UNIVERSITY MATHEMATICS I

A SERIES OF BOOKS IN MATHEMATICS

Editors: R. A. Rosenbaum, G. Philip Johnson

UNIVERSITY MATHEMATICS

I

JACK R. BRITTON
University of Colorado

R. BEN KRIEGH
University of Colorado

LEON W. RUTLAND
Virginia Polytechnic Institute

W. H. FREEMAN AND COMPANY

SAN FRANCISCO AND LONDON

Preface

This is the first of two volumes that are intended to provide college and university students with a sensible continuation of the modern approach to mathematics that is being introduced in most elementary and secondary schools, with more emphasis than in the past placed on an understanding of fundamental concepts. Certain advanced topics in algebra and trigonometry, along with analytic geometry and calculus, are unified into a sequential exposition that eliminates much unnecessary duplication and is conducive to an efficient development and use of ideas and techniques. Fundamental concepts are discussed in a reasonably rigorous fashion, with adequate emphasis on important skills, and without an excess of sophistication. Many applications of mathematics have been included, and they have frequently been made the motivation for the introduction of mathematical concepts. An intuitive discussion often precedes the formal treatment of a new idea.

Although the books were written with students in engineering and the sciences in mind, they are also well suited for a good liberal arts course in mathematics. The exposition has, in the main, been kept at a level that has proved to be reasonable for the average student. However, a number of optional sections, problems, and proofs, each of which is marked by a star and may be omitted without loss of continuity, have been included as a challenge to the better students.

Important definitions, axioms, and theorems are clearly labeled, and a conscientious effort has been made to utilize each new idea and notation as frequently as possible in order to promote its intelligent use by the student. New materials and new points of view are not introduced merely for the sake of novelty, but are brought in only if they make a genuine contribution to the understanding that can be imparted to the reader.

There are several features of particular interest that we have found helpful in providing the student with a deeper understanding of elementary mathematical analysis, as well as a better background for mathematics beyond the sophomore level. First, there is the development and consistent use of the neighborhood concept in the treatment of limits. This approach gives the student a better intuitive feeling for the meaning of a limit than the more usual formal ϵ-δ attack. The second significant feature is the introduction and use of matrices for the solution of systems of linear equations and for the discussion of linear transformations in reducing a quadratic polynomial to a canonical form, as well as the application of these ideas to the solution of simple systems of differential equations. A third important feature is the use of vector algebra for the discussion of geometric ideas relating to the line and the plane in three-dimensional space, and the use of vector calculus for the development of a number of basic notions relating to curves and surfaces as well as to velocity and acceleration. The introduction and application of some elementary ideas in the calculus of complex-valued functions motivates and simplifies the use of the exponential function with an imaginary exponent.

The material in these books has been taught quite successfully for the past three years—first in the form of notes and then in an offset preliminary edition—to ordinary freshman and sophomore classes. The point of view of the exposition, the organization, and the development of the mathematical ideas, the new topics, and the intuitive development that often precedes a more rigorous formal discussion, have all been enthusiastically received by both faculty and students. We believe that this approach has enabled students to attain a desirable level of mathematical maturity in a shorter time than they could have with the more traditional approaches.

The first seven chapters of Volume I are concerned with basic ideas and the development of a consistent language and terminology for the remainder of the book. A good modern course in analytic geometry and calculus can be based on Chapters 4 and 5, the first three sections of Chapter 6, and Chapters 8 to 15 of Volume I, plus Chapters 1 to 11 of Volume II. Chapters 12 and 13 of Volume II contain adequate material for a short course in differential equations. Chapter 14 consists of an elementary treatment of the Laplace transformation, and Chapter 15 is a brief introduction to probability.

The material in Volume I can easily be covered in two five-semester-hour courses in the freshman year. The material in the first thirteen of the fifteen chapters of Volume II can be covered (with minor omissions) in two four-semester-hour courses in the sophomore year. It is, however, quite possible for a well-prepared class to complete both volumes in the two-year sequence by omitting the more elementary portions of Volume I. In order to establish the language and point of view for such students, it is advisable to study the concept of a set and the set notation in Sections 1.6, 1.7, and 1.8. The summary of Chapter 2 gives the symbols that are consistently used to denote certain special sets of numbers. Basic work on inequalities occurs in Sections 3.8 and 3.9. Chapters 4, 5, and 6, which contain the introductory work in analytic geometry and the discussion of relations and functions, should be taken in more or less detail, depending on the preparation of the class. Chapter 7, which is concerned with basic trigonometry, may be omitted for students with good high school preparation in this subject. Not more than two or three weeks is needed to cover the preceding topics, so that students with adequate high school background are then able to begin the serious work on limits and continuity in Chapter 8.

We wish to thank Professors R. A. Rosenbaum and Morris Kline for their editorial suggestions, which contributed in a notable fashion to the clarity of the exposition. Many other valuable suggestions came from our colleagues in the Department of Applied Mathematics at the University of Colorado and from the long-suffering students who have seen the book through the many pains of its birth. To these students and colleagues we owe a debt that can be repaid only by the gratitude of a newer generation of students for whom the exposition has been made simpler and clearer. We are particularly appreciative of the intelligent effort put in by Mrs. Dorothy Vaughn in typing the manuscript in its many revisions. Finally, we wish to express our gratitude to our families for putting up with us during the trials and tribulations of this project.

March 1965   JACK R. BRITTON
                                                                R. BEN KRIEGH
                                                                LEON W. RUTLAND

Contents

Chapter 8. Limits and Continuity   242

Chapter 9. The Derivative and the Inverse Derivative   276

Chapter 10. Theorems on Derivatives   295

Chapter 11. Further Applications of the Derivative   327

Chapter 12. The Definite Integral   368

Chapter 1   Fundamental Ideas

1.1 INTRODUCTION

What is mathematics? Mathematicians and philosophers have been trying for centuries—and without much success—to give a simple answer to this apparently simple question. A logician might say that mathematics is an extension of logic. A philosopher might say that mathematics is a language. A mathematician is likely to say that the question cannot be answered in any simple or concise way. Indeed, it is only by actual experience in mathematics itself that the question can be answered at all.

Most basic mathematical concepts have their roots in the physical situations that men face in their daily lives. For instance, one of the most primitive and basic of all concepts is that of counting, which is the root of the more abstract concepts of number and arithmetic. Thus, statements of the form

Two spears and three spears are five spears,

or

Two stones and three stones are five stones

have led to the more general kind of statement that

Two things and three things are five things,

or, in the most abstract and concise form,

$$2 + 3 = 5.$$

Man's ability to formulate concepts related to physical experience in short, concise "abstract" statements of this type has been the basis for his development of a civilization founded on an understanding of his environment. Much of mathematics consists of the formulation and development of abstract concepts from specific situations that arise in connection with the development of a social structure and a civilization. For example, the ancient Arab merchants developed a convenient and systematic notation as an aid to keeping track of their money. The ancient Egyptians developed many of the fundamental ideas of trigonometry so that they could relocate property lines after a flood along the Nile river bottom. In more recent times, Sir Isaac Newton was led to consider the fundamental concepts of the mathematical subject now called the calculus in order to describe the behavior of moving objects. In each case, these fundamental concepts have arisen as a result of necessity and as a supplement to our ordinary language.

Since it is clearly impossible to discuss mathematics without making use of a language, we shall consider a few fundamental concepts that are concerned with language. A language is useful only when the words in the language have a reasonably clear meaning. Thus it is important to understand just how words are given a meaning.

Without careful consideration, we might say that words are defined in terms of other words. However, it soon becomes apparent that this procedure is not always possible. For example, suppose we look in a dictionary for the meaning of the word *riddle*. The definition given may read "an enigma propounded for solution by guessing." In order to understand the meaning of *riddle* we must know the meaning of the word *enigma*. Another reference to the dictionary reveals that an enigma is "an obscure saying such as a riddle." Hence the meaning of the word *riddle* is made to depend upon itself. Just what is a riddle seems to be an enigma!

The problem of trying to define a word thus assumes a somewhat perplexing aspect. However, all is not yet lost. It is possible to give meaning to a word without using other words. This may be done by means of gesturing, pointing, and making noises. It is in just this way that young children learn the meaning of their first words. Of course, meaning does not come easily in this fashion; it is acquired only after much effort and repetition.

Nevertheless, by this crude approach a child acquires a basic vocabulary. With the aid of this vocabulary new words are defined and old words are given a refined meaning. Hence an ultimate meaning of some words is not obtained by a direct definition, but is achieved by means of a "feedback" principle. Words that are a part of the basic vocabulary of a language are often called "undefined" terms. Whatever meaning such words have is given to them by the manner in which they are allowed to be used.

Thus, the development of mathematics begins with language. New ideas are described in terms of a basic set of primitive words, the undefined terms of the language, and other words such as *which, the, for*, and so on, which are used in their customary fashion with no specific technical mathematical meaning. An example of an undefined word is the word *point*. A dictionary definition of *point* is "an undefined geometric element concerning which it is postulated that at least two exist and that two suffice to determine a straight line." The actual meaning of *point* lies in the geometry that may be built on this definition.

The feedback principle applies equally well to the learning and understanding of mathematical concepts. For example, each of us first learns the most elementary ideas associated with counting, such as addition and multiplication. Yet even after having had this knowledge for a number of years, we have never really considered the question "What is a number?" We simply use numbers, and, in doing so, we expand our knowledge of them. It is only after a considerable length of time that one acquires the maturity necessary to understand what is *meant* by the question, a much easier task than answering it.

Accordingly, although the purpose of the early portions of this book is to give at least a partial answer to the preceding questions, we shall draw freely on illustrations from algebra and arithmetic in order to provide an intuitive approach to the abstract ideas that are introduced.

1.2 EQUALITY

Some misunderstanding has arisen from time to time in connection with the symbol for equality, $=$. It is a result of the fact that the symbol is often used in at least two (and sometimes three) different senses. In order to clarify this point we shall use the equals sign as indicated in the following definitions:

Definition 1.2a. The statement

$$a = b$$

means that a is another name for the object whose name is b.

Definition 1.2b. The statement

$$a \neq b$$

means that a and b are names of different objects.

Definition 1.2c. The statement

$$a .=. b$$

means that a is *defined* to be another name for the object whose name is b.

The symbol $.=.$ may be read "is equal, by definition, to," or "is defined to be the same as."

At first sight there may appear to be no significant difference between the two notations $.=.$ and $=$, and it is true that the difference is essentially conceptual. However, this alone is sufficient reason for us to make such a distinction. An illustration based on the next definition will help to clarify this point.

Definition 1.2d. The symbol

$$[\![x]\!] .=. n,$$

where n is the largest integer less than or equal to x.

The sentence of Definition 1.2d gives the bracket symbol $[\![x]\!]$ meaning. Once this meaning has been given, we may use the symbol in connection with ordinary equality. For example, we have $[\![2.34]\!] = 2$. Here the symbol $.=.$ is not used because $[\![2.34]\!]$ is not being defined as 2, but instead, $[\![2.34]\!] = 2$ by virtue of Definition 1.2d. Another example will illustrate this idea further.

Example 1.2a. Let $a_1 .=. 1$, and let $a_{n+1} .=. \frac{1}{2}a_n$, $n = 1, 2, 3, \ldots$. (The ellipsis customarily means "and so forth.") These statements define a sequence of numbers, denoted by $a_1, a_2, a_3, \ldots$. Which of the following statements is correct?

(a) $a_5 .=. \frac{1}{16}$.
(b) $a_5 = \frac{1}{16}$.

The formula $a_{n+1} = \frac{1}{2}a_n$ is called a **recurrence formula** because it can be used to determine a_{n+1} when a_n is known. For example,

$$a_2 = \frac{1}{2}a_1 = \frac{1}{2} \cdot 1 = \frac{1}{2},$$

$$a_3 = \frac{1}{2}a_2 = \frac{1}{2} \cdot \frac{1}{2} = \frac{1}{2^2},$$

$$a_4 = \frac{1}{2}a_3 = \frac{1}{2} \cdot \frac{1}{2^2} = \frac{1}{2^3},$$

and

$$a_5 = \frac{1}{2}a_4 = \frac{1}{2} \cdot \frac{1}{2^3} = \frac{1}{2^4} = \frac{1}{16}.$$

In each case, the expression obtained for a_n is a **consequence** of the given definition so that it is *not* correct to say that

$$a_5 .=. \frac{1}{16},$$

but it is correct to say that

$$a_5 = \frac{1}{16}.$$

1.3 LOGIC

While it is not our purpose to make a detailed study of logic, there are certain of its principles that we need in order to develop the succeeding mathematics.

Definition 1.3a. A **proposition** is a complete declarative sentence with a definite meaning.

For example, the following sentences are all propositions:

$$2 + 3 = 5,$$
$$2 + 3 = 8,$$

Gold is a precious metal,
If it rains tonight, then tomorrow it will be fair.

A sentence of the form

x is a cat

may be interpreted in two ways. In one sense, it asserts that the 24th letter of the alphabet is a cat. In another sense, it is intended to be an incomplete sentence, where the symbol x is used to represent an arbitrary element of language. In this second sense, until x is replaced by a meaningful word or symbol, the sentence is not really complete and is therefore not to be regarded as a proposition according to Definition 1.3a.

In order to indicate that a letter represents an arbitrary element, we shall sometimes underline the symbol, as in

$$\underline{x} \text{ is a cat.}$$

Sentences of this kind are important enough in mathematics to merit special consideration.

Definition 1.3b. An **open sentence** is an incomplete sentence which contains an arbitrary element and which becomes a proposition when the arbitrary element is replaced by a definite element.

Thus,

$$\underline{x} \text{ is a cat,}$$
$$x + 7 = 0,$$
$$x \text{ is an integer,}$$

are examples of open sentences.

Logic is concerned with the rules according to which propositions and/or open sentences may be combined in order to give valid conclusions. The most fundamental rule of logic is

Law 1.3a. *The Law of the Excluded Middle.* Every proposition in the language must be either true or false, but it cannot be both, nor can it be neither.

Thus, $2 + 3 = 8$ is a false proposition, whereas $2 + 3 = 5$ is a true proposition.

An immediate consequence of Law 1.3a is that if a given proposition is true, then its denial is false, and, conversely, if a proposition is false then its denial is true. For example, since $2 + 3 = 8$ is false, it follows that $2 + 3 \neq 8$ is true. It is upon these facts that the technique of proof by contradiction is based. This technique is discussed in detail in Section 1.5.

In the development of a science, we are frequently interested in establishing a chain of valid reasoning from a given proposition, called the **hypothesis,** to another proposition, called the **conclusion.** For example, if we are told that it is raining, then we conclude at once that the sky must be cloudy. In other words, the statement "It is raining" suggests that certain other conditions must also be true. In this example, the conclusion that it is cloudy is suggested by the meaning of the statement "It is raining" and our own physical experience that rain must be associated with clouds. In mathematics, it is not always so easy to obtain conclusions from given hypotheses, since we must rely only upon the previously established rules or theorems and definitions, rather than on actual physical experience.

The assertion that a given hypothesis leads to a certain conclusion is called an **implication.** For example, if x is a number such that $x + 3 = 5$, then according to the rules of ordinary arithmetic, it follows that $x = 2$. In mathematics it is important to indicate clearly what propositions are used as hypotheses and what propositions follow as conclusions from these hypotheses. Since an implication is usually stated in the form

$$\text{if } p, \text{ then } q \quad \text{or} \quad p \text{ implies } q,$$

where p denotes the hypothesis and q denotes the conclusion, it is convenient to use a special symbol to denote an implication.

Definition 1.3c. The symbol

$$p \Rightarrow q$$

means that the hypothesis, p, implies the conclusion, q, according to some rule. The sign $\Rightarrow$ is usually read "implies."

The sentences

$$x + 3 = 5 \Rightarrow x = 2$$

and

It is raining $\Rightarrow$ there are clouds in the sky

illustrate correct uses of the implication symbol.

It sometimes happens that each of two propositions implies the other. In that case we write

$$p \Leftrightarrow q$$

to mean that an implication exists both ways. For example,

A triangle has three equal sides $\Leftrightarrow$ the triangle has three equal angles.

This proposition is often written as "A triangle has three equal sides *if and only if* it has three equal angles" or "For a triangle to have three equal sides, it is *necessary and sufficient* that it have three equal angles." The symbol $\Leftrightarrow$ will be used in place of the phrase "if and only if" or "necessary and sufficient," since these phrases are often a source of confusion for the student. However, $\Leftrightarrow$ may be read "if and only if" or "implies and is implied by." The statement $p \Leftrightarrow q$ is a combination of the two statements

$$p \Rightarrow q, \quad q \Rightarrow p.$$

Definition 1.3d. The statement $q \Rightarrow p$ is called the **converse** of the statement $p \Rightarrow q$.

It is necessary for the reader to realize that $p \Rightarrow q$ does not guarantee that $q \Rightarrow p$. The statement,

It is raining $\Rightarrow$ there are clouds in the sky

is valid, but it does not follow that the converse

There are clouds in the sky $\Rightarrow$ it is raining

is valid. Again,

$$a = 2 \quad \text{and} \quad b = 3 \Rightarrow ab = 6,$$

is valid, but the converse

$$ab = 6 \Rightarrow a = 2, \quad b = 3,$$

is not valid.

Even though a proposition may imply a second proposition in the sense of Definition 1.3c, there is no guarantee that the second proposition is true. It is still necessary to specify the conditions under which the conclusion of an implication will be true. This is done by

Law 1.3b. *The Law of Inference.* Suppose that

(1) a proposition, p, is true, and that
(2) $p \Rightarrow q$ is a valid implication.

Then q is also true.

To make clear the significance of this law, consider the following examples.

Example 1.3a. Does the proposition "two sides of a triangle are equal" imply the proposition "the angles opposite these sides are equal?"

By drawing a line from the vertex of the third angle to the midpoint of the third side, we divide the triangle into two triangles with the sides of one equal, respectively, to the sides of the other. Thus, the two triangles are congruent and the corresponding angles are equal.

This is the essential chain of reasoning used in high school geometry to arrive at the fact that the implication proposed in this example is correct. If p is the proposition, "two sides of a triangle are equal," and q the proposition, "the angles opposite these sides are equal," then we have shown that

$$p \Rightarrow q.$$

Consequently, for any triangle for which p is true, the Law of Inference guarantees that q is also true.

The next example illustrates another situation.

Example 1.3b. With the usual rule that "equals may be added to equals," is

$$2 = 10 \Rightarrow 3 = 11$$

a correct implication?

The reader should note that this question is not concerned with the truth or falsity of either of the propositions $2 = 10$ or $3 = 11$, it is concerned only with the validity of the implication. Here the proposition p is $2 = 10$, and, by adding 1 to both sides, we get

$$2 + 1 = 10 + 1 \quad \text{or} \quad 3 = 11.$$

Hence the given implication is correct.

It is important to understand, in Example 1.3b, that the Law of Inference guarantees that *if* $2 = 10$ were true, then $3 = 11$ would also be true. However, since $2 = 10$ is not true, no conclusion may be drawn regarding the truth or falsity of $3 = 11$ from the implication $2 = 10 \Rightarrow 3 = 11$ alone. It is easy to show that a false proposition may imply a true one. For example, let the proposition p be $-2 = 2$, which is patently false. However, by multiplying "equals by equals," we get

$$(-2)(-2) = (2)(2) \quad \text{or} \quad 4 = 4.$$

Thus, if q is the true proposition $4 = 4$, we have

$$p \Rightarrow q,$$

even though p is false.

These illustrations show that a false proposition may imply a true proposition or a false one. Moreover, if $p \Rightarrow q$ and q is true, no conclusion as to the truth or falsity of p may be drawn. For instance, both the false proposition $-2 = 2$ and the true proposition $2 = 2$ imply the true proposition $4 = 4$.

However, if $p \Rightarrow q$ and q is false, then we may conclude that p is also false. Otherwise the Law of Inference is contradicted. Thus, the facts that $2 = 10 \Rightarrow 3 = 11$ and $3 = 11$ is false may be regarded as proof that $2 = 10$ is also false.

In order to emphasize another important point, we consider one of the popular fallacies.

Let x and y represent two nonzero numbers for which

$$x = y.$$

Assuming that the usual rules of arithmetic are valid, we may write

$$x^2 = xy$$

(by multiplying both members by x) and

$$x^2 - y^2 = xy - y^2$$

(by subtracting y^2 from both sides). From the rules of factoring, we may write

$$(x - y)(x + y) = (x - y)y.$$

By division, we have

$$(x + y) = y$$

or, since $y = x$,

$$x + y = x, \quad 2x = x, \quad \text{or} \quad 2 = 1.$$

Here we have reached a contradiction with an accepted fact. The initial statement, $x = y$, may be considered true without causing difficulty. What, then, is wrong with the reasoning process? Is

$$x = y \Rightarrow 2 = 1$$

a valid statement? If not, we evidently do not have a valid implication, which is to say that some basic rule of algebra must have been violated. Indeed the violation occurred when the factor $(x - y)$ was "divided" from both sides of the equation. Since $x = y$, this factor is 0 and therefore may not be divided into the members of the equation.

This fallacy is intended to illustrate the need for obeying the rules of the "game," and to show that the validity of the process of obtaining conclusions depends upon following these rules. As a further illustration of the same point, consider the following example.

Example 1.3c. Determine if

$$ac = bc \Rightarrow a = b.$$

Before the problem can be solved, we must know what the symbols a, b, and c represent. If they are ordinary numbers, then

$$ac = bc \Rightarrow ac - bc = 0$$

or

$$(a - b)c = 0.$$

If we can be sure that $c \neq 0$, then we may assert that

$$a - b = 0,$$

so that

$$a = b.$$

Hence, we have $ac = bc \Rightarrow a = b$ *if a, b*, and *c are ordinary numbers, and if $c \neq 0$.* If these stipulations were changed, then the implication might no longer be valid. It is on this account that the conditions under which manipulations are carried out must be clear.

Exercises 1.3

1. Let $\bar{n} .=. k$, where n is a positive integer and where k is the largest positive integer for which $k^2 \leq n$.
   (a) What is the value of $\bar{n}$ for $n = 18$? 120? -3? 641? 0?
   (b) Does the fact that $\bar{n}$ is defined above imply that $\bar{\bar{n}}$ is defined?
   (c) If the answer to (b) is yes, which of the following is correct?

$$\bar{\bar{7}} .=. 1, \quad \bar{\bar{7}} = 1, \quad \bar{\bar{7}} \neq 1.$$

2. Let $1! .=. 1$ and $n! .=. n(n-1)!$ for $n = 2, 3, 4, \ldots$.
   (a) Is it true that $4! = 1 \cdot 2 \cdot 3 \cdot 4$? Why or why not?
   (b) Does $n! .=. n(n-1)! \Rightarrow 0! = 1$ if $n = 1$? Why or why not?
   (c) Which of the following statements, if any, is (are) correct?

$$\frac{10!}{8!} .=. 10 \cdot 9, \quad \frac{10!}{8!} = \frac{10}{8}, \quad \frac{10!}{8!} \neq \frac{10}{8}, \quad \frac{10!}{8!} \text{ is undefined.}$$

Give reasons for your answers.

3. Let $a_1 .=. 2$ and $a_n .=. 2a_{n-1}$. Which of the following expressions is (are) correct?

$$a_n = 2n, \quad a_n .=. 2^n, \quad a_n = 2^n, \quad a_n \neq 2^n, \quad a_n .=. 2n.$$

4. Are the following implications valid or not?
   (a) Two lines in three-dimensional space are both perpendicular to the same line $\Rightarrow$ the two lines are perpendicular to each other.
   (b) One side of a triangle is shorter than a second side $\Rightarrow$ the angle opposite the first side is smaller than that opposite the second side.
   (c) The diagonals of a parallelogram bisect each other $\Rightarrow$ the parallelogram is a rhombus.

5. Are the following implications valid or not? Explain why. (Assume that x and y represent integers.)
   (a) $x = 3 \Rightarrow x^2 = 9$.
   (b) $x^2 = 9 \Rightarrow x = 3$.
   (c) $x^2 = 4 \Rightarrow x^2 - 2x + 2 \neq 5$.
   (d) $\dfrac{x^2 - y^2}{x - y} = 0 \Rightarrow x = y$.
   (e) $2 = 1 \Rightarrow 2 = 2$.
   (f) $xy + y = 0 \Rightarrow y = 0$.

6. State the converse of each of the following implications. Is the converse valid? Why?
   (a) $a = 3$ and $b = 4 \Rightarrow ab = 12$.
   (b) Two straight lines in a plane are parallel $\Rightarrow$ the two lines do not intersect.
   (c) Two triangles are congruent $\Rightarrow$ the corresponding angles are equal.
   (d) $a = 2$ and $b = 3 \Rightarrow a + b = 5$.
   (e) $x = 3 \Rightarrow x^2 = 9$.
   (f) $3 = 5 \Rightarrow 4 = 6$.
   (g) Two angles of a triangle are equal, respectively, to two angles of a second triangle $\Rightarrow$ the third angles of the two triangles are equal.

7. Let x and y be two unequal numbers, and let $x - y = 2c$. Then

$$
\begin{aligned}
x - y = 2c &\Rightarrow x^2 - xy = 2cx \\
&\Rightarrow y^2 + x^2 - xy = 2cx + y^2 \\
&\Rightarrow y^2 + x^2 - 2xy = 2cx + y^2 - xy \\
&\Rightarrow y^2 - 2xy + x^2 = 2cx - y(x - y) \\
&\Rightarrow y^2 - 2xy + x^2 = 2cx - y(2c) \\
&\Rightarrow (y - x)^2 = 2c(x - y) \\
&\Rightarrow (y - x)^2 = 4c^2 \\
&\Rightarrow y - x = 2c \\
&\Rightarrow y - x = x - y \\
&\Rightarrow y = x.
\end{aligned}
$$

This result contradicts the assumption that $x \neq y$. What is wrong?

1.4 AXIOMS

Just as not every word can be defined in terms of other words, not every proposition can be proved true or false by using other propositions. A circular type of reasoning is no better than a circular type of definition. Hence it is necessary to assume that some propositions are true to start with, and from these propositions to deduce the truth or falsity of other propositions.

A proposition that is assumed to be true is called an **axiom**. However, an axiom can not be considered to be a "self-evident truth," even though this definition can be found in many dictionaries. An axiom may be true in the sense that it is consistent with experience, but in mathematics it is immaterial if axioms are true in this sense. The mathematician is interested only in the consequences of the *supposed* truth of the axiom. Of course, the branches of mathematics that are of most value to us in a practical sense are those that can best be used to describe our experiences. Thus we ordinarily use axioms that seem to be consistent with experience, so that many axioms *appear* to be "self-evident truths." The important point is that axioms are propositions which are *assumed* to be true.

One of the most notable examples of a supposed "self-evident truth" is the famous euclidean axiom that *one and only one line parallel to a given line can be drawn through a point not on the given line.* This axiom was considered a "self-evident truth" for nearly twenty centuries until a brilliant Russian mathematician, Nikolai Lobachevsky, who lived from 1793 to 1856, questioned its truth.

He discovered several other kinds of geometry by means of modifications of this axiom.

There are two axioms fundamental to all of mathematics. These may be stated as

Axiom 1.4a. *Axiom of Identity.* For any object a, $a = a$.

Axiom 1.4b. *Axiom of Substitution.* If $a = b$, then a may be used to replace b in any part of a proposition containing b without altering the validity of the proposition.

We have discussed briefly the use of undefined words, definitions, axioms, and certain rules of logic in mathematics. Using these primitive concepts, we can establish the validity of certain implications. Those valid implications that are regarded as basic to the development of mathematics are called **theorems.** The undefined terms, the definitions, the axioms, and the theorems together constitute what is called a **mathematical structure.**

These remarks are illustrated very simply by two theorems that follow immediately from Axioms 1.4a and 1.4b.

Theorem 1.4a. *The symmetry property of* $=$:
$$a = b \Rightarrow b = a.$$

PROOF: A proof of this theorem is given by the following observations:

$b = b$ by the Identity Axiom,
$b = a$ by the Substitution Axiom and the given proposition, $a = b$.

Theorem 1.4b. *The transitive property of* $=$:
$$a = b \quad \text{and} \quad b = c \Rightarrow a = c.$$

PROOF: $a = b$ (by hypothesis) and
$b = c$ (by hypothesis),

so that by substituting from the second equality into the first, we may write
$$a = c \quad \text{(by Axiom 1.4b)}.$$

1.5 METHODS OF PROOF

The preceding laws of logic, definitions, axioms, and theorems form the basis on which the mathematics of this book rests. It would be possible for us to build, detail by detail, upon this basis to obtain the structure with which we shall work. Such a procedure would, however, become quite tedious. Consequently, we shall prove most of the key theorems, but we shall not hestitate to introduce some ideas in an intuitive fashion.

There are, of course, various ways of proving theorems. It may be possible to prove a proposition *directly* by starting with something known (a definition, an axiom, or a previously proved theorem) and proceeding step by step, using the laws of logic and other known results to arrive at the desired result. This process has been illustrated in the simple proofs of Theorems 1.4a and 1.4b.

It may also be possible to prove a theorem *indirectly* by demonstrating that the denial of the theorem cannot be true. This procedure is based on the **Law of the Excluded Middle** (Law 1.3a) and is illustrated by

---

Example 1.5a. Prove that the square of the ratio of two integers cannot be exactly 2.

In this example the proposition states that if a and b are integers, then $(a/b)^2 \neq 2$. In order to prove this statement, we shall show that its denial cannot be true. Accordingly, we must show that if a and b are integers, then $(a/b)^2 = 2$ is not possible.

As a preliminary step, we note that a is an even integer if, and only if, a^2 is divisible by 4. This follows easily from the fact that a is an even integer $\Leftrightarrow a = 2n$, where n is an integer, and so $a^2 = (2n)^2 = 4n^2$.

We may assume, without loss of generality, that a/b is in its lowest terms, that is, that a and b have no common factors. Why? Suppose now that the negation of the proposition to be proved is true—that is, that

$$\left(\frac{a}{b}\right)^2 = 2.$$

Then

$$a^2 = 2b^2.$$

The right member of this equation is divisible by 2, so the left member must also be divisible by 2. However, a is an integer; so if a^2 is divisible by 2, then it must be divisible by 4. Explain.

Thus, we may write $a = 2c$, where c is an integer. Then $a^2 = 4c^2$ so that we have

$$4c^2 = 2b^2 \quad \text{or} \quad 2c^2 = b^2.$$

Application of the same argument again shows that b^2 must be divisible by 2 and hence by 4. Thus, $b = 2d$, where d is some integer. Now we have a contradiction. The fact that $a = 2c$ and $b = 2d$ means that a and b have the common factor 2, contrary to the assumption that a/b is in its lowest terms. Consequently, it is *not* true that $(a/b)^2 = 2$. This completes the proof.

An indirect proof of this type, in which the denial of a proposition is proved false, is called a **proof by contradiction.** The procedure of constructing a proof by contradiction may be expressed symbolically in terms of implication. Suppose we are given a true proposition, p, and are required to demonstrate the truth of a proposition, q, by the use of the Law of Inference. Now it may not be clear how to establish the implication

$$p \Rightarrow q,$$

by starting with p and proceeding to q. In that case it may be possible to prove the implication *indirectly* by establishing another implication that is equivalent to $p \Rightarrow q$. For this purpose we introduce the notation $-p$ to denote the negation or denial of the proposition p. If p represents the statement "It is raining," then $-p$ represents "It is not raining." Again, if p is "$x = 2$," then $-p$ is "$x \neq 2$."

If p is the *compound* proposition "$a = b$ and $b \neq c$," then $-p$ is "$a \neq b$, or $b = c$, or $a \neq b$ and $b = c$"; that is, $-p$ is the negation of at least one of the simple propositions of which p is compounded. It is clear, by the Law of the Excluded Middle (Law 1.3a), that *if p is true, then $-p$ is false; and, if p is false, then $-p$ is true.*

The technique of proof by contradiction is based on the equivalence of the two statements

$$p \Rightarrow q \quad \text{and} \quad -q \Rightarrow -p.$$

The latter implication is called the **contrapositive** of the former. To see why these statements are logically equivalent, let us first consider some examples of contrapositive statements. The contrapositive of

$$\text{It is raining} \Rightarrow \text{it is cloudy}$$

is

$$\text{It is not cloudy} \Rightarrow \text{it is not raining.}$$

Similarly, the contrapositive of

$$x = 2 \Rightarrow x^2 = 4$$

is

$$x^2 \neq 4 \Rightarrow x \neq 2.$$

The reader is cautioned to observe the difference between the *converse* of an implication and the *contrapositive* of the same implication. In particular, if the implication is $p \Rightarrow q$, then the converse is

$$q \Rightarrow p$$

and the contrapositive is

$$-q \Rightarrow -p.$$

In general, these two statements are distinct. Thus, if $p \Rightarrow q$ is

$$\text{It is raining} \Rightarrow \text{it is cloudy}$$

the converse is

$$\text{It is cloudy} \Rightarrow \text{it is raining,}$$

which is certainly not a valid implication.

To show that the statements $p \Rightarrow q$ and $-q \Rightarrow -p$ are equivalent, let us refer again to Law 1.3b of logic. In order to prove that a statement q is true whenever another statement p is true, we must establish that $p \Rightarrow q$. In case this cannot be done directly, we may be able to establish the connection indirectly by using the fact that if q is false, then $-q$ is true. Now, suppose that we can show that $-q \Rightarrow -p$, so that $-p$ is true by Law 1.3b. Then p is false, contrary to the originally given statement that p is true. Evidently the contradiction arises from the assumption that q is false. Thus, in order to avoid the contradiction, we must conclude that q is true and that $p \Rightarrow q$ is therefore also true, since a true statement can never imply a false one. In other words, we have established that

$$(-q \Rightarrow -p) \Rightarrow (p \Rightarrow q).$$

In a similar way, we may establish that

$$(p \Rightarrow q) \Rightarrow (-q \Rightarrow -p)$$

so that the statements $p \Rightarrow q$ and $-q \Rightarrow -p$ are logically equivalent. That is, one of the statements is true if, and only if, the other is true.

To illustrate this concept again, let us *prove* that if a, b, and x are numbers, where $x \neq 0$, then

$$ax = bx \Rightarrow a = b.$$

That is, we shall prove the "cancellation" law for multiplication.

In this illustration, p is the proposition "$ax = bx$," and q is the proposition "$a = b$." Hence, $-p$ is "$ax \neq bx$," and $-q$ is "$a \neq b$." We want to show that $-q \Rightarrow -p$. Suppose that $-q$ is true; that is, suppose that $a \neq b$, and let

$$a - b = c,$$

where c cannot be 0. Then,

$$(a - b)x = cx$$

or

$$ax - bx = cx.$$

Since $c \neq 0$ and $x \neq 0$, it follows that $ax - bx \neq 0$ and that

$$ax \neq bx.$$

Thus, we have established the implication

$$a \neq b \Rightarrow ax \neq bx,$$

or $-q \Rightarrow -p$. Therefore, $p \Rightarrow q$, or

$$ax = bx \Rightarrow a = b,$$

as was to be shown.

Example 1.5b. Archimedes (287–212 B.C.), who was undoubtedly the greatest of the ancient mathematicians, proved a number of theorems in Mechanics on the basis of a set of simple axioms that were suggested to him by common experience with weights and levers. Suppose that two weights, W_1 and W_2, rest on a lever on opposite sides of the fulcrum and at distances d_1 and d_2, respectively, from the fulcrum. Then the first two of Archimedes' axioms are equivalent to

Axiom 1. If $W_1 = W_2$ and $d_1 = d_2$, the system is in equilibrium (the weights balance); if $W_1 = W_2$ but $d_1 \neq d_2$, then the system is not in equilibrium and the lever inclines toward the weight at the greater distance.

Axiom 2. If the system is in equilibrium for some set of weights and distances, and additional weight is added to W_1, then equilibrium will not be maintained and the lever will incline toward W_1; similarly, if weight is taken from W_1, the lever will incline toward W_2.

Prove that if the system is in equilibrium, then $W_1 \neq W_2 \Rightarrow d_1 \neq d_2$.

This again is a good example of a simple proof by contradiction. We assume the negation of the proposition that is to be proved; that is, we assume that $d_1 = d_2$.

Now, if $W_1 \neq W_2$, then either W_1 is greater than W_2 or W_1 is less than W_2. First, suppose that W_1 is the greater. Then let $W_1 - W_2 = W_3$. Subtract W_3 from W_1 to get W, which is equal to W_2. The new system, in which $W = W_2$ and $d_1 = d_2$, is in equilibrium by Axiom 1.

Now, add W_3 to W to get W_1 again. By Axiom 2, the system will not remain in equilibrium but will be inclined toward W_1. But this is the original system, so we have a contradiction of the hypothesis that the system is in equilibrium. Therefore it cannot be true that W_1 is greater than W_2 and $d_1 = d_2$. (The reader may construct a proof similar to this in order to show that it cannot be true that W_1 is less than W_2 and $d_1 = d_2$.) Consequently, we have shown that $d_1 = d_2 \Rightarrow W_1 = W_2$, which is contrary to the given assumption that $W_1 \neq W_2$. It therefore follows that

$$W_1 \neq W_2 \Rightarrow d_1 \neq d_2,$$

as was to be shown.

In mathematics, we frequently use the term **conjecture** to mean a proposition that has not been proved but is suspected of being true. Usually a conjecture is an "educated" guess, but we have to be careful not to be led astray by plausible conjectures. This has happened even to famous and renowned mathematicians. For example, Fermat (French, 1601–1665) believed that every number of the form

$$2^{2^n} + 1,$$

with n a positive integer, is a prime number. Thus,

$$2^{2^1} + 1 = 2^2 + 1 = 5,$$
$$2^{2^2} + 1 = 2^4 + 1 = 17,$$
$$2^{2^3} + 1 = 2^8 + 1 = 257,$$

and, since these are all primes, Fermat's conjecture does appear plausible. (Furthermore, it is tempting to accept the conjecture, since the numbers to be tested become exceedingly large with increasing n, and the testing would not be easy.) Yet the danger of drawing conclusions without adequate proof is demonstrated by the fact that for $n = 5$, we have

$$2^{2^5} + 1 = 2^{32} + 1 = 4{,}294{,}967{,}297$$
$$= (641)(6{,}700{,}417),$$

a factorization that was pointed out by Euler (Swiss, 1707–1783).

A conjecture is, of course, disproved by a single example showing that it is not true. Such an example is called a **counterexample.** Thus Euler's calculation for $n = 5$ furnished a counterexample that disproved Fermat's conjecture. It is not to be supposed that a counterexample is always easy to find.

Example 1.5c. Another conjecture ascribed to Fermat is that the equation $x^n + y^n = z^n$, where n is a positive integer, can be satisfied by positive integral values of x, y, z only if $n = 1$ or if $n = 2$.

This conjecture has not yet been proved or disproved. No counterexample has ever been found.

Exercises 1.5

1. Write (i) the converse and (ii) the contrapositive for each of the following statements, and determine which are valid.
   (a) Two triangles are congruent $\Rightarrow$ the triangles have corresponding angles equal.
   (b) A polygon has 4 equal sides $\Rightarrow$ the polygon is a parallelogram.
   (c) $x = 2 \Rightarrow x^2 = 4$.
   (d) A triangle is isosceles $\Rightarrow$ the triangle has two equal sides.
   (e) x is a factor of a and x is a factor of $b \Rightarrow x$ is a factor of $a + b$.
2. Does the statement "You cannot enjoy smoking if you do not smoke Blotto cigarettes," guarantee smoking enjoyment if you smoke Blotto cigarettes? Explain.
3. Does the statement "If you do not elect A. Crook, then you cannot have honest government," guarantee honest government if A. Crook is elected? Explain.
4. Let α and β be two *distinct* objects (not numbers) for which the following axioms hold.
   Axiom 1. $\alpha\beta = \alpha$.
   Axiom 2. $\alpha\alpha = \beta$.
   Axiom 3. $(xy)z = x(yz) = xyz$, where x, y, z are separately either α or β.
   Prove the following statements:
   Theorem A. $\beta\beta = \beta$.
   Theorem B. $\alpha\beta = \beta\alpha$.
5. With the axioms of Example 1.5b, prove:
   (a) If the system is in equilibrium, then $W_1 = W_2 \Rightarrow d_1 = d_2$.
   (b) If the system is in equilibrium, then $d_1 = d_2 \Rightarrow W_1 = W_2$
6. Consider a system, called a **miniature geometry**, of "points" and "lines" for which the following axioms are satisfied.
   Axiom 1. Each pair of lines has exactly one point in common.
   Axiom 2. Every point is on exactly two lines.
   Axiom 3. There are exactly four lines in the system.
   Prove the following theorems:
   Theorem A. There are exactly six points in the system.
   Theorem B. There are exactly three points on each line.
7. Let a, b, c, d, e, f, g denote objects called "points."
   Definition: A "line" is a collection of two or more points. Suppose lines and points satisfy the following axioms.
   Axiom 1. Each pair of lines has exactly one point in common.
   Axiom 2. All lines contain the same number of points.
   Axiom 3. Every pair of points must determine exactly one line.
   Axiom 4. There is more than one line.
   Prove that
   (a) every point must lie on exactly three lines;
   (b) there are seven lines.
   How is Axiom 4 used?
8. Let a B denote a collection of objects called A's, and suppose the following axioms hold.
   Axiom 1. There are at least two A's—A_1 and A_2.
   Axiom 2. Any two A's are in one and only one B.

Axiom 3. Any given *B* contains two or more *A*'s.

Axiom 4. For a given *B*, there is exactly one *A* not in that *B*.

Prove that

(a) there are at least two *A*'s;

(b) there are at least three *B*'s;

(c) there cannot be four *A*'s.

9. Is it true or false that the number of sides of a polygon is always equal to the number of its vertices?

10. Try to obtain a formula that will give the number of regions into which a plane is partitioned by *n* straight lines, no two of which are parallel and no three of which are concurrent. *Note*: You are not asked to prove that the formula is correct. This will be done in Exercises 2.2, Number 26.

11. In a plane there are *n* straight lines, no two of them being parallel and no three of them concurrent. Determine how many points of intersection there are. (See Exercises 2.2, Number 27.)

12. Let $d(n)$ be the number of distinct divisors of the positive integer *n*. For example, $d(1) = 1$, $d(2) = 2$, $d(3) = 2$, $d(4) = 3$, $d(5) = 2$, $d(9) = 3$, etc. Is the statement "$d(n)$ is odd $\Leftrightarrow n$ is a perfect square" a reasonable conjecture? If you think so, try to prove it.

13. Let *F* denote the number of faces of a polyhedron, *V* the number of its vertices, and *E* the number of its edges. Is the statement

$$F + V = E + 2$$

a reasonable conjecture? (In connection with this problem, you might like to read pages 236–240, of Courant and Robbins, *What is Mathematics?*)

1.6 THE CONCEPT OF SET

The concept of set is the most primitive and fundamental concept underlying any mathematical structure. It arises as a generalization of a concept familiar in daily life. For example, a collection of atoms forms a larger unit called a *molecule*. The furniture in a bedroom is sometimes called a *set* or *suite*. The collection of books owned by a particular individual is his *library*. In each case the word—molecule, suite, or library—is a name used to designate a collection of objects. The collection itself is considered as an individual object.

A gathering of distinct objects into a whole need not be confined to physical objects. A collection may equally well consist of several abstract ideas. For example, the *Ten Commandments* is the name of a collection of moral laws.

It is generally accepted in mathematics that the word *set* is an undefined term. Rather than adopt this point of view here, we shall consider the word to be definable in terms of other words in the basic vocabulary. Thus, we have

Definition 1.6a. A **set** is a collection of well-defined objects regarded as a single unit. The objects belonging to a set are called **elements** of the set.

As an example, let us consider the objects *a, e, i, o, u* as a unit. If we choose a name, say $\mathcal{V}$, for this unit, then we write

$$\mathcal{V} .=. \{a, e, i, o, u\}.$$

This collection of symbols is read, "$\mathcal{U}$ is defined to be the set of elements a, e, i, o, u." The braces will consistently be used to designate a set, and the symbols written within the braces indicate the elements that constitute the set. Script capital letters will be used for names of sets.

The set $\mathcal{U}$ can be defined in another way. We may say that it is the set of vowels of the English alphabet. Indeed, this example illustrates a second way in which a set may be defined. In the first method, the elements in the set are explicitly listed. In the second method the set is defined by means of a property possessed by the elements and only by the elements that are to be in the set. By this method, we write

$$\mathcal{U} .=. \{*: * \text{ is a vowel of the English alphabet}\},$$

which is read "$\mathcal{U}$ is defined to be the set of objects $*$ such that $*$ is a vowel of the English alphabet." If $*$ is replaced by the name of some object, and if the resulting statement is true, then that object is considered to be an element of the set $\mathcal{U}$; if the resulting statement is false, or if it is meaningless, then the object is not an element of the set. Thus, in the definition of $\mathcal{U}$, if we replace $*$ by 3, we obtain the false statement, "3 is a vowel of the English alphabet." Hence 3 is not an element of $\mathcal{U}$.

Similarly, we may write

$$\mathcal{N} .=. \{x: x \text{ is a positive integer}\}.$$

That is, $\mathcal{N}$ is the collection of objects x such that x is a positive integer. This set cannot be defined by listing all its elements, so that the method of defining a set by means of a property is an essential one. The statement giving the property for the elements in the set being defined is called a **defining relation.**

Some other examples of sets are

(a) $\mathcal{A} .=. \{x: x = a, x = b, \text{ or } x = c\}$ or, more concisely,
$\mathcal{A} .=. \{a, b, c\}$;

(b) $\mathcal{P} .=. \{x: x \text{ is a prime number}\}$;

(c) $\mathcal{B} .=. \{x: x \text{ is an animal}\}$;

(d) $\mathcal{S} .=. \{x: x \text{ is a planet of Sol}\}$.

Some of the elements of $\mathcal{P}$ are 2, 3, 5, 641. Some objects that are not in $\mathcal{P}$ are 12, *dog*, *Venus*, *pencil*, and *a*.

The following notations are convenient for indicating that an object does or does not belong to a set.

Definition 1.6b. The notation $a \in \mathcal{S}$ means that the object a is an element of the set $\mathcal{S}$.

Definition 1.6c. The notation $a \notin \mathcal{S}$ means that a is not an element of $\mathcal{S}$.

Referring to the preceding examples of sets, we may write $2 \in \mathcal{P}$, Venus $\in \mathcal{S}$, dog $\notin \mathcal{A}$, $a \notin \mathcal{B}$, cat $\in \mathcal{B}$, etc.

In Definition 1.6a, a set was described as a collection of well-defined objects. The adjective *well-defined* has been inserted in order to indicate that not every "defining relation" may be adequate to define a set. A careless use of defining relations may lead to paradoxical situations. For example, may

$$\mathcal{Q} .=. \{x: x \text{ is } a \text{ or } b \text{ or } \mathcal{Q}\}$$

be properly considered to define a set? This is clearly a case of trying to define a set in terms of itself. Such a definition cannot be considered valid, and we shall not regard it as defining any set at all. It is necessary that a defining relation clearly determine the elements that belong to the set.

It is also necessary to distinguish between an *element* of a set and the *set* to which the element belongs. There is little danger of confusion when there are several elements in the set, but if a set contains only one element the situation may become delicate. For example, let

$$\mathcal{S} .=. \{a\}.$$

The name of the set consisting of the one object, *a*, is $\mathcal{S}$. It is desirable to maintain a distinction between the two entities—the element and the set consisting of that element.

Sometimes sets having other sets as elements are important. For example, let

$$\mathcal{Q} .=. \{a, b\},$$
$$\mathcal{B} .=. \{b, d, e\},$$
$$\mathcal{C} .=. \{2, 3, 4, 5\}.$$

Then we may wish to consider a set

$$\mathcal{J} .=. \{\mathcal{Q}, \mathcal{B}, \mathcal{C}\}.$$

The elements of $\mathcal{J}$ are $\mathcal{Q}$, $\mathcal{B}$, and $\mathcal{C}$. However, the elements of $\mathcal{Q}$, $\mathcal{B}$, and $\mathcal{C}$ are *not* elements of $\mathcal{J}$.

In working with sets, we might encounter a defining relation such as "*x* is a prime number less than 2." Since 1 is not considered a prime, we find that there are no objects for which the defining relation is true. Rather than prohibit the use of such a definition, we regard it as a defining relation for a set having no elements.

Definition 1.6d. A defining relation that is satisfied by no element is said to define a set called the **empty set,** denoted by $\varnothing$.

It is generally agreed that there can be only one empty set, since there is no way of distinguishing between two such sets. Accordingly, we speak of *the* empty set rather than *an* empty set.

As a further illustration of the difference between a set and the elements of a set, consider the set

$$\mathcal{Q} .=. \{\varnothing\}.$$

This set consists of the single element $\varnothing$, itself a set that contains no elements.

Suppose we consider a set consisting of elements that belong to another set. The fact that such a relationship exists between the two sets is indicated by saying the first set is a **subset** of the given set. To indicate this relationship between two sets α and $\mathfrak{B}$, we introduce a special notation.

Definition 1.6e. $\alpha \subset \mathfrak{B}$ (read "α is a subset of $\mathfrak{B}$") means that every element of α is also an element of $\mathfrak{B}$.

Definition 1.6f. If there is at least one element in $\mathfrak{B}$ that is not also in α, then α is called a **proper** subset of $\mathfrak{B}$.

Definition 1.6g. $\alpha \not\subset \mathfrak{B}$ means that α is *not* a subset of $\mathfrak{B}$, which means that there is at least one element of α that is not in $\mathfrak{B}$.

For example, if

$$\alpha .=. \{a, b, c, d\},$$
$$\mathfrak{B} .=. \{c, d\},$$
$$\mathcal{C} .=. \{d, b, a, c\},$$

then $\mathfrak{B}$ is a proper subset of α and $\mathcal{C}$, and $\mathcal{C}$ is a subset but not a proper subset of α. In fact, α and $\mathcal{C}$ both consist of the same elements, so that

$$\alpha \subset \mathcal{C} \quad \text{and} \quad \mathcal{C} \subset \alpha.$$

Also, we have $\alpha \not\subset \mathfrak{B}$ because there are elements in α that are not in $\mathfrak{B}$.

A simple consequence of the definition of subset is

Theorem 1.6a. The empty set is a subset of every set.

PROOF: If the empty set is not a subset of an arbitrary set α, then there must be an element in $\varnothing$ that is not in α. But since $\varnothing$ contains no elements, this relationship is impossible. Hence $\varnothing$ must be considered a subset of α.

To illustrate the difference in meaning between the symbols $\in$ and $\subset$, observe that $\subset$ may stand only between sets, and $\in$ may stand only between an object in a set and a set. Thus, all of the subsets of $\alpha .=. \{a, b, c\}$ are $\varnothing$, $\{a\}$, $\{b\}$, $\{c\}$, $\{a, b\}$, $\{b, c\}$, $\{a, c\}$, and α itself. Hence, we may write

$$\{a\} \subset \alpha \quad \text{or} \quad \{b\} \subset \alpha \quad \text{or} \quad \{a, b\} \subset \alpha$$

and

$$a \in \alpha \quad \text{or} \quad b \in \alpha$$

but *not*

$$a \subset \alpha \quad \text{or} \quad \{a\} \in \alpha.$$

The reader should notice the difference in the treatment of the object a and the set $\{a\}$, whose only element is a.

Example 1.6a. If $\alpha .=. \{2, 4, 7, 9\}$ and $\mathfrak{B} .=. \{2, 3, 4\}$, show that neither set is a subset of the other.

We have
$$7 \in \alpha \quad \text{and} \quad 7 \notin \mathfrak{B} \Rightarrow \alpha \not\subset \mathfrak{B}.$$

Similarly,
$$3 \in \mathfrak{B} \quad \text{and} \quad 3 \notin \alpha \Rightarrow \mathfrak{B} \not\subset \alpha.$$

Thus, neither set is a subset of the other.

The last example shows that a subset relationship need not exist between two arbitrary sets. It is clear already that a set may be defined in many ways. Hence, an important question that must sometimes be answered is whether or not two sets defined in different ways are really the same set. In fact, although we may have an intuitive idea of what is meant by saying that two sets α and $\mathcal{B}$ are the same, it is necessary to state formally the circumstances under which two sets shall be considered identical.

Definition 1.6h. Two sets α and $\mathcal{B}$ are the same if, and only if, they contain the same elements. In this case, we write $\alpha = \mathcal{B}$.

This definition is almost equivalent to

Theorem 1.6b. If α and $\mathcal{B}$ are sets,

$$\alpha = \mathcal{B} \Leftrightarrow \alpha \subset \mathcal{B} \quad \text{and} \quad \mathcal{B} \subset \alpha.$$

The next example illustrates these ideas in an elementary way.

Example 1.6b. Let $\mathcal{P}$ and $\mathcal{Q}$ be two sets such that

$\mathcal{P} .=. \{x: x \text{ is the square of a positive integer}\},$

and

$\mathcal{Q} .=. \{y: y \text{ is a positive integer having an odd number of distinct divisors}\}.$

Are the sets $\mathcal{P}$ and $\mathcal{Q}$ the same?

In other words, while we may think that we have defined two *different* sets by using different defining relations, it may happen that we have not. In fact, in view of Exercises 1.5, Number 12, we know that if $x = n = p^2$, then $d(n)$ is an odd number, so that $\mathcal{P} \subset \mathcal{Q}$. Also, if n has an odd number of divisors, then n is a perfect square, so that $\mathcal{Q} \subset \mathcal{P}$. Hence $\mathcal{P} = \mathcal{Q}$.

Example 1.6c. Let $\mathcal{P}$ and $\mathcal{Q}$ be two sets such that

$\mathcal{P} .=. \{y: y \text{ is the sum of consecutive odd positive integers}\},$
$\mathcal{Q} .=. \{x: x \text{ is the square of a positive integer}\}.$

Are the sets $\mathcal{P}$ and $\mathcal{Q}$ the same, or is one a subset of the other?

In order to demonstrate a method of argument that is applicable to more difficult problems, we shall make a slightly more detailed analysis than is necessary. Let x be an element of $\mathcal{Q}$. Then $x = n^2$, where n is a positive integer. It can be shown (as will be done later) that, for each positive integer n,

$$n^2 = 1 + 3 + 5 + \cdots + (2n - 1).$$

Hence x is the sum of consecutive odd integers and is therefore an element of $\mathcal{P}$. This shows that $\mathcal{Q} \subset \mathcal{P}$.

Next, let $y \in \mathcal{P}$, so that

$$y = (2k + 1) + (2k + 3) + \cdots + (2m + 1), \qquad k < m.$$

Now y may be written in the form

$$y = (m + 1)^2 - k^2.$$

(Why?) This expression is not always the square of an integer. (Prove this.) Hence, $\mathcal{P} \not\subset \mathcal{Q}$, and $\mathcal{Q}$ is a proper subset of $\mathcal{P}$.

Exercises 1.6

1. For each of the following descriptions, write out specifically the elements of the set $\mathcal{Q}$.

   (a) $\mathcal{Q} .=. \{x: x \text{ is a positive even integer not exceeding } 10\}$.
   (b) $\mathcal{Q} .=. \{x: x^2 - 1 = 0\}$.
   (c) $\mathcal{Q} .=. \{x: x = [\![y]\!] \text{ and } 0 < y < 10\}$.
   (d) $\mathcal{Q} .=. \{x: x \text{ is a prime number between 30 and 40}\}$.

2. What common property is possessed by the elements of each set $\mathcal{Q}$ if

   (a) $\mathcal{Q} .=. \{1, 3, 5, 7, 9\}$;
   (b) $\mathcal{Q} .=. \{4, 8, 12, 16, 20\}$;
   (c) $\mathcal{Q} .=. \{[\![2.1]\!], [\![2.67]\!], [\![2.78]\!], [\![2.95]\!]\}$;
   (d) $\mathcal{Q} .=. \{\frac{1}{2}, \frac{3}{2}, \frac{5}{2}, \frac{7}{2}, \frac{9}{2}, \frac{11}{2}\}$.

3. Determine for each of the following if (i) $\mathcal{Q}$ is a subset of $\mathcal{B}$; (ii) $\mathcal{B}$ is a subset of $\mathcal{Q}$; (iii) $\mathcal{Q}$ is a proper subset of $\mathcal{B}$; (iv) $\mathcal{B}$ is a proper subset of $\mathcal{Q}$.

   (a) $\mathcal{Q} .=. \{1, 3, 5, 6, 8\}$, $\mathcal{B} .=. \{1, 5, 7\}$.
   (b) $\mathcal{Q} .=. \{1, 3, 7\}$, $\mathcal{B} .=. \{x: x \text{ is an odd integer}\}$.
   (c) $\mathcal{Q} .=. \{a, b, c, d\}$, $\mathcal{B} .=. \{d, c, a, b\}$.
   (d) $\mathcal{Q} .=. \{2, 4, 5\}$, $\mathcal{B} .=. \{x: x \text{ is an even integer}\}$.
   (e) $\mathcal{Q} .=. \{x: 0 < x < 1\}$, $\mathcal{B} .=. \{x: 0 \leq x \leq 1\}$.

4. If

$$\mathcal{Q} .=. \{a, b\} \quad \text{and} \quad \mathcal{B} .=. \{a, c, \mathcal{Q}\},$$

   which of the following statements is (are) correct?

   (a) $a \in \mathcal{Q}$.
   (b) $a \subset \mathcal{Q}$.
   (c) $a \notin \mathcal{Q}$.
   (d) $a \not\subset \mathcal{Q}$.
   (e) $\mathcal{Q} \in \mathcal{Q}$.
   (f) $\mathcal{Q} \notin \mathcal{Q}$.
   (g) $\mathcal{Q} \subset \mathcal{Q}$.
   (h) $\mathcal{Q} \not\subset \mathcal{Q}$.

   (i) $b \in \mathcal{B}$.
   (j) $b \notin \mathcal{B}$.
   (k) $b \subset \mathcal{B}$.
   (l) $b \not\subset \mathcal{B}$.
   (m) $\mathcal{Q} \in \mathcal{B}$.
   (n) $\mathcal{Q} \notin \mathcal{B}$.
   (o) $\mathcal{Q} \subset \mathcal{B}$.
   (p) $\mathcal{Q} \not\subset \mathcal{B}$.

5. Let $\mathcal{Q}$, $\mathcal{B}$, $\mathcal{C}$ be sets. Which of the following is (are) valid?

   (a) $\mathcal{Q} \neq \mathcal{B}$ and $\mathcal{B} \neq \mathcal{C} \Rightarrow \mathcal{Q} \neq \mathcal{C}$.
   (b) $\mathcal{Q} \not\subset \mathcal{B}$ and $\mathcal{B} \not\subset \mathcal{C} \Rightarrow \mathcal{Q} \not\subset \mathcal{C}$.

6. A set $\mathcal{Q}$ contains n elements. How many subsets of $\mathcal{Q}$ are there?

7. The fact that there can be only one empty set—that is, that the empty set is unique—can be proved by means of Theorem 1.6b. Assume that $\varnothing'$ is another empty set, and prove that $\varnothing = \varnothing'$.

1.7 CORRESPONDENCE OF SETS

Suppose that α is the set of chairs in a classroom and that $\mathcal{B}$ is the set of students attending a class in that room. If every chair is occupied by one student, and if there is no student without a chair, then we say that to each chair there corresponds a student and to each student there corresponds a chair. A relationship of this kind between sets is described by

Definition 1.7a. If, with every $a \in \alpha$ there is associated a unique element $b \in \mathcal{B}$, and conversely, if $a \in \alpha$ is uniquely associated with $b \in \mathcal{B}$, then α and $\mathcal{B}$ are said to be in a **one-to-one correspondence**. The association between elements is denoted by writing $a \leftrightarrow b$.

To illustrate, let $\alpha .=. \{1, 2, 3, 4\}$ and let $\mathcal{B} .=. \{a, b, c, d\}$. The manner in which the elements of α are associated with the elements of $\mathcal{B}$ is entirely arbitrary, so long as the correspondence is one-to-one. For example, we might have

$$1 \leftrightarrow a, \quad 2 \leftrightarrow d, \quad 3 \leftrightarrow b, \quad 4 \leftrightarrow c.$$

Since each element in each set is used exactly once, and since there are no elements of either set left unused, a one-to-one correspondence has been established. Clearly, a correspondence between these two sets can be established in a number of ways.

To describe a one-to-one correspondence between sets α and $\mathcal{B}$, we have

Definition 1.7b. $\alpha \sim \mathcal{B}$ (read "α is equivalent to $\mathcal{B}$") means that there exists a one-to-one correspondence between α and $\mathcal{B}$.

The problem of establishing a one-to-one correspondence between sets is not always as simple as it may seem from the preceding illustration. Often a correspondence must be established by means of a rule that prescribes the association of the elements of the sets in question. For example, if $\mathfrak{N}$ is the set of natural numbers, and if $\mathcal{I}_3$ is the set of positive integers that are multiples of 3, then we may establish a one-to-one correspondence between the sets by associating with the element n in $\mathfrak{N}$ the element $3n$ in $\mathcal{I}_3$; that is, $n \leftrightarrow 3n$. While this formula does not explicitly list corresponding elements from each set, it can be used to determine which element of $\mathcal{I}_3$ is associated with a given element of $\mathfrak{N}$, or conversely. For example, with the element 7 in $\mathfrak{N}$ is associated the element 21 in $\mathcal{I}_3$, and with 69 in $\mathcal{I}_3$ is associated the element 23 in $\mathfrak{N}$. The correspondence may be indicated, in this case, by the array

$$\mathfrak{N}: 1, 2, 3, \ 4, \ \ldots, n, \ \ldots,$$
$$\mathcal{I}_3: 3, 6, 9, 12, \ldots, 3n, \ldots,$$

in which the corresponding elements of the two sets are matched in vertical columns.

The correspondence between the sets $\mathfrak{N}$ and $\mathcal{I}_3$ illustrates a case in which a subset ($\mathcal{I}_3$) of a set ($\mathfrak{N}$) is equivalent to the original set $\mathfrak{N}$. If a set α has a proper subset $\mathcal{B}$ such that $\mathcal{B} \sim \mathcal{A}$, then $\mathcal{A}$ must have an infinite number of elements. Sets that are equivalent to the set $\mathfrak{N}$ of natural numbers are called **denumerable** sets. Other infinite sets, such as the set of real numbers, are said to be **non-denumerable,** and the problem of establishing a correspondence between two equivalent nondenumerable sets is often tricky. We shall not pursue the matter in detail here.

However, to illustrate the situation if x and y are real numbers, let

$$\mathcal{A} .=. \{x: 0 \leq x \leq 1\},$$
$$\mathcal{B} .=. \{y: 5 \leq y \leq 8\}.$$

Then we can show that $\mathcal{A} \sim \mathcal{B}$. With the number x we associate the number $(y - 5)/3$, and write $x = (y - 5)/3$. By means of this formula, we can obtain a unique number x in $\mathcal{A}$ for a given y in $\mathcal{B}$; conversely, for a given x there is a corresponding value of y—namely, $y = 3x + 5$. Hence, $\mathcal{A} \sim \mathcal{B}$.

It is important for the reader to realize that many kinds of correspondences between elements of two sets may be established. Some of these correspondences will *not* be one-to-one. However, this fact does *not* mean that there exists no one-to-one correspondence between the two sets. Whether or not a one-to-one correspondence is exhibited may depend on the way in which elements are associated. In order to prove that a one-to-one correspondence exists, it is sufficient to exhibit at least one method by which the correspondence is established. But to prove that a one-to-one correspondence does not exist between two sets can be very difficult. (Note that the definition of equivalence of sets requires every nonempty set to be equivalent to itself.)

Exercises 1.7

In each of the following problems, decide whether or not $\mathcal{A} \sim \mathcal{B}$, and prove that your answer is correct.

1. $\mathcal{A} .=. \{1, 3, 7, 9\}, \mathcal{B} .=. \{2, 4, 6, 8\}$.
2. $\mathcal{A} .=. \{a, b, c, d\}, \mathcal{B} .=. \{1, 3, 5, 7, 9\}$.
3. $\mathcal{A} .=. \{3, 6, 9, \ldots, 3k, \ldots\}, k \in \mathfrak{N}, \mathcal{B} .=. \{5, 10, 15, \ldots, 5n, \ldots\}, n \in \mathfrak{N}$.
4. $\mathcal{A} .=. \{x: x \text{ is a positive integer}\}, \mathcal{B} .=. \{(x, y): x, y \text{ are positive integers}\}$.
5. $\mathcal{A} .=. \{x: 0 \leq x \leq 1\}, \mathcal{B} .=. \{y: 0 \leq y \leq 3\}$.
6. $\mathcal{A} .=. \{x: 0 < x \leq 1\}, \mathcal{B} .=. \{y: 1 \leq y\}$.
7. $\mathcal{A} .=. \{x: x \text{ is a seat in your classroom}\}, \mathcal{B} .=. \{y: y \text{ is a student in your classroom}\}$.
8. $\mathcal{A} .=. \{x: 2 \leq x \leq 3\}, \mathcal{B} .=. \{y: 7 \leq y \leq 70\}$.
9. $\mathcal{A} .=. \{x: a \leq x \leq b\}, \mathcal{B} .=. \{y: c \leq y \leq d\}, a < b, c < d$.
10. $\mathcal{A} .=. \{x: 0 < x \leq 1\}, \mathcal{B} .=. \{y: 0 \leq y < 1\}$.

1.8 OPERATIONS ON SETS

It is frequently convenient to consider new sets constructed in some prescribed manner from given sets. There are two particularly important ways in which such a construction can be accomplished.

Let α and $\mathcal{B}$ be sets. Then the **union** of the two sets, written $\alpha \cup \mathcal{B}$, is described in

Definition 1.8a. $\quad \alpha \cup \mathcal{B} .=. \{x: x \in \alpha \text{ and/or } x \in \mathcal{B}\}.$

Thus, $\alpha \cup \mathcal{B}$ represents the set obtained by putting the elements of α and $\mathcal{B}$ together into one set. To illustrate, let

$$\alpha .=. \{a, b\} \quad \text{and} \quad \mathcal{B} .=. \{a, c, d\}.$$

Then

$$\alpha \cup \mathcal{B} = \{a, b, c, d\}.$$

Notice that the element common to both sets is *not* counted twice in the union of α and $\mathcal{B}$.

The second important set construction consists of the elements that are common to α and $\mathcal{B}$ and is called the **intersection** of the sets α and $\mathcal{B}$. The intersection of α and $\mathcal{B}$ is denoted by $\alpha \cap \mathcal{B}$ and is described by

Definition 1.8b. $\quad \alpha \cap \mathcal{B} .=. \{x: x \in \alpha \text{ and } x \in \mathcal{B}\}.$

In the preceding illustration,

$$\alpha \cap \mathcal{B} = \{a\}.$$

Example 1.8a. Let

$$\mathcal{I}_e .=. \{x: x \text{ is an even integer}\},$$
$$\mathcal{I}_o .=. \{x: x \text{ is an odd integer}\}.$$

Describe the sets $\mathcal{I}_e \cup \mathcal{I}_o$ and $\mathcal{I}_e \cap \mathcal{I}_o$.

Since $\mathcal{I}_e \cup \mathcal{I}_o$ is the set $\mathcal{I}$ of all the integers, we have

$$\mathcal{I}_e \cup \mathcal{I}_o = \mathcal{I}.$$

Furthermore, no integer can be both odd and even, so

$$\mathcal{I}_e \cap \mathcal{I}_o = \varnothing.$$

In addition to the operations of union and intersection, it is useful to have an operation on sets that picks out the elements in one set that are not in another. Such an operation is given by

Definition 1.8c. $\quad \alpha - \mathcal{B} .=. \{x: x \in \alpha \text{ and } x \notin \mathcal{B}\}.$

The operation is called the **set difference**. It removes from α those elements that are in $\alpha \cap \mathcal{B}$. In certain special cases the operation yields what at first sight may appear to be rather surprising results. For example, let

$$\alpha .=. \{a, b, c\} \quad \text{and} \quad \mathcal{B} .=. \{a, d\}.$$

Then

$$\alpha - \mathcal{B} = \{b, c\},$$

and

$$\mathcal{B} - \alpha = \{d\}.$$

Moreover, if

$$\mathcal{C} .=. \{d, e\} \quad \text{and} \quad \mathcal{D} .=. \{d, e, f\},$$

then
$$\mathcal{D} - \mathcal{C} = \{f\},$$
and
$$\mathcal{C} - \mathcal{D} = \varnothing.$$

Sets formed by unions or intersections may be represented pictorially by means of diagrams (called Venn diagrams) as shown in Figure 1.8a.

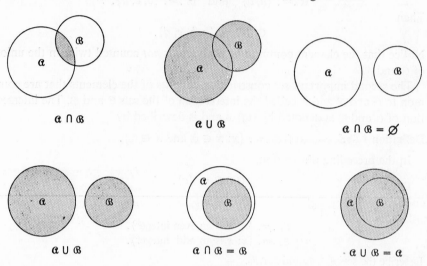

The sets $\mathcal{C}$ and $\mathcal{B}$ are represented by the regions interior to the closed curves. The shaded region is the region indicated below each diagram. Note that $\mathcal{C} \cap \mathcal{B} \subset \mathcal{C} \cup \mathcal{B}$.

FIGURE 1.8a

Occasionally, we shall be interested only in sets that are contained in a fixed given set, called a **universal set** or a **universe.** For example, we may wish to carry out an extended discussion using only sets whose elements are letters of the English alphabet. In this case, we call the alphabet the universal set, since every set in the discussion is a subset of it. Two particular subsets are

$$\mathcal{V} .= . \{a, e, i, o, u\}$$
and
$$\mathcal{C} .= . \{b, c, d, f, g, h, j, k, l, m, n, p, q, r, s, t, v, w, x, y, z\},$$

that is, the set of vowels and the set of consonants. These two sets have the property that their union is the universal set and their intersection is the empty set. When two sets are so related, we say that one set is the **complement** of the other with respect to the universe. Hence, if $\mathcal{U}$ denotes a universe (the alphabet in the above illustration) and $\mathcal{C}'$ the complement of a given set $\mathcal{C}$, we have

Definition 1.8d. $\qquad \mathcal{C}' .= . \mathcal{U} - \mathcal{C}.$

This is read "the complement of $\mathcal{C}$ is defined to be the set of elements in the universe that are not in $\mathcal{C}$." Hence, in the previous illustration, $\mathcal{C}' = \mathcal{V}$ and $\mathcal{V}' = \mathcal{C}$, with respect to $\mathcal{U}$. It is important that a statement of complementation be qualified unless it is clearly understood what is the universe.

For example, if we wish to form the complement of a set $\mathcal{A}$ with respect to a set $\mathcal{U}$ on one occasion and with respect to a set $\mathcal{V}$ on another occasion, we must so indicate. A notation such as $\mathcal{A}'_\mathcal{U}$ or $\mathcal{A}'_\mathcal{V}$ may be used for this purpose.

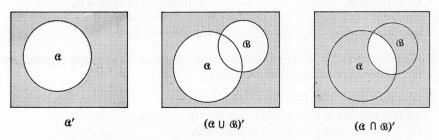

$\mathcal{A}'$ $\qquad$ $(\mathcal{A} \cup \mathcal{B})'$ $\qquad$ $(\mathcal{A} \cap \mathcal{B})'$

The shaded region is the region indicated below each diagram.

FIGURE 1.8b

The complement can also be illustrated by means of Venn diagrams. Let the universe be the region enclosed within a rectangle. The complements of various sets are shown in Figure 1.8b.

Exercises 1.8

1. Given the sets $\mathcal{A} .=. \{a, b, c, d\}$, $\mathcal{B} .=. \{a, b, e, f, g\}$, $\mathcal{C} .=. \{b, c, e, h\}$, and the universe $\mathcal{U} .=. \{a, b, c, d, e, f, g, h\}$, express each of the following sets in terms of its elements.

   (a) $\mathcal{A} \cap \mathcal{C}$.
   (b) $\mathcal{A} \cup \mathcal{C}$.
   (c) $\mathcal{A} - \mathcal{B}$.
   (d) $\mathcal{A}'$.
   (e) $\mathcal{A}' \cup \mathcal{B}'$.
   (f) $\mathcal{B}' \cap \mathcal{C}$.

   (g) $(\mathcal{A} \cap \mathcal{B}) - \mathcal{B}$.
   (h) $(\mathcal{B} \cap \mathcal{C}')'$.
   (i) $\mathcal{B}' - \mathcal{A}'$.
   (j) $(\mathcal{C} - \mathcal{B}) - \mathcal{A}$.
   (k) $\mathcal{C} - (\mathcal{B} - \mathcal{A})$.

2. Given the sets $\mathcal{A} .=. \{x: 0 \leq x \leq 3\}, \mathcal{B} .=. \{x: 1 < x < 4\}, \mathcal{C} .=. \{x: 2 \leq x < 5\}$, where the universe is the set $\mathcal{U} .=. \{x: 0 \leq x \leq 6\}$, find each of the following sets.

   (a) $\mathcal{A} \cap \mathcal{B}$.
   (b) $\mathcal{A} \cup \mathcal{C}$.
   (c) $\mathcal{A} - \mathcal{B}$.
   (d) $\mathcal{B} - \mathcal{A}$.
   (e) $(\mathcal{B} \cap \mathcal{C}) - \mathcal{A}$.
   (f) $\mathcal{A}' - \mathcal{B}$.

   (g) $\mathcal{A}' - \mathcal{C}'$.
   (h) $(\mathcal{A} \cap \mathcal{B}) - \mathcal{C}'$.
   (i) $\mathcal{B}' \cap \mathcal{C}'$.
   (j) $(\mathcal{A} - \mathcal{B}')'$.
   (k) $(\mathcal{A} \cup \mathcal{B}) - \mathcal{C}'$.
   (l) $(\mathcal{A}' \cap \mathcal{B}')'$.

3. If $\mathcal{A} .=. \{0, 1, 2\}$, $\mathcal{B} .=. \{0, 2, 4\}$, and $\mathcal{C} .=. \{1, 2, 3\}$, find the following.

   (a) All possible sets obtained from $\mathcal{A}$, $\mathcal{B}$, and $\mathcal{C}$ by using only the operations $\cup$ and $\cap$.
   (b) All possible sets obtained from $\mathcal{A}$, $\mathcal{B}$, and $\mathcal{C}$ by using only the operation $-$.

4. Let $\mathfrak{U}$ denote a universal set. Study the following list, in which some of the relations are incorrect. Determine which are incorrect and correct them.

(a) $\mathfrak{A} \cup \varnothing = \mathfrak{A}$.

(b) $\mathfrak{A} \cap \mathfrak{U} = \mathfrak{A}$.

(c) $\mathfrak{A} \cup \mathfrak{A}' = \mathfrak{U}$.

(d) $\mathfrak{A} \cap \mathfrak{A}' = \mathfrak{A}$.

(e) $\mathfrak{A} \cup \mathfrak{A} = \mathfrak{A}$.

(f) $\mathfrak{A} \cap \mathfrak{A} = \varnothing$.

(g) $\mathfrak{A} \cup \mathfrak{U} = \mathfrak{U}$.

(h) $\mathfrak{A} \cap \varnothing = \varnothing$.

(i) $(\mathfrak{A}')' = \mathfrak{U}$.

(j) If $\mathfrak{A} = \mathfrak{B}'$ then $\mathfrak{B} = \mathfrak{A}'$.

(k) $(\mathfrak{A} - \mathfrak{B}) \cup \mathfrak{B} = \mathfrak{A} - \mathfrak{B}$.

(l) $(\mathfrak{A} \cup \mathfrak{B}) - \mathfrak{B} = \mathfrak{A} - \mathfrak{B}$.

(m) $\mathfrak{A} \cap (\mathfrak{A} - \mathfrak{B}) = \mathfrak{A} \cup \mathfrak{B}$.

(n) $(\mathfrak{A} - \mathfrak{B})' = \mathfrak{A}' - \mathfrak{B}'$.

5. Find three sets, $\mathfrak{A}$, $\mathfrak{B}$, and $\mathfrak{C}$, such that any two of them have nonempty intersections but all three have an empty intersection.

6. If $\mathfrak{A}$, $\mathfrak{B}$, $\mathfrak{C}$, and $\mathfrak{D}$ are sets, show that

(a) if $\mathfrak{A} \subset \mathfrak{C}$ and $\mathfrak{B} \subset \mathfrak{D}$, then $\mathfrak{A} \cup \mathfrak{B} \subset \mathfrak{C} \cup \mathfrak{D}$;

(b) if $\mathfrak{A} \subset \mathfrak{C}$ and $\mathfrak{B} \subset \mathfrak{D}$, then $\mathfrak{A} \cap \mathfrak{B} \subset \mathfrak{C} \cap \mathfrak{D}$.

7. Let $\mathfrak{A}$ and $\mathfrak{B}$ be sets such that

(i) $\mathfrak{A} \cup \mathfrak{B} = \{a, b, c, d\}$;

(ii) $\mathfrak{A} \cap \mathfrak{B} = \{a, c\}$;

(iii) $\mathfrak{A} - \mathfrak{B} = \{b\}$.

Find $\mathfrak{A}$ and $\mathfrak{B}$.

*1.9 SET ALGEBRA

The set compositions or operations defined in the preceding section have some interesting properties. These properties are often associated with an operation in an algebraic system. In the following theorems, $\mathfrak{A}$, $\mathfrak{B}$, and $\mathfrak{C}$ denote sets.

Theorem 1.9a. *The commutative property for set unions:*

$$\mathfrak{A} \cup \mathfrak{B} = \mathfrak{B} \cup \mathfrak{A}.$$

Theorem 1.9b. *The commutative property for set intersections:*

$$\mathfrak{A} \cap \mathfrak{B} = \mathfrak{B} \cap \mathfrak{A}.$$

PROOF: The proof of each of these theorems is almost trivial. Thus, if $x \in \mathfrak{A} \cup \mathfrak{B}$, then $x \in \mathfrak{A}$ or $x \in \mathfrak{B}$. It follows that "$x \in \mathfrak{B}$ or $x \in \mathfrak{A}$" also is true. Hence, $x \in \mathfrak{B} \cup \mathfrak{A}$. That is, $\mathfrak{A} \cup \mathfrak{B} \subset \mathfrak{B} \cup \mathfrak{A}$. By a similar argument, $\mathfrak{B} \cup \mathfrak{A} \subset \mathfrak{B} \cup \mathfrak{A}$, so that $\mathfrak{A} \cup \mathfrak{B} = \mathfrak{B} \cup \mathfrak{A}$. This completes the proof of Theorem 1.9a. The reader may construct a proof of Theorem 1.9b along similar lines.

The notation $\mathfrak{A} \cup (\mathfrak{B} \cup \mathfrak{C})$ means that the union of $\mathfrak{B}$ and $\mathfrak{C}$ is to be obtained first, then the union of the resulting set with $\mathfrak{A}$ is formed. That is, the parentheses prescribe an order for performing the set operations. The next two theorems show that the order of forming unions and intersections is immaterial.

Theorem 1.9c. *The associative property of union:*

$$\mathcal{Q} \cup (\mathcal{B} \cup \mathcal{C}) = (\mathcal{Q} \cup \mathcal{B}) \cup \mathcal{C}.$$

Theorem 1.9d. *The associative property of intersection:*

$$\mathcal{Q} \cap (\mathcal{B} \cap \mathcal{C}) = (\mathcal{Q} \cap \mathcal{B}) \cap \mathcal{C}.$$

These properties indicate that we may, without ambiguity, write $\mathcal{Q} \cup \mathcal{B} \cup \mathcal{C}$ for either expression in Theorem 1.9c and $\mathcal{Q} \cap \mathcal{B} \cap \mathcal{C}$ for either expression in Theorem 1.9d. The proof of each theorem is elementary and is left for the reader. Each theorem can be simply illustrated by means of Venn diagrams.

The next relationships are also fundamental to the algebra of sets.

Theorem 1.9e. *The distributive law of union with respect to intersection:*

$$\mathcal{Q} \cup (\mathcal{B} \cap \mathcal{C}) = (\mathcal{Q} \cup \mathcal{B}) \cap (\mathcal{Q} \cup \mathcal{C}).$$

Theorem 1.9f. *The distributive law of intersection with respect to union:*

$$\mathcal{Q} \cap (\mathcal{B} \cup \mathcal{C}) = (\mathcal{Q} \cap \mathcal{B}) \cup (\mathcal{Q} \cap \mathcal{C}).$$

Again, the proofs of these theorems are not difficult and may be left for the reader. As stated, Theorem 1.9e is a distributive law from the left. Since set union is commutative, we may write

$$(\mathcal{B} \cap \mathcal{C}) \cup \mathcal{Q} = (\mathcal{B} \cup \mathcal{Q}) \cap (\mathcal{C} \cup \mathcal{Q}),$$

which states that union is also distributive with respect to intersections from the right. Since the distributive property holds from both sides, we say that union is distributive with respect to intersection without qualification. For some operations the distributive law may hold only from the right or only from the left, but not from both sides. (See Exercises 1.9, Number 5.)

With the help of the preceding theorems and the following three additional fundamental relationships, an entire algebra of sets can be developed. This algebra will be illustrated only briefly here.

Theorem 1.9g. $\qquad\qquad \mathcal{Q} - \mathcal{B} = \mathcal{Q} \cap \mathcal{B}'.$

PROOF: Let $x \in \mathcal{Q} - \mathcal{B}$. Then, $x \in \mathcal{Q}$ and $x \notin \mathcal{B}$, or $x \in \mathcal{Q}$ and $x \in \mathcal{B}'$. Hence, $x \in \mathcal{Q} \cap \mathcal{B}'$, and $\mathcal{Q} - \mathcal{B} \subset \mathcal{Q} \cap \mathcal{B}'$. By reversing the argument, we obtain the result that $\mathcal{Q} \cap \mathcal{B}' \subset \mathcal{Q} - \mathcal{B}$ so that

$$\mathcal{Q} \cap \mathcal{B}' = \mathcal{Q} - \mathcal{B}.$$

Theorem 1.9h. De Morgan's Laws:

$$\text{(i) } (\mathcal{Q} \cup \mathcal{B})' = \mathcal{Q}' \cap \mathcal{B}',$$
$$\text{(ii) } (\mathcal{Q} \cap \mathcal{B})' = \mathcal{Q}' \cup \mathcal{B}'.$$

PROOF: The proofs of these statements may be carried out in a manner similar to the proof of Theorem 1.9g, and are left for the reader.

The following example illustrates the use of the fundamental properties in proving other relationships between sets.

Example 1.9a. Show that $\alpha - (\mathfrak{B} \cup \mathfrak{C}) = (\alpha - \mathfrak{B}) \cap (\alpha - \mathfrak{C})$.
We have

$$\begin{aligned}
\alpha - (\mathfrak{B} \cup \mathfrak{C}) &= \alpha \cap (\mathfrak{B} \cup \mathfrak{C})' && \text{(Theorem 1.9g)} \\
&= \alpha \cap (\mathfrak{B}' \cap \mathfrak{C}') && \text{(Theorem 1.9h)} \\
&= (\alpha \cap \mathfrak{B}') \cap (\alpha \cap \mathfrak{C}'),
\end{aligned}$$

where an extra α term has been inserted (which is permissible since $\alpha \cap \alpha = \alpha$). Since $\alpha \cap \mathfrak{B}' = \alpha - \mathfrak{B}$ and $\alpha \cap \mathfrak{C}' = \alpha - \mathfrak{C}$, we have

$$\alpha - (\mathfrak{B} \cup \mathfrak{C}) = (\alpha - \mathfrak{B}) \cap (\alpha - \mathfrak{C}).$$

Exercises 1.9

1. Prove De Morgan's Laws (Theorem 1.9h).
2. Show that $\alpha \subset \mathfrak{B} \Rightarrow \mathfrak{B}' \subset \alpha'$.
3. Show that $(\alpha - \mathfrak{B})' = \alpha' \cup \mathfrak{B}$.
4. Does the operation of set difference have commutative or associative properties?
5. Is set difference distributive either from the right or from the left with respect to unions or intersections?
6. In each of the following, write an expression equivalent to the given one, using the operation of complementation rather than that of set difference.

   (a) $\alpha - (\mathfrak{B} \cup \mathfrak{C})$.   (d) $\alpha - (\mathfrak{B} - \mathfrak{C})$.

   (b) $\alpha - (\mathfrak{B} \cap \mathfrak{C})$.   (e) $(\alpha - \mathfrak{B}) - \mathfrak{C}$.

   (c) $\alpha \cup (\mathfrak{B} - \mathfrak{C})$.   (f) $\alpha \cap (\mathfrak{B} - \mathfrak{C})$.

7. Show that $(\alpha - \mathfrak{B}) - \mathfrak{C} = (\alpha - \mathfrak{C}) - (\mathfrak{B} - \mathfrak{C})$.
8. Show that $\alpha \cup \mathfrak{B} \cup \mathfrak{C} = (\alpha - \mathfrak{B}) \cup (\mathfrak{B} - \mathfrak{C}) \cup (\mathfrak{C} - \alpha) \cup (\alpha \cap \mathfrak{B} \cap \mathfrak{C})$.
9. Prove that $(\alpha - \mathfrak{B}) \cup (\mathfrak{B} - \alpha) = (\alpha \cup \mathfrak{B}) - (\alpha \cap \mathfrak{B})$.
10. Prove that $(\alpha \cap \mathfrak{B}) \cap \mathfrak{C} = \alpha \cap (\mathfrak{B} \cap \mathfrak{C})$ by using set algebra and the associative law for unions and De Morgan's Laws.
11. Prove that $\alpha - (\mathfrak{B} \cup \mathfrak{C}) = (\mathfrak{B}' - \alpha') \cap (\mathfrak{C}' - \alpha')$.
12. Prove that $\alpha \cup (\mathfrak{B} - \mathfrak{C}) = (\alpha' - \mathfrak{C}')' - (\alpha' - \mathfrak{B})$.

Summary of Chapter 1

The reader should clearly understand the fundamental ideas and concepts underlying any mathematical structure, which are

    (1) a basic vocabulary of undefined terms (Section 1.1);

    (2) propositions and open statements (Section 1.3);

    (3) the Law of the Excluded Middle (Section 1.3);

    (4) the Law of Inference (Section 1.3);

    (5) axioms (Section 1.4).

Special emphasis should be given to understanding

    (6) the meaning of implication (Section 1.3);

    (7) the converse of a proposition (Section 1.5);

(8) the contrapositive of a proposition (Section 1.5);
(9) the meaning of a conjecture (Section 1.5);
(10) the concept of an axiomatic system (Section 1.5);
(11) the concept of theorem (Section 1.4);
(12) methods of formulating proofs, such as direct proof, indirect proof, and proof by counterexample (Section 1.5);
(13) the concept of set (Section 1.6);
(14) the meanings of the symbols $\in$, $\notin$, $\subset$, $\not\subset$, $\cap$, $\cup$, $'$, $-$, in relation to sets (Sections 1.6, 1.7, 1.8);
(15) the concept of one-to-one correspondence (Section 1.7);
(16) the meanings of finite, denumerable, and nondenumerable (Section 1.7).

Chapter 2   The Complex Number System

2.1 THE NATURAL NUMBERS

When a small child wants to indicate "how many," he usually holds up an appropriate number of fingers (when possible). For example, if he wants to say

that he has ⊖⊖ (marbles), he will say that he has 🖐 marbles.

What he is doing then is to exhibit a set (of fingers) containing as many elements as he has marbles, without using a particular name for that many objects. Thus, using the language of the preceding chapter, we may say that the child has established a one-to-one correspondence between the set of fingers and the

set of marbles. There are, of course, many sets other than 🖐 that could

be used to represent ⊖⊖ . For example, the same information could be

conveyed by using a set such as ///// (sticks).

This method of conveying information regarding a number of objects is rather cumbersome, especially when the number of objects exceeds the number of fingers available. Since all the sets used in reference to the number of marbles,

⊖⊖ , have a common property—that the elements of any two of the sets

can be put into a one-to-one correspondence—it is convenient to give this common property a name. In the case of the set of marbles, we call the property

common to all sets equivalent to ⊖⊖ marbles by the name *four*, which

we write 4.

Thus, when one states that he has 4 marbles, he means that he has

marbles, or ⫽⫽⫽⫽ marbles, and so on. Hence, the number 4 may be regarded

as the name of a set of sets, each of which has the property that its elements

can be put into a one-to-one correspondence with ◎ ◎ ◎ ◎ , or with $\{a, b, c, d\}$,

or with the elements of any other equivalent set.

Definition 2.1a. The **cardinal number** of the set α is the name of the set of equivalent sets to which α belongs, and is designated by the symbol

$$C(\alpha).$$

Some special cardinal numbers are

$$1 .=. \ C(\{a\}),$$
$$2 .=. \ C(\{a, b\}),$$
$$3 .=. \ C(\{a, b, c\}).$$

For example, the second statement indicates that the name for the set of sets each of whose elements can be put into a one-to-one correspondence with the elements of the set $\{a, b\}$, is 2 or *two*. Although we use the set $\{a, b\}$ here, any other set that is in one-to-one correspondence with $\{a, b\}$ would serve as well.

Definition 2.1b. The cardinal numbers commonly denoted by

1, 2, 3, 4, 5, and so on,

constitute the set, $\mathfrak{N}$, of **natural numbers,** our ordinary counting numbers.

The reader is assumed to be familiar with the operations of addition and multiplication for the natural numbers. He has undoubtedly made much use of the following basic laws which are here taken as axioms. Let a, b, and c be natural numbers in the following axioms.

Axiom 2.1a. *The Closure Law of Addition:* The sum $a + b$ of any two natural numbers is a unique natural number c.

We say that the set $\mathfrak{N}$ of natural numbers is *closed* under the operation of addition.

Axiom 2.1b. *The Commutative Law of Addition:*

$$a + b = b + a.$$

This axiom states that *the sum of any two natural numbers does not depend on the order in which the numbers are added.*

Axiom 2.1c. *The Associative Law of Addition:*

$$(a + b) + c = a + (b + c).$$

This law states that *the sum of three (or more) natural numbers is independent of the way in which the numbers are grouped.* Since both groupings yield the same result, the notation $a + b + c$ is unambiguous. However, the reader should note that this statement does *not* concern itself with a rearrangement of the order of the numbers; such a rearrangement was dealt with by Axiom 2.1b.

Axiom 2.1d. *The Closure Law of Multiplication.* The product ab of any two natural numbers is a unique natural number c.

Axiom 2.1e. *The Commutative Law of Multiplication:*

$$ab = ba.$$

Axiom 2.1f. *The Associative Law of Multiplication:*

$$(ab)c = a(bc).$$

The reader should state both the preceding laws in his own words in order to be certain he understands them.

Axiom 2.1g. *The Distributive Law:*

$$a(b + c) = ab + ac.$$

This law is the basic principle on which is based the operation of factoring in algebra.

Although the preceding laws are stated as axioms, it is possible to derive them as formal consequences of fundamental operations on sets. This derivation will not be attempted here. On the other hand, it is important to know that many of the results of arithmetic may be obtained as theorems from the preceding axioms.

Theorem 2.1a. $\quad a = b \Rightarrow a + c = b + c, \qquad a, b, c \in \mathfrak{N}.$

PROOF: By the Axiom of Identity,

$$a + c = a + c.$$

By hypothesis, $a = b$, so that the Substitution Axiom justifies the replacement of a on the right side of the equation by b, to obtain

$$a + c = b + c.$$

Thus the theorem is proved.

It is not our intention to develop algebra in the manner indicated by the preceding theorem and its proof; however, the student should realize that it is possible to make a complete and rigorous development along these lines. Much of this type of treatment now appears in a number of elementary books.

An order relation among the natural numbers is set up in

Definition 2.1c. If a and b are two natural numbers, and if there is a natural number c such that $a + c = b$, then a is said to be *less than b*, and we write $a < b$, or b is said to be *greater than a*, and we write $b > a$.

In brief, the inequality signs, $>$ and $<$, point toward the smaller number.

For example,
$$5 > 3, 3 < 5,$$
and, in general,
$$1 < 2 < 3 < 4 < 5 < \cdots.$$

It follows from the preceding arrangement that every natural number has a **successor**; the successor of 1 is 2, the successor of 2 is 3, and so on. Similarly, every natural number except 1 has a **predecessor**; the predecessor of 5 is 4, the predecessor of 126 is 125, and so on.

Certain subsets of $\mathfrak{N}$ occur frequently and are important enough to be worth noting.

Definition 2.1d. The set of **even** natural numbers is the set
$$\{2k\}, \qquad k = 1, 2, 3, \ldots.$$

That is, the set of even natural numbers consists of those natural numbers that are divisible by two.

Definition 2.1e. The set of **odd** natural numbers is the set
$$\{2k - 1\}, \qquad k = 1, 2, 3, \ldots.$$

That is, the set of odd natural numbers consists of those natural numbers that are not divisible by two.

Definition 2.1f. If a natural number has exactly two distinct divisors (itself and unity), it is called a **prime** number. The set of prime numbers will be denoted by the symbol $\mathfrak{P}$. Thus,
$$\mathfrak{P} .=. \{2, 3, 5, 7, 11, 13, 17, 19, 23, 29, 31, 37, 41, \ldots\}.$$

Note that 1 is not a prime number according to this definition. Every number not in $\mathfrak{P}$, except 1, can be expressed as a product of two or more of the prime numbers. Hence, the primes are of special significance in work dealing with the natural numbers. It has been proved that the set of primes is not finite; that is, there is no "largest" prime. (See Exercises 2.1, Number 5.)

Exercises 2.1

1. Is the set of even natural numbers closed with respect to addition? multiplication? subtraction?
2. Is the set of odd natural numbers closed with respect to addition? multiplication? subtraction?
3. Is the operation of subtraction in $\mathfrak{N}$ a commutative or associative operation?
4. Using the fundamental properties of the natural numbers, prove the following statements about elements of $\mathfrak{N}$.

   (a) $a(b + c + d) = ab + ac + ad$.
   (b) If $a + b + c + d .=. [(a + b) + c] + d$, prove that
   $$a + b + c + d = a + [b + (c + d)].$$
   (c) If $abcd .=. [(ab)c]d$, prove that $abcd = a[b(cd)]$.

5. It can be shown that there is no greatest prime by assuming the contrary and showing that this assumption leads to a contradiction. Thus, suppose that there is a greatest prime, say p_n. Form the number

$$m .=. (2)(3)(5)\cdots(p_{n-1})(p_n) + 1,$$

where the first term is the product of all the primes from 2 to p_n, inclusive. Is m divisible by 2? by 3? by 5? $\cdots$ by p_{n-1}? by p_n? What conclusion may be drawn? This proof is essentially that of Euclid (Greek, about 300 B.C.)

2.2 MATHEMATICAL INDUCTION

Discovery in mathematics sometimes results from an astute observation of an apparent pattern that appears in several similar types of statements. For example, from the equations

$$1 = 1^2$$
$$1 + 3 = 4 = 2^2$$
$$1 + 3 + 5 = 9 = 3^2$$
$$1 + 3 + 5 + 7 = 16 = 4^2$$

emerges an apparent pattern which seems to state that the sum of successive odd numbers, beginning with 1, is equal to the square of the number of odd integers in the sum. This is a conjecture, namely, that

$$1 + 3 + 5 + \cdots + (2n - 1) = n^2$$

for every natural number n.

This conjecture is based upon the very meager evidence of four explicit examples, and, although this evidence is suggestive, it does *not* constitute a proof of the general statement. Indeed, even though we may write down additional examples to illustrate the statement, we must not regard *any* number of such examples as constituting a *proof* that the formula is true in all cases. We might demonstrate the validity of the formula for every natural number from $n = 1$ to $n = 1000$; but this verification alone in no way guarantees that the conjecture is valid for $n = 1,000,000$. Consequently, it is necessary to have available a logical procedure that can be used to establish the validity of a proposed formula (if it is valid) without depending solely on a relatively few verifications. The procedure used for this purpose is based on

Theorem 2.2a. *The Theorem of Mathematical Induction.* Let $p(n)$ be a proposition associated with a natural number n. If $p(1)$ is true, and if $p(k) \Rightarrow p(k + 1)$ for an arbitrary natural number k, then $p(n)$ is true for all n.

A rigorous proof of this theorem is beyond the scope of our work here. However, the principal idea upon which the theorem is based is the establishing of the implication $p(k) \Rightarrow p(k + 1)$ which is sometimes called an **inheritance property**. In effect, if k is a number for which $p(k)$ is true and if $p(k) \Rightarrow p(k + 1)$, it follows by Law 1.3b that $p(k + 1)$ is also true. If it has been shown explicitly that $p(1)$ is true, then, taking $k = 1$, we see that the general implication

$p(k) \Rightarrow p(k + 1)$ guarantees the validity of $p(2)$. In turn, $p(2) \Rightarrow p(3)$, $p(3) \Rightarrow p(4)$, and so on, so that we have an unending chain of implications:

$$p(1) \Rightarrow p(2) \Rightarrow p(3) \Rightarrow p(4) \Rightarrow p(5) \Rightarrow \cdots.$$

To illustrate the Theorem of Mathematical Induction, let us provide a proof of the conjectured formula given at the beginning of this section.

Example 2.2a. Prove that $1 + 3 + 5 + \cdots + (2n - 1) = n^2$ for every $n \in \mathfrak{N}$.

The proposition $p(n)$ associated with the integer n in this case is the equation

$$1 + 3 + 5 + \cdots + (2n - 1) = n^2.$$

For $n = 1$, $p(1)$ is the statement $1 = 1^2$, which is true.

The proposition $p(k)$ is the statement

$$1 + 3 + \cdots + (2k - 1) = k^2.$$

We want to show that this statement implies $p(k + 1)$. In this particular case, we may add the next odd integer to both sides of the equation $p(k)$, to get

$$1 + 3 + \cdots + (2k - 1) + (2k + 1) = k^2 + (2k + 1),$$

or

$$1 + 3 + \cdots + (2k - 1) + (2k + 1) = (k + 1)^2.$$

This equation is exactly $p(k + 1)$. Hence we have established that

$$p(k) \Rightarrow p(k + 1).$$

Since $p(1)$ is true, it follows by Theorem 2.2a that $p(n)$ is true for all $n \in \mathfrak{N}$.

Mathematical induction is useful in a number of ways in connection with propositions that do not involve equations.

Example 2.2b. Prove that $x - y$ is a factor of $x^n - y^n$ for every $n \in \mathfrak{N}$.

The expression $x - y$ is said to be a factor of $x^n - y^n$ provided that $x^n - y^n = (x - y)Q_n(x, y)$, where $Q_n(x, y)$ is some polynomial in x and y. Hence the proposition $p(n)$ may be taken as the mathematical statement $x^n - y^n = (x - y)Q_n(x, y)$ for all $n \in \mathfrak{N}$. If $n = 1$, we have the statement $p(1)$, which is

$$x - y = (x - y) \cdot 1 = x - y,$$

an obviously true proposition.

The statement $p(k)$ is

$$x^k - y^k = (x - y)Q_k(x, y).$$

We must now show that this statement implies $p(k + 1)$. In order to demonstrate this implication, we subtract and add $x^k y$ in the expression $x^{k+1} - y^{k+1}$ so as to make use of the factorization of $x^k - y^k$ described by the statement $p(k)$. Thus,

$$x^{k+1} - y^{k+1} = x^{k+1} - x^k y + x^k y - y^{k+1}$$
$$= x^k(x - y) + y(x^k - y^k).$$

Since $p(k)$ states that $x^k - y^k = (x - y)Q_k(x, y)$, we have

$$x^{k+1} - y^{k+1} = x^k(x - y) + y(x - y)Q_k(x, y)$$
$$= (x - y)[x^k + yQ_k(x, y)].$$

The expression $x^k + yQ_k(x, y)$ is another polynomial in x and y which we may call $Q_{k+1}(x, y)$. Thus,

$$x^{k+1} - y^{k+1} = (x - y)Q_{k+1}(x, y),$$

and we have established that

$$p(k) \Rightarrow p(k + 1).$$

Hence, by the Theorem of Mathematical Induction, $p(n)$ is true for all $n \in \mathfrak{N}$.

It is often convenient to use an alternate form of mathematical induction.

Theorem 2.2b. Suppose a proposition $p(n)$ associated with the natural number n is true for $n = 1, 2, 3, \ldots, k - 1$, and suppose

$$p(1), p(2), p(3), \ldots \quad \text{and} \quad p(k - 1) \Rightarrow p(k).$$

Then $p(n)$ is true for all $n \in \mathfrak{N}$.

PROOF: The theorem may be proved by means of Theorem 2.2a, and is left for the reader.

The use of Theorem 2.2b is illustrated in

Example 2.2c. Let $a_1 .=. 1$, and for $n \geq 2$ let

$$a_n .=. a_1 + \frac{a_2}{2} + \cdots + \frac{a_{n-1}}{n - 1}.$$

Prove that

$$a_n = \frac{n}{2} \quad \text{for all } n \geq 2.$$

In this case, the starting point for the inductive process is at $n = 2$. The proposition $p(n)$ is that $a_n = n/2$ for $n \geq 2$. If $n = 2$, $a_2 = 1$, according to this formula. This result agrees with the value given by the definition for a_n for $n = 2$. Now suppose that $a_r = r/2$ for $1 < r < k$. Then, according to the definitions of a_n and a_1,

$$a_k = 1 + \frac{a_2}{2} + \frac{a_3}{3} + \ldots + \frac{a_{k-1}}{k - 1}, \quad k \geq 2.$$

Now, by substituting $a_r = r/2$ for $r = 2, 3, 4, \ldots, k - 1$, we get

$$a_k = 1 + \frac{2/2}{2} + \frac{3/2}{3} + \frac{4/2}{4} + \cdots + \frac{(k - 1)/2}{k - 1}$$

$$= 1 + \frac{1}{2} + \frac{1}{2} + \frac{1}{2} + \cdots + \frac{1}{2}$$

$$= 1 + \frac{k - 2}{2} = \frac{k}{2}.$$

Thus, the propositions $p(2), p(3), \ldots, p(k - 1)$ and $a_1 .=. 1$ together imply $p(k)$. Hence, by Theorem 2.2b, $p(n)$ is true for all $n \in \mathfrak{N}$.

In order to illustrate common errors in the attempt to use mathematical induction, consider the following two examples.

Example 2.2d. Is the formula

$$2 + 4 + 6 + 8 + \cdots + 2n = n^2 + n + 1$$

valid for all n?

Suppose the formula is true for the number k. Then

$$2 + 4 + 6 + 8 + \cdots + 2k = k^2 + k + 1,$$

and by adding $2(k + 1)$ to both sides of the equation we get

$$2 + 4 + 6 + \cdots + 2k + 2(k + 1) = k^2 + k + 1 + 2(k + 1)$$
$$= (k + 1)^2 + (k + 1) + 1,$$

which is $p(k + 1)$. Hence, $p(k) \Rightarrow p(k + 1)$.

However, the reader must not jump to the conclusion that the proposed formula is true by virtue of the preceding implication. Actually, this formula is valid for *no* values of n. For instance, $n = 1$ gives 2 for the left side and 3 for the right; $n = 2$ gives 6 for the left side and 7 for the right. In fact, the student should be able to see that the left side always yields an even sum and the right side is always odd.

Example 2.2d shows that it is necessary to *know* that the proposition being examined is true for *at least one* particular value of n.

Example 2.2e. Let $p(n)$ be the proposition: $n^2 + n + 41$ is a prime number.

A so-called "proof" might go as follows. It is easily verified that $p(1)$, $p(2)$, $p(3)$ are true. It therefore appears that $p(n)$ is true for all n. Just to be sure, let us check $p(4)$, $p(5)$, $p(6)$, $p(7)$, and $p(8)$. The expression $n^2 + n + 41$ is found to be a prime number in each case. Hence, it must be a prime for all n.

How naive we would have to be to accept such a hasty conclusion! In this case, it is obvious that $n = 41$ gives $(41)^2 + 41 + 41$, which, being divisible by 41, is surely *not* a prime. In order to have completed a proof by mathematical induction, we would have had to show that

$$p(k) \Rightarrow p(k + 1),$$

that is, that

$$k^2 + k + 41 \text{ is a prime} \Rightarrow (k + 1)^2 + (k + 1) + 41 \text{ is a prime.}$$

It must clearly be impossible to do this, since this would imply that $p(41)$ is true, contrary to fact.

Exercises 2.2

In Numbers 1 to 11, prove the given statement by mathematical induction.

1. $1 + 2 + 3 + \cdots + n = \frac{1}{2}n(n + 1)$.
2. $2a + 4a + 6a + \cdots + 2na = n(n + 1)a$.
3. $1 \cdot 2 + 2 \cdot 3 + 3 \cdot 4 + \cdots + n(n + 1) = \frac{1}{3}n(n + 1)(n + 2)$.
4. $2 + 5 + 8 + \cdots + (3n - 1) = \frac{1}{2}n(3n + 1)$.
5. $1 \cdot 2 + 2 \cdot 2^2 + 3 \cdot 2^3 + \cdots + n \cdot 2^n = 2 + (n - 1)2^{n+1}$.
6. $1^2 + 2^2 + 3^2 + \cdots + n^2 = \frac{1}{6}n(n + 1)(2n + 1)$.
7. $1^2 + 3^2 + 5^2 + \cdots + (2n - 1)^2 = \frac{1}{3}n(4n^2 - 1)$.

8. $\dfrac{1}{1\cdot3} + \dfrac{1}{3\cdot5} + \cdots + \dfrac{1}{(2n-1)(2n+1)} = \dfrac{n}{2n+1}.$

9. $\dfrac{1}{1\cdot5} + \dfrac{1}{5\cdot9} + \cdots + \dfrac{1}{(4n-3)(4n+1)} = \dfrac{n}{4n+1}.$

10. $a + a^2 + a^3 + \cdots + a^n = \dfrac{a(a^n - 1)}{a - 1},$ where $a \neq 1.$

11. $\dfrac{1}{1\cdot2} + \dfrac{1}{2\cdot3} + \dfrac{1}{3\cdot4} + \cdots + \dfrac{1}{n(n+1)} = \dfrac{n}{n+1}.$

12. Refer to Example 2.2b and show that
$$x^n - y^n = (x - y)(x^{n-1} + x^{n-2}y + x^{n-3}y^2 + \cdots + xy^{n-2} + y^{n-1}).$$

13. Which of the following (if any) are valid for all n?
   (a) $1 + 2 + 6 + \cdots + n! = 3^{n-1}$;

   (b) $1 + r + r^2 + \cdots + r^n = \dfrac{1 - r^{n+1}}{1 - r}$;

   (c) $a_n = 2^{2^{n-1}}$ if $a_1 .=. 2$ and $a_n .=. 2^{a_{n-1}}.$

14. Let $a_1 .=. 1$ and $a_n .=. na_{n-1}$, with $n = 2, 3, 4, \ldots$. Prove that $a_n = n!$

15. Let $a_1 .=. 2$ and $a_n .=. 2a_{n-1}$, with $n = 2, 3, 4, \ldots$. Prove that $a_n = 2^n.$

16. Is the following a valid formula?
$$1^3 + 2^3 + \cdots + n^3 = (1 + 2 + 3 + \cdots + n)^2.$$

17. Prove that $2^{4n} - 1$ is divisible by 15 for $n = 1, 2, 3, \ldots$. *Hint*:
$$2^{4(n+1)} - 1 = 2^4(2^{4n} - 1) + (2^4 - 1).$$

18. Is the equation
$$[1 + 3 + 5 + \cdots + (2n - 1)]^2 = 10n^3 - 35n^2 + 50n - 24$$
   true for all n?

19. Is the formula
$$4 + 5 + 6 + \cdots + (n + 3) = n^3 + 3$$
   true for all n?

20. Is the formula
$$(1 + a)^n \geq na + 1 \quad \text{for } a > 0$$
   true for all n?

21. If $u_1 .=. 1$, $u_2 .=. 2$, and $u_n .=. u_{n-1} + u_{n-2}$, for $n = 3, 4, 5, \ldots$, prove that $u_n < (7/4)^n$. (The numbers u_n in this problem form the so-called "Fibonacci sequence.")

22. Given $a_1 .=. 1$, $a_2 .=. 2$, $2a_n .=. a_{n-1} + a_{n-2}$, for $n = 3, 4, 5, \ldots$. Prove that $\frac{3}{2} \leq a_n \leq \frac{7}{4}$, for $n = 3, 4, 5, \ldots$.

23. Prove Theorem 2.2b.

24. Let $p(n)$ be a proposition known to be true for $n = n_0$, where $n_0 > 1$, and suppose $p(k) \Rightarrow p(k + 1)$. Prove that $p(n)$ is true for all $n > n_0$.

25. A pile of balls is arranged in the form of a pyramid. Find a formula for the number of balls in the pyramid when the base is
    (a) an equilateral triangle having n balls on a side;
    (b) a square with n balls on a side.

26. In Exercises 1.5, Number 10, prove that your answer is correct.

27. In Exercises 1.5, Number 11, prove that $\frac{1}{2}n(n-1)$ is the correct answer.

28. Let p_n and p_{n+1} be two consecutive odd prime numbers (for example, 3 and 5, or 13 and 17). Is $p_n p_{n+1} + 2$ always a prime number for every n? If your answer is yes, try to prove it; if your answer is no, try to find a counterexample.

2.3 THE SET OF INTEGERS

The set of natural numbers, together with the operations of addition and multiplication, is an example of a very simple mathematical system. Most of the fundamental properties of the system have already been discussed. However, there is one additional property that leads to a number of interesting ideas.

Among the elements of $\mathfrak{N}$, there is one that has a unique property not possessed by the other elements in $\mathfrak{N}$. The number 1 has the property that

$$1x = x$$

for all $x \in \mathfrak{N}$. In other words, the multiplication of any element x in $\mathfrak{N}$ by 1 yields the element x again. Since, under multiplication by 1, the "identity" of x is preserved, 1 is called the **multiplicative identity** for the set $\mathfrak{N}$. Furthermore, it can be shown that 1 is the only element of $\mathfrak{N}$ that possesses this property.

Another important property of the natural numbers may be stated as

Theorem 2.3a. If $a, b, c \in \mathfrak{N}$, then

$$ac = bc \Leftrightarrow a = b.$$

The proof of this theorem, which can be based directly on the order properties of the set $\mathfrak{N}$, is omitted as being beside the purposes of the present development. The implication in this theorem, however, applies much more generally than just to the natural numbers, as we shall see later. The reader should keep in mind that the number zero is *not* an element of the set $\mathfrak{N}$.

It is natural now to ask if there is also in $\mathfrak{N}$ an **additive identity** for the elements of $\mathfrak{N}$. In other words, is there an element s such that

$$x + s = x$$

for every $x \in \mathfrak{N}$? The answer is, of course, that there is no such element in $\mathfrak{N}$.

As will be evident later, the lack of an additive identity in $\mathfrak{N}$ impairs its usefulness in arithmetic operations, and it is desirable to try to "enlarge" the set $\mathfrak{N}$ by adjoining to it a new element that will be such an additive identity. Therefore, we assume that there exists a unique element (a number not in $\mathfrak{N}$) that is an additive identity for the elements of $\mathfrak{N}$.

Definition 2.3a. The symbol 0 (read "zero") denotes the unique number for which

$$0 + x = x + 0 = x$$

for all $x \in \mathfrak{N}$, and

$$0 + 0 = 0.$$

The set $\mathfrak{N} \cup \{0\}$ is denoted by $\mathfrak{N}_0$. It follows from Definition 2.3a and the basic axioms for the natural numbers that the set $\mathfrak{N}_0$ is closed with respect to addition and that the commutative and associative laws of addition hold. We make the further basic assumption that $\mathfrak{N}_0$ is closed with respect to multiplication and that the commutative and associative laws of multiplication as well as the distributive law apply to $\mathfrak{N}_0$.

On the basis of these assumptions and Definition 2.3a, we may obtain as theorems all the fundamental properties of the element zero.

Theorem 2.3b. $\qquad\qquad 0x = 0 \qquad$ for all $x \in \mathfrak{N}_0$.

PROOF: Since

$$0 + 1 = 1,$$

then

$$(0 + 1)x = x,$$

or, by the Distributive Law,

$$0x + x = x$$

for every $x \in \mathfrak{N}_0$. Therefore, $0x$ must be the additive identity, which is unique. Hence,

$$0x = 0.$$

The next theorem is fundamental in solving equations.

Theorem 2.3c. $\qquad ab = 0 \Rightarrow a = 0 \quad$ or $\quad b = 0$.

PROOF: Let us assume that $b \neq 0$. Then

$$ab = 0 \Rightarrow ab + b = b$$

or, by the use of the Distributive Law,

$$(a + 1)b = b.$$

Therefore, by Theorem 2.3a,

$$a + 1 = 1,$$

which, by the uniqueness of the additive identity, implies that

$$a = 0.$$

A similar argument applies if it is assumed that $a \neq 0$, rather than $b \neq 0$. Of course, if $a = 0$ and $b = 0$, the theorem is clearly true.

Another important concept associated with the solution of equations is based on the idea of an additive inverse. A number b is said to be an additive inverse of a number a if

$$a + b = 0.$$

The only element in $\mathfrak{N}_0$ with an additive inverse in $\mathfrak{N}_0$ is 0, since $0 + 0 = 0$, and since $a + b \neq 0$ if $a, b \in \mathfrak{N}_0$ and at least one of a, b is not zero. The lack of additive inverses may be considered a defect in the set $\mathfrak{N}_0$ since the usefulness of the set is thereby greatly impaired. For instance, if $b \in \mathfrak{N}_0$, the equation $x + b = 0$ has no solution $x \in \mathfrak{N}_0$ unless $b = 0$. It is therefore desirable to extend the set $\mathfrak{N}_0$ in such a way that there is a new set of objects containing $\mathfrak{N}_0$ as a subset and including the additive inverses of the elements of $\mathfrak{N}_0$. Hence, we assume that for each $x \in \mathfrak{N}$ there is an object that is its additive inverse.

Definition 2.3b. Let $x \in \mathfrak{N}$. Then $-x$ is defined to be an object such that
$$x + (-x) = 0.$$
The object $-x$ is called an **additive inverse** of x.

By adjoining the additive inverses of the natural numbers to the set $\mathfrak{N}_0$, we have constructed a new set which we shall denote by $\mathscr{I}$, the set of all integers:
$$\mathscr{I} .=. \{\ldots, -4, -3, -2, -1, 0, 1, 2, 3, 4, \ldots\}.$$
We again make the basic assumption that the fundamental laws of addition and multiplication apply to the elements of the set $\mathscr{I}$. Thus, except for the substitution of "integer" for "natural number," Axioms 2.1a through 2.1g apply to the set of integers. The next theorem is a direct result of these axioms.

Theorem 2.3d. Every $x \in \mathfrak{N}_0$ has a unique additive inverse.

PROOF: By Definition 2.3b, x has an additive inverse $-x$. We wish to show that if y is also an additive inverse of x, then $y = -x$; that is,
$$x + y = 0 \Rightarrow y = -x.$$
Since
$$x + (-x) = -x + x = 0,$$
we have
$$(-x + x) + y = 0 + y = y.$$
Moreover, by the Associative Law of Addition,
$$(-x + x) + y = -x + (x + y)$$
$$= -x + 0 = -x.$$
Consequently, $y = -x$, as was to be shown.

It follows from this theorem and Definition 2.3b that x is the additive inverse of $-x$; that is, $-(-x) = x$. For example, -5 is the additive inverse of 5, and 5 is the additive inverse of -5, which is to say that $-(-5) = 5$.

An additional important consequence of the axioms is the rule of signs for multiplication.

Theorem 2.3e. $(a)(-b) = -(ab)$ for any natural numbers a and b.

PROOF: We have, by the definition of $(-b)$,
$$b + (-b) = 0.$$
Hence
$$a[b + (-b)] = a0 = 0.$$

(Why?) Then, by the Distributive Law,
$$ab + (a)(-b) = 0.$$
It follows that $(a)(-b)$ must be the additive inverse of ab; that is,
$$(a)(-b) = -(ab),$$
which is what we desired to prove.

It is left for the reader to prove

Theorem 2.3f. Let a and b be natural numbers; then
$$(-a)(-b) = ab.$$

It follows at once from Theorem 2.3e that 1 is the multiplicative identity element for the set $\mathcal{I}$.

For the set $\mathfrak{N}$ of natural numbers, subtraction is an operation described by

Definition 2.3c. If $p, q \in \mathfrak{N}$, and if there is an $x \in \mathfrak{N}$ such that
$$p + x = q,$$
then
$$q - p .=. x.$$

This operation is not defined for all pairs of natural numbers, since $x \in \mathfrak{N}$ only if q is greater than p. This is to say that the set $\mathfrak{N}$ is not closed with respect to subtraction. However, if we use the same definition but allow p and q to be integers, then $x = q - p$ is always an integer; that is, the set $\mathcal{I}$ is closed with respect to subtraction.

Theorem 2.3g. If $p, q \in \mathcal{I}$, then there always exists $x \in \mathcal{I}$ such that
$$p + x = q.$$

PROOF: Consider the number $(-p) + q$, which is an integer. We have
$$p + [(-p) + q] = [p + (-p)] + q$$
$$= 0 + q$$
$$= q.$$

This shows that $x = (-p) + q$ is an integer such that
$$p + x = q.$$

The preceding proof also shows that if we write
$$x = q - p$$
whenever
$$p + x = q,$$
then we must have
$$q + (-p) = q - p;$$
that is, the addition of $-p$ is the same as the subtraction of p. It is for this reason that we may regard subtraction as the inverse of addition.

Corresponding to each natural number a in $\mathcal{I}$, there is an additive inverse $-a$ in $\mathcal{I}$ that is customarily called a **negative** integer. The natural numbers themselves are frequently called the **positive** integers. We use this terminology in extending the notion of ordering to the set $\mathscr{I}$.

Definition 2.3d. If $a, b \in \mathscr{I}$, then

$$a > b \quad \text{if} \quad a - b = p \text{ is a positive integer,}$$
$$a < b \quad \text{if} \quad a - b = q \text{ is a negative integer.}$$

For example, we have $2 > -5$ since $2 - (-5) = 7$, and $-10 < -2$ since

$$-10 - (-2) = -8.$$

Exercises 2.3

1. Prove that $x \cdot 0 = 0$ for all $x \in \mathscr{I}$. (See Theorem 2.3b.)

2. Prove that if a and b are integers, then $ab = 0 \Rightarrow a = 0$ or $b = 0$. (See Theorem 2.3c.)

3. Prove that $(-x)(-y) = xy$ for all $x, y \in \mathscr{I}$.

4. Prove that if $x \in \mathscr{I}$, then $-(-x) = x$.

5. Show that $a + (-b) = a - b$.

6. Prove that the additive inverse $-a$ is equivalent to a subtracted from 0, or that $0 - a = -a$.

7. In "factoring," we write $27x^2 + 36x = 9x(3x + 4)$. This is an illustration of the use of what basic law?

8. Suppose there were a distributive law of addition with respect to multiplication. What would be another form for $a + bc$? Show by the use of specific numbers that this is *not* a correct law.

2.4 GROUPS

The operations of addition and multiplication on $\mathfrak{N}$ are examples of an operation that combines two elements of a set of objects to produce a third element of the set. Such operations are worth some additional study.

Definition 2.4a. A **binary operation** on a set $\mathcal{C}$ is any operation or rule that associates with two elements of $\mathcal{C}$ a third element of $\mathcal{C}$.

A binary operation on a set is characterized by the fact that the set is *closed* with respect to this operation. That is, a combination of two elements of the set yields a third element of the set. To illustrate, the set of natural numbers $\mathfrak{N}$ is *not* closed with respect to the operation of subtraction. Hence, subtraction is *not* a binary operation on $\mathfrak{N}$. This means that the difference of two natural numbers is not always a natural number. Of course, the set of integers is closed with respect to subtraction, and so subtraction is a binary operation on that set.

Binary operations occur in many ways and in several varieties. Let the symbol $*$ denote a binary operation on a set $\mathcal{C}$. (For example, on the set $\mathfrak{N}$, $*$

may represent either addition or multiplication.) Then the element c associated to the pair of elements a and b is denoted by $a * b = c$. For example, $2 + 3 = 5$ and $2 \cdot 3 = 6$ express in specific cases the same idea that is expressed by $a * b = c$ in the general case.

Definition 2.4b. If $*$ is a binary operation on a set $\mathcal{Q}$, and if

$$x * y = y * x$$

for *all* elements x and y in $\mathcal{Q}$, then $*$ is said to be a *commutative* operation on $\mathcal{Q}$.

For example, since $a + b = b + a$ for all integers in $\mathcal{J}$, we say that addition is a commutative operation on $\mathcal{J}$.

Definition 2.4c. If $*$ is a binary operation on a set $\mathcal{Q}$, and if

$$x * (y * z) = (x * y) * z$$

for all x, y, and z in $\mathcal{Q}$, then $*$ is said to be an *associative* operation on $\mathcal{Q}$.

Thus, since $a + (b + c) = (a + b) + c$ for all a, b, c in $\mathcal{J}$, we say that addition is an associative operation on $\mathcal{J}$. A binary operation need not be commutative or associative, although many familiar binary operations have both these properties. Subtraction is a simple example of an operation that has neither property. In later sections of this book we shall encounter examples of other operations that are not commutative or associative.

Definition 2.4d. A set of objects on which there is defined one or more binary operations is called an **algebraic structure.**

The set of objects in $\mathfrak{N}$ with the binary operations of addition and multiplication is an example of an algebraic structure. The set of integers, $\mathcal{J}$, is also an algebraic structure, but it is not at all like the structure on $\mathfrak{N}$.

An algebraic structure is necessarily determined whenever a binary operation on a set is given. The most familiar examples of algebraic structures are, of course, associated with the number system. However, it is frequently necessary to consider more abstract examples of algebraic structures. For example, it is possible to establish an algebraic structure on *any* set of objects merely by introducing, in an arbitrary way, a binary operation on the set.

For example, let $\mathcal{Q} . = . \{a, b, c\}$. Then a binary operation, $*$ (which is neither addition nor multiplication) can be established by means of an *operation table*, analogous to the addition tables of arithmetic. Such a table is given in Figure 2.4a.

$*$	a	b	c
a	b	c	a
b	c	a	b
c	a	b	c

FIGURE 2.4a

The element $b * c$, for example, is found in the b row and the c column, and is b. Similarly, $a * b$ is found in the a row and b column and is c. That is, $a * b = c$. We call attention next to a simple but important kind of algebraic structure.

Definition 2.4e. A **group** is a set $\mathcal{a}$ on which is defined a binary operation $*$ for which the following axioms are satisfied:

> G_1. the operation $*$ is associative;
> G_2. the set contains an identity element, e, for which
> $\quad x * e = e * x = x$ for every $x \in \mathcal{a}$;
> G_3. for each element $x \in \mathcal{a}$, there exists an inverse
> $\quad$ element x^{-1} in $\mathcal{a}$, such that $x * x^{-1} = x^{-1} * x = e$.

For example, the set $\mathcal{g}$ of integers is a group with respect to the operation of addition because (i) addition is a binary operation on $\mathcal{g}$, (ii) it is an associative operation, (iii) the identity element is 0, and (iv) each element x in $\mathcal{g}$ has an additive inverse $(-x)$ in $\mathcal{g}$. The set $\mathcal{N}$ is *not* a group with respect to addition because it does not contain 0 and it does not have *additive inverses*—that is, inverses with respect to addition. In fact, the extension of the set $\mathcal{N}$ of natural numbers to the set $\mathcal{g}$ of integers was made in order to obtain a group with respect to addition.

The set $\{0, \pm 2, \pm 4, \ldots, \pm 2n, \ldots\}$, with $n \in \mathcal{N}$, is another example of a group with respect to addition, as the reader may verify. A set that is a group with respect to the operation of addition is called an **additive group**. A simple example of a set that is a group with respect to multiplication is $\{1, -1\}$. It is clear that the set $\mathcal{g}$ is *not* a **multiplicative group;** that is, it is not a group with respect to multiplication.

Other examples of groups can be obtained by means of a **modular arithmetic** for integers.

Definition 2.4f. The notation $a \equiv b \,(\mathrm{mod}\, p)$ means that $a = mp + b$, where $a, m, p,$ and b are integers.

That is, $a \equiv b \,(\mathrm{mod}\, p)$ means that b is the remainder after dividing a by p. The notation is read "a is congruent to b modulo p." For example,

$$7 \equiv 2 \;(\mathrm{mod}\; 5),$$
$$11 \equiv 4 \;(\mathrm{mod}\; 7),$$

and

$$6 \equiv 0 \;(\mathrm{mod}\; 3).$$

By using this concept of "congruence," we may construct other examples of additive and multiplicative groups. For example, the set of numbers $\{0, 1, 2\}$ is an *additive group*, modulo 3, if we agree that the ordinary sum of two of the elements of the set $\{0, 1, 2\}$ will be replaced by the remainder (mod 3) if the sum is equal to or greater than 3. Thus, $0 + 0 = 0, 0 + 1 = 1, \ldots, 1 + 2 = 3$, but $3 \equiv 0 \;(\mathrm{mod}\; 3)$. Likewise, $2 + 2 = 4$, but $4 \equiv 1 \;(\mathrm{mod}\; 3)$. The *addition table* in this system is given in Figure 2.4b. The operation is called addition, modulo 3, and is denoted by $+_3$.

$+_3$	0	1	2
0	0	1	2
1	1	2	0
2	2	0	1

FIGURE 2.4b

In a similar way, if we agree to replace the *product* of two elements of the set $\{1, 2, 3, 4\}$ by its remainder, modulo 5, then the set is a multiplicative group. The operation table is given in Figure 2.4c. The operation is called multiplication, modulo 5, and is denoted by $\times_5$.

$\times_5$	1	2	3	4
1	1	2	3	4
2	2	4	1	3
3	3	1	4	2
4	4	3	2	1

FIGURE 2.4c

The examples of groups that we have considered are all examples of *commutative* groups, in which the operation is commutative. Noncommutative groups exist, but a discussion of this type of group is beyond the scope of our work here. However, in Exercises 2.4, Number 12, there is an example of a noncommutative group.

Exercises 2.4

1. Is subtraction a binary operation on $\mathfrak{N}$? on $\mathcal{J}$? Explain.

2. Is subtraction an associative or commutative operation on $\mathcal{J}$? Explain.

3. Let $\mathcal{Q} .=. \{a, b, c, d\}$, and let $\mathcal{S}$ denote the following set of subsets of $\mathcal{Q}$:

$$\mathcal{S} = \{\{a\}, \{b\}, \{a, b\}, \{c, d\}, \mathcal{Q}\}.$$

Are the operations of union and intersection binary operations on $\mathcal{S}$? Why or why not?

4. Is division a binary operation on $\mathfrak{N}$? on $\mathcal{J}$? Explain.

5. Is the operation given in Figure 2.4a commutative or associative? Is the set $\{a, b, c\}$ a group under this operation? Explain.

6. Construct an example of a binary operation on the set $\alpha .=. \{a, b, c\}$ that is
   (a) not commutative and not associative;
   (b) commutative but not associative;
   (c) associative but not commutative.

7. Is the set of numbers $\mathcal{G}_3 .=. \{x: x = 3k, k \in \mathcal{G}\}$ a group with respect to addition? Explain.

8. Is the set $\mathcal{G}_0 .=. \{x: x = 2k + 1, \ k \in \mathcal{G}\}$ a group with respect to addition? Explain.

9. Is the set $\{1, 2, 3, 4, 5\}$ a group with respect to multiplication, modulo 6? Explain.

10. Is the set $\{3, 6, 9, 12\}$ a group with respect to multiplication, modulo 15?

11. Let I denote an initial position of an equilateral triangle ABC having its center at O. Let P denote a 120° counterclockwise rotation of ABC about O, and let Q denote a 240° counterclockwise rotation of ABC about O. The effect of these rotations is shown in Figure 2.4d.

FIGURE 2.4d

Let the "sum" of two rotations be defined as the rotation obtained by carrying out successively the two given rotations. For example, $P + Q$ denotes a rotation of 120° followed by an *additional* rotation of 240°. The net effect is a rotation of 360° (since the amounts of rotation are added), which returns the triangle to its original position, I. Hence, we may write

$$P + Q = I.$$

Show that under this "addition" operation, the set $\{I, P, Q\}$ forms a group.

12. Besides the rotations in Number 11, other rotations of a triangle that leave the triangle relatively unchanged are possible. For example, let S, T, and U denote 180° rotations of triangle ABC about the lines s, t, and u, respectively, as shown in Figure 2.4e.

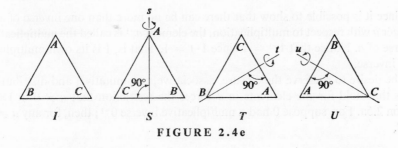

FIGURE 2.4e

(The lines s, t, u are *not* to be moved with the triangle; they remain fixed in the plane.) If "addition" is extended to include these rotations, then show that the set $\{I, P, Q, S, T, U\}$ forms a group. (To illustrate "addition" with these new elements, consider $Q + S$. If we start from the initial position I and perform rotation Q, we get the position shown by Figure 2.4f.

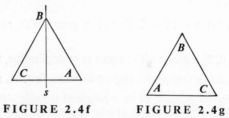

FIGURE 2.4f   FIGURE 2.4g

Since S is a 180° rotation about the line s, rotation S changes the position of Figure 2.4f into that of Figure 2.4g. The position of Figure 2.4g is obtained directly from the initial position by the operation U. Hence, we have

$$Q + S = U.$$

The reader should observe that $S + Q \neq U$.)

2.5 THE RATIONAL NUMBERS

As we have seen, the set $\mathcal{I}$ is not a group with respect to multiplication, because $\mathcal{I}$ does not contain multiplicative inverses of its elements. Therefore, in an effort to construct a mathematical structure of greater breadth and versatility, we shall enlarge the set $\mathcal{I}$ in such a way that the resulting set satisfies the following conditions as nearly as possible:

(i) the set is an additive group;
(ii) the set is a multiplicative group;
(iii) the set contains $\mathcal{I}$ as a subset.

For this purpose, we assume that there exist elements that are the inverses of the elements of $\mathcal{I}$ with respect to multiplication.

Definition 2.5a. If $a \in \mathcal{I}$, with $a \neq 0$, then let a^{-1} denote an element such that

$$aa^{-1} = a^{-1}a = 1.$$

Since it is possible to show that there can be no more than one inverse of any integer a with respect to multiplication, the element a^{-1} is called the **multiplicative inverse** of a. Notice that $1^{-1} = 1$ since $1 \cdot 1 = 1$. That is, 1 is its own multiplicative inverse.

The desire to preserve the closure, associative, commutative, and distributive laws that hold for the elements in $\mathcal{I}$ forces the restriction that $a \neq 0$ in Definition 2.5a. For, suppose 0 had a multiplicative inverse 0^{-1}; then, for any $a \neq 0$ in $\mathcal{I}$,

$$a = a \cdot 1 = a(0 \cdot 0^{-1}) = (a \cdot 0) \cdot 0^{-1}$$
$$= 0 \cdot 0^{-1} = 1.$$

This absurdity forces us to omit 0^{-1} as an element of the new set. Consequently, it will henceforth be understood that the symbol a^{-1} is meaningful *only* when a is a number other than 0.

The introduction of the new elements of the form a^{-1} leads at once to the discovery that the set containing only the integers and their multiplicative inverses is not closed with respect to addition or multiplication. For example, $3^{-1} + 3^{-1}$ is neither an integer nor the inverse of an integer. This follows because

$$3(3^{-1} + 3^{-1}) = (3)(3^{-1}) + (3)(3^{-1}) = 1 + 1 = 2,$$

and, if $3^{-1} + 3^{-1}$ is an integer, then it and 3 are positive integral factors of 2. But the only positive integral factors of 2 are 1 and 2, so that $3^{-1} + 3^{-1}$ is not an integer. The reader may show in a similar fashion that the assumption that $3^{-1} + 3^{-1} = n^{-1}$, the inverse of an integer, leads again to a contradiction.

The preceding discussion shows that in order to have closure for addition, we must include still other elements of the form

$$a^{-1} + a^{-1} + \cdots + a^{-1}$$

in the set.

Definition 2.5b. Let $n \in \mathfrak{N}$. If $a \neq 0$, then

$$na^{-1} .=. a^{-1} + a^{-1} + \cdots + a^{-1}.$$

(There are n terms.)

Thus, na^{-1} denotes a new element that is the sum of n of the elements a^{-1} as well as being the product of n and a^{-1}. The definition is easily extended to include the case when n is a negative integer. Since $(-n) = (-1)n$, we may write

$$-(na^{-1}) = (-n)a^{-1} .=. (-1)(na^{-1}).$$

We now have a considerably extended set of elements of the type ab^{-1} where $a, b \in \mathfrak{g}$ and $b \neq 0$.

Definition 2.5c. The set of elements ab^{-1} where $a, b \in \mathfrak{g}$ and $b \neq 0$ is called the set of **rational numbers** and is denoted by $\mathfrak{F}$.

Since 1 is its own multiplicative inverse, it follows that $a \cdot 1^{-1} = a \cdot 1 = a$ for every $a \in \mathfrak{g}$. Hence the set $\mathfrak{g}$ is a subset of $\mathfrak{F}$. It is customary to write

$$a/b \quad \text{or} \quad \frac{a}{b}$$

for the element ab^{-1}.

Of course, we assume that the commutative, associative, and distributive laws still hold. On the basis of these laws, we may derive all the properties of the set of rational numbers on an axiomatic basis. Since we want the commutative law to hold, it follows that $ab^{-1} = b^{-1}a$. It is easily shown that 0 is the unique additive identity and that 1 is the unique multiplicative identity. The following examples illustrate a few of the techniques and processes involved with making such proofs. Although a complete axiomatic development of the rational numbers will not be given here, it is important to know that this can be done. The essential aspect of such a development for the reader is an understanding of the mathematical processes involved rather than the detailed development itself.

Theorem 2.5a. Let $a \in \mathcal{G}$. Then

$$(a^{-1})^{-1} = a.$$

PROOF: Since

$$a[(a^{-1})(a^{-1})^{-1}] = a \cdot 1 = a$$

and

$$[a(a^{-1})](a^{-1})^{-1} = 1(a^{-1})^{-1} = (a^{-1})^{-1},$$

it follows by the associative law that

$$(a^{-1})^{-1} = a.$$

Theorem 2.5b. Let $a, b \in \mathcal{G}$. Then

$$a^{-1}b^{-1} = (ab)^{-1}.$$

PROOF: Consider

$$\begin{aligned}
(a^{-1}b^{-1})(ab) &= (a^{-1}b^{-1})(ba) \\
&= (a^{-1})[(b^{-1}b)a] \\
&= a^{-1}(1a) = a^{-1}a = 1.
\end{aligned}$$

Evidently $(a^{-1}b^{-1})$ is the multiplicative inverse for ab; that is, $a^{-1}b^{-1} = (ab)^{-1}$.

The next theorem shows that many elements in $\mathfrak{F}$ are equivalent to each other.

Theorem 2.5c. Let $a, b \in \mathcal{G}$. Then

$$ab^{-1} = (ma)(mb)^{-1}, \qquad m \neq 0.$$

PROOF:
$$\begin{aligned}
ab^{-1} &= (a \cdot 1)b^{-1} = [a(mm^{-1})]b^{-1} \\
&= (am)(m^{-1}b^{-1}) = (am)(mb)^{-1} \\
&= (ma)(mb)^{-1}.
\end{aligned}$$

That is, we have shown that

$$\frac{a}{b} = \frac{ma}{mb}, \qquad m \neq 0.$$

We now obtain a general rule for the addition of elements in $\mathfrak{F}$ which shows that $\mathcal{G}$ is closed with respect to addition.

Theorem 2.5d. Let $a, b \in \mathcal{G}$. Then

$$ab^{-1} + cd^{-1} = (ad + bc)(bd)^{-1}.$$

PROOF:
$$ab^{-1} = (ad)(bd)^{-1},$$
and
$$cd^{-1} = (bc)(bd)^{-1},$$
by Theorem 2.5c. Hence
$$ab^{-1} + cd^{-1} = (ad)(bd)^{-1} + (bc)(bd)^{-1}$$
$$= (ad + bc)(bd)^{-1},$$
by the Distributive Law.

In the usual notation of fractions, Theorem 2.5d states that
$$\frac{a}{b} + \frac{c}{d} = \frac{ad + bc}{bd}.$$

Since the element 0 has no multiplicative inverse, it is not possible for the set $\mathfrak{F}$ to be a multiplicative group. However, the set $\mathfrak{F} - \{0\}$ is a commutative multiplicative group, which is a sufficient achievement of our original goal. Therefore, we have established a new and more complex type of mathematical structure illustrated by the set $\mathfrak{F}$, which satisfies the following definition.

Definition 2.5d. Any set $\mathfrak{A}$ on which two binary operations (usually denoted by $+$ and $\cdot$) are defined is called a **field,** provided that

 F_1. the set $\mathfrak{A}$ is a commutative group with respect to $+$;
 F_2. the set $\mathfrak{A} - \{0\}$, where 0 is the additive identity, is a commutative group with respect to $\cdot$;
 F_3. the operation $\cdot$ is distributive with respect to $+$.

Examples of fields other than $\mathfrak{F}$ will be considered later.

Since $a/b = -a/(-b)$ (see Number 6, Exercises 2.5), a rational number may always be written with a positive denominator. Accordingly, we state

Definition 2.5e. A rational number is called positive or negative according to the sign of its numerator when the number is written with a positive denominator.

If r and s are unequal rational numbers, they can be ordered by means of the same formal definition as was used for the integers.

Definition 2.5f. $r < s$ means that $s - r = p$ is a positive number.

It follows that if $s - r$ and $q - s$ are both positive, then $q - r = (q - s) + (s - r)$ must be positive. That is, if $r < s$ and $s < q$, then $r < q$ (the **transitive property** of $<$). Also, since $r \neq s$ if, and only if, $r < s$ or $s < r$, the rational numbers form an ordered set.

One property possessed by the rational numbers, but clearly not by the integers, is that between any two given rational numbers there is always at least one other rational number. For, if a and b are rational, then $\frac{1}{2}(a + b)$ is a rational number that is greater than the lesser and less than the greater of a and b. It follows easily that infinitely many rational numbers exist between a and b. Because of this property, the set of rational numbers is said to be **dense.**

In spite of this "denseness," the rational numbers can be arranged in one-to-one correspondence with the positive integers, so that $\mathfrak{F}$ is a denumerable set. In order to establish the correspondence, we first arrange the positive fractions a/b in groups for which $a + b = 2, 3, 4, 5, 6, \ldots$:

$$\frac{1}{1}; \frac{1}{2}, \frac{2}{1}; \frac{1}{3}, \frac{2}{2}, \frac{3}{1}; \frac{1}{4}, \frac{2}{3}, \frac{3}{2}, \frac{4}{1}; \frac{1}{5}, \frac{2}{4}, \frac{3}{3}, \frac{4}{2}, \frac{5}{1}; \ldots$$
$$1, 2, 3, 4, \quad 5, 6, 7, 8, 9, 10, \quad 11, \ldots$$

In this arrangement, each positive fraction will occur repeatedly, but if each repetition is deleted, then a sequence remains in which each positive rational number occurs just once and in a definite position. Hence, these numbers are in a one-to-one correspondence with the natural numbers.

All the rational numbers may now be put into such a correspondence with the positive integers. It is sufficient to start with zero and then to write each negative rational number following its additive inverse in the preceding sequence:

$$0, \frac{1}{1}, -\frac{1}{1}, \frac{1}{2}, -\frac{1}{2}, \frac{2}{1}, -\frac{2}{1}, \frac{1}{3}, -\frac{1}{3}, \frac{3}{1}, -\frac{3}{1}, \ldots$$
$$1, 2, \quad 3, 4, \quad 5, 6, \quad 7, 8, \quad 9, 10, 11, \ldots$$

We have thus shown that the set $\mathfrak{F}$ of rational numbers is a denumerable set.

Exercises 2.5

1. Use the Associative Law to prove that for any element $x \in \mathfrak{F}$, $1 \cdot x = x$. (Note that if $x \in \mathfrak{F}$, then x is of the form ab^{-1}, $b \neq 0$, and $a, b \in \mathcal{I}$.)

2. Prove that $0 \cdot a^{-1} = 0$. *Hint*: Use the Associative law, and observe that
$$0 = 0 \cdot 1 = 0(aa^{-1}).$$

3. Prove that $x \in \mathfrak{F} \Rightarrow 0 \cdot x = 0$. (See Number 2.)

4. Prove that $x \in \mathfrak{F} \Rightarrow x + 0 = x$.

5. Prove that $a \in \mathfrak{R} \Rightarrow (-a)^{-1} = -a^{-1}$. (Consider the product $(-a)(-a^{-1})$ and use the fact that $(-a) = (-1)a$, along with the Commutative and Associative Laws and the uniqueness of the multiplicative inverse.)

6. Prove that $a, b \in \mathcal{I} \Rightarrow ab^{-1} = (-a)(-b)^{-1}$.

7. Prove that $(ab^{-1})(cd^{-1}) = (ac)(bd)^{-1}$; that is, prove that
$$\frac{a}{b} \cdot \frac{c}{d} = \frac{ac}{bd}.$$

8. Prove that $(-a)/b = a/(-b) = -(a/b)$, for $a, b \in \mathfrak{R}$.

9. Is division a binary operation on the set $\mathfrak{F} - \{0\}$?

10. Show that the set of numbers $\{0, 1, 2\}$ with operations $+_3$ and $\times_3$ is a field.

11. Does the set of numbers $\{0, 1, 2, 3, 4\}$ with operations $+_5$ and $\times_5$ form a field? Explain.

12. Does the set of numbers $\{0, 1, 2, 3\}$ with operations $+_4$ and $\times_4$ form a field? Explain.

13. Let θ be a "number" such that $\theta^2 = 2$. Show that the set of numbers of the form $a + b\theta$, where $a, b \in \mathfrak{F}$, is a field with respect to ordinary addition and multiplication.

14. If $a, b \in \mathfrak{F}$, is the statement that

$$\left(\frac{a}{b} + 1\right) \Big/ \left(\frac{a}{b} - 1\right) \in \mathfrak{F}$$

always true? Explain fully.

15. If fractions are added according to Theorem 2.5d, show that the Associative Law of Addition holds.

2.6 THE FIELD OF REAL NUMBERS

By ordinary long division, a rational number a/b can be expressed in decimal form. If the denominator contains no prime factors other than 2 or 5, the decimal terminates. Otherwise, the decimal is periodic; that is, eventually a sequence of digits will repeat endlessly. For example, consider the division of a by b. Once the remainder is less than b, only the $b - 1$ natural numbers less than b are possible remainders. After at most $b - 1$ divisions, a remainder must occur for the second time. Thereafter, all remainders will repeat indefinitely in the same order. Thus, every rational number can be represented in repeating or else in terminating decimal form.

As a specific illustration, we may divide 4 by 7 to show that

$$\frac{4}{7} = 0.571428 + \frac{0.000004}{7},$$

and the remainders from this point on repeat in the same order in which they have already occurred. This means that the rational number 4/7 may be expressed in the form of an endless repeating decimal, $0.571428 \cdots$, where the six digits following the decimal point are repeated again and again without end.

It is also possible to show that every repeating decimal represents a rational number. In order to illustrate the argument, consider

$$2.1353535 \ldots,$$

and let

$$x = 2.1\overline{35},$$

where the line above the digits 3 and 5 indicates the repeating part. Then,

$$100x = 213.5\overline{35}$$

and

$$100x - x = 213.5\overline{35} - 2.1\overline{35}$$

or

$$99x = 211.4.$$

Hence,

$$x = \frac{2114}{990} = \frac{1057}{495}.$$

Since $2.13\overline{5}$ is not a terminating decimal, the preceding manipulations require justification, which we shall give at a later point. However, since every repeating decimal may be dealt with in the same manner, we may assume that every such decimal represents a rational number.

It is not difficult to show by the same method that the terminating decimal 0.2 and the repeating decimal 0.1999 . . . represent the same number, 2/10 or 1/5. If we agree always to diminish the last digit of a terminating decimal by unity and annex an endless sequence of nines, as in

$$0.348 = 0.347999 \ldots,$$

then we may state that *every rational number is a repeating decimal*, and conversely, *every repeating decimal is a rational number.*

On the other hand, not every *infinite* (endless) *decimal* corresponds to a rational number. For example,

$$0.202002000200002 \ldots,$$

in which the nth 2 is followed by n zeros, does not correspond to a rational number since it is not a repeating decimal. Evidently, the rational number system is full of "gaps"; it contains no representatives of the nonrepeating infinite decimals.

But, as we saw in Example 1.5a, there is no rational number a/b such that $(a/b)^2 = 2$. This suggests that $\sqrt{2}$ might be represented by a nonrepeating decimal. Indeed, we can construct this decimal in the following intuitive fashion.

Since $1^2 < 2$ and $2^2 > 2$, the first required digit is 1. By trial, we find $(1.4)^2 < 2$ and $(1.5)^2 > 2$, so that the next digit is 4. Again, by examining $(1.41)^2$, $(1.42)^2$, $(1.43)^2, \ldots, (1.49)^2$, we find that $(1.41)^2 < 2$ and $(1.42)^2 > 2$, so that the third digit is 1. Clearly, we can continue with one digit at a time to construct a nonrepeating decimal with the following property: If we break off this decimal at any point and consider the rational number r_1 so obtained, and also the rational number r_2 obtained from r_1 by increasing the last digit of r_1 by unity, then

$$r_1^2 < 2 < r_2^2.$$

The infinite decimal that we conceive to be constructed by continuing the preceding stepwise process endlessly is defined to be $\sqrt{2}$.

The preceding discussion indicates that we can once again enlarge the number system in such a way that there are no "gaps" in the new system and so that there will be, for instance, a number x such that $x^2 = 2$. The desired enlargement is obtained by means of

Definition 2.6a. An **irrational number** is a number corresponding to a nonrepeating infinite decimal.

In view of this definition, we say that 0.2020020002 . . . represents a certain irrational number. Furthermore, irrational numbers occur in many ways. The most common way is perhaps in the process of finding roots such as $\sqrt[3]{4}$, $\sqrt{5}$,

$\sqrt[10]{15}$, and so on. Other well-known irrational numbers are π, the ratio of the circumference of a circle to its diameter, and the number called e, which is used as the base of the system of "natural logarithms." From an elementary point of view, we regard all of these numbers as being represented by infinite decimals obtained in a manner similar to that used for $\sqrt{2}$.

Definition 2.6b. The set of all irrational numbers is denoted by $\mathcal{R}_i$.

Definition 2.6c. The set

$$\mathcal{R} . = . \mathcal{R}_i \cup \mathcal{F}$$

is called the set of **real numbers**. The set $\mathcal{R}$ includes all decimals, repeating and nonrepeating.

Infinite decimals may be considered from another point of view that is suggested by our construction for $\sqrt{2}$ and that is valuable in obtaining properties of the real numbers. Let an infinite decimal x be written as

$$x = a_0.a_1a_2 \ldots a_n \ldots,$$

where a_0 is an integer and $a_1, a_2, \ldots, a_n, \ldots$ are the digits in the decimal part of the number. Let

$$b_n = a_0.a_1a_2 \ldots a_n.$$

It is clear that b_n is a rational number. In fact,

$$b_n = a_0 + \frac{a_1a_2 \ldots a_n}{10^n}.$$

The rational number b_n is called the *n-place decimal approximation* to the infinite decimal x. Thus the number

$$1.41421$$

is the five-place approximation to $\sqrt{2}$, and

$$3.141592653$$

is the nine-place approximation to π.

Evidently, the larger the value of n, the closer the nth approximation is to the number x. This fact is expressed by saying that the difference

$$x - b_n$$

may be made as near zero as we wish by taking n sufficiently large. In other words, we say that as n increases without bound, b_n "approaches" the number x. Since this discussion applies to *every* infinite decimal, we may consider such an infinite decimal to be the number approached by the set of approximating rational numbers $b_1, b_2, b_3, \ldots, b_n, \ldots$.

Definition 2.6d. An infinite decimal that is approached by a set of *positive* approximating rational numbers is called a **positive real number**.

Definition 2.6e. An infinite decimal that is approached by a set of *negative* approximating rational numbers is called a **negative real number**.

Positive and negative real numbers are distinguished in the usual way, with $+$ or $-$ signs.

As in the previous cases, we require all the basic laws of the fundamental operations to hold for the numbers in $\mathcal{R}$. It can then be shown that the set $\mathcal{R}$ is a field. However, it is beyond the scope of this book to include the details of such a proof.

The real numbers can be ordered in the same way that the rational numbers were ordered.

Definition 2.6f. If $a, b \in \mathcal{R}$, then $a < b$ means that $b - a$ is a positive number p, and we say that a is less than b.

A similar definition can be given for $a > b$ (read "a is greater than b" or "b is less than a").

With Definition 2.6f, the real numbers form an **ordered field** just as the rational numbers do. However, the field of real numbers has two important properties not possessed by the field of rational numbers.

First, it was shown that the field $\mathcal{F}$ is denumerable. It can be shown that $\mathcal{R}$ *is nondenumerable*, although we shall not include the argument here. (See, for example, Courant and Robbins, *What is Mathematics?*, pages 81–82.)

In order to understand the second difference between the two fields, we need two additional concepts.

Definition 2.6g. Let $\mathcal{S}$ be a subset of $\mathcal{R}$. A number p is said to be an upper bound of $\mathcal{S}$ if

$$x \in \mathcal{S} \Rightarrow x \leqq p.$$

For example, if $\mathcal{S} .=. \{x: 0 \leq x < 2\}$, then $5, \pi, 2.34$, and 2 are upper bounds of $\mathcal{S}$. If $\mathcal{S} .=. \{x: x = \pi/n, n \in \mathcal{N}\}$, then $4, 3.1416, 2\pi$, and 1001 are upper bounds of $\mathcal{S}$. It is clear that if a subset $\mathcal{S}$ of $\mathcal{R}$ has one upper bound p, then it has infinitely many since every number greater than p is also an upper bound of $\mathcal{S}$. It is also possible that a subset $\mathcal{S}$ of $\mathcal{R}$ have no upper bound. Such a set is $\{x: x = n\pi, n \in \mathcal{N}\}$.

Among the upper bounds of a set $\mathcal{S}$, there may be a smallest one.

Definition 2.6h. If M is an upper bound for a set $\mathcal{S}$ and if every other upper bound p of $\mathcal{S}$ is such that $M \leqq p$, then M is called the **least upper bound** of $\mathcal{S}$.

For example, if $\mathcal{S} .=. \{x: 0 \leq x < 2\}$, then 2 is the least upper bound of $\mathcal{S}$. If $\mathcal{S} .=. \{x: x = \pi/n, n \in \mathcal{N}\}$, then π is the least upper bound of $\mathcal{S}$.

Now, suppose we consider the subset $\mathcal{S}$ of $\mathcal{F}$, where

$$\mathcal{S} .=. \left\{x: x = 1 - \frac{1}{2^n}, n \in \mathcal{N}\right\}.$$

Then the least upper bound of $\mathcal{S}$ is 1, which is an element of $\mathcal{F}$. Similarly, if $\mathcal{S} .=. \{x: x = b_n$, where b_n is the nth decimal approximation to the number $1/3\}$, then $\mathcal{S} \subset \mathcal{F}$ and the least upper bound of $\mathcal{S}$ is $1/3$. (That is, $\mathcal{S}$ contains the elements 3/10, 33/100, 333/1000, etc., and this set of elements has 1/3 as a least upper bound.) Again, the least upper bound is in $\mathfrak{F}$.

Now consider the set $\mathcal{S} .=. \{x: x = b_n,$ where b_n is the nth decimal approximation to $\sqrt{2}\}$. Then $\mathcal{S}$ contains the rational numbers 14/10, 141/100, 1414/1000, 14142/10000, and so on, and $\mathcal{S} \subset \mathfrak{F}$. In this case, the least upper bound of $\mathcal{S}$ is $\sqrt{2}$, which is *not* a rational number. This illustration shows that even if a subset $\mathcal{S}$ of $\mathfrak{F}$ has a least upper bound, then that least upper bound is *not* necessarily in $\mathfrak{F}$.

However, as the preceding discussion has shown, it is reasonable to assume that if $\mathcal{S}$ is any subset of $\mathfrak{R}$ that has a least upper bound, then the least upper bound is a number in $\mathfrak{R}$. Hence, $\mathfrak{R}$ has a kind of *completeness* that $\mathfrak{F}$ does not possess. Accordingly, $\mathfrak{R}$ is called a **complete ordered field,** whereas $\mathfrak{F}$ is *not* a complete ordered field.

Exercises 2.6

1. Show that there is no rational number whose square is 3.
2. Is $\sqrt{2} + \sqrt{3}$ a rational number? Prove that your answer is correct.
3. Is the sum of two irrational numbers always irrational? What about the product?
4. If a and b are rational numbers and c is irrational, prove that

$$a + bc = 0 \Rightarrow a = b = 0.$$

(*Hint*: Suppose $b \neq 0$; then solve for c.)

In Numbers 5 to 10, find the simple fraction equivalent to the given repeating decimal.

5. $2.200200\overline{200}$.

6. $0.\overline{285714}$.

7. $0.1\overline{30}$.

8. $0.9\overline{8}$.

9. $0.\overline{1101}$.

10. $0.1\overline{3}$.

In Numbers 11 to 17, find the repeating decimal representation of the given fraction.

11. 4/7.

12. 3/5.

13. 11/17.

14. 22/7. (Compare this with the best value of π that you are able to find.)

15. 100/101.

16. 1/9.

17. 2/3.

18. Verify that

$$0.2020\overline{20} + 0.0303\overline{03} = 0.2323\overline{23}$$

by calculating the corresponding simple fractions.

19. Consider the set of numbers of the form $a\sqrt{2} + b\sqrt{3}$, where a and b are both rational. Do these numbers form a field? Explain.

In numbers 20 to 24, find the least upper bound of the given set $\mathcal{S}$. State whether $\mathcal{S} \subset \mathfrak{F}$ or $\mathcal{S} \not\subset \mathfrak{F}$, and indicate to which of $\mathfrak{F}$ or $\mathfrak{R}_i$ the least upper bound belongs.

20. $\mathcal{S} .=. \left\{x: x = \dfrac{n}{2n + 1}, n \in \mathfrak{N}\right\}.$

21. $\mathcal{S} .=. \left\{x: x = (-1)^n + \dfrac{1}{n}, n \in \mathfrak{N}\right\}.$

22. $S.=.\{x: x = b_n,$ where b_n is the nth decimal approximation to the infinite decimal $2.\overline{13}\}$.
23. $S.=.\{x: x \in \mathfrak{F}, x \geq 0, x^2 < 5\}$.
24. $S.=.\{x: x \in \mathfrak{F}, x \geq 0, x^2 < 0.25\}$.

2.7 THE FIELD OF COMPLEX NUMBERS

It follows from the discussion in the preceding section that within the field of real numbers, we can always find numbers x such that $x^2 = a$, if a is nonnegative. But what about the equation $x^2 = -a$, if a itself is positive? There is no real number that will satisfy this equation since the square of any real number is positive or zero. Hence, in order to be able to solve the equation, we must make a further extension of the number system.

First, let us suppose that we have defined a new "number," θ, such that $\theta^2 = -1$. Then we may investigate the set of "numbers" of the form $a + b\theta$, where a and b are chosen from the set of real numbers. Since we should like to preserve as much of our familiar algebra as possible, let us consider what would be likely properties of such "numbers."

If we should have $a + b\theta = 0$, then we might use the rules of our ordinary algebra to write

$$a = -b\theta,$$

and, by squaring both members,

$$a^2 = b^2\theta^2.$$

Now, $\theta^2 = -1$, so that

$$a^2 = -b^2,$$

an equation that is not possible for real a and b unless $a = b = 0$. Thus, it seems desirable to say that

$$a + b\theta = 0 \text{ if, and only if, } a = b = 0.$$

Again, if we have

$$a + b\theta = c + d\theta,$$

then

$$(a - c) + (b - d)\theta = 0$$

follows with just a little manipulation, assuming that we may operate with the "number" θ using the ordinary rules of algebra. However, the last equation, by the preceding agreement, can be valid only if $a = c$ and $b = d$.

Addition would present no problem, since it would seem reasonable to ask that

$$(a + b\theta) + (c + d\theta) = (a + c) + (b + d)\theta.$$

For multiplication, we have

$$(a + b\theta)(c + d\theta) = ac + ad\theta + bc\theta + bd\theta^2$$
$$= (ac - bd) + (ad + bc)\theta,$$

where we have again used $\theta^2 = -1$, as well as the ordinary algebraic manipulations.

Since a, b, c, d are all real, it appears that the results of adding or multiplying "numbers" of the form $a + b\theta$ and $c + d\theta$ are again "numbers" of the same form. This looks so promising that we make our extension of the number system on the basis of these results.

Quantities of the form $a + b\theta$ are actually pairs of real numbers, where the symbol θ serves only to keep the two numbers separate. Another way of specifying a pair of numbers so that each is distinguished from the other is by the notation (a, b) where a denotes the first element and b the second element of the pair. That is, (a, b) is called an **ordered pair** of real numbers. Because of the order concept associated with the numbers, we may not say that (a, b) and (b, a) are the same. They are *different* pairs.

Definition 2.7a. A **complex number** is an ordered pair of real numbers, (a, b), that obeys the following rules.

 (1) Equality: $(a, b) = (c, d) \Leftrightarrow a = c$ and $b = d$.
 (2) Addition: $(a, b) + (c, d) .=. (a + c, b + d)$.
 (3) Multiplication: $(a, b)(c, d) .=. (ac - bd, ad + bc)$.

Notice that we have used exactly the number pairs that seemed desirable from our preliminary investigations. It is now easy to see that a one-to-one correspondence exists between the number pairs of the form $(a, 0)$ and the real numbers. To illustrate, observe that

$$(a, 0) + (b, 0) = (a + b, 0)$$

and that

$$(a, 0)(b, 0) = (ab, 0).$$

It follows that the element $(a, 0)$ behaves exactly like the real number a in relation to other elements of the form $(b, 0)$. For example, $(1, 0)$ is the multiplicative identity for the elements $(a, 0)$, and $(a^{-1}, 0)$ is the multiplicative inverse for $(a, 0)$. Therefore, let us agree to write a for $(a, 0)$. Under this condition we may, for any complex number, write

$$
\begin{aligned}
(a, b) &= (a, 0) + (0, b) \\
&= (a, 0)(1, 0) + (b, 0)(0, 1) \\
&= a \cdot 1 + b(0, 1) \\
&= a + b(0, 1).
\end{aligned}
$$

Since $(0, 1)(0, 1) = (-1, 0) = -1$, it appears that the θ, which was introduced earlier, represents the number pair $(0, 1)$. Since $\theta^2 = -1$, it is natural to call θ a square root of -1.

Let us now examine the problem of finding (a, b) so that

$$[(a, b)]^2 = -1 = (-1, 0).$$

Since $[(a, b)]^2 = (a, b)(a, b) = (a^2 - b^2, 2ab)$, we must have, by the preceding definition of equality,

$$a^2 - b^2 = -1 \quad \text{and} \quad 2ab = 0.$$

From the second equation it follows that

$$a = 0 \quad \text{or} \quad b = 0.$$

But, keeping in mind that a and b are real, we see that $b \neq 0$. (If it were zero, the first equation would reduce to $a^2 = -1$, an impossibility for any real number a.) Thus, we must have $a = 0$, so that $b^2 = 1$, and $b = 1$ or -1. Consequently, we have two candidates for square roots of -1; they are $(0, 1)$ and $(0, -1)$. The student should verify that $[(0, -1)]^2$ is the same as $(-1, 0)$, or -1.

In order to have a handier symbol, it is customary to designate the number pair $(0, 1)$ by the symbol i, and the pair $(0, -1)$ by $-i$. The result of the last discussion can then be written in usual algebraic fashion:

$$i^2 = -1 \quad \text{and} \quad (-i)^2 = -1.$$

The square roots of -1 are accordingly i and $-i$. The number i has unfortunately been called the **imaginary unit,** a name that must not be interpreted literally since it should be evident that the number pairs (a, b) that we have called complex numbers are no more "imaginary" than the pairs a/b that we called rational numbers earlier.

With the preceding agreements, we may replace the number pair (a, b) by the symbol $a + bi$. Our preliminary discussion has shown that we may operate with these symbols in a formal algebraic manner, replacing i^2 by -1, and that the results will be consistent with the definitions that we have set down for the complex numbers.

For any complex number, $a + bi$, the real number a is known as the *real part*, and the real number b as the *coefficient of the imaginary part* of the complex number. If $a = 0$ and $b \neq 0$, the complex number is called a **pure imaginary number.** If $b = 0$, the complex number is identified with the real number a.

We shall use the symbol $\mathfrak{C}$ for the set of all complex numbers so that the set $\mathfrak{R}$ of real numbers is a proper subset of the complex numbers; that is, $\mathfrak{R} \subset \mathfrak{C}$. Any complex number with a nonzero imaginary part is called **imaginary.** Thus, $2 - 3i$, $2.48 + 0.93i$, and $-i\sqrt{3}$ are all examples of imaginary numbers. The set $\mathfrak{C}$ includes all such numbers as well as all the real numbers.

The definition of equality means that two complex numbers are equal if, and only if, their real parts are equal and the coefficients of their imaginary parts are equal.

The definition of addition indicates that we add the real parts of the two complex numbers to get the real part of the sum, and we add the coefficients of the imaginary parts to get the coefficient of the imaginary part of the sum.

The subtraction of complex numbers is defined as the inverse of addition. Hence, if z represents a complex number,

$$z_1 - z_2 = z_3 \text{ means } z_1 = z_2 + z_3.$$

We can thus develop a formula for subtraction. Let

$$(a, b) - (c, d) = (e, f);$$

then

$$(a, b) = (c, d) + (e, f)$$
$$= (c + e, d + f).$$

This means that $a = c + e$ and $b = d + f$, or $e = a - c$ and $f = b - d$. Consequently, we have the formula

$$(a, b) - (c, d) = (a - c, b - d)$$

or

$$(a + bi) - (c + di) = (a - c) + (b - d)i.$$

The division of complex numbers is defined as the inverse of multiplication, so

$$\frac{z_1}{z_2} = z_3 \text{ means } z_1 = z_2 z_3.$$

Let us find an expression for the quotient of the complex numbers (a, b) and (c, d).

$$\frac{(a, b)}{(c, d)} = (e, f) \text{ means}$$

$$(a, b) = (c, d)(e, f)$$
$$= (ce - df, de + cf).$$

Thus, $a = ce - df$, and $b = de + cf$. Solving for e and f, we have

$$e = \frac{ac + bd}{c^2 + d^2},$$

$$f = \frac{bc - ad}{c^2 + d^2},$$

or

$$\frac{(a, b)}{(c, d)} = \left(\frac{ac + bd}{c^2 + d^2}, \frac{bc - ad}{c^2 + d^2} \right).$$

If we think of the complex numbers in the form $a + bi$ and $c + di$, we may get the same result by multiplying numerator and denominator of the fraction by $c - di$, which is called the **conjugate** of $c + di$. Thus,

$$\frac{a + bi}{c + di} = \frac{(a + bi)(c - di)}{(c + di)(c - di)}$$

$$= \frac{ac + bd}{c^2 + d^2} + i \frac{bc - ad}{c^2 + d^2}.$$

The set of complex numbers is closed under the four fundamental operations of addition, subtraction, multiplication, and division (except for division by zero), and the associative, commutative, and distributive laws are satisfied. Hence, the complex numbers form a field.

It is reasonable to ask if it is possible to continue making extensions of the number system to obtain an even more comprehensive kind of number system, and it is rather surprising to learn that it can be shown that any further extension of the complex number system entails the loss of at least one of the properties possessed by the field of complex numbers. The discussion in Chapter 3 will show, however, that no further extension is needed for the purposes of ordinary elementary algebra.

To summarize the results of this chapter, we point out that we have gone through a succession of constructions to obtain a number system—the complex number system—that is most versatile and useful in solving mathematical problems. In addition, as the reader will discover in his progress through this book, the complex number system embodies many surprising and important relationships that make the system most useful in dealing with problems in engineering and physics.

The following chart illustrates the relationship between the various number systems that we have discussed:

natural numbers ⎫
zero   ⎬ integers ⎫
negative integers ⎭   ⎬ rational numbers ⎫
        ratios of   ⎬ real numbers ⎫
        integers ⎭   ⎬   ⎬ complex
        irrational numbers ⎭   imaginary   ⎬ numbers
                                                    numbers ⎭

That is,

$$\mathfrak{N} \subset \mathfrak{N}_0 \subset \mathcal{I} \subset \mathcal{F} \subset \mathcal{R} \subset \mathcal{C}.$$

Exercises 2.7

1. Verify the Commutative Law of Multiplication for complex numbers.
2. Verify the Associative Law of Addition for complex numbers.
3. Verify the Distributive Law for complex numbers.
4. Verify the Associative Law of Multiplication for complex numbers.
5. Show that the set of complex numbers forms a field.

In Numbers 6 to 22, inclusive, perform the indicated operation, and write the answer in the form $a + bi$.

6. $(4 + i) + (3 - 5i)$.
7. $(2 + 7i) - (3 - 2i)$.
8. $(5 + 7i)(3 + i)$.
9. $(1 + 2i)(3 - 4i)$.
10. $(3 - i)(4 + 2i)$.
11. $(x + iy)(x - iy)$.
12. $(8 - i\sqrt{3})(8 + i\sqrt{3})$.
13. $(1 - i)(1 - i)(1 + i)$.

14. $\dfrac{3 - 2i}{4 + 5i}$.

15. $\dfrac{5 + 4i}{3 - 4i}$.

16. $\dfrac{1}{2 - 3i}$.

17. $\dfrac{3 + 4i}{3 - 4i}$.

18. $\dfrac{5 + i}{1 - 3i}$.

19. $\dfrac{2 + 10i}{5 - i}$.

20. $i^5 + i^8$.

21. $\dfrac{6 - i}{5 + 2i} - \dfrac{3 + 4i}{2 - 5i}$.

22. $\dfrac{7 + 2i}{3 - 4i} + \dfrac{2 + 5i}{4 + 5i}$.

In Numbers 23 to 25, show that the given set of complex numbers is a multiplicative group.

23. $\{1, -1, i, -i\}$.

24. $\{1, \omega, \omega^2\}$, where $\omega = \dfrac{-1 + i\sqrt{3}}{2}$.

25. $\left\{1, -1, \dfrac{1 + i\sqrt{3}}{2}, \dfrac{-1 + i\sqrt{3}}{2}, \dfrac{-1 - i\sqrt{3}}{2}, \dfrac{1 - i\sqrt{3}}{2}\right\}$.

26. In Definition 2.7a, suppose (1) and (2) are retained as they are, but that (3) is replaced by
$$(a, b)(c, d) .=. (ac + bd, ad - bc).$$

(a) Is there a subset of the set $\{(a, b)\}$ that corresponds to the real numbers?
(b) Is there a pair that can serve as a square root of -1?
(c) Which pairs would serve as square roots of 1?

Summary of Chapter 2

The reader should understand what is meant by the following fundamental concepts, and be able to give examples of each:

(1) a binary (closed) operation (Section 2.4);
(2) an associative operation (Sections 2.1, 2.4);
(3) a commutative operation (Sections 2.1, 2.4);
(4) the Distributive Law (Section 2.1);
(5) the Theorem of Mathematical Induction (Section 2.2);
(6) an algebraic structure (Section 2.4);
(7) a group (Section 2.4);
(8) a field (Section 2.5).

The following sets of numbers should be recognized by the reader to the extent that (a) he is familiar with the notation for each set, and (b) he knows the structural differences between them:

(9) $\mathfrak{N} .=. \{x: x$ is a natural number$\}$ (Section 2.1);
(10) $\mathfrak{N}_0 .=. \mathfrak{N} \cup \{0\}$ (Section 2.3);
(11) $\mathcal{I} .=. \{x: x$ is an integer$\}$ (Section 2.3);
(12) $\mathfrak{F} .=. \{x: x$ is a rational number$\}$ (Section 2.5);
(13) $\mathfrak{R}_i .=. \{x: x$ is an irrational number$\}$ (Section 2.6);

(14) $\mathfrak{R} . = .$ {x: x is a real number} (Section 2.6);

(15) $\mathfrak{C} . = .$ {x: x is a complex number} (Section 2.7).

Finally, the reader should be able to prove some of the elementary properties of a system of numbers by using the fundamental laws for that system, as illustrated in

(16) Theorems 2.3a, b, c, d, e, f, g, h;

(17) Theorems 2.5a, b, c, d.

Chapter 3   Algebraic Expressions, Equations, and Inequalities

3.1 POSITIVE INTEGRAL EXPONENTS

When it is known that a set of elements is a field with respect to the operations of addition and multiplication, many rules governing expressions that involve elements of the field can be obtained. These rules may then be used to compare different expressions or to simplify expressions so as to make such a system a useful tool in solving problems.

In the discussion that follows, letters of the alphabet will be used to represent arbitrary elements of a given field. For example, if we are discussing the field of real numbers, then the letters a, b, c, and so on, may be replaced by arbitrarily chosen real numbers. The result of making such a replacement is a special statement about particular elements of the field. Thus, we might write

$$2x + 3x = 5x, \qquad x \in \mathfrak{R}.$$

If x is replaced by $\frac{1}{2}$, then

$$2(\tfrac{1}{2}) + 3(\tfrac{1}{2}) = 5(\tfrac{1}{2})$$

is a true statement about the elements 2, 3, 5, and $\frac{1}{2}$ in the field. However, the first statement is true for the elements 2, 3, 5, and for any other element x, whatever x may be, in the field. Hence the first statement conveys a much more general idea than the second. Herein lies a great power of the mathematical method—that of generalizing from particular examples to a general rule.

In algebra we are accustomed to considering expressions such as

$$a + b - (2a - b); \frac{a + b}{a - c}, \text{ with } a \neq c; a^2 + 2ab + b^2; \frac{x^2 - y^2}{x - y}, \text{ with } x \neq y; \sqrt{c}.$$

(Notice that since division by zero is not defined, the expressions involving division have a side condition.)

These expressions are formed by making use of letters of the alphabet, which represent elements from some basic set of numbers, along with one or more of the operations of addition, subtraction, multiplication, division, and extraction of roots. If these operations are used only a finite number of times to combine only a finite number of elements of the basic set of numbers, then the resulting expression is usually called an **algebraic expression.** Thus, all the preceding expressions are of this type.

The algebraic operations that are carried out with algebraic expressions are valid for *all* permissible numerical values that may be substituted for the letters. Hence, a statement involving algebraic expressions is a general statement about numbers rather than a specific statement about certain numbers. To illustrate further, we may replace statements such as

$$2(3 + 5) = (2)(3) + (2)(5)$$

and

$$7(1 + 3) = (7)(1) + (7)(3)$$

by the more general form

$$a(b + c) = ab + ac$$

This last statement, the Distributive Law, expresses at once a property possessed by *all* numbers, whereas the preceding statements are statements about specific numbers. As the reader proceeds through this book, he will realize more and more the basic importance of being able to deal with general statements in order to obtain results that are useful, not only in mathematics itself but also in all areas of application.

Consider the expression $a + a$. By the Distributive and Commutative Laws we may write

$$a + a = a(1 + 1) = a \cdot 2 = 2a.$$

Similarly, $a + a + a = 3a$, $a + a + a + a = 4a$, and so on. In each case we may use the laws of the field in order to obtain a simpler expression for the sum, and in each case the numerical coefficient counts the number of a's occurring in the original sum.

Similarly, it would be convenient to have a simple way of writing a repeated product of an element with itself. For example, it is cumbersome to write $a \cdot a \cdot a \cdot a \cdot a$ for the product of five a's. We have already made use of a notation that would enable us to write such forms in a simpler way; we have used the symbol a^2 for $a \cdot a$.

Definition 3.1a. For any positive integer n, $a^n .=. a \cdot a \cdot \cdots \cdot a$, where there are n a's on the right side. The number n, when used in this manner, is called an **exponent.**

Thus, $a^2 = a \cdot a$, $a^5 = a \cdot a \cdot a \cdot a \cdot a$, etc. Several rules follow immediately from this definition. The reader should prove each part of the following theorem.

Theorem 3.1a. If $a, b \in \mathfrak{R}$ and $n, m, p \in \mathfrak{N}$, then

(1) $a^n a^m = a^{n+m}$,

(2) $(a^n)^m = a^{nm}$,

(3) $(ab)^p = a^p b^p$.

For example,

$$a^2a^3 = (a \cdot a) \cdot (a \cdot a \cdot a) = a \cdot a \cdot a \cdot a \cdot a = a^5,$$

and

$$(a^2)^3 = a^2 \cdot a^2 \cdot a^2 = (a \cdot a) \cdot (a \cdot a) \cdot (a \cdot a) = a^6.$$

By means of these rules many expressions involving products and exponents may easily be simplified.

Example 3.1a. Find a simpler expression for $(ab^3)^2(a^3b)^3$.

Applying the rules in Theorem 3.1a, we get

$$\begin{aligned}
(ab^3)^2(a^3b)^3 &= a^2(b^3)^2(a^3)^3b^3 && \text{[by (3)]}\\
&= a^2b^6a^9b^3 && \text{[by (2)]}\\
&= a^{11}b^9 && \text{[by the Commutative Law of}\\
& && \text{Multiplication and (1)].}
\end{aligned}$$

Example 3.1b. Find the product of $(x^2 - xy + y^2)$ and $(x^2 + 2xy - 3y^2)$.

By the Distributive, Associative, and Commutative Laws, we have

$$\begin{aligned}
(x^2 &- xy + y^2)(x^2 + 2xy - 3y^2)\\
&= x^2(x^2 + 2xy - 3y^2) - xy(x^2 + 2xy - 3y^2) + y^2(x^2 + 2xy - 3y^2)\\
&= x^4 + 2x^3y - 3x^2y^2 - x^3y - 2x^2y^2 + 3xy^3 + x^2y^2 + 2xy^3 - 3y^4\\
&= x^4 + x^3y - 4x^2y^2 + 5xy^3 - 3y^4.
\end{aligned}$$

Example 3.1c. Suppose θ is a number for which $\theta^2 - \theta + 1 = 0$. Express the product of $(\theta^2 + \theta + 1)$ and $(\theta^2 - 2\theta - 1)$ in terms of powers of θ less than the second.

Since

$$\theta^2 - \theta + 1 = 0,$$

then

$$\theta^2 = \theta - 1.$$

Hence,

$$\theta^2 + \theta + 1 = (\theta - 1) + \theta + 1 = 2\theta,$$

and

$$\theta^2 - 2\theta - 1 = (\theta - 1) - 2\theta - 1 = -\theta - 2.$$

Therefore,

$$\begin{aligned}
(\theta^2 + \theta + 1)(\theta^2 - 2\theta - 1) &= (2\theta)(-\theta - 2) = -2\theta^2 - 4\theta\\
&= -2(\theta - 1) - 4\theta = -6\theta + 2.
\end{aligned}$$

Exercises 3.1

In Numbers 1 to 18, find the product of the given expressions in as simple a form as you can.

1. $(a^2b^3)^3(ab^2)^2$.
2. $(x^3y^3)^3(x^2y^2z)^2$.
3. $(a^3b^4c^2)^4(ab^3c^2)^3$.
4. $(a^nb^p)^2(a^2b^p)^3$.
5. $(a^nbc^{2n})^2(abc^3)^n$.
6. $(a^pb^q)^p(ab^q)^p$.
7. $(a^2 - b^2)(a - b)$.
8. $(a^3 - b^3)(a^6 + a^3b^3 + b^6)$.
9. $(x^2 + 2xy + y^2)(x^2 - 2xy + y^2)$.
10. $(x + 2y - z)(x - 2y + z)$.

11. $(a^2 + ab + b^2 + a - b + 1)(a - b - 1)$.
12. $(x^{n+1} - x^n y^n + y^{n+1})(x + y)$.
13. $(x^{n+1} - x^n y^n + y^{n+1})(x^{n+1} + x^n y^n + y^{n+1})$.
14. $(x^{2n} - x^n y^n + y^{2n})(x^{2n} + x^n y^n + y^{2n})$.
15. $(1 + x + x^2)(1 - x + x^2 - x^3)$.   17. $(a - b + c)^2$.
16. $(x - y)(x^2 + xy + y^2)(x + y)(x^2 - xy + y^2)$.   18. $(a - b)^2(a^2 + 2ab + b^2)$.

19. In Example 3.1c, first find the product $(\theta^2 + \theta + 1)(\theta^2 - 2\theta - 1)$, and then use the fact that $\theta^2 - \theta + 1 = 0$ to show that the product is $-6\theta + 2$.

In Numbers 20 to 23, suppose u is a number for which $u^3 + u^2 + u + 1 = 0$, and find the following products in terms of powers of u lower than the third.

20. $(u^2 + u + 1)(u^3 - 1)$.   22. $(u^2 - u + 1)(u^2 + 2u + 2)$.
21. $(u^4 - 1)(u^2 + 2u + 3)$.   23. $(u^2 + 1)(u^3 - u - 1)(u + 1)$.

3.2 FACTORIZATION OVER A FIELD

It was pointed out earlier that a composite integer may be expressed as a product of prime integers. This concept can be extended to certain types of algebraic expressions having coefficients belonging to a field.

Definition 3.2a. An algebraic expression of the form

$$a_0 x^n + a_1 x^{n-1} + \cdots + a_{n-1} x + a_n, \qquad a_0 \neq 0,$$

where n is a nonnegative integer and the numbers a_i are numbers in a specified field (say $\mathfrak{F}$ or $\mathfrak{R}$ or $\mathfrak{C}$), is called a *polynomial of degree n in x on this field*.

Since polynomials occur frequently in the following discussions, it is worthwhile to give them special attention. We shall use notations such as $p(x)$, $q(x)$, $r(x)$, and $s(x)$ to represent polynomials in x. Thus,

$$p(x) .=. 4x^3 - 7x^2 + \sqrt{2}x - 1$$

is a polynomial of degree three on the field $\mathfrak{R}$.

In a similar fashion, a *polynomial in x and y* on a given field is a sum of terms of the type $a_i x^m y^n$, where the a_i are numbers in the field and the m and n are nonnegative integers. We may denote such polynomials by $p(x, y)$, $q(x, y)$, and so on. For example,

$$x^3 + \sqrt{3}\, xy^2 + y^4 - \pi y + 2$$

is a polynomial in x and y on the field $\mathfrak{R}$.

Evidently, the sum of two polynomials is another polynomial, and if 0 is considered to be a polynomial in which all the coefficients are 0, then the set of all polynomials in x, $\{p(x)\}$, over the field $\mathfrak{F}$, $\mathfrak{R}$, or $\mathfrak{C}$ has an additive identity. Also, if $p(x)$ is a polynomial, $-p(x)$ is also a polynomial such that $p(x) + (-p(x)) = 0$. Finally, addition of polynomials is an associative operation so that the set $\{p(x)\}$ of polynomials on a given field forms an additive group.

The set $\{p(x)\}$ is closed and has the associative property with respect to ordinary multiplication. Furthermore, 1 is the multiplicative identity, but the multiplicative inverse of a polynomial is generally not a polynomial. Consequently, the set $\{p(x)\} - \{0\}$ is not a multiplicative group. For example, the multiplicative inverse of $1 - x$, is not a polynomial, although we may write

$$\frac{1}{1-x} = 1 + x + x^2 + \cdots + x^{n-1} + \frac{x^n}{1-x}.$$

It follows from this discussion that the set $\{p(x)\}$ of polynomials is not a field. However, the set possesses many of the properties possessed by the set of integers. The set $\{p(x)\}$ is an additive group; it is closed with respect to multiplication, possesses a multiplicative identity element, and its elements obey the Associative Law of Multiplication and the Distributive Law.

The concepts of prime and composite numbers in the set of natural numbers have analogies in the set of polynomials over a field.

Definition 3.2b. A polynomial $p(x)$ is said to be **factorable** in a given field if the polynomial can be written as a product of polynomials of degree greater than 0 with coefficients in that field. The polynomials in the product are called **factors** of $p(x)$.

Example 3.2a. Factor the polynomial $x^2 - 1$ in $\mathfrak{F}$.

In this case, we may write
$$x^2 - 1 = (x - 1)(x + 1)$$
by inspection and trial. The expressions $x - 1$ and $x + 1$ are the factors of $x^2 - 1$.

The expression $2x + 4$ may be written as $2(x + 2)$. However, since the factor 2 is a polynomial of degree 0, the factorization is considered to be a trivial one. Hence, we are led to

Definition 3.2c. If a polynomial *cannot* be expressed as a product of other polynomials of degree greater than 0 over a given field, then the polynomial is said to be **irreducible** in that field.

Thus, $2x + 4$ is irreducible in the fields $\mathfrak{F}$, $\mathfrak{R}$, and $\mathfrak{C}$.

Example 3.2b. Show that $x^2 - 2$ is irreducible in the field $\mathfrak{F}$ of rational numbers, but is reducible in the field $\mathfrak{R}$ of real numbers.

Suppose that $x^2 - 2$ is reducible. Then it must be the product of two first degree factors $x - a$ and $x - b$. But it is easy to see by trial that if $b \neq -a$, then $(x - a)(x - b)$ will have a term $-(a + b)x$. Consequently, $b = -a$ and the factors are $x - a$ and $x + a$, so that
$$(x - a)(x + a) = x^2 - a^2 = x^2 - 2.$$
This means that $a^2 = 2$, which we have shown impossible for rational a. Therefore, $x^2 - 2$ is irreducible in $\mathfrak{F}$.

If a does not have to be rational, we may write $a = \sqrt{2}$, and
$$x^2 - 2 = (x - \sqrt{2})(x + \sqrt{2}),$$
which displays the fact that $x^2 - 2$ is reducible in $\mathfrak{R}$.

Example 3.2c. Show that $x^2 + 2$ cannot be factored in the field $\mathfrak{R}$, but can be factored in the field $\mathfrak{C}$.

By the same argument as that in the preceding example, we are led to

$$x^2 + 2 = (x - a)(x + a) = x^2 - a^2$$

in any field where $x^2 + 2$ is reducible. This requires that $a^2 = -2$, which is impossible in $\mathfrak{R}$ but gives $a = \pm i\sqrt{2}$ in $\mathfrak{C}$. Hence, the factorization is possible in $\mathfrak{C}$, and we have

$$x^2 + 2 = (x - i\sqrt{2})(x + i\sqrt{2}).$$

There is no routine procedure that can always be used to obtain the factors of a given expression. A student must become well enough acquainted with certain standard forms so that he can easily recognize a type form into which a given expression may be factored.

The preceding three examples are special cases of the general form, $a^2 - b^2$, called the difference of two squares. The difference of two squares can always be factored as $(a - b)(a + b)$ in an appropriate field. Note that, in the case of $a^2 + b^2$, which is not factorable in the field $\mathfrak{R}$, we may write $a^2 + b^2 = a^2 - (i)^2b^2 = a^2 - (ib)^2$ in the field $\mathfrak{C}$. *Hence, it is always necessary to specify with respect to what field a factorization is to be done.*

There are several other common types of expressions that can be factored easily in the field of rational numbers. By studying the patterns for each of these forms, one can easily extend the forms to apply in fields other than the field of rational numbers. Some of the more usual forms and their factors are

$$a^2 - b^2 = (a - b)(a + b),$$
$$a^3 - b^3 = (a - b)(a^2 + ab + b^2),$$
$$a^3 + b^3 = (a + b)(a^2 - ab + b^2),$$
$$x^2 + (b + c)x + bc = (x + b)(x + c),$$
$$ax + by + ay + bx = (a + b)(x + y).$$

Any proposed factorization can be checked simply by multiplying the factors together to see if the resulting product is equivalent to the original expression.

The use of the preceding forms in factoring is illustrated in the following examples.

Example 3.2d. Factor $27x^3 + 8y^6$ in the field $\mathfrak{F}$.

This expression may be written as $(3x)^3 + (2y^2)^3$. Hence, this fits the form $a^3 + b^3$, and we have the factorization

$$(3x)^3 + (2y^2)^3 = [(3x) + (2y^2)][(3x)^2 - (3x)(2y^2) + (2y^2)^2]$$
$$= (3x + 2y^2)(9x^2 - 6xy^2 + 4y^4).$$

Example 3.2e. Factor $x^2 + 2x - 48$ in the field $\mathfrak{F}$.

If this expression can be factored in the field $\mathfrak{F}$, we should expect factors of the form $(x - a)(x + b)$. Hence, we need two numbers, a and b, whose product is 48 and whose difference is 2. Two such numbers are 6 and 8. Hence,

$$x^2 + 2x - 48 = (x - 6)(x + 8).$$

Note that if the 6 and 8 are interchanged in these factors, we get

$$(x - 8)(x + 6) = x^2 - 2x - 48,$$

and the sign of the middle term does not agree with the corresponding sign in the given expression.

Example 3.2f. Factor $a^4 - b^4$ in the field $\mathcal{C}$.

$$a^4 - b^4 = (a^2 - b^2)(a^2 + b^2)$$
$$= (a - b)(a + b)(a + ib)(a - ib).$$

Note that if the field $\mathcal{F}$ had been specified, then we would have written

$$a^4 - b^4 = (a - b)(a + b)(a^2 + b^2).$$

Example 3.2g. In what field is $x^2 + 2y^2$ factorable?

Since we may write $x^2 + 2y^2 = (x + i\sqrt{2}y)(x - i\sqrt{2}y)$, the expression is factorable in the field $\mathcal{C}$.

Example 3.2h. Factor $a^2 + ab + b^2$ in the field $\mathcal{C}$.

In this case it is necessary to add to and subtract from the expression a quantity that will form a perfect square with the first two terms. By doing this, a form for the sum or difference of two squares may be obtained and the usual factoring techniques may then be applied to this result. Thus,

$$a^2 + ab + b^2 = \left(a^2 + ab + \frac{b^2}{4}\right) - \frac{b^2}{4} + b^2$$

$$= \left(a + \frac{b}{2}\right)^2 + \frac{3b^2}{4}$$

$$= \left(a + \frac{b}{2} + \frac{i\sqrt{3}}{2}b\right)\left(a + \frac{b}{2} - \frac{i\sqrt{3}}{2}b\right).$$

Example 3.2i. Factor $a^4 + 5a^2b^2 + 9b^4$ in the field $\mathcal{F}$.
We may use the technique employed in Example 3.2h. Thus,

$$a^4 + 5a^2b^2 + 9b^4 = a^4 + 6a^2b^2 + 9b^4 - a^2b^2$$
$$= (a^2 + 3b^2)^2 - a^2b^2$$
$$= (a^2 + 3b^2 - ab)(a^2 + 3b^2 + ab).$$

Exercises 3.2

In Numbers 1 to 14, write the given polynomial as a product of irreducible polynomials in the field $\mathcal{F}$.

1. $4x^2 - 9$.
2. $x^2 - 3$.
3. $8a^3 - 27b^6$.
4. $64 - y^3$.
5. $4x^4 + y^4$.
6. $x^2 + y^2$.
7. $x^2 - 7x + 10$.

8. $6y^2 - 11y + 3$.
9. $16x^4 - y^4$.
10. $125 + 27a^3$.
11. $27x^6 + 8x^3y^3z^6$.
12. $6x^2 - xy - 12y^2$.
13. $4x^2 - 12xy + 9y^2$.
14. $a^4 + 4$.

In Numbers 15 to 26, write the given polynomial as a product of irreducible polynomials in the field $\mathfrak{R}$.

15. $x^2 - 3$.
16. $x^2 + y^2$.
17. $x^2 - 2\sqrt{3}x + 3$.
18. $16x^4 - y^4$.
19. $x^3 + 9x$.
20. $5a^2 - b^2$.

21. $z^4 + 2z^2 + 4$.
22. $w^4 - 4$.
23. $x^3 + 2x^2 - 2x - 4$.
24. $b^3 + b^2 - 3b - 3$.
25. $x^3 + 8y^3$.
26. $x^4 + 1$.

In Numbers 27 to 38, write the given polynomial as a product of irreducible polynomials in the field $\mathfrak{C}$.

27. $x^2 + y^2$.
28. $16x^4 - y^4$.
29. $a^2 - 5ai - 6$.
30. $x^3 + 9x$.
31. $a^2 + 5b^2$.
32. $z^3 - 1$.

33. $2x^2 - ix + 6$.
34. $8x^3 + y^3$.
35. $a^3 + 3a$.
36. $x^3 + 2x^2 + 2x + 1$.
37. $b^3 - b^2 + 2b - 2$.
38. $x^4 - 4y^4$.

In Numbers 39 to 60, factor each expression in the field $\mathfrak{R}$.

39. $3^{2n} + 2 \cdot 3^n + 1$.
40. $6 - 3^n - 3^{2n}$.
41. $2x^2 - xy^k - y^{2k}$.
42. $x^2 - 9 + 6y - y^2$.
43. $9a^2 - (3b - 6)^2$.
44. $(u^2 + u + 1)^2 - (u - 3)^2$.
45. $x - xy + 1 - y^2$.
46. $a^3 + a^3b^3 - b^3 - 1$.
47. $ax + ay - a - bx - by + b$.
48. $4n^3 - n - 4n^2 + 1$.
49. $a^2b^2 - b^2 + c^2 - a^2c^2$.

50. $(x - 1)^3 - 1 + x^3$.
51. $(x - a)(x^2 - b^2) + (x^2 - a^2)(x - b)^2$.
52. $x^4 + x^2y^2 + y^4 - x^2 + xy - y^2$.
53. $4(a + b)^2 - 4(a^2 - b^2) + (a - b)^2$.
54. $x^3 - x^2y - x^2 + xy - 6x + 6y$.
55. $(a + b)^2 + a + b - 6$.
56. $a^2 - ab - 2b^2 - ac + 2bc$.
57. $x^2 + y^2 + 2y - 2x - 2xy$.
58. $a^2 - x^2 + b^2 - 4 - 2ab + 4x$.
59. $16 - 16y^3 - x^4 + x^4y^3$.
60. $ab^2 + (a^2 - a)b - a^2$.

3.3 FRACTIONAL EXPRESSIONS

Algebraic expressions involving the operation of division are called **fractional expressions**. Some examples of fractional expressions are

$$\frac{a}{b} + 2c, \quad \frac{2 + x}{x^2 - 4}, \quad \frac{a/b}{2 + (b/a)}.$$

The third expression is an example of a complex fractional expression, that is, a fraction that has fractions as terms of its numerator or denominator. It should be understood that *no values leading to a division by zero may be substituted in these expressions.*

Fractional expressions occur quite frequently in mathematics and it is often necessary to reduce complex fractions to simple fractions, or to change the form of such expressions so that they may be combined by addition into a single fraction. In order to accomplish these changes, we need to make use of some additional ideas.

Definition 3.3a. A **multinomial** is an algebraic expression consisting of more than one term. (An expression of one term is usually called a **monomial**.)

Some examples of multinomials are

$$a^3 + a^2b + ab^3 + b^3,$$
$$2x^2 + 3x + 1,$$
$$x^2 - a^2,$$
$$\frac{a}{b} + \frac{c}{d} + \frac{e}{f}.$$

The third of these is called a **binomial**; the second is called a **trinomial**.

Definition 3.3b. A multinomial A is said to divide a multinomial B if A is a factor of B. If A divides B, we write $A|B$.

Illustration:

$$(a + b)|(a^2 - b^2).$$

Definition 3.3c. A **common multiple** of a set of multinomials A, B, C is a multinomial M such that A, B, C each divides M.

A common multiple for the expressions x, $x^2 - 4$, $x + 2$, x^3 may be obtained by simply multiplying all the expressions together. Thus, $M = x^4(x + 2)(x^2 - 4)$ is a common multiple since each of the expressions certainly divides M. However, we can write many other expressions that will be common multiples merely by multiplying M by any arbitrary multinomial. It is usually desirable to obtain a certain unique common multiple that is of simplest form.

Definition 3.3d. A common multiple, L, of a set of multinomials is said to be a **lowest common multiple** (L.C.M.), if L divides every other common multiple M of the set. That is, $L|M$ for every M.

For example, several common multiples of the expressions

$$ab, \quad 2a^2, \quad 6b^2, \quad 4ab^3$$

are

$$48a^4b^6, \quad 12a^4b^3, \quad 24a^2b^3, \quad 12a^2b^3.$$

Of these, $12a^2b^3$ divides each of the others. While this result suggests that $12a^2b^3$ may be the L.C.M., it is by no means conclusive evidence that this is the case. Since it is not possible to make an actual comparison between this common multiple and all other common multiples, it is necessary to determine some means of deducing the L.C.M.

Let us write each of the expressions in a factored form over the field of rational numbers. Then we have

$$ab, \quad 2a^2, \quad 2\cdot3b^2, \quad 2^2ab^3.$$

The L.C.M. of these expressions must contain each factor to the highest power to which it occurs in any of the given expressions. For example, since 2 appears to the second power in the last expression, the L.C.M. must contain 2^2. Similarly, it must contain b^3, a^2, and 3. If the exponent on any of these factors is increased, the resulting common multiple is divisible by the original common multiple. On the other hand, if any of the exponents is decreased, then the resulting expression ceases to be a common multiple. Hence the L.C.M. must be a product of these factors; that is, the L.C.M. is $3 \cdot 2^2 a^2 b^3$.

Example 3.3a. Find the L.C.M. for the expressions

$$6x, \quad x^2 - 4, \quad x^2 + 4x + 4, \quad 4x - 8.$$

These expressions, in factored form, are

$$2 \cdot 3 \cdot x, \quad (x - 2)(x + 2), \quad (x + 2)^2, \quad 2^2(x - 2).$$

Hence, the L.C.M. is

$$2^2 \cdot 3 \cdot x \cdot (x - 2) \cdot (x + 2)^2.$$

We are now in a position to discuss the addition of fractional expressions in any field. For fractions with a common denominator, we have

Theorem 3.3a.
$$\frac{a}{d} + \frac{b}{d} = \frac{a + b}{d}.$$

PROOF: It follows from the Distributive Law that

$$\frac{a}{d} + \frac{b}{d} = (a)\left(\frac{1}{d}\right) + (b)\left(\frac{1}{d}\right) = (a + b)\left(\frac{1}{d}\right) = \frac{a + b}{d}.$$

By means of this theorem we may combine any number of fractions if we first find equivalent fractions, all of which have the same denominator.

Example 3.3b. Combine

$$\frac{2}{3ab} + \frac{b}{2a^2} + \frac{3a}{b^2}.$$

The L.C.M. of the denominators is $6a^2b^2$. Hence we may replace each of the fractions by an equivalent fraction:

$$\frac{2}{3ab} \quad \text{by} \quad \frac{4ab}{6a^2b^2},$$

$$\frac{b}{2a^2} \quad \text{by} \quad \frac{3b^3}{6a^2b^2},$$

and

$$\frac{3a}{b^2} \quad \text{by} \quad \frac{18a^3}{6a^2b^2}.$$

These equivalent fractions may be obtained as follows. Since

$$\frac{2}{3ab} = \frac{2x}{3abx},$$

we must try to choose a quantity for x such that $3abx = 6a^2b^2$. Hence,

$$x = 2ab,$$

$$\frac{2}{3ab} = \frac{2(2ab)}{3ab(2ab)} = \frac{4ab}{6a^2b^2}.$$

A similar procedure may be used on each of the other terms. Hence,

$$\frac{2}{3ab} + \frac{b}{2a^2} + \frac{3a}{b^2} = \frac{4ab}{6a^2b^2} + \frac{3b^3}{6a^2b^2} + \frac{18a^3}{6a^2b^2}$$

$$= \frac{4ab + 3b^3 + 18a^3}{6a^2b^2}.$$

Example 3.3c. Combine

$$\frac{x - a}{by - bx - xy + x^2} + \frac{y - a}{bx - by - xy + y^2}.$$

The denominators, in factored form, are $(b - x)(y - x)$ and $(x - y)(b - y)$, respectively. The factor $x - y$ may be replaced by $(-1)(y - x)$, so that there are essentially three distinct factors in the L.C.M., which is $(b - x)(y - x)(b - y)$. Hence

$$\frac{x - a}{(b - x)(y - x)} + \frac{y - a}{(-1)(y - x)(b - y)}$$

$$= \frac{(x - a)(b - y)}{(b - x)(y - x)(b - y)} + \frac{(-1)(y - a)(b - x)}{(b - x)(y - x)(b - y)}$$

$$= \frac{bx - ab - xy + ay - by - ax + ab + xy}{(b - x)(y - x)(b - y)}$$

$$= \frac{bx + ay - by - ax}{(y - x)(b - x)(b - y)}.$$

At this stage, the result appears to be a satisfactory form for the answer. However, it is generally agreed that a fractional form should always be replaced by an equivalent fractional form in lowest terms; that is, in terms such that the numerator and denominator do not have common factors. Hence, further examination is necessary.

$$\frac{bx + ay - by - ax}{(y - x)(b - x)(b - y)} = \frac{(b - a)(x - y)}{(y - x)(b - x)(b - y)}$$

$$= \frac{(-1)(b - a)}{(b - x)(b - y)} = \frac{a - b}{(b - x)(b - y)}, \qquad x \neq y.$$

(Why is the restriction $x \neq y$ needed?)

Note that expressions of the form $(-1)a/b$ may be written in several equivalent forms:

$$\frac{(-1)a}{b} = \frac{-a}{b} = -\frac{a}{b} = \frac{a}{-b}.$$

Thus

$$A + \frac{a}{-b} = A - \frac{a}{b} = A + \frac{-a}{b}.$$

Multiplication and division of fractional forms may be carried out by first factoring each numerator and denominator over the field of rational numbers, then multiplying the numerators and denominators according to the rules obtained by means of the laws governing the field.

Theorem 3.3b.
$$\frac{A}{B} \cdot \frac{C}{D} = \frac{AC}{BD}.$$

PROOF: This follows from the definition of multiplication for rational numbers.

Theorem 3.3c.
$$\frac{A}{B} \div \frac{C}{D} = \frac{AD}{BC}.$$

PROOF: If $X = A/B \div C/D$, then, by the definition of division, we may write $X \cdot C/D = A/B$. Since the expressions A, B, C, D, X represent elements in a field, we know that the inverse of an element always exists, and since the inverse of C/D is D/C, we may write

$$\left(X \cdot \frac{C}{D}\right) \cdot \frac{D}{C} = \frac{A}{B} \cdot \frac{D}{C}$$

or

$$X \cdot \left(\frac{C}{D} \cdot \frac{D}{C}\right) = \frac{AD}{BC}$$

and

$$X = \frac{AD}{BC}.$$

This is the familiar rule that division by a fraction may be carried out by inverting the divisor and multiplying.

Example 3.3d. Simplify

$$\frac{x - 2}{x^2 - a^2} \cdot \frac{x^3 - a^3}{x^2 - 4} \div \frac{bx^2 + abx + a^2b}{x^2 + 4x + 4}.$$

We write

$$\frac{x - 2}{x^2 - a^2} \cdot \frac{x^3 - a^3}{x^2 - 4} \div \frac{bx^2 + abx + a^2b}{x^2 + 4x + 4}$$

$$= \frac{x - 2}{(x - a)(x + a)} \cdot \frac{(x - a)(x^2 + ax + a^2)}{(x - 2)(x + 2)} \cdot \frac{(x + 2)^2}{b(x^2 + ax + a^2)}$$

$$= \frac{(x - 2)(x - a)(x^2 + ax + a^2)(x + 2)^2}{b(x - a)(x + a)(x - 2)(x + 2)(x^2 + ax + a^2)} = \frac{x + 2}{b(x + a)}.$$

Usually, we omit the next to the last step and go directly into the final form of the answer. Notice that we have written a series of expressions that are equivalent to each other. For instance, the next to the last step in the development is put in to emphasize that Theorem 3.3b was used first to multiply the fractional forms in order to obtain an equivalent form. Finally, the last form is reached by making the observation that a fraction of the form AM/BM is equivalent to the fraction A/B. Simplification of complex fractions can be accomplished by first converting the problem into one involving multiplication and division of individual fractions.

Example 3.3e. Simplify

$$\frac{\dfrac{a}{b} - \dfrac{b}{a}}{\dfrac{1}{a^3} - \dfrac{1}{b^3}}.$$

First, we express the numerator and denominator as single fractions. Thus,

$$\frac{a}{b} - \frac{b}{a} = \frac{a^2 - b^2}{ab} = \frac{(a - b)(a + b)}{ab}$$

and

$$\frac{1}{a^3} - \frac{1}{b^3} = \frac{b^3 - a^3}{a^3 b^3} = \frac{(b - a)(a^2 + ab + b^2)}{a^3 b^3}.$$

Hence

$$\frac{\dfrac{a}{b} - \dfrac{b}{a}}{\dfrac{1}{a^3} - \dfrac{1}{b^3}} = \frac{\dfrac{(a - b)(a + b)}{ab}}{\dfrac{(b - a)(a^2 + ab + b^2)}{a^3 b^3}}$$

$$= \frac{(a - b)(a + b)}{ab} \cdot \frac{a^3 b^3}{(b - a)(a^2 + ab + b^2)}$$

$$= -\frac{a^2 b^2 (a + b)}{a^2 + ab + b^2}.$$

Example 3.3f. Let

$$\mathfrak{X} .=. \left\{ x, \frac{1}{x}, 1 - x, \frac{1}{1 - x}, \frac{x - 1}{x}, \frac{x}{x - 1} \right\}, \qquad x \in \mathfrak{R} \text{ and } x \neq 0, 1.$$

An operation can be defined on this set by a "substitution" process. If Ⓢ denotes this operation, and if $u, v \in \mathfrak{X}$, then u Ⓢ v means that the expression u is to be substituted for x in the expression v. Thus,

$$\frac{1}{1 - x} \text{ Ⓢ } \frac{x}{x - 1} = \frac{\dfrac{1}{1 - x}}{\dfrac{1}{1 - x} - 1} = \frac{1}{x}.$$

Show that

$$\left(\frac{x - 1}{x} \right) \text{ Ⓢ } \left(\frac{x}{x - 1} \right) \in \mathfrak{X}.$$

We perform the substitution indicated by Ⓢ to get

$$\frac{x - 1}{x} \text{ Ⓢ } \frac{x}{x - 1} = \frac{\dfrac{x - 1}{x}}{\dfrac{x - 1}{x} - 1} = 1 - x.$$

It is clear by inspection that the result is an element of $\mathfrak{X}$. It can furthermore be shown that the set $\mathfrak{X}$ is closed under the substitution operation Ⓢ. In fact, the reader may verify that the set $\mathfrak{X}$ is a group with respect to this operation. (See Exercises 3.3, Number 53.)

Exercises 3.3

In Numbers 1 to 8, reduce the fractions to lowest terms.

1. $\dfrac{a^2 - a - 2}{a^2 + a - 6}$.

2. $\dfrac{6x^3y^2 - 6x^3}{3x^3y^3 - 3x^3}$.

3. $\dfrac{4xy^2z}{8x^2y - 4xy^2}$.

4. $\dfrac{a^3 - 27}{a^2 - 6a + 9}$.

5. $\dfrac{ax - ay - x + y}{ax + ay - x - y}$.

6. $\dfrac{(a - b)^2 - c^2}{a^2 - (b + c)^2}$.

7. $\dfrac{x^2 - a^2 + 2ab - b^2}{x^2 + a^2 + 2ax - b^2}$.

8. $\dfrac{(x^3 - 1)(x^2 - 1)}{(x - 1)^2(x + 1)^3}$.

In Numbers 9 to 20, combine the fractions and simplify.

9. $2y + \dfrac{9}{y + 3} - \dfrac{9}{3 - y}$.

10. $\dfrac{m^2 + n^2}{m^2 - n^2} - \dfrac{m - n}{m + n} + \dfrac{1}{m - n}$.

11. $\dfrac{a}{a - b} + \dfrac{a}{a + b} + \dfrac{b}{b - a}$.

12. $\dfrac{y^3}{x^3 - y^3} - \dfrac{y}{x - y}$.

13. $\dfrac{1}{a + b} - \dfrac{b - a}{b(b + a)} - \dfrac{2a - b}{b^2 - a^2}$.

14. $\dfrac{4 - x}{(y - x)(2 - x)} - \dfrac{y - 4}{(x - y)(2 - y)}$.

15. $\dfrac{x + 1}{x^2 - x - 6} - \dfrac{x - 4}{x^2 - 4x + 3} + \dfrac{x + 4}{x^2 + x - 2}$.

16. $\dfrac{2}{x + y} - \dfrac{x - y}{x^2 - xy + y^2} + \dfrac{6xy}{x^3 + y^3}$.

17. $\dfrac{x}{y + 3} - \dfrac{x^2 - 1}{xy + 3x} - \dfrac{1 - 6x}{y^2 - 9}$.

18. $\dfrac{b}{(a - b)(a - c)} + \dfrac{c}{(b - c)(b - a)} + \dfrac{a}{(a - c)(b - c)}$.

19. $\dfrac{a^2 - (b - c)^2}{(c + a)^2 - b^2} + \dfrac{b^2 - (c - a)^2}{(a + b)^2 - c^2} + \dfrac{c^2 - (a - b)^2}{(b + c)^2 - a^2}$.

20. $\dfrac{x + y}{(y - z)(z - x)} + \dfrac{y + z}{(z - x)(x - y)} + \dfrac{z + x}{(x - y)(y - z)}$.

In Numbers 21 to 48, simplify the given expressions.

21. $(x^2 - 1)\left(x + 1 + \dfrac{2}{x - 1}\right)$.

22. $\dfrac{x}{y} \cdot \dfrac{xy - y}{x^3 - x} \cdot (x + 1)$.

23. $x^2 \cdot \dfrac{x}{x^2 - xy} \cdot \left(\dfrac{1}{x} - \dfrac{1}{y}\right)$.

24. $\dfrac{a^3 - 27}{a^2 - 4} \div \dfrac{a^2 + 3a + 9}{a - 2}$.

25. $\left(\dfrac{1}{x - y} - \dfrac{1}{x + y}\right) \div \left(\dfrac{1}{x - y} + \dfrac{1}{x + y}\right)$.

26. $\dfrac{(1 - x)^2 - y^2}{(x - y)^2 - 1} \cdot \dfrac{1 - (x + y)^2}{x^2 - (y + 1)^2}$.

27. $\dfrac{b^2 - 16}{3b^2 - 4b} \div \dfrac{b^2 + 6b + 8}{3b^2 - b - 4}$.

28. $\dfrac{2u^2 - 3u + 1}{u^2 - 4} \cdot \dfrac{u^2 - u - 6}{3u^2 - u - 2} \cdot \dfrac{3u^2 - 4u - 4}{2u^2 - 7u + 3}$

29. $\left(1 + \dfrac{2b^3}{a^3 - b^3}\right)\left(\dfrac{a - b}{a + b}\right) \div \left(1 - \dfrac{a}{b} + \dfrac{a^2}{b^2}\right).$

30. $\left(\dfrac{a + 1}{a - 1} + \dfrac{a - 1}{a + 1}\right) \div \left(\dfrac{a + 1}{a - 1} - \dfrac{a - 1}{a + 1}\right).$

31. $\dfrac{x^4 - 1}{x^3 - 1}\left[1 - \dfrac{x}{(x + 1)^2}\right] \div \left[\dfrac{1}{x} + x\right].$

32. $\dfrac{(x - y)^2}{x^3 - y^3} \cdot \dfrac{x^6 - y^6}{x^2 - y^2} \cdot \dfrac{x^2 + xy + y^2}{x^4 + x^2y^2 + y^4}.$

33. $\dfrac{x^2 - y^2}{x^3 - y^3}\left(\dfrac{1}{x^2} + \dfrac{1}{xy} + \dfrac{1}{y^2}\right)\dfrac{x^3y^3}{(x - y)^2} + \dfrac{x^2}{x - y}.$

34. $\left(\dfrac{x + 3}{x - 1} - x\right)\left(2x - \dfrac{x^2}{x + 1}\right) \div \left(\dfrac{2x}{x - 1} - x\right).$

35. $\dfrac{1 + \dfrac{x}{x - 1}}{1 - \dfrac{x}{x - 1}}.$

36. $\dfrac{1}{1 - \dfrac{1}{1 + \dfrac{1}{a}}}.$

37. $\dfrac{\dfrac{x}{a - x} - \dfrac{a - x}{x}}{\dfrac{1}{x + a} + \dfrac{2x}{a^2 - x^2}}.$

38. $\dfrac{\dfrac{x}{y^2} + \dfrac{y}{x^2}}{\dfrac{1}{x^2} - \dfrac{1}{xy} + \dfrac{1}{y^2}}.$

39. $\dfrac{x - 2}{x - 2 - \dfrac{x}{x - \dfrac{x - 1}{x - 2}}}.$

40. $\dfrac{1 - \dfrac{x^2 + y^2}{x^2 - y^2}}{\dfrac{x - y}{x + y} - \dfrac{x + y}{x - y}}.$

41. $\dfrac{x - y - \dfrac{(x + y)^2}{x - y}}{x + y - \dfrac{x^2 + y^2}{x - y}}.$

42. $\dfrac{x - 1}{x + 1 + \dfrac{2}{x - 1}} \div \left[\dfrac{1}{2} - \dfrac{1}{x + \dfrac{1}{x}}\right].$

43. $\dfrac{\dfrac{x^2}{y^2} - \dfrac{1 - x^2}{1 - y^2}}{\dfrac{x - 1}{y + y^2} + \dfrac{x + 1}{y - y^2}}.$

44. $\dfrac{a - \dfrac{a - 1}{a + 1}}{a - 1} - \dfrac{a - \dfrac{a + 1}{a - 1}}{a + 1}.$

45. $\dfrac{y - \dfrac{2y - 1}{y + 1}}{y^3 + 1} - \dfrac{1 - \dfrac{2y}{y + 1}}{y^2 - 1}.$

46. $\left[3 - \dfrac{x + 3}{x - \dfrac{2}{x - 1}}\right]\dfrac{x - \dfrac{2}{x - 1}}{2x - 3\dfrac{x + 1}{x - 1}}.$

47. $\dfrac{x - 1}{x - 1 - \dfrac{x^2 - x + 1}{x + \dfrac{1}{x + 1}}}.$

48. $\dfrac{\dfrac{1}{x} + \dfrac{x}{x + 1}}{x^3 - 1} - \dfrac{\dfrac{x^2 + 1}{x^4 - x^3} - \dfrac{1}{x^3 - x^2}}{x^3 + 1}.$

49. Are there any real numbers a and b such that $\dfrac{1}{a} + \dfrac{1}{b} = \dfrac{2}{a+b}$?

50. For what set of values of x is the expression $\frac{1}{3}(x+1)$ an integer?
51. For what set of values of x is the expression $\frac{1}{3}(x+1)$ a positive rational number?
52. For what set of real values of a is $\frac{1}{4}(a^2+1)$ a positive integer?
53. The following problems all refer to the set $\mathfrak{X}$ in Example 3.3f.
    (a) Write out a complete operation table for $\circledS$ on $\mathfrak{X}$.
    (b) If $u, v \in \mathfrak{X}$, is it generally true that $u \circledS v = v \circledS u$?
    (c) What is the identity element in the set $\mathfrak{X}$ for the operation $\circledS$? This means for what object $u \in \mathfrak{X}$ is it true that $u \circledS a = a$ for every $a \in \mathfrak{X}$?
    (d) What is the inverse of the element $1/(1-x)$ with respect to $\circledS$? That is, for what element $v \in \mathfrak{X}$ is it true that

$$v \circledS \frac{1}{1-x} = u,$$

    where u is the identity element?
    (e) Identify the inverse of each element.
    (f) Is it true that if v^{-1} is the inverse of v, then v is also the inverse of v^{-1}, that is,

$$v^{-1} \circledS v = v \circledS v^{-1} = u,$$

    where u is the identity element?

3.4 NEGATIVE AND RATIONAL EXPONENTS

We shall now consider how exponents are used in connection with division. For example, to divide a^5 by a^3, we write

$$\frac{a^5}{a^3} = \frac{a \cdot a \cdot a \cdot a \cdot a}{a \cdot a \cdot a} = a \cdot a = a^2,$$

and similarly,

$$\frac{a^3}{a^5} = \frac{a^3}{a^3 a^2} = \frac{1}{a^2}.$$

In the first of these illustrations, we might conceivably write

$$\frac{a^5}{a^3} = a^{5-3} = a^2,$$

which seems reasonable since the exponent 5 counts the number of factors in the numerator and the exponent 3 counts the number of factors in the denominator, and the process of division removed 3 factors from the numerator. However, if we follow the same rule in the second case, we would have

$$\frac{a^3}{a^5} = a^{3-5} = a^{-2}.$$

The a^{-2} is a symbol that has not yet been defined. If it is to have a meaning, it should be $1/a^2$, in view of the earlier results. The preceding discussion suggests

Definition 3.4a. Let $n \in \mathfrak{N}$. Then

$$a^{-n} .=. \frac{1}{a^n}, \qquad a \neq 0, a \in \mathfrak{R}.$$

In making this definition, we must be confident that contradictions to previously established theorems are not implied. A brief investigation shows that the consequences of this definition are consistent with previous results. Thus, since

$$a^{-n} \cdot a^{-m} = \frac{1}{a^n} \cdot \frac{1}{a^m} = \frac{1}{a^n \cdot a^m} = \frac{1}{a^{n+m}} = a^{-(n+m)},$$

Theorem 3.1a (1) holds for negative as well as for positive exponents. Similarly,

$$(a^n)^{-m} = \frac{1}{(a^n)^m} = \frac{1}{a^{nm}} = a^{-nm}$$

and

$$(a^{-n})^m = a^{-nm}.$$

Finally,

$$(a^{-n})^{-m} = \frac{1}{(a^{-n})^m} = \frac{1}{a^{-nm}} = a^{nm},$$

so that Theorem 3.1a (2) holds for negative exponents. The reader may show that Theorem 3.1a (3) also holds. Hence, these rules may be applied to the new exponents, and the results will be consistent.

Furthermore, the definition enables us to formulate a new rule for division.

Theorem 3.4a. If $a \in \mathfrak{R}$, $a \neq 0$ and $m, n \in \mathfrak{N}$, $m \neq n$, then

$$\frac{a^n}{a^m} = a^{n-m}.$$

Theorem 3.4a is not yet complete in that no provision is made for the case where $n = m$. If Theorem 3.4a were to apply in this case, then

$$\frac{a^n}{a^n} = a^{n-n} = a^0,$$

which is again an undefined symbol. Evidently if the symbol a^0 is to have a meaning, it should be 1, since $a^n/a^n = 1$. Hence, we make the following definition.

Definition 3.4b. If $a \in \mathfrak{R}$,

$$a^0 .=. 1, \qquad a \neq 0.$$

Here, a cannot be permitted to be 0 since consistent results cannot be obtained from any tentative definition for 0^0. To illustrate, suppose $0^0 .=. 1$. Then, we may write

$$\frac{0}{0} = 0^0 = 1$$

and

$$2 = 2 \cdot 1 = 2 \cdot 0^0 = 2 \cdot \frac{0}{0} = \frac{2 \cdot 0}{0} = \frac{0}{0} = 0^0 = 1.$$

Consequently, the symbol 0^0 will remain undefined, just as division by 0 is undefined. This is an example in which any attempt to define a symbol will lead to inconsistent results.

Example 3.4a. Find a simpler expression for $(a^{-2}b^3)^{-2} \cdot (a^3b^{-1})^2$.

We have

$$(a^{-2}b^3)^{-2} \cdot (a^3b^{-1})^2 = (a^4b^{-6})(a^6b^{-2}) = a^{10}b^{-8} = \frac{a^{10}}{b^8}.$$

The student must use special care in applying the rules for exponents to expressions involving sums or differences. We have no right to expect $(a + b)^2$ to be equal to $a^2 + b^2$. The following example illustrates a *correct* handling of exponents in connection with sums or differences.

Example 3.4b. Simplify

$$(a^{-2} - b^{-2})^{-1} \cdot (a \cdot b)^{-2}.$$

Since

$$(a^{-2} - b^{-2})^{-1} = \left(\frac{1}{a^2} - \frac{1}{b^2} \right)^{-1},$$

we have

$$(a^{-2} - b^{-2})^{-1} \cdot (ab)^{-2} = \left(\frac{b^2 - a^2}{a^2b^2} \right)^{-1} \cdot \frac{1}{a^2b^2}$$

$$= \frac{1}{\dfrac{b^2 - a^2}{a^2b^2}} \cdot \frac{1}{a^2b^2} = \frac{1}{b^2 - a^2}.$$

We have already seen that there exists no rational number x such that $x^2 = 2$. We can show in the same way that there exists no rational number x such that $x^n = a$ for $a, n \in \mathfrak{N}$, unless a is an exact nth power of an integer. Thus, $x^5 = 32$ is true for the rational number 2, but $x^5 = 20$ is true for no rational value of x. Besides the fact that statements of the type $x^n = a$ are usually not true for any rational number x, it is the case, as we shall see later, that such equations are generally true for n different complex values of x.

For the present we shall assume that if a is a positive number, the equation $x^n = a$ has a unique *positive* solution, which is designated in the next definition.

Definition 3.4c. Let $a, b > 0$, and let $n \in \mathfrak{N}$. If $b^n = a$, then

$$a^{1/n} . = . b.$$

The number b is called the *principal nth root of a*.

For example, since $2^5 = 32$, we have $(32)^{1/5} = 2$. Similarly, $2^4 = 16$ implies that $(16)^{1/4} = 2$. Notice carefully that we have restricted the meaning of $(16)^{1/4}$ to the single real positive fourth root of 16.

Definition 3.4d. If $b > 0$ and $m \in \mathcal{I}$, $n \in \mathfrak{N}$, then

$$b^{m/n} .=. (b^m)^{1/n}.$$

This interpretation for rational exponents is particularly valuable since these exponents obey the same laws as were developed for positive integral exponents.

Example 3.4c. Show that $b > 0$, $m \in \mathcal{I}$, $n \in \mathfrak{N} \Rightarrow (b^m)^{1/n} = (b^{1/n})^m$.

Let $b^{1/n} = x$. Then $b = x^n$ and $b^m = (x^n)^m$. But $(x^n)^m = (x^m)^n$, so that $(b^m)^{1/n} = x^m = (b^{1/n})^m$.

It will be left as an exercise for the reader to prove

Theorem 3.4b. If $x, y \in \mathcal{F}$ and $a > 0$, then

$$
\begin{align}
&(1) & a^x a^y &= a^{x+y}, \\
&(2) & (a^x)^y &= a^{xy}, \\
&(3) & a^x/a^y &= a^{x-y}.
\end{align}
$$

It is often necessary to determine an expression involving exponents that is equivalent to a given expression, but that is in a more desirable form, as illustrated in

---

Example 3.4d. Simplify $(4^{1/3})(6^{1/2})$.

Since the bases 4 and 6 are not the same, the rule of adding exponents does not apply. Instead, we write

$$
\begin{align}
(4^{1/3})(6^{1/2}) &= (4^{2/6})(6^{3/6}) & &= (4^2 \cdot 6^3)^{1/6} \\
&= (2^4 \cdot 2^3 \cdot 3^3)^{1/6} & &= (2^7 \cdot 3^3)^{1/6} \\
&= 2(2 \cdot 3^3)^{1/6} & &= 2(54)^{1/6}.
\end{align}
$$

In the preceding example, we were able to find an equivalent expression that

(1) *contains no fractional exponent greater than unity,*
(2) *contains no negative exponent,* and
(3) *contains no fractional exponents in a denominator.*

An expression satisfying these conditions is said to be in its **simplest** form.

Example 3.4e. Find the simplest form for

$$\text{(a)} \ \frac{2^{1/2}}{2^{1/2} - 1}, \quad \text{(b)} \ \frac{2^3 ab^{-2}}{3^{2/3}}, \quad \text{(c)} \ 2^{8/3} a^{5/4}.$$

We may proceed as follows:

(a) $\dfrac{2^{1/2}}{2^{1/2} - 1} = \dfrac{2^{1/2}(2^{1/2} + 1)}{(2^{1/2} - 1)(2^{1/2} + 1)} = \dfrac{2 + 2^{1/2}}{2 - 1} = 2 + 2^{1/2}.$

(b) $\dfrac{2^3 ab^{-2}}{3^{2/3}} = \dfrac{8a}{b^2 3^{2/3}} \cdot \dfrac{3^{1/3}}{3^{1/3}} = \dfrac{8a}{3b^2}(3^{1/3}).$

(c) $2^{8/3} a^{5/4} = 2^2 \cdot 2^{2/3} \cdot a \cdot a^{1/4} = 4a(2^{2/3} a^{1/4}).$

Notice in (a) of Example 3.4e that we multiplied numerator and denominator by the factor $2^{1/2} + 1$, which serves as a "rationalizing factor" for the number $2^{1/2} - 1$.

Another notation that is widely used to denote the principal nth root of the real number a is $\sqrt[n]{a}$. Although it seems preferable not to use this notation except in the case of square roots, its frequent occurrence in the literature requires that the student be familiar with it.

Definition 3.4e. $\quad \sqrt[n]{a^m} .=. a^{m/n}, \qquad a \in \mathfrak{R}, a > 0, n,m \in \mathfrak{N}.$

(It is customary in the case of the square root to write $\sqrt{a}$, where the index 2 is understood but not written.)

The $\sqrt{\ }$ sign is called a **radical sign**. By means of Definition 3.4e, all manipulations involving radicals can be carried out by the use of exponents.

Example 3.4f. Show that

$$(\sqrt[n]{a})^m = \sqrt[n]{a^m}.$$

Since $\sqrt[n]{a} = a^{1/n}$ by definition, then

$$(\sqrt[n]{a})^m = (a^{1/n})^m = a^{m/n} = \sqrt[n]{a^m}.$$

It is to be emphasized that the radical sign invariably indicates the *principal* root. For example,

$$\sqrt{x^2} = \begin{cases} x & \text{if } x \geq 0, \\ -x & \text{if } x < 0. \end{cases}$$

Another notation usually used in this sense is given in the next definition.

Definition 3.4f. $\qquad |x| .=. \begin{cases} x & \text{if } x \geq 0, \\ -x & \text{if } x < 0, \end{cases}$

and is read "the **absolute value** of x." The vertical bars are called *absolute value bars*.

Thus,

$$|x| = \sqrt{x^2} \quad \text{and} \quad |-2| = 2.$$

Similarly,

$$|x - a| = \begin{cases} x - a & \text{if } x - a \geq 0, \\ a - x & \text{if } x - a < 0, \end{cases}$$

by virtue of Definition 3.4f. The use of this notation will be discussed more fully later.

Exercises 3.4

In Numbers 1 to 10, simplify the given expression and write the answer with positive exponents only.

1. $(a^3b^{-2})^{-3}(a^2b^{-2})^0(a^{-2}b^{-1})^{-1}$.

2. $(x^{-1} - y^{-1})^{-1}(x^{-1}y^{-1})^{-1}$.

3. $(x + y)^{-2}(x + y)^3(x^2y^3)^{-2}$.

4. $\left(\dfrac{a^{-2}}{bc^{-4}}\right)^{-2}\left(\dfrac{a^2}{b^{-1}c^{-2}}\right)^{-3}$.

5. $\dfrac{9a^{-4} - 1}{3a^{-1} + a}$.

6. $(x^2y^{-2} - 2^2)^{-2}\left(\dfrac{y}{x + 2y}\right)^{-2}$.

7. $(a^{-1} - b^{-1})^{-1}(a^{-1} + b^{-1})^{-1}$.

8. $\dfrac{4x^{-4} - 1}{x^{-2} + 2^{-1}}$.

9. $(ax^{-2} + b^{-1})^3(b^{-3}x^{-6})^{-1}(ab + x^2)^{-3}$.

10. $\left(\dfrac{a^{-2} - 2b^{-1}}{a^{-4} - 4b^{-2}}\right)^{-1}(b - 2a)^{-1}$.

In Numbers 11 to 18, evaluate the given expression, using principal roots.

11. $8^{-2/3} - 25^{-3/2}$.

12. $(27^{-4/3})(3^3)$.

13. $8^{1/5}2^{2/5}$.

14. $-8^{-2/3}$.

15. $-8^{2/3}$.

16. $64^{-5/6}$.

17. $(0.0016)^{3/4}$.

18. $(4^{-3/2})(32^{4/5})$.

In Numbers 19 to 28, perform the indicated operations and express the result in simplest form.

19. $(2^{1/2})(2^{2/3})$.

20. $(3^{1/2}2^{1/3})^2 2^{1/3}$.

21. $(a^{-1/2}b^{-1/3})^{-3}(a^{1/2}b^{1/2})^{-1}$.

22. $(a^{-1/2}a^{-1/3})^{-2}$.

23. $\dfrac{a^{1/3}b^{1/4}}{a^{1/5}b^{1/5}}$.

24. $(x^{-1/2} + y^{-1/2})^{-1}$.

25. $(a^{-1/5}b^{-2/3})^{-1/2}(ab^{-2})^{-1/3}$.

26. $(a^{1/2}b^{1/4})^0(a^{-1/2}a^{-1/4})^{-2}$.

27. $(3^{-1/2}2^{-2/3})^{-5}$.

28. $(a^{1/3} + b^{-1/3})(a^{2/3} - a^{1/3}b^{-1/3} + b^{-2/3})$.

In Numbers 29 to 32, use principal roots to solve the given equation.

29. $x^{-3} = 8$.

30. $x^{-2/3} = 16$.

31. $x^{3/2} = 1/8$.

32. $x^{-4/5} = 16$.

Simplify the expressions in Numbers 33 to 64 as much as you can.

33. $\sqrt{8} - 2\sqrt{18} + \sqrt{32}$.

34. $3\sqrt{27} - \sqrt{48} + \dfrac{4}{\sqrt{12}}$.

35. $2\sqrt{27} - 3\sqrt{48} + \frac{1}{5}\sqrt{75}$.

36. $\sqrt{8} + \sqrt{\frac{1}{2}} - \sqrt{32} + \sqrt{50}$.

37. $2\sqrt[3]{320} - \sqrt[3]{40} - 3\sqrt[3]{135}$.

38. $\sqrt[3]{27} + \sqrt[3]{4} - \sqrt[6]{8}$.

39. $\sqrt{18y^2} - 3\sqrt{8y^2} + 2\sqrt{50y^2}$.

40. $\sqrt{\dfrac{4x^2}{y^4}} + \sqrt{\dfrac{y^4}{4x^2}}$.

41. $x\sqrt[3]{xy^5} + 2y\sqrt[3]{x^4y^2} + 3\sqrt[3]{x^4y^5}$.

42. $(\sqrt[3]{3a})(\sqrt[3]{9a})$, $a > 0$.

43. $\sqrt{3}(\sqrt{2} + \sqrt{6})$.

44. $(\sqrt[3]{\frac{4}{9}})(\sqrt[3]{18})$.

45. $(\sqrt[3]{\frac{2}{27}})(\sqrt[3]{\frac{9}{8}})$.

46. $(\sqrt[3]{xy^2})(\sqrt[3]{x^2y})$.

47. $(\sqrt[3]{9} - 2\sqrt[3]{4})(2\sqrt[3]{3} + 3\sqrt[3]{2})$.

48. $\dfrac{a^2}{b^2}\sqrt[n]{\dfrac{b^{2n+2}}{a^{2n-1}}}$, $a > 0$, $b > 0$.

49. $(x\sqrt{y} + y\sqrt{x})\sqrt{xy}$.

50. $\sqrt[4]{\dfrac{32x^7}{125w^9}}$, $x > 0$, $w > 0$.

51. $\sqrt{25\sqrt{5}}$.

52. $\sqrt{\dfrac{5a}{b}} + \sqrt{\dfrac{b}{5a}} - \sqrt{\dfrac{5b}{a}}$, $a > 0$, $b > 0$.

53. $(\sqrt[3]{4})(\sqrt{2})$.

54. $(\sqrt[3]{12})(\sqrt{6})$.

55. $\dfrac{\sqrt{10}}{\sqrt{5} - 2\sqrt{2}}$.

56. $\dfrac{2\sqrt{3} + 4\sqrt{2}}{\sqrt{6} - \sqrt{2}}$.

57. $\dfrac{3\sqrt{2} - 2\sqrt{3}}{\sqrt{2} + \sqrt{3}}$.

58. $\dfrac{2 + \sqrt{3} - \sqrt{7}}{2 - \sqrt{3} - \sqrt{7}}$.

59. $\dfrac{12}{\sqrt{3} - \sqrt{3}}$.

60. $\dfrac{1}{2\sqrt[3]{a} + \sqrt[3]{b}}$.

61. $\sqrt{3^{25} + 2^{25}}$.

62. $\sqrt[n]{\dfrac{4^n \cdot 6}{4^{2n+1} + 2^{4n+1}}}$.

63. $\dfrac{2 + i\sqrt{3}}{2 - i\sqrt{3}}$.

64. $\dfrac{\sqrt{3} + i\sqrt{2}}{\sqrt{3} - i\sqrt{2}}$.

65. If a and b are real numbers, simplify the expression

$$\frac{\sqrt{(a - b)^2}}{a - b}.$$

66. If $a = \sqrt{(2 + \sqrt{5})^2}$ and $b = \sqrt{(2 - \sqrt{5})^2}$, find $a - b$.

67. By writing each of the following in terms of positive exponents, show that they are *not* equivalent.

$$(a + b)^{-3} \quad \text{and} \quad a^{-3} + b^{-3}.$$

68. In decimal notation, the number 576.23 stands for

$$5(10^2) + 7(10^1) + 6(10^0) + 2(10^{-1}) + 3(10^{-2}).$$

In order to indicate a base other than 10, we frequently write the base as a subscript in parentheses immediately following the number. For example, $412.03_{(5)}$ stands for

$$4(5^2) + 5^1 + 2(5^0) + 0(5^{-1}) + 3(5^{-2}).$$

(a) Write $412.03_{(5)}$ to the base 10.

(b) Write 412.184 to the base 5.

(c) Write 110.75 to the base 2.

69. Prove Theorem 3.4b.

70. Select the equivalent expressions in each of the following sets:

(a) $\{(12)^{1/2}, \frac{1}{2}(48)^{1/2}, (48)^{1/4}, (144)^{1/4}, 2(216)^{1/6}\}$.

(b) $\left\{ -2^{1/2} + 3^{1/2}, \dfrac{1}{2^{1/2} + 3^{1/2}}, \dfrac{3^{1/2}}{6^{1/2} + 1}, \dfrac{6^{1/2}}{2(3^{1/2}) + 3(2^{1/2})}, \dfrac{2(3^{1/2}) - 3(2^{1/2})}{3^{1/2} + 2^{1/2}} \right\}$.

71. Suppose θ is an imaginary number such that $\theta^6 = 1$. Without finding θ, do the following:

(a) Show that θ must satisfy one of the two equations

$$\theta^2 + \theta + 1 = 0, \quad \theta^2 - \theta + 1 = 0.$$

(b) Show that $\{1, \theta, \theta^2, \theta^3, \theta^4, \theta^5\}$ is a group with respect to multiplication.

72. By the use of fractional exponents, algebraic expressions such as $a - b$ can be factored. For example,

$$a - b = (a^{1/2} - b^{1/2})(a^{1/2} + b^{1/2}).$$

(a) Factor $a - b$ using exponents having 3 as denominators.
(b) Factor $a^2 - b^2$ using exponents having 3 as denominators.
(c) Factor $a^2 - b$ using exponents having 4 as denominators.
(d) Factor $a - b$ using exponents having 6 as denominators.

3.5 SYNTHETIC DIVISION

It is assumed that the reader is familiar with the usual algebraic procedure for multiplication and division of polynomials. He may, however, not realize that it is possible by means of simple devices to shorten the work considerably in division. For example, we can save the writing of many symbols by not writing down the power of a number such as x, provided we keep the coefficients in some kind of order. If we agree to write coefficients in order of decreasing powers of x, then we might write a division as shown in the next example.

Example 3.5a. Divide $2x^3 + x^2 - 3$ by $x - 2$.

Let us characterize $2x^3 + x^2 - 3$ by the coefficients 2, 1, 0, -3, where 0 is the coefficient of the missing x term. Similarly, we may characterize $x - 2$ by 1, -2. The division form becomes

$$
\begin{array}{r}
2 \quad 5 \quad 10 \\
1 \,-2 \overline{\smash{\big)}\, 2 \quad 1 \quad\ \ 0 \quad -3} \\
\underline{2 \,-4} \\
5 \\
\underline{5 \,-10} \\
10 \\
\underline{10 \,-20} \\
17
\end{array}
$$

Thus, the coefficients of the quotient are 2, 5, and 10 and the remainder is 17, so that we may write

$$\frac{2x^3 + x^2 - 3}{x - 2} = 2x^2 + 5x + 10 + \frac{17}{x - 2}.$$

This procedure still does not eliminate all of the repetitious writing. Observe that each number in the quotient, 2, 5, 10, has appeared three times. This repetition seems to be unnecessary. Also, if the first term of the divisor is 1, then it is apparent that the number to be written in the quotient is always the same as the first number in the dividend row. Hence, the only number in the divisor that determines the numbers actually written is the -2. Therefore, let us write

$$
\begin{array}{r}
2 \quad\ 5 \quad\ 10 \\
-2 \overline{\smash{\big)}\, 2 \quad\ 1 \quad\ \ 0 \quad -3} \\
\underline{-4 \,-10 \,-20} \\
5 \quad\ 10 \quad\ 17
\end{array}
$$

Now, if we use the lower row of numbers and simply carry down the 2, we may perform the division using the neat form

$$
\begin{array}{r|rrrr}
-2 & 2 & 1 & 0 & -3 \\
 & & -4 & -10 & -20 \\
\hline
 & 2 & 5 & 10 & 17
\end{array}
\quad \text{or} \quad
\begin{array}{rrrr|r}
2 & 1 & 0 & -3 & -2 \\
 & -4 & -10 & -20 & \\
\hline
2 & 5 & 10 & 17 &
\end{array}
$$

Since we prefer to add rather than to subtract, and we can change from subtraction to addition by changing the sign on the divisor from minus to plus, we arrive at the following final form:

$$
\begin{array}{rrrr|r}
2 & 1 & 0 & -3 & 2 \\
 & 4 & 10 & 20 & \\
\hline
2 & 5 & 10 & 17 &
\end{array}
$$

and

$$\frac{2x^3 + x^2 - 3}{x - 2} = 2x^2 + 5x + 10 + \frac{17}{x - 2}.$$

The preceding schematic procedure, which is known as **synthetic division**, is illustrated further in the next two examples.

Example 3.5b. Divide $2x^3 + 3x^2 - 2x + 2$ by $x + 3$.

We write the synthetic division and the result as follows:

$$
\begin{array}{rrrr|r}
2 & 3 & -2 & 2 & -3 \\
 & -6 & 9 & -21 & \\
\hline
2 & -3 & 7 & -19 &
\end{array}
$$

and

$$\frac{2x^3 + 3x^2 - 2x + 2}{x + 3} = 2x^2 - 3x + 7 - \frac{19}{x + 3}.$$

Example 3.5c. Perform the indicated division:

$$\frac{2x^3 + 2x^2 - 2x - 3}{2x + 1}.$$

Since the leading coefficient in the denominator is not 1, we rewrite the problem as

$$\frac{2x^3 + 2x^2 - 2x - 3}{2x + 1} = \frac{2x^3 + 2x^2 - 2x - 3}{x + \frac{1}{2}} \cdot \frac{1}{2}.$$

The synthetic division and the final result are next shown:

$$
\begin{array}{rrrr|r}
2 & 2 & -2 & -3 & -\frac{1}{2} \\
 & -1 & -\frac{1}{2} & \frac{5}{4} & \\
\hline
2 & 1 & -\frac{5}{2} & -\frac{7}{4} &
\end{array}
$$

and

$$
\frac{2x^3 + 2x^2 - 2x - 3}{2x + 1} = \tfrac{1}{2}\left[\frac{2x^3 + 2x^2 - 2x - 3}{x + \frac{1}{2}}\right]
$$

$$
= \tfrac{1}{2}\left[2x^2 + x - \tfrac{5}{2} - \frac{\frac{7}{4}}{x + \frac{1}{2}}\right]
$$

$$
= x^2 + \tfrac{1}{2}x - \tfrac{5}{4} - \frac{7}{4(2x + 1)}.
$$

Exercises 3.5

Perform the indicated division using synthetic division.

1. $(x^3 + x^2 - 5x - 2) \div (x - 2)$.
2. $(3x^3 + 5x^2 + x - 1) \div (x + 1)$.
3. $(4x^3 + 5x + 3) \div (2x + 1)$.
4. $(2x^3 + 4x^2 - 3x - 1) \div (x - 3)$.
5. $(x^3 - 5x^2 - 15) \div (x - 4)$.
6. $(2y^4 - y^3 + 2y^2 - 3y - 5) \div (y + 2)$.
7. $(4x^4 - 34x^2 - 17x + 30) \div (x - 3)$.
8. $(w^3 - 3w^2 + 9w - 27) \div (w - 3i)$, $(i^2 = -1)$.
9. $(y^3 + 2y^2 + y + 1) \div (y + i)$.
10. $(4x^3 + 20x^2 + 11x - 35) \div (2x + 5)$.
11. $(6x^3 - 17x^2 + 17) \div (2x - 3)$.
12. $(2w^3 + 9aw^2 + 8a^2w - 3a^3) \div (w + 3a)$.
13. $(3y^3 - 6ay^2 - 2a^2y + 5a^3) \div (y - 2a)$.
14. $(x^4 + x^3 - x^2 - 2x - 2) \div (x + \sqrt{2})$.
15. $(2u^4 + 3u^3 - 5u^2 - 9u - 7) \div (u - \sqrt{3})$.
16. $(15x^3 - 41x^2 + 24x - 8) \div (5x - 2)$.
17. $(6x^3 - 17x^2 + 15x - 6) \div (3x - 4)$.

3.6 POLYNOMIAL EXPRESSIONS

In Section 3.2 it was shown that the set of polynomials over a given field forms an additive group, but that the set is *not* closed with respect to division. Nevertheless, it is possible to develop a number of interesting and important properties of polynomials associated with the operation of division. The following basic theorem is essentially a statement of the result of dividing a polynomial $p(x)$ by a polynomial $q(x)$.

Theorem 3.6a. For any two polynomials $p(x)$ and $q(x)$ in a given field, where the degree of $q(x)$ is less than or equal to the degree of $p(x)$, there exist polynomials $r(x)$ and $s(x)$ in the field such that

$$p(x) = q(x)s(x) + r(x),$$

where the degree of $r(x)$ is less than the degree of $q(x)$, and the sum of the degrees of $q(x)$ and $s(x)$ is equal to the degree of $p(x)$.

The formal proof, which is in essence a description of the division process, is omitted. The equation

$$p(x) = q(x)s(x) + r(x)$$

is a direct consequence of the equation resulting from the division—namely,

$$\frac{p(x)}{q(x)} = s(x) + \frac{r(x)}{q(x)}.$$

Example 3.6a. Find the polynomials $r(x)$ and $s(x)$ required by Theorem 3.6a, if

$$p(x) .=. x^4 + 1 \quad \text{and} \quad q(x) .=. x + 1.$$

We may write, by division,

$$\frac{x^4 + 1}{x + 1} = x^3 - x^2 + x - 1 + \frac{2}{x + 1}.$$

Hence,

$$r(x) = 2, \quad s(x) = x^3 - x^2 + x - 1.$$

An important special case of Theorem 3.6a occurs when the polynomial $q(x)$ is simply $x - c$.

Theorem 3.6b. *The Remainder Theorem.* Under the conditions of Theorem 3.6a, if $q(x) = x - c$, so that

$$p(x) = (x - c)s(x) + r(x),$$

then $r(x)$ is a constant equal to the value of $p(x)$ when x is replaced by c. The symbol $p(c)$ is used to indicate this value.

PROOF: This theorem follows immediately from Theorem 3.6a by replacing x by c in the equation

$$p(x) = (x - c)s(x) + r(x),$$

a procedure that gives $p(c) = r(c)$. Furthermore, since the degree of $r(x)$ is less than that of $x - c$, its degree must be zero; that is, $r(x)$ is a constant and has the value $p(c)$.

It follows from Theorem 3.6b that the division of $p(x)$ by $x - c$ yields a constant remainder, $p(c)$, the value of $p(x)$ when x is replaced by the number c.

Example 3.6b. What is the value of

$$p(x) .=. x^4 + 3x^3 - 2x^2 - 6x - 7,$$

when x is replaced by -3?

In Theorem 3.6b, we put $c = -3$ so that $x - c$ is $x + 3$. Division of the polynomial $p(x)$ by $x + 3$ yields a remainder of -7, which shows that $p(-3) = -7$.

In the special case when $p(c) = 0$ in Theorem 3.6b, it follows that $x - c$ is a factor of $p(x)$, since then

$$p(x) = (x - c)s(x).$$

Definition 3.6a. A number c for which the value of a polynomial $p(x)$ is 0 is called a **zero** of the polynomial.

For example, if

$$p(x) .=. x^3 - 2x^2 + 4x - 8,$$

then $p(2) = 0$ and 2 is a zero of the polynomial $p(x)$.

The next theorem is an important one concerning the zeros of a polynomial over the field $\mathfrak{C}$ of complex numbers.

Theorem 3.6c. *The Fundamental Theorem of Algebra.* Every polynomial of degree greater than 0 in the field $\mathcal{C}$ has at least one zero in $\mathcal{C}$.

The proof of this theorem is too elaborate to be included here. However, a proof may be found in Schreier and Sperner, *Introduction to Modern Algebra and Matrix Theory* (Chelsea, 1952).

It is a direct consequence of the preceding theorem that every polynomial of degree greater than 0 in $\mathcal{C}$ has at least one factor of the form $x - r$, or $\alpha x + \beta$, where r (or α and β) $\in \mathcal{C}$. Factors of this form are called **linear factors**. This result follows from Theorem 3.6b, where the remainder is 0.

The preceding remarks and Theorem 3.6c lead to a result of considerable importance in practical and theoretical work involving polynomials.

Theorem 3.6d. A polynomial $p(x)$ of degree n in $\mathcal{C}$ is reducible to a product of exactly n linear factors in $\mathcal{C}$.

PROOF: The proof can be made by mathematical induction. Let $p(x)$ be a polynomial of degree 1. Then it is of the form

$$p(x) = a_0 x + a_1, \qquad a_0 \neq 0,$$

or

$$p(x) = a_0(x - r_1),$$

where

$$r_1 = -a_1/a_0,$$

as required by the theorem.

Now suppose that every polynomial of degree $n - 1$ in $\mathcal{C}$ is reducible to a product of $n - 1$ linear factors in $\mathcal{C}$, in the form

$$s(x) = a_0(x - r_1)(x - r_2) \cdots (x - r_{n-1}).$$

Let $p(x)$ be a polynomial of degree n. Then, by Theorem 3.6c, we know that

$$p(x) .=. a_0 x^n + a_1 x^{n-1} + \cdots + a_n$$

has at least one zero in $\mathcal{C}$. If this zero is r_n, then, by Theorem 3.6b,

$$p(x) = (x - r_n)s(x),$$

where the remainder is 0, since r_n is a zero of $p(x)$, and the degree of $s(x)$ is $n - 1$. By the inductive assumption, $s(x)$ is reducible to a product of $n - 1$ linear factors, so that

$$p(x) = a_0(x - r_1)(x - r_2) \cdots (x - r_{n-1})(x - r_n).$$

This completes the proof.

It is clear that each of the numbers r_i in the preceding proof is a zero of $p(x)$. However, it is possible that some of the r_i's are equal. In that case, we make the following

Definition 3.6b. If exactly k of the factors $(x - r_i)$ in the expression

$$p(x) = a_0(x - r_1)(x - r_2) \cdots (x - r_n)$$

are identical, then the zero r_i is said to have **multiplicity** k.

For example, the polynomial

$$p(x) = x^5 - 4x^4 + x^3 + 10x^2 - 4x - 8$$

may be written as

$$p(x) = (x - 2)(x - 2)(x - 2)(x + 1)(x + 1).$$

The zero 2 has a multiplicity 3 and the zero -1 has a multiplicity 2.

Theorem 3.6d is equivalent to the statement that a polynomial in $\mathbb{C}$ of degree n has exactly n zeros in $\mathbb{C}$, provided that the multiplicity of each zero is counted according to Definition 3.6b. Thus, the preceding polynomial is of the fifth degree and has five zeros, -1 counted twice and 2 counted three times.

As a further illustration of Theorem 3.6d, the polynomial

$$p(x) = x^3 + 2x^2 + 2x + 4$$

must have 3 zeros in $\mathbb{C}$. Since

$$p(x) = (x^2 + 2)(x + 2)$$
$$= (x + i\sqrt{2})(x - i\sqrt{2})(x + 2),$$

it is apparent that the zeros of $p(x)$ are $i\sqrt{2}$, $-i\sqrt{2}$, and -2.

The preceding theorems lead to a useful result that specifies a condition that two polynomials be identical.

Theorem 3.6e. If the value of a polynomial $p(x)$ of degree n is equal to the value of a polynomial $q(x)$ of degree m, where $m \leq n$, for at least $n + 1$ values of x, then the polynomials are identical and have equal values for all values of x.

PROOF: Suppose that $p(x) = q(x)$ for the values

$$x_1, x_2, \ldots, x_{n+1},$$

and consider the polynomial

$$s(x) = p(x) - q(x).$$

Then, $s(x)$ is of degree n or less and each x_i is a zero of $s(x)$.

If

$$p(x) = a_0 x^n + a_1 x^{n-1} + \cdots + a_n$$

and

$$q(x) = b_0 x^n + b_1 x^{n-1} + \cdots + b_n,$$

where b_0, b_1, and so on, may be 0 if $m < n$, then

$$s(x) = (a_0 - b_0)x^n + (a_1 - b_1)x^{n-1} + \cdots + (a_n - b_n) = 0.$$

If $a_0 \neq b_0$, then $s(x)$ is actually of degree n. However, by hypothesis, $s(x)$ has at least $n + 1$ zeros, which contradicts Theorem 3.6d. Therefore, $a_0 = b_0$. If $a_1 \neq b_1$, then $s(x)$ is of degree $n - 1$ and the same contradiction results. Thus, $a_1 = b_1$, and it follows similarly that $a_i = b_i$, $i = 2, 3, \ldots, n - 1$. This leaves the equation $a_n - b_n = 0$, which implies that $a_n = b_n$.

Accordingly, all the coefficients of $s(x)$ are zero, the polynomials $p(x)$ and $q(x)$ are identical and, of course, have equal values for all values of x.

Example 3.6c. For what values of A, B, and C will

$$(x^2 + 3x + 4) = A(x + 1)^2 + B(x + 1) + C$$

for all x?

Since the two polynomials are to be identical, we may equate coefficients of corresponding powers of x by the proof of Theorem 3.6e. Thus,

$$1 = A,$$
$$3 = 2A + B,$$
$$4 = A + B + C.$$

The last two equations yield $B = 1$, $C = 2$, so that we have

$$x^2 + 3x + 4 = (x + 1)^2 + (x + 1) + 2.$$

There are a number of theorems pertaining to the zeros of a polynomial over the field $\mathfrak{R}$, and of these the following one is fundamental.

Theorem 3.6f. If $p(x)$ is a polynomial in the field $\mathfrak{R}$, then

$$p(a + ib) = 0 \Rightarrow p(a - ib) = 0, \qquad b \neq 0.$$

That is, if $a + ib$ is a zero of a polynomial with real coefficients, then $a - ib$ is also a zero of the polynomial.

PROOF: The product $(x - a - ib)(x - a + ib) = (x - a)^2 + b^2$ is a polynomial in $\mathfrak{R}$. By Theorem 3.6a,

$$p(x) = q(x)[(x - a)^2 + b^2] + r(x),$$

where the degree of $r(x)$ is *less* than 2. Hence, it must be that

$$r(x) = cx + d.$$

Since $p(a + ib) = 0$ and $(x - a)^2 + b^2 = 0$ for $x = a + ib$, it follows that

$$0 = c(a + ib) + d$$

or that

$$(ca + d) + bci = 0.$$

Thus, $bc = 0$ so that $c = 0$ because $b \neq 0$ by hypothesis. Consequently, $d = 0$ also, and thus $r(x) = 0$, which shows that

$$p(x) = q(x)[(x - a)^2 + b^2].$$

If $x = a - ib$, then, since $(x - a)^2 + b^2 = 0$ for $x = a - ib$,

$$p(a - ib) = 0.$$

Hence, $a - ib$ is a zero of $p(x)$, as was to be shown.

In Theorem 3.6d, allowance was made for the fact that some of the linear factors of a polynomial might have imaginary coefficients. As a consequence of Theorems 3.6d and 3.6f, it follows that every polynomial with *real* coefficients may be factored into an essentially unique product of *real linear* and/or *quadratic* factors. For instance, as an illustration of Theorem 3.6d, we had

$$x^3 + 2x^2 + 2x + 4 = (x^2 + 2)(x + 2),$$

where the factor $x^2 + 2$ is irreducible in the field $\mathfrak{R}$.

Exercises 3.6

1. For each of the following find the polynomials $r(x)$ and $s(x)$ required by Theorem 3.6a.
   (a) $p(x) .=. 2x^4 - x^3 + 5x^2 - x + 3, q(x) .=. x^2 + 1$.
   (b) $p(x) .=. 3x^3 + 2x^2 - 2x - 1, q(x) .=. 2x^2 - 2$.

In each of Numbers 2 to 9, use synthetic division and the remainder theorem to find the indicated values of the given polynomial.

2. $p(x) .=. 2x^4 - 3x^3 + 2x^2 + x - 7; p(-2), p(3)$.
3. $g(x) .=. x^5 - 4x^3 + 2x - 5; g(2), g(-2)$.
4. $r(x) .=. 3x^4 + 2x^2 - 7x; r(3), r(-2)$.
5. $s(x) .=. 3x^4 + 2x^3 - 5x^2 - 3x - 1; s(-3), s(2)$.
6. $p(x) .=. 5x^4 - 6x^2 + 2x + 3; p(-2), p(4)$.
7. $r(y) .=. y^5 + 4y^4 + 16y^3 + 96; r(-2), r(2)$.
8. $s(w) .=. 9w^4 - 2w^2 + w; s(3), s(-3)$.
9. $g(x) .=. 3x^3 - 7x^2 + 5x - 2; g(-4), g(2)$.

10. Show that the set of polynomials on the field of complex numbers forms an additive group.

In each of Numbers 11 to 14, show by synthetic division that the given value is or is not a zero of the given polynomial.

11. $p(x) .=. 6x^3 - 4x^2 + 5x - 42; x = 2$.
12. $p(s) .=. s^4 + s^2 + 27s - 9; s = -3$.
13. $q(t) .=. t^4 - 3t^3 + t + 4; t = 2$.
14. $q(x) .=. x^5 - 6x^4 - x^3 + 2x; x = 3$.

In each of Numbers 15 to 17, find the values of the constants A, B, C, D so that the given polynomials will be equal for all values of x.

15. $2x^2 - 3x - 1 = A(x - 1)^2 + B(x - 1) + C$.
16. $x^3 - 3x^2 + 2x - 7 = A(x - 1)^3 + B(x - 2)^2 + C(x + 1) + D$.
17. $16x^3 + 1 = A(2x + 1)^3 + B(x - 1)^2 + C(x + 1) + D$.
18. Prove that if $a + b\sqrt{c}$, where c is not a perfect square, is a zero of a polynomial $p(x)$ with rational coefficients, then $a - b\sqrt{c}$ is also a zero of $p(x)$. *Hint*: See the proof of Theorem 3.6f.

Use the given zero to obtain the other zeros of the polynomials in Numbers 19 to 30.

19. $x^3 + 6x^2 + 11x + 6$; one zero is -3.
20. $x^3 - 2x^2 - 9x + 18$; one zero is 2.
21. $3x^3 - 2x^2 - 11x + 10$; one zero is $5/3$.
22. $5x^3 + 28x^2 + 45x + 18$; one zero is $-3/5$.
23. $x^4 - x^3 + 2x^2 - 4x - 8$; one zero is $2i$.
24. $x^4 - 2x^3 + 10x^2 - 18x + 9$; one zero is $-3i$.

25. $x^4 - 3x^3 - x^2 + 13x - 10$; one zero is $2 + i$.
26. $x^3 + (3 - 2i)x^2 + (2 - 6i)x - 4i$; one zero is $2i$.
27. $x^3 + (4 + i)x^2 + 4x(1 + i) + 4i$; one zero is $-i$.
28. $x^4 + x^3 - 4x^2 - 2x + 4$; one zero is $\sqrt{2}$. *Hint:* See Number 18.
29. $x^4 - x^3 - 9x^2 - 5x + 2$; one zero is $2 + \sqrt{3}$.
30. $x^3 - x^2(1 + \sqrt{3}) + x(-2 + \sqrt{3}) + 2\sqrt{3}$; one zero is $\sqrt{3}$.

3.7 SOLUTION SETS OF EQUATIONS

Much of the power of mathematics as a practical tool in science and engineering lies in its applicability to physical problems. A physical problem is frequently represented by a mathematical model in the form of an expression called an *equation*. A solution to the physical problem is then obtained when a solution to the mathematical problem is found. Since a mathematical equation arising in connection with a physical problem is usually in the form of an open statement, the problem of finding a solution to the mathematical problem is simply that of finding elements of a given set for which the open statement is true.

Definition 3.7a. A statement of equality between two mathematical expressions is called an **equation.**

Some examples of equations are

(a) $1 + 1 = 2$,

(b) $1 = 2$,

(c) $2x - 3 = 5$,

(d) $x(x - 1) = x^2 - x$,

(e) $\dfrac{1}{x} - \dfrac{1}{x + 1} = \dfrac{1}{x(x + 1)}$,

(f) $x^2 = x^2 + 1$.

Thus, an equation is an open statement or a proposition, and in the latter case may be either true or false. Example (a) is a true proposition, whereas (b) is false. The remaining examples are open statements and are therefore not classified as either true or false without additional restrictions on x. Thus, (c) is true if $x = 4$, and (d) is true for all $x \in \mathcal{C}$. Also, (e) is true for the set $\mathcal{C} - \{-1, 0\}$, and (f) is true for no $x \in \mathcal{C}$.

Quite often it is necessary to specify with respect to what set a given equation is or is not true. For example, the equation

$$x^2 + 1 = 0$$

is true for no $x \in \mathcal{R}$, but is true if $x = \pm i$ in the field $\mathcal{C}$.

Because equations involving open statements are of two types, it is convenient to have

Definition 3.7b. An **identity** on a set S is an equation that is true whenever its members are defined for elements of S.

Of the preceding examples of equations, (a), (d), and (e) are identities on either $\mathcal{R}$ or $\mathcal{C}$. But the equation

$$1 - \sqrt{x^2} = 1 - x$$

is an identity on the set of nonnegative real numbers, but not on $\mathcal{R}$ or $\mathcal{C}$.

The reader may find it instructive to prove the next theorem.

Theorem 3.7a. If $p(x) = q(x)$ is an identity on $\mathcal{C}$, then it is an identity on $\mathcal{R}$.

We call particular attention to the set of elements described in

Definition 3.7c. The set S of elements for which a given equation, $p(x) = q(x)$, is true is called the **solution set** of the equation, and is denoted by $S[p(x) = q(x)]$.

For example,

$$S[2x - 3 = 5] = \{4\},$$
$$S[x^2 = x^2 + 1] = \varnothing$$

and

$$S[x(x - 1) = x^2 - x] = \mathcal{C}.$$

The process of finding the solution set of a simple algebraic equation is based on several fundamental theorems. In each of these it is to be understood that $a, b, c, d \in \mathcal{R}$ unless it is otherwise indicated.

Theorem 3.7b. $\qquad a = b \Leftrightarrow a + c = b + c.$

This theorem states that *a given equation implies the equation that results if the same number c is added to or subtracted from both members.*

PROOF:

(a) First, we show that $a = b \Rightarrow a + c = b + c$.

Since $a + c = a + c$,   by the Identity Axiom 1.4a,

then $a + c = b + c$,   by the Substitution Axiom 1.4b.

(b) To show that $a + c = b + c \Rightarrow a = b$, we write

$$(a + c) + (-c) = (b + c) + (-c),$$

by part (a). Then we have

$$a + [c + (-c)] = b + [c + (-c)]$$

(why?)   or

$$a + 0 = b + 0,$$

so that

$$a = b.$$

Proofs of the following three theorems may be constructed in a manner similar to that used for Theorem 3.7b and are left for the reader, who should also restate these theorems verbally for himself, as we did for Theorem 3.7b.

Theorem 3.7c. If $c \neq 0$, then

$$a = b \Leftrightarrow ac = bc.$$

Theorem 3.7d. If $c \neq 0$, then

$$a = b \Leftrightarrow a/c = b/c.$$

Theorem 3.7e. $\quad a = b$ and $c = d \Rightarrow ac = bd.$

The solution set for an equation can sometimes be found with the aid of these theorems. To illustrate, let us find the solution set of

$$2x - 3 = 5.$$

It follows that

$$(2x - 3) + 3 = 5 + 3,$$

by Theorem 3.7b, or

$$2x = 8.$$

Then

$$(\tfrac{1}{2})(2x) = (\tfrac{1}{2})(8),$$

by Theorem 3.7c, or

$$x = 4.$$

The next example illustrates another situation.

Example 3.7a. Find the solution set of the equation

$$\frac{x+1}{x} = \frac{1}{x}.$$

It is clear that $x = 0$ is *not* a solution of this equation since both members are meaningless for this value of x. If we assume that there is a nonzero solution, so that Theorem 3.7c applies, then we have

$$\frac{x+1}{x} = \frac{1}{x} \Leftrightarrow \frac{x+1}{x} \cdot x = \frac{1}{x} \cdot x$$

$$\Leftrightarrow \quad x + 1 = 1$$
$$\Leftrightarrow \quad\quad x = 0.$$

by Theorem 3.7b. Thus we arrive at a contradiction, and so the solution set of the given equation is empty.

Example 3.7a suggests that for operations involving the variable the preceding theorems may not be applicable; there is apparently no guarantee that the solution set of the new equation is also a solution set for the original equation. This situation is clarified by Theorems 3.7f–j.

Theorem 3.7f. Let $g(x)$ and $h(x)$ be algebraic expressions, and let $p(x)$ be a polynomial. Then

$$\mathcal{S}[g(x) = h(x)] = \mathcal{S}[g(x) + p(x) = h(x) + p(x)].$$

That is, *a polynomial expression may be added to both sides of an equation without altering the solution set.*

PROOF: Let $b \in \mathcal{S}[g(x) = h(x)]$. This means that

$$g(b) = h(b).$$

By Theorem 3.7b it follows that

$$g(b) + p(b) = h(b) + p(b).$$

Hence,

$$b \in S[g(x) + p(x) = h(x) + p(x)]$$

and

$$S[g(x) = h(x)] \subset S[g(x) + p(x) = h(x) + p(x)].$$

Now we must show that

$$S[g(x) + p(x) = h(x) + p(x)] \subset S[g(x) = h(x)].$$

If

$$b \in S[g(x) + p(x) = h(x) + p(x)],$$

then

$$g(b) + p(b) = h(b) + p(b).$$

By Theorem 3.7b it follows that

$$g(b) = h(b),$$

so that

$$b \in S[g(x) = h(x)].$$

Hence

$$S[g(x) + p(x) = h(x) + p(x)] \subset S[g(x) = h(x)],$$

and the two solution sets are therefore the same.

The situation is different if both sides of an equation $g(x) = h(x)$ are multiplied by a polynomial $p(x)$.

Theorem 3.7g. If $g(x)$ and $h(x)$ are algebraic expressions in x and if $p(x)$ is a polynomial in x, then

$$S[g(x) = h(x)] \subset S[g(x) \cdot p(x) = h(x) \cdot p(x)].$$

The proof is left for the reader.

Example 3.7b. Find the solution set of the equation

$$2x = x^2.$$

By Theorem 3.7f, we may write

$$2x - x^2 = 0$$

or

$$x(2 - x) = 0.$$

It follows that $x = 0$ or $2 - x = 0$, so that the solution set is

$$S[2x = x^2] = \{0, 2\}.$$

As an illustration of Theorem 3.7g, observe that $2x = x^2$ is the equation

$$2 = x$$

multiplied by x, so that $S[2 = x] = \{2\}$, and

$$S[2 = x] \subset S[2x = x^2].$$

However, suppose we had tried to use Theorem 3.7c to obtain

$$\frac{1}{x} \cdot 2x = \frac{1}{x} \cdot x^2$$

or

$$2 = x.$$

This result leaves the impression that the solution set of $x^2 = 2x$ is simply $\{2\}$. However, the multiplication by $1/x$ is valid only so long as $x \neq 0$, and, in this illustration, the multiplication by $1/x$ results in an equation having a different solution set. This idea is summarized in a general form in

---

Theorem 3.7h. If $g(x)$ and $h(x)$ are algebraic expressions and if $p(x)$ is a polynomial, then

$$S\left[\frac{g(x)}{p(x)} = \frac{h(x)}{p(x)}\right] \subset S[g(x) = h(x)].$$

The proof is left for the reader.

The next theorem is a kind of extension of Theorem 3.7f that is needed in connection with problems of the form in the next example.

Example 3.7c. Find the solution set of the equation

$$\sqrt{x} = -2, \qquad x \in \mathfrak{R}.$$

Notice the restriction $x \in \mathfrak{R}$, which is necessary since we have not defined the symbol $\sqrt{x}$ for $x \in \mathfrak{C}$. According to Theorem 3.7e, by squaring both sides of the equation, we get $x = 4$. But $\sqrt{4} \neq -2$. In fact, $S[\sqrt{x} = -2] = \emptyset$. Hence the equation resulting from the squaring process does not have the same solution set as the original one.

In general, we have the following theorem, which should be proved by the reader.

Theorem 3.7i. If $g(x)$ and $h(x)$ are algebraic expressions, then

$$S[g(x) = h(x)] \subset S[g^2(x) = h^2(x)].$$

In Example 3.7b we illustrated the fact that if the product of two factors is zero, then at least one of the factors is zero. In connection with the determination of the solution set of an equation, this idea takes on a general form as stated in

Theorem 3.7j. Let $p(x)$ and $p_1(x), p_2(x), \ldots, p_n(x)$ be polynomials such that

$$p(x) = p_1(x)p_2(x) \cdots p_n(x).$$

Then

$$S[p(x) = 0] = S[p_1(x) = 0] \cup S[p_2(x) = 0] \cup \cdots \cup S[p_n(x) = 0].$$

The proof is left for the reader.

In order to summarize the preceding theorems, we state that (1) *addition of a polynomial to both sides of an algebraic equation will not alter the solution set*; (2) *multiplication by a polynomial may yield an equation with a larger solution set*; and (3) *division by a polynomial may give an equation with a smaller solution set.*

The process of solving a given equation begins with the *assumption* that the equation has a solution. We then apply the preceding theorems to obtain successively simpler equations until we arrive at an equation whose solution set is apparent. The elements of this set must be checked in the given equation in order to eliminate extraneous values. It may happen, of course, that the beginning assumption is not justified and that the equation has no solution in the number field in which we are working. Since division by a polynomial $p(x)$ may result in the loss of solutions belonging to $S[p(x) = 0]$, we should check the latter set for possible solutions of the original equation.

Example 3.7d. Solve the equation

$$\frac{1}{x - 2} + \frac{1}{x} = \frac{1}{x(x - 2)}.$$

Multiplying each side of the equation by the L.C.M., $x(x - 2)$, of the denominators, we obtain

$$x + (x - 2) = 1,$$

so that

$$x = \tfrac{3}{2}.$$

We know from the preceding theorems that

$$S\left[\frac{1}{x - 2} + \frac{1}{x} = \frac{1}{x(x - 2)}\right] \subset \{\tfrac{3}{2}\}.$$

Thus, either 3/2 is the only element of the solution set or else the solution set is empty. Substituting 3/2 for x in the original equation produces an identity so that $S = \{3/2\}$.

Example 3.7e. Determine the solution set for the equation $[\![x]\!] = 2$, $x \in \mathcal{R}$.

Since $[\![x]\!] = 2$ for all $x \in \mathcal{R}$ such that $2 \leq x < 3$, it follows that $S = \{x : 2 \leq x < 3\}$.

Example 3.7f. Find the solution set for the equation

$$x + 2|x - 2| = 5, \qquad x \in \mathcal{R}.$$

This equation may be considered as a combination of two other equations. If $x - 2 \geq 0$, that is, if $x \geq 2$, then $|x - 2| = x - 2$, and if $x - 2 < 0$, that is, if $x < 2$, then $|x - 2| = 2 - x$. Hence, we may write the given equation in the form

$$x + 2(x - 2) = 5, \quad \text{if } x \geq 2,$$

and in the form

$$x + 2(2 - x) = 5, \quad \text{if } x < 2.$$

In the first case we obtain a valid result for $x = 3$ only, and in the second case the equation is true for $x = -1$ only. Hence $S = \{-1, 3\}$ for the given equation.

Exercises 3.7

Determine the solution set in the field $\mathfrak{R}$ for each of Numbers 1 to 29.

1. $x^2 - 7x + 12 = 0$.
2. $x^2 - x - 2 = 0$.
3. $x^3 + 3x^2 + 2x = 0$.
4. $y^3 + 5y^2 - 14y = 0$.
5. $x^3 - 4x^2 + x + 6 = 0$. (Use synthetic division.)
6. $x^3 + 2x^2 - 9x - 18 = 0$.

7. $\dfrac{2}{t} + \dfrac{3}{t^2 + t} = 0$.

8. $\dfrac{1}{w} - \dfrac{4}{w^2 + 3} = 0$.

9. $\dfrac{1}{2x} + \dfrac{1}{2x - 1} = \dfrac{4x - 1}{2x(2x - 1)}$.

10. $\dfrac{x + 4}{x^2 - 2x} = \dfrac{5x}{x^2 - 4} - \dfrac{4}{x - 2}$.

11. $\dfrac{4w^2}{w^2 - 9} + \dfrac{w - 3}{w + 3} = \dfrac{w + 3}{w - 3} + 4$.

12. $\sqrt{x + 1} + 2 = \sqrt{x - 3}$.

13. $\sqrt{t - 1} + \sqrt{t + 4} = 5$.

14. $\sqrt{u + 2} = \sqrt{u - 3} + 1$.

15. $\sqrt{x + 4} - \sqrt{2} = \sqrt{x - 6}$.
16. $|x| + 3 = 0$.
17. $|s| = 2$.
18. $2w - |w| = 3$.
19. $[\![x - 1]\!] = 3$.
20. $2[\![t]\!] = 3$.
21. $[\![x]\!] - |x| = 2$.
22. $2|x - 1| - 3|x| = 4$.
23. $|s + 1| - 2|s| + 3|s - 2| = 6$.
24. $w - [\![w]\!] = \frac{1}{2}$.
25. $\sqrt{x^2} = 2$.
26. $\sqrt{(x - 1)^2} = -3$.
27. $u + [\![u]\!] = 4.5$.
28. $|w| + [\![w]\!] = 3.5$.
29. $(x^{-1} + 1)^{-1} = x + 1$.

Using principal roots only, find the solution set in each of Numbers 30 to 33.

30. $3x^{-1/4} = 6$.
31. $2x^{1/3} = -3$.
32. $w^{-3/4} = \frac{1}{27}$.
33. $3x^{1/5} = -1$.

34. Prove Theorem 3.7c.
35. Prove Theorem 3.7d.
36. Prove Theorem 3.7e.
37. Find the altitude and side of an equilateral triangle whose area is $144 \sqrt{3}$ square inches.
38. Find two positive numbers if their difference is 20 and the difference of their square roots is 2.
39. What is the area A of a face of a cube in terms of the volume V?
40. Find the area of a regular hexagon whose perimeter is 18 inches.
41. A man bought 100 ounces of an alloy that was supposed to be sterling silver, which is legally defined to be 92.5% pure silver and 7.5% copper. He checked the weight of the alloy in water and found it to be 90-2/3 ounces. If silver loses 2/23 of its weight and copper 1/6 of its weight in water, by how much did the alloy miss being sterling?
42. The electrical resistance R_s equivalent to two resistances R_1 and R_2 in series is given by

$$R_s = R_1 + R_2.$$

The resistance R_p equivalent to the two resistances in parallel is given by

$$1/R_p = 1/R_1 + 1/R_2.$$

Two resistances in series are found to be equivalent to a resistance of 90 ohms. When the resistances are wired in parallel, the equivalent resistance is found to be one-third the larger of the original resistances. Find the original resistances.

43. A sports car that is 12 feet long overtakes a truck that is 32 feet long and that is traveling at the rate of 40 miles per hour. How fast must the sports car be traveling in order to pass the truck in two seconds?

3.8 INEQUALITIES

It was found in Chapter 2 that each of the sets $\mathfrak{N}$ of natural numbers, $\mathfrak{I}$ of integers, $\mathfrak{F}$ of rational numbers, and $\mathfrak{R}$ of real numbers has an order property. This property is customarily denoted by the symbol $<$. For any two elements $a, b \in \mathfrak{R}$, one and only one of the following is valid:

$$a < b, \quad a = b, \quad a > b.$$

This statement is called the **trichotomy law** of numbers.

An expression of the form

$$a < b, \quad b > a,$$

where $a, b \in \mathfrak{R}$, is called an **inequality.** Inequalities are perhaps as important in the applications of mathematics as are equations. In fact, insofar as our knowledge of the physical world is obtained by measurement (not mere counting), that knowledge is described by inequalities rather than by equations. For instance, if we say that the diameter d of the planet Venus is 7,700 miles, we mean that

$$7650 < d < 7750.$$

A moment's reflection shows that an absolutely exact measurement of any physical quantity such as distance, weight, velocity, and so on, is completely impossible; the accuracy depends on the measuring instruments, and such instruments can be made to measure only within certain specified tolerances— never exactly. We shall also see later that inequalities are essential in clarifying such fundamental concepts as that of a limit, on which the entire calculus is built. It is for these reasons that a good basic understanding of inequalities is necessary, and we shall next develop a number of fundamental laws concerning them.

Theorem 3.8a. *The Transitive Property of Inequalities:*

$$a > b \quad \text{and} \quad b > c \Rightarrow a > c, \qquad a, b, c \in \mathfrak{R}.$$

PROOF: $a > b \Rightarrow a - b = p$, where p is a positive number. Similarly,

$$b > c \Rightarrow b - c = q,$$

where $q > 0$. Then, by adding the two equations $a - b = p$ and $b - c = q$, we obtain

$$a - c = p + q,$$

where $p + q$ is a positive number. Hence,

$$a > c.$$

That we may add (subtract) the same real number to (from) both members of an inequality and retain the direction or the "sense" of the inequality is contained in the following theorem.

Theorem 3.8b. $a > b \Rightarrow a + c > b + c,$ $a, b, c \in \mathcal{R}.$

PROOF: $a > b \Rightarrow a - b = p$, a positive number. Furthermore,

$$a - b = (a + c) - (b + c),$$

so that

$$(a + c) - (b + c) = p,$$

a positive number. Therefore

$$a + c > b + c.$$

Subtraction of the same real number from both sides of an equality is also taken care of since in Theorem 3.8b, c may be either positive or negative.

Another important result is that both members of an inequality may be multiplied by the same *positive* number without changing the sense of the inequality.

Theorem 3.8c. $a > b$ and $c > 0 \Rightarrow ac > bc,$ $a, b, c \in \mathcal{R}.$

PROOF: Since $a - b = p$, a positive number, and c is also positive, then

$$(a - b)c = pc,$$

a positive number. Thus,

$$ac - bc = pc,$$

and

$$ac > bc.$$

Division is also taken care of, since c is any positive number and could be of the form $1/b$.

Theorem 3.8d. $a > b$ and $c < 0 \Rightarrow ac < bc,$ $a, b, c \in \mathcal{R}.$

The proof is left for the exercises.

Still another important theorem is that if all the members of two inequalities of the same sense are positive, and the corresponding members are multiplied together, an inequality of the same sense is obtained.

Theorem 3.8e. $a > b > 0$ and $c > d > 0 \Rightarrow ac > bd,$ $a, b, c \in \mathcal{R}.$

PROOF: We have $a - b = p, c - d = q$, with p and q positive. Thus

$$a = b + p, c = d + q,$$

and

$$ac = (b + p)(d + q),$$

or

$$ac = bd + bq + pd + pq.$$

Accordingly,

$$ac - bd = bq + pd + pq,$$

which is a positive number. Therefore,

$$ac > bd.$$

(Why?)

A number of useful results concerning rational exponents and inequalities can be obtained from Theorem 3.8e. If both members of an inequality are positive, the same positive integral powers of both members are unequal in the same sense.

Theorem 3.8f. $a > b > 0$ and $p \in \mathfrak{N} \Rightarrow a^p > b^p,$ $a, b \in \mathfrak{R}.$

PROOF: The proof is a simple exercise in mathematical induction using Theorem 3.8e, and is left for the reader.

Sometimes inequality signs are combined with equals signs to give symbols such as $\geq$ (read "greater than or equal to") and $\leq$ (read "less than or equal to"). For example, if m is any real number whatsoever, we have $m^2 \geq 0$. (Why?)

Theorem 3.8f can be extended to include rational values for p.

Theorem 3.8g. $a > b > 0,$ $p > 0,$ and $p \in \mathfrak{F} \Rightarrow a^p > b^p,$ $a, b \in \mathfrak{R}.$

PROOF: The proof is by contradiction. Let $p = m/n$, where m and n are positive integers, and assume that

$$a^{m/n} \leq b^{m/n}.$$

Then

$$(a^{m/n})^n \leq (b^{m/n})^n$$

or

$$a^m \leq b^m.$$

But since $a > b$, $a^m > b^m$, which is a contradiction of the preceding result. Evidently, $a^{m/n} > b^{m/n}$.

The preceding theorems of this section are useful in establishing many important relationships of inequality. The following examples illustrate the use of these theorems.

Example 3.8a. Show that the arithmetic mean of two positive numbers is never less than their positive geometric mean; that is,

$$a > 0 \text{ and } b > 0 \Rightarrow \tfrac{1}{2}(a + b) \geq \sqrt{ab}.$$

We shall illustrate two possible procedures for proving this result. The first goes directly back to the definition of $a > b$. Thus, we write

$$\tfrac{1}{2}(a + b) - \sqrt{ab} = \tfrac{1}{2}(a - 2\sqrt{ab} + b)$$
$$= \tfrac{1}{2}(\sqrt{a} - \sqrt{b})^2,$$

which cannot be a negative number. Hence

$$\tfrac{1}{2}(a + b) \geq \sqrt{ab}.$$

The second procedure consists of an analysis in which the required proposition is assumed true. Then we attempt to derive a known result. A reversal of these steps can then be used as the needed proof.

1. We assume that $\tfrac{1}{2}(a + b) \geq \sqrt{ab}$ is true.
2. $a + b \geq 2\sqrt{ab}.$ Why?
3. $a + b - 2\sqrt{ab} \geq 0.$ Why?
4. $(\sqrt{a} - \sqrt{b})^2 \geq 0.$ Why?

This last result is known to be valid since the square of any real number is nonnegative. Therefore, we may construct the *proof*:

1. $(\sqrt{a} - \sqrt{b})^2 \geq 0.$ $m^2 \geq 0$ for any real number m.
2. $a + b - 2\sqrt{ab} \geq 0.$ Why?
3. $a + b \geq 2\sqrt{ab}.$ Why?
4. $\tfrac{1}{2}(a + b) \geq \sqrt{ab}.$ Why?

Example 3.8b. If a, b, c are positive numbers, and $d/a < e/b < f/c$, show that

$$\frac{d}{a} < \frac{d + e + f}{a + b + c} < \frac{f}{c}.$$

Let $f/c = r$. Then we have $e/b < r$, and $d/a < r$.
Since a and b are positive, we have $d < ar$, and $e < br$. Also, $f = cr$. Consequently,

$$d + e + f < ar + br + cr$$

(why?) or

$$d + e + f < (a + b + c)r$$

and

$$\frac{d + e + f}{a + b + c} < r$$

(why?); that is,

$$\frac{d + e + f}{a + b + c} < \frac{f}{c}.$$

The left portion of the inequality may be proved in a similar manner.

Example 3.8c. Without using decimal approximations, determine the proper order relationship $>$, $=$, or $<$ between the numbers $\sqrt{15} - \sqrt{14}$ and $\sqrt{32} - \sqrt{31}$.

Let θ denote the proper one of the three symbols. Then,

$$\sqrt{15} - \sqrt{14} \; \theta \; \sqrt{32} - \sqrt{31} \Leftrightarrow \sqrt{15} + \sqrt{31} \quad \theta \; \sqrt{32} + \sqrt{14}$$
$$\Leftrightarrow (\sqrt{15} + \sqrt{31})^2 \; \theta \; (\sqrt{32} + \sqrt{14})^2$$
$$\Leftrightarrow 46 + 2\sqrt{465} \quad \theta \; 46 + 2\sqrt{448}$$
$$\Leftrightarrow \sqrt{465} \quad \theta \; \sqrt{448}.$$

Clearly, the proper symbol is $>$, and the preceding analysis can be made into a proof by proceeding through the steps in reverse order, that is, by starting with the true inequality $\sqrt{465} > \sqrt{448}$, and deriving the desired result $\sqrt{15} - \sqrt{14} > \sqrt{32} - \sqrt{31}$.

Exercises 3.8

In Numbers 1 to 5, show the validity of the inequalities.

1. $\dfrac{d}{3c} > 1 - \dfrac{3c}{4d}$, where $c > 0$, $d > 0$, $2d \neq 3c$.

2. $x^2 + \dfrac{9}{x^2} \geq 6$, where $x \neq 0$.

3. $\dfrac{\sqrt{x}}{\sqrt{y}} + \dfrac{\sqrt{y}}{\sqrt{x}} > 2$, if $x > 0$, $y > 0$, $x \neq y$.

4. $\dfrac{3a}{5b} + \dfrac{5b}{3a} > 2$, if $a > 0$, $b > 0$, $3a \neq 5b$.

5. $a^2 + b^2 + c^2 > ab + ac + bc$, unless $a = b = c$.

In each of Numbers 6 to 9, without using decimal expansions, determine which of the symbols, $>$, $=$, $<$ should be substituted for θ.

6. $\sqrt{6} - \sqrt{8} \ \theta \ \sqrt{3} - 2$.

7. $\sqrt{15} - \sqrt{5} \ \theta \ 3 - \sqrt{2}$.

8. $\sqrt{22} - \sqrt{17} \ \theta \ \sqrt{37} - \sqrt{31}$.

9. $\sqrt{19} - \sqrt{14} \ \theta \ \sqrt{29} - \sqrt{22}$.

10. Prove Theorem 3.8d.

11. Prove Theorem 3.8f.

12. Prove that $0 < a < b \Rightarrow 1/a > 1/b$.

13. Prove that if $a < b$, then $-a > -b$.

14. Prove that for any real numbers a, b, c, d,

$$(ab + cd)^2 \leq (a^2 + c^2)(b^2 + d^2).$$

(Cauchy's Inequality).

15. Is the statement

$$a, b, c, d > 0 \Rightarrow (ab + cd)(ac + bd) \leq 4abcd$$

true or false?

16. For what positive numbers, if any, is the sum of the number and its reciprocal less than 2?

17. Prove that if $a > b > 0$, then $p \in \mathfrak{N} \Rightarrow a^{1/p} > b^{1/p}$.

18. Prove that if $0 < a < 1$, then $p \in \mathfrak{N} \Rightarrow a \leq a^{1/p} < 1$.

19. Prove that if $1 < a$, then $p \in \mathfrak{N} \Rightarrow 1 < a^{1/p} \leq a$.

20. Show that if a, b, $c > 0$, then

$$3abc \leq a^3 + b^3 + c^3.$$

Hint: One factor of $a^3 + b^3 + c^3 - 3abc$ is $a + b + c$.

21. For a, b, c real, show that $ax^2 + bx + c$ is positive for all real x if and only if $a > 0$, $b^2 - 4ac < 0$. *Hint*: Try to convert most of the expression into a perfect square involving x.

22. Prove by mathematical induction that

$$\left(\frac{1}{2}\right)\left(\frac{3}{4}\right)\left(\frac{5}{6}\right) \cdots \left(\frac{2n-1}{2n}\right) \leq \frac{1}{\sqrt{3n+1}}.$$

3.9 SOLUTION SETS OF INEQUALITIES

In the preceding section the fundamental properties of inequalities were introduced. Now we propose to combine the results of that section with open statements involving inequalities to obtain results similar to those obtained for equations in Section 3.7. For example, corresponding to the idea of the solution set of an equation, we have the following definition for inequalities.

Definition 3.9a. The set of values for which a given inequality is true is called the **solution set** of the inequality.

It is now evident that we are faced with the same question as in the case of equations—that is, to determine what operations may be performed on an inequality in order to arrive at the solution set. The pertinent ideas are based on the discussion in the preceding section.

By the use of Theorem 3.8b, the reader should be able to prove

Theorem 3.9a. The solution set of an inequality

$$f(x) > g(x)$$

is not altered by adding a polynomial $p(x)$ to both sides; that is,

$$S[f(x) > g(x)] = S[f(x) + p(x) > g(x) + p(x)].$$

Similarly, Theorem 3.8c suffices to prove

Theorem 3.9b. The solution set of an inequality

$$f(x) > g(x)$$

is not altered by multiplying both members by a factor $p(x)$ that is *positive* for all $x \in \mathcal{R}$; that is,

$$p(x) > 0 \quad \text{for } x \in \mathcal{R} \Rightarrow S[f(x) > g(x)] = S[p(x)f(x) > p(x)g(x)].$$

In order to find the solution set of a given inequality, we apply the preceding theorems to obtain simpler inequalities until the solution set is apparent. This will be illustrated in the next examples.

Example 3.9a. Solve the inequality $5x + 7 > 3x + 15$.

We apply Theorem 3.9a by adding $-3x - 7$ to both members to obtain

$$2x > 8.$$

Then dividing both members by 2, we find the solution set to be $\{x: x > 4\}$.

Example 3.9b. Solve the inequality $x^2 - 5x + 6 > 0$.

We note that $x^2 - 5x + 6 = (x - 2)(x - 3)$. But a product of two factors is positive (> 0) only if both factors are positive or if both are negative. The set of numbers for which both factors are positive may be expressed as the intersection of two sets:

$$S[x - 2 > 0] \cap S[x - 3 > 0].$$

This is the same as $\{x: x > 3\}$. Why?

Similarly, the set of numbers for which both factors are negative may be written

$$\mathcal{S}[x - 3 < 0] \cap \mathcal{S}[x - 2 < 0],$$

and this is the set $\{x: x < 2\}$.

Since any number in either of the sets $\{x: x < 2\}$ and $\{x: x > 3\}$ is an element of $\mathcal{S}[x^2 - 5x + 6 > 0]$, the desired solution set is

$$\{x: x < 2\} \cup \{x: x > 3\}.$$

Example 3.9c. Solve the inequality $1/(x - 1) > 1$.

By subtracting 1 from both members, we get

$$\frac{1}{x - 1} > 1 \Leftrightarrow \frac{1}{x - 1} - 1 > 0$$

or

$$\frac{2 - x}{x - 1} > 0.$$

The last inequality is satisfied if, and only if, both $2 - x$ and $x - 1$ are positive or both are negative. We find

$$\mathcal{S}[2 - x > 0] \cap \mathcal{S}[x - 1 > 0] = \{x: x < 2\} \cap \{x: x > 1\}$$
$$= \{x: 1 < x < 2\}.$$

Also,

$$\mathcal{S}[2 - x < 0] \cap \mathcal{S}[x - 1 < 0] = \{x: x > 2\} \cap \{x: x < 1\}$$
$$= \varnothing.$$

Accordingly, the required solution set is

$$\{x: 1 < x < 2\}.$$

Example 3.9d. Determine the solution set for the inequality $|x - 3| + 2|x| < 5$.

We know that

$$|x| = \begin{cases} x & \text{if } x \geq 0, \\ -x & \text{if } x < 0, \end{cases}$$

and that

$$|x - 3| = \begin{cases} x - 3 & \text{if } x \geq 3, \\ 3 - x & \text{if } x < 3. \end{cases}$$

Consequently, it proves useful to split the domain of definition of $|x - 3| + 2|x|$ into the intervals $x < 0$, $0 \leq x < 3$, and $3 \leq x$. Then we have

$$|x - 3| + 2 \cdot |x| = 3 - x - 2x = 3 - 3x, \qquad x < 0,$$
$$|x - 3| + 2 \cdot |x| = 3 - x + 2x = 3 + x, \qquad 0 \leq x < 3,$$

and

$$|x - 3| + 2 \cdot |x| = x - 3 + 2x = 3x - 3, \qquad 3 \leq x.$$

Hence, we have to solve three problems:

(a) $\qquad\qquad\qquad 3 - 3x < 5$ along with $x < 0$.

Since $3 - 3x < 5$ for $-2/3 < x$, both these conditions are satisfied for $-2/3 < x < 0$.

(b) $\qquad\qquad\qquad\qquad 3 + x < 5$ along with $0 \leq x < 3$.

Since $3 + x < 5$ for $x < 2$, both conditions are satisfied for $0 \leq x < 2$.

(c) $\qquad\qquad\qquad\qquad 3x - 3 < 5$ along with $3 \leq x$.

Since $3x - 3 < 5$ for $x < 8/3$ only, there are no numbers that satisfy both these conditions.

The solution of the given inequality is thus

$$\{x: -\tfrac{2}{3} < x < 0\} \cup \{x: 0 \leq x < 2\} \cup \varnothing = \{x: -\tfrac{2}{3} < x < 2\}.$$

Example 3.9e. Find the solution set of the inequality

$$\frac{4}{y} + 9y > 12.$$

Excluding $y = 0$, we have $y^2 > 0$ so that we may multiply both members by y^2. Thus, for $y \neq 0$,

$$\frac{4}{y} + 9y > 12 \Leftrightarrow 4y + 9y^3 > 12y^2$$

$$\Leftrightarrow 9y^3 - 12y^2 + 4y > 0$$
$$\Leftrightarrow y(9y^2 - 12y + 4) > 0$$
$$\Leftrightarrow y(3y - 2)^2 > 0.$$

The last inequality is true for $y > 0$ and $y \neq 2/3$. Hence the required solution set is $\{y: y > 0 \text{ and } y \neq 2/3\}$.

Example 3.9f. The resistance R (ohms) of a metal conductor of electricity can be represented quite accurately by

$$R = R_0(1 + \alpha t),$$

where R_0 is the resistance at temperature $t = 0$, and α is the temperature coefficient of resistivity. A German-silver standard resistor of 10 ohms at 0°C has a temperature coefficient of 0.00036 per degree C. Within what temperature limits must this resistor be kept if it is not to vary from its nominal resistance by more than 0.01 ohm?

Since the resistance is required to be greater than $(10 - 0.01)$ ohms and less than $(10 + 0.01)$ ohms, we have

$$9.99 < 10(1 + \alpha t) < 10.01 \Leftrightarrow 0.999 < 1 + \alpha t < 1.001$$
$$\Leftrightarrow -0.001 < \alpha t < 0.001$$

$$\Leftrightarrow -\frac{0.001}{\alpha} < t < \frac{0.001}{\alpha}.$$

For $\alpha = 0.00036$, we have approximately

$$-2.8 < t < 2.8;$$

that is, the temperature must lie between -2.8°C and 2.8°C.

Exercises 3.9

Determine the solution set for the given inequality in each of Numbers 1 to 15.

1. $\dfrac{1}{3x - 5} > 0.$

2. $\dfrac{4}{2x + 9} < 0.$

3. $6x + 27 < 2x + 9.$
4. $\frac{2}{3}x - 15 > 6 - \frac{1}{2}x.$
5. $x + [\![x]\!] < 2x.$
6. $2 \leq [\![x]\!] \leq 5.$
7. $|x| + 1 < x.$
8. $2|x| + x < 6.$

9. $3|x - 1| + |x| < 1.$
10. $|x - 1| + |x + 1| < 4.$
11. $\sqrt{2x + 3} \geq 5.$

12. $x + \dfrac{4}{x} > 4.$

13. $y + \dfrac{1}{y} \geq 2.$

14. $4a + \dfrac{25}{a} > 20.$

15. $|x| \geq x.$

16. Express the inequalities $-1 < x < 5$ by a single inequality, making use of absolute values.
17. A person found what he thought to be the solution set of the inequality $x + 1 < 4x + 4$ as follows:

$$x + 1 < 4x + 4 \Rightarrow x + 1 < 4(x + 1)$$
$$\Rightarrow 1 < 4$$
$$\Rightarrow \text{the given inequality is true for all } x \in \mathfrak{R}.$$

Criticize his solution.
18. Prove Theorem 3.9a.
19. Prove Theorem 3.9b.
20. A student makes grades of 60, 70, and 80 on three tests. How well must he do on two more tests in order to average 80 or better on all five?
21. The specific gravity s of a body is given by the formula $s = A/(A - W)$, where A is the weight in air and W the weight in water. Show, for bodies with specific gravity greater than 3, that $A > W > \frac{2}{3}A.$
22. For bodies having specific gravities between 1.25 and 1.50, show that $\frac{1}{5}A < W < \frac{1}{3}A.$ (See the preceding problem.)
23. If air friction is neglected, the height h (feet) above the ground of an "upper atmosphere" rocket t seconds after lift-off is given approximately by $h = 6800t - 16t^2.$ Find the interval of time during which the rocket is above 160,000 feet.

Summary of Chapter 3

The reader should understand clearly the following concepts:

(1) the factorization of a polynomial in a field (Section 3.2);
(2) the irreducibility of a polynomial in a field (Section 3.2);

(3) the factorization of various basic forms (such as $a^2 - b^2$, $a^3 + b^3$, etc.) (Section 3.2);

(4) the method of completing the square (Section 3.2);

(5) the least common multiple of polynomial expressions (Section 3.3);

(6) the laws governing the addition, multiplication, and division of fractions (Section 3.3);

(7) operations with negative and rational exponents (Section 3.4);

(8) undefined forms such as 0^0 (Section 3.4);

(9) the principal nth root of a positive number (Section 3.4);

(10) the absolute value of a number (Section 3.4);

(11) operations with radicals (Section 3.4);

(12) synthetic division (Section 3.5);

(13) the Remainder Theorem (Section 3.6);

(14) the Fundamental Theorem of Algebra (Section 3.6);

(15) the reducibility of polynomials in the field $\mathfrak{C}$ (Section 3.6);

(16) the multiplicity of factors of a polynomial (Section 3.6);

(17) The solution sets of equations and inequalities, and the effect upon solution sets resulting from multiplication and division by polynomials (Sections 3.7, 3.9);

(18) the laws governing inequalities (Section 3.8);

(19) the techniques of proving relationships of inequality (Section 3.8).

Chapter 4   Geometry and The Real Numbers

4.1 A GEOMETRIC INTEPRETATION OF THE REAL NUMBERS

The reader is undoubtedly familiar with the idea of interpreting real numbers geometrically on a straight line, as is done on a ruler, for example. Such an interpretation is based on the assumption that geometry is a mathematical entity distinct from algebra, and on the following fundamental axiom.

Axiom 4.1a. A one-to-one correspondence exists between the set of real numbers and the set of points on a straight line.

This axiom is simply an existence postulate. It does not indicate in what manner a one-to-one correspondence actually can be established. One of the simplest ways of establishing such a correspondence is based on the concept of distance.

Let us begin by defining what is meant by the "distance" between two elements of $\mathcal{R}$.

Definition 4.1a. Let a and b be two real numbers. The quantity

$$d(a, b) .=. \sqrt{(a - b)^2}$$

is called the **distance** between the two numbers a and b.

According to this definition, distance is a numerical quantity that is always positive or zero. In fact, the reader may easily verify the following properties of distance:

(1) $d(a, b) = 0 \Leftrightarrow a = b.$
(2) $d(a, b) = d(b, a).$
(3) $d(a, c) = d(a, b) + d(b, c), \qquad a \leqq b \leqq c.$

We now have the set $\mathcal{R}$ of real numbers on which is defined a quantity called distance. Let us attempt to associate these numbers with points on a straight line m in such a way that "distance" will have a consistent geometric interpretation. On the line m, an arbitrary point, called the origin, is chosen to be associated with the number 0. For the present, this point will be denoted by (0).

Another arbitrary point distinct from (0), and usually located to the right of (0), is chosen to be associated with the number 1, and is denoted by (1) (see Figure 4.1a).

$$(-1) \qquad (0) \qquad\qquad (1) \qquad (a)\ (2) \qquad m$$

FIGURE 4.1a

Since $d(0, 1) = 1$, the line segment on m between (0) and (1) is a geometrical representation of a distance of one unit, and is called a **unit length**. Furthermore, once we have established the correspondence between points on m and the real numbers, we may define the **length** of a line segment on m as the distance between the numbers associated with the points that determine the line segment. However, it is desirable to establish the correspondence so that the following axiom is satisfied.

Axiom 4.1b. Two line segments that are geometrically congruent have the same length.

This requirement forces us to locate the point (2) in such a way that the line segment from (1) to (2) is geometrically congruent to the segment from (0) to (1). Consequently, the two points (0) and (1), with the concept of distance in Definition 4.1a, and Axiom 4.1b, determine the point on m to be associated with the real number a. On occasion, where it is necessary to distinguish between the number a and the point associated with this number, we shall use the notation (a) for the point. However, this notation is often clumsy, and when there is no danger of confusion we shall use a to denote both the real number a and the point associated with the number.

The following example illustrates some of the preceding ideas.

Example 4.1a. Find the length of the line segment determined by the following pairs of points: (a) (-2) and (3); (b) $(\sqrt{2})$ and $(\sqrt{5})$.

Using the expression in Definition 4.1a, we get

(a) $$d(-2, 3) = \sqrt{(-2 - 3)^2} = 5,$$

and

(b) $$d(\sqrt{2}, \sqrt{5}) = \sqrt{(\sqrt{2} - \sqrt{5})^2} = \sqrt{5} - \sqrt{2}.$$

In (b) of Example 4.1a, why is

$$d(\sqrt{2}, \sqrt{5}) = \sqrt{2} - \sqrt{5}$$

an incorrect statement?

For convenience in specifying the location of a point P with respect to a point Q, we need to introduce the concept of a **directed line segment**. Since points associated with positive numbers are located to the right of (0), the direction of a line m from (0) to any point (a), where $a > 0$, is called the *positive direction* of m. The opposite direction is the *negative direction* of m. If the direction from a point P on m to a point Q on m is in the positive direction of m, then the line segment PQ is called a *positively directed* line segment. Otherwise it is called a *negatively directed* line segment. Hence, the segment from (0) to (1) is positively directed, and the segment from (1) to (0) is negatively directed.

The straight line m is usually called the **real number axis**, or the *x-axis*, and the set of points on m is said to constitute a **one-dimensional space**. The real number a that corresponds to a point $A = (a)$ on the axis is called the coordinate of the point. Thus, the point $(-1/2)$ has the coordinate $-1/2$. Accordingly, the real number a, by means of its sign and magnitude, determines the distance and the direction of the point (a) from the origin.

The next definition is useful in relating distance to a directed line segment.

Definition 4.1b. The **directed distance** from a point P_1 to a point P_2 on the real axis is a number whose magnitude is the number of units in the length of the segment joining the two points and whose sign is plus or minus, according as the direction is the same as or is opposite from the positive direction of the axis.

The directed distance will be designated by P_1P_2. Note that P_2P_1 is in the opposite direction from P_1P_2 so that we have $P_2P_1 = -P_1P_2$.

It follows at once from Definition 4.1a that the directed distance OP from the origin to any point P on the axis is given by the coordinate of P. Thus if P has the coordinate x, then $OP = x$. Another important consequence of Definition 4.1a is given in

Theorem 4.1a. On the real axis, the directed distance P_1P_2 is always given by

$$P_1P_2 = OP_2 - OP_1.$$

PROOF: The proof of this theorem consists of direct verification from the few possible different placements of the points P_1 and P_2 relative to the origin. Figure 4.1b shows three of the possibilities. For example, in the middle line

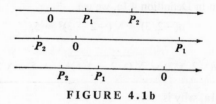

FIGURE 4.1b

of the figure we see that OP_1 is positive, OP_2 is negative, and P_1P_2 is negative. Clearly, $OP_2 - OP_1$ will be negative and will have the correct magnitude so that $P_1P_2 = OP_2 - OP_1$. The reader should make a careful analysis for all other possible placements of P_1 and P_2. Note that, if P_1 and P_2 coincide, the theorem correctly gives zero for the directed distance.

Theorem 4.1b. If the coordinates of P_1 and P_2 are x_1 and x_2, respectively, then

$$P_1P_2 = x_2 - x_1.$$

In view of our recognition that $OP_1 = x_1$ and $OP_2 = x_2$, this theorem is essentially a restatement of Theorem 4.1a.

We have, for instance,

(a) $x_1 = 5, \quad x_2 = -3 \Rightarrow P_1P_2 = -3 - 5 = -8;$
(b) $x_1 = -4, \quad x_2 = 2 \Rightarrow P_1P_2 = 2 + 4 = 6.$

An order relation is established among the points on the real number axis corresponding to the order relation among the real numbers. The point (a) is said to *precede* the point (b) if and only if the real number a is *less* than the real number b. Thus we have a geometric picture that corresponds to the statement $a < b$.

A set of points on the real number axis is defined by stating a certain property which the elements of the set possess, but which other points of the x-axis do not possess. A set such as $\{(x): a \leq x \leq b\}$, where $a < b$, is called a **closed interval**. It is important to notice that the end points (a) and (b) must be elements of the set if the interval is closed. If neither end point is included, the set is said to be an **open** interval; if only one end point is included, the set is said to be a **half-open** interval.

We frequently need to refer to sets of points such as

$$\{(x): x > a\} \quad \text{or} \quad \{(x): x \leq b\},$$

where a and b are fixed real numbers. These sets correspond, respectively, to the entire real axis to the right of the point (a) and the entire real axis to the left of and including the point (b). Such intervals are termed **semi-infinite**, since they correspond to half-lines which are endless in one direction. We shall not employ the adjectives open or closed with semi-infinite intervals.

Example 4.1b. Describe the interval $\{(x): 1 \leq x \leq 2\}$.

This set consists of all the points on the segment of the x axis between and including the points (1) and (2). The interval is closed since both end points are included. In sketching a point set consisting of a segment of the axis, we indicate the end points by small circles. If the end point is included, the interior of the circle is black, and if the end point is not included, the interior of the circle is white (see Figures 4.1c and 4.1d).

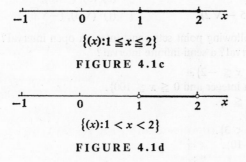

$\{(x): 1 \leq x \leq 2\}$

FIGURE 4.1c

$\{(x): 1 < x < 2\}$

FIGURE 4.1d

Example 4.1c. Describe the interval $\{(x): 1 < x < 2\}$.

This set consists of the same points as in Example 4.1b with the exception of the end points. This interval is open, since neither end point is included (see Figure 4.1d).
Note: In contrast to the preceding examples, the interval $\{(x): 1 \leq x < 2\}$ is half-open, since only one of the end points is included (see Figure 4.1e).

$$\{(x): 1 \leq x < 2\}$$

FIGURE 4.1e

If (x_0) is a given point on the real number axis and h is a given positive number, then the interval

$$\{(x): x_0 - h < x < x_0 + h\}$$

consists of all points of the segment between $(x_0 - h)$ and $(x_0 + h)$ (see Figure 4.1f). This important type of open interval is called a **neighborhood** of the

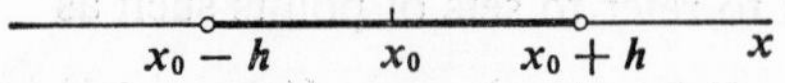

$$\{(x): x_0 - h < x < x_0 + h\}$$

FIGURE 4.1f

point (x_0), and the positive number h is often called the **radius** of the neighborhood. For instance, the neighborhood of radius 0.5 of the point (-2) is the open interval $\{(x): -2.5 < x < -1.5\}$. The idea of a neighborhood will play an important role in some of our later discussions.

Exercises 4.1

1. Find the distance between the following points on the real number axis. What is the directed distance from the first to the second of the given points in each case?

(a) $(-3), (-7)$.

(b) $(\sqrt{3}), (\sqrt{6})$.

(c) $(2 - \sqrt{2}), (5 - \sqrt{2})$.

(d) $(2 - \sqrt{2}), (\sqrt{2} - 5)$.

(e) $(3), (-10)$.

(f) $(\sqrt{3}), (-\sqrt{6})$.

2. Which of the following point sets constitutes an open interval? a closed interval? a half-open interval? a semi-infinite interval?

(a) $\{(x): -4 < x \leq -2\}$.

(b) $\{(x): x$ is an integer and $0 \leq x \leq 100\}$.

(c) $\{(x): 0 \leq x \leq 1\}$.

(d) $\{(x): x \geq 4\}$.

(e) $\{(x): 2 < x < 3\}$.

(f) $\{(x): x < -10\}$.

3. Represent each of the following sets graphically.

(a) $\mathcal{A} .=. \{(x): 2 < x \leq 5\}$.
(b) $\mathcal{B} .=. \{(x): -2 \leq x \leq 3\}$.
(c) $\mathcal{C} .=. \{(x): -1 < x < 4\}$.
(d) $\mathcal{D} .=. \{(x): -3 \leq x < 1\}$.

4. If $\mathcal{A}, \mathcal{B}, \mathcal{C}, \mathcal{D}$ are the sets in Number 3, describe each of the following sets and represent it graphically. For example, we would describe $\mathcal{A} \cup \mathcal{C}$ by writing

$$\mathcal{A} \cup \mathcal{C} = \{(x): -1 < x \leq 5\}.$$

(a) $\mathcal{A} \cap \mathcal{B}$.
(b) $\mathcal{A} \cup \mathcal{B}$.
(c) $(\mathcal{A} \cup \mathcal{B}) \cap \mathcal{C}$.
(d) $(\mathcal{A} \cup \mathcal{B}) \cap (\mathcal{C} \cup \mathcal{D})$.

(e) $\mathcal{B} \cap \mathcal{C} \cap \mathcal{D}$.
(f) $(\mathcal{A} \cap \mathcal{C}) \cup (\mathcal{B} \cap \mathcal{D})$.
(g) $\mathcal{A} \cap \mathcal{B} \cap \mathcal{C} \cap \mathcal{D}$.
(h) $\mathcal{A} \cup \mathcal{B} \cup \mathcal{C} \cup \mathcal{D}$.

5. If complementation is with respect to the set $\mathcal{R}$ of all real numbers and we refer to the sets in Number 3, then $\mathcal{A}'$, for example, would be the set

$$\{(x): x \leq 2 \text{ or } x > 5\}.$$

Describe each of the following sets.

(a) $\mathcal{A}' \cap \mathcal{B}'$.
(b) $(\mathcal{A}' \cup \mathcal{C}') \cap \mathcal{D}'$.
(c) $(\mathcal{A}' \cup \mathcal{C}') \cap (\mathcal{A}' \cup \mathcal{D}')$.
(d) $(\mathcal{A} \cup \mathcal{C}') \cap (\mathcal{B} \cup \mathcal{D}')$.

6. If the *distance* between two closed intervals, $\mathcal{I}_1$ and $\mathcal{I}_2$, is defined to be the least distance between P_1 and P_2, where $P_1 \in \mathcal{I}_1$ and $P_2 \in \mathcal{I}_2$, find the distance between the pairs of intervals given in each of the following.

(a) $\mathcal{I}_1 .=. \{(x): 0 \leq x \leq 3\}$, $\mathcal{I}_2 .=. \{(x): 5 \leq x \leq 7\}$.
(b) $\mathcal{I}_1 .=. \{(x): -5 \leq x \leq -3\}$, $\mathcal{I}_2 .=. \{(x): 2 \leq x \leq 5\}$.
(c) $\mathcal{I}_1 .=. \{(x): -3 \leq x \leq 1\}$, $\mathcal{I}_2 .=. \{(x): 1 \leq x \leq 2\}$.
(d) $\mathcal{I}_1 .=. \{(x): -4 \leq x \leq -2\}$, $\mathcal{I}_2 .=. \{(x): -3 \leq x \leq 4\}$.

7. The definition in Number 6 does not apply to intervals that are not closed. (Why?) Can you modify the definition to handle such intervals? For instance, state what you think should be the "distance" between $\mathcal{I}_1$ and $\mathcal{I}_2$ if

$$\mathcal{I}_1 .=. \{(x): 1 < x < 3\}, \quad \mathcal{I}_2 .=. \{(x): 5 < x < 10\}.$$

4.2 TWO-DIMENSIONAL EUCLIDEAN SPACE

We may construct a reference system for two-dimensional euclidean geometry by choosing two perpendicular lines in a plane and using the same number scale on each line with the zero points coincident. The common zero point of the two lines is called the **origin**, O. One of the lines is designated the x-axis and the other the y-axis. Usually the x-axis is taken as the horizontal axis, with the positive direction to the right, and the y-axis as the vertical axis, with the positive direction upward (see Figure 4.2a).

In order to locate a point P of the plane, we construct a line L_1 through P perpendicular to the x-axis and a line L_2 through P perpendicular to the y-axis, as shown in Figure 4.2a. If the point where L_1 meets the x-axis is P_1, and the

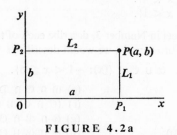

FIGURE 4.2a

point where L_2 meets the y-axis is P_2, then the directed distance a from the origin to P_1 is called the **x-coordinate** or the **abscissa** of the point P, and the directed distance b from the origin to P_2 is called the **y-coordinate** or the **ordinate** of the point P. Thus, a point in the plane is located relative to O by means of the numbers, a and b. We regard the point as being represented by the ordered pair of numbers (a, b), the x-coordinate being given first. It is a basic assumption that there is a one-to-one correspondence between the ordered pairs of real numbers (x, y) and the points of the plane.

The points $(3, 4)$, $(-2, 6)$, $(-7, -3)$, and $(5, -2)$ are plotted as indicated in Figure 4.2b. Notice that the x- and y-axes divide the plane into four parts.

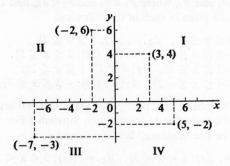

FIGURE 4.2b

These parts are called **quadrants,** and are numbered counterclockwise, the quadrant where both of the coordinates are positive being quadrant I (see Figure 4.2b).

The distance between the points (x_1, a) and (x_2, a) is $\sqrt{(x_2 - x_1)^2}$, as can be shown by drawing the rectangle with the line from (x_1, a) to (x_2, a) as one side and with the opposite side on the x-axis (see Figure 4.2c). Similarly, the distance between the points (b, y_1) and (b, y_2) is $\sqrt{(y_2 - y_1)^2}$.

Using the preceding results, it is easy to obtain a formula for the distance

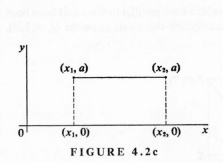

FIGURE 4.2c

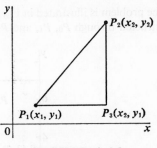

FIGURE 4.2d

P_1P_2 between any two points P_1 and P_2 in the plane. We first apply the Theorem of Pythagoras to the right triangle $P_1P_2P_3$ in Figure 4.2d to obtain

$$(P_1P_2)^2 = (P_2P_3)^2 + (P_1P_3)^2.$$

If the distances P_1P_3 and P_2P_3 are now replaced by their values in terms of the coordinates, the result is

$$(P_1P_2)^2 = (x_2 - x_1)^2 + (y_2 - y_1)^2.$$

Thus, by taking the positive square root on both sides of this equation, we have the proof of

Theorem 4.2a. The distance d between the point P_1 with coordinates (x_1, y_1) and the point P_2 with coordinates (x_2, y_2) is given by

$$d(P_1, P_2) = \sqrt{(x_2 - x_1)^2 + (y_2 - y_1)^2}.$$

The following example illustrates how some geometric questions can be answered by the use of the concept of distance in conjunction with the representation of points in a plane by means of ordered number pairs.

Example 4.2a. Do the points $A(1, 3)$, $B(5, 6)$, $C(8, 2)$ determine an equilateral triangle?

To answer the question we need only to find the distance between each pair of points Thus,

$$d(A, B) = [(5 - 1)^2 + (6 - 3)^2]^{1/2} = 5,$$
$$d(B, C) = [(8 - 5)^2 + (2 - 6)^2]^{1/2} = 5,$$
$$d(C, A) = [(8 - 1)^2 + (2 - 3)^2]^{1/2} = \sqrt{50} = 5\sqrt{2}.$$

Since $d(C, A) \neq d(B, C)$ the triangle is not equilateral. However, it is an isosceles right triangle. (Why?)

Another illustration of the use of coordinates in geometry is given next.

Example 4.2b. Determine the point $P_0(x_0, y_0)$ on the line segment from $P_1(2, 3)$ to $P_2(5, 7)$ that is two-thirds of the distance from P_1 to P_2.

The problem is illustrated in Figure 4.2e, where lines parallel to the y-axis have been constructed through P_0, P_1, and P_2, and intersecting the x-axis at points Q, $A(2, 0)$,

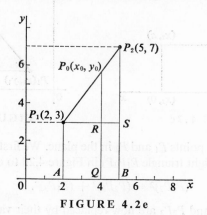

FIGURE 4.2e

and $B(5, 0)$, respectively. Similarly, a line parallel to the x-axis has been constructed through P_1. The triangles P_1P_0R and P_1P_2S are similar, so that corresponding sides are proportional. Thus

$$\frac{P_1P_0}{P_1P_2} = \frac{P_1R}{P_1S} = \frac{AQ}{AB}.$$

In terms of coordinates of the points, these ratios are

$$\frac{x_0 - 2}{5 - 2} = \frac{4 - 2}{5 - 2} = \frac{2}{3}.$$

Hence

$$x_0 = 2 + \left(\frac{2}{3}\right)(3) = 4.$$

In the same way,

$$\frac{P_1P_0}{P_1P_2} = \frac{P_0R}{P_2S} \quad \text{or} \quad \frac{2}{3} = \frac{y_0 - 3}{7 - 3}.$$

This gives

$$y_0 = 5\tfrac{2}{3},$$

so that P_0 is the point $(4, 17/3)$.

Example 4.2b illustrates a method that can be used to locate a point on a line segment which divides that line segment in a specified manner. Perhaps the most important special instance of such a problem is that of locating the mid-point of a given line segment. If the line segment joins $P_1(x_1, y_1)$ to $P_2(x_2, y_2)$, then the reader may easily show that the coordinates of the midpoint, say $P_0(x_0, y_0)$, are given by

$$x_0 = x_1 + \tfrac{1}{2}(x_2 - x_1) = \tfrac{1}{2}(x_1 + x_2),$$
$$y_0 = y_1 + \tfrac{1}{2}(y_2 - y_1) = \tfrac{1}{2}(y_1 + y_2).$$

Notice that *the coordinates of the midpoint are the simple arithmetic averages of the corresponding coordinates of the end points of the segment.*

The use of coordinates and algebra frequently makes it possible to write down quite simple proofs for certain theorems in geometry. The next problem is an illustration of this procedure.

Example 4.2c. Show that the line segment joining the midpoints of the nonparallel sides of a trapezoid is equal in length to one-half the sum of the parallel sides.

Place the axes so that one end of the base of the trapezoid is at the origin and the *x*-axis runs along this base as in Figure 4.2f. Then the other end of the base will have

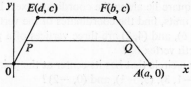

FIGURE 4.2f

coordinates $(a, 0)$ and the remaining vertices will be labeled (b, c) and (d, c). The *y*-coordinates of the last two points are the same, since the bases of the trapezoid are parallel.

If P and Q are the midpoints of the nonparallel sides as shown in the figure, then the coordinates of P are $(\frac{1}{2}d, \frac{1}{2}c)$ and those of Q are $[\frac{1}{2}(a + b), \frac{1}{2}c]$. Consequently,

$$PQ = \frac{a + b}{2} - \frac{d}{2} = \frac{a + b - d}{2}.$$

The sum of the lengths of the two bases is

$$OA + EF = a + (b - d) = a + b - d,$$

so that

$$PQ = \tfrac{1}{2}(OA + EF),$$

as was to be shown.

The reader should notice the convenient placement of the coordinate axes in the preceding problem. Such a wise choice frequently is the key to a simple proof. The study of geometry using coordinates and algebra is called **coordinate geometry** or **analytic geometry**. The preceding proof is an example of a proof by the methods of analytic geometry.

Exercises 4.2

1. In each of (a) and (b), use the distance formula to determine if the given three points lie in a straight line.
   (a) $(-3, -2)$, $(6, 1)$, $(0, -1)$.
   (b) $(-2, 3)$, $(7, -1)$, $(1, 2)$.

2. In each of (a) and (b), use the distance formula to determine if the quadrilateral whose vertices are at the given points is a parallelogram.
   (a) $(0, 0)$, $(5, 1)$, $(8, -4)$, $(3, -5)$.
   (b) $(-1, 8)$, $(1, 2)$, $(-3, -2)$, $(-5, 4)$.

3. Work Number 2 by another method.
4. Determine which of the triangles whose vertices are at the given points is an equilateral triangle or an isosceles triangle.

    (a) $(0, 5)$, $(-3, 4)$, $(-1, 2)$.
    (b) $(-1, 4)$, $(-4, -1)$, $(-1, -2)$.
    (c) $(-3, 2)$, $(1, -1)$, $(-2, -5)$.

5. Is the triangle with vertices at $(-2, 1)$, $(-1, -1)$, and $(-5, -3)$ a right triangle? Explain.
6. The diagonals of a square lie along the coordinate axes. If the length of the side of the square is four units, find the coordinates of the vertices.
7. The points $(1, 3)$, $(1, 6)$, and $(4, 2)$ are three vertices of a parallelogram. At what points could the fourth vertex be?
8. Is it possible to draw a circle that has its center at the point $(2, 1)$ and that passes through the points $(-1, 3)$, $(5, -1)$, and $(0, -2)$?
9. Find the point equidistant from the points $(-3, 1)$, $(2, -4)$, and $(1, 1)$.
10. Find the center and radius of the circle passing through the points $(0, 6)$, $(7, 5)$, and $(6, -2)$.
11. Let $P_0(x_0, y_0)$ be a point on the line through the points $P_1(-3, 4)$ and $P_2(5, -7)$. If $P_1P_0/P_1P_2 = k$, find the coordinates of P_0 for each of the following values of k.

    (a) $k = \frac{2}{5}$.
    (b) $k = \frac{3}{4}$.
    (c) $k = \frac{4}{3}$. (Remember that P_1P_0 and P_1P_2 are directed distances.)
    (d) $k = -\frac{1}{2}$.
    (e) $k = -\frac{3}{2}$.

12. A triangle has one vertex at the origin and another at the point $(2, 3)$. If the midpoint of the side opposite the origin is at $(0, 5)$, what are the coordinates of the third vertex?
13. Find the vertices of a triangle having the midpoints of its sides at $(3, 2)$, $(5, -1)$, $(6, 4)$.

Use the methods of analytic geometry to prove the following theorems.

14. The diagonals of a rectangle are equal.
15. If the diagonals of a parallelogram are equal, the figure is a rectangle.
16. The sum of the squares of the medians of a triangle is equal to three-fourths the sum of the squares of the sides.
17. If two medians of a triangle are equal, the triangle is isosceles.
18. If the midpoints of the opposite sides of a quadrilateral are joined by line segments, these segments bisect each other.

4.3 DIRECTION NUMBERS

Consider the line determined by the points $(2, 1)$ and $(5, 5)$ in Figure 4.3a. How can we determine other points on this line? Since the straight line is characterized by the fact that its "direction" is fixed, we should be able to use this property in answering the question. If we let (x, y) be a point on the line and construct lines parallel to the coordinate axes, as shown in Figure 4.3a, it is

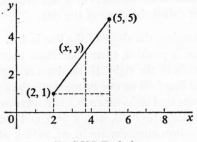

FIGURE 4.3a

apparent that the two triangles formed are similar. Hence, the corresponding sides are proportional and we may write

$$\frac{y-1}{4} = \frac{x-2}{3}.$$

If we denote this common ratio by k, then we have

$$x - 2 = 3k \quad \text{and} \quad y - 1 = 4k.$$

The numbers 3 and 4 in the right members of these equations characterize the line to the extent that its direction is determined by these numbers. For example, if $k = 1$, then there is a 4-unit increase in the y direction for a 3-unit increase in the x-direction in reaching the point $(5, 5)$ from the point $(2, 1)$. Furthermore, starting at any point on the line, a 4-unit increase in y and a 3-unit increase in x will yield a second point on the line. Similarly, if $k = \frac{1}{2}$, then a second point on the line is reached by moving $\frac{3}{2}$ units to the right and 2 units up from any starting point on the line. In fact, k may have any nonzero value and statements similar to the preceding ones may be made. These facts constitute the basis for

Definition 4.3a. Any ordered pair of numbers, p and q, that completely characterize the direction of a straight line are called **direction numbers** of the line. A number-pair used in this fashion is denoted by $[p, q]$.

For the line given by the two equations

$$x - 2 = 3k, \quad y - 1 = 4k,$$

a set of direction numbers is $[3, 4]$, $[3/2, 2]$, $[-6, -8]$, or any other pair obtained by the choice of some nonzero value of k. It follows that if (x_1, y_1) and (x_2, y_2) are two distinct points on a line, then a set of direction numbers of the line is

$$[x_2 - x_1, y_2 - y_1].$$

The direction numbers of a nonvertical line determine another number described in the next definition and often used to characterize the direction of a line.

Definition 4.3b. If the direction numbers of a line are $[p, q]$, where $p \neq 0$, then the ratio $m = q/p$ is called the **slope** of the line.

In the preceding illustration, the slope of the line is $4/3$.

If the slope of a line is positive, then y increases as x increases, so that the line rises as one proceeds to the right. If the slope is negative, then y decreases as x increases, and the line falls as one proceeds to the right. Thus, if the slope is $-4/3$, then y decreases by 4 units for each 3 unit increase in x. For a horizontal line, the direction numbers are $[k, 0]$, with $k \neq 0$, and the slope is $0/k = 0$. For a vertical line, the direction numbers are $[0, k]$, with $k \neq 0$, but the slope does *not* exist, since the ratio $k/0$ is not defined.

As will be seen in the following theorems, direction numbers are helpful in describing geometric relationships between two or more lines.

Theorem 4.3a. Two lines are parallel $\Leftrightarrow$ the direction numbers of the lines are proportional.

PROOF: In Figure 4.3b, suppose that L_1 and L_2 are two parallel lines, with P_1

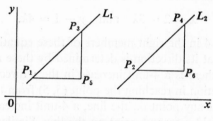

FIGURE 4.3b

and P_3 two points on L_1 and P_2 and P_4 two points on L_2. Then the right triangles $P_1P_5P_3$ and $P_2P_6P_4$, which have their legs parallel to the respective axes, are similar, and their corresponding sides are proportional. The converse of this result also follows from the same considerations. Hence, the theorem is proved.

Example 4.3a. Is the line through the points $P_1(-1, 3)$ and $P_2(2, 9)$ parallel to the line through the points $P_3(1, 2)$ and $P_4(5, 10)$?

We find that a set of direction numbers for the first line is $[3, 6]$ and a set of direction numbers for the second line is $[4, 8]$. Since $\frac{3}{4} = \frac{6}{8}$, the direction numbers are proportional and so the lines are parallel.

Notice in the preceding example that the slope of P_1P_2 is $6/3 = 2$ and that the slope of P_3P_4 is $8/4 = 2$. This suggests the following theorem, whose proof is left to the reader.

Theorem 4.3b. Two nonvertical lines are parallel if, and only if, their slopes are equal.

The next theorem gives an important criterion for determining by means of direction numbers whether or not two lines are perpendicular.

Theorem 4.3c. A line L_1 with direction numbers $[m, n]$ is perpendicular to a line L_2 with direction numbers $[p, q] \Leftrightarrow mp + nq = 0$.

PROOF: Figure 4.3c will aid in visualizing the basis for this proof. Let the

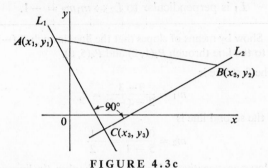

FIGURE 4.3c

point of intersection of L_1 and L_2 be denoted by $C(x_3, y_3)$ and let $A(x_1, y_1)$ and $B(x_2, y_2)$, respectively, be second points on L_1 and L_2. Then, since $[m, n]$ and $[p, q]$ are direction numbers of the respective lines,

$$x_3 - x_1 = k_1m, \quad y_3 - y_1 = k_1n, \quad k_1 \neq 0,$$

and

$$x_3 - x_2 = k_2p, \quad y_3 - y_2 = k_2q, \quad k_2 \neq 0.$$

Then, L_1 is perpendicular to $L_2 \Leftrightarrow$ triangle ABC is a right triangle with AB as its hypotenuse

$$\Leftrightarrow (AB)^2 = (AC)^2 + (BC)^2$$
$$\Leftrightarrow (x_2 - x_1)^2 + (y_2 - y_1)^2 = (x_3 - x_1)^2 + (y_3 - y_1)^2 + (x_3 - x_2)^2 + (y_3 - y_2)^2$$
$$\Leftrightarrow x_3^2 - x_1x_3 - x_2x_3 + x_1x_2 + y_3^2 - y_1y_3 - y_2y_3 + y_1y_2 = 0$$
$$\Leftrightarrow (x_3 - x_1)(x_3 - x_2) + (y_3 - y_1)(y_3 - y_2) = 0$$
$$\Leftrightarrow k_1k_2mp + k_1k_2nq = 0$$
$$\Leftrightarrow mp + nq = 0.$$

Example 4.3b. Find direction numbers of a line perpendicular to the line through the two points $P_1(1, -2)$ and $P_2(-3, 4)$.

A set of direction numbers of the line P_1P_2 may be taken to be

$$[-3 - 1, 4 - (-2)] = [-4, 6].$$

It then follows, from Theorem 4.3c, if $[m, n]$ is a set of direction numbers of a line perpendicular to P_1P_2, that

$$-4m + 6n = 0.$$

Any values of m and n, not both zero, that satisfy this equation may be chosen as the desired direction numbers. Thus a suitable set is $[6, 4]$ or any other numbers proportional to these, such as $[3, 2]$.

The next theorem is a direct consequence of Theorem 4.3c and its proof is left to the reader.

Theorem 4.3d. Let m_1 and m_2 be the slopes of two lines L_1 and L_2, respectively. Then

$$L_1 \text{ is perpendicular to } L_2 \Leftrightarrow m_1 m_2 = -1.$$

Example 4.3c. Show by means of slopes that the line through $P_1(-1, 3)$ and $P_2(2, 9)$ is perpendicular to the line through $P_3(1, 2)$ and $P_4(5, 0)$.

The slope of the first line is

$$m_1 = \frac{9 - 3}{2 - (-1)} = 2,$$

and the slope of the second line is

$$m_2 = \frac{0 - 2}{5 - 1} = -\frac{1}{2}.$$

Since these two slopes are negative reciprocals of each other, the lines are perpendicular, as was to be shown.

Exercises 4.3

1. Plot the points $A(-3, -4)$, $B(5, -2)$, $C(4, 2)$, and $D(0, 1)$, and then answer the following questions about the quadrilateral $ABCD$.

   (a) Is the figure a trapezoid, a parallelogram, or neither?
   (b) Does the figure include any right angles?

2. Show that the midpoints of the sides of the quadrilateral in Number 1 are the vertices of a parallelogram.

3. Describe at least two ways in which you can determine whether or not three points lie in a straight line.

4. Show by two different methods that the points $(1, -1)$, $(-7, 1)$, and $(5, -2)$ lie in a straight line.

5. Prove in two ways that the points $(3, 0)$, $(4, 5)$, and $(6, 2)$ are vertices of a right triangle.

6. If the three points in Number 5 are three of the vertices of a rectangle, what are the coordinates of the fourth vertex?

7. If a wedge DEF is placed on an inclined plane, as shown in Figure 4.3d, find direction numbers of faces DE and DF.

8. Find the direction numbers of the shortest line segment that can be drawn from the point $(-4, 2)$ to the line through the points $(0, 2)$ and $(1, -1)$.

9. Find the direction numbers of the altitudes and medians of the triangle with vertices at $(-2, 3)$, $(-1, -2)$, $(-3, -4)$.

10. If a line through the points $(1, 2)$ and $(-1, -1)$ is perpendicular to a line through $(-4, 1)$ and $(a, -3)$, find a.

11. If a line through the points $(1, 2)$ and $(-1, -1)$ is parallel to a line through $(-4, 1)$ and $(a, -3)$, find a.
12. Prove Theorem 4.3b.
13. Which of the points $(-3, 0)$, $(6, 3)$, $(1, 1)$ lie on the line through the points $(-6, -1)$ and $(3, 2)$?

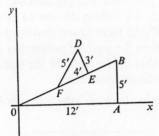

FIGURE 4.3d

Use the methods of analytic geometry to prove the following theorems.

14. The diagonals of a square are mutually perpendicular.
15. If the midpoints of the successive sides of a rectangle are joined by line segments, the resulting figure is a rhombus.
16. If the midpoints of the successive sides of a quadrilateral are joined by line segments, the resulting figure is a parallelogram.
17. In a parallelogram the sum of the squares of the diagonals is equal to the sum of the squares of the sides.

4.4 THREE-DIMENSIONAL EUCLIDEAN SPACE

The preceding ideas pertaining to a two-dimensional space can be quite easily extended to a three-dimensional space. Points in a euclidean three-space can be described in much the same way as in a euclidean two-space. In order to accomplish this, three mutually perpendicular planes are first chosen as reference planes. The lines of intersection of these planes are called the **coordinate axes** and are named the x-, y-, and z-axes. The three planes are called **coordinate planes** and are designated as the xy-, yz-, and xz-planes.

If the point of intersection of the planes is taken as the *origin*, and if a common

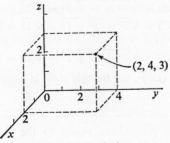

FIGURE 4.4a

number scale is associated with each axis, then points in space are located relative to the origin by an ordered number-triple (x, y, z). The numbers in the triple are called the coordinates of the point located x units from the yz-plane, y units from the xz-plane, and z units from the xy-plane. Coordinates are customarily given in the x, y, z order. See Figure 4.4a.

The three coordinate axes are usually chosen so as to form a right-handed system. In such a system, if one faces in the positive y-direction with his head in the positive z-direction, then the positive x-direction is to his right.

The next theorem shows that the formula for the distance between two points extends easily to the three-dimensional case.

Theorem 4.4a. The distance between the two points $P_1(x_1, y_1, z_1)$ and $P_2(x_2, y_2, z_2)$ is given by

$$d(P_1, P_2) = \sqrt{(x_2 - x_1)^2 + (y_2 - y_1)^2 + (z_2 - z_1)^2}.$$

PROOF: Geometrically, this expression is the result of calculating the length of a diagonal of a "box" by means of the Pythagorean Theorem, as indicated

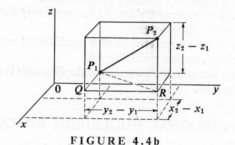

FIGURE 4.4b

in Figure 4.4b. By considering the right triangles P_1QR and P_1RP_2, the reader may verify that the length of the diagonal is given by the expression in the theorem.

Example 4.4a. Show that the triangle with vertices at the points $A(1, 2, 1)$, $B(5, 3, 4)$, and $C(8, -3, 2)$ is a right triangle and find its area.

The lengths of the sides are

$$d(A, B) = \sqrt{4^2 + 1^2 + 3^2} = \sqrt{26},$$
$$d(A, C) = \sqrt{7^2 + 5^2 + 1^2} = \sqrt{75} = 5\sqrt{3},$$

and

$$d(B, C) = \sqrt{3^2 + 6^2 + 2^2} = \sqrt{49} = 7.$$

Since $(AC)^2 = (AB)^2 + (BC)^2$, the triangle ABC is a right triangle, and its area is

$$\tfrac{1}{2}(\text{base})(\text{altitude}) = \tfrac{7}{2}\sqrt{26}.$$

Another concept that generalizes easily to the three-dimensional case is that of direction numbers of a line.

Definition 4.4a. An ordered set of three numbers, denoted by $[m, n, p]$, which characterizes the direction of a line in three-dimensional space, is called a set of **direction numbers** of the line.

These numbers specify the number of units change in the y- and z-directions for a given number of units change in the x-direction. It is clear that a set of direction numbers such as $[2, 3, 6]$ specify the same direction as the set $[2k, 3k, 6k]$, where k is any real number other than zero.

Example 4.4b. Obtain direction numbers for the line through the points $P_1(-2, 3, 4)$ and $P_2(3, -1, 1)$ and show how to obtain other points on this line (see Figure 4.4c).

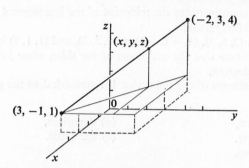

FIGURE 4.4c

In order to get to the second point from the first, we must move five units in the positive x-direction, four units in the negative y-direction, and three units in the negative z-direction. Since the direction of the line is fixed, the number-triple $[5, -4, -3]$ characterizes this particular direction. This same direction is given by any other set of numbers proportional to these, such as $[5k, -4k, -3k]$, with $k \neq 0$. These numbers are therefore direction numbers of the line.

If (x, y, z) is another point on the line through P_1 and P_2, then we have the following equal ratios:

$$\frac{x - 3}{5} = \frac{y + 1}{-4} = \frac{z - 1}{-3} = k.$$

Hence, other points on the line can be found by giving k different values. For instance, $k = 1$ yields the point $(8, -5, -2)$; $k = -2$ yields $(-7, 7, 7)$; and so on.

Exercises 4.4

1. Find the distance between the following pairs of points.

   (a) $(3, 5, 2)$, $(-2, 3, 1)$.
   (b) $(-2, -1, 4)$, $(3, -1, 0)$.
   (c) $(3, -4, -2)$, $(-2, 3, -5)$.

2. Find direction numbers of the lines determined by the pairs of points in Number 1.
3. Plot the points $P(-2, 3, -4)$, $Q(2, 0, -3)$, $R(3, 4, 5)$. Determine whether or not PQR is a right triangle.

4. Find a point one-third of the distance from the point (3, 6, 4) to the point (−1, 3, 2). *Hint*: Use a direct extension of the corresponding method in two-dimensional space.

5. Find a point three-fifths of the distance from the point (−1, −2, 4) to the point (−3, 1, 5).

6. Is the straight line joining the points (−2, −3, 4) and (−1, 2, −1) parallel to the straight line joining the points (3, −7, −1) and (4, −2, −6)?

7. Prove that the following three points are on a straight line by using the distance formula and also by using direction numbers: (−1, 3, −4), (5, 0, 5), and (1, 2, −1).

8. What are the direction numbers of each of the coordinate axes? What are the direction numbers of a line through the point (2, −3, 1) parallel to the *x*-axis? to the *y*-axis? to the *z*-axis?

9. What are the coordinates of the midpoint of the line segment joining the points (x_1, y_1, z_1) and (x_2, y_2, z_2)?

10. Let the points (2, 3, 5), (2, −1, −1), (−2, 5, 3), and (1, 1, 2) be the vertices of a quadrilateral. Show that the midpoints of the sides, when joined in succession, form a parallelogram.

11. Find the coordinates of the point that is symmetrical to the point (2, 5, 3) with respect to

(a) the *yz*-plane,
(b) the *xz*-plane,
(c) the *xy*-plane,
(d) the origin,
(e) the *z*-axis.

12. What are the coordinates of the point on the *z*-axis that is equidistant from (2, 1, 3) and (−4, 5, −2)?

13. How many lines are there in the *yz*-plane that have each of their points equidistant from the *y*-axis and *z*-axis? Find direction numbers of each line.

14. Describe and sketch the set of points in three-dimensional space satisfying the following conditions.

(a) $y = 0$.
(b) $y = 0$ and $x = 0$.
(c) $z = 3$.
(d) $y = 2$ and $z = 3$.
(e) $y = z$.

4.5 VECTORS

The study of physical problems is a rich source of many mathematical concepts, which are particularly valuable because they in turn lead to simple methods of describing and analyzing other physical situations. In this section, we shall introduce one such concept from mathematical physics.

In physics, we are often concerned with an entity called a **force**. It has been found, as a result of many experiments, that a force is characterized by a magnitude, a direction, and a rule of combination with other forces. The first two characteristics suggest that a force can be represented geometrically by a directed line segment such as *OP* in Figure 4.5a. The length of the line segment is proportional to the magnitude of the force and the direction of the segment is the direction in which the force acts. Directed line segments used for such a representation may be called **arrows** and are frequently denoted by symbols such as **a, b, r,** and so on. (In this book, boldface type will be used to denote these directed quantities. In writing by hand, it is customary to use a half-

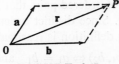

FIGURE 4.5a

arrow over a letter or a wavy line under the letter, as $\overrightarrow{a}$ or $\underset{\sim}{a}$ for the same purpose.)

It is known from experiment that two forces, **a** and **b**, acting at a common point, are equivalent to a single **resultant** force, **r**. Furthermore, this single force is correctly represented by the diagonal of the parallelogram having the arrows representing **a** and **b** as its sides (see Figure 4.5a). The force **r** is called the sum of the forces **a** and **b**, and we write

$$\mathbf{r} = \mathbf{a} + \mathbf{b}.$$

Notice that this equation uses the plus sign in a different sense from that of ordinary algebraic addition. The plus sign here means that the quantities represented by **a** and **b** are combined by the **parallelogram law of composition.**

Definition 4.5a. Quantities that can be represented by arrows and that combine according to the parallelogram law are called **vectors.**

Examples of such quantities are forces, displacements, and velocities. (There are also other quantities that can be represented by arrows, but that do not combine according to the parallelogram law.)

Although we now have a geometrical representation for vectors, we do not yet have a convenient analytical representation for them. However, that it is possible to represent vector quantities by sets of numbers is already suggested by our earlier considerations in locating points in a two- or three-dimensional space by means of ordered pairs or ordered triples of numbers. To illustrate, recall that the symbol (4, 3) represents a certain point P, with respect to an origin O (see Figure 4.5b). This pair of numbers determines, with reference to O,

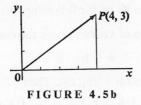

FIGURE 4.5b

a direction and a magnitude, the direction being given by the direction numbers $[4k, 3k]$ and the magnitude by the length of the line segment from O to P.

Hence, it appears reasonable to interpret an ordered pair of numbers (a_1, a_2), where a_1 and a_2 are not both zero, as an arrow whose *tip* is at the point (a_1, a_2) and whose *tail* is at the origin.

Finally, (a_1, a_2) may be regarded as a vector provided a condition for equality and a definition for addition of ordered pairs that is equivalent to the parallelogram rule can be prescribed. Since distinct ordered pairs are associated with distinct points, the following definition is reasonable.

Definition 4.5b. $(a_1, a_2) = (b_1, b_2) \Leftrightarrow a_1 = b_1$ and $a_2 = b_2$.

The geometrical illustration in Figure 4.5c suggests the definition for addition.

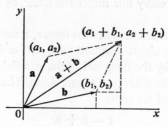

FIGURE 4.5c

Definition 4.5c. $(a_1, a_2) + (b_1, b_2) .=. (a_1 + b_1, a_2 + b_2)$.

Thus, if
$$\mathbf{a} = (2, 4), \quad \mathbf{b} = (-3, 2),$$
then
$$\mathbf{a} + \mathbf{b} = (2, 4) + (-3, 2)$$
$$= (2 - 3, 4 + 2) = (-1, 6).$$

It follows at once that if $\mathbf{a} = (a_1, a_2)$ is a vector, then the magnitude of $\mathbf{a}$, denoted by $|\mathbf{a}|$, is given by the number

$$[a_1^2 + a_2^2]^{1/2}.$$

The vector $\mathbf{0} .=. (0, 0)$ is called the **zero vector**. This vector has magnitude zero but does not have direction.

The representation of vectors by pairs of real numbers implies that some properties of vectors can be deduced from properties of real numbers. This idea is illustrated in the proofs of the following three theorems.

Theorem 4.5a. The addition of vectors obeys the commutative law:

$$\mathbf{a} + \mathbf{b} = \mathbf{b} + \mathbf{a}.$$

PROOF: Let $\mathbf{a} = (a_1, a_2)$ and $\mathbf{b} = (b_1, b_2)$. Then

$$\mathbf{a} + \mathbf{b} = (a_1 + b_1, a_2 + b_2),$$
and
$$\mathbf{b} + \mathbf{a} = (b_1 + a_1, b_2 + a_2).$$

By the commutative law of addition for real numbers, we have

$$a_1 + b_1 = b_1 + a_1, \quad a_2 + b_2 = b_2 + a_2,$$

so that

$$\mathbf{a} + \mathbf{b} = \mathbf{b} + \mathbf{a},$$

as was to be shown.

Theorem 4.5b. Vector addition is associative:

$$(\mathbf{a} + \mathbf{b}) + \mathbf{c} = \mathbf{a} + (\mathbf{b} + \mathbf{c}).$$

PROOF: The proof is a simple consequence of the definition of addition for vectors and the associative law for real numbers, and is left for the reader.

Let $\mathbf{a} = (a_1, a_2)$. Then by the definition of addition we may write $2(a_1, a_2) = (a_1, a_2) + (a_1, a_2) = (2a_1, 2a_2)$. If this process is repeated $k - 1$ times, we arrive at a relation $k(a_1, a_2) = (ka_1, ka_2)$, where k is an integer. This suggests the more general relationship given by

Definition 4.5d. If k is a real number, then

$$k(a_1, a_2) .=. (a_1, a_2)k .=. (ka_1, ka_2).$$

Note: The first part of this definition is equivalent to the statement

$$k\mathbf{a} = \mathbf{a}k.$$

The real number k is often called a **scalar** and the operation defined in Definition 4.5d is called **scalar multiplication.**

Theorem 4.5c. $\qquad k(\mathbf{a} + \mathbf{b}) = k\mathbf{a} + k\mathbf{b}, \qquad k \in \mathcal{R}.$

PROOF: This result follows directly from Definition 4.5d and Definition 4.5c. The details are left for the reader.

It is not difficult to see that the multiplication of a vector by a positive real number does not alter the direction of the vector, but it may change the magnitude or the length of the vector. Multiplication of a vector by a negative number reverses the direction of the vector and may also change the magnitude. Multiplication of a vector by zero always yields the zero vector.

Vector subtraction may be defined by means of the following two definitions.

Definition 4.5e. $\qquad\qquad -\mathbf{a} .=. (-1)\mathbf{a}.$

Definition 4.5f. $\qquad\qquad \mathbf{a} - \mathbf{b} .=. \mathbf{a} + (-\mathbf{b}).$

The vector sum and difference of $\mathbf{a}$ and $\mathbf{b}$ are shown in Figure 4.5d.

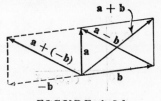

FIGURE 4.5d

Figure 4.5d illustrates an important fact about vectors. Since $\mathbf{a} - \mathbf{b}$ is a vector $\mathbf{x}$ such that $\mathbf{a} = \mathbf{b} + \mathbf{x}$, it may be represented in the diagram as the vector that extends from the tip of $\mathbf{b}$ to the tip of $\mathbf{a}$. But $\mathbf{x}$ is also the vector $\mathbf{a} + (-\mathbf{b})$ which is shown in the diagram. We know that $\mathbf{a} - \mathbf{b}$ and $\mathbf{a} + (-\mathbf{b})$ are the same vector $\mathbf{x}$, yet they appear as two different line segments in the figure. Evidently, the location of the arrow in the diagram is unimportant; only the magnitude and direction are of fundamental importance insofar as a vector is concerned. (*Note:* There are certain applications in which the location of the arrow *is* important and attention will be called to this fact when it is necessary.)

For example, the vector $\mathbf{a} = (3, 1)$ can be written as the sum or difference of two other vectors in infinitely many ways. Thus, $\mathbf{a} = (7, 5) - (4, 4)$ or $\mathbf{a} = (-2, 5) - (-5, 4)$, and $\mathbf{a}$ may be drawn as shown in Figure 4.5e. In other

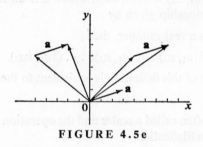

FIGURE 4.5e

words, we may regard a given vector to be represented by an arrow of the correct length and direction but located anywhere in the plane, simply by writing the vector as the difference of two appropriate vectors.

In view of Definition 4.5d and the rule for addition of vectors, we may write an arbitrary vector $\mathbf{a}$ in a special form as follows:

$$\mathbf{a} = (a_1, a_2) = (a_1, 0) + (0, a_2)$$
$$= a_1(1, 0) + a_2(0, 1).$$

In other words, *every* vector in two-dimensional space may be expressed as a sum of just the two vectors $(1, 0)$ and $(0, 1)$, each multiplied by a properly chosen scalar. Since each of the two vectors $(1, 0)$ and $(0, 1)$ has a magnitude of one unit, it is called a **unit vector**. The following notation is customarily employed:

$$\mathbf{i} .=. (1, 0), \quad \mathbf{j} .=. (0, 1),$$

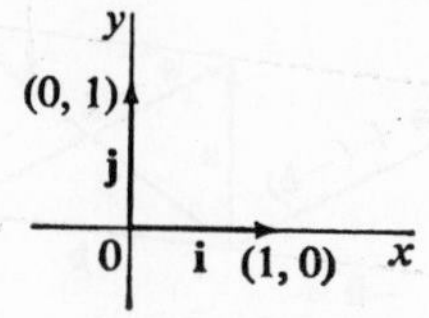

FIGURE 4.5f

and the vectors **i** and **j** may be represented as in Figure 4.5f. In terms of these two vectors, we may now write any vector $\mathbf{a} = (a_1, a_2)$ as

$$\mathbf{a} = a_1\mathbf{i} + a_2\mathbf{j}.$$

The numbers a_1 and a_2 are called the *components of* **a** *with respect to the* **i** *and* **j** *vectors*. The **i** and **j** vectors are called a **base set** or simply a **basis**, because every other vector may be written in terms of these two vectors in the manner just indicated. These ideas will be of considerable value later in obtaining important results in a simple way.

Exercises 4.5

1. If $\mathbf{a} .=. (2, 4)$, $\mathbf{b} .=. (4, -3)$, $\mathbf{c} .=. (-3, 2)$, determine

   (a) $\mathbf{a} + \mathbf{b}$,
   (b) $\mathbf{b} - \mathbf{a}$,
   (c) $|\mathbf{c}|$,
   (d) $|\mathbf{c} - \mathbf{b}|$,
   (e) $2\mathbf{a} + 3\mathbf{b}$,
   (f) $|3\mathbf{a} - \mathbf{b}|$.

2. Suppose a vector **v** has its tail at the point $\mathbf{a} .=. (-2, -3)$ and its tip at $\mathbf{b} .=. (3, 9)$. Express **v** in terms of **a** and **b**. Is this the same as the vector $\mathbf{p} = (5, 12)$? Explain.

3. Suppose the sides of a closed polygon represent vectors arranged tip to tail. What is the sum of these vectors?

4. The resultant of $\mathbf{a} .=. (3, 2)$ and **b** is $\mathbf{r} .=. (8, 8)$. What is the magnitude of **b**?

5. If $\mathbf{a} .=. 2\mathbf{i} + 3\mathbf{j}$ and $\mathbf{b} .=. 4\mathbf{i} - \mathbf{j}$, determine

   (a) $\mathbf{a} + \mathbf{b}$,
   (b) $\mathbf{a} - \mathbf{b}$,
   (c) $2\mathbf{a} - 3\mathbf{b}$,
   (d) $|\mathbf{a}| \cdot |\mathbf{b}|$,
   (e) $|\mathbf{a} + \mathbf{b}|$,
   (f) $|\mathbf{a}| + |\mathbf{b}|$,
   (g) $|3\mathbf{a} - 2\mathbf{b}|$,
   (h) $|3\mathbf{a}| - |2\mathbf{b}|$.

6. In general, does $|\mathbf{a} + \mathbf{b}| = |\mathbf{a}| + |\mathbf{b}|$?

7. Demonstrate *geometrically* the associative law for vector addition.

8. Do vectors form a group with respect to addition?

9. Prove Theorem 4.5b.

10. Prove Theorem 4.5c.

11. Find a unit vector parallel to the resultant of the vectors $\mathbf{a} .=. 2\mathbf{i} + 5\mathbf{j}$ and $\mathbf{b} .=. 3\mathbf{i} - \mathbf{j}$.

12. Demonstrate graphically that $-(\mathbf{a} - \mathbf{b}) = -\mathbf{a} + \mathbf{b}$.

13. Show that $|\mathbf{a} - \mathbf{b}| \geq ||\mathbf{a}| - |\mathbf{b}||$.

14. Show that $|\mathbf{a} + \mathbf{b} + \mathbf{c}| \leq |\mathbf{a}| + |\mathbf{b}| + |\mathbf{c}|$.

15. If $\mathbf{a} .=. -2\mathbf{i} + 3\mathbf{j}$, $\mathbf{b} .=. 3\mathbf{i} - 4\mathbf{j}$, and $\mathbf{c} .=. -\mathbf{i} - \mathbf{j}$, find $|2\mathbf{a} - 3\mathbf{b} - \mathbf{c}|$.

16. Suppose we want to discuss vectors in three-dimensional space.

   (a) How may they be represented in terms of numbers?
   (b) How would addition be defined for the representation in part (a)?
   (c) What would be the direction and magnitude of a vector in terms of the representation in part (a)?
   (d) What vectors would form a base set in three dimensions?

17. The vectors **i** and **j** form a base set for vectors in two dimensions. Is this the only base set possible? If you think not, give an example.

18. Do the vectors in a base set need to be unit vectors?
19. A rotation of a body through a given angle about a given line as axis can be represented by an arrow of length proportional to the angle and pointing along the axis in the direction from which the angle appears to be counterclockwise. Are such arrows vectors? That is, can such arrows be combined like vectors so that the associative and commutative laws are obeyed? *Hint*: Consider the simple case of a rotation through 90° about the *x*-axis followed by a rotation through 90° about the *y*-axis.

4.6 APPLICATIONS OF VECTORS

Vectors are indispensable in analyzing problems involving velocities, accelerations, and forces. Some of the simpler applications to velocity problems and force problems are discussed in this section.

Since a velocity is completely characterized by a magnitude and a direction, it is ideally represented by a vector whose magnitude represents the speed and whose direction is that of the velocity. This idea is illustrated in the following examples.

Example 4.6a. A man can row a boat at a rate of 4 mph in still water. If he attempts to row straight across a river 100 yards wide, and flowing at a rate of 3 mph, where will he land on the opposite shore? What will be the actual speed of the boat?

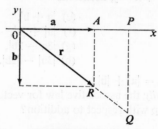

FIGURE 4.6a

If the origin of coordinates is chosen at the starting point of the boat, then the rate of rowing is represented by the vector **a** = 4**i**, and the rate of the stream is represented by the vector **b** = −3**j**, as shown in Figure 4.6a. The resulting direction of travel is therefore that of the vector

$$\mathbf{r} = \mathbf{a} + \mathbf{b} = 4\mathbf{i} - 3\mathbf{j},$$

which has the direction [4, −3]. The rate of travel in this direction is $|\mathbf{r}| = 5$ mph. Furthermore, triangle *OAR* is similar to triangle *OPQ*, so that

$$\frac{PQ}{OP} = \frac{AR}{OA} = \frac{3}{4}.$$

Since *OP* = 100,

$$PQ = (100)\left(\frac{3}{4}\right) = 75 \text{ yards.}$$

Thus the boat lands 75 yards downstream.

The next example offers a slight variation of the problem in the preceding example.

Example 4.6b. A wind is blowing from the south at 50 mph. The pilot of a plane, whose speed in still air is 130 mph, wants to fly due east. In what direction should he head the plane?

If the plane were to head due east, the wind would cause it to drift north. Hence, the plane must head in a southeasterly direction in order to compensate for the wind

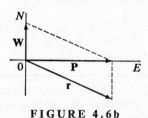

FIGURE 4.6b

Since the wind is due north, let its velocity be represented by the vector **W** = 50**j**, and let

$$r = xi + yj$$

represent a vector of magnitude 130 mph in the direction in which the plane heads (see Figure 4.6b). Since it is required that the plane actually travel due east, the vector **p** = *u***i** may be used to represent the resultant velocity of the plane. Hence, we must have

$$\mathbf{W} + \mathbf{r} = \mathbf{p} \Rightarrow 50j + xi + yj = ui$$
$$\Rightarrow xi + (y + 50)j = ui + 0j$$
$$\Rightarrow x = u, \text{ and } y + 50 = 0, \text{ or } y = -50.$$

Furthermore, since

$$|\mathbf{r}| = \sqrt{x^2 + y^2} = 130,$$

we have

$$\sqrt{x^2 + 50^2} = 130.$$

It follows that

$$x = 120, \quad \mathbf{p} = 120\mathbf{i}.$$

This result means that if the plane heads in the direction given by $[12, -5]$, then it will actually travel due east at a speed of 120 mph.

Example 4.6c. Two forces, F_1 and F_2, are acting on an object. If F_1 is 12 pounds and acts in the northeast direction and F_2 is 6 pounds and acts in the northwest direction, find their resultant.

If the origin is chosen at the object, then

$$F_1 = 6\sqrt{2}i + 6\sqrt{2}j,$$

and

$$F_2 = -3\sqrt{2}i + 3\sqrt{2}j,$$

as shown in Figure 4.6c. The resultant vector **r** is simply the sum of F_1 and F_2, so that

$$r = (6\sqrt{2}i + 6\sqrt{2}j) + (-3\sqrt{2}i + 3\sqrt{2}j)$$
$$= 3\sqrt{2}i + 9\sqrt{2}j.$$

Thus, the direction of **r** is given by [1, 3], and its magnitude is

$$|r| = [(3\sqrt{2})^2 + (9\sqrt{2})^2]^{1/2} = 6\sqrt{5} \text{ pounds.}$$

Problems involving a set of forces that are in equilibrium often make use of the following fundamental law of mechanics.

Law 4.6a. If a rigid mechanical system is at rest, then the vector sum of all the external forces acting on the system is zero.

An application of this law is illustrated in

Example 4.6d. An object weighing 7000 pounds is suspended by two cables. Relative to the horizontal and vertical directions, one cable is in the [4, 3] direction and the other is in the [−12, 5] direction. What is the tension in each of the cables?

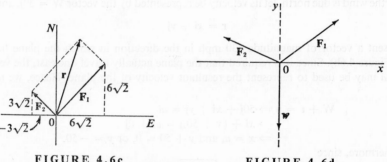

FIGURE 4.6c   **FIGURE 4.6d**

It is convenient to introduce a coordinate system with the origin at the object and the cables in the *xy*-plane, as shown in Figure 4.6d. If F_1 is the force along the cable in the [4, 3] direction, F_2 the force along the cable in the [−12, 5] direction, and **w** the downward force due to the weight of the object, then, by Law 4.6a, the sum of these forces must be zero; that is,

$$F_1 + F_2 + w = 0.$$

Since the vector F_1 is in the [4, 3] direction, its components are proportional to 4 and 3. Thus we may write

$$F_1 = 4ki + 3kj.$$

Similarly,

$$F_2 = -12mi + 5mj,$$

and

$$w = -7000j.$$

Hence, from

$$F_1 + F_2 + w = 0,$$

we get

$$(4k - 12m)\mathbf{i} + (3k + 5m - 7000)\mathbf{j} = 0,$$

and

$$4k - 12m = 0 \quad \text{and} \quad 3k + 5m - 7000 = 0.$$

It follows that

$$k = 3m \quad \text{and} \quad 3(3m) + 5m = 7000,$$

so that

$$m = 500 \quad \text{and} \quad k = 1500.$$

Thus,

$$\mathbf{F}_1 = 6000\mathbf{i} + 4500\mathbf{j}$$

and

$$\mathbf{F}_2 = -6000\mathbf{i} + 2500\mathbf{j}.$$

The tension in the first cable is

$$|\mathbf{F}_1| = \sqrt{(6000)^2 + (4500)^2} = 7500 \text{ pounds}$$

and in the second cable is

$$|\mathbf{F}_2| = \sqrt{(6000)^2 + (2500)^2} = 6500 \text{ pounds}.$$

Exercises 4.6

In each of Numbers 1 to 3, find the resultant of the given set of vectors.

1. 10 units upward, 8 units to the right, 3 units downward.
2. 5 units in the northeast direction, 7 units in the northwest direction.
3. 3 units in the northeast direction, 6 units in the east direction, 5 units in the southeast direction.
4. Find the resultant of a force of 200 pounds acting in the [3, 4] direction and a force of 500 pounds acting in the [−8, 15] direction.
5. Find the resultant of a force of 50 pounds acting in the [−5, −12] direction, a force of 100 pounds acting in the [3, −4] direction, and a force of 75 pounds acting in the [8, 15] direction.
6. A plane is headed west at right angles to a 50 mph wind blowing from the north. If the plane's speed with no wind is 700 mph, find the actual speed and direction of flight.
7. A ship sailing north meets an ocean current flowing from west to east at a speed of 4 knots. If the ship's speed in still water is 25 knots, find the resultant speed and direction.
8. A man pushes a lawn mower with a force of 50 pounds acting in the direction of the handle. If the handle is held at a 30° angle with the horizontal, what part of the force actually is used in pushing the lawn mower in the horizontal direction? What is the useful part of the force if the handle is held at 45°? at 60°?
9. Two men were pushing a heavy box across a floor. One man pushed on the box in an easterly direction with a force of 60 pounds and the other pushed in a northerly direction with a force of 25 pounds. Find the magnitude and direction of the resultant force. If the second man had pushed in a northeasterly direction with the same force, what would be the resultant force on the box?
10. A boat can travel 9 mph in still water. In what direction should the boat head in

order to reach a point 20 miles below its starting point on the opposite bank of a river that is $2\sqrt{65}$ miles wide and that flows at a rate of 6 mph?

11. If the wind blows in a southeasterly direction at 40 mph, in what direction should a pilot fly a plane at 120 mph in order that the plane will travel straight east?

12. A car is stuck in the mud. The enterprising driver ties a rope to the car and to a tree 40 feet in front of the car. Assuming that the rope is initially taut and won't stretch, what force can the driver apply to pull the car straight forward if he can displace the center of the rope 1 foot with a force of 100 pounds in a direction perpendicular to the rope?

13. A crane is holding a 3-ton beam above the ground. There is a 6-foot length of cable between the beam and the top of the crane. What force would be required to push the beam 2 feet sideways? If the cable is lengthened 12 feet, what force would be required to push the beam 2 feet sideways?

14. A boom 20 feet long is attached to the base of a vertical pole 20 feet high, and is supported at its upper end by a cable passing through a pulley at the top of the pole. Find the tension in the cable when the boom supports a weight of 5000 pounds from its upper end when it is in a direction of [3, 4] relative to the horizontal and vertical directions. Neglect the weight of the boom.

Summary of Chapter 4

The following ideas must be clearly understood since they are fundamental to much of the work to come later:

(1) one-dimensional euclidean space and distance between two points in the space (Section 4.1);

(2) length of a line segment (Section 4.1);

(3) directed distance (Section 4.1);

(4) open, closed, and half-open intervals (Section 4.1);

(5) neighborhoods (Section 4.1);

(6) two-dimensional euclidean space and distance between two points in the space (Section 4.2);

(7) direction numbers (Section 4.3);

(8) slope of a line (Section 4.3);

(9) location of points on a line (Section 4.3);

(10) conditions for two lines to be perpendicular (Section 4.3);

(11) three-dimensional euclidean space and distance between two points in the space (Section 4.4);

(12) direction numbers in three-dimensional space (Section 4.4);

(13) vectors and vector quantities (Section 4.5);

(14) parallelogram law of composition (Section 4.5);

(15) representation of vectors in two dimensions by number-pairs (Section 4.5);

(16) properties of vector addition and scalar multiplication (Section 4.5);

(17) the set of base vectors, **i** and **j** (Section 4.5);

(18) the magnitude of a vector (Section 4.5);

(19) simple applications of vectors to force and velocity problems (Section 4.6).

Chapter 5　Relations and Functions

5.1 RELATIONS

The concept of an ordered pair of numbers has been fundamental in much of the preceding work. Ordered pairs of integers were used to represent rational numbers in the form a/b. Ordered pairs of real numbers were used to define complex numbers, and we have associated to each point of a two-dimensional euclidean plane an ordered pair of real numbers.

Most applications of mathematics in practical problems make use of sets of ordered pairs of numbers. For example, suppose we are interested in the temperature of a cold storage room at any time as its temperature is lowered to 0°F from an initial temperature of 50°F. We know that at any time t (minutes) when we look at a thermometer in the room, we can read the temperature u. Thus, when $t = 1$, we might read 48.5°; at $t = 5$, we might read 36.3°; and so on. It is clear that we are making use of ordered pairs of real numbers (t, u), with $t \geqq 0$, where the first number gives the time and the second gives the temperature at that time.

A study of an object moving in a straight line also requires the use of ordered pairs of numbers in specifying the location of the object as x units from an origin 0 at a given time t. In fact, in physics, the well-known law for the distance traversed by a falling object is expressed in approximate form by the equation $x = \frac{1}{2}gt^2$, where x is the number of feet the object falls in t seconds and g is the gravitational acceleration. If the value $g = 32$ is used, then the equation is $x = 16t^2$, giving $x = 16$ for $t = 1$, $x = 64$ for $t = 2$, and so on. Thus, again we are concerned with a set of ordered pairs of real numbers,

$$\{(t, x): x = 16t^2, t \geqq 0\}.$$

A somewhat different type of illustration is obtained from a study of the frequency of occurrence of the letter e in a piece of writing. Such studies are of importance, for example, in the science of cryptography. Consider the following poem, where each line is followed by a number pair (L, n), the first element of the pair being the number of the line and the second being the number of e's in that line.

Euclid*
Vachel Lindsay (L, n)

Old Euclid drew a circle	(1, 3)
On a sand-beach long ago.	(2, 1)
He bounded and enclosed it	(3, 4)
With angles thus and so.	(4, 1)
His set of solemn graybeards	(5, 3)
Nodded and argued much	(6, 2)
Of arc and of circumference	(7, 3)
Diameters and such.	(8, 2)
A silent child stood by them	(9, 2)
From morning until noon	(10, 0)
Because they drew such charming	(11, 4)
Round pictures of the moon.	(12, 2)

In this case, we have a set

$$P = \{(1, 3), (2, 1), (3, 4), (4, 1), (5, 3), (6, 2),$$
$$(7, 3), (8, 2), (9, 2), (10, 0), (11, 3), (12, 2)\},$$

which serves to list the number of e's in each line of the poem.

Since sets of ordered pairs of numbers are encountered in so many important ways, it is essential that we consider such sets in greater detail. These sets are, of course, subsets of the set $\{(x, y): x, y \in \mathcal{R}\}$. Illustrations of this type of set are

(a) $S_1 .=. \{(0, 3), (0, 4), (6, 1)\}$,
(b) $S_2 .=. \{(x, y): y = x^2\}$,
(c) $S_3 .=. \{(x, y): x^2 + y^2 = 25\}$,
(d) $S_4 .=. \{(x, y): x > y\}$.

Thus, in (b) the pairs $(1, 1)$, $(3, 9)$, $(-2, 4)$ are all in S_2, whereas pairs such as $(0, 4)$, $(2, 2)$, and $(5, 3)$ are not in S_2. In illustration (c) it is understood that x and y are to be real numbers so that a value of x leading to an imaginary value for y is not allowed. Hence, pairs such as $(3, 4)$, $(-3, 4)$, $(-3, -4)$, $(5, 0)$, and $(-2, \sqrt{21})$ are all in S_3, whereas pairs with $x > 5$ or $x < -5$ are not in S_3. Notice that the sets S_2, S_3, and S_4 are defined by means of a characteristic property of their elements but that S_1 is defined by simply stating what its elements are.

Sets of the type just described are important in many mathematical problems and they are given a special name.

Definition 5.1a. A set of ordered pairs of real numbers is called a **binary relation** in $\mathcal{R}$.

Definition 5.1b. The set of first elements of a binary relation is called the **domain** of the relation, and the set of second elements is called the **range** of the relation.

---

* Reprinted with permission of the publisher from *Collected Poems* by Vachel Lindsay. Copyright 1914 by The Macmillan Company, renewed 1942 by Elizabeth C. Lindsay.

For a given set $\{(x, y)\}$, we frequently call x and y **variables**. The variable x which takes on values in the domain is usually called the **independent** variable, and y, which takes on values in the range, is called the **dependent** variable. When the number of variables is clear from the context, we often drop the adjective "binary" and speak simply of a *relation*.

Example 5.1a. Describe the domain and range of the relation

$$Q .=. \{(0, 5), (0, 6), (1, 4), (2, 5), (3, 6), (4, 4)\}.$$

The domain of Q is the set $\{0, 1, 2, 3, 4\}$ and the range of Q is the set $\{4, 5, 6\}$. It is, of course, possible to construct many other relations with the same domain and range as those in this example. For instance, the relation

$$T .=. \{(0, 4), (1, 5), (2, 6), (3, 4), (4, 5)\}$$

has the same domain and range as Q.

Example 5.1b. Describe the relation

$$Q .=. \{(x, y): x > y, x \in \mathcal{I}, y \in \mathcal{I}\}.$$

Since Q is the set of pairs (x, y) of integers such that $x > y$, some elements of the relation are the pairs $(7, 3)$, $(7, 4)$, $(7, 5)$, $(-4, -5)$, $(-2, -5)$, and $(3, -5)$. The domain of Q is the set of all integers and the range of the relation is also the set of all integers. Notice that this is not the same relation as in illustration (d). Why?

Example 5.1c. Let a relation Q be defined as the set of ordered pairs (x, y) of real numbers such that $y = x^2$; that is,

$$Q .=. \{(x, y): y = x^2, x \in \mathcal{R}\}.$$

Some of the elements of the relation are the pairs $(0, 0)$, $(2, 4)$, $(-2, 4)$, $(\sqrt{3}, 3)$, and $(-\sqrt{3}, 3)$. What is the domain and what is the range of Q?

The domain of Q is the set $\mathcal{R}$ and the range is the set of all nonnegative numbers. Why can no negative number belong to the range?

Example 5.1d. Describe the relation

$$T .=. \{(x, y): y = x^2, 0 \leqq x \leqq 1\}.$$

The set of first elements in the pairs—that is, the domain of the relation T—is the set $\{x: 0 \leqq x \leqq 1\}$. The rule used for determining the elements of the range is the same as that used in the preceding example, except that the domain has been restricted.

It is often necessary to restrict the domain of a relation in setting up mathematical equations to describe physical problems. In fact, different rules may be used to determine the second element of a pair corresponding to different parts of the domain.

Example 5.1e. What are the domain and range of

$$T .=. \{(x, y): y = x^2 \text{ if } 0 \leqq x \leqq 1, y = 2 - x \text{ if } 1 < x < 2, \text{ and } y = 2 \text{ if } x = 2\}.$$

The domain of T is the set $\{x: 0 \leqq x \leqq 2\}$, and the range is $\{y: 0 \leqq y \leqq 1, y = 2\}$.

This example illustrates the importance of not confusing a relation with the rule used to determine the pairs belonging to the relation.

It is to be emphasized that in many examples of relations a rule is given that determines the range and the domain of the relation, provided it is understood that we are concerned with pairs of *real* numbers. Hence, if no additional information is given, it is to be understood that the permissible values in the domain and range are those *real* numbers for which the given rule is satisfied.

Example 5.1f. Describe the domain and range of

$$T .=. \{(x, y): x^2 + y^2 = 1\}.$$

Since it is not specified that the values of x and y are to be taken from some particular set, we may use any pair of real numbers (x, y) for which $x^2 + y^2 = 1$. Several such pairs are

$$(1, 0), \left(\frac{1}{2}, \frac{\sqrt{3}}{2}\right), \left(\frac{3}{5}, \frac{4}{5}\right), \left(-\frac{1}{2}, \frac{\sqrt{3}}{2}\right), \left(-\frac{1}{2}, -\frac{\sqrt{3}}{2}\right), \left(\frac{1}{2}, -\frac{\sqrt{3}}{2}\right).$$

Note that there can be no pair where $x > 1$, since there is no corresponding real value for y. Hence we conclude that the domain is $\{x: -1 \leqq x \leqq 1\}$ and the range is $\{y: -1 \leqq y \leqq 1\}$.

Exercises 5.1

Give the domain and range of each of the following relations.

1. $Q .=. \{(1, 3), (3, 2), (2, 2), (3, 1), (4, 3), (3, 3)\}$.
2. $S .=. \{(1, 5), (2, 5), (3, 5), (4, 5), (5, 5)\}$.
3. $T .=. \{(x, y): y = x^2 \text{ and } x \leqq 10, x \in \mathfrak{N}\}$.
4. $S .=. \{(x, y): y = \sqrt{x} \text{ and } y \leqq 10, y \in \mathfrak{N}\}$.
5. $S .=. \{(x, y): y^2 = x \text{ and } |y| \leqq 10, y \in \mathcal{G}\}$.
6. $S .=. \{(x, y): y^2 = x, x \in \mathcal{G}\}$.
7. $Q .=. \{(x, y): x < y\}$.
8. $Q .=. \{(x, y): x \geqq y\}$.
9. $T .=. \{(x, y): y = 2x + 3 \text{ for } 0 \leqq x \leqq 1 \text{ and } y = -5x + 10 \text{ for } 1 < x \leqq 2\}$.
10. $T .=. \{(x, y): y = 2 \text{ if } 0 < x < 1 \text{ and } y = 3 \text{ if } 1 < x < 2\}$.
11. $Q .=. \{(x, y): y = x \text{ if } 0 \leqq x < 1 \text{ and } y = x^2 \text{ if } 1 \leqq x \leqq 2\}$.
12. $T .=. \{(x, y): y = \sqrt{x - 1}\}$.
13. $T .=. \{(x, y): y = 1/x, y \in \mathfrak{N}\}$.
14. $T .=. \{(x, y): y^2 = 1/x\}$.
15. $T .=. \{(x, y): x^2 + y^2 = 4\}$.
16. $T .=. \{(x, y): x^2 - y^2 = 4\}$.
17. $Q .=. \{(x, y): x + y = 1\}$.
18. $Q .=. \{(x, y): \sqrt{x} + \sqrt{y} = 1\}$.
19. $P .=. \{(x, y): y = 1/x \text{ if } 0 < x < 2\} \cup \{(x, y): y = x^2 \text{ if } 1 \leqq x \leqq 3\}$.
20. $P .=. \{(x, y): y = 2 \text{ if } -2 \leqq x \leqq 0\} \cap \{(x, y): y = 2 \text{ if } 0 \leqq x < 2\}$.
21. $P .=. \{(x, y): x^2 + y^2 = 1\} \cap \{(x, y): y = 3/5\}$.
22. $P .=. \{(x, y): y = x, 0 \leqq x \leqq 1\} \cup \{(x, y): y = x + 1, -1 \leqq x \leqq 0\}$.

5.2 DEFINITION OF A FUNCTION

In the definition of a binary relation, no restriction was placed on the number of elements of the range that may correspond to a particular element of the domain. However, a very important type of relation is one in which a multiplicity of values corresponding to a given element of the domain is not allowed. Relations of this kind are given a special name.

Definition 5.2a. A **function** is a relation such that to each element of the domain there corresponds *one and only one* element of the range.

According to this definition, it is apparent that every function is a relation, but not every relation is a function. Thus, in the preceding section, only Examples 5.1c, 5.1d, and 5.1e give relations that are functions.

Example 5.2a. Consider the relation $\{(0, 1), (1, 1), (2, 3), (3, 2)\}$. The domain of this relation is the set $\{0, 1, 2, 3\}$ and the range is the set $\{1, 2, 3\}$. Is this relation a function?

Since each element of the domain has exactly one element of the range associated with it, this relation is a function. It is immaterial that one element of the range is associated with more than one element of the domain, as in $(0, 1)$ and $(1, 1)$.

Example 5.2b. Consider the set $\{(x, y)\}$ of ordered pairs of real numbers where $y = x^2$. Is this relation a function?

Note that the domain is the set of all real numbers, and the range is the set of all nonnegative real numbers. Since to each element of the domain there corresponds exactly one element of the range, this relation is also a function.

There is an important special notation for functions that is used to indicate the element of the range corresponding to an element of the domain. If f denotes a function $\{(x, y)\}$, then the number y associated with a given x is denoted by $f(x)$, read "f of x." With this notation, the set of pairs defining f may then be written as $\{(x, f(x))\}$.

Using the functional notation just described, we may write for the function defined in Example 5.2b, the set of pairs

$$\{(x, f(x)): f(x) = x^2, x \in \mathcal{R}\}.$$

Thus, corresponding to $x = 3$, we should have $f(3) = 3^2 = 9$, and the pair is $(3, 9)$. Similarly, $f(-2) = (-2)^2 = 4$ means that $(-2, 4)$ is one of the set of pairs that belong to the given function. More generally, we have $f(a) = a^2$. It is important to notice that, in each case, x in the defining rule has been replaced by the number in the parentheses in $f(\ )$.

In the preceding illustrations, we have specifically indicated a restriction to real numbers. In most of our work, this is a natural restriction and from now on is to be understood, unless the contrary is stated. It is to be further understood that, unless otherwise stated, the domain of a given function $\{(x, f(x))\}$ is that subset of the set of real numbers for which $f(x)$ is a real number.

For example, the domain of the function $\{(x, \sqrt{x})\}$ is the set $\{x: x \geq 0\}$, since $\sqrt{x}$ is a real number if and only if x is a nonnegative number. However, the domain of the function $\{(x, \sqrt{x}): 1 \leq x \leq 4\}$ is the interval $\{x: 1 \leq x \leq 4\}$, as specifically stated in the description of the function.

Suppose a function is given by $\{(x, g(x)): g(x) = x + 1/x\}$. The domain of this function is the set of all real numbers with the exception of zero. Why? Notice that the letter g has been used here in place of the symbol f. Other letters, as F, G, φ, Γ, and so on, are frequently used in the same manner, and indicate a name for the function. The formula $g(x) = x + 1/x$ tells us how to form the second member of the pair whose first member is x. Such a formula is said to define the function, although the function itself is *not the formula* but is the set of number-pairs $\{(x, g(x))\}$.

Example 5.2c. For the function g, defined by $g(x) = x + (1/x)$, find the formula that corresponds to

$$\text{(a) } g\left(\frac{1}{x}\right), \quad \text{(b) } g\left(x - \frac{1}{x}\right), \quad \text{(c) } xg(x) - g(1).$$

(a) The symbol $g(1/x)$ means that, in the formula for $g(x)$, the x is to be replaced by $1/x$. Thus,

$$g\left(\frac{1}{x}\right) = \frac{1}{x} + \frac{1}{\dfrac{1}{x}} = \frac{1}{x} + x.$$

Notice that for this special case we have $g(x) = g(1/x)$.

(b) Similarly,

$$g\left(x - \frac{1}{x}\right) = x - \frac{1}{x} + \frac{1}{x - \dfrac{1}{x}}$$

$$= x - \frac{1}{x} + \frac{x}{x^2 - 1}$$

$$= \frac{x^4 - x^2 + 1}{x(x^2 - 1)}.$$

(c) Finally,

$$xg(x) - g(1) = x\left(x + \frac{1}{x}\right) - \left(1 + \frac{1}{1}\right)$$

$$= x^2 + 1 - 2$$

$$= x^2 - 1.$$

Exercises 5.2

1. Given the sets $\mathcal{A} .=. \{2, 4, 6\}$ and $\mathcal{B} .=. \{3, 5\}$.

   (a) Define a relation on $\mathcal{A}$ and $\mathcal{B}$ which is not a function by indicating a correspondence between the elements of $\mathcal{A}$ and the elements of $\mathcal{B}$. Use $\mathcal{A}$ as the domain and $\mathcal{B}$ as the range of the relation.

(b) How many different *functions* can be defined on these two sets if $\mathcal{Q}$ is the domain of the function, and the range is a subset of $\mathcal{B}$?

In each of Numbers 2 to 15, if the set $\{(x, y)\}$ of pairs of real numbers formed according to the given rule is a function, give the domain and range of the function. If the set is not a function, tell why it is not.

2. $y = x^2 + 3$.
3. $y = 2x + 3$.
4. $y = \pm\sqrt{4 - x^2}$.
5. $y = -\sqrt{4 - x^2}$.
6. $y = \sqrt{4 - x^2}$.
7. $y = 1/x$.
8. $y = 1/(x^2 - 4)$.

9. $y = (x^2 - 4)/(x - 2)$.
10. $y = \sqrt{x^2 - 9}$.
11. $y^2 = x$.
12. $x + y = 1$.
13. $x^2 + y = 1$.
14. $x^2 + y^2 = 1$.
15. $y = \pm\sqrt{6 - x - x^2}$.

16. If $f(x) = x^2 - 2x$, find $f(2)$; $f(1/2)$; $f(a)$; $f(1/h)$.
17. If $g(x) = 1/(x - 4)$, find $g(3)$; $g(4)$; $g(1/h)$; $g(1/x)$.
18. If $h(x) = x/(x - 1)$, find $h(0)$; $h(1/2)$; $h(1/x)$; $h(x + k)$.
19. If $f(x) = 2x + 3$, find $f(x + h)$; $f(1/x)$.
20. If $f(x) = 1/x$, find $2f(4) - f(2)$; $f(a) + f(b)$; $af(a)$; $1/f(a)$.
21. If $g(x) = 2x - x^2$, find $g(3) - g(2)$; $g(1) \cdot g(3)$; $g(1/2)/g(1/3)$.
22. If $f(x) = x^3$, find $f(a + h) - f(a)$; $f(a) + 1/f(a)$; $[f(a)]^2$.

5.3 GRAPHS OF RELATIONS AND FUNCTIONS

In Chapter 4, a two-dimensional rectangular coordinate system was established by choosing two perpendicular lines in the plane and setting up a number scale on each axis. In the definition of a relation, each ordered pair, or element of the relation, may be considered to be the x and y coordinates of a point in two-dimensional space. Consequently, a pictorial representation, or **graph**, of a relation may be obtained by plotting the number-pairs belonging to the relation.

Graphs play an important role in mathematics by providing a geometric visualization for many problems. It is frequently helpful to graph a function in order to arrive at the proper procedure for setting up a problem. Graphs are nearly always employed in experimental work where an attempt is made to discover a natural law or a pattern for the data obtained. When such a pattern is found, it is sometimes possible to describe the natural phenomenon by a mathematical formula. Consequently, it is important that we examine the process of making graphs in some detail.

Example 5.3a. Graph the relation

$$\{(0, 2), (0, 1), (1, 3), (2, -1), (3, 2), (4, 0)\}.$$

The graph is shown in Figure 5.3a. In this case, the graph consists of just the six isolated points.

Example 5.3b. Graph the function consisting of the set of ordered pairs (x, y) such that $y = 4$.

The fact that every number-pair in this set has 4 for its second element means that all the points are at a distance of 4 units above the *x*-axis. Hence, the set of points constitutes a straight line parallel to the *x*-axis and 4 units above it (see Figure 5.3b).

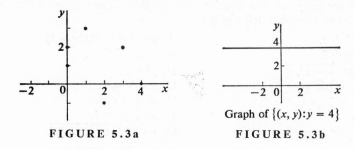

FIGURE 5.3a

Graph of $\{(x, y): y = 4\}$

FIGURE 5.3b

Example 5.3c. Graph the relation $\{(x, y): x = 2\}$.

It can easily be seen that this set of points describes a straight line parallel to the *y*-axis and 2 units to the right of it (see Figure 5.3c).

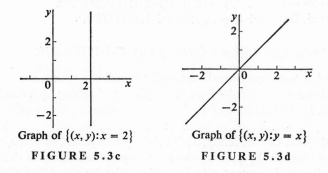

Graph of $\{(x, y): x = 2\}$

FIGURE 5.3c

Graph of $\{(x, y): y = x\}$

FIGURE 5.3d

Example 5.3d. Graph the function defined by the set of ordered pairs (x, y) of real numbers where $y = x$.

The graph is shown in Figure 5.3d. The statement $y = x$ means that each point is just as far from the *x*-axis as it is from the *y*-axis, and that the two coordinates have the same sign. Thus, the graph is the bisector of the angles formed by the two axes in the first and third quadrants.

Example 5.3e. Graph the relation defined by the set of ordered pairs (x, y) of real numbers such that $x > y$.

The graph consists of all points below the line $y = x$, as indicated by the shaded area in Figure 5.3e.

Example 5.3f. Graph the relation $\{(x, y): y^2 = x\}$.

We first plot a few points of the graph such as $(0, 0)$, $(1, 1)$, $(1, -1)$, $(4, 2)$, $(4, -2)$,

(9, 3), and (9, −3). As we plot more and more points whose coordinates satisfy the equation $y^2 = x$, these points suggest the curve that is shown in Figure 5.3f. We call

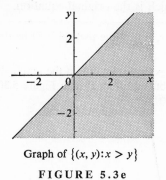

Graph of $\{(x, y): x > y\}$

FIGURE 5.3e

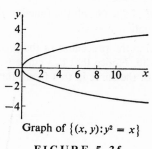

Graph of $\{(x, y): y^2 = x\}$

FIGURE 5.3f

this curve the graph of the given relation. We shall later discuss certain concepts of calculus that will justify the smooth curve drawn here.

If the coordinates of every point on a graph satisfy an equation (as in the preceding example), and no other points satisfy the same equation, then the equation is called *an equation of the graph* and the graph is called *the graph of the equation*. In accordance with standard custom, we shall use this terminology so that we may speak of the graph in Figure 5.3f as the graph of the equation $y^2 = x$. Also, $y^2 = x$ is an equation of this graph.

The graph in Figure 5.3f displays a certain symmetry that will be of interest in the succeeding work. If the figure were folded along the x-axis, the part of the curve below the axis would coincide exactly with the part above the axis. We call the x-axis a **line of symmetry** of the curve.

In general, a line L is said to be a line of symmetry of a graph if to each point P on the graph there corresponds another point P_1 on the graph such that L is the perpendicular bisector of the segment PP_1 (see Figure 5.3g).

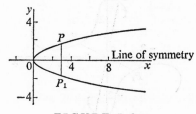

FIGURE 5.3g

If a point (x, y) is on a graph that is symmetric with respect to the x-axis, then, by the definition of symmetry, the point $(x, -y)$ must also be on the graph. Conversely, if both (x, y) and $(x, -y)$ are on the graph, then the graph is symmetric with respect to the x-axis. This means that the coordinates $(x, -y)$ must satisfy an equation of the graph, so that the replacement of y by $-y$ in this equation should yield the original equation. Thus, in Example 5.3f, if we replace y by $-y$ we get $(-y)^2 = x$ or $y^2 = x$, which is the original equation.

Example 5.3g. Graph the function $f. =. \{(x, x^2)\}$. Note that this will be the graph of the equation $y = x^2$.

Following the procedure of the preceding example, we obtain the graph shown in Figure 5.3h. Notice that this curve can be obtained from that in Figure 5.3f by the rotation of the curve in that figure through $90°$.

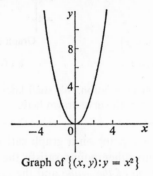

Graph of $\{(x, y):y = x^2\}$

FIGURE 5.3h

The graph of $y = x^2$ is symmetric with respect to the y-axis, since replacement of x by $-x$ does not change the equation. That is, if (x, y) is a point on the graph, then $(-x, y)$ must also be a point on the graph.

A point O is said to be a **point of symmetry** with respect to a given graph if and only if for every point P on the graph, there is another point P_1 on the graph such that O is the midpoint of the line segment PP_1 (see Figure 5.3i). If

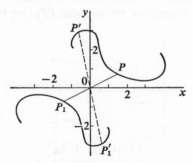

FIGURE 5.3i

the point (x, y) lies on a graph that is symmetric with respect to the origin, then the point $(-x, -y)$ must also lie on the graph. This is illustrated in the following example.

Example 5.3h. Graph the function $f .=. \{(x, x^3)\}$. An equation that connects the elements of the ordered pairs is $y = x^3$.

The graph of this function is not symmetric to the x-axis or to the y-axis, but if we replace x by $-x$ and y by $-y$ in the equation $y = x^3$, we get $-y = (-x)^3$ or $y = x^3$. Hence, the graph is symmetric with respect to the origin. The curve is shown in Figure 5.3j.

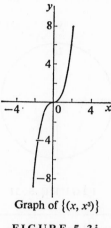

Graph of $\{(x, x^3)\}$

FIGURE 5.3j

Example 5.3i. Graph the function f consisting of the set of ordered pairs $\{(x, y)\}$, where

$$y = 1 \qquad \text{if} \quad x \leqq 0,$$
$$y = x^2 + 1 \quad \text{if} \quad 0 < x \leqq 1,$$
$$y = 2 \qquad \text{if} \quad 1 < x.$$

The graph of f is shown in Figure 5.3k. Notice that the pieces join to form a continuous graph.

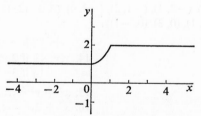

FIGURE 5.3k

Example 5.3j. Graph the relation $S .=. \{(x, y): x^2 + y^2 = 1\}$.

The graph is symmetric with respect to the x-axis, the y-axis, and the origin. It several points are plotted, they appear to lie on a circle of radius 1 with its center at the origin (see Figure 5.3l). Since a circle is defined as a set of points all equidistant from a given point, this conjecture can be verified by determining the condition on the coordinates (x, y) of a point P so that P is at a distance of one unit from the origin. In that case, we have

$$(x - 0)^2 + (y - 0)^2 = 1,$$

or

$$x^2 + y^2 = 1.$$

This result shows that every point (x, y) in S is on the circle and that every point on the circle must be in S. Hence, the graph of S is the circle shown in Figure 5.31.

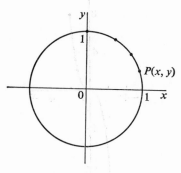

FIGURE 5.31

It is easy to see from the special case in the preceding example that a relation described by the equation $x^2 + y^2 = a^2$ must have a graph that is a circle of radius a and has its center at the origin. Verify this.

Exercises 5.3

In each of the following, a relation consists of a set of ordered pairs (x, y), determined by the indicated rule. State whether the relation is also a function; give the domain and range; discuss the symmetry of the graph of the relation, and sketch the graph.

1. $\{(0, 0), (3, 0), (1, 2), (-2, 1), (-1, 2), (-3, 0), (0, 3), (2, 1)\}$.
2. $\{(0, 0), (0, -3), (0, 1), (0, 3), (0, -1)\}$.

3. $y = -x$.
4. $y = -3$.
5. $x = -4$.
6. $x = 2y$.
7. $y^2 = -4x$.
8. $y = 2x^2$.
9. $y = 4 - x^2$.
10. $x = 9 - y^2$.

11. $y = \begin{cases} x \text{ if } x \geq 0, \\ -x \text{ if } x \leq 0. \end{cases}$

12. $y = \begin{cases} 1 \text{ if } 0 \leq x \leq 1, \\ 2 \text{ if } x = 3. \end{cases}$

13. $y = \begin{cases} 1 - x \text{ if } x \leq 1, \\ 1 + x \text{ if } x > 1. \end{cases}$

14. $y = \begin{cases} 2 \text{ if } x \leq 2, \\ 3 \text{ if } 2 < x \leq 3, \\ 4 \text{ if } 3 < x \leq 4. \end{cases}$

15. $x^2 + y^2 = 16$.
16. $x^2 + 2y^2 = 4$.
17. $2x^2 + y^2 + 4 = 0$.
18. $x^2 - 2y^2 = 4$.
19. $2y^2 - x^2 = 4$.
20. $x^2 + y = 1$.
21. $y > x$.
22. $0 \leq x \leq 1, 0 \leq y \leq 1$.
23. $x^2 + (y - 1)^2 = 0$.
24. $x^2 - y^2 = 0$.
25. $xy - x - y + 1 = 0$.

5.4 GRAPHS OF CERTAIN SPECIAL FUNCTIONS

If the equation $y^2 = x$, with $x > 0$, is solved for y, then $y = \sqrt{x}$ or $y = -\sqrt{x}$. Thus there are two values of y which satisfy the equation for a given positive value of x; the two y values are negatives of each other. Recall (Section 3.4) that for $x > 0$ we have restricted $\sqrt{x}$ to mean the positive square root of x. If both roots are intended, then the symbol $\pm\sqrt{x}$ must be employed.

Example 5.4a. Graph

$$f .=. \{(x, \sqrt{x})\}, \; g .=. \{(x, -\sqrt{x})\}, \text{ and } Q .=. \{(x, \pm\sqrt{x})\}.$$

The graphs are shown in Figure 5.4a. Notice that f and g are functions but that Q is not. Why?

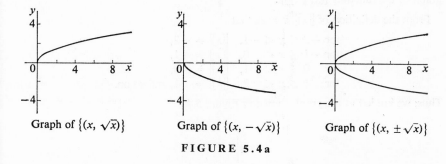

Graph of $\{(x, \sqrt{x})\}$ Graph of $\{(x, -\sqrt{x})\}$ Graph of $\{(x, \pm\sqrt{x})\}$

FIGURE 5.4a

Furthermore, it is important for the reader to recall (Definition 3.4e) that

$$\sqrt{x^2} = \begin{cases} x & \text{for } x \geq 0, \\ -x & \text{for } x < 0. \end{cases}$$

Thus, we have $\sqrt{2^2} = 2$ and $\sqrt{(-2)^2} = \sqrt{4} = 2$. It is imperative to realize that -2 is an *incorrect* result for $\sqrt{4}$.

Another symbol, which for real values of x, is equivalent to $\sqrt{x^2}$, is $|x|$, the absolute value of x, which was defined in Section 3.4. The reader should recall that

$$|x| .=. \begin{cases} x & \text{for } x \geq 0, \\ -x & \text{for } x < 0. \end{cases}$$

Example 5.4b. Graph the function $\{(x, f(x)): f(x) = |x - 2|\}$.

The statement $f(x) = |x - 2|$ means that

$$f(x) = \begin{cases} x - 2 \text{ for } x - 2 \geq 0, \text{ or } x \geq 2, \\ -(x - 2) \text{ for } x - 2 < 0, \text{ or } x < 2. \end{cases}$$

The graph is shown in Figure 5.4b.

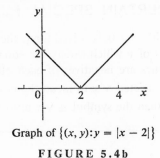

Graph of $\{(x, y): y = |x - 2|\}$

FIGURE 5.4b

Example 5.4c. In Section 1.2 we introduced the "greatest integer" symbol, $[\![x]\!]$, where $[\![x]\!]$ stands for the greatest integer that is less than or equal to x. Sketch the graph of the function $\{(x, [\![x]\!])\}$.

From the definition of $[\![x]\!]$, we see that

$$\text{for } -2 \leq x < -1, \quad [\![x]\!] = -2,$$
$$\text{for } -1 \leq x < \quad 0, \quad [\![x]\!] = -1,$$
$$\text{for } \quad 0 \leq x < \quad 1, \quad [\![x]\!] = \quad 0,$$
$$\text{for } \quad 1 \leq x < \quad 2, \quad [\![x]\!] = \quad 1, \text{ and so on.}$$

Thus, we are led to the graph shown in Figure 5.4c.

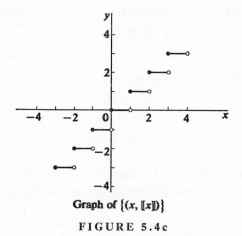

Graph of $\{(x, [\![x]\!])\}$

FIGURE 5.4c

Example 5.4d. Graph the function $f. =. \{(x, x - [\![x]\!])\}$.

Since $f(x) = x - [\![x]\!]$, then for $0 \leq x < 1$, the greatest integer in x is 0, and $f(x) = x$. For $1 \leq x < 2$, the greatest integer in x is 1, and $f(x) = x - 1$. For $-1 \leq x < 0$, $[\![x]\!] = -1$, and $f(x) = x + 1$. The reader should check the values of $x - [\![x]\!]$ for additional portions of the domain. The graph is shown in Figure 5.4d.

It appears from Figure 5.4d that the graph of the function $\{(x, x - [[x]])\}$ can be easily constructed once we have the graph of this function for the interval $0 \leq x < 1$. The remainder of the graph is obtained by moving this portion

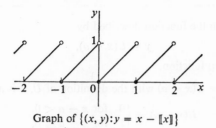

Graph of $\{(x, y): y = x - [[x]]\}$

FIGURE 5.4d

to the right or left exactly one unit, then to the right or left exactly two units, then three units, four units, and so on. A function whose graph has the repetitive character of this one is called **periodic.** Using the notation $\{(x, y): y = f(x)\}$, we may define a periodic function as one for which there exists a fixed real number k such that

$$f(x + k) = f(x)$$

for all x for which $f(x)$ is defined. The smallest such positive number k is called the **period** of the function. For the function in Example 5.4d, we have $f(x + 1) = f(x)$, and, since no positive number smaller than 1 will serve here, the function has a period of 1. Periodicity is an important characteristic of many of the functions that occur in the applications of mathematics. We shall be particularly concerned with this in our study of the trigonometric functions.

Another function that is quite useful in various applications is given in

Definition 5.4a. Let

$$U(x) .=. \begin{cases} 0 & \text{for } x < 0, \\ 1 & \text{for } x \geq 0. \end{cases}$$

The function $U .=. \{(x, y): y = U(x)\}$ is called the **unit step function.**

The graph of the function $U(x)$ is shown in Figure 5.4e.

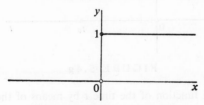

Graph of the Unit Step Function

FIGURE 5.4e

Many of the functions that are important in scientific and engineering practice may be constructed in a rather simple fashion by the use of the unit step function. The next two examples illustrate the procedure.

Example 5.4e. Graph the function described by

$$y = U(x - a),$$

where U is the unit step function.

Upon comparing $y = U(x - a)$ with the definition of U, it is apparent that

$$U(x - a) = \begin{cases} 0 & \text{for } x - a < 0, \\ 1 & \text{for } x - a \geq 0, \end{cases}$$

or

$$U(x - a) = \begin{cases} 0 & \text{for } x < a, \\ 1 & \text{for } x \geq a. \end{cases}$$

Hence, the "step" occurs at $x = a$, and the graph is shown in Figure 5.4f.

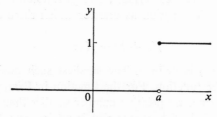

Graph of $y = U(x - a)$

FIGURE 5.4f

Example 5.4f. It is common practice to check the behavior of an electric circuit under the influence of a "pulse" of voltage such as that supplied by a battery that can be switched in and out of the circuit. Figure 5.4g shows a graph of such a pulse. Rep-

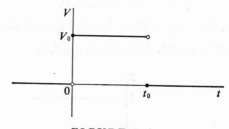

FIGURE 5.4g

resent the corresponding function of the time t by means of the unit step function.

A step voltage of magnitude V_0 and starting at $t = 0$ is given by

$$V_1(t) = V_0 U(t).$$

This follows directly from Definition 5.4a. Furthermore,

$$V_2(t) = V_0 U(t - t_0)$$

would correspond to a step voltage of the same magnitude but starting at $t = t_0$. Consequently, the desired representation is

$$V(t) = V_0[U(t) - U(t - t_0)].$$

It should be noted that the "pulse" type function may also represent a constant force acting for a finite time interval. A pulse of this kind is sometimes used as an idealized representation of the force exerted on a pile by a pile driver. Such representations are frequently used in order to make an analysis of the effect of forces of this type.

A large part of scientific research consists of gathering data about a given phenomenon, and then trying to find a mathematical function that can be used to describe these data. Once such a function is found, it can serve as a basis for the prediction of future events or it may be employed to indicate ways in which changes in the environment may affect the phenomenon.

Exercises 5.4

Let a function consist of the set of ordered pairs (x, y), where y is related to x as indicated in each of Numbers 1 to 19. Give the domain and the range, discuss the symmetry of the graph of the function, and sketch it. If a function is periodic, specify the period.

1. $y = [\![x + 1]\!]$.
2. $y = -\sqrt{4 - x^2}$.
3. $y = \sqrt{x^2 - 4}$.
4. $y = |x + 1|$.
5. $y = |x| + x$.
6. $y = x|x|$.
7. $y = [\![x]\!] - x$.
8. $x = \sqrt{y + 1}$.

9. $y = [\![x]\!]$ for $-1 \leq x < 1$, and the function is periodic with a period of 2.
10. $y = |x|$ for $-2 \leq x < 0$, and the function is periodic with a period of 2.
11. $y = x - |[\![x]\!]|$.
12. $y = x - [\![|x|]\!]$.

13. $y = \begin{cases} \dfrac{|x|}{x} & \text{for } x \neq 0, \\ 0 & \text{for } x = 0. \end{cases}$

14. $y = \dfrac{1 + (-1)^n}{2}$, where $n = [\![x]\!]$.

15. $y = x^2 - [\![x^2]\!]$.
16. $y = U(x) - 2U(x - 1) + U(x - 2)$, where U is the unit step function.
17. $y = xU(x) - (x - 1)U(x - 1)$.
18. $y = xU(x) - 2(x - 1)U(x - 1) + (x - 2)U(x - 2)$.
19. $y = U(x) - U(x - 2)$ for $0 < x \leq 4$, and the function is periodic of period 4.

20. For the function defined in Example 5.4d, show that for $n \leq x < n + 1$, where $n \in \mathcal{I}$, $f(x) = x - n$. Use this result to show that f is periodic with period 1.

21. The load on a beam of length $2c$ is 1000 pounds per foot on the portion of the beam from one end to the middle and 3000 pounds per foot on the remainder of the beam. Represent the loading function by means of the unit step function U.

22. A battery of voltage E is connected to a circuit in such a manner that a switch can reverse the connections so that the polarity of the voltage is reversed. Suppose that the impressed voltage is E for 2 seconds and $-E$ for the next 2 seconds, and zero thereafter. (The battery is shunted out after 4 seconds.) Describe the impressed voltage by means of the unit step function.

5.5 CLUSTER POINTS

In Section 4.1, a neighborhood of a point a was defined to be the set $\{x: a - h < x < a + h\}$. Recall that this set is an open interval of length $2h$ with the point a as its midpoint. We shall denote such an interval by $\mathfrak{N}(a, h)$, or simply by $\mathfrak{N}(a)$ if we wish to speak of a neighborhood in general without specifying its radius. Since the neighborhood concept is frequently used to advantage in discussing some of the properties of functions and their graphs, we need to examine the consequences of the definition in some detail.

It is sometimes necessary to consider half-open intervals for which a given point a is one of the end points. That is, the interval may extend only to the right or only to the left of the given point. The neighborhood concept is specialized to handle these situations by the following definitions.

Definition 5.5a. A **right neighborhood** of a point a is the set

$$\mathfrak{N}(a^+, h) .=. \{x: a \leq x < a + h\},$$

and a **left neighborhood** of a is the set

$$\mathfrak{N}(a^-, h) .=. \{x: a - h < x \leq a\}.$$

We may denote a general right or left neighborhood by $\mathfrak{N}(a^+)$ or $\mathfrak{N}(a^-)$, respectively, if the specific size of the neighborhood is not important for the discussion.

Example 5.5a. If $\mathbb{S} .=. \{x: x = 0 \text{ or } 1 \leq x < 2\}$, what points of $\mathbb{S}$ have at least one neighborhood contained entirely within $\mathbb{S}$?

We see that any point a, where $1 < a < 2$, has a neighborhood that is contained entirely in $\mathbb{S}$ (see Figure 5.5a). Thus if $a = 1.99$, then a neighborhood of a that is contained entirely in $\mathbb{S}$ is the set $\mathfrak{N}(1.99, 0.005) = \{x: 1.985 < x < 1.995\}$. Of course there are many other possible neighborhoods, since we may choose for h any value such that $0 < h < 0.01$. The reader should describe for himself neighborhoods of 1.9999 and 1.0005 that are contained in $\mathbb{S}$. As Figure 5.5a illustrates, the point 0 has

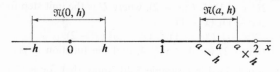

FIGURE 5.5a

no neighborhood *contained entirely in* S, even though 0 does have neighborhoods. Furthermore, the points 1 and 2 do not have neighborhoods contained entirely in S, although 1 does have right neighborhoods and 2 has left neighborhoods that do belong to S.

Another useful concept is that of the **deleted neighborhood** of a point—that is, a neighborhood with the point itself excluded from the set. For such a set, we shall use the notation $\mathfrak{N}^*(a)$ given by the following definition.

Definition 5.5b. $\qquad\qquad \mathfrak{N}^*(a) .=. \mathfrak{N}(a) - \{a\}.$

Note that $\mathfrak{N}^*(a) = \mathfrak{N}^*(a^+) \cup \mathfrak{N}^*(a^-)$. (It is usually desirable to read the symbol $\mathfrak{N}(a)$ as "neighborhood"; for example, read the symbol $\mathfrak{N}(a, h)$ as "neighborhood of a of radius h." Similarly, the symbol $\mathfrak{N}^*(a, h)$ is to be read "deleted neighborhood of a of radius h." We shall write "a $\mathfrak{N}(a, h)$" with the expectation that it will be read "a neighborhood.")

In Example 5.5a, every $\mathfrak{N}(0, h)$, where $0 < h < 1$, contains only one point of S, namely 0, and no $\mathfrak{N}^*(0, h)$, where $0 < h < 1$, contains any points of S. Also, the point 1 has a deleted right neighborhood contained entirely in S, and the point 2 has a deleted left neighborhood contained entirely in S, even though 2 does not belong to S.

Consider next the set $\mathfrak{I} .=. \{x : x = 1/10^n, n \in \mathfrak{N}\}$. This set consists of the numbers with decimal representations 0.1, 0.01, 0.001, and so on. None of the points of this set has a deleted neighborhood contained entirely in the set. For instance, for $h \leq 0.0009$, the $\mathfrak{N}^*(0.001, h)$ contains no points of $\mathfrak{I}$. On the other hand, if $h > 0.0009$, then the $\mathfrak{N}^*(0.001, h)$ contains both points that do and points that do not belong to $\mathfrak{I}$. There is one point of particular interest relative to the set $\mathfrak{I}$. This is the point 0, which has the property that every $\mathfrak{N}^*(0)$ contains points that are in $\mathfrak{I}$. In this respect, the point 0 relative to the set $\mathfrak{I}$ is like every point in the closed interval $\{x : 1 \leq x \leq 2\}$ relative to the set S of Example 5.5a. That is, every $\mathfrak{N}^*(a)$, where $1 \leq a \leq 2$, contains points that are in S. Points with this property relative to the domain of a given function are important in describing the behavior of the function, as we shall soon see. This is the reason for making the next definition.

Definition 5.5c. A point a is called a **cluster point** of a set S if every $\mathfrak{N}^*(a, h)$ contains at least one point of S.

Thus, it follows from the preceding discussion that for the set S in Example 5.5a, every point x where $1 \leq x \leq 2$ is a cluster point of S. However, 0 is not a cluster point of S since not every deleted neighborhood of 0 contains points of S. For instance, the $\mathfrak{N}^*(0, \frac{1}{2})$ contains no points of S. Notice that 2 is a cluster point of S even though $2 \notin$ S. Furthermore, for the set $\mathfrak{I} .=. \{x : x = 1/10^n, n \in \mathfrak{N}\}$, 0 is a cluster point although $0 \notin \mathfrak{I}$. Does $\mathfrak{I}$ have any other cluster points?

Example 5.5b. Determine the cluster points of S if

$$S .=. \{x: x = 1/n, n \in \mathfrak{N}\}.$$

The only possible cluster point is 0, since for $x = 1/n$ we need only take a $\mathfrak{N}^*(1/n, h)$, where $h < 1/n - 1/(n + 1)$, to have a deleted neighborhood containing no points of S. That 0 is a cluster point follows from the fact that for every value of h there will always be a value of n large enough so that $1/n < h$ and therefore $1/n \in \mathfrak{N}^*(0, h)$.

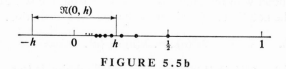

FIGURE 5.5b

Thus, if $h = 1/10^6$, then the point $1/(10^6 + 1)$ is in the $\mathfrak{N}^*(0, 1/10^6)$ (see Figure 5.5b).

Example 5.5c. Determine the cluster points, if there are any, of the set

$$S .=. \{(x): x = n, n \in \mathfrak{N}\}.$$

There are no cluster points for S because, for any n, a $\mathfrak{N}^*(n, \frac{1}{2})$ contains no points of S.

The following example illustrates how the concept of cluster point is of value to us in describing the behavior of functions in the neighborhood of certain special points.

Example 5.5d. Discuss the behavior of the function

$$f .=. \left\{(x, y): y = \frac{x^3 - 1}{x - 1}\right\}$$

in the neighborhood of the point 1.

Although f is not defined at $x = 1$, it is defined in every $\mathfrak{N}^*(1, h)$, so that 1 is a cluster point of the domain S of f. For values of $x \in \mathfrak{N}^*(1, h)$, the function may be described by

$$y = \frac{(x - 1)(x^2 + x + 1)}{(x - 1)} = x^2 + x + 1.$$

From this equation, it is apparent that for values of x very near to 1, the values of y are very near to 3, as the following table of values illustrates:

x	0.9	1.1	0.99	1.01	0.999	1.001
y	2.71	3.31	2.9701	3.0301	2.997001	3.003001

Hence, it appears intuitively that the point 3 is a cluster point of the range of f corresponding to the cluster point 1 of the domain of f. This situation is described by saying that "as x approaches 1, y approaches 3."

This idea is illustrated again in the next example.

Example 5.5e. If $f .=. \{(x, y): y = x^3, x \in \mathbb{R}\}$, what cluster point of the range of f corresponds to the cluster point 2 of the domain?

On an intuitive basis it seems clear that as x approaches 2, y approaches 8. That is, if we choose any value of x very near 2, the corresponding value of y is very near 8. For example, if

$$x = 2.001, \quad y = 8.012006001.$$

Conversely, if we choose any value of y very near 8, then we can find a corresponding value of x very near 2. Of course, although we may demonstrate that these statements are true in particular cases, it is desirable that we be able to make a general statement that will hold for *all* values of x or y in suitable neighborhoods. It is for this reason that the neighborhood concept becomes important.

We may convert the statement "as x approaches 2, y approaches 8" into a more precise mathematical statement by saying that for any $\mathfrak{N}(8, k)$ in the range of f, a corresponding $\mathfrak{N}^*(2, h)$ can be found in the domain of f such that

$$x \in \mathfrak{N}^*(2, h) \Rightarrow y \in \mathfrak{N}(8, k).$$

The details of actually finding the $\mathfrak{N}^*(2, h)$ for a given $\mathfrak{N}(8, k)$ are somewhat involved and will be postponed until Chapter 8. For the present, we shall rely entirely on the intuitive point of view that is suggested by the results of direct calculation, as in Examples 5.5d and 5.5e.

The terminology introduced in the preceding discussion is so useful that it is convenient to have a symbolic way of writing it.

Definition 5.5d. If a is a cluster point of the domain of a function $f .=. \{(x, y)\}$ and if,

(i) b is a corresponding cluster point of the range such that for each prescribed $\mathfrak{N}(b, k)$, there is a $\mathfrak{N}^*(a, h)$ such that

$$x \in \mathfrak{N}^*(a, h) \Rightarrow y \in \mathfrak{N}(b, k),$$

or if

(ii) y has a constant value b for all values of x in some $\mathfrak{N}^*(a)$,

then we write

$$\text{as } x \to a, \quad y \to b.$$

which is read "as x approaches a, y approaches b."

It is sometimes necessary to consider the behavior of a function on a one-sided neighborhood of a cluster point of its domain. In that case, a modification of the notation in Definition 5.5d may be used. For instance,

$$\text{as } x \to 2^-, \quad y \to 8^-$$

means that 2 and 8 are corresponding cluster points of the domain and range, respectively, of a function f such that whenever $x \in \mathfrak{N}^*(2^-, h)$, then $y \in \mathfrak{N}(8^-, k)$, where $\mathfrak{N}^*(2^-, h)$ is a one-sided neighborhood in the domain of f that is determined by the corresponding one-sided neighborhood $\mathfrak{N}(8^-, k)$ in the range of f. The notation

$$\text{as } x \to 2^-, \quad y \to 8^-$$

may be read "as x approaches 2 from below (or from the left), y approaches 8 from below." Similarly,

$$\text{as } x \to 2^+, \quad y \to 8^-$$

is read "as x approaches 2 from above, y approaches 8 from below." (How would the notation "as $x \to 2^+$, $y \to 2^+$" be read?)

In any case, the statement that $x \to a^+$ means that the values of the independent variable x are restricted to a deleted right neighborhood of a, and $x \to a^-$ means that the values of x are restricted to a deleted left neighborhood of a. For example, if $y = -\sqrt{x - 1}$, then

$$\text{as } x \to 1^+, \quad y \to 0^-.$$

This statement means that 0 is the cluster point of the range corresponding to the cluster point 1 of the domain. In this case, y is real only if $x \geq 1$, and for such values of x, $y \leq 0$.

Definition 5.5e. The domain S of a function is said to be **unbounded above** if there exists no number M_1 such that for all $x \in S$, $x < M_1$. The domain is said to be **unbounded below** if there exists no number M_2 such that for all $x \in S$, $x > M_2$.

If the domain S of a function $f .=. \{(x, y)\}$ is unbounded above, then it is frequently desirable to know the behavior of y for "all very large values of $x \in S$," that is, for all values of $x > M$, where M is any given positive number no matter how large. In this connection, the following notation, to be read "x increases without bound," is used:

$$x \to \infty.$$

For instance, a correct statement using this notation is

$$\text{as } x \to \infty, \quad 1/x \to 0^+.$$

This may be read "as x increases without bound, $1/x$ approaches zero through positive values."

In a similar fashion, the notation

$$x \to -\infty,$$

to be read "x decreases without bound," is employed if the domain is unbounded below. Thus, it is correct to write

$$\text{as } x \to -\infty, \quad 1 - \frac{1}{x} \to 1^+,$$

or

$$\text{as } x \to -\infty, \quad x^2 \to \infty.$$

The reader should translate these statements into meaningful English for himself.

Exercises 5.5

1. Determine which points of each of the following sets have neighborhoods contained entirely within the set.

   (a) $S .=. \{x: x = 1/n, n \in \mathfrak{N}\}$.
   (b) $S .=. \{x: 0 \leqq x \leqq 1\}$.
   (c) $S .=. \{x: 0 < x < 1\} \cup \{x: 1 < x < 2\}$.
   (d) $S .=. \{x: 0 \leqq x \leqq 1 \text{ and } x \in \mathfrak{F}\}$.

2. What is the set of cluster points for each of the following sets?

   (a) $\{x: x = 1 - (1/n), n \in \mathfrak{N}\}$.
   (b) $\{x: 0 < x < 1\}$.
   (c) $\{t: t = (1/n) + (-1)^n, n \in \mathfrak{N}\}$.
   (d) $\{x: 0 < x < 1\} \cup \{x: 1 < x < 2\}$.
   (e) $\{x: 0 < x < 1 \text{ and } x \in \mathfrak{F}\}$.
   (f) $\{x: 0 < x < 1 \text{ and } x \in \mathfrak{R} - \mathfrak{F}\}$.

3. Use the neighborhood concept or the discussion that follows Definition 5.5e to explain what is meant by each of the following statements.

   (a) If $y = x^2 + 2x$, then as $x \to 1$, $y \to 3$.

   (b) If $y = \dfrac{x^2 - 4}{x - 2}$, then as $x \to 2$, $y \to 4$.

   (c) If $y = [\![x]\!]$, then as $x \to 2^-$, $y \to 1$,
   and as $x \to 2^+$, $y \to 2$.

   (d) If $y = \dfrac{1}{x}$, then as $x \to \infty$, $y \to 0^+$,

   and as $x \to -\infty$, $y \to 0^-$.

   (e) If $y = \dfrac{x^2}{x^2 - 1}$, then as $x \to 1^-$, $y \to -\infty$,

   and as $x \to 1^+$, $y \to \infty$.

   (f) If $y = x - [\![x]\!]$, then as $x \to 2^-$, $y \to 1^-$,
   and as $x \to 2^+$, $y \to 0^+$.

4. Discuss the behavior of y

   (a) as $x \to 0$ if $y = |x|$,
   (b) as $x \to 1$ if $y = x^2 - x + 1$,
   (c) as $x \to 0$ if $y = 1/|x|$,

   (d) as $x \to 0^+$ if $y = \dfrac{1}{x + |x|}$,

   (e) as $x \to \infty$ if $y = 1/|x|$,

   (f) as $x \to 0^+$ if $y = \dfrac{x}{x + |x|}$,

   (g) as $x \to \infty$ if $y = \dfrac{x}{x + |x|}$.

In many problems in applied mathematics, part of the solution consists of finding the values of arbitrary constants so that a function will satisfy certain conditions called boundary conditions (such as one end of a rod being held at constant temperature, or the ends of a vibrating string being fixed at certain points). In Numbers 5 to 9, find the values of the constants A and B so that the given function satisfies the stated conditions.

5. $x(t) = t^2 + 2Bt + 4A$; as $t \to 0$, $x(t) \to 5$, and as $t \to 3$, $x(t) \to 2$.

6. $u(x) = \dfrac{Ax}{B + |x|}$; as $x \to -1$, $u(x) \to \dfrac{1}{3}$, and as $x \to \infty$, $u(x) \to -1$.

7. $s(x) = \dfrac{Ax}{Bx + |x|}$; as $x \to 1$, $s(x) \to 2$, and as $x \to -\infty$, $s(x) \to 3$.

8. $u(x) = \dfrac{Ax^2}{1 - Bx^2}$; as $x \to \infty$, $u(x) \to -\dfrac{4}{3}$, and as $x \to -2$, $u(x) \to -\dfrac{32}{23}$.

9. $u(t) = -2t + \sqrt{At - Bt^2}$; as $t \to 1$, $u(t) \to 0$, and as $t \to -1$, $u(t) \to 2$.

5.6 SIMPLE ALGEBRAIC FUNCTIONS

It is frequently advantageous to be able to visualize the graph of a function from the properties of the function. Certain of such properties—the domain and range of the function, symmetry, and periodicity—have already been discussed. With the aid of these and additional properties to be discussed in this section, the student should be able to sketch the graphs of many functions with a minimum of point plotting.

In many of the examples that we have previously considered, we were concerned with simple algebraic expressions that did not involve fractional forms. In this section we shall concentrate on expressions involving these forms.

Example 5.6a. Graph the function

$$\left\{(x, y): y = \frac{1}{x}\right\}.$$

The domain of this function is the set of all real numbers with the exception of zero; the range is the same set of numbers. It should be clear that zero is not a permissible value for either x or y because of the prohibition on division by zero.

Since the equation $y = 1/x$ or $xy = 1$ is unchanged when x and y are simultaneously replaced by $-x$ and $-y$, respectively, its graph must be symmetric with respect to the origin. Furthermore, the product xy is to be positive, so that x and y must have the same sign. Consequently, the graph appears in the first and third quadrants only.

It is to be particularly noticed that this graph does not intersect either axis. However, as smaller and smaller positive values are chosen for x, the corresponding values of y are larger and larger. In fact, by taking x sufficiently small, we may force the y values to be arbitrarily large—the smaller the x value, the larger the y. This is an appropriate place to employ the notation of the preceding section, since the sense of the last two sentences is given precisely by the statement

$$\text{as } x \to 0^+, \quad \text{then } y \to \infty.$$

Also, the graph becomes straighter and more nearly vertical and gets closer and closer to the positive *y*-axis as $x \to 0^+$. This kind of geometric behavior is described by saying that the *y*-axis is an **asymptote** to the curve, or that the graph approaches the *y*-axis asymptotically.

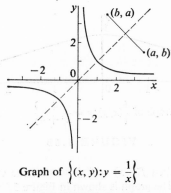

Graph of $\left\{(x, y) : y = \dfrac{1}{x}\right\}$

FIGURE 5.6a

In a similar fashion, we have $y \to 0^+$ as $x \to \infty$ and the graph approaches the line $= 0$. Furthermore, as $x \to 0^-$, $y \to -\infty$, and as $x \to -\infty$, $y \to 0^-$, so that we may also say that the *x*-axis is an asymptote to the curve, or that the graph approaches the -axis asymptotically. The curve is shown in Figure 5.6a.

The concepts of asymptote introduced in the preceding example are summarized in the next definition.

Definition 5.6a. If $y = f(x)$, where $f(x)$ is an algebraic expression, and if a is a cluster point of the domain of f such that $|y| \to \infty$ as $x \to a^+$ or $x \to a^-$, then the line $x = a$ is called a **vertical asymptote** to the curve. If b is a cluster point of the range of f such that $y \to b^+$ or $y \to b^-$ as $|x| \to \infty$, then the line $y = b$ is called a **horizontal asymptote** to the curve.

As Figure 5.6a shows, the graph of $y = 1/x$ is symmetric to the line $y = x$. In general, as the reader may easily verify, the point (b, a) is symmetric to the point (a, b) with respect to the line $y = x$. Consequently, a test for such symmetry in the graph of an equation is as follows. In the given equation, interchange the two variables. If the equation is unchanged, then its graph is symmetric with respect to the line $y = x$. For example, $x^2 + y^2 - 3xy = 0$ and $y^2 + x^2 - 3yx = 0$ express the same relationship between x and y. Hence the graph of this equation is symmetric with respect to the line $y = x$.

Example 5.6b. Graph the equation

$$y = \frac{4}{x^2 + 4}.$$

The domain for this equation is $\mathfrak{R}$. From the form of the fraction, it follows that as

$x \to 0$, $y \to 1^-$ and that $y = 1$ is the largest possible value for y. Furthermore, cannot be zero or negative for any value of $x \in \mathcal{R}$, so that the range of y is $0 < y \leq 1$ Also, as $x \to \infty$, $y \to 0^+$ and as $x \to -\infty$, $y \to 0^+$. Thus the x-axis is an asymptote to the curve.

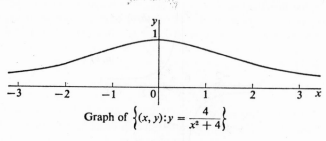

Graph of $\left\{(x, y):y = \dfrac{4}{x^2 + 4}\right\}$

FIGURE 5.6b

If $f(x) .=. 4/(x^2 + 4)$, then $f(-x) = f(x)$ so that the curve must be symmetric with respect to the y-axis. The graph is shown in Figure 5.6b.

Example 5.6c. Graph the function $\{(x, y)\}$ described by

$$y = \frac{x^2}{x^2 - 1}.$$

The domain of the function consists of all real numbers except 1 and -1. Solving for x^2, we get $x^2 = y/(y - 1)$, from which it follows that the range is $\{y: y \leq 0$ or $y > 1\}$. (For any value of y in the interval $0 < y < 1$, x^2 is negative, and for $y = 1$, x^2 is undefined.)

The curve passes through the origin but intersects the axes at no other point. Since x may be replaced by $-x$ without changing the equation, the curve is symmetric to the y-axis.

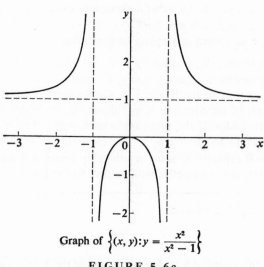

Graph of $\left\{(x, y):y = \dfrac{x^2}{x^2 - 1}\right\}$

FIGURE 5.6c

As $x \to 1^-$, $y \to -\infty$. For example, $x = 0.9 \Rightarrow y = -4.26$, $x = 0.99 \Rightarrow y = -49.8$, and so on. Thus the curve is asymptotic on the left to the lower portion of the line $x = 1$. Similarly, as $x \to 1^+$, $y \to \infty$, so that the curve is asymptotic on the right to the upper portion of the line $x = 1$ (see Figure 5.6c). It follows by the symmetry previously noted that the line $x = -1$ is also an asymptote to the curve.

Moreover, as $x \to \infty$ or as $x \to -\infty$, $y \to 1^+$, since for x large in absolute value, the corresponding value of y is close to 1 but a little greater than 1. This conclusion follows from the fact that the numerator of $x^2/(x^2 - 1)$ is one unit greater than the denominator. Hence, $y = 1$ is a horizontal asymptote to the curve.

The work on asymptotes which has been presented in connection with the preceding examples will now be summarized in order to help clarify the concept. This discussion is restricted to equations of the form $y = f(x)$, where $f(x)$ is a **rational fraction**—that is, a fraction whose numerator and denominator are each polynomials in x. This means that

$$f(x) = \frac{a_0 x^m + a_1 x^{m-1} + \cdots + a_m}{b_0 x^n + b_1 x^{n-1} + \cdots + b_n}.$$

It is assumed that numerator and denominator have no common factors.

Upon setting the denominator equal to zero and solving the resulting equation for x, we obtain the real values of x (if any) that describe the *vertical asymptotes*. This follows from the fact that in a sufficiently small deleted neighborhood of such a value of x, the fraction becomes arbitrarily large in absolute value.

There are three separate cases to discuss in connection with *horizontal asymptotes*.

(a) If the degree of the numerator is less than the degree of the denominator, then, as in Example 5.6a and Example 5.6b, $y \to 0$ as $x \to \infty$ or as $x \to -\infty$, and the x-axis is a horizontal asymptote.

(b) If the degree of the numerator is equal to the degree of the denominator, then, as in Example 5.6c, $y \to a_0/b_0$ as $x \to \pm\infty$, and the line $y = a_0/b_0$ is a horizontal asymptote.

(c) If the degree of the numerator is greater than the degree of the denominator, then $|y| \to \infty$ as $|x| \to \infty$, and there is no horizontal asymptote.

To illustrate Case (b), let $y = (2x^2 + 3x + 4)/(3x^2 + 7x + 8)$. Then, as $x \to \pm\infty$, $y \to \frac{2}{3}$. This is apparent if the numerator and denominator are divided by x^2, so that, for $x \neq 0$,

$$\frac{2x^2 + 3x + 4}{3x^2 + 7x + 8} = \frac{2 + \dfrac{3}{x} + \dfrac{4}{x^2}}{3 + \dfrac{7}{x} + \dfrac{8}{x^2}}.$$

As x increases, all the terms of both numerator and denominator, except the coefficients of x^2 in the original fraction, approach zero.

Exercises 5.6

In Numbers 1 to 24, discuss and sketch the graph of the given equation.

1. $xy = -1$.

2. $x^2 y = -1$.

3. $y = \dfrac{3}{x - 1}$.

4. $y = \dfrac{4}{x^2 + 1}$.

5. $y = \dfrac{x}{x^2 + 1}$.

6. $y = \dfrac{x^2}{(x - 1)(x - 4)}$.

7. $y = \dfrac{-x^2}{x^2 - 4x + 3}$.

8. $y = \dfrac{x^2}{1 - x^2}$.

9. $y = \dfrac{2}{4 - x^2}$.

10. $y = \dfrac{x + 4}{x - 4}$.

11. $y = \dfrac{x}{x^2 - 1}$.

12. $y = \dfrac{x}{x - 4}$.

13. $y = \dfrac{x}{(x - 3)^2}$.

14. $y = \dfrac{2x}{(x + 4)^2}$.

15. $y = \dfrac{x^2 - 9}{x^2 + 9}$.

16. $y = \dfrac{4x^2}{x^2 - 9}$.

17. $y = \dfrac{4 - x^2}{x^2 - 9}$.

18. $y = \dfrac{1}{\sqrt{x^2 - 1}}$.

19. $y = \dfrac{x - 2}{x^2 - 4}$.

20. $y^2 = \dfrac{x}{x + 1}$.

21. $y = \sqrt{\dfrac{x}{x + 1}}$.

22. $y^2 = \dfrac{x^2 - 4x}{x - 2}$.

23. $y^2 = \dfrac{4}{9 + x^2}$.

24. $y^2 = \dfrac{x^2}{x^2 - 1}$.

25. Since

$$\frac{2x^2 + 3}{6x} = \frac{x}{3} + \frac{1}{2x},$$

sketch the graph of

$$y = \frac{2x^2 + 3}{6x}$$

by sketching the graphs of $y = x/3$ and $y = 1/(2x)$ and adding the ordinates. Does this curve have an oblique asymptote?

26. Since

$$\frac{x^2 - 8}{x - 3} = x + 3 + \frac{1}{x - 3},$$

sketch the graph of

$$y = \frac{x^2 - 8}{x - 3}$$

by sketching the graphs of $y = x + 3$ and $y = 1/(x - 3)$ and adding the ordinates. Does this curve have an oblique asymptote?

27. The lateral area of a right circular cone is equal to one-half the perimeter of the base times the slant height, and the total surface area is the lateral area plus the area of the base. If the total surface area of a right circular cone is 4π square units, find its altitude as a function of the radius and sketch the graph of this function.

28. A right circular cone of height h is circumscribed about a sphere of radius 4 inches. Express the volume of the cone as a function of its height and sketch the graph of this function.

5.7 INVERSE FUNCTIONS

Suppose that $\$P$ is invested at an interest rate r compounded annually for n years. It is quite easy to show by mathematical induction that the total amount A (original principal P plus all interest) is given by

$$A = P(1 + r)^n.$$

In order to simplify matters, let $P = 100$ and $n = 10$. Then we have

$$A = 100(1 + r)^{10},$$

which defines a function $f = \{(r, A): A = 100(1 + r)^{10}\}$. This is a natural form to consider if we wish to study the way in which A changes with r, since the formula for A shows exactly how A depends on r.

However, suppose we are interested in the way in which r depends on A, having in mind perhaps such questions as what interest rate will double our money in ten years. This suggests that we solve the equation $A = 100(1 + r)^{10}$ for r to get

$$(1 + r)^{10} = 0.01A,$$
$$1 + r = \sqrt[10]{0.01A},$$
$$r = \sqrt[10]{0.01A} - 1.$$

The last equation may be regarded as defining a function

$$g = \{(A, r): r = \sqrt[10]{0.01A} - 1\},$$

a study of which will answer many of our questions concerning the dependence of r on A. For instance, if $A = 200$, then $r = \sqrt[10]{2} - 1 = 0.072$ (approximately).

There are many applications which lead to considerations similar to those in the preceding discussion. These are problems in which it is desirable to interchange the roles of the two variables in a given function and to study the resulting relation. These ideas are made more precise in the following paragraphs.

Consider a function f that consists of the set $\{(0, 1), (1, 3), (2, 4), (3, 2)\}$ and let the elements of each pair in this set be interchanged so that there is obtained a new relation $\{(1, 0), (3, 1), (4, 2), (2, 3)\}$, whose domain is the range of f and whose range is the domain of f. For this particular f, the new relation is also a function, since one and only one element of the range corresponds to each element of the domain.

The domain and range of any relation may be interchanged in like manner to form a new relation. Each pair in the new relation is obtained by interchanging the elements of a corresponding pair in the original relation. Two such sets of pairs are called **inverse relations;** each relation is said to be the inverse of the other.

In the special case where both relations are functions, they are called **inverse functions.** The inverse of a function f is denoted by the symbol f^{-1}. It is essential to realize that the superscript -1 in this notation is *not* an exponent; it signifies only that f^{-1} is the inverse of f. For example, in the preceding illustration, it would be proper to use the notation f^{-1} for the second set of pairs, since it is the inverse of the first set f. These important ideas are summarized in

Definition 5.7a. If a function f is such that to each element of its range there corresponds one and only one element of its domain, then the set obtained by interchanging the elements in each of the pairs of the function f is called the *inverse function* of f and is denoted by f^{-1}.

Example 5.7a. Let $g .=. \{(x, y): y = 2x - 1\}$. For each value of x, there is just one value of y, and conversely. Determine the inverse function g^{-1}, and graph both functions on the same set of axes.

A representative element of g may be indicated by $(x, 2x - 1)$, so that the corresponding element of g^{-1} is $(2x - 1, x)$. For most purposes, this way of giving the pair is awkward; we prefer to specify directly the manner in which the second element of the pair may be formed from the first one. Thus, if we write $s = 2x - 1$, then we find $x = \frac{1}{2}(s + 1)$, so that the same pair may be indicated by $(s, \frac{1}{2}(s + 1))$. Consequently, we have

$$g^{-1} = \{(s, t): t = \tfrac{1}{2}(s + 1)\}.$$

Since the particular letters used to indicate numbers of the domain and the range are immaterial, we may also write, as is customary,

$$g^{-1} = \{(x, y): y = \tfrac{1}{2}(x + 1)\}.$$

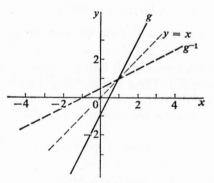

FIGURE 5.7a

The graphs of the two functions g and g^{-1} are shown in Figure 5.7a. Notice that the two graphs are symmetric with respect to the line $y = x$. Explain why this should be so.

Example 5.7b. Find the inverse of the function $F .=. \{(x, y)\}$, where $x = \sqrt{y}$.

Observe that the specification $x = \sqrt{y}$ means that the domain of F is $x \geq 0$. Also $y = x^2$, so that an equivalent definition of F is $\{(x, x^2): x \geq 0\}$.

From this last result, it follows that the inverse function is $F^{-1} = \{(x^2, x): x \geq 0\}$. Thus, if we write $x^2 = t$, with $x \geq 0$, then $x = \sqrt{t}$ and $F^{-1} = \{(t, \sqrt{t})\}$, or, in terms of the letters x and y,

$$F^{-1} = \{(x, \sqrt{x})\} = \{(x, y): y = \sqrt{x}\}.$$

The graphs of the two functions are shown in Figure 5.7b. Notice again the symmetry with respect to the line $y = x$.

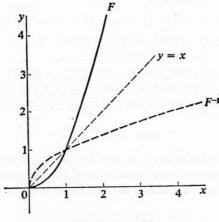

FIGURE 5.7b

In Example 3.3f we considered a set of algebraic expressions with respect to a substitution operation ⑤. For example,

$$\frac{1}{1 - x} \;⑤\; \frac{x}{x - 1} = \frac{\frac{1}{1 - x}}{\frac{1}{1 - x} - 1} = \frac{1}{x}.$$

Suppose each of these expressions is associated with a function as follows:

$$f(x) .=. \frac{1}{1 - x},$$

$$g(x) .=. \frac{x}{x - 1},$$

$$h(x) .=. \frac{1}{x}.$$

Then the result of substituting $1/(1 - x)$ for x in $x/(x - 1)$ can be expressed in functional notation as

$$f(x) \circledS g(x) = h(x)$$

or as

$$g[f(x)] = h(x).$$

A functional form obtained by the substitution of one form into another is described in

Definition 5.7b. If $y .=. f(x)$ and $u .=. g(y)$, and if

$$u = g[f(x)] .=. h(x),$$

then h is called the g **composite** of f.

Example 5.7c. If $f(x) .=. x^2 - x - 1$ and $g(x) .=. x - 1$, find $f[g(x)]$ and $g[f(x)]$.

We have, by direct substitution,

$$f[g(x)] = (x - 1)^2 - (x - 1) - 1 = x^2 - 3x + 1,$$

and

$$g[f(x)] = (x^2 - x - 1) - 1 = x^2 - x - 2.$$

This example illustrates that, in general, $f[g(x)] \neq g[f(x)]$.

The notion of a composite function is often useful in describing functions in terms of other functions that may be simpler in some desirable respect. To illustrate, consider

$$h(x) .=. \sqrt{1 - x^2}.$$

If $f(x) .=. 1 - x^2$ and $g(y) .=. \sqrt{y}$, then $h(x)$ is the g composite of f. In order that $h(x) \in \mathfrak{R}$, we must restrict the domain of f to the interval $-1 \leq x \leq 1$ so that the range of f will be a subset of the domain of g.

Exercises 5.7

1. In each of the following, does the function have a corresponding inverse function? If so, find the inverse function and sketch.
   (a) $f .=. \{(1, 10), (2, 20), (3, 30)\}$.
   (b) $g .=. \{(1, 5), (2, 4), (3, 3), (4, 2), (5, 1)\}$.
   (c) $h .=. \{(2, 1), (4, 3), (6, 5), (8, 1), (10, 2)\}$.
   (d) $F .=. \{(1, 2), (2, 3), (3, 2), (4, 1)\}$.
   (e) $H .=. \{(x, x)\}$.
   (f) $G .=. \{(u, -u^2)\}, u \geq 0$.
   (g) $f .=. \{(x, y): y = -x\}$.
   (h) $F .=. \{(x, y): y = 2 - 2x\}$.
   (i) $G .=. \{(t - 1, t + 1)\}$.
2. In each of the following, the inverse relation is not a function. Make an alteration in the domain of the given function so that the new relation is a function with an inverse, and sketch the graphs of both functions.
   (a) $\{(x, y): y = x^2 + 1\}$.
   (b) $\{(x, y): y = 1 - x^2\}$.
   (c) $\{(u, v): v = \sqrt{1 - u^2}\}$.
   (d) $\{(s, t): t = |s|\}$.

3. Attention was called to the fact that in f^{-1}, the -1 is not an exponent. However, we can justify writing $(f^{-1})^{-1} = f$. How?

4. Find $f[g(x)]$ and $g[f(x)]$ and state any necessary restrictions on the domain of g or of f, if

(a) $f(x) = \dfrac{1}{x-1}$, $g(x) = \dfrac{x^2}{x^2-1}$;

(b) $f(x) = \dfrac{x}{1-x}$, $g(x) = \dfrac{x}{x-1}$;

(c) $f(x) = g(x) = \dfrac{x-1}{x+1}$;

(d) $f(x) = \sqrt{x-1}$, $g(x) = \dfrac{1}{x+1}$.

5. Express each of the following as a composite of two "simpler" functions, and state any necessary restrictions on the domains.

(a) $h(x) = \dfrac{x-1}{\sqrt{x}}$.   (b) $h(x) = \sqrt{\dfrac{x}{x-1}}$.

6. The following data, showing the variation in thermal conductivity of copper with changes in temperature, were obtained by experimentation:

Absolute Temperature	10	15	20	30	40	60	80
Thermal Conductivity	1.5	2.4	4.1	3.8	3.1	2.4	1.8

(a) Plot these points to display the thermal conductivity as a function of the absolute temperature, and draw a smooth curve through them.

(b) What do you think happens to the thermal conductivity as the absolute temperature approaches zero? Estimate the thermal conductivity for an absolute temperature of 5°.

(c) What restrictions would be necessary to make the inverse of the function represented by this graph a function? For what absolute temperature is the thermal conductivity 3?

7. (a) Show that $f[f^{-1}(x)] = x$ if
$$f(x) = \frac{x-1}{x+1}, \quad x \neq 1.$$

(b) Is it true in general that $f[f^{-1}(x)] = f^{-1}[f(x)] = x$?

8. If $f(x+2) = x^2 + 1$, then $f(x)$ can be found as follows. Let $x + 2 = t$ so that $x = t - 2$. Then
$$f(t) = (t-2)^2 + 1 = t^2 - 4t + 5 \Rightarrow f(x) = x^2 - 4x + 5.$$
This method may always be applied in case we have given $f[g(x)]$, where g^{-1} is a function. Use this procedure in each of the following.

(a) $f(\tfrac{1}{2}x + 1) = \tfrac{1}{2}x - 1$; $f(x) = ?$ (c) $F(\sqrt{x} - 1) = x^3$; $F(x) = ?$

(b) $g(x-1) = \dfrac{x+1}{x-1}$; $g(x) = ?$ (d) $G\left(\dfrac{1}{x}\right) = \dfrac{x-1}{x+1}$; $G(x) = ?$

9. Suppose a function f has an inverse function f^{-1}, and that f obeys a "functional equation" such as

$$f(x) + f(y) = f(xy).$$

What is the corresponding property of the function f^{-1}?

The given equation may be solved for xy by "taking inverses" of both sides to get

$$f^{-1}[f(x) + f(y)] = f^{-1}[f(xy)] = xy.$$

Now, let $u = f(x)$ and $v = f(y)$ so that

$$x = f^{-1}(u) \quad \text{and} \quad y = f^{-1}(v).$$

Then substitution yields

$$f^{-1}(u + v) = f^{-1}(u)f^{-1}(v),$$

which is the desired result.

(a) Use the same procedure to obtain the result

$$f^{-1}(x^n) = nf^{-1}(x)$$

from the equation

$$[f(x)]^n = f(nx).$$

(b) If $f(ax + by) = af(x) + bf(y)$, a and b being specified numbers, show that f^{-1} obeys this same equation; that is,

$$f^{-1}(ax + by) = af^{-1}(x) + bf^{-1}(y).$$

10. If $g(x) = x^2 + 1$, find $g[g(x)]$.
11. What formula defines $f(g)$ if $f(x) = \sqrt{x - 1}$ and $g(x) = x^2 - 3$? Give the domain and range of each of f, g, and $f(g)$.
12. What formula defines $G(H)$ if $G(x) = \sqrt{4 - x}$ and $H(x) = 1/x$? Give the domain and range of each of G, H, and $G(H)$.
13. Suppose $f(xy) = f(x) + f(y)$ and that f^{-1} is a function.

(a) Show that $f(1) = 0$.
(b) If $f(2) = 1$, show that $f(4) = 2$ and $f^{-1}(3) = 8$.

Summary of Chapter 5

A number of important terms and intuitive ideas have been introduced in this chapter. The reader should have a clear understanding of each of the following items:

(1) relation, domain, range (Section 5.1);
(2) dependent and independent variables (Section 5.1);
(3) function, and the difference between a relation and a function (Section 5.2);
(4) graphs, lines and points of symmetry (Section 5.3);
(5) the difference between a function, the equation (or equations) defining the function, and the graph of a function (Section 5.3);
(6) periodic function and its characteristics (Section 5.4);
(7) step function and its properties (Section 5.4);

(8) right and left neighborhoods of a point, deleted neighborhoods (Section 5.5);
(9) cluster points of a set of points (Section 5.5);
(10) the meaning of symbols such as "as $x \to a$, $y \to b$," "$x \to \infty$," etc., and their use in describing the behavior of functions (Section 5.5);
(11) the meaning of boundedness and unboundedness of a function (Section 5.5);
(12) asymptotes of a graph (Section 5.6);
(13) inverse of a function (Section 5.7);
(14) composite functions (Section 5.7).

Chapter 6

Linear and Quadratic Functions

6.1 LINEAR EQUATIONS

An equation of the form

(1)
$$Ax + By + C = 0$$

is called a **linear equation** because of its close connection with the straight line in plane geometry. Assuming $B \neq 0$, we may solve Equation (1) for y to obtain a result of the form

(2)
$$y = mx + b,$$

where $m = -A/B$ and $b = -C/B$. Equation (2) clearly determines a unique value of y for each real value of x, so that we may associate with it the solution set

$$\{(x, y): y = mx + b\}.$$

The function defined by this set is called a **linear function.**

The equations

$$Ax + C = 0 \qquad A \neq 0,$$

and

$$By + C = 0, \qquad B \neq 0,$$

are special cases of Equation (1). The graph of the first equation is a straight line parallel to the y-axis, as can be seen from the fact that the equation is equivalent to $x = d$, where $d = -C/A$ is a constant. Thus this equation is satisfied by the set of points $\{(d, y)\}$, where y is any real number. Figure 5.3c shows the graph for the special case $d = 2$. The student should make a similar analysis to convince himself that the second equation will have for its graph a straight line parallel to the x-axis (compare Figure 5.3b).

Before proceeding to a discussion of the relationship between the general linear equation and the straight line, it should be made clear that a straight line is regarded as being completely determined by any given point on the line and the direction of the line. Thus, a line is considered to be specified by a pair of coordinates (x_1, y_1) and a set of direction numbers $[m, n]$ (see Section 4.3).

Theorem 6.1a. Every straight line has an equation of the form

$$Ax + By + C = 0.$$

PROOF: Let the line be specified by the coordinates (x_1, y_1) of a point P_1 on the line and the direction numbers $[m, n]$ of the line. Let $P(x, y)$ be any second point on the line. Then $[x - x_1, y - y_1]$ must also be direction numbers of the line (compare Section 4.3), so that

$$x - x_1 = km, \quad y - y_1 = kn.$$

If k is eliminated by multiplying both members of the first of these equations by n and of the second equation by m and subtracting, the result is

$$n(x - x_1) - m(y - y_1) = 0$$

or

$$nx - my + my_1 - nx_1 = 0.$$

With $A = n$, $B = -m$, and $C = my_1 - nx_1$, the equation is of the form $Ax + By + C = 0$, which was to be shown.

The next theorem is essentially the converse of Theorem 6.1a, and completes the description of the connection between the straight line and the general linear equation (1).

Theorem 6.1b. The equation $Ax + By + C = 0$, where at least one of A, B is different from zero, has a straight line for its graph.

PROOF: In order to prove this theorem, we must show two things: (i) that the solution set of the equation consists of points all on a straight line, and (ii) that every point on this line is in the solution set of the equation.

(i) Let $P_1(x_1, y_1)$ and $P_2(x_2, y_2)$ be two points whose coordinates satisfy the given equation. This means that

$$Ax_1 + By_1 + C = 0$$

and

$$Ax_2 + By_2 + C = 0.$$

By subtraction, we get

$$A(x_2 - x_1) + B(y_2 - y_1) = 0.$$

It is not difficult to see that this equation is equivalent to the pair of equations

(3) $$x_2 - x_1 = kB, \quad y_2 - y_1 = -kA,$$

where k is a constant. (The reader may check this statement in case $A \neq 0$, by setting $y_2 - y_1 = -kA$ and solving for $x_2 - x_1$. If $B \neq 0$, he may set $x_2 - x_1 = kB$ and solve for $y_2 - y_1$.) It follows from the discussion in Section 4.3 that the direction from any point $P_1(x_1, y_1)$ to any other point $P_2(x_2, y_2)$ has the direction numbers $[B, -A]$. Thus, all points in the solution set lie on the line specified by the point $P_1(x_1, y_1)$ and the set of direction numbers $[B, -A]$.

(ii) Now suppose that $P_3(x_3, y_3)$ is any other point on the line specified by $P_1(x_1, y_1)$ and the direction numbers $[B, -A]$. Then

$$x_3 - x_1 = pB, \quad y_3 - y_1 = -pA.$$

If these two equations are solved for x_3 and y_3, respectively, and the results substituted into the left member of Equation (1), we find

$$Ax_3 + By_3 + C = A(x_1 + pB) + B(y_1 - pA) + C$$
$$= Ax_1 + By_1 + C = 0,$$

since (x_1, y_1) was assumed to be in the solution set of Equation (1). We have thus shown that every point on the line is in the solution set of the equation. Hence the proof of the theorem is complete.

The following examples illustrate the application of the preceding theorems and of some of the ideas that occurred in their proofs. It is important to note that Equations (3) show that $[B, -A]$ may be taken as a set of direction numbers for the line $Ax + By + C = 0$.

Example 6.1a. Find an equation for the straight line passing through the points $P_1(2, -1)$ and $P_2(4, 5)$.

It follows from the work in Section 4.3 that these two points determine the direction characterized by the direction numbers $[2, 6]$. Suppose $P(x, y)$ is any point on the line determined by P_1 and P_2 (Figure 6.1a). Then direction numbers that characterize the

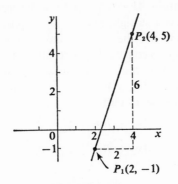

FIGURE 6.1a

line through P and P_1 are $[x - 2, y + 1]$. Since the two sets of direction numbers must be proportional, we may write

$$x - 2 = 2t, \quad y + 1 = 6t,$$

where t, the proportionality factor, may be any real number. For each value of t, the two equations determine a point on the line. For instance, if $t = 0$, we get $x = 2$, $y = -1$, that is, the point $(2, -1)$; if $t = 1$, then the point is $(4, 5)$; if $t = -3$, the point is $(-4, -18)$, and so on.

In this example, since neither direction number is zero, we may solve for t in both equations to obtain

$$t = \frac{x - 2}{2} \quad \text{and} \quad t = \frac{y + 1}{6},$$

so that

$$\frac{x-2}{2} = \frac{y+1}{6} \quad \text{or} \quad 3x - y - 7 = 0.$$

Thus, every point P that lies on the straight line determined by P_1 and P_2 must have coordinates that satisfy the equation $3x - y - 7 = 0$. As a check, notice that direction numbers of this line are indicated to be $[-1, -3]$ which are proportional to $[2, 6]$.

In the solution of Example 6.1a, there occurred the equations $x - 2 = 2t$ and $y + 1 = 6t$. Equations of this form constitute a useful way of describing a straight line. It is clear from the proofs of the preceding theorems that a pair of equations

(4) $$x - x_1 = mt, \quad y - y_1 = nt$$

always describes the straight line specified by the point (x_1, y_1) and the direction numbers $[m, n]$. Equations (4) are called **parametric equations** of the line and the auxiliary variable t is called a **parameter.**

Example 6.1b. A straight line is described by the equations $x = 2 + t, y = 3 - 3t$. Write an equation for this line in the general linear form.

This problem can be solved by eliminating the parameter t. This can be done by adding $3x$ and y to get

$$3x + y = 6 + 3t + 3 - 3t$$

or

$$3x + y - 9 = 0.$$

(See Figure 6.1b.)

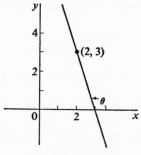

FIGURE 6.1b

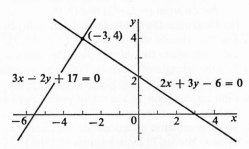

FIGURE 6.1c

Example 6.1c. Find an equation of the straight line that is perpendicular to the line $2x + 3y - 6 = 0$ and that passes through the point $(-3, 4)$ (Figure 6.1c).

Direction numbers of the given line are $[B, -A] = [3, -2]$. If $[m, n]$ is a set of direction numbers of a line perpendicular to the given line, then by Theorem 4.3c,

$$3m - 2n = 0.$$

A set of numbers satisfying this condition is $[2, 3]$. Hence the desired equation is of the form

$$3x - 2y + C = 0.$$

(Why?) The value of C may be determined from the fact that the point $(-3, 4)$ must be on this line. Thus, by substituting the coordinates of this point into the equation, we get

$$3(-3) - 2(4) + C = 0 \quad \text{or} \quad C = 17.$$

Therefore the desired equation is $3x - 2y + 17 = 0$.

Exercises 6.1

1. Find an equation of the line passing through the two given points.

   (a) $(-2, 3)$ and $(4, -1)$.   (d) $(-1, -2)$ and $(2, -2)$.
   (b) $(-2, -3)$ and $(-2, 1)$.   (e) $(3, 0)$ and $(0, -4)$.
   (c) $(-2, -3)$ and $(3, 2)$.   (f) $(0, -2)$ and $(-5, 0)$.

2. Write an equation for the straight line that passes through the point $(2, -2)$ and is parallel to the line $3x - 5y = 8$. (After determining the direction numbers of the desired line, use the method of Example 6.1c.)

3. A line L passes through the point $(2, \frac{3}{2})$ and is perpendicular to the line $3x + 4y = 12$. At what point does L cut the x-axis?

4. (a) Find the area of the triangle enclosed by the coordinate axes and the line $5x - 4y = 20$.

   (b) Use the result of (a) to find the length of the altitude to the hypotenuse of the triangle.

   (c) Can you find another method to work (b)?

5. Write an equation for a line that passes through the points (x_1, y_1), (x_2, y_2), with $x_1 \neq x_2$.

6. (a) Express by an algebraic equation the statement that the point (x, y) is equidistant from $(-5, -2)$ and $(3, 0)$.

   (b) Determine the algebraic equation of (a) by another method.

7. For the triangle with vertices at $(2, 6)$, $(5, 3)$, and $(3, 1)$, find the coordinates of the point where the altitude from the vertex $(5, 3)$ intersects the base.

8. For the triangle of Number 7, find an equation of the line passing through the vertex $(5, 3)$ and the midpoint of the opposite side.

9. Find an equation of the set of points equidistant from the points $(3, -1)$ and $(-3, 3)$.

10. Write parametric equations for the same line as in Number 5. Is the restriction $x_1 \neq x_2$ needed in these equations? Why?

11. Write an equation for a line having direction numbers $[k, 1]$ and passing through (x_0, y_0). What would have to be the value of k if the line also passes through the origin?

12. Find parametric equations for the line that passes through $(2, 3)$ and is parallel to the line $4x - y = 6$.

13. Find parametric equations for the line that passes through $(2, 3)$ and is perpendicular to the line $4x - y = 6$.

14. Where does the line $x = 2 - 3t$, $y = 1 + 4t$ cut the coordinate axes?

15. Does the line $x = 5 - 3t$, $y = -3 + 2t$ pass through the point $(14, 2)$? Explain.

16. A line passes through the point $(0, 2)$ and has direction numbers $[1, -4]$. Does the point $(100, -392)$ lie on this line? Explain.
17. Find the point on the line $3x - 2y - 15 = 0$ that is equidistant from the points $(-3, -1)$ and $(5, 3)$.
18. Find the point on the line $x + y + 7 = 0$ that is equidistant from the points $(-4, 1)$ and $(2, -3)$.
19. Find the center of the circle that passes through the points $(1, -3)$, $(-3, -7)$, and $(-1, -1)$.
20. Prove that the lines $ax + by = c_1$ and $ax + by = c_2$ are parallel.
21. Prove that the lines $ax + by = c_1$ and $bx - ay = c_2$ are perpendicular.

6.2 SPECIAL FORMS OF THE LINEAR EQUATION

The direction of any nonvertical line may be characterized by its slope, which was defined in Section 4.3 to be the ratio $m = k_2/k_1$ of its direction numbers $[k_1, k_2]$. An equation for a line having the slope m and passing through a given point (a, b) may easily be obtained by equating slopes. Thus, if (x, y) is any point other than (a, b) on the line, then

$$\frac{y - b}{x - a} = m \quad \text{or} \quad y - b = m(x - a).$$

The last equation is called the **point-slope form** of the equation of a straight line.

A special case of the point-slope form of the equation occurred in Equation (2) of Section 6.1. There, the point is $(0, b)$, which is where the line cuts the y-axis. The number b is called the **y-intercept** of the line and the equation

$$y = mx + b$$

is the **slope-intercept form** of the equation of a straight line.

Example 6.2a. Find an equation of the line that passes through the point $(2, 3)$ with a slope of -3 (see Figure 6.1b).

If (x, y) is a point on the line, then the slope determined by (x, y) and $(2, 3)$ is $(y - 3)/(x - 2)$, which must equal -3. Hence an equation of the line is $y + 3x = 9$.

Sometimes the points where the line cuts the two axes are of special interest. Suppose these points are denoted by $(a, 0)$ and $(0, b)$ so that a and b, respectively, are the x- and y-intercepts of the line (see Figure 6.2a). Then, if (x, y) is any

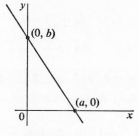

FIGURE 6.2a

other point on the line, an equation of the line can be found by equating two expressions for the slope. Thus

$$\frac{y-0}{x-a} = \frac{0-b}{a-0} \quad \text{or} \quad bx + ay = ab.$$

By division by ab, the usual **intercept form** is obtained:

$$\frac{x}{a} + \frac{y}{b} = 1.$$

Example 6.2b. The y-intercept of a line exceeds the x-intercept by 1 and the line passes through the point $(10, -6)$ (see Figure 6.2b). Find an equation of the line.

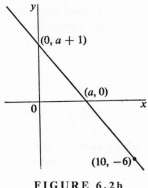

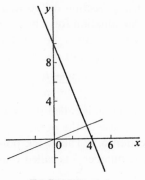

FIGURE 6.2b   **FIGURE 6.2c**

If the x-intercept is a, then the y-intercept must be $a + 1$. Hence, the equation may be written in the form

$$\frac{x}{a} + \frac{y}{a+1} = 1.$$

Since the line is to pass through $(10, -6)$, then

$$\frac{10}{a} - \frac{6}{a+1} = 1,$$

or

$$a^2 - 3a - 10 = 0,$$

or

$$(a - 5)(a + 2) = 0.$$

Thus,

$$a = 5 \quad \text{and} \quad a + 1 = 6$$

or

$$a = -2 \quad \text{and} \quad a + 1 = -1.$$

Consequently, there are two lines that satisfy the given conditions, and their equations are

$$\frac{x}{5} + \frac{y}{6} = 1 \quad \text{or} \quad 6x + 5y - 30 = 0$$

and

$$\frac{x}{-2} + \frac{y}{-1} = 1 \quad \text{or} \quad x + 2y + 2 = 0.$$

Example 6.2c. A line has an x-intercept of 4 and a y-intercept of 10. Find the perpendicular distance from the origin to this line (see Figure 6.2c).

The equation of the line may be written

$$\frac{x}{4} + \frac{y}{10} = 1$$

or

$$y = -\frac{5}{2}x + 10.$$

This equation shows that the slope of the line is $-5/2$, so that the slope of a line perpendicular to it is $2/5$. Hence, the line through the origin and perpendicular to the given line has an equation

$$y = \frac{2}{5}x.$$

In order to solve the equations of the two lines for their point of intersection, the values of y may be equated to get

$$\frac{2}{5}x = -\frac{5}{2}x + 10$$

or

$$29x = 100 \quad \text{and} \quad x = \frac{100}{29}.$$

Since $y = \frac{2}{5}x$, the corresponding value of y is $\frac{40}{29}$.

Accordingly, the distance from the origin to the line is

$$d = \sqrt{\left(\frac{100}{29}\right)^2 + \left(\frac{40}{29}\right)^2} = \frac{20}{\sqrt{29}}.$$

Exercises 6.2

1. Find the slope and the y-intercept of each of the following lines.

   (a) $2x - 3y + 7 = 0.$
   (b) $3x - 5y = 0.$
   (c) $1.2x + 0.04y = 2.4.$
   (d) $x = 1 + 2t, y = 3 - 4t.$
   (e) $x = -2 + 5t, y = 4t.$
   (f) $x/2 + y/3 = 4.$

2. Find the equation of a line having the sum of its intercepts equal to 5 and passing through the point $(2, -4)$.

3. Determine the slope and intercepts of the line passing through the two given points.

   (a) $(-2, 5), (3, -2).$
   (b) $(-4, -1), (2, -3).$
   (c) $(3, 4), (-2, -1).$
   (d) $(a, b), (c, d).$

4. What is the x-intercept of the line that has a slope -3 and a y-intercept 4?

5. A line has a slope -4 and a y-intercept 2. Does the point $(100, -392)$ lie on this line? Explain.

6. What is the y-intercept of the line that has a slope -2 and an x-intercept -3?
7. Find the distance from the origin to the line having an x-intercept of 4 and a y-intercept of -2.
8. A certain line has its y-intercept twice its x-intercept and passes through the point $(1, 4)$. Find an equation for this line.
9. Find the point of intersection of the altitudes of the triangle with vertices at $(1, 5)$, $(3, -2)$, $(-1, 1)$.
10. Find the equations of the perpendicular bisectors of the sides of the triangle in Number 9. Do all three bisectors intersect in a single point?
11. Find the point of intersection of the medians of the triangle in Number 9.
12. Are the three points found in Numbers 9, 10, and 11 collinear?
13. Do the lines $2x + 3y = 7$, $6x = 4y + 5$, $3x - 2y - 4 = 0$, and $6y = 9 - 4x$ form a rectangle?
14. Under standard atmospheric pressure, the freezing point of water is 32° on the Fahrenheit scale (F) and the boiling point is 212°. On the centigrade scale (C), the freezing point is 0° and the boiling point is 100°. Assuming that C is a linear function of F such that $C = mF + b$, find the centigrade temperature corresponding to 0° Fahrenheit.
15. Will the centers of all circles tangent to the line $2x - 3y = 6$ at the point $(6, 2)$ lie on a line? If so, find the equation of the line.
16. As shown in Figure 6.2d, a strut CD stays a beam AB. If the perpendicular distance from D to the wall AC is 2 feet, find the length of the strut.

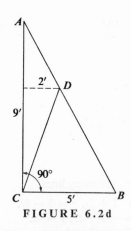

FIGURE 6.2d

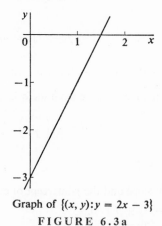

Graph of $\{(x, y): y = 2x - 3\}$

FIGURE 6.3a

17. According to Hooke's law, if a spring is stretched or compressed, its change in length (x) is proportional to the force (F) exerted upon it, and when the force is removed, the spring will return to its original position. If a force of 10 pounds stretches a spring $\frac{1}{4}$ inch, write an equation showing the relation between F and x and draw the graph.

6.3 FUNCTIONS AND SOLUTION SETS

In discussing an equation such as $2x - 3 = 0$, we may associate with it the function $\{(x, y): y = 2x - 3\}$, whose graph is shown in Figure 6.3a. The point

$(\frac{3}{2}, 0)$ is a point on this graph, and the x-coordinate of this point satisfies the equation $2x - 3 = 0$. This fact is interpreted geometrically by saying that the solution of the equation $2x - 3 = 0$ is the x-coordinate of the point where the line $y = 2x - 3$ crosses the x-axis. This idea will be of great value in discussing the solution sets of other types of equations.

Example 6.3a. Compare the solution set of $x + 2|x - 2| = 5$ with the graph of an appropriate function.

The function that is associated with the given equation is
$$\{(x, y): y = x + 2|x - 2| - 5\}.$$
In order to obtain the graph of this function easily, we shall rewrite
$$y = x + 2|x - 2| - 5$$
as
$$y = 3x - 9 \quad \text{if } 2 \leqq x \quad \text{and} \quad y = -x - 1 \quad \text{if } x < 2.$$
The graph is shown in Figure 6.3b. Among the points corresponding to the function

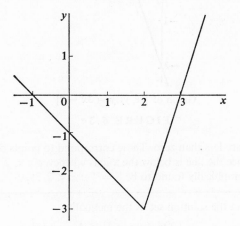

Graph of $\{(x, y): y = x + 2|x - 2| - 5\}$

FIGURE 6.3b

are the points for which $y = 0$, namely, $(3, 0)$ and $(-1, 0)$. In this case these points may be obtained easily from the defining equations of the function. The solution set of the original equation is $S = \{-1, 3\}$. The elements in the solution set of an equation in one unknown are called **roots** of the equation. Thus, the roots of the given equation are -1 and 3.

In a more general case, we may not be able to find the exact roots of an equation of the form $f(x) = 0$, and we may be obliged to use an approximation to a root. Such an approximation can be obtained geometrically by drawing the graph of the associated function $\{(x, y): y = f(x)\}$, and then determining the points where this graph crosses the x-axis. The accuracy of the approximation so obtained depends on the accuracy with which the graph can be drawn and the accuracy with which the coordinates of a point can be read.

The solution set for an inequality can be related to the graph of a function by exploiting more fully than in the preceding discussion the relationship between the graph and the order properties of the real numbers. The following examples will illustrate this idea.

Example 6.3b. Obtain the solution set of the inequality $3x < 2$ by means of the graph of an appropriate function.

The inequality may be rewritten as $3x - 2 < 0$. A function associated with this form is $\{(x, y): y = 3x - 2\}$, whose graph is shown in Figure 6.3c. We are interested in

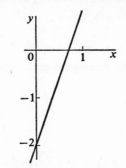

Graph of $\{(x, y): y = 3x - 2\}$

FIGURE 6.3c

the values of y that are less than zero. These correspond to points on the line that are below the x-axis. Since the line is below the x-axis whenever $x < 2/3$, the solution set of the inequality is graphically found to be $\mathcal{S} = \{x: x < 2/3\}$.

Example 6.3c. Find the solution set of the inequality
$$2|x| + |x - 1| < 4.$$
Since
$$|x| = \begin{cases} -x & \text{for } x < 0, \\ x & \text{for } x \geq 0, \end{cases}$$
it follows that
$$|x - 1| = \begin{cases} -x + 1 & \text{for } x < 1, \\ x - 1 & \text{for } x \geq 1. \end{cases}$$

Thus it is natural to divide the domain of definition of the left side of the inequality into three parts: $x < 0$, $0 \leq x < 1$, and $x \geq 1$.

For $x < 0$, the given inequality is the same as
$$-2x - (x - 1) < 4 \quad \text{or} \quad -3x - 3 < 0.$$

Similarly, for $0 \leq x < 1$, we must have
$$2x - (x - 1) < 4 \quad \text{or} \quad x - 3 < 0.$$

And, for $x \geqq 1$,
$$2x + (x - 1) < 4 \quad \text{or} \quad 3x - 5 < 0.$$

The function defined by
$$y = \begin{cases} -3x - 3 & \text{for } x < 0, \\ x - 3 & \text{for } 0 \leqq x < 1, \\ 3x - 5 & \text{for } 1 \leqq x, \end{cases}$$

has the graph that is shown in Figure 6.3d. From this graph it appears that the solution set of the original inequality is $\{x : -1 < x < 5/3\}$.

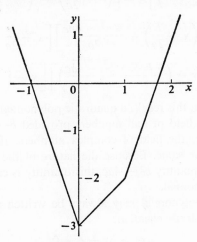

FIGURE 6.3d

Exercises 6.3

Determine solution sets for each of the following equations or inequalities by using the graph of an appropriate function.

1. $|2x| - 3 = 4$.
2. $2|x - 2| = x - 1$.
3. $|x - 2| < 1$.
4. $[\![x + 1]\!] = 2$.
5. $[\![x + \frac{1}{2}]\!] < 3$.
6. $ax - b|x| = c$, with $a, b, c > 0$.
7. $|x + 1| - 2|x| = 3$.
8. $|x + 1| - 2|x| < 3$.
9. $[\![x]\!] + |x - 2| = 3$.
10. $2|x - 2| - |x + 1| < 2$.
11. $|x| + |x - 1| + |x - 2| < 3$.
12. $|x| + 2|x - 1| - 3|x - 2| = 4$.

6.4 QUADRATIC EXPRESSIONS AND EQUATIONS

An expression of the form
$$ax^2 + bx + c, \qquad a \neq 0,$$
is called a **quadratic polynomial** in x. We shall show that it is always possible to write such a polynomial as the product of two linear factors in the field of complex numbers. First, the form of the expression can be modified by factoring out a to obtain
$$ax^2 + bx + c = a\left(x^2 + \frac{b}{a}x + \frac{c}{a}\right).$$

Then, upon adding and subtracting the square of one-half of the coefficient of x inside the parentheses, we get

$$a\left(x^2 + \frac{b}{a}x + \frac{b^2}{4a^2} - \frac{b^2}{4a^2} + \frac{c}{a}\right) = a\left[\left(x + \frac{b}{2a}\right)^2 - \frac{b^2 - 4ac}{4a^2}\right].$$

This last expression may be written as the difference of two squares, as follows:

$$a\left[\left(x + \frac{b}{2a}\right)^2 - \left(\frac{b^2 - 4ac}{4a^2}\right)\right] = a\left[\left(x + \frac{b}{2a}\right)^2 - \left(\frac{\sqrt{b^2 - 4ac}}{2a}\right)^2\right]$$

$$= a\left[\left(x + \frac{b}{2a}\right) - \frac{\sqrt{b^2 - 4ac}}{2a}\right]\left[x + \frac{b}{2a} + \frac{\sqrt{b^2 - 4ac}}{2a}\right]$$

$$= a\left[x - \left(\frac{-b + \sqrt{b^2 - 4ac}}{2a}\right)\right]\left[x - \left(\frac{-b - \sqrt{b^2 - 4ac}}{2a}\right)\right].$$

As may be seen from this result, a quadratic polynomial with real coefficients is factorable over the field of real numbers provided $b^2 - 4ac > 0$, and it is always factorable over the field of complex numbers. If $b^2 - 4ac = 0$, then the two factors are the same. Because the nature of the factorization can be ascertained from the quantity $b^2 - 4ac$, this quantity is called the **discriminant** of the quadratic polynomial.

Since a quadratic polynomial may always be written as a product of two linear factors, any **quadratic equation**

$$ax^2 + bx + c = 0$$

can be solved for the unknown x. The solution set is obtained simply by determining the value of x for which each of the linear factors will be zero. Thus for the general quadratic equation, we may write

$$\mathsf{S}[ax^2 + bx + c = 0] = \left\{\frac{-b - \sqrt{b^2 - 4ac}}{2a}, \frac{-b + \sqrt{b^2 - 4ac}}{2a}\right\}.$$

This means that the roots of the equation $ax^2 + bx + c = 0$ are

$$\frac{-b + \sqrt{b^2 - 4ac}}{2a} \quad \text{and} \quad \frac{-b - \sqrt{b^2 - 4ac}}{2a}.$$

Example 6.4a. Determine the solution set of the equation

$$3x^2 + 4x - 4 = 0.$$

The given equation may be written in the factored form

$$(3x - 2)(x + 2) = 0.$$

Since the factor $3x - 2$ is zero when $x = \frac{2}{3}$, and $x + 2$ is zero if $x = -2$, the solution set S is $\{\frac{2}{3}, -2\}$.

Example 6.4b. Determine the solution set of the equation

$$2x^2 + x + 1 = 0.$$

By using the formula, we obtain

$$S = \left\{ \frac{-1 \pm i\sqrt{7}}{4} \right\}.$$

The reader should verify that these complex numbers satisfy the equation.

Many expressions may be put into a quadratic form or into a form that displays a quadratic factor, as the following examples illustrate.

(1) The expression $x^4 + 5x^2 - 6$ is a quadratic polynomial in x^2. In order to bring out this fact more clearly, it is sometimes helpful to change the variable appearing in the expression. In this case, if $y = x^2$, then $x^4 + 5x^2 - 6 = y^2 + 5y - 6$.

(2) The expression $x + 1 - 2x^{-1}$ may be made to display a quadratic factor if x^{-1} is factored out. Thus we get $x^{-1}(x^2 + x - 2)$, and the second factor is a quadratic polynomial.

(3) A fourth-degree polynomial such as $x^4 - 4x^3 + 6x^2 - 4x - 3$ can sometimes be put into a quadratic form by grouping terms in an appropriate way. Thus, we have

$$x^4 - 4x^3 + 6x^2 - 4x - 3 = x^4 - 4x^3 + 4x^2 + 2x^2 - 4x - 3$$
$$= (x^2 - 2x)^2 + 2(x^2 - 2x) - 3.$$

Hence, the expression is a quadratic polynomial in the quantity $(x^2 - 2x)$.

It follows from this discussion that an equation that is quadratic in form may often be solved by first solving a quadratic equation.

Example 6.4c. Solve the equation

$$x^4 - 4x^3 + 6x^2 - 4x - 3 = 0.$$

As the preceding discussion in (3) shows, this equation is the same as

$$(x^2 - 2x)^2 + 2(x^2 - 2x) - 3 = 0.$$

Accordingly, let $u = x^2 - 2x$, so that the equation becomes

$$u^2 + 2u - 3 = 0 \quad \text{or} \quad (u + 3)(u - 1) = 0.$$

The roots of this equation are -3 and 1, so that we have two equations in x:

$$x^2 - 2x = -3 \quad \text{and} \quad x^2 - 2x = 1.$$

The reader may show that these two equations have the roots $1 \pm i\sqrt{2}$ and $1 \pm \sqrt{2}$, respectively. Hence, the solution set of the given equation is

$$S = \{1 + \sqrt{2}, 1 - \sqrt{2}, 1 + i\sqrt{2}, 1 - i\sqrt{2}\}.$$

Just as we were able to associate a function with a linear equation $ax + b = 0$, so we may associate a function $\{(x, y): y = ax^2 + bx + c\}$ with a quadratic equation $ax^2 + bx + c = 0$. For example, to the equation $x^2 - 4x + 3 = 0$, we may associate the function $\{(x, y): y = x^2 - 4x + 3\}$, whose graph is shown in Figure 6.4a. This curve, which is characteristic of the quadratic function, is called a **parabola**. As we might expect, the solution set of the equation $x^2 - 4x + 3 = 0$ consists of the x-coordinates of the points at which the graph of the related function crosses the x-axis.

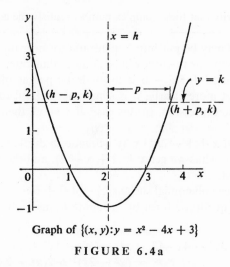

Graph of $\{(x, y): y = x^2 - 4x + 3\}$

FIGURE 6.4a

A study of the graph in Figure 6.4a suggests that we investigate certain properties that the parabola seems to possess. In particular, we might consider the possibility of determining the lowest point or vertex of the curve and whether or not there is a line of symmetry. Such information would be useful in obtaining the graphs of other functions that are similar to this one.

It is easy to see that the line $x = 2$ is a line of symmetry by completing the square in x:

$$y = x^2 - 4x + 3$$
$$= (x^2 - 4x + 4) - 1$$
$$= (x - 2)^2 - 1$$

or

$$y + 1 = (x - 2)^2.$$

This equation implies that $x - 2 = \pm\sqrt{y + 1}$, so that for each value of $y > -1$ there are two values of x equidistant from the value 2. For $y = -1$, the equation gives $0 = (x - 2)^2$ so that $x = 2$ is the only corresponding value.

The line of symmetry of a parabola is called the **axis** of the parabola. The point where the axis intersects the curve is called the **vertex** of the parabola. A perpendicular to the line of symmetry must intersect the parabola at two symmetrically located points, at just one point, or at no points at all. If a perpendicular to the line of symmetry intersects the parabola at only one point, then that point is the vertex of the parabola. From the equation $y = x^2 - 4x + 3$, we found that $y = -1 \Rightarrow x = 2$, so that the vertex of this parabola is the point $(2, -1)$. The axis and the vertex of a parabola $y = Ax^2 + Bx + C$ can always be found by completing the square in x as in the preceding discussion. Thus, if the final equation is of the form $(x - h)^2 = m(y - k)$, then the vertex is at the point (h, k) and the axis is the line $x = h$.

Exercises 6.4

In each of Numbers 1 to 10, find the solution set of the given equation.

1. $x^2 + 2x + 2 = 0$.
2. $-3x^2 + 4x - 3 = 0$.
3. $4x^2 - 3x - 2 = 0$.
4. $x^2 + x + 1 = 0$.
5. $x^2 + 2px + q = 0$.

6. $x^2 + \sqrt{2}x - 4 = 0$.
7. $x^2 + 2\sqrt{3}x + 3 = 0$.
8. $x^2 - 0.1x + 0.05 = 0$.
9. $1000x^2 + 5x - 2 = 0$.
10. $x^2 - 3ix - 2 = 0$.

11. Find the sum of the roots of the equation $ax^2 + bx + c = 0$.
12. Find the product of the roots of the equation $ax^2 + bx + c = 0$.
13. Show that the roots of the equation $ax^2 + bx + a = 0$ are reciprocals of each other.
14. One root of the equation $ax^2 - bx + 2a = 0$ is 4. What is the other root?
15. Find the roots of $2x^2 + 9x + c = 0$ if it is known that the product of the roots is 2.
16. Is it always possible to put an equation of the form $x^4 + ax^3 + bx^2 + cx + d = 0$ into the form $(x^2 + mx)^2 + p(x^2 + mx) + d = 0$?
17. Put the equation $x^4 + 4x^3 + 5x^2 + 2x - 2 = 0$ into the form suggested in Number 16 and then find the solution set.
18. Use the method of Number 17 to solve the equation

$$x^4 + 6x^3 + 8x^2 - 3x - 6 = 0.$$

In each of Numbers 19 to 22, solve the given equation.

19. $x + 1 - 2x^{-1} = 0$.
20. $x^2 + 5 - 6x^{-2} = 0$.

21. $x^{1/2} - 1 = 12x^{-1/2}$.
22. $27x^{3/2} - 217x^{3/4} + 8 = 0$.

23. Show that the axis of symmetry of the graph of $y = Ax^2 - 2Bx + C$ is given by $x = B/A$.
24. Sketch each of the following parabolas. Find the equation of the axis and the coordinates of the vertex.

   (a) $y = 4x^2 + 6x + 3$.
   (b) $y = 2x^2 + 4x$.

   (c) $y = -3x^2 + 6x + 2$.
   (d) $2x^2 + 8x + 1 + y = 0$.

25. Find the value of b so that the graph of the equation $y = 8x^2 + bx + 8$ will have its vertex on the line $y = 4$.
26. Find the equation of a parabola with vertex at the origin, axis along the y-axis, and passing through the point $(3, -1)$.
27. Find the equation of a parabola with vertex at the point $(-3, 2)$, axis the line $x = -3$, and passing through the point $(0, 5)$.
28. Find the number that exceeds its square by the greatest amount.
29. Find a number such that the sum of it and its reciprocal is 1.
30. A rectangular piece of cardboard is to have a square 4 inches on a side cut from each corner. The remaining piece is to be folded up to form an open box. It is required that the box be 4 inches longer than it is wide and that it have a volume of 48 cubic inches. What must be the dimensions of the original rectangle?

31. Find the area of the largest rectangle that can be cut from a piece of cardboard in the shape of a right triangle with sides 5 inches and 12 inches, respectively, if one side of the rectangle is to be along the hypotenuse of the triangle.

6.5 INEQUALITIES INVOLVING QUADRATIC POLYNOMIALS

The results obtained in the preceding section are useful in finding solution sets for inequalities that involve quadratic polynomials. Such problems will be considered both from the algebraic and from the geometric point of view.

Example 6.5a. Determine the solution set of the inequality

$$x^2 - x < 6.$$

First Method: We first complete the square on the left by adding 1/4 to both sides of the given inequality which becomes

$$x^2 - x + \frac{1}{4} < \frac{25}{4}$$

or

$$\left(x - \frac{1}{2}\right)^2 < \left(\frac{5}{2}\right)^2.$$

Since, for $a > 0$, $x^2 < a^2 \Leftrightarrow -a < x < a$, we have

$$-\frac{5}{2} < x - \frac{1}{2} < \frac{5}{2},$$

which can be simplified to yield

$$-2 < x < 3.$$

Thus

$$\mathbb{S}[x^2 - x < 6] = \{x: -2 < x < 3\}.$$

Second Method: This time we use the function

$$\{(x, y): y = x^2 - x - 6\},$$

where the defining equation is obtained from the left side of the inequality

$$x^2 - x - 6 < 0$$

that results by subtracting 6 from both sides of the given one. The graph of the function is shown in Figure 6.5a. This graph is easily sketched by first noting that

$$x^2 - x - 6 = (x - 3)(x + 2)$$

so that $y = 0$ for $x = -2$ and for $x = 3$. Since the equation is that of a parabola, the reader should be able to make the sketch on the basis of the preceding information.

Now the solution set required is that set of values of x for which $y < 0$, that is, for which the graph lies below the x-axis. From the graph it is easy to see that

$$y < 0 \quad \text{for } -2 < x < 3,$$

which gives the same solution set as before.

Example 6.5b. Find the solution set of the inequality

$$\left|\frac{x-1}{x+1}\right| \leq 2.$$

From the definition of absolute value, it follows that the given inequality is equivalent to

$$-2 \leq \frac{x-1}{x+1} \leq 2.$$

The required solution set must accordingly be the intersection of the solution sets of the two inequalities

(i) $-2 \leq \dfrac{x-1}{x+1}$, (ii) $\dfrac{x-1}{x+1} \leq 2.$

We shall solve (ii) in detail.

An equivalent inequality that involves a linear or quadratic polynomial rather than a fractional expression can be obtained from the given inequality by means of the theorems governing inequalities. We have

$$\frac{x-1}{x+1} \leq 2 \Leftrightarrow \frac{x-1}{x+1} - 2 \leq 0$$

$$\Leftrightarrow \frac{-x-3}{x+1} \leq 0$$

$$\Leftrightarrow \frac{x+3}{x+1} \geq 0.$$

For $x \neq -1$, the last inequality is equivalent to

$$\frac{(x+3)(x+1)}{(x+1)^2} \geq 0,$$

and since $(x+1)^2 > 0$, we have

$$(x+3)(x+1) \geq 0, \qquad x \neq -1.$$

A graph (Figure 6.5b) of the equation

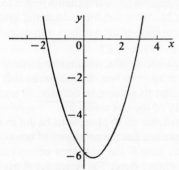

Graph of $\{(x, y): y = x^2 - x - 6\}$

FIGURE 6.5a

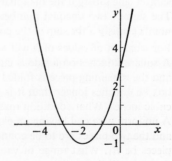

Graph of $\{(x, y): y = x^2 + 4x + 3\}$

FIGURE 6.5b

$$y = (x + 3)(x + 1)$$

shows that $y \geq 0$ for $x \geq -1$, and for $x \leq -3$. Since $x \neq -1$, the solution set of (ii) is

$$S = \{x: x \leq -3\} \cup \{x: x > -1\}.$$

By a procedure precisely identical with the preceding one, the reader may show that the solution set of (i) is

$$\mathfrak{I} = \{x: x \leq -1\} \cup \{x: x \geq -\tfrac{1}{3}\}.$$

The solution set of the given inequality is therefore

$$S \cap \mathfrak{I} = \{x: x \leq -3\} \cup \{x: x \geq -\tfrac{1}{3}\}.$$

Exercises 6.5

In each of Numbers 1 to 16, find the solution set of the given inequality.

1. $x^2 - 2x - 3 > 0$.
2. $x^2 - x - 12 \leq 0$.
3. $2w^2 - 3w - 2 \leq 0$.
4. $2x^2 + 5x + 1 > 0$.

5. $\dfrac{1}{x - 2} < 2$.

6. $\left|\dfrac{1}{x - 2}\right| < 2$.

7. $\dfrac{1}{x + 3} > 1$.

8. $\left|\dfrac{1}{x + 3}\right| > 1$.

9. $y^2 + y + 2 \leq 0$.

10. $x - \dfrac{2}{x} > 1$.

11. $\sqrt{2x + 3} > x$.

12. $\left|\dfrac{x - 2}{x + 3}\right| \geq 2$.

13. $\left|\dfrac{1}{(x + 1)(x - 2)}\right| \leq 1$.

14. $\dfrac{1}{x^2 - 2x + 2} > 4$.

15. $\dfrac{x - 2}{x + 2} < \dfrac{x + 1}{x - 1}$.

16. $\left|\dfrac{1}{x + 2}\right| < \dfrac{1}{x - 1}$.

17. A wire 14 inches long is to be bent into a rectangle. What condition must the shorter side satisfy if the diagonal of the rectangle is to be less than 5 inches long?
18. The sum of two unequal numbers is to be 25. What condition must the smaller number satisfy if the sum of the positive square roots of the numbers is to exceed 7?
19. For what set of values of x will $\sqrt{(x + 1)(x - 3)}$ be real?
20. A square 2 inches on a side is cut from each corner of a rectangular piece of tin and the remaining piece is folded up to form an open box. It is required that the box be 4 inches longer than it is wide and that its volume be between 40 and 50 cubic inches. What condition must the width of the box satisfy?
21. A uniform wire coil having an electrical resistance of 10 ohms is to be cut in two and the two pieces are to be connected in parallel. Let the resistance of one of the pieces be R_1. What range of values may R_1 have if the resistance equivalent to the two coils in parallel is not to exceed 1.6 ohms? *Note:* The resistance R equivalent to two resistances R_1 and R_2 in parallel is given by

$$1/R = 1/R_1 + 1/R_2.$$

6.6 OTHER QUADRATIC POLYNOMIAL EQUATIONS

In Section 6.4 it was stated that the graph of an equation of the form

$$y = ax^2 + bx + c, \qquad a \neq 0,$$

is a parabola, and this curve was discussed there. The axis and the vertex of the parabola can easily be found by completing the square in x.

The preceding equation is a special case of a more general type of polynomial equation of the second degree which will be considered in this section.

Definition 6.6a. A polynomial expression of the form

$$q(x, y) .=. Ax^2 + Bxy + Cy^2 + Dx + Ey + F,$$

where the coefficients A, B, C, D, E, F are constants, is called a **quadratic polynomial in two variables.**

Our attention here will be confined to polynomials with real coefficients. The expression

$$5x^2 - 2\sqrt{2}xy + 6y^2 - 1.2x + 15y - \pi$$

is such a polynomial with

$$A = 5, \quad B = -2\sqrt{2}, \quad C = 6, \quad D = -1.2, \quad E = 15, \quad F = -\pi.$$

Certain simple special cases of the general quadratic equation $q(x, y) = 0$, are of considerable interest in mathematics as well as of great importance in many applications of mathematics. In the particular cases to be considered now, the coefficient B will be zero so that the xy term will be absent from the equation. If, in addition, $A = 0$ or $C = 0$, then the equation is of the form

$$Cy^2 + Dx + Ey + F = 0,$$

or

$$Ax^2 + Dx + Ey + F = 0.$$

If $E \neq 0$ in the second of these equations, then it can be solved for y to obtain the form $y = ax^2 + bx + c$, which describes a parabola. Similarly, if $D \neq 0$ in the first of the equations, it can be solved for x to give the form $x = ay^2 + by + c$. The following definition is thus consistent with the discussion in Section 6.4.

Definition 6.6b. The graph of an equation of the form

$$y = ax^2 + bx + c, \qquad a \neq 0,$$

or of the form

$$x = ay^2 + by + c, \qquad a \neq 0,$$

is called a **parabola.**

In the discussion of the parabola in Section 6.4, the roles of x and y may be interchanged in order to determine the salient features of the parabola corresponding to an equation of the form $x = ay^2 + by + c$. Evidently, in this case, the curve will have a horizontal axis rather than a vertical one, but the axis and the vertex can easily be found by completing the square in y.

Example 6.6a. Locate the axis and the vertex of the parabola described by $x = 2y^2 - 4y$, and sketch the curve.

By completing the square in y, we may write the equation in the form

$$x + 2 = 2(y^2 - 2y + 1)$$

or

$$x + 2 = 2(y - 1)^2.$$

This shows that the vertex is at the point $(-2, 1)$ and the axis is the line of symmetry $y = 1$. The graph appears in Figure 6.6a.

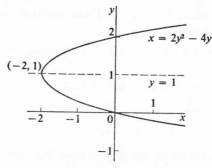

FIGURE 6.6a

Some additional special cases of the equation $q(x, y) = 0$ will be considered next. In these cases, $B = D = E = 0$, so that the equation is of the form

$$Ax^2 + Cy^2 + F = 0.$$

If $F = 0$ and $AC > 0$, then this equation has only $(0, 0)$ for a real solution and has a graph consisting only of the origin. If $F = 0$ and $AC < 0$, then the equation may be written as

$$\alpha^2 x^2 - \beta^2 y^2 = 0.$$

It follows that $(\alpha x - \beta y)(\alpha x + \beta y) = 0$ and this equation is satisfied if either $\alpha x - \beta y = 0$ or $\alpha x + \beta y = 0$. The graph of each of these equations is a straight line through the origin, so that the graph of the original equation consists of two intersecting straight lines. As an illustration of these remarks, consider the equation

$$4x^2 - 3y^2 = 0,$$

which may be written

$$(2x - \sqrt{3}y)(2x + \sqrt{3}y) = 0.$$

The graph consists of the two intersecting lines having the respective equations $2x - \sqrt{3}y = 0$ and $2x + \sqrt{3}y = 0$. If $ACF \neq 0$ and A, C, F are all of the same sign, then the equation has no real solutions at all.

The more interesting graphs occur for $ACF \neq 0$ and A, C, F not all of the same sign. Under these circumstances, the equation may be written in one of the following three forms, in which the numbers α, β, γ, *are all positive*:

(i) $\alpha x^2 + \beta y^2 = \gamma$,   (ii) $\alpha x^2 - \beta y^2 = \gamma$,   (iii) $\alpha y^2 - \beta x^2 = \gamma$.

Since these three equations involve only the squares of x and y, their graphs must be symmetric with respect to both axes and the origin.

Definition 6.6c. The graph of an equation of the form

$$\alpha x^2 + \beta y^2 = \gamma, \qquad \alpha, \beta, \gamma \text{ all positive,}$$

is called an **ellipse**.

Note that if $\alpha = \beta$, the graph will be a circle with an equation of the form $x^2 + y^2 = a^2$, which has already been discussed. The circle is thus regarded as a special form of an ellipse.

Example 6.6b. Sketch the ellipse given by the equation

$$x^2 + 4y^2 = 16.$$

The intercepts on the axes are easily found by setting $y = 0$ to get $x = \pm 4$, and setting $x = 0$ to get $y = \pm 2$. Additional points can be obtained by solving for y with the result $y = \pm \frac{1}{2}\sqrt{16 - x^2}$. Notice that the domain of the relation defined by this equation is the set $\{x: -4 \leq x \leq 4\}$. The values $x = \pm 2$ each yields $y = \pm\sqrt{3}$, so that four points are found: $(-2, -\sqrt{3})$, $(-2, \sqrt{3})$, $(2, -\sqrt{3})$, and $(2, \sqrt{3})$. Other points can be calculated in a similar fashion. The graph in Figure 6.6b shows the ellipse described by the given equation.

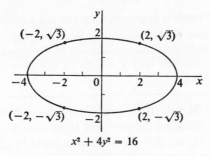

$$x^2 + 4y^2 = 16$$

FIGURE 6.6b

Definition 6.6d. The graph of an equation of the form

$$\alpha x^2 - \beta y^2 = \gamma \quad \text{or} \quad \alpha y^2 - \beta x^2 = \gamma, \qquad \alpha, \beta, \gamma \text{ all positive,}$$

is called a **hyperbola**.

Example 6.6c. Sketch the hyperbola given by the equation

$$x^2 - 4y^2 = 16.$$

The solution of this equation for y is $y = \pm\frac{1}{2}\sqrt{x^2 - 16}$, which shows that y is real only if $|x| \geq 4$. Hence, the interval $-4 < x < 4$ is not part of the domain of the relation defined by the given equation. The graph cuts the x-axis at $(\pm 4, 0)$, and other points can be found by setting x equal to additional values in the domain. For instance, $x = 5$ (or -5) yields $y = \pm 3/2$ so that the four points $(-5, -3/2)$, $(-5, 3/2)$, $(5, -3/2)$, $(5, 3/2)$ are all on the curve (see Figure 6.6c).

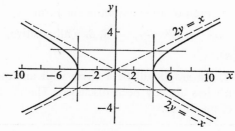

FIGURE 6.6c

It is reasonable to conjecture that for very large values of x the value of $\sqrt{x^2 - 16}$ is closely approximated by the value of x itself. Indeed, it is easy to show that

$$(x - \sqrt{x^2 - 16}) \to 0 \quad \text{as } x \to \infty.$$

Thus

$$x - \sqrt{x^2 - 16} = \frac{(x - \sqrt{x^2 - 16})(x + \sqrt{x^2 - 16})}{x + \sqrt{x^2 - 16}}$$

$$= \frac{16}{x + \sqrt{x^2 - 16}},$$

from which the stated result is apparent, since the last numerator is a constant. The geometrical interpretation of this estimate is that the graph of $y = \frac{1}{2}\sqrt{x^2 - 16}$ has the line $y = \frac{1}{2}x$ as an asymptote. A consideration of the symmetry of the curve shows that it is asymptotic to the two lines $y = \pm\frac{1}{2}x$ or $x \pm 2y = 0$. These lines are quite helpful in making the sketch.

The asymptotes in the preceding example can be obtained from the equation of the hyperbola by replacing the constant 16 by zero and factoring the result. It can, moreover, be shown that the hyperbola given by either of the equations in Definition 6.6d has as asymptotes the lines obtained by replacing γ by zero and factoring the resulting equation. (The method used in Example 6.6c can also be used to prove this general statement.)

Another special case of the equation $q(x, y) = 0$ that is important in various applications is the equation

$$xy = \gamma.$$

It will be shown later that the graph is again a hyperbola. The asymptotes of the curve are the coordinate axes as can be seen by comparing Example 5.6a. The equation $PV = k$, which relates the volume V and the pressure P of a gas according to Boyle's Law, is an important instance of this last type of equation.

Exercises 6.6

In Numbers 1 to 16, identify and sketch the curves defined by the given equations.

1. $y + 2x^2 = 0$.
2. $x + 4y^2 = 0$.
3. $4x^2 + 4y^2 = 9$.
4. $4x^2 - y^2 = 4$.
5. $4x^2 - 8y^2 = 0$.
6. $y^2 - x^2 - 9 = 0$.
7. $y = 3x^2 - 6x + 5$.
8. $y^2 - 4x + 6y + 9 = 0$.
9. $4y^2 + x - 16y + 19 = 0$.
10. $4x^2 + 9y^2 = 36$.
11. $9x^2 + 4y^2 = 36$.
12. $xy = 5$.
13. $xy + 4 = 0$.
14. $xy = 0$.
15. $y^2 + 2x^2 + 1 = 0$.
16. $4x^2 + 8y^2 = 0$.

17. Find the equation of a circle with center at the origin and passing through the point $(-1, -4)$.
18. Does the condition that the curve pass through the point $(3, 4)$ determine a unique ellipse of the type described in Definition 6.6c? Explain.
19. How many parabolas, with equations of the type given in Definition 6.6b, can be drawn with vertices at $(-1, -4)$ and passing through the origin? Find their equations and sketch them.
20. Find A if the longer axis of the ellipse $Ax^2 + 4y^2 = 9$ is to be 4.
21. Figure 6.6d shows the dimensions of a parabolic arch. What is the height h of the arch at a distance of 3 feet from the axis of symmetry?

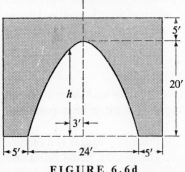

FIGURE 6.6d

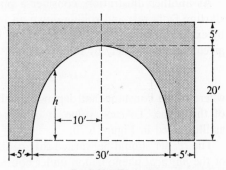

FIGURE 6.6e

22. Figure 6.6e shows the dimensions of a semi-elliptic arch. What is the height h of the arch at a distance of 10 feet from the center?
23. Sketch the line $2y + x = 4$ and the parabola $y^2 = -4x$ on the same set of axes. Do you think the line is tangent to the parabola? Defend your answer.

6.7 FAMILIES OF CURVES

In many of the applications of mathematics, it is necessary to work with an equation in which certain coefficients may assume various values corresponding to the physical constants that describe the particular problem. For example, Boyle's Law states that if the temperature of a given mass of an ideal gas is constant, then the product of the pressure P and the volume V of the gas is a constant k. This statement may be expressed in mathematical form by the equation

$$PV = k.$$

The coefficient k, however, is different for each different temperature. Thus, for each value of k, the equation describes the branch of a hyperbola that lies in the first quadrant, since P and V must both be positive. Some of these curves are shown in Figure 6.7a.

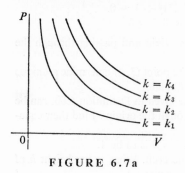 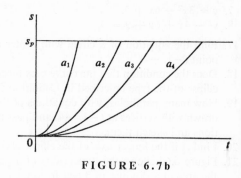

FIGURE 6.7a   FIGURE 6.7b

As another illustration, consider a physical problem associated with a ball starting from rest and rolling down an inclined plane of length s_p. It is known by experiment that the distance s of the ball from its starting point at time t is given quite accurately by the equation

$$s = \tfrac{1}{2}at^2, \qquad 0 \leq s \leq s_p,$$

where a is a constant that depends on the force of gravity and the inclination of the plane. To each value of a, there corresponds a piece of a parabola, as illustrated in Figure 6.7b.

The reader should be warned that neither of the preceding figures is a picture of the *physical* phenomenon under consideration. The graphs, being geometric representations of the equations that give a more or less accurate description of some phases of the physical picture, are essentially only mathematical devices for studying the phenomenon.

In the preceding examples, k is a constant for each particular curve, but varies from curve to curve in Figure 6.7a, and a similar statement applies to a in Figure 6.7b. A letter used in this manner is called a **parameter**. [Although this is a slightly different usage of the word parameter from that in Section 6.1, the context will always make clear which usage is intended. Students have suggested (not without reason) the name "variable constant" for the usage of the present section.]

Definition 6.7a. An equation in two variables in which there occurs a single parameter is said to represent a **one-parameter family of curves**.

In general, a family of curves is characterized by the fact that all members of the family have some property in common. For example, the family of hyperbolas in Figure 6.7a all have the coordinate axes as asymptotes, and the family of parabolas in Figure 6.7b all have their vertices at the origin, with the *s*-axis as their common axis.

We shall be concerned here with two types of problems: (i) to write an equation for a set of curves with a given geometric property in common; (ii) to find the common property of a family of curves described by a given equation.

Example 6.7a. Find the equation of the family of straight lines all passing through the point (2, 3).

In this problem, as in similar ones, we must choose some parameter representing a geometric condition which varies from member to member of the family, but is fixed for any one of the curves. This is relatively easy here since the slope, say *m*, varies from line to line but is fixed for any one line. Thus, if *m* is the slope of any line in the family, then an equation of the line is

$$y - 3 = m(x - 2) \quad \text{or} \quad y = mx + 3 - 2m.$$

This equation represents all the nonvertical lines through the point (2, 3). See Figure 6.7c.

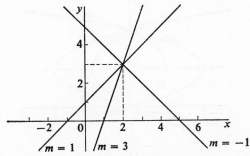

FIGURE 6.7c

Note: In the preceding example, if it is desired to represent all lines without exception through the point (2, 3), then it is preferable to use direction numbers, say [*a*, *b*], rather than slope. In this case, the equation is of the form

$$a(y - 3) = b(x - 2) \quad \text{or} \quad bx - ay = 2b - 3a.$$

Example 6.7b. Find the equation of the family of lines all having slope 2.

In this case, it is convenient to choose as a parameter the *y*-intercept, *b*. Then the slope-intercept form of the equation yields

$$y = 2x + b.$$

(Of course, it is possible to choose some other quantity as a parameter, but the choice of *b* leads to the simplest form for an equation of the family.)

Example 6.7c. What common property is possessed by each member of the family of lines described by $kx + py = 0$?

At first sight it appears that there are two parameters in the equation. However, if $k \neq 0$, we may write $x + (p/k)y = 0$, and then consider the ratio p/k as the parameter. It is easy to see that, regardless of the values assigned to k and p, the point $(0, 0)$ will lie on the graph of the resulting equation. Hence, the given equation represents a family of lines passing through the origin.

If $p \neq 0$, the preceding family can be characterized by the equation $y = mx$, where m is the parameter that represents the slope. In many cases, where it is difficult to recognize the family property, it may be necessary to put the given equation into various equivalent forms, one of which may reveal the desired property.

Example 6.7d. Find an equation of the family of parabolas, each of which has its axis parallel to the x-axis and passes through the origin and the point $(0, 2)$. See Figure 6.7d.

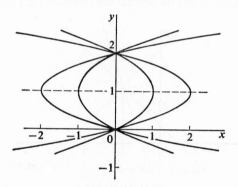

FIGURE 6.7d

We know from the discussion in Section 6.6 that the desired equation must be of the form

$$x = ay^2 + by + c.$$

Furthermore, the equation must be satisfied by $(0, 0)$ and by $(0, 2)$. Hence

$$0 = 0 + 0 + c$$

and

$$0 = 4a + 2b + c.$$

Therefore $c = 0$ and $b = -2a$, so that the desired equation is

$$x = ay^2 - 2ay.$$

The reader should check to see that this one-parameter family does satisfy the given conditions.

Example 6.7e. Describe the one-parameter family of curves represented by the equation

$$x^2 + y^2 = a^2,$$

where a is the parameter.

For any given value of a, the equation represents a circle of radius a having its center at the origin. Hence, the family of curves described by the equation is the family of concentric circles whose centers are at the origin (see Figure 6.7e).

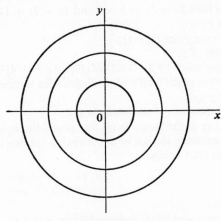

FIGURE 6.7e

Exercises 6.7

In Numbers 1 to 5, determine an equation for the family of straight lines satisfying the given condition.

1. The lines all pass through the point $(3, -1)$.
2. The lines are all parallel to the line $3x - y - 6 = 0$.
3. The lines are all perpendicular to the line $-2x + 3y - 6 = 0$.
4. Each line has the same constant, k, for the sum of its intercepts.
5. Each line has a slope equal numerically to its y-intercept.

In Numbers 6 to 10, determine the property common to all members of the family of lines whose equation is given.

6. $3x - ky = 4.$

7. $mx + 2y = 6.$

8. $2x - y = k.$

9. $mx + (m - 1)y = 6.$

10. $3x + my = m + 4.$

11. Let $L(x, y)$ stand for the linear expression $Ax + By + C$. We shall understand that $L(x_1, y_1)$ means $Ax_1 + By_1 + C$. Accordingly, we see that (x_1, y_1) is a point on the line

$$Ax + By + C = 0 \Leftrightarrow L(x_1, y_1) = 0.$$

Now suppose that

$$L_1(x, y) .=. A_1x + B_1y + C_1$$

and

$$L_2(x, y) .=. A_2x + B_2y + C_2.$$

If the two lines $L_1(x, y) = 0$ and $L_2(x, y) = 0$ intersect in the point (x_1, y_1), then for any real constants a and b (not both zero),

$$aL_1(x, y) + bL_2(x, y) = 0$$

is an equation of a line through (x_1, y_1). Prove this last statement. Note that we may regard the last equation as that of a family of lines all passing through the intersection of the given two lines.

12. Use the idea of Number 11 to find an equation of the line that passes through the intersection of the lines $2x + 3y - 5 = 0$ and $4x - 7y + 11 = 0$, and
    (a) has a slope of 1;
    (b) passes through the point $(1, -1)$;
    (c) has a y-intercept of 3.

13. What property is possessed by the family of ellipses $ax^2 + 4y^2 = 4a$, where $a > 0$?

14. (a) Find the equation of the family of parabolas with vertices at $(-2, 3)$ and axes parallel to the y-axis.
    (b) Sketch several members of the family in (a).
    (c) Find the member of the family in (a) that passes through the origin.

15. What property is common to each of the following families of parabolas? Sketch several members of each family.

    (a) $x^2 = ay$.
    (b) $y^2 = ax$.
    (c) $(x - a)^2 = 2y$.

    (d) $(y + b)^2 + x = 0$.
    (e) $y^2 + 2y + ax = 0$.

16. What property is possessed by the family of curves $ax^2 + (1 - a)y^2 = 1$? Identify and sketch members of the family such that

    (a) $a > 1$;
    (b) $a = 1$;
    (c) $0 < a < 1$ (note especially $a = \frac{1}{2}$);

    (d) $a = 0$;
    (e) $a < 0$.

Summary of Chapter 6

The reader should understand the following fundamental items before going on to the succeeding work:

(1) the meaning of linear equation and linear function (Section 6.1);
(2) parametric equations of a straight line (Section 6.1);
(3) standard forms for the equation of a straight line (Section 6.2);
(4) the use of graphs in determining solution sets of equations and inequalities (Section 6.3);
(5) quadratic polynomials in one variable and factorization of them by completing the square (Section 6.4);
(6) the quadratic formula for the solution of quadratic equations (Section 6.4);
(7) the solution of inequalities involving quadratic polynomials (Section 6.5);
(8) the characteristic forms for the equations of the parabola, ellipse, hyperbola, and circle (Section 6.6);
(9) families of curves (Section 6.7).

Chapter 7   Trigonometric Functions

7.1 ANGULAR MEASURE

In elementary geometry a plane angle is defined as the geometric figure consisting of two rays (half-lines) with their end points in common. This common end point is the **vertex** and the rays are the **sides** of the angle. It is frequently necessary to compare angles with respect to their "size," an intuitive concept that we wish to make precise.

To do this, we first construct a circle of arbitrary radius with its center at the vertex of the angle. The angle is then called a **central angle** of the circle, and the portion of the circumference between the sides of the angle is called the **subtended arc** (see Figure 7.1a).

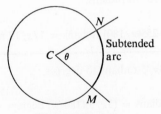

FIGURE 7.1a

Definition 7.1a. If an angle, regarded as a central angle of a circle, subtends an arc of length equal to the radius of the circle, then the angle is said to have a measure of **one radian;** if the arc length is 1/360 of the circumference of the circle, then the measure of the angle is **one degree** (1°).

The units given in this definition are the fundamental ones, and all angles may have their measures expressed in terms of these. Common subdivisions are the *milliradian* (mil), which is 1/1000 of a radian, and the *minute* ('), which is 1/60 of a degree. The minute is sometimes divided into sixty equal parts called *seconds* ("), but it is also common to use decimal parts of degrees or minutes.

The concept of angular measure is important in connection with rotations in a plane. If a ray is made to execute a plane rotation about its end point, then the initial and terminal positions of the ray determine an angle. Since it is sometimes necessary to distinguish the directions of rotation, we agree to call a *counterclockwise* rotation positive and a *clockwise* rotation negative. With this convention, we call the measure of an angle *positive* or *negative* according to the direction in which the ray was rotated from its initial to its terminal position (see Figure 7.1b).

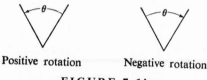

Positive rotation   Negative rotation

FIGURE 7.1b

Since the circumference of a circle is equal to 2π times the radius, it follows that a ray generates an angle of 2π radians in making one complete revolution. Hence, $360° = 2\pi$ radians, $180° = \pi$ radians, $90° = \pi/2$ radians, $1° = \pi/180$ radians, and $180°/\pi = 1$ radian. Note that each of the preceding equations is an abbreviation for a statement of the form, "a rotation of so many degrees is equivalent to a rotation of so many radians." Thus, the statement "$360° = 2\pi$ radians" is to be understood in the same way that the statement "12 inches = 1 foot" is understood.

Example 7.1a. Convert 255° to radians.

We have

$$255° = 255(\pi/180) \text{ radians} = 17\pi/12 \text{ radians}.$$

Example 7.1b. Convert $3\pi/5$ radians to degrees.

We have

$$3\pi/5 \text{ radians} = (3\pi/5)(180/\pi) \text{ degrees} = 108°.$$

Since there are rotations which are greater than one complete rotation (360° or 2π radians), it is clear that the measure of an angle may be any real number of radians (or degrees). Notice, however, that rotations of θ radians and $(\theta + 2n\pi)$ radians, where $n \in \mathcal{J}$, result in the same geometric figure, even though the measures are quite different (see Figure 7.1c).

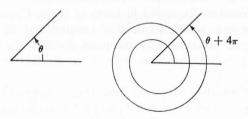

FIGURE 7.1c

It is a universal convention that whenever no units are specified for the measure of an angle, the unit is understood to be the radian. We shall use this convention consistently so that, for example, "an angle 2" is understood to mean "an angle of measure 2 radians."

A sector of a circle is a figure bounded by two radii and the intercepted arc. Let us use the idea of radian measure to find the length of the arc and the area of the sector. From the definition of radian measure, we see that if θ is the central angle in radians, and s is the intercepted arc on a circle of radius r, then

$$\theta = \frac{s}{r} \quad \text{or} \quad s = r\theta.$$

Since there are 2π radians in one revolution, we have

$$\frac{\text{area sector}}{\text{area circle}} = \frac{\theta}{2\pi}$$

or

$$\text{area sector} = \frac{\theta}{2\pi}(\pi r^2) = \frac{1}{2}r^2\theta.$$

Exercises 7.1

1. Convert the following to radian measure:

   (a) 135°; (b) 285°; (c) 275°; (d) 359°.

2. Convert the following to degree measure:

   (a) $7\pi/4$ radians;   (c) $5\pi/6$ radians;
   (b) $3\pi/2$ radians;   (d) $2\pi/7$ radians.

3. An angular speed of five revolutions per second is how many radians per minute?
4. An angular speed of 120 radians per minute is how many degrees per second?
5. Give in degrees one other positive and one other negative measure of each of the following angles:

   (a) an angle of 65°;   (c) an angle of $-115°$;
   (b) an angle of 215°;   (d) an angle of $-333°$.

6. What is the angular speed in radians per second of the minute hand of a clock?
7. Find the area of a sector of a circle of radius 4 inches if the central angle is

   (a) 120°;   (d) 330°;
   (b) 225°;   (e) $2\pi/3$ radians;
   (c) 260°;   (f) $\pi/6$ radians.

8. Two cars have wheels of diameters 26 inches and 28 inches, respectively. In what distance would the smaller wheels make 600 more revolutions than the larger ones?
9. Do you get more for your money by buying one-third of a 12-inch diameter pizza for 75 cents or one-fourth of a 16-inch diameter pizza for 95 cents?
10. A sector of angle θ is to be cut from a circular disk of tin and the balance of the disk is to be formed into a right circular cone. It is required that the area of the base of the cone be one-third of the lateral surface area. Find the radian measure of θ.

11. Let the elements of a set be rotations of a plane figure about the origin. In particular, let R_n stand for a rotation through $n\pi/3$ radians, where n is an integer. Suppose that $R_m \oplus R_n$ stands for the rotation symbolized by R_m followed by that symbolized by R_n. Also, let $R_m = R_n$ mean that the final positions of the plane figure are identical; for example, $R_5 = R_{-1}$. Does the set $\{R_n : n = 1, 2, 3, 4, 5, 6\}$ form a group under the operation $\oplus$? Explain fully.

12. The length L of a metal bar is quite accurately given by the formula $L = L_0(1 + \beta t)$, where L_0 is the length at temperature $t = 0$ and β is the coefficient of linear expansion. In a critical experiment involving an artificial earth satellite, it was

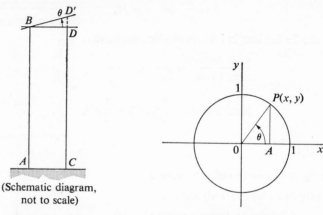

(Schematic diagram, not to scale)

FIGURE 7.1d   **FIGURE 7.2a**

essential to control the lengths of two parallel bars AB and CD (Figure 7.1d) closely enough that a platform BD supported by the bars would not be tilted by more than 5 seconds of arc because of temperature differences in the two bars. If the two bars are 10 centimeters apart and are each 2 meters long at 0°C, and if $\beta = 2.38 \times 10^{-5}$ per degree C, find the range of temperature difference allowable. *Hint*: It is sufficiently accurate to consider one bar fixed at 0°C, and to investigate the tilt caused by temperature changes in the other bar. Furthermore, for the extremely small angle of tilt, say θ, being considered, a very accurate formula is $\theta = (L_0\beta t/10)$ radians, where L_0 is in centimeters.

7.2 DEFINITION OF THE TRIGONOMETRIC FUNCTIONS

In Section 5.4, the concept of a periodic function f was introduced as one for which $f(x + k) = f(x)$ for some $k \neq 0$. Because of the important role played by the periodic functions in pure and applied mathematics, we need to make a detailed study of certain of the more frequently occurring functions of this kind.

Let us consider a point P on the circumference of a circle with unit radius and with center at the origin of a rectangular coordinate system (see Figure 7.2a). As P assumes various positions on the circumference, the x- and y-coordinates of P vary between 1 and -1. The location of P is, however, determined by the angle θ which OP makes with the positive x-axis. Consequently, the coordinates x and y are also completely determined by the angle θ.

For reasons that will appear later, we agree to use radian measure for the angle θ. The set of permissible values of θ is the set $\mathfrak{R}$ of all real numbers. Corresponding to each value of θ, there is a unique value of x and a unique value of y. Hence, each of the sets $\{(\theta, x)\}$ and $\{(\theta, y)\}$ is a function, with $\mathfrak{R}$ as its domain and with the set $\{u: -1 \leq u \leq 1\}$ as its range.

Definition 7.2a. Let $P(x, y)$ be a point on the unit circle with its center at the origin O, and let θ be the radian measure of the angle from the positive x-axis to OP. Then the set of pairs $\{(\theta, x)\}$ is called the **cosine** function and the set of pairs $\{(\theta, y)\}$ is called the **sine** function.

Just as we write $y = f(x)$ when f is the function $\{(x, y)\}$, we also write $x = \cos \theta$ when x is the value associated with θ by the cosine function, and $y = \sin \theta$ when y is the value associated with θ by the sine function.

Returning to Figure 7.2a, we see that an increase of 2π in the measure of the angle AOP leaves the position of P unaltered and hence the values of x and y unchanged. Thus we have the results

$$\cos (\theta + 2\pi) = \cos \theta \quad \text{and} \quad \sin (\theta + 2\pi) = \sin \theta.$$

This means that the sine and cosine functions are both periodic with the period 2π.

In Figure 7.2a, the line segment OA represents $\cos \theta$ or $\cos (\theta + 2n\pi)$, for $n \in \mathcal{I}$, and AP represents $\sin \theta$ or $\sin (\theta + 2n\pi)$.

It is clear that as θ varies from 0 to $\pi/2$, $\cos \theta$ varies from 1 to 0 and $\sin \theta$ varies from 0 to 1. Graphs of the two functions are shown in Figure 7.2b.

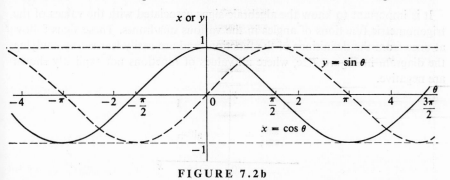

FIGURE 7.2b

By virtue of the periodicity of these functions, the following equations are true for every $n \in \mathcal{I}$:

$$\cos (\theta + 2n\pi) = \cos \theta \quad \text{and} \quad \sin (\theta + 2n\pi) = \sin \theta.$$

Since $P(x, y)$ in Figure 7.2a is a point on the unit circle with center at the origin, and the equation of this circle is

$$x^2 + y^2 = 1,$$

it follows immediately that

$$\cos^2 \theta + \sin^2 \theta = 1.$$

This formula is fundamental in many relationships involving the sine and cosine functions since it can readily be used to change from one function to the other. The reader should observe that the relationship holds regardless of the value of θ.

The sine and cosine functions are called **trigonometric** functions because of their relationship to triangles. Using these two functions, it is possible to define other trigonometric functions that are useful.

Definition 7.2b.

(a) The **tangent** function is defined by the equation

$$\tan \theta = \frac{\sin \theta}{\cos \theta}.$$

(b) The **cotangent** function is defined by the equation

$$\cot \theta = \frac{\cos \theta}{\sin \theta}.$$

(c) The **secant** function is defined by the equation

$$\sec \theta = \frac{1}{\cos \theta}.$$

(d) The **cosecant** function is defined by the equation

$$\csc \theta = \frac{1}{\sin \theta}.$$

It is important to know the algebraic signs associated with the values of the trigonometric functions of angles in the various quadrants. These signs follow at once from the definitions of the functions and are easily learned by studying the diagram in Figure 7.2c, where all values of functions not explicitly shown are negative.

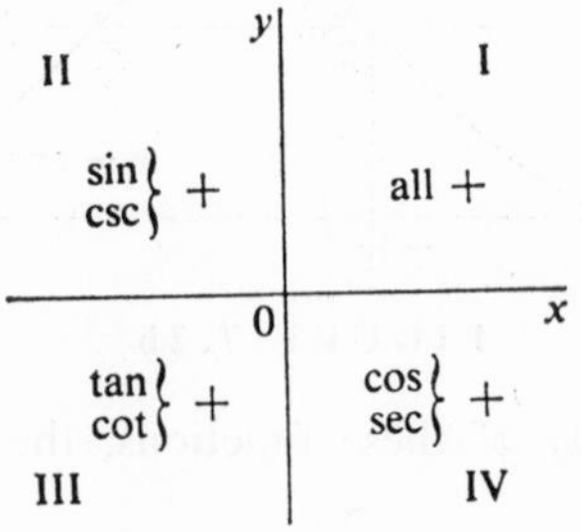

FIGURE 7.2c

The range of the tangent function may be obtained as follows. Since $\sin 0 = 0$ and $\cos 0 = 1$, $\tan 0 = 0/1 = 0$. As $\theta \to (\pi/2)$, $\sin \theta \to 1$ and $\cos \theta \to 0^+$. Thus $\tan \theta \to \infty$ as $\theta \to (\pi/2)^-$ and $\tan (\pi/2)$ is not defined. From Figure 7.2b, we note that for values of θ between 0 and $-(\pi/2)$, sin θ is negative and cos θ is positive, so tan θ is negative. Also, as $\theta \to -(\pi/2)^+$, sin $\theta \to -1$ and cos $\theta \to 0^+$, so tan $\theta \to -\infty$. The graph of the tangent function is shown in Figure 7.2d. Note

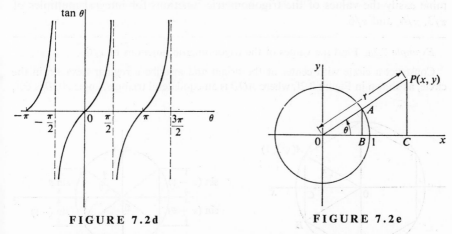

FIGURE 7.2d   FIGURE 7.2e

that the period of tan θ is π. The construction of the graphs of cot θ, sec θ, and csc θ is left for the exercises.

An angle whose terminal side coincides with one of the coordinate axes is called a **quadrantal** angle. The values of the trigonometric functions for the quadrantal angles are summarized in the following table.

θ	sin θ	cos θ	tan θ	cot θ	sec θ	csc θ
0	0	1	0	undef.	1	undef.
$\dfrac{\pi}{2}$	1	0	undef.	0	undef.	1
π	0	-1	0	undef.	-1	undef.
$\dfrac{3\pi}{2}$	-1	0	undef.	0	undef.	-1

The value of any of the trigonometric functions may be expressed as a ratio by making use of similar triangles. Thus, if $P(x, y)$ is a point in the plane, then triangles OAB and OPC in Figure 7.2e are similar. If we let r represent the distance OP, then

$$\sin \theta = \frac{AB}{1} = \frac{PC}{OP} = \frac{y}{r}, \qquad \csc \theta = \frac{1}{\sin \theta} = \frac{r}{y},$$

$$\cos \theta = \frac{OB}{1} = \frac{OC}{OP} = \frac{x}{r}, \qquad \sec \theta = \frac{1}{\cos \theta} = \frac{r}{x},$$

$$\tan \theta = \frac{\sin \theta}{\cos \theta} = \frac{AB}{OB} = \frac{y}{x}, \qquad \cot \theta = \frac{1}{\tan \theta} = \frac{x}{y}.$$

We have already found the values of the trigonometric functions for quadrantal angles. For angles with terminal sides in the quadrants, we usually have to resort to a book of tables, but geometric considerations enable us to determine easily the values of the trigonometric functions for integral multiples of $\pi/3$, $\pi/4$, and $\pi/6$.

Example 7.2a. Find the values of the trigonometric functions of $\pi/6$.

Construct a circle with center at the origin and inscribe a regular hexagon in the circle, as shown in Figure 7.2f, where *AOB* is an equilateral triangle, angle *AOB* is 60°,

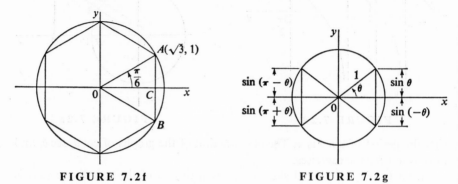

| FIGURE 7.2f | FIGURE 7.2g |

and thus angle *AOC* is 30°. If we let the radius be 2 units, then $AC = 1$ unit, and, by the Pythagorean Theorem, $OC = \sqrt{3}$ units. Thus,

$$\sin \frac{\pi}{6} = \frac{1}{2}, \qquad \csc \frac{\pi}{6} = 2,$$

$$\cos \frac{\pi}{6} = \frac{\sqrt{3}}{2}, \qquad \sec \frac{\pi}{6} = \frac{2}{\sqrt{3}},$$

$$\tan \frac{\pi}{6} = \frac{1}{\sqrt{3}}, \qquad \cot \frac{\pi}{6} = \sqrt{3}.$$

We have already noted that the values of the trigonometric functions are unchanged if the angle is increased or decreased by an integral multiple of 2π, so that the values of the trigonometric functions for any angle may be expressed in terms of the values of the same functions of some angle between 0 and 2π. Furthermore, from Figure 7.2g, it is seen that for $0 \leq \theta \leq \pi/2$,

$$\sin (\pi - \theta) = \sin \theta,$$
$$\sin (\pi + \theta) = -\sin \theta,$$

and

$$\sin (-\theta) = -\sin \theta.$$

Similar arguments hold for the other trigonometric functions, so that changing the angle by adding or subtracting $n\pi$, $n = 0, \pm1, \pm2, \ldots$, does *not* change the *absolute value* of a trigonometric function, although it *may* change the *sign*.

Example 7.2b. Express the values of the trigonometric functions of $7\pi/6$ in terms of the values of trigonometric functions of θ with $0 \leqq \theta \leqq \pi/2$.

Since $7\pi/6 = \pi + (\pi/6)$, we know that the absolute value of any trigonometric function of $7\pi/6$ is equal to the value of the same trigonometric function of $\pi/6$, and that the algebraic sign is the sign of that function in the third quadrant. Accordingly, we have

$$\sin \frac{7\pi}{6} = -\sin \frac{\pi}{6}, \qquad \csc \frac{7\pi}{6} = -\csc \frac{\pi}{6},$$

$$\cos \frac{7\pi}{6} = -\cos \frac{\pi}{6}, \qquad \sec \frac{7\pi}{6} = -\sec \frac{\pi}{6},$$

$$\tan \frac{7\pi}{6} = \tan \frac{\pi}{6}, \qquad \cot \frac{7\pi}{6} = \cot \frac{\pi}{6}.$$

If two trigonometric functions f and g are related so that

$$f(\tfrac{1}{2}\pi - \theta) = g(\theta) \quad \text{or} \quad f(\theta) = g(\tfrac{1}{2}\pi - \theta),$$

then f and g are called **cofunctions**. From Figure 7.2h, we see that for $0 < \theta < \tfrac{1}{2}\pi$

$$\sin \theta = \cos [(\pi/2) - \theta];$$

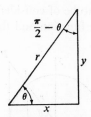

FIGURE 7.2h

hence the sine and cosine functions are cofunctions. Note that θ and $(\pi/2) - \theta$ are **complementary** angles. Other pairs of cofunctions are $\tan \theta$ and $\cot \theta$, and $\sec \theta$ and $\csc \theta$. By using the fact that $(\pi/2) - (\pi/6) = \pi/3$, we may write the answers in the preceding example in terms of the cofunctions of the functions used there. For instance,

$$\sin \frac{7\pi}{6} = -\sin \frac{\pi}{6} = -\cos \left(\frac{\pi}{2} - \frac{\pi}{6} \right) = -\cos \frac{\pi}{3},$$

$$\tan \frac{7\pi}{6} = \tan \frac{\pi}{6} = \cot \left(\frac{\pi}{2} - \frac{\pi}{6} \right) = \cot \frac{\pi}{3}.$$

In a similar fashion, the reader may obtain corresponding results for the other four functions.

These results are special cases of a more general type of "reduction" formula which may be stated as

Theorem 7.2a. Let f denote one of the six fundamental trigonometric functions. Then, for each $n \in \mathscr{I}$,

$$f(\theta + n\pi) = \pm f(\theta)$$

and

$$f\left(\theta + n\pi + \frac{\pi}{2}\right) = \pm \text{co-}f(\theta)$$

where the appropriate sign must be chosen to correspond to the given function f and the quadrant of the original angle, $\theta + n\pi$, or $\theta + n\pi + (\pi/2)$.

PROOF: Complete details of the proof will not be given here. However, by the periodicity of the function f, we have

$$f(\theta + n\pi) = f(\theta) \qquad \text{if } n \text{ is even,}$$

and

$$f(\theta + n\pi) = f(\theta + \pi) \quad \text{if } n \text{ is odd.}$$

If $0 \leq \theta \leq \pi/2$, the reader may verify from sketches similar to that in Figure 7.2g that the first formula in the theorem is correct. In a similar fashion, he may verify the second formula. As a matter of fact, the formulas will all fall out as special cases of the so-called "addition" formulas to be discussed in a later section.

To conclude this section, we shall establish some inequalities between θ, $\sin \theta$, and $\tan \theta$ that will prove to be of considerable importance in later work. Using the definition of the sine function and the fact that a chord of a circle

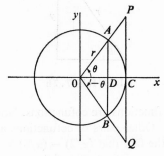

FIGURE 7.2i

is shorter than the arc it subtends, we see from Figure 7.2i, where θ is an acute angle, that

$$0 < \text{chord } AB < \text{arc } ACB.$$

That is,

$$0 < 2r \sin \theta < 2r\theta$$

or

$$0 < \sin \theta < \theta.$$

Furthermore,

$$\text{area of sector } AOC < \text{area of triangle } POC.$$

That is,

$$\tfrac{1}{2}r^2\theta < \tfrac{1}{2}r^2 \tan \theta$$

or

$$\theta < \tan \theta.$$

These two results are combined in

Theorem 7.2b. $\qquad 0 < \theta < \dfrac{\pi}{2} \Rightarrow 0 < \sin\theta < \theta < \tan\theta.$

Exercises 7.2

In Numbers 1 to 12, find the values of the six trigonometric functions of the given numbers.

1. $\frac{1}{4}\pi.$
2. $-\frac{1}{6}\pi.$
3. $\frac{4}{3}\pi.$
4. $\frac{5}{3}\pi.$

5. $\frac{13}{4}\pi.$
6. $\frac{3}{4}\pi.$
7. $\frac{7}{4}\pi.$
8. $\frac{3}{2}\pi.$

9. $4\pi.$
10. $\pi.$
11. $-\frac{3}{2}\pi.$
12. $\frac{7}{6}\pi.$

In Numbers 13 to 18, express the values of the trigonometric functions of the given numbers in terms of the values of the trigonometric functions of a number between 0 and $\pi/4$; for example,

$$\sin\frac{5\pi}{3} = \sin\left(\frac{3\pi}{2} + \frac{\pi}{6}\right) = -\cos\frac{\pi}{6}.$$

13. $\frac{5}{12}\pi.$
14. $\frac{5}{9}\pi.$

15. $-\frac{1}{7}\pi.$
16. $\frac{11}{12}\pi.$

17. $\frac{10}{7}\pi.$
18. $-\frac{4}{7}\pi.$

In Numbers 19 to 32, graph the functions defined by the given equations.

19. $f(\theta) = \cot\theta.$
20. $f(\theta) = \sec\theta.$
21. $f(\theta) = \csc\theta.$
22. $f(\theta) = \sin 2\theta.$
23. $f(\theta) = \cos\frac{1}{2}\theta.$
24. $f(\theta) = 3\sin 2\theta.$
25. $f(\theta) = \tan\frac{1}{2}\theta.$

26. $f(\theta) = \frac{1}{2}\sec 2\theta.$
27. $f(\theta) = \frac{1}{2}\cos\frac{1}{2}\theta.$
28. $f(\theta) = \cot 2\theta.$
29. $f(\theta) = 3\csc\frac{1}{2}\theta.$
30. $f(\theta) = 2\tan\theta.$
31. $f(\theta) = 3\tan\frac{1}{3}\theta.$
32. $f(\theta) = \cos 4\theta.$

33. Show from Figure 7.2i that

$$0 < \theta < \frac{\pi}{2} \Rightarrow \cos\theta < \frac{\theta}{\sin\theta} < \sec\theta.$$

34. For what values of θ such that $0 < \theta < \pi/2$ will the following statements be true?

(a) $\tan\theta < \cot\theta.$
(b) $\sec\theta > \csc\theta.$

(c) $\sin\theta > \cos\theta.$
(d) $\sec\theta < 2.$

7.3 SIMPLE APPLICATIONS OF THE TRIGONOMETRIC FUNCTIONS

The importance of land measurement and of surveying undoubtedly led to the development of the trigonometric functions for the solution of problems involving triangles. The expression of the trigonometric functions as ratios of the sides of a right triangle already suggests how they were used in solving problems involving right triangles. Since, in this type of work, it is customary to employ degree measure rather than radian measure, it is useful to have a table that gives to several decimal places the values of the sine, cosine, and tangent functions of angles from 0° to 90°.

Example 7.3a. Find the other sides of a right triangle if the side a is 5 and the angle A is 25°. (By convention, the triangle is lettered so that the angle A is opposite the side a and correspondingly for the other sides and angles, as shown in Figure 7.3a.)

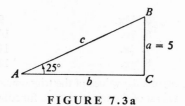

FIGURE 7.3a

From the figure, we have

$$\sin 25° = \frac{5}{c},$$

so that

$$c = \frac{5}{\sin 25°} = \frac{5}{0.42262} = 11.83.$$

If the book of tables also includes the cosecant, then we can conveniently replace the division by multiplication and write

$$c = 5 \csc 25° = 5(2.3662) = 11.83.$$

Since the values of $\sin 25°$ and $\csc 25°$ are only approximations, the two computed values of c may differ slightly if carried to additional decimal places.
We also have

$$\tan 25° = \frac{5}{b}$$

and

$$b = \frac{5}{\tan 25°} = 5 \cot 25° = 5(2.1445) = 10.73.$$

Since $a^2 + b^2 = c^2$, we may easily check our results:

$$a^2 + b^2 = 5^2 + (10.73)^2 = 140.1,$$
$$c^2 = (11.83)^2 = 140.0.$$

The angle α from the positive x-direction to a line is called the **angle of inclination** of the line. The definition of slope in Section 4.3 implies that $\tan \alpha$ is the slope of the line. Thus, the equation of a line with angle of inclination 60° and y-intercept 4 is $y = \sqrt{3}x + 4$. The notion of slope frequently appears in applications.

Example 7.3b. If the slope of a railroad track is to be 5/100, find the angle the tracks will make with the horizontal.

Since the slope is the tangent of the angle θ in Figure 7.3b, we have

$$\tan \theta = \tfrac{5}{100},$$

and

$$\theta = 2°52'.$$

Example 7.3c. An airplane is flying at a speed of 500 miles per hour in a direction 15° north of east. Find the north and east components of the vector representing the velocity.

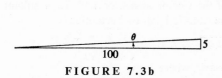

FIGURE 7.3b

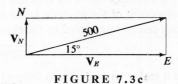

FIGURE 7.3c

From Figure 7.3c, we find

$$\cos 15° = \frac{|V_E|}{500}.$$

Thus,

$$
\begin{aligned}
|V_E| &= 500 \cos 15° \\
&= 500(0.96593) \\
&= 483 \text{ mph.}
\end{aligned}
$$

Also

$$\sin 15° = \frac{|V_N|}{500},$$

so that

$$
\begin{aligned}
|V_N| &= 500 \sin 15° \\
&= 500(0.25882) \\
&= 129 \text{ mph.}
\end{aligned}
$$

Example 7.3d. Find the resultant of the vectors shown in Figure 7.3d.

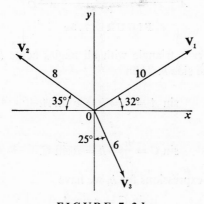

FIGURE 7.3d

We use the method of resolving each of the given vectors into its components along the axes and then combining these components. The details of the calculation are as follows:

Vector	x-component		y-component	
V_1	10 cos 32° =	8.48	10 sin 32° =	5.30
V_2	−8 cos 35° =	−6.55	8 sin 35° =	4.59
V_3	6 cos 65° =	2.54	−6 sin 65° =	−5.44
Resultant	sum =	4.47	sum =	4.45

The x-component of the resultant is the sum of the x-components, or 4.47, and the y-component of the resultant is the sum of the y-components, or 4.45. The resultant vector can be represented by the number-pair (4.47, 4.45). Its magnitude is

$$\sqrt{(4.47)^2 + (4.45)^2} = 6.31,$$

and it makes an angle θ with the positive x-axis, where

$$\tan \theta = \frac{4.45}{4.47} = 0.996,$$

$$\theta = 44°55'.$$

In order to solve oblique triangles, it is convenient to use two theorems called the Law of Sines and the Law of Cosines, respectively.

Theorem 7.3a. *The Law of Sines.* In any triangle, the sides are proportional to the sines of the opposite angles.

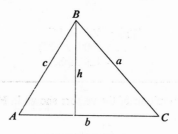

FIGURE 7.3e

PROOF: First, consider a triangle with all angles acute (Figure 7.3e). Let h be the altitude to the side b. Then

$$\sin A = \frac{h}{c} \Rightarrow h = c \sin A.$$

Also,

$$\sin C = \frac{h}{a} \Rightarrow h = a \sin C.$$

Equating these two expressions for h, we have

$$a \sin C = c \sin A,$$

from which it follows that

$$\frac{c}{\sin C} = \frac{a}{\sin A}.$$

By constructing a perpendicular to the side a and using the same argument as before, we obtain

$$\frac{c}{\sin C} = \frac{b}{\sin B}.$$

Hence, we have

$$\frac{a}{\sin A} = \frac{b}{\sin B} = \frac{c}{\sin C}.$$

A similar construction may be used for an obtuse triangle and the proof of this case is left for the exercises.

The Law of Sines may be used to aid in the solution of an oblique triangle when one side and two angles are given, or when two sides and the angle opposite one of them is given.

Example 7.3e. Solve the triangle for which

$$A = 35°, \quad B = 65°, \quad \text{and} \quad a = 3.$$

From

$$\frac{a}{\sin A} = \frac{b}{\sin B},$$

we get

$$\frac{3}{\sin 35°} = \frac{b}{\sin 65°},$$

so that

$$b = \frac{3 \sin 65°}{\sin 35°} = \frac{3(0.90631)}{0.57358} = 4.74.$$

We have

$$C = 180° - A - B = 80°,$$

and by the use of

$$\frac{a}{\sin A} = \frac{c}{\sin C},$$

we find

$$c = \frac{3 \sin 80°}{\sin 35°} = \frac{3(0.98481)}{0.57358} = 5.15.$$

If two sides and the included angle of a triangle are given, or if the three sides are given, the Law of Sines will not suffice to solve the triangle. It is necessary to use the Law of Cosines.

Theorem 7.3b. *The Law of Cosines.* The square of any side of a triangle is equal to the sum of the squares of the other two sides minus twice the product of these two sides multiplied by the cosine of the included angle.

PROOF: Let the triangle AOB be placed so that the vertex O is at the origin and the side a is along the positive x-axis, as in Figure 7.3f. Then the co-

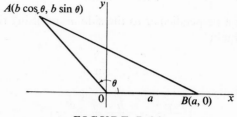

FIGURE 7.3f

ordinates of B are $(a, 0)$ and the coordinates of A are $(b \cos \theta, b \sin \theta)$. We use the distance formula for the length of c to obtain

$$c^2 = (a - b \cos \theta)^2 + (b \sin \theta)^2,$$

or, with the aid of the formula $\cos^2 \theta + \sin^2 \theta = 1$,

$$c^2 = a^2 + b^2 - 2ab \cos \theta.$$

A similar derivation can be used to obtain the formulas

$$a^2 = b^2 + c^2 - 2bc \cos A$$

and

$$b^2 = c^2 + a^2 - 2ca \cos B$$

Example 7.3f. Solve the triangle for which

$$a = 2, \quad b = 3, \quad \text{and} \quad c = 4.$$

We write

$$a^2 = b^2 + c^2 - 2bc \cos A,$$

giving

$$4 = 9 + 16 - 24 \cos A,$$

from which it follows that

$$\cos A = \frac{7}{8}$$

and

$$A = 28°57.3'.$$

The reader may find angles B and C in the same manner by writing the Law of Cosines twice more, once with B and then with C as the included angle.

Exercises 7.3

In Numbers 1 to 13, solve the triangle with the given parts.
  1. $b = 4, B = 35°, C = 90°$.
  2. $a = 3, b = 4, c = 5$.
  3. $B = 28°, A = 62°, c = 6$.
  4. $A = 55°, C = 90°, b = 2$.
  5. $A = 48°, B = 22°, c = 4$.

6. $a = 5, b = 6, c = 7$.
7. $a = 5, b = 4, B = 22°$ (two solutions).
8. $a = 6, c = 5, C = 15°$ (two solutions).
9. $a = 6, c = 7, C = 15°$.
10. $a = 3, b = 4, C = 27°32'$.
11. $a = 6, b = 7, c = 8$.
12. $b = 5, c = 6, A = 42°$.
13. $a = 4, b = 5, C = 37°$.
14. Find the acute angle between the line $x = -2$ and the line $3x - 2y = 6$.
15. What is the equation of a line with angle of inclination $150°$ and x-intercept -3?
16. (a) Find the equation of the system of lines with angle of inclination $135°$.
    (b) Find the member of the system in (a) that has a y-intercept of -2.
17. If an equilateral triangle has one side along the y-axis and the third vertex in the first quadrant, find the angle of inclination of each side.
18. Find the x- and y-components of a vector with a magnitude of 7 making an angle of $67°$ with the positive x-axis.
19. Find the resultant of the forces F_1 and F_2 acting on a body, if F_1 is inclined at an angle of $46°$ to the x-axis and has a magnitude of 25 pounds, and F_2 is inclined at an angle of $115°$ to the x-axis and has a magnitude of 37 pounds.
20. Prove the Law of Sines for an obtuse triangle.
21. Find the resultant of the forces F_1, F_2, and F_3 acting on a body, if F_1 is inclined at an angle of $63°$ to the x-axis and has a magnitude of 7 pounds, F_2 is inclined at an angle of $155°$ to the x-axis and has a magnitude of 12 pounds, and F_3 is inclined at an angle of $219°$ to the x-axis and has a magnitude of 8 pounds.
22. Find the tension in each rope if a weight is suspended as shown in Figure 7.3g.

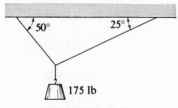

FIGURE 7.3g

23. If the speed of an airplane is 600 miles per hour and the plane is climbing at an angle of $27°$ with the horizontal, find the rate at which the plane is gaining altitude.
24. A block weighing 15 pounds rests on an inclined plane making an angle of $18°$ with the horizontal. Find the least force required to keep the block from moving if all forces other than gravity are disregarded.
25. If three forces of 50, 75, and 85 pounds are in equilibrium, find the angles the vectors representing the forces make with each other.
26. An enemy plane is spotted at a point P, 1000 miles due north of an air field O. The plane is flying at a speed of 500 miles per hour in a direction S $30°$ E straight toward a target that is 600 miles from P. Can a plane that is immediately dispatched from O and whose speed is 600 miles per hour fly in a straight line and intercept the enemy plane before it reaches the target? If so, in what direction should the intercepting plane fly? Ignore the heights of the planes.

7.4 BASIC TRIGONOMETRIC FORMULAS

From the definitions of the fundamental trigonometric functions there can be obtained a number of basic identities involving these functions. These identities are useful not only in changing one trigonometric form into another, but also in investigating the essential properties of the functions.

Theorem 7.4a. $\cos^2 \theta + \sin^2 \theta = 1.$

PROOF: As was pointed out in Section 7.2, this formula follows from the fact that $(\cos \theta, \sin \theta)$ is a point on the unit circle with center at the origin. See Figure 7.2a.

The reader may prove the following theorems by dividing both members of the preceding identity by $\cos^2 \theta$ and $\sin^2 \theta$, respectively.

Theorem 7.4b. $\sec^2 \theta = 1 + \tan^2 \theta.$

Theorem 7.4c. $\csc^2 \theta = 1 + \cot^2 \theta.$

These relationships, with the definitions given for tangent, cotangent, secant, and cosecant can be used in establishing other identities.

Example 7.4a. Prove that

$$\frac{\sin \theta \cot \theta + \cos \theta}{\cot \theta} = 2 \sin \theta.$$

We shall prove the proposed identity by transforming the left side of the equation into the right. Thus,

$$\frac{\sin \theta \cot \theta + \cos \theta}{\cot \theta} = \frac{\sin \theta \dfrac{\cos \theta}{\sin \theta} + \cos \theta}{\dfrac{\cos \theta}{\sin \theta}}$$

$$= \frac{2 \cos \theta \sin \theta}{\cos \theta}$$

$$= 2 \sin \theta.$$

Example 7.4b. Prove that

$$\csc \theta + \cot \theta = \frac{\sin \theta}{1 - \cos \theta}.$$

Again it is convenient to express the trigonometric functions on the left side of the equation in terms of the sine and cosine functions. Hence,

$$\csc \theta + \cot \theta = \frac{1}{\sin \theta} + \frac{\cos \theta}{\sin \theta}$$

$$= \frac{1 + \cos \theta}{\sin \theta} \left(\frac{1 - \cos \theta}{1 - \cos \theta} \right)$$

$$= \frac{1 - \cos^2 \theta}{\sin \theta (1 - \cos \theta)}$$

$$= \frac{\sin^2 \theta}{\sin \theta (1 - \cos \theta)}$$

$$= \frac{\sin \theta}{1 - \cos \theta}.$$

The fundamental identities and definitions are also useful in solving trigonometric equations as the next examples illustrate.

Example 7.4c. Solve the equation

$$2 \cos^2 x + \cos x - 1 = 0.$$

Since this is a quadratic equation in cos x, we factor the left side to get

$$(2 \cos x - 1)(\cos x + 1) = 0.$$

It now follows that

$$\cos x = \frac{1}{2} \quad \text{or} \quad \cos x = -1$$

and

$$x = \pm \frac{\pi}{3} + 2n\pi \quad \text{or} \quad x = \pi + 2n\pi, \qquad n \in \mathcal{G}.$$

Thus the solution set is

$$\mathcal{S} = \left\{ x : x = 2n\pi \pm \frac{\pi}{3} \right\} \cup \{ x : x = (2n + 1)\pi \}, \qquad n \in \mathcal{G}.$$

It is easy to check in the given equation that all these values do actually satisfy it.

Example 7.4d. Solve the equation

$$2 \sin^2 x - \cos x - 1 = 0.$$

By making use of the identity $\sin^2 x = 1 - \cos^2 x$, and rearranging terms, we get

$$2 \cos^2 x + \cos x - 1 = 0.$$

Since this is exactly the equation in the preceding example, it is evident that the desired solution set is the same as there.

The last example illustrates that the use of the trigonometric identities sometimes serves to transform the equation into one in which only one trigonometric function of the unknown occurs. If the equation can be solved for that function of the unknown, then the desired unknown itself can be found from tables of values of the trigonometric functions.

Example 7.4e. Find the solution set of the equation

$$\tan^2 x + \sec^2 x = 7.$$

Since $\sec^2 x = 1 + \tan^2 x$, the equation becomes

$$\tan^2 x + (1 + \tan^2 x) = 7$$

or

$$\tan^2 x = 3.$$

Hence

$$\tan x = \pm \sqrt{3}.$$

It follows that

$$x = \frac{\pi}{3} + n\pi, \quad \frac{2\pi}{3} + n\pi, \qquad n \in \mathcal{G},$$

which determines the solution set of the equation.

Exercises 7.4

In each of Numbers 1 to 13, verify the given identity by transforming the left side into the right.

1. $\tan \alpha + \cot \alpha = \sec \alpha \csc \alpha$,
2. $\sec A - \cos A = \tan A \sin A$.
3. $\sec^2 x + \csc^2 x = \sec^2 x \csc^2 x$.
4. $\dfrac{\cos \theta}{1 - \sin \theta} - \dfrac{1 - \sin \theta}{\cos \theta} = 2 \tan \theta$.
5. $\dfrac{1}{1 + \sin A} + \dfrac{1}{1 - \sin A} = 2 \sec^2 A$.
6. $\cot \alpha + \tan \alpha = \cot \alpha \sec^2 \alpha$.
7. $\dfrac{\sin A + \sin B}{\sin A - \sin B} = \dfrac{\csc B + \csc A}{\csc B - \csc A}$.
8. $\dfrac{1 - \sec^2 \alpha}{1 - \csc^2 \alpha} = \tan^4 \alpha$.
9. $\cot A + \csc A = \dfrac{\sin A}{1 - \cos A}$.
10. $\cos \alpha + \sin \alpha \tan \alpha = \sec \alpha$.
11. $1 + \sin^2 \theta \sec^2 \theta = \sec^2 \theta$.
12. $\csc^4 A - \cot^4 A = \csc^2 A(\sin^2 A + 2 \cos^2 A)$.
13. $\sec^2 \theta \csc^2 \theta = (\tan \theta + \cot \theta)^2$.

Solve the trigonometric equations of Numbers 14 to 29.

14. $2 \sin 2\theta - 1 = 0$.
15. $\cos 3\theta = 0$.
16. $\cos^2 A - \sin A - 1 = 0$.
17. $\tan 2\alpha = 1$.
18. $2 \sin^2 x - 1 = 0$.
19. $\sqrt{3} \sin \theta - \sec \theta \cos^2 \theta = 0$.
20. $2 \sin^2 \theta + 3 \sin \theta = 2$.
21. $\tan^4 B - 9 = 0$.
22. $\sin^3 A + \cos^3 A = 0$.
23. $\sin^2 \alpha + \sin \alpha + 1 = 0$.
24. $\sin A \cos A - \cos A + \sin A = 1$.
25. $\cos^3 x - 2 \cos^2 x + \cos x - 2 = 0$.
26. $3 \tan^3 x + 3 \tan^2 x + \tan x + 1 = 0$.
27. $\sec^2 A - \tan A = 1$.
28. $3 \sec^2 x = 4 \tan^2 x$.
29. $2 \sin^2 x + \sqrt{3} \sin x + 2 \sin x + \sqrt{3} = 0$.

7.5 TRIGONOMETRIC FORMULAS INVOLVING THE SUM AND DIFFERENCE OF TWO ANGLES

It is often useful to be able to write such expressions as $\cos(\alpha - \beta)$ or $\tan(\alpha + \beta)$ in terms of trigonometric functions of the separate angles α and β. In order to see how this may be done, we begin with

Theorem 7.5a. $\cos(\alpha - \beta) = \cos \alpha \cos \beta + \sin \alpha \sin \beta$.

PROOF: Let α and β be represented by the angles shown in Figure 7.5a. There is no essential loss in generality involved in this representation since only the fact that A and B are points on the unit circle is actually used in the proof. If A, O, and B are in a straight line, the formula can be verified directly.

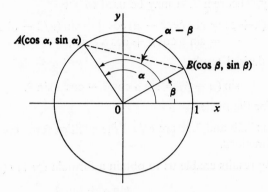

FIGURE 7.5a

Also the angle from OB to OA is always $\alpha - \beta$, $\beta - \alpha$, or 2π minus one of these. The value of the cosine function is $\cos(\alpha - \beta)$ for each of these angles. The fact that A and B are on the circle implies that the coordinates of A are $(\cos\alpha, \sin\alpha)$, and those of B are $(\cos\beta, \sin\beta)$.

The square of the distance AB is therefore

$$(AB)^2 = (\cos\alpha - \cos\beta)^2 + (\sin\alpha - \sin\beta)^2$$
$$= \cos^2\alpha - 2\cos\alpha\cos\beta + \cos^2\beta + \sin^2\alpha - 2\sin\alpha\sin\beta + \sin^2\beta$$
$$= 2 - 2\cos\alpha\cos\beta - 2\sin\alpha\sin\beta.$$

Now, using the law of cosines in triangle AOB, we get

$$(AB)^2 = (OB)^2 + (OA)^2 - 2(OB)(OA)\cos(\alpha - \beta)$$

or

$$(AB)^2 = 2 - 2\cos(\alpha - \beta).$$

Equating the two expressions for $(AB)^2$, we have

$$2 - 2\cos\alpha\cos\beta - 2\sin\alpha\sin\beta = 2 - 2\cos(\alpha - \beta)$$

or

$$\cos(\alpha - \beta) = \cos\alpha\cos\beta + \sin\alpha\sin\beta.$$

Theorem 7.5b. $\quad \cos(\alpha + \beta) = \cos\alpha\cos\beta - \sin\alpha\sin\beta.$

PROOF: The formula for $\cos(\alpha + \beta)$ may be obtained by writing

$$\cos(\alpha + \beta) = \cos[\alpha - (-\beta)]$$
$$= \cos\alpha\cos(-\beta) + \sin\alpha\sin(-\beta)$$
$$= \cos\alpha\cos\beta - \sin\alpha\sin\beta.$$

Theorem 7.5c. $\quad \sin(\alpha + \beta) = \sin\alpha\cos\beta + \cos\alpha\sin\beta.$

PROOF: Since $\sin \alpha = \cos (\pi/2 - \alpha)$, then

$$\begin{aligned} \sin (\alpha + \beta) &= \cos [\pi/2 - (\alpha + \beta)] \\ &= \cos [(\pi/2 - \alpha) - \beta]. \end{aligned}$$

Consequently, Theorem 7.5a may be used to get

$$\begin{aligned} \sin (\alpha + \beta) &= \cos (\pi/2 - \alpha) \cos \beta + \sin (\pi/2 - \alpha) \sin \beta \\ &= \sin \alpha \cos \beta + \cos \alpha \sin \beta, \end{aligned}$$

which is the desired result.

Theorem 7.5d. $\sin (\alpha - \beta) = \sin \alpha \cos \beta - \cos \alpha \sin \beta$.

PROOF: Left for the reader.

Note: Theorems 7.5b and 7.5c are called the **addition formulas** for the trigonometric functions.

The preceding results enable us to obtain a formula for $\tan (\alpha + \beta)$.

Theorem 7.5e. $\qquad \tan (\alpha + \beta) = \dfrac{\tan \alpha + \tan \beta}{1 - \tan \alpha \tan \beta}$.

PROOF: $\qquad \tan (\alpha + \beta) = \dfrac{\sin (\alpha + \beta)}{\cos (\alpha + \beta)}$

$$= \frac{\sin \alpha \cos \beta + \cos \alpha \sin \beta}{\cos \alpha \cos \beta - \sin \alpha \sin \beta}$$

$$= \frac{\dfrac{\sin \alpha \cos \beta}{\cos \alpha \cos \beta} + \dfrac{\cos \alpha \sin \beta}{\cos \alpha \cos \beta}}{\dfrac{\cos \alpha \cos \beta}{\cos \alpha \cos \beta} - \dfrac{\sin \alpha \sin \beta}{\cos \alpha \cos \beta}}.$$

Thus, we find

$$\tan (\alpha + \beta) = \frac{\tan \alpha + \tan \beta}{1 - \tan \alpha \tan \beta}.$$

Theorem 7.5f. $\qquad \tan (\alpha - \beta) = \dfrac{\tan \alpha - \tan \beta}{1 + \tan \alpha \tan \beta}$.

PROOF: Left for the reader.

If we add the formulas for $\sin (\alpha + \beta)$ and $\sin (\alpha - \beta)$ and divide by 2, we obtain

Theorem 7.5g. $\quad \sin \alpha \cos \beta = \frac{1}{2}[\sin (\alpha + \beta) + \sin (\alpha - \beta)]$.

In a similar fashion we may add the formulas for $\cos (\alpha + \beta)$ and $\cos (\alpha - \beta)$ and divide by 2 to get

Theorem 7.5h. $\quad \cos \alpha \cos \beta = \frac{1}{2}[\cos (\alpha + \beta) + \cos (\alpha - \beta)]$.

By subtracting the formula for $\cos (\alpha + \beta)$ from the formula for $\cos (\alpha - \beta)$ and dividing by 2, we have

Theorem 7.5i. $\quad \sin \alpha \sin \beta = \frac{1}{2}[\cos (\alpha - \beta) - \cos (\alpha + \beta)]$.

The following examples illustrate the use of the formulas derived in this section.

Example 7.5a. Find $\cos 75°$ without using tables.

Since $75° = 45° + 30°$, we may write

$$\cos 75° = \cos (45° + 30°)$$
$$= \cos 45° \cos 30° - \sin 45° \sin 30°$$
$$= \frac{\sqrt{2}}{2} \cdot \frac{\sqrt{3}}{2} - \frac{\sqrt{2}}{2} \cdot \frac{1}{2}$$
$$= \tfrac{1}{4}(\sqrt{6} - \sqrt{2}).$$

Example 7.5b. Use an addition formula to verify the identity

$$\sin (180° + A) = -\sin A.$$

We use Theorem 7.5c and $\sin 180° = 0$, $\cos 180° = -1$ to get

$$\sin (180° + A) = \sin 180° \cos A + \cos 180° \sin A$$
$$= -\sin A.$$

Example 7.5c. Show that

$$\cos 2\theta + \sin 2\theta \tan \theta = 1.$$

Since $\tan \theta = \sin \theta / \cos \theta$, we have

$$\cos 2\theta + \sin 2\theta \tan \theta = \cos 2\theta + \sin 2\theta \frac{\sin \theta}{\cos \theta}$$

$$= \frac{\cos 2\theta \cos \theta + \sin 2\theta \sin \theta}{\cos \theta}$$

$$= \frac{\cos (2\theta - \theta)}{\cos \theta} \qquad \text{(Theorem 7.5a)}$$

$$= \frac{\cos \theta}{\cos \theta} = 1.$$

Example 7.5d. Express $\sqrt{3} \cos \theta + \sin \theta$ in the form $A \sin (\theta + \alpha)$, with α the smallest nonnegative angle possible.

By Theorem 7.5c, we have

$$A \sin (\theta + \alpha) = A \sin \theta \cos \alpha + A \cos \theta \sin \alpha.$$

Consequently, in order for the equation

$$\sqrt{3} \cos \theta + \sin \theta = A \sin (\theta + \alpha)$$

to be an identity, it is necessary that

$$A \sin \alpha = \sqrt{3} \quad \text{and} \quad A \cos \alpha = 1.$$

Making use of the fact that $\cos^2 \alpha + \sin^2 \alpha = 1$, we square and add corresponding members of the last two equations to get

$$A^2 = 4 \quad \text{and} \quad A = \pm 2.$$

If $A = 2$, then $\sin \alpha = \sqrt{3}/2$ and $\cos \alpha = 1/2$, so that $\alpha = \pi/3$. If $A = -2$, then $\alpha = 4\pi/3$, so that the value $A = 2$ should be used.

It has thus been shown that

$$\sqrt{3} \cos \theta + \sin \theta = 2 \sin (\theta + \pi/3).$$

The method of the preceding example is widely used in many applied problems. This method shows that any expression of the form

$$a \cos \theta + b \sin \theta$$

can be put into either of the forms

$$A \sin (\theta + \alpha) \quad \text{or} \quad B \cos (\theta + \beta).$$

Example 7.5e. Solve the equation

$$\tan 2\theta \cot \theta + 1 = \sec 2\theta \csc \theta.$$

Upon multiplying the equation by $\cos 2\theta \sin \theta$, we get

$$\sin 2\theta \cos \theta + \cos 2\theta \sin \theta = 1$$

or

$$\sin 3\theta = 1.$$

It follows that

$$3\theta = \pi/2 + 2\pi k, \quad k \in \mathcal{J},$$

and that

$$\theta = \pi/6 + 2\pi k/3, \quad k \in \mathcal{J}.$$

These values of θ constitute the solution set of

$$\sin 3\theta = 1,$$

an equation that was obtained by multiplication by $\cos 2\theta \sin \theta$. Hence, this solution set may conceivably have elements that are not in the solution set of the original equation. (Compare Theorem 3.7g.) It is therefore necessary to check these values in the given equation. The reader may check the values $\pi/6$, $\pi/6 + 2\pi/3$, and $\pi/6 + 4\pi/3$. Why is it not necessary to carry out separate checks for any other values?

Exercises 7.5

In Numbers 1 to 6, find the value of the given expression without using tables.

1. $\sin 75°$.
2. $\cos \pi/12$.
3. $\tan 105°$.
4. $\sin \pi/12$.
5. $\cos 105°$.
6. $\tan 5\pi/12$.

7. Find a formula for $\cot (A + B)$ in terms of $\cot A$ and $\cot B$.
8. Find a formula for $\cot (A - B)$ in terms of $\cot A$ and $\cot B$.
9. Find a formula for $\cos (A + B + C)$ in terms of sines and cosines of A, B, and C.
10. Find a formula for $\cos (A + B - C)$ in terms of cosines and sines of A, B, and C.

In Numbers 11 to 15, use the addition formulas to verify the given identity.

11. $\cos (180° + A) = -\cos A$.
12. $\sin (90° + A) = \cos A$.
13. $\tan (3\pi/2 - A) = \cot A$.
14. $\sin (2\pi - A) = -\sin A$.
15. $\cos [(\pi/2) + A] = -\sin A$.

16. Express each of the following in the form $A \cos (\theta - \alpha)$, where α is the smallest nonnegative angle possible.

   (a) $\cos \theta + \sqrt{3} \sin \theta$.   (b) $\cos \theta + \sin \theta$.

   In Numbers 17 to 24, verify the given identity by transforming the left side into the right.

17. $\cos (A + B) \cos B + \sin (A + B) \sin B = \cos A$.
18. $\sin [\theta + (\pi/3)] - \cos [\theta - (\pi/6)] = 0$.
19. $\sin (A - B) \cos B + \cos (A - B) \sin B = \sin A$.

20. $\sec (A + B) = \dfrac{\sec A \sec B}{1 - \tan A \tan B}$.

21. $\sin \alpha + \sin \beta = 2 \sin \frac{1}{2}(\alpha + \beta) \cos \frac{1}{2}(\alpha - \beta)$. *Hint:* Let $u = \frac{1}{2}(\alpha + \beta)$, $v = \frac{1}{2}(\alpha - \beta)$.
22. $\sin \alpha - \sin \beta = 2 \sin \frac{1}{2}(\alpha - \beta) \cos \frac{1}{2}(\alpha + \beta)$. See Number 21.
23. $\cos \alpha + \cos \beta = 2 \cos \frac{1}{2}(\alpha + \beta) \cos \frac{1}{2}(\alpha - \beta)$. See Number 21.
24. $\cos \alpha - \cos \beta = -2 \sin \frac{1}{2}(\alpha + \beta) \sin \frac{1}{2}(\alpha - \beta)$. See Number 21.

25. If α is in the second quadrant, β is in the third quadrant, and $\cos \alpha = -4/5$, $\sin \beta = -12/13$, find

   (a) $\sin (\alpha + \beta)$;   (b) $\cos (\alpha - \beta)$;   (c) $\tan (\alpha + \beta)$.

26. If A is in the fourth quadrant, B is in the third quadrant, and $\sin A = -2/3$, $\tan B = 4/3$, find

   (a) $\sin (A - B)$;   (b) $\cos (A + B)$;   (c) $\tan (A - B)$.

   In Numbers 27 to 32, solve the given equations.

27. $\cos 3x \cos x + \sin 3x \sin x = 0$.
28. $\sin 3\varphi \cos \varphi - \cos 3\varphi \sin \varphi + 1 = 0$.

29. $\tan [x + (\pi/4)] = 1 + \tan x$.   31. $3 \cos \theta - 4 \sin \theta = 2$.
30. $2 \sin [x + (\pi/6)] = \sqrt{3}$.   32. $12 \sin \theta - 5 \cos \theta = 13$.

33. A rocket h feet long stands on its launching pad d feet away from an observer. The observer's line of sight to the tip of the rocket's nose makes an angle α with the horizontal (Figure 7.5b). Shortly after launching in a vertical path, the line

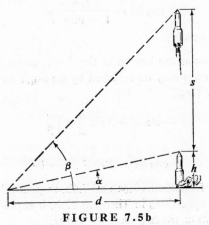

FIGURE 7.5b

of sight to the same point on the rocket makes an angle β with the horizontal. Show that the distance s that the rocket has risen is given by

$$s = \frac{d \sin (\beta - \alpha)}{\cos \alpha \cos \beta}.$$

34. A picture 5 feet high hangs on a wall so that the bottom edge of the picture is 4 feet from the floor. A man whose eye level is 5 feet above the floor looks at the picture from a point x feet away from the wall. Show that the angle α subtended by the picture at the man's eye is given by

$$\tan \alpha = \frac{5x}{x^2 - 4}.$$

7.6 MULTIPLE-ANGLE FORMULAS

One of the important uses of the formulas developed in Section 7.5 is in the derivation of formulas for trigonometric functions of multiples of a given angle.

Theorem 7.6a. $\qquad \sin 2\alpha = 2 \sin \alpha \cos \alpha.$

PROOF: This result is obtained directly from Theorem 7.5c by letting $\beta = \alpha$. Thus,

$$\begin{aligned}
\sin 2\alpha = \sin (\alpha + \alpha) &= \sin \alpha \cos \alpha + \cos \alpha \sin \alpha \\
&= 2 \sin \alpha \cos \alpha.
\end{aligned}$$

Theorem 7.6b.
$$\begin{aligned}
\cos 2\alpha &= \cos^2 \alpha - \sin^2 \alpha \\
&= 2 \cos^2 \alpha - 1 \\
&= 1 - 2 \sin^2 \alpha.
\end{aligned}$$

PROOF: Use the formula for $\cos (\alpha + \beta)$ with $\beta = \alpha$. The details are left for the reader.

Theorem 7.6c. $\qquad \tan 2\alpha = \dfrac{2 \tan \alpha}{1 - \tan^2 \alpha}.$

PROOF: Left for the reader.

The preceding formulas are known as the *double-angle formulas*. The reader should understand that α may be replaced by an angle in any other form and the result is still valid. Thus,

$$\sin \alpha = 2 \sin \frac{\alpha}{2} \cos \frac{\alpha}{2}$$

or

$$\cos 6\alpha = 2 \cos^2 3\alpha - 1$$

are valid statements of Theorems 7.6a and 7.6b, respectively.

From the various expressions in Theorem 7.6b, it is possible to obtain some useful formulas known as the *half-angle formulas*.

Theorem 7.6d.
$$\sin \frac{\theta}{2} = \pm\sqrt{\frac{1 - \cos \theta}{2}},$$

where the correct choice of sign is to be made to agree with the sign of $\sin \theta/2$.

PROOF: Since $\cos 2\alpha = 1 - 2 \sin^2 \alpha$,
we have

$$\sin^2 \alpha = \frac{1 - \cos 2\alpha}{2}$$

or

$$\sin \alpha = \pm\sqrt{\frac{1 - \cos 2\alpha}{2}}.$$

If $2\alpha = \theta$, then

$$\sin \frac{\theta}{2} = \pm\sqrt{\frac{1 - \cos \theta}{2}},$$

as was to be shown.

Theorem 7.6e.
$$\cos \frac{\theta}{2} = \pm\sqrt{\frac{1 + \cos \theta}{2}},$$

where the correct choice of sign is to be made to agree with the sign of $\cos \theta/2$.

PROOF: This theorem may be proved by following the same procedure as that in Theorem 7.6d, but using the formula

$$\cos 2\alpha = 2 \cos^2 \alpha - 1.$$

The details are left for the reader.

Theorem 7.6f.
$$\tan \frac{\theta}{2} = \pm\sqrt{\frac{1 - \cos \theta}{1 + \cos \theta}},$$

where the sign is to agree with the sign of $\tan \theta/2$. Alternate forms are

$$\tan \frac{\theta}{2} = \frac{1 - \cos \theta}{\sin \theta},$$

and

$$\tan \frac{\theta}{2} = \frac{\sin \theta}{1 + \cos \theta}.$$

PROOF: The proof is left for the reader, who should note that the correct sign is given in each case in the last two forms.

The application of these formulas is illustrated in the following examples.

Example 7.6a. If $\sin \alpha = -1/3$ and α is in the third quadrant, find $\sin \alpha/2$ and $\tan \alpha/2$.

In order to use Theorems 7.6d and 7.6f, we need to know $\cos \alpha$. Since α is in the third quadrant, $\cos \alpha$ is negative, so that

$$\cos \alpha = -\sqrt{1 - \sin^2 \alpha} = -\sqrt{1 - \frac{1}{9}} = -\frac{2\sqrt{2}}{3}.$$

Furthermore, $\alpha/2$ is in the second quadrant, so that

$$\sin \frac{\alpha}{2} = \sqrt{\frac{1 - \cos \alpha}{2}} = \sqrt{\frac{1 + (2\sqrt{2}/3)}{2}} = \frac{\sqrt{6 + 2\sqrt{3}}}{6},$$

and

$$\tan \frac{\alpha}{2} = \frac{1 - \cos \alpha}{\sin \alpha} = \frac{1 + (2\sqrt{2}/3)}{-1/3} = -(3 + 2\sqrt{2}).$$

Example 7.6b. Show that

$$\sec \alpha + \tan \alpha = \tan \left(\frac{\alpha}{2} + \frac{\pi}{4} \right).$$

We may write

$$\sec \alpha + \tan \alpha = \frac{1 + \sin \alpha}{\cos \alpha}$$

$$= \frac{1 - \cos [\alpha + (\pi/2)]}{\sin [\alpha + (\pi/2)]} \qquad \text{(Why?)}$$

$$= \tan \frac{1}{2} \left(\alpha + \frac{\pi}{2} \right) \qquad \text{(By Theorem 7.6f)}$$

$$= \tan \left(\frac{\alpha}{2} + \frac{\pi}{4} \right).$$

Example 7.6c. Express $\cos^4 \alpha$ in terms of first powers of the cosine function.

We have

$$\cos^4 \alpha = \left(\frac{1 + \cos 2\alpha}{2} \right)^2 = \frac{1}{4} (1 + 2 \cos 2\alpha + \cos^2 2\alpha)$$

$$= \frac{1}{4} \left(1 + 2 \cos 2\alpha + \frac{1 + \cos 4\alpha}{2} \right)$$

$$= \frac{3}{8} + \frac{1}{2} \cos 2\alpha + \frac{1}{8} \cos 4\alpha.$$

As in the preceding sections, the trigonometric formulas derived here are often useful in solving trigonometric equations.

Example 7.6d. Solve the equation

$$\sin 2\theta + \cos \theta = 0.$$

By using the identity $\sin 2\theta = 2 \sin \theta \cos \theta$, and factoring, we obtain

$$\cos \theta (2 \sin \theta + 1) = 0.$$

Thus

$$\cos \theta = 0 \quad \text{or} \quad \sin \theta = -\frac{1}{2},$$

from which the values of θ may be obtained as

$$\theta = \frac{\pi}{2} + n\pi \quad \text{or} \quad \theta = (2n + 1)\pi + \frac{\pi}{6} \quad \text{or} \quad 2n\pi - \frac{\pi}{6}, \qquad n \in \mathscr{I}.$$

The last two sets of answers may be combined by writing

$$\theta = n\pi + (-1)^{n+1} \frac{\pi}{6}, \qquad n \in \mathcal{I}.$$

Accordingly, the solution set of the given equation is

$$S = \left\{ n\pi + \frac{\pi}{2} \right\} \cup \left\{ n\pi + (-1)^{n+1} \frac{\pi}{6} \right\}, \qquad n \in \mathcal{I}.$$

Example 7.6e. Find the solution set of the equation

$$\cos 4\theta + \cos 2\theta = 0.$$

Since $\cos 4\theta = 2 \cos^2 2\theta - 1$, the equation becomes

$$2 \cos^2 2\theta - 1 + \cos 2\theta = 0$$

or

$$(2 \cos 2\theta - 1)(\cos 2\theta + 1) = 0.$$

If

$$2 \cos 2\theta - 1 = 0,$$

then

$$\cos 2\theta = 1/2,$$

so that

$$2\theta = \pm \pi/3 + 2\pi n, \qquad n \in \mathcal{I},$$

or

$$\theta = \pm \pi/6 + \pi n, \qquad n \in \mathcal{I}.$$

If

$$\cos 2\theta + 1 = 0,$$

then

$$\cos 2\theta = -1,$$

and

$$2\theta = \pi + 2\pi n, \qquad n \in \mathcal{I},$$

so that

$$\theta = \pi/2 + \pi n, \qquad n \in \mathcal{I}.$$

Hence, the required solution set is

$$S = \left\{ \pm \frac{\pi}{6} + n\pi \right\} \cup \left\{ \frac{\pi}{2} + n\pi \right\}, \qquad n \in \mathcal{I}.$$

Exercises 7.6

1. Find a formula for $\sin 3A$ in terms of trigonometric functions of A alone.
2. If $\cos A = 3/4$ and $\sin A < 0$, find $\sin 2A$.
3. Find the value of each of the following, without using tables.

   (a) $\sin 112\frac{1}{2}°$. \qquad\qquad (b) $\cos 22\frac{1}{2}°$.

4. Find an expression for $\cos^3 A \sin^4 A$ in terms of trigonometric functions of integral multiples of A where the trigonometric functions are to the first power only.

5. Express $\dfrac{\sin 4B - \sin 2B}{\cos 4B + \cos 2B}$ in terms of $\tan B$.

6. Prove Theorem 7.6c.
7. Prove Theorem 7.6e.
8. Prove Theorem 7.6f.

In each of Numbers 9 to 19, verify the given identity by transforming the left side into the right.

9. $\tan B + \cot B = 2 \csc 2B$.

10. $\cos^4 \theta - \sin^4 \theta = \cos 2\theta$.

11. $\tan x/2 + \cot x/2 = 2 \csc x$.

12. $\sin^4 A/2 + \cos^4 A/2 = 1 - \frac{1}{2} \sin^2 A$.

13. $\dfrac{1 - \tan^2 \varphi}{1 + \tan^2 \varphi} = \cos 2\varphi$.

14. $\cos 3A = 4 \cos^3 A - 3 \cos A$.

15. $\cos 4\alpha = 1 - 8 \sin^2 \alpha \cos^2 \alpha$.

16. $\cot x - \tan x = 2 \cot 2x$.

17. $\dfrac{1 + \sin A - \cos A}{1 + \sin A + \cos A} = \tan \dfrac{A}{2}$.

18. $1 - \cos \alpha = 2 \sin^2 \alpha/2$.

19. $\csc 2\theta + \cot 2\theta = \cot \theta$.

20. Express $\sin^4 \theta$ in terms of first powers of the cosine function.

21. If A and B are the acute angles of a right triangle, is it true that

$$\cos 2B = \sin (A - B)?$$

22. If $\cos \alpha = 1/3$ and α is in the fourth quadrant, find:

(a) $\sin \alpha/2$; (b) $\cos \alpha/2$; (c) $\tan \alpha/2$.

In each of Numbers 23 to 32, solve the given trigonometric equation.

23. $\cos 2\theta + \sin 2\theta + 1 = 0$.

24. $\cos 2\theta - \cos \theta = 0$.

25. $\tan \theta/2 = \sin \theta$.

26. $\cos^2 B/2 - \sin^2 B/2 = \cos^2 B$.

27. $2 \cos^2 A/2 = \cos A$.

28. $\cot \alpha/2 + \sin \alpha = 0$.

29. $2 \csc 2A + \sec A = 0$.

30. $\tan \theta/2 + \cot \theta/2 = 1$.

31. $4 \cos^2 A/2 - 2 = \sqrt{3}$.

32. $2 \cos^2 2\theta - \sin 2\theta - 1 = 0$.

33. The upper stages of a space rocket are h feet long and stand on a booster rocket that is b feet long, as shown in Figure 7.6a. Find the point on the ground where the upper stages and the booster rocket subtend equal angles.

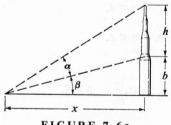

FIGURE 7.6a   FIGURE 7.6b

34. Let α denote the angle that a simple pendulum of length l makes with the vertical, as shown in Figure 7.6b. Show that the height h of the end of the pendulum above its lowest position is $2l \sin^2 (\alpha/2)$.

7.7 THE TRIGONOMETRIC FORM OF A COMPLEX NUMBER

In Section 2.7, a complex number was defined to be an ordered pair of real numbers that obeys certain rules of equality, addition, and multiplication. In

Section 4.5, a vector in a two-dimensional space was defined to be an ordered pair of real numbers, the rules for equality and addition being the same as for complex numbers. The multiplication of a vector by a scalar corresponds exactly to the multiplication of a complex number by a real number. Therefore, it is both interesting and useful to associate the complex number (a, b) or $a + ib$ with the vector (a, b). Thus, we may regard the arrow (see p. 134) that represents a vector (a, b) as a geometric representation of the complex number $a + ib$. For example, in Figure 7.7a the arrow labeled **a**, which represents the

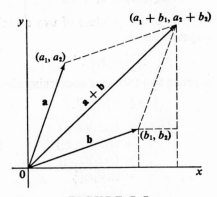

FIGURE 7.7a

vector $\mathbf{a} .=. (a_1, a_2)$, may also represent the complex number $a_1 + ia_2$. Figure 7.7a illustrates further that the geometric representation of the sum of two vectors (a_1, a_2) and (b_1, b_2) is the same as the representation of the sum of two complex numbers $a_1 + ia_2$ and $b_1 + ib_2$.

Since the number-pair (a, b) may also be represented as a point with x-coordinate a and y-coordinate b in the xy-plane, the complex number $a + ib$ may be associated with the point (a, b). We shall find that both the point representation and the vector representation of a complex number are useful, and we may employ either of these at our convenience.

The absolute value of a real number may be interpreted geometrically as the distance between the origin and the point representing the number on the number scale. The absolute value of a complex number (sometimes called the modulus) is defined in a similar manner.

Definition 7.7a. The quantity

$$|a + ib| .=. \sqrt{a^2 + b^2}$$

is called the **absolute value** or **modulus** of the complex number $a + ib$.

Notice that this definition agrees with the definition of the magnitude $|\mathbf{a}|$ of the vector **a**, and with the meaning of $|x|$ when x is real.

In the work that follows the letter z will be used to represent a complex number. The conjugate of the number $z = a + ib$ was previously defined as the number $a - ib$. The conjugate of z will be denoted by $\bar{z}$. The absolute value of $z = a + ib$ is then given by

(1) $$|z|^2 = a^2 + b^2 = (a + ib)(a - ib) = z\bar{z}.$$

The following two theorems will be helpful. Proofs are left for the exercises.

Theorem 7.7a. The conjugate of the sum of two complex numbers is the sum of their conjugates; that is,

$$\overline{z_1 + z_2} = \bar{z}_1 + \bar{z}_2.$$

Theorem 7.7b. The conjugate of the product of two complex numbers is the product of their conjugates; that is,

$$\overline{z_1 z_2} = \bar{z}_1 \bar{z}_2.$$

We are ready now to prove two theorems concerning absolute values.

Theorem 7.7c. $\qquad\qquad |z_1 z_2| = |z_1||z_2|.$

PROOF:

$$
\begin{aligned}
|z_1 z_2|^2 &= (z_1 z_2)(\overline{z_1 z_2}) && \text{(By (1))}\\
&= (z_1 z_2)(\bar{z}_1\, \bar{z}_2) && \text{(By Theorem 7.7b)}\\
&= (z_1 \bar{z}_1)(z_2 \bar{z}_2) && \text{(Why?)}\\
&= |z_1|^2 |z_2|^2. && \text{(Why?)}
\end{aligned}
$$

Thus

$$|z_1 z_2| = |z_1||z_2|.$$

Theorem 7.7d. $\qquad \left|\dfrac{z_1}{z_2}\right| = \dfrac{|z_1|}{|z_2|}, \qquad z_2 \neq 0.$

PROOF: Let

$$z = \frac{z_1}{z_2},$$

then

$$z z_2 = z_1,$$

and

$$|z z_2| = |z_1|,$$

and, by Theorem 7.7c,

$$|z||z_2| = |z_1|.$$

Thus,

$$|z| = \frac{|z_1|}{|z_2|}, \qquad z_2 \neq 0.$$

Example 7.7a. Verify geometrically that $|z_1 + z_2| \leq |z_1| + |z_2|$.

The inequality is apparent from Figure 7.7b, since the length of any side of a triangle is less than or equal to the sum of the lengths of the other two sides.

From the geometric interpretation we may obtain a useful trigonometric form for a complex number. In Figure 7.7c, let the modulus of the nonzero complex number $a + ib$ be represented by the letter r and let θ be the angle from the positive x axis to the line OP. The angle θ is called the *argument* (or *amplitude*) of the complex number. Since

$$a = r \cos \theta \quad \text{and} \quad b = r \sin \theta,$$

we may write

$$a + ib = r \cos \theta + ir \sin \theta$$
$$= r(\cos \theta + i \sin \theta).$$

The fact that $\cos \theta + i \sin \theta = \cos (\theta + 2n\pi) + i \sin (\theta + 2n\pi)$, $n \in \mathcal{I}$ shows that any integral multiple of 2π may be added to the argument of a complex number to obtain another representation of the number.

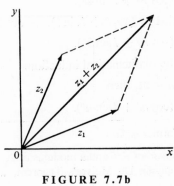

FIGURE 7.7b

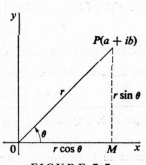

FIGURE 7.7c

The trigonometric form is useful for finding the product of two complex numbers, z_1 and z_2. If $z_1 = r_1(\cos \theta_1 + i \sin \theta_1)$ and $z_2 = r_2(\cos \theta_2 + i \sin \theta_2)$, then

$$z_1 z_2 = r_1 r_2 [(\cos \theta_1 \cos \theta_2 - \sin \theta_1 \sin \theta_2) + i(\sin \theta_1 \cos \theta_2 + \cos \theta_1 \sin \theta_2)]$$

or

(2) $$z_1 z_2 = r_1 r_2 [(\cos (\theta_1 + \theta_2) + i \sin (\theta_1 + \theta_2)].$$

Similarly, the reciprocal of a nonzero complex number may be expressed in trigonometric form as follows:

$$\frac{1}{r(\cos \theta + i \sin \theta)} = \frac{(\cos \theta - i \sin \theta)}{r(\cos \theta + i \sin \theta)(\cos \theta - i \sin \theta)}$$

$$= \frac{1}{r}(\cos \theta - i \sin \theta)$$

or

(3) $$\frac{1}{r(\cos \theta + i \sin \theta)} = \frac{1}{r}[\cos (-\theta) + i \sin (-\theta)].$$

This formula and Formula (2) for a product may be used to obtain a formula for expressing the quotient of two complex numbers in trigonometric form:

$$\frac{r_1(\cos \theta_1 + i \sin \theta_1)}{r_2(\cos \theta_2 + i \sin \theta_2)} = \frac{r_1}{r_2} (\cos \theta_1 + i \sin \theta_1)\left(\frac{1}{\cos \theta_2 + i \sin \theta_2}\right)$$

$$= \frac{r_1}{r_2} (\cos \theta_1 + i \sin \theta_1)[\cos (-\theta_2) + i \sin (-\theta_2)]$$

or

(4) $$\frac{r_1(\cos \theta_1 + i \sin \theta_1)}{r_2(\cos \theta_2 + i \sin \theta_2)} = \frac{r_1}{r_2} [\cos (\theta_1 - \theta_2) + i \sin (\theta_1 - \theta_2)].$$

The product formula leads to an interesting result if $z_1 = z_2$. Let $r_1 = r_2 = 1$ and $\theta_1 = \theta_2 = \theta$. Then we have

$$(\cos \theta + i \sin \theta)^2 = (\cos 2\theta + i \sin 2\theta).$$

If each side of this equation is multiplied by $(\cos \theta + i \sin \theta)$, we obtain

$$(\cos \theta + i \sin \theta)^3 = (\cos 3\theta + i \sin 3\theta).$$

The following general result is obtained by mathematical induction.

Theorem 7.7e. *De Moivre's Theorem.* If $n \in \mathfrak{N}$, then

(5) $$[(\cos \theta + i \sin \theta]^n = (\cos n\theta + i \sin n\theta).$$

Example 7.7b. Express $(\sqrt{3} + i)^8$ in the form $a + ib$.

The complex number $\sqrt{3} + i$ has an argument of $\pi/6$ and a modulus of 2. Writing the number in trigonometric form and applying De Moivre's Theorem, we have

$$(\sqrt{3} + i)^8 = [2(\cos 30° + i \sin 30°)]^8$$
$$= 2^8(\cos 240° + i \sin 240°)$$
$$= 256 \left(-\frac{1}{2} - i\frac{\sqrt{3}}{2}\right)$$
$$= -128 - i\, 128 \sqrt{3}.$$

Example 7.7c. Express $(-1/2 - i\sqrt{3}/2)^{50}$ in the form $a + ib$.

Writing the number in trigonometric form and applying De Moivre's Theorem, we obtain

$$(-1/2 - i\sqrt{3}/2)^{50} = [1(\cos 240° + i \sin 240°)]^{50}$$
$$= 1^{50}(\cos 12{,}000° + i \sin 12{,}000°)$$
$$= \cos 120° + i \sin 120°$$
$$= -1/2 + i\sqrt{3}/2.$$

In order to verify that De Moivre's Theorem is true if n is a negative integer, we write $n = -m$, with m a positive integer. Then, we have

$$[(\cos \theta + i \sin \theta)]^n = \frac{1}{(\cos \theta + i \sin \theta)^m}$$
$$= \left(\frac{1}{\cos m\theta + i \sin m\theta}\right) \quad \text{(By Formula 5)}$$
$$= [\cos (-m\theta) + i \sin (-m\theta)] \quad \text{(By Formula 3)}$$
$$= (\cos n\theta + i \sin n\theta).$$

Exercises 7.7

1. Prove Theorem 7.7a.
2. Prove Theorem 7.7b.
3. Verify geometrically that $|z_1 + z_2| \geq \big||z_1| - |z_2|\big|$.
4. Prove $\overline{z_1 z_2 z_3} = \bar{z}_1 \bar{z}_2 \bar{z}_3$.
5. Show that if $z_2 z_3 \neq 0$, then

$$\left|\frac{z_1}{z_2 z_3}\right| = \frac{|z_1|}{|z_2||z_3|}.$$

★6. Give an algebraic proof that

$$|z_1 + z_2| \leq |z_1| + |z_2|.$$

Hint: $|z_1 + z_2|^2 = (z_1 + z_2)(\bar{z}_1 + \bar{z}_2)$. After multiplying out the right side, use Cauchy's Inequality, Exercises 3.8, Number 14.

In Numbers 7 to 16, perform the indicated operations and express the answers in the form $a + ib$.

7. $[3(\cos 37° + i \sin 37°)][2(\cos 23° + i \sin 23°)]$.

8. $\dfrac{12(\cos 52° + i \sin 52°)}{4(\cos 7° + i \sin 7°)}$.

9. $[\frac{1}{2}(\cos 10° + i \sin 10°)]^6$.
10. $(1 + i)^8$.
11. $(1/2 + i\sqrt{3}/2)^{100}$.

12. $[2(\cos 36° + i \sin 36°)]^5$.
13. $[2(\cos 15° + i \sin 15°)]^{-4}$.
14. $(\sqrt{2}/2 - i\sqrt{2}/2)^{60}$.
15. $(-1/2 + i\sqrt{3}/2)^{-50}$.
16. $(-\sqrt{2}/2 - i\sqrt{2}/2)^{100}$.

Summary of Chapter 7

The reader should understand the following basic items:

(1) radian measure and its relationship to degree measure (Section 7.1);
(2) formulas for the length of an arc of a circle and the area of a sector of a circle (Section 7.1);
(3) the definitions of the six fundamental trigonometric functions (Section 7.2);
(4) the periodicity properties and graphs of the trigonometric functions (Section 7.2);
(5) the signs of the trigonometric functions in each of the four quadrants, and values of the functions for special angles (Section 7.2);
(6) the "reduction rule," Theorem 7.2a;
(7) the use of the trigonometric functions in solving triangles (Section 7.3);
(8) the Law of Sines and the Law of Cosines (Section 7.3);
(9) the fundamental trigonometric identities and their use in simplifying expressions involving trigonometric functions (Section 7.4);
(10) the addition formulas and their applications (Section 7.5);
(11) the multiple-angle formulas and their applications (Section 7.6);
(12) the use of trigonometric identities in solving trigonometric equations (Sections 7.4, 7.5, 7.6);
(13) the trigonometric form of a complex number (Section 7.7);
(14) de Moivre's Theorem (Section 7.7).

Chapter 8   Limits and Continuity

The ideas and concepts which are introduced in this chapter are the basic notions necessary for any genuine understanding of the calculus, which we shall begin in Chapter 9. The reader is urged to devote the greatest effort to make certain that he attains as full a comprehension of these ideas as possible. Without this comprehension it is impossible to understand exactly the technical meaning of such things as velocity, acceleration, area enclosed by a curved line, the work done by the exploding gasoline-air mixture in an automobile motor, and many other everyday notions in the highly technological civilization of the present and of the foreseeable future.

8.1 THE INTUITIVE NOTION OF LIMIT

The definition of function as given in Chapter 5 is quite broad and includes many relations that are too general to be of use in most applications of mathematics to physical problems. For example, we are often interested in functions whose graphs exhibit certain properties of "connectedness" and "smoothness." In fact, in the graphing of functions, we have often assumed a great deal concerning the behavior of the function.

Example 8.1a. Graph the function f described by
$$y = (x - 1)(2 - x).$$
First, the points $(1, 0)$, $(2, 0)$, $(3/2, 1/4)$, $(3, -2)$, $(0, -2)$ are plotted, as in Figure 8.1a. These points are then connected by a curve as shown in the figure. But what

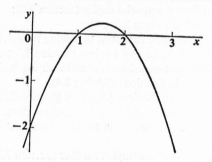

FIGURE 8.1a

right do we have to assume that the plotted points should be connected in this manner? The procedure seems intuitively sound; we have simply assumed that if we choose a particular point, say 2, then as $x \to 2$, $y \to 0$, as discussed in Section 5.5. That is, we have assumed that for values of x in a small neighborhood of 2, $\mathfrak{N}(2, h)$, the corresponding values of y are in a small neighborhood of 0, $\mathfrak{N}(0, \epsilon)$. However, we have not actually proved this to be the case.

Our intuitive feeling about the matter can be strengthened by numerical calculations such as those given in the following table:

x	y
2.4	-0.56
2.2	-0.24
2.1	-0.11
2.01	-0.0101
2.001	-0.001001
2.0001	-0.00010001

The table seems to show that the nearer x is to 2, the nearer y is to 0. But this process of numerical verification is tedious and not very practical since it doesn't really prove anything. Therefore, it is desirable to find a reasonably simple and general way of showing precisely what seems to be suggested intuitively.

Rather than making calculations for different values of x near 2, such as 2.01, 2.001, and so on, let us simply investigate what happens to y when x is in a general neighborhood of 2, say $\mathfrak{N}(2, h)$. In this way we may be able to determine the behavior of the function for *all* values of x in $\mathfrak{N}(2, h)$ rather than for just particular values of x. Consequently, in order to insure that only values of x near 2 will be considered, we shall require that $h < 1$ for any neighborhood $\mathfrak{N}(2, h)$ under consideration.

Since it appears that $y \to 0$ as $x \to 2$, let us consider the difference between the apparent value approached by y and other values of y corresponding to values of x in $\mathfrak{N}(2, h)$. That is, we shall consider

$$|y - 0|,$$

which is

$$|y| = |x - 1||x - 2|$$

when y is written in terms of x. From the fact that $x \in \mathfrak{N}(2, h)$, it follows that

$$2 - h < x < 2 + h.$$

Hence

$$-h < x - 2 < h,$$

which is equivalent to

$$|x - 2| < h.$$

Also, since $h < 1$, the first inequality implies that

$$1 < x < 3$$

or

$$0 < x - 1 < 2,$$

so that surely

$$|x - 1| < 2,$$

Thus, by the use of this inequality and the fact that $|x - 2| < h$, we get

$$|y| = |x - 1||x - 2| < 2h,$$

or

$$-2h < y < 2h,$$

which is equivalent to the statement that $y \in \mathfrak{N}(0, 2h)$.

It has therefore been established that as long as $h < 1$,

$$x \in \mathfrak{N}(2, h) \Rightarrow y \in \mathfrak{N}(0, 2h).$$

In other words, for any small neighborhood of 0 in the range of the function, there is a corresponding neighborhood of 2 in the domain such that if x is in this neighborhood

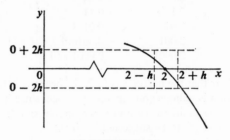

FIGURE 8.1b

of 2, then y is in the specified small neighborhood of 0. See Figure 8.1b. Accordingly, we may write

$$\text{as } x \to 2, \quad y \to 0.$$

Another example will help to illustrate the idea further.

Example 8.1b. Show that if $y = x^2 - 3$, then as $x \to 2$, $y \to 1$.

Since we are interested in values of y near 1, it is natural to consider the difference between 1 and values of y corresponding to values of x near 2. Thus,

$$|y - 1| = |x^2 - 4| = |x - 2||x + 2|.$$

For values of $x \in \mathfrak{N}(2, h)$, we have

$$2 - h < x < 2 + h$$

or

$$|x - 2| < h.$$

Again, we may restrict x to be near 2 by requiring $h < 1$ so that

$$1 < x < 3.$$

By adding 2 to each member of this inequality, we get

$$3 < x + 2 < 5,$$

so that surely

$$|x + 2| < 5.$$

The last result and the inequality $|x - 2| < h$ together imply that

$$|y - 1| = |x - 2||x + 2| < 5h,$$

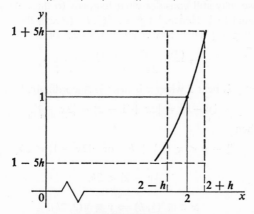

FIGURE 8.1c

which means that $y \in \mathfrak{N}(1, 5h)$. That is, $x \in \mathfrak{N}(2, h) \Rightarrow y \in \mathfrak{N}(1, 5h)$ (see Figure 8.1c), no matter how small h may be, and we may write

$$\text{as } x \to 2, \quad y \to 1.$$

In each of the two preceding examples, the radius of the neighborhood in the range of the function was found to be related to the radius of the neighborhood in the domain. In fact, the smaller the first neighborhood, the smaller must be the second, so that the two neighborhoods may be thought of as shrinking to a point together as $h \to 0$. The relationship between the radii of the two neighborhoods is the essentially important result obtained in the preceding examples.

The result illustrated in the last example may be stated in another way. If $\mathfrak{N}(1, \epsilon)$ is a given arbitrarily small neighborhood of 1 in the range of f, and if there is a corresponding neighborhood $\mathfrak{N}(2, \delta)$ in the domain such that

$$x \in \mathfrak{N}(2, \delta) \Rightarrow y \in \mathfrak{N}(1, \epsilon),$$

then we say that as $x \to 2$, $y \to 1$. In this form, for a given $\mathfrak{N}(1, \epsilon)$, the existence of $\mathfrak{N}(2, \delta)$ must be demonstrated by finding an appropriate δ. This can be done by using the result of the preceding example and letting $5h = \epsilon$, from which it follows that the required $\delta = h = \epsilon/5$.

The next example illustrates a somewhat different case, in which we consider the behavior of a function in a neighborhood of a point at which the function is undefined.

Example 8.1c. Discuss the behavior as $x \to \frac{1}{2}$ of the function described by

$$y = \frac{4x^2 - 1}{2x - 1}.$$

In this case, the functional value is not defined at $x = \frac{1}{2}$. However, the behavior of the function still may be considered for values of x in a *deleted* neighborhood of $\frac{1}{2}$. In other words, we may still consider what happens to the function for values of x near $\frac{1}{2}$, but not equal to $\frac{1}{2}$. Hence, let $x \in \mathfrak{N}^*(\frac{1}{2}, h)$. (Recall that $\mathfrak{N}^*(\frac{1}{2}, h)$ denotes the neighborhood with $x = \frac{1}{2}$ deleted.) For all such values of x,

$$y = \frac{(2x - 1)(2x + 1)}{2x - 1} = 2x + 1,$$

and it appears that y is near 2 when x is near $\frac{1}{2}$. Accordingly, let us consider

$$|y - 2| = |2x + 1 - 2| = |2x - 1|.$$

If $x \in \mathfrak{N}^*(\frac{1}{2}, h)$, then

$$\tfrac{1}{2} - h < x < \tfrac{1}{2} + h, \quad \text{or} \quad |2x - 1| < 2h,$$

so that

$$|y - 2| < 2h.$$

That is,

$$x \in \mathfrak{N}^*(\tfrac{1}{2}, h) \Rightarrow y \in \mathfrak{N}(2, 2h).$$

Even though y is not defined at $x = \frac{1}{2}$, we still may write

$$y \to 2 \quad \text{as} \quad x \to \tfrac{1}{2}.$$

The examples thus far have dealt with fairly simple situations. There are other examples in which the behavior of a function near a point must be analyzed on either side of the point by means of right or left neighborhoods.

Example 8.1d. Discuss the behavior of

$$y = \frac{x}{|x| + x^2} \quad \text{as} \quad x \to 0.$$

Again, the given expression is undefined at the point of interest. Since $y > 0$ if $x > 0$, and $y < 0$ if $x < 0$, it appears that a separate investigation of the behavior of y must be made (i) for $x > 0$ and (ii) $x < 0$.

(i) If $x > 0$, then $|x| = x$ and $y = 1/(1 + x)$. Let $x \in \mathfrak{N}^*(0^+, h)$ so that $0 < x < h$.

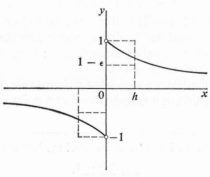

FIGURE 8.1d

Then,
$$1 < 1 + x < 1 + h$$

and

$$1 > \frac{1}{1+x} > \frac{1}{1+h} = 1 - \frac{h}{1+h}.$$

In other words,

$$x \in \mathfrak{N}^*(0^+, h) \Rightarrow y \in \mathfrak{N}(1, \epsilon),$$

where $\epsilon = h/(1 + h)$. Again, we have been able to establish a connection between the radii of the neighborhoods in the domain and range of the function. Accordingly, we say that as $x \to 0^+$, $y \to 1$.

(ii) Similarly, if $x \in \mathfrak{N}^*(0^-, h)$ so that $-h < x < 0$, it follows that $y \in \mathfrak{N}(-1, \epsilon)$, where $\epsilon = h/(1 + h)$. This shows that as $x \to 0^-$, $y \to -1$. (The reader should supply the details.) A graph of

$$y = \frac{x}{|x| + x^2}$$

in the vicinity of $x = 0$ is shown in Figure 8.1d.

Exercises 8.1

1. If $g(x) .=. x^2 + 2$, find values of h such that

   (a) $g(x) \in \mathfrak{N}(6, \frac{1}{10})$ for all $x \in \mathfrak{N}^*(2, h)$;
   (b) $g(x) \in \mathfrak{N}(6, \frac{1}{100})$ for all $x \in \mathfrak{N}^*(2, h)$;
   (c) $g(x) \in \mathfrak{N}(6, \epsilon)$ for all $x \in \mathfrak{N}^*(2, h)$.
   Note: In (c) the h will be given in terms of ϵ.

2. If $f(x) .=. 2x^2 - 2x - 1$, find values of h such that

   (a) $f(x) \in \mathfrak{N}(3, \frac{1}{10})$ for all $x \in \mathfrak{N}^*(2, h)$;
   (b) $f(x) \in \mathfrak{N}(3, \frac{1}{100})$ for all $x \in \mathfrak{N}^*(2, h)$;
   (c) $f(x) \in \mathfrak{N}(3, \epsilon)$ for all $x \in \mathfrak{N}^*(2, h)$.

3. If $g(x) .=. \dfrac{x - 2}{x + 3}$, find values of h such that

   (a) $g(x) \in \mathfrak{N}(\frac{1}{6}, \frac{1}{10})$ for all $x \in \mathfrak{N}^*(3, h)$;
   (b) $g(x) \in \mathfrak{N}(\frac{1}{6}, \frac{1}{100})$ for all $x \in \mathfrak{N}^*(3, h)$;
   (c) $g(x) \in \mathfrak{N}(\frac{1}{6}, \epsilon)$ for all $x \in \mathfrak{N}^*(3, h)$.

4. If $f(x) .=. \dfrac{x + 2}{x - 1}$, find values of h such that

   (a) $f(x) \in \mathfrak{N}(4, 10^{-2})$ for all $x \in \mathfrak{N}^*(2, h)$;
   (b) $f(x) \in \mathfrak{N}(4, 10^{-4})$ for all $x \in \mathfrak{N}^*(2, h)$;
   (c) $f(x) \in \mathfrak{N}(4, \epsilon)$ for all $x \in \mathfrak{N}^*(2, h)$.

5. Let

$$f(x) .=. \begin{cases} x^3 & \text{if } x < 0, \\ x^2 + 1 & \text{if } x \geq 0. \end{cases}$$

Explain why you *cannot* find a value for h so that $f(x) \in \mathfrak{N}(1, \frac{1}{10})$ for all $x \in \mathfrak{N}^*(0, h)$.

6. 1

$$g(x) .=. \begin{cases} \dfrac{x^2}{x^2 + 1} & \text{if } x \le 4, \\ \dfrac{4}{x} & \text{if } x > 4, \end{cases}$$

is it possible to find an h for each $\mathfrak{N}(1, \epsilon)$ so that $g(x) \in \mathfrak{N}(1, \epsilon)$ for all $x \in \mathfrak{N}^*(4, h)$? Explain why or why not.

7. If $y .=. \sqrt{x}$, find the values of h for which

(a) $x \in \mathfrak{N}^*(0^+, h) \Rightarrow y \in \mathfrak{N}(0^+, 0.1)$;
(b) $x \in \mathfrak{N}^*(0^+, h) \Rightarrow y \in \mathfrak{N}(0^+, 0.001)$;
(c) $x \in \mathfrak{N}^*(0^+, h) \Rightarrow y \in \mathfrak{N}(0^+, \epsilon)$.

8. If

$$g(x) .=. \frac{x^2 + 8x + 15}{x + 3},$$

find a value of h such that

$$x \in \mathfrak{N}^*(-3, h) \Rightarrow g(x) \in \mathfrak{N}(2, \epsilon).$$

9. Let

$$y .=. \begin{cases} |1 - x| & \text{for } x > 0, \\ \frac{1}{2} & \text{for } x = 0, \\ |x| & \text{for } x < 0. \end{cases}$$

Is it possible to find an h corresponding to each arbitrary ϵ such that the following statements are true? Explain.

(a) $x \in \mathfrak{N}^*(0, h) \Rightarrow y \in \mathfrak{N}(\frac{1}{2}, \epsilon)$.
(b) $x \in \mathfrak{N}^*(1, h) \Rightarrow y \in \mathfrak{N}(0, \epsilon)$.

10. Suppose $n \in \mathfrak{N}$, and let

$$g(x) .=. \begin{cases} 0 & \text{for } x \ne 1/n. \\ 1 & \text{for } x = 1/n. \end{cases}$$

Is there any value of h such that the following statement is true?

$$x \in \mathfrak{N}^*(0^+, h) \Rightarrow g(x) \in \mathfrak{N}(0^+, \epsilon).$$

Explain.

8.2 LIMITS

In the preceding section, we discussed in an intuitive fashion the set of values of a function when the independent variable is restricted to a small neighborhood of a given point. The ideas presented there form the basis for a major portion of the ensuing work in mathematical analysis and motivate the following precise statement.

Definition 8.2a. A number A is said to be the limit of $f(x)$ as $x \to a$ if for each given $\mathfrak{N}(A, \epsilon)$ there is a corresponding $\mathfrak{N}^*(a, h)$ in the domain of f such that

$$x \in \mathfrak{N}^*(a, h) \Rightarrow y \in \mathfrak{N}(A, \epsilon).$$

The limit is denoted by writing

$$\lim_{x \to a} f(x) = A.$$

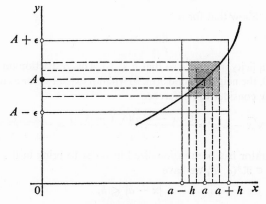

FIGURE 8.2a

This concept is illustrated geometrically in Figure 8.2a. For every $\mathfrak{N}(A, \epsilon)$, no matter how small, there must be a deleted neighborhood $\mathfrak{N}^*(a, h)$ such that the points of f are in the rectangle as shown, for all values of $x \in \mathfrak{N}^*(a, h)$.

Example 8.2a. Prove that

$$\lim_{x \to 2} x^3 = 8.$$

We shall follow the procedure illustrated by the examples of the preceding section. For simplicity, we restrict h so that $h < 1$, and then consider the difference

$$x^3 - 8 = (x - 2)(x^2 + 2x + 4).$$

For values of $x \in \mathfrak{N}^*(2, h)$, we have

$$2 - h < x < 2 + h$$

or

$$|x - 2| < h.$$

Also for $h < 1$, it is true that $1 < x < 3$, so that for these values of x, $x^2 < 9$ and $|2x| < 6$. Therefore

$$|x^2 + 2x + 4| < 19,$$

and

$$|x^3 - 8| = |x - 2||x^2 + 2x + 4| < 19h.$$

Accordingly,

$$x \in \mathfrak{N}^*(2, h) \Rightarrow x^3 \in \mathfrak{N}(8, 19h).$$

If it is required that $x^3 \in \mathfrak{N}(8, \epsilon)$ for some given ϵ, then we may choose $h = \epsilon/19$, as long as $\epsilon < 19$, in order to be sure that

$$x \in \mathfrak{N}^*(2, h) \Rightarrow x^3 \in \mathfrak{N}(8, \epsilon).$$

Although a neighborhood of radius greater than 19 about the value 8 would ordinarily not be of interest, it may be stated, for those who insist on knowing what to do if

$\epsilon \geq 19$, that in this case the choice should be $h = 1$. As a general conclusion, the choice $h = \min(1, \epsilon/19)$, that is, the minimum of 1 and $\epsilon/19$, makes the preceding implication true for each ϵ. This completes the required proof.

Example 8.2b. Show that for $a > 0$,

$$\lim_{x \to a} \sqrt{x} = \sqrt{a}.$$

Again, for simplicity, restrict h so that $h < \frac{1}{2}a$. This restriction on h is made so that if a is very near 0, the neighborhood $\mathfrak{N}(a, h)$ will not extend so far as to include negative values of x. Now consider the difference

$$\sqrt{x} - \sqrt{a} = \frac{(\sqrt{x} - \sqrt{a})(\sqrt{x} + \sqrt{a})}{\sqrt{x} + \sqrt{a}} = \frac{x - a}{\sqrt{x} + \sqrt{a}},$$

where the numerator has been rationalized in order to bring in the difference $x - a$. For values of $x \in \mathfrak{N}^*(a, h)$, we have

$$|x - a| < h,$$

and for $h < \frac{1}{2}a$,

$$\tfrac{1}{2}a < x < \tfrac{3}{2}a.$$

Therefore,

$$\sqrt{x} > \sqrt{\tfrac{1}{2}a}$$

and

$$\sqrt{x} + \sqrt{a} > \sqrt{\tfrac{1}{2}a} + \sqrt{a} = \left(1 + \frac{1}{\sqrt{2}}\right)\sqrt{a}.$$

Since $\dfrac{1}{\sqrt{2}} > 0.5$, we may replace the last inequality by

$$\sqrt{x} + \sqrt{a} > 1.5\sqrt{a},$$

We now have

$$|\sqrt{x} - \sqrt{a}| = \left|\frac{x - a}{\sqrt{x} + \sqrt{a}}\right| < \frac{h}{1.5\sqrt{a}},$$

so that

$$x \in \mathfrak{N}^*(a, h) \Rightarrow \sqrt{x} \in \mathfrak{N}\left(\sqrt{a}, \frac{h}{1.5\sqrt{a}}\right).$$

It is certain then that

$$\sqrt{x} \in \mathfrak{N}(\sqrt{a}, \epsilon) \quad \text{if } x \in \mathfrak{N}^*(a, h),$$

where $h = \min(a/2, 1.5\epsilon\sqrt{a})$—that is, the minimum of $a/2$ and $1.5\epsilon\sqrt{a}$. This proves that $\lim_{x \to a} \sqrt{x} = \sqrt{a}$ for $a > 0$.

If we wish to discuss the behavior of $f(x)$ as $x \to a^+$, we modify Definition 8.2a by considering $\mathfrak{N}^*(a^+, h)$ and, if the limit exists, by writing

$$\lim_{x \to a^+} f(x) = A.$$

A similar procedure can be followed for $x \to a^-$ and $\lim_{x \to a^-} f(x) = A$. These limits are called one-sided limits, or limits from the right or left, respectively.

Example 8.2c. Examine $\lim_{x\to 0} (1/x)$.

Suppose $x \in \mathfrak{N}^*(0, h)$. Then $|x| < h$, and

$$\left|\frac{1}{x}\right| > \frac{1}{h}.$$

This shows that the smaller the value of h, the larger is the absolute value of $1/x$. Hence, there can be no limit as $x \to 0$. For, let any fixed number, say A, be proposed as the limit; then, for $x > 0$, we have

$$\frac{1}{x} > \frac{1}{h},$$

and

$$\frac{1}{x} - A > \frac{1}{h} - A.$$

For all sufficiently small values of h, $(1/h) - A$ is arbitrarily large. Thus, for all values of h so small that $(1/h) - A > \epsilon$, that is $h < 1/(A + \epsilon)$, we have

$$x \in \mathfrak{N}^*(0^+, h) \Longrightarrow \frac{1}{x} \notin \mathfrak{N}(A, \epsilon).$$

This proves the statement that $\lim_{x\to 0} (1/x)$ does not exist. The student should compare this discussion with that in Example 5.6a.

A further general result is given in

Theorem 8.2a. $\quad \lim_{x\to a} f(x) = A \Leftrightarrow \lim_{x\to a^-} f(x) = \lim_{x\to a^+} f(x) = A.$

PROOF:

(a) If $\lim_{x\to a} f(x) = A$, then for a given $\mathfrak{N}(A, \epsilon)$ there is a $\mathfrak{N}^*(a, h)$ such that $x \in \mathfrak{N}^*(a, h) \Longrightarrow y \in \mathfrak{N}(A, \epsilon)$. Hence, if $x \in \mathfrak{N}^*(a^-, h)$, then it is still true that $y \in \mathfrak{N}(A, \epsilon)$. Similarly, if $x \in \mathfrak{N}^*(a^+, h)$ then $y \in \mathfrak{N}(A, \epsilon)$. Accordingly,

$$\lim_{x\to a^-} f(x) = A \quad \text{and} \quad \lim_{x\to a^+} f(x) = A.$$

(b) The proof of the converse part of the theorem is left for the reader.

It is important to observe that the definition of limit as $x \to a$ does not require the function under consideration to be defined at $x = a$. The limit of a function is concerned with the behavior of the function in the *deleted neighborhood* of the point $x = a$, but *not* with the value of the function at the point. The preceding definition of limit unfortunately requires some knowledge of the limit number A in order to be used in a practical way. Since such knowledge is not always available, other methods of discussing limits are needed. Some of these methods will be discussed in a later chapter.

The next example illustrates a slightly more complex situation.

Example 8.2d. Find $\lim_{x\to 0} \sin (1/x)$ if it exists.

Since we have no hint as to a possible limit number or value of A, we must examine the behavior of $\sin (1/x)$ in a different way. Because

$$\sin \frac{(2n - 1)\pi}{2} = (-1)^{n+1},$$

it follows that

$$\sin \frac{1}{x} = (-1)^{n+1} \quad \text{if } x = \frac{2}{(2n-1)\pi}, \quad n \in \mathfrak{N}.$$

Hence, $\sin (1/x)$ oscillates infinitely often between $+1$ and -1 as $x \to 0$. Consequently, for a given $\mathfrak{N}(A, \epsilon)$, there exists no $\mathfrak{N}(0, h)$ such that

$$x \in \mathfrak{N}^*(0, h) \Rightarrow y \in \mathfrak{N}(A, \epsilon)$$

for any number A. That is, no matter how small a neighborhood about $x = 0$ we consider, there is no number A such that the value of the function is always between

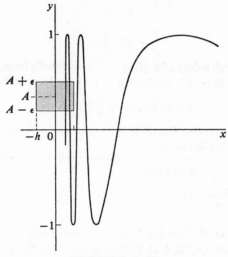

FIGURE 8.2b

$A - \epsilon$ and $A + \epsilon$ (see Figure 8.2b). The functional value oscillates between $+1$ and -1 more and more "rapidly" as $x \to 0$. Evidently, a limit does not exist.

To sum up the preceding discussion, we may conclude that a function will fail to possess a limit at a point if the functional value "oscillates violently" without settling down, or increases without bound in absolute value, or if the limits from the right and from the left are different as $x \to a$.

Exercises 8.2

In each of Numbers 1 to 9, show that the given statement is correct.

1. $\lim\limits_{x \to 2} (x^2 - x + 1) = 3.$

2. $\lim\limits_{x \to 1} (x^2 + 3x + 1) = 5.$

3. $\lim\limits_{x \to 2} (x^3 - 2x^2 + x) = 2.$

4. $\lim\limits_{x \to -1} \dfrac{x + 3}{x + 2} = 2.$

5. $\lim\limits_{x \to 2} |x - 2| = 0.$

6. $\lim\limits_{x \to -3} |x + 3| = 0.$

7. $\lim\limits_{x \to 3} \dfrac{x^2 - 9}{x - 3} = 6.$

8. $\lim\limits_{x \to -1} \dfrac{x^2 - 1}{x + 1} = -2.$

9. $\lim\limits_{x \to 2} \dfrac{x - 2}{x^2 + 2x - 8} = \dfrac{1}{6}.$

10. Prove the second part of Theorem 8.2a.

11. Examine $\lim\limits_{x \to 0} \dfrac{x}{|x|}$.

12. Examine $\lim\limits_{x \to 0} \dfrac{x^2}{|x|}$.

13. Examine $\lim\limits_{x \to 0} \dfrac{|x|}{x^2}$.

14. Examine $\lim\limits_{x \to 0} \cos \dfrac{1}{x}$.

15. Does $\lim\limits_{x \to 0} x \sin \dfrac{1}{x}$ exist?

16. Prove that $\lim\limits_{x \to 2} \dfrac{1}{x^2 - 4}$ does not exist.

17. Does $\lim\limits_{x \to 2^+} \dfrac{1}{\sqrt{x - 2}}$ exist?

18. Examine $\lim\limits_{x \to 2^+} \dfrac{\sqrt{x^2 - 4}}{x - 2}$.

8.3 THEOREMS ON LIMITS

The apparently complicated procedure of evaluating limits directly from the definition can frequently be replaced by a simpler procedure based on certain important theorems on limits. These theorems are concerned with limits of sums, differences, products, and quotients of functions and justify the intuitive arguments used in the next illustration.

Example 8.3a. Evaluate

$$\lim_{x \to 0} \frac{2x^2 - 3x + 1}{3x^2 - x + 2}.$$

On a moment's reflection, it seems natural to say that

$$\text{as } x \to 0, \quad \frac{2x^2 - 3x + 1}{3x^2 - x + 2} \to \frac{1}{2}.$$

However, in order to arrive at this conclusion, we mentally argue perhaps as follows:

$$\lim_{x \to 0} \frac{2x^2 - 3x + 1}{3x^2 - x + 2} = \frac{\lim\limits_{x \to 0} (2x^2 - 3x + 1)}{\lim\limits_{x \to 0} (3x^2 - x + 2)}$$

$$= \frac{\lim\limits_{x \to 0} (2x^2) + \lim\limits_{x \to 0} (-3x) + 1}{\lim\limits_{x \to 0} (3x^2) + \lim\limits_{x \to 0} (-x) + 2}$$

$$= \frac{0 + 0 + 1}{0 + 0 + 2} = \frac{1}{2}.$$

The seeming reasonableness of these steps is, of course, no justification for the argument; it is not difficult to produce an example for which the procedure does not work.

Example 8.3b. Evaluate

$$\lim_{x \to -2} \frac{x^3 + 8}{|x| - 2}.$$

If we attempt to use the same steps here as in Example 8.3a, we get

$$\frac{\lim_{x \to -2} (x^3 + 8)}{\lim_{x \to -2} (|x| - 2)} = \frac{0}{0},$$

a *meaningless* symbol. This "dead-end" result must by no means be regarded as show-ing that the original limit does not exist. Instead, it illustrates the necessity for knowing the conditions under which the limits may be handled as in Example 8.3a.

By the definition of $|x|$, it is clear that for $x \in \mathfrak{N}(-2, h)$ and $h < 1$, $|x| = -x$. Hence, we have

$$\lim_{x \to -2} \frac{x^3 + 8}{|x| - 2} = \lim_{x \to -2} \frac{x^3 + 8}{-x - 2}$$

$$= \lim_{x \to -2} \frac{(x + 2)(x^2 - 2x + 4)}{-(x + 2)}$$

$$= \lim_{x \to -2} [-(x^2 - 2x + 4)]$$

$$= -12.$$

The last step in the preceding example is justified by the following two the-orems. The first theorem is quite simple, and its proof is left as an exercise for the reader, after he has studied the proof of the second theorem.

Theorem 8.3a. $\lim_{x \to a} f(x) = A$ and $c \in \mathfrak{R}$

$$\Rightarrow \lim_{x \to a} cf(x) = c \lim_{x \to a} f(x) = cA.$$

Theorem 8.3b. $\lim_{x \to a} f(x) = A$ and $\lim_{x \to a} g(x) = B$

$$\Rightarrow \lim_{x \to a} [f(x) + g(x)] = \lim_{x \to a} f(x) + \lim_{x \to a} g(x) = A + B.$$

In words, Theorem 8.3b states that the limit of a sum is equal to the sum of the limits *provided the limits exist!*

PROOF: In order to prove the theorem, we must show that for each given $\mathfrak{N}(A + B, \epsilon)$ there is a $\mathfrak{N}^*(a, h)$ such that

$$x \in \mathfrak{N}^*(a, h) \Rightarrow [f(x) + g(x)] \in \mathfrak{N}(A + B, \epsilon).$$

The statements that $\lim_{x \to a} f(x) = A$ and $\lim_{x \to a} g(x) = B$ may be rewritten as

$$x \in \mathfrak{N}_1^*(a, h_1) \Rightarrow f(x) \in \mathfrak{N}(A, \epsilon_1)$$

and

$$x \in \mathfrak{N}_2^*(a, h_2) \Rightarrow g(x) \in \mathfrak{N}(B, \epsilon_2).$$

These are equivalent to saying that

for $x \in \mathfrak{N}_1^*(a, h_1)$,

$$A - \epsilon_1 < f(x) < A + \epsilon_1,$$

and for $x \in \mathfrak{N}_2^*(a, h_2)$,

$$B - \epsilon_2 < g(x) < B + \epsilon_2.$$

Since ϵ_1 and ϵ_2 are arbitrary, let each be taken equal to $\epsilon/2$. Then, by adding corresponding parts of the last inequalities, we get

$$A + B - \epsilon < f(x) + g(x) < A + B + \epsilon$$

for $x \in \mathfrak{N}_1^* \cap \mathfrak{N}_2^*$. (Why?) That is, given any ϵ, there is a $\mathfrak{N}^*(a, h)$ such that $x \in \mathfrak{N}^*(a, h) \Rightarrow [f(x) + g(x)] \in \mathfrak{N}(A + B, \epsilon)$.

There is a similar theorem on the limit of a product of two functions

Theorem 8.3c. $\lim\limits_{x \to a} f(x) = A$ and $\lim\limits_{x \to a} g(x) = B$

$$\Rightarrow \lim_{x \to a} [f(x) \cdot g(x)] = \lim_{x \to a} f(x) \cdot \lim_{x \to a} g(x) = AB.$$

PROOF: This time we must show that for each $\mathfrak{N}(AB, \epsilon)$, there is a $\mathfrak{N}^*(a, h)$ such that

$$x \in \mathfrak{N}^*(a, h) \Rightarrow f(x) \cdot g(x) \in \mathfrak{N}(AB, \epsilon),$$

or that for $x \in \mathfrak{N}^*(a, h)$,

$$|f(x)g(x) - AB| < \epsilon.$$

The statements that $\lim_{x \to a} f(x) = A$ and $\lim_{x \to a} g(x) = B$ mean that $|f(x) - A|$ and $|g(x) - B|$ can both be made arbitrarily small by restricting x to a sufficiently small neighborhood of a. This suggests that we introduce these two differences into the inequality by subtracting and adding the product $f(x)B$. Thus, we write

$$\begin{aligned} |f(x)g(x) - AB| &= |f(x)g(x) - f(x)B + f(x)B - AB| \\ &= |f(x)[g(x) - B] + [f(x) - A]B| \\ &\leq |f(x)||g(x) - B| + |f(x) - A||B|. \end{aligned}$$

But

$$|g(x) - B| < \epsilon_1 \quad \text{when } x \in \mathfrak{N}_1^*(a, h_1)$$

and

$$|f(x) - A| < \epsilon_2 \quad \text{when } x \in \mathfrak{N}_2^*(a, h_2),$$

so that

$$|f(x)g(x) - AB| \leq |f(x)|\epsilon_1 + |B|\epsilon_2$$

when $x \in \mathfrak{N}_1^* \cap \mathfrak{N}_2^*$. Also, the statement that

$$|f(x) - A| < \epsilon_2$$

shows that $|f(x)|$ is bounded. (Why?) Hence, we know that $|f(x)| < M$, where M is a positive constant. Since ϵ_1 and ϵ_2 are arbitrary, ϵ_1 may be chosen equal to $\epsilon/(2M)$ and ϵ_2 equal to $\epsilon/(2|B|)$. It follows that

$$x \in \mathfrak{N}_1^* \cap \mathfrak{N}_2^* \Rightarrow |f(x)g(x) - AB| < \epsilon,$$

and the proof is complete.

The next theorem frequently makes it possible to consider the limit of a quotient $f(x)/g(x)$ as a special case of the limit of a product.

Theorem 8.3d. If $\lim\limits_{x \to a} f(x) = A$ and $A \neq 0$, then

$$\lim_{x \to a} \frac{1}{f(x)} = \frac{1}{A}.$$

PROOF: We shall prove this theorem under the assumption that A is positive. (The argument for $A < 0$ is similar and is left for the reader.) It is necessary to show that there exists an h corresponding to a given $\epsilon > 0$ such that

$$x \in \mathfrak{N}^*(a, h) \Rightarrow \left| \frac{1}{f(x)} - \frac{1}{A} \right| < \epsilon.$$

First, we establish an auxiliary result—namely, that there exists an h_1 such that

$$x \in \mathfrak{N}^*(a, h_1) \Rightarrow f(x) > \tfrac{1}{2}A.$$

The truth of this follows at once from the definition of limit. Thus $\lim_{x \to a} f(x) = A$ means that there exists an h_1 such that

$$x \in \mathfrak{N}^*(a, h_1) \Rightarrow f(x) \in \mathfrak{N}(A, A/2),$$

so that

$$\tfrac{1}{2}A < f(x) < \tfrac{3}{2}A.$$

Now let us write

$$\left| \frac{1}{f(x)} - \frac{1}{A} \right| = \frac{|A - f(x)|}{|Af(x)|}.$$

As a further consequence of $\lim_{x \to a} f(x) = A$, there is an h_2 such that

$$x \in \mathfrak{N}^*(a, h_2) \Rightarrow f(x) \in \mathfrak{N}(A, \epsilon_2),$$

and thus

$$|f(x) - A| < \epsilon_2.$$

Accordingly, for $h = \min(h_1, h_2)$,

$$x \in \mathfrak{N}^*(a, h) \Rightarrow \frac{|A - f(x)|}{|Af(x)|} < \frac{\epsilon_2}{A^2/2}.$$

If ϵ_2 is chosen equal to $\tfrac{1}{2}A^2\epsilon$, then it has been shown that there is an h such that

$$x \in \mathfrak{N}^*(a, h) \Rightarrow \frac{1}{f(x)} \in \mathfrak{N}\left(\frac{1}{A}, \epsilon\right),$$

and the proof of the theorem is complete.

Using Theorem 8.3c, the reader should be able to prove the next result quite easily.

Theorem 8.3e. $\lim\limits_{x \to a} f(x) = A$, $\lim\limits_{x \to a} g(x) = B$, $B \neq 0$

$$\Rightarrow \lim_{x \to a} \frac{f(x)}{g(x)} = \frac{A}{B}.$$

The preceding theorems show at once that

$$\lim_{x \to a} x^2 = (\lim_{x \to a} x)(\lim_{x \to a} x) = a^2.$$

It follows by induction that

$$\lim_{x \to a} x^n = a^n, \qquad n \in \mathfrak{N}$$

We also have $\lim_{x \to a} cx^n = ca^n$, with c a constant. Thus, by a simple extension of the theorem on the limit of a sum, it follows that for a polynomial $P(x)$

$$\lim_{x \to a} P(x) = P(a),$$

that is,

$$\lim_{x \to a} (p_0 x^n + p_1 x^{n-1} + \cdots + p_n) = p_0 a^n + p_1 a^{n-1} + \cdots + p_n.$$

The following examples illustrate further the use of the fundamental limit theorems.

Example 8.3c. Find

$$\lim_{x \to 1} \frac{2x^2 - x + 1}{x^2 - 2}.$$

Since $\lim_{x \to 1} (2x^2 - x + 1) = 2$ and $\lim_{x \to 1} (x^2 - 2) = -1$, we get, by Theorem 8.3e,

$$\lim_{x \to 1} \frac{2x^2 - x + 1}{x^2 - 2} = \frac{2}{-1} = -2.$$

Example 8.3d. Evaluate

$$\lim_{x \to 4} \frac{x^{5/2} - 16x^{1/2}}{x - 4}.$$

First, the given fraction may be written in the form

$$\left(\frac{x^2 - 16}{x - 4} \right) x^{1/2}.$$

It follows from Example 8.2b that

$$\lim_{x \to 4} x^{1/2} = 2.$$

Also,

$$\lim_{x \to 4} \frac{x^2 - 16}{x - 4} = \lim_{x \to 4} \frac{(x - 4)(x + 4)}{x - 4}$$

$$= \lim_{x \to 4} (x + 4) \qquad \text{(Why?)}$$

$$= 8.$$

Therefore,

$$\lim_{x \to 4} \left(\frac{x^2 - 16}{x - 4} \cdot x^{1/2} \right) = (8)(2) = 16.$$

The theorems on limits have all been stated for the case $x \to a$, where a is a real number. The theorems can also be shown to be valid for $x \to \infty$, provided, of course, that the other conditions of the theorems are satisfied.

Example 8.3e. Find

$$\lim_{x \to \infty} \frac{x^2 - 2x + 4}{3x^2 + x - 1},$$

if it exists.

As the problem stands, the limits of the numerator and denominator do not exist. However, if the fraction is rewritten as

$$\frac{1 - \frac{2}{x} + \frac{4}{x^2}}{3 + \frac{1}{x} - \frac{1}{x^2}},$$

then, as $x \to \infty$, the limits of the new numerator and denominator do exist, since $1/x \to 0$ as $x \to \infty$. Hence

$$\lim_{x \to \infty} \frac{x^2 - 2x + 4}{3x^2 + x - 1} = \lim_{x \to \infty} \frac{1 - \frac{2}{x} + \frac{4}{x^2}}{3 + \frac{1}{x} - \frac{1}{x^2}} = \frac{1}{3}.$$

Example 8.3f. Find

$$\lim_{x \to 0} x \sin \frac{1}{x},$$

if it exists.

Since $\lim_{x \to 0} \sin (1/x)$ does not exist, the theorems on limits cannot be used. However, we know $|\sin (1/x)| \leq 1$ so that

$$\left| x \sin \frac{1}{x} \right| \leq |x|,$$

and since $x \to 0$, $|x \sin (1/x)| \to 0$. Therefore,

$$\lim_{x \to 0} x \sin \frac{1}{x} = 0.$$

The preceding result suggests the following general theorem on limits.

Theorem 8.3f. $\qquad \lim_{x \to a} f_1(x) = A, \quad \lim_{x \to a} f_2(x) = A,$

and

$$f_1(x) \leq g(x) \leq f_2(x) \text{ for all } x \in \mathfrak{N}^*(a, h) \Rightarrow \lim_{x \to a} g(x) = A.$$

PROOF: The proof is left for the reader.

In using the basic theorems, one must be certain that the proper conditions are fulfilled. Thus, Example 8.3f shows that

$$\lim_{x \to 0} x \sin \frac{1}{x} = 0.$$

Nevertheless, it does *not* follow that $\lim_{x \to 0} \sin (1/x)$ exists!

Occasionally it is necessary to use the theorems on limits when the limits are of the one-sided variety.

Example 8.3g. Let

$$f(x) .=. \begin{cases} x^2 + 2x, & x \leq 1, \\ 2x, & x > 1, \end{cases}$$

and let

$$g(x) .=. \begin{cases} 2x^3, & x \leq 1, \\ 3, & x > 1. \end{cases}$$

Find $\lim_{x \to 1} [f(x) \cdot g(x)]$ if it exists.

Neither $f(x)$ nor $g(x)$ have limits as $x \to 1$, but one-sided limits exist for both functions. Thus

$$\lim_{x \to 1^-} f(x) = 3, \quad \lim_{x \to 1^+} f(x) = 2,$$
$$\lim_{x \to 1^-} g(x) = 2, \quad \lim_{x \to 1^+} g(x) = 3.$$

Therefore, $\lim_{x \to 1^-} [f(x) \cdot g(x)] = 6$ and $\lim_{x \to 1^+} [f(x) \cdot g(x)] = 6$. Consequently, $\lim_{x \to 1} [f(x) \cdot g(x)] = 6$.

This example shows that even though two functions do not individually have limits at a particular point, the product function may have a limit.

The reader should be warned that although the preceding theorems on limits are useful in many problems, they cannot always be used, and other techniques must be employed. We shall return to this question at a later time.

Exercises 8.3

In Numbers 1 to 18, find the specified limit, provided it exists.

1. $\lim_{x \to 2} \dfrac{8 - x^3}{x^2 - 2x}$.

2. $\lim_{x \to 3} \dfrac{x^3 - 27}{x^2 - 9}$.

3. $\lim_{x \to -1} \dfrac{3x^2 + 2x - 1}{2x^2 + 5x + 3}$.

4. $\lim_{x \to \infty} \dfrac{x^2 + x - 1}{2x^2 + 2x - 3}$.

5. $\lim_{x \to \infty} \dfrac{5x^3 - 7x + 3}{25x^2 + 10x + 1}$.

6. $\lim_{x \to \infty} \dfrac{2x^2 - x}{x^3 + 2x^2}$.

7. $\lim_{x \to \infty} \dfrac{3x^2 - 2x + 3}{2x^2 + x - 4}$.

8. $\lim_{h \to 0} \dfrac{(3 + h)^3 - 3^3}{h}$.

9. $\lim_{x \to 1} \dfrac{x^3 - 1}{|x - 1|}$.

10. $\lim_{x \to \frac{1}{2}} \dfrac{x^{-2} - x^{-1} - 2}{2x - 1}$.

11. $\lim_{x \to \infty} \dfrac{\cos 2x}{x}$.

12. $\lim_{x \to \infty} \dfrac{\tan x}{x}$.

13. $\lim_{x \to 0} \dfrac{1}{1 - (1/x)}$.

14. $\lim_{x \to 0} x^2 \sin \dfrac{1}{x}$.

15. $\lim_{x \to \infty} (\sqrt{x^2 + 1} - x)$.

16. $\lim_{h \to 0} \dfrac{\sqrt{2} - \sqrt{2 + h}}{h}$.

17. $\lim_{x \to -1} \dfrac{|x| - 1}{x + 1}$.

18. $\lim_{h \to 0} \dfrac{1}{h} \left[\dfrac{1}{\sqrt{2 + h}} - \dfrac{1}{\sqrt{2}} \right]$.

19. Prove Theorem 8.3a.
20. Prove Theorem 8.3e.
21. Define what is meant by $\lim_{x \to \infty} f(x) = A$.
22. Prove Theorem 8.3b for the case $x \to \infty$.
23. Prove Theorem 8.3f.

8.4 CONTINUOUS AND DISCONTINUOUS FUNCTIONS

The graph of a function frequently indicates a lack of connectedness or smoothness that the reader might be inclined to regard as peculiar and worthy of closer
investigation. Figures 8.4a, 8.4b, and 8.4c illustrate three simple instances of
such behavior which will be of interest to us in the following discussion. For
the first function, the limit as $x \to a$ of $f(x)$ exists, but $f(a)$ is not the same as
the limit. For the second, the functional value simply increases without bound
as $x \to a$. For the third, the functional value has different limits from the right
and from the left.

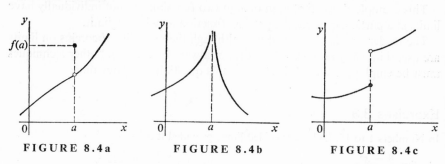

| FIGURE 8.4a | FIGURE 8.4b | FIGURE 8.4c |

A study of the peculiarities of various functions is of considerable interest
both in advanced mathematics and in its applications. However, from an elementary point of view, we rather expect functions that describe simple physical
phenomena to be fairly "well-behaved." Well-behaved functions have a number
of intuitively characteristic properties, which we shall now consider.

Definition 8.4a. A function f for which $\lim_{x \to a} f(x) = f(a)$ is called a **continuous**
function at $x = a$. A function that is continuous at every point in an interval
$b \leq x \leq c$ is said to be *continuous on that interval*.

Notice carefully that the statement, $\lim_{x \to a} f(x) = f(a)$, implies that

(i) $f(a)$ is defined;
(ii) $\lim_{x \to a} f(x)$ exists; and
(iii) $\lim_{x \to a} f(x) = f(a)$.

In fact, it is worthwhile to compare this definition with that for limit. If
$\lim_{x \to a} f(x) = A$, then there is an h for each given ϵ such that

$$x \in \mathfrak{N}^*(a, h) \Rightarrow f(x) \in \mathfrak{N}(A, \epsilon),$$

where $\mathfrak{N}^*(a, h)$ is contained in the domain of f. If f is *continuous*, then we may replace A by $f(a)$ and $\mathfrak{N}^*(a, h)$ by $\mathfrak{N}(a, h)$, since we are now concerned with what happens *at* $x = a$ as well as what happens *near* $x = a$. Hence, if f is continuous at $x = a$, we have

$$x \in \mathfrak{N}(a, h) \Rightarrow f(x) \in \mathfrak{N}(f(a), \epsilon)$$

when $\mathfrak{N}(a, h)$ is in the domain of f.

If either $f(a)$ is undefined or $\lim_{x \to a} f(x)$ does not exist, the statement that $\lim_{x \to a} f(x) = f(a)$ becomes meaningless. Thus, in examining a function for continuity, it is helpful to determine the values in $\mathfrak{R}$ for which the function is undefined. If a function is not defined at a point, it cannot be continuous there; nevertheless it is often necessary to consider the behavior of the function in a neighborhood of such a point.

In general, a function f is said to be **discontinuous** at $x = a$ if (1) the domain of f includes some deleted neighborhood of a, and (2) f is not continuous at $x = a$. We shall usually not be concerned with questions of continuity at a point that possesses no deleted neighborhood contained in the domain of the function. This applies in particular to points that possess neighborhoods lying entirely outside this domain.

Figures 8.4a, 8.4b, and 8.4c illustrate three kinds of discontinuities. For further illustration, consider a function f having a graph as shown in Figure 8.4d.

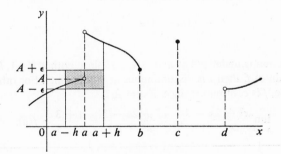

FIGURE 8.4d

At $x = a$, the function is undefined and there is a $\mathfrak{N}^*(a, h)$ contained in the domain of f, so that f is discontinuous at $x = a$. For values of x for which $b < x < d$ and $x \neq c$, $f(x)$ is undefined. At $x = c$, the function is defined at an *isolated point* of the domain of f. Nothing more need be said about f on this interval.

For values of x in the interior of an interval contained entirely in the domain of a function, the theorems on limits can be used to demonstrate continuity in many cases where the function is described by a "simple" formula.

For example, in the preceding section it was shown that

$$\lim_{x \to a} x^n = a^n \quad \text{for } n \in \mathfrak{N}.$$

This result shows that $f(x) = x^n$ describes a continuous function for all values of x since $a^n = f(a)$. It can be extended, as in the following theorem, to include every $n \in \mathcal{I}$.

Theorem 8.4a. The function f described by $f(x) .=. x^n$, for $n \in \mathcal{I}$, is continuous for all values of x when $n > 0$, and is continuous for all values of $x \neq 0$ when $n \leq 0$.

PROOF: Left for the reader.

Furthermore, it was shown for a polynomial $P(x)$ that,

$$\lim_{x \to a} P(x) = P(a),$$

which proves the following theorem.

Theorem 8.4b. A function f for which $f(x) .=. P(x)$, a polynomial in x, is continuous for all $x \in \mathcal{R}$.

The next theorem also follows easily.

Theorem 8.4c. Every function for which $y = P(x)/Q(x)$, where $P(x)$ and $Q(x)$ are polynomials, is continuous at every value of x for which $Q(x) \neq 0$.

PROOF: Left for the reader.

Example 8.4a. At what values of x is the function

$$f .=. \left\{ (x, y): y = \frac{x^2 + 2x - 3}{x^2 - 1} \right\}$$

continuous?

Since the function is undefined at $x = \pm 1$, and since both $\mathfrak{N}^*(-1, h)$ and $\mathfrak{N}^*(1, h)$ are in the domain of f, then f is discontinuous at these points. For other values of x, by Theorem 8.4c, f is continuous since, if $a \neq \pm 1$,

$$\lim_{x \to o} \frac{x^2 + 2x - 3}{x^2 - 1} = \frac{a^2 + 2a - 3}{a^2 - 1} = \frac{a + 3}{a + 1} = f(a).$$

The concept of continuity can be extended to include continuity at an end point of an interval.

Definition 8.4b. If $f(x)$ is defined on the interval $a \leq x \leq b$, where $a < b$, then f is said to be continuous from the right at the point a if

$$\lim_{x \to a^+} f(x) = f(a)$$

and continuous from the left at the point b if

$$\lim_{x \to b^-} f(x) = f(b).$$

Example 8.4b. Let $f .=. \{(x, y): y = [\![x]\!], 0 \leq x \leq 2\}$. At what points is f continuous?

At any point for which $0 < a < 1$, $[\![a]\!] = 0$, so that

$$\lim_{x \to a} [\![x]\!] = 0 = f(a)$$

and f is continuous there. Since f is defined at $x = 0$ but is not defined for $x < 0$, we must consider the limit from the right. Then,

$$\lim_{x \to 0^+} f(x) = 0 = f(0)$$

so that f is continuous from the right at $x = 0$ (see Figure 8.4e). At $x = 1$, however, $[\![1]\!] = 1$, but

$$\lim_{x \to 1^-} f(x) = 0,$$

so that f is not continuous from the left at this point.

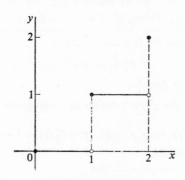

FIGURE 8.4e

In the same way, f is continuous at every point a for which $1 < a < 2$. At $x = 1$, f is continuous from the right, since $f(1) = 1$ and $\lim_{x \to 1^+} f(x) = 1$. At $x = 2$, the function is discontinuous, since $f(2) = 2$ and $\lim_{x \to 2^-} f(x) = 1$.

Although it is fairly easy to determine the points at which a "simple" function is continuous or discontinuous, the techniques developed so far are not adequate to handle most functions. Even though we may intuitively feel that functions described by formulas such as

$$y = \sin x \quad \text{or} \quad y = \sqrt{1 - x^2}$$

are continuous at certain points, we do not yet have the means for *proving* such a conjecture. This lack of tools will be remedied to a large extent in the succeeding work.

One very important result enables us to evaluate a limit of a composite function in a simple manner.

Theorem 8.4d. Let $y = f(x)$ and $u = g(y)$. If $\lim_{x \to a} f(x) = A$ and g is continuous at $y = A$, then

$$\lim_{x \to a} g[f(x)] = g[\lim_{x \to a} f(x)] = g(A).$$

PROOF: Since g is continuous at $y = A$, we know that there is a δ such that

$$y \in \mathfrak{N}(A, \delta) \Rightarrow g(y) \in \mathfrak{N}[g(A), \epsilon]$$

for each given ϵ. Also, since $f(x) \rightarrow A$ as $x \rightarrow a$, there is an h for which

$$x \in \mathfrak{N}^*(a, h) \Rightarrow f(x) \in \mathfrak{N}(A, \delta).$$

Hence, since $y = f(x)$,

$$x \in \mathfrak{N}^*(a, h) \Rightarrow y \in \mathfrak{N}(A, \delta) \Rightarrow g(y) \in \mathfrak{N}[g(A), \epsilon],$$

which is to say that

$$\lim_{x \to a} g[f(x)] = g[\lim_{x \to a} f(x)].$$

This result often allows us to interchange the taking of a limit with the formation of a functional value, as in the next illustration.

Example 8.4c. Show that the function F, where

$$F(x) .=. \sqrt{1 - x^2},$$

is continuous on its entire domain.

Since we may regard the given function as a composite of the two functions described by

$$g(y) .=. \sqrt{y} \quad \text{and} \quad y = f(x) .=. 1 - x^2,$$

we try to apply Theorem 8.4d.

It has been shown in Example 8.2b that

$$\lim_{x \to a} \sqrt{x} = \sqrt{a} \quad \text{for } a > 0,$$

which means that the square root function is continuous for $x > 0$. It is almost trivial, and it is left to the reader to show that

$$\lim_{x \to 0^+} \sqrt{x} = 0,$$

which completes the demonstration that the square root function is continuous on its entire domain.

Since $y = 1 - x^2$ defines a polynomial function that is continuous for all real values of x and is nonnegative for $|x| \leq 1$, then, by Theorem 8.4d, the function F, given by

$$F(x) = \sqrt{1 - x^2} = g[f(x)],$$

is continuous for $-1 \leq x \leq 1$.

Occasionally it is possible to "improve" discontinuous functions at points where the function is undefined. In Example 8.4a the function described by $f(x) = (x^2 + 2x - 3)/(x^2 - 1)$ was discussed, and was found to be discontinuous at $x = 1$ and at $x = -1$, because it is undefined there. However, $\lim_{x \to 1} [(x^2 + 2x - 3)/(x^2 - 1)] = 2$. Is it possible to define a function g, which is identical to f everywhere that f is defined, and which will also be defined and continuous at $x = 1$? If such a function g exists, it must be defined at $x = 1$ so that

$$\lim_{x \to 1} g(x) = g(1).$$

If $g(x) = f(x)$ everywhere else, then we must have $g(1).=.2$. Hence,

$$g(x).=.\begin{cases} \dfrac{x^2 + 2x - 3}{x^2 - 1}, & x \neq 1, -1, \\ 2, & x = 1. \end{cases}$$

The discontinuity of f at $x = 1$ is said to be **removable**. We may ask if the discontinuity at $x = -1$ is also removable. The reader can soon convince himself that it is not. As this discussion suggests, a discontinuity at a point $x = a$ is removable only if $\lim_{x \to a} f(x)$ exists.

The simpler types of discontinuities are classified as *removable* (Figure 8.4a); *finite* (Figure 8.4c); and *infinite* (Figure 8.4b). The discontinuity at $x = a$, illustrated in Figure 8.4a, is regarded as removable even though $f(a)$ is defined, because a new function g can be defined that is identical to $f(x)$ everywhere except at $x = a$, where $g(a).=.\lim_{x \to a} f(x)$.

Another more complicated type of discontinuity is shown in Figure 8.2b, which illustrates the failure of $\lim_{x \to 0} \sin(1/x)$ to exist because of the badly oscillatory character of the function.

An additional example will further illustrate some of these ideas.

Example 8.4d. Discuss the continuity of the function described by

$$f(x) = \frac{x - 1}{x\sqrt{x^2 - 1}}.$$

We see that $f(x)$ is undefined for $|x| \leq 1$. As $x \to -1^-$, $f(x) \to \infty$, so that f has an infinite discontinuity at -1. As $x \to 1^+$, $f(x) \to 0^+$ (why?), so that f has a removable discontinuity at $x = 1$ if only the one-sided limit is considered.

Exercises 8.4

In each of Numbers 1 to 17, for the function described by the given equation, determine the points of continuity and discontinuity, and describe the discontinuities. If a discontinuity is removable, explain how it can be removed.

1. $y = \dfrac{x}{x^2 - 1}$.

2. $y = \dfrac{x}{x^2 + 1}$.

3. $y = |x + 1|$.

4. $y = \dfrac{x + 4}{x^2 - 16}$.

5. $f(x).=.\begin{cases} x, & x \leq 2, \\ x - 2, & x > 2. \end{cases}$

6. $g(x).=.\begin{cases} x, & x \leq 0, \\ \dfrac{1}{x}, & x > 0. \end{cases}$

7. $y = \dfrac{x - 2}{x^2 + x - 6}$.

8. $y = \sqrt{1 - x^2}$.

9. $y = \dfrac{x - 1}{\sqrt{1 - x}}$.

10. $y = \dfrac{x + 3}{x^2 + 7x + 12}$.

11. $s = \dfrac{a - t}{\sqrt{|a^2 - t^2|}}$.

12. $f(x).=.\begin{cases} |x|, & |x| < 1, \\ x^2 - 1, & |x| > 1. \end{cases}$

13. $g(t).=.\begin{cases} \dfrac{t^2}{2} - 2, & 0 < t < 2, \\ 2 - \dfrac{8}{t^2}, & 2 < t \end{cases}$

14. $h(x) .=. \dfrac{[\![\frac{1}{2} + x]\!] - [\![\frac{1}{2}]\!]}{x}$, $\quad 0 \leq x \leq 3$.

15. $f(x) .=. \dfrac{|1 + x| - |x| - 1}{x}$, $\quad -2 \leq x < 2$.

16. $f(s) .=. \begin{cases} s^2, & s \leq 1, \\ s^2 - 8s^{-1}(s - 1)^3, & s > 1. \end{cases}$

17. $g(t) .=. [\![t\, [\![\frac{1}{t}]\!]]\!]$, $\quad t > 0$.

18. Prove Theorem 8.4a.
19. Prove Theorem 8.4c.
20. Prove that if $P(x)$ is a polynomial, then $\sqrt{|P(x)|}$ is continuous for all values of x.
21. Prove that $y = x^{1/3}$ describes a continuous function for all values of x. *Hint:* Compare Example 8.2b and consider $x \in \mathfrak{N}^*(a, \frac{7}{8}a)$, $a > 0$.
22. In Example 8.4d, prove that $\lim_{x \to 1^+} f(x) = 0$.
23. Suppose g is a continuous function for $a \leq x \leq b$ and h is a continuous function for $b < x \leq c$. Is the function f, where

$$f(x) .=. \begin{cases} g(x), & a \leq x \leq b, \\ h(x), & b < x \leq c, \end{cases}$$

necessarily continuous on the interval $a \leq x \leq c$? Why or why not?
24. Let f and g be functions that are discontinuous at $x = a$. Is it possible for the function described by the following equations to be continuous at $x = a$?

(a) $y = f(x) + g(x)$.   (b) $y = f(x) \cdot g(x)$.   (c) $y = f(x)/g(x)$.

8.5 PROPERTIES OF CONTINUOUS FUNCTIONS

As we indicated in the preceding section, continuous functions have a number of interesting and important properties, some of which are simple consequences of the theorems on limits. In the following discussion, if f is given as continuous over a closed interval $a \leq x \leq b$, then it is understood to have one-sided continuity at a and b.

Theorem 8.5a. Let f and g be continuous functions defined on the interval $a \leq x \leq b$. Then

$$\text{(i) } f(x) + g(x), \text{ and}$$
$$\text{(ii) } f(x) \cdot g(x)$$

define continuous functions on $a \leq x \leq b$, and

$$\text{(iii) } \frac{f(x)}{g(x)}$$

defines a continuous function at points where $g(x) \neq 0$.

PROOF: The proof of (i) will be given, the remaining proofs being left to the reader.

Let F be defined by $F(x) = f(x) + g(x)$. The hypothesis that f and g are continuous implies that for each c, such that $a \leq c \leq b$,

$$\lim_{x \to c} f(x) = f(c) \quad \text{and} \quad \lim_{x \to c} g(x) = g(c).$$

Accordingly, by the basic theorem on the limit of a sum,

$$\lim_{x \to c} [f(x) + g(x)] = f(c) + g(c),$$

or

$$\lim_{x \to c} F(x) = F(c).$$

This means that F is continuous at c. Since c is any point in the interval, the proof of the statement that F is continuous on the interval $a \leq x \leq b$ is complete. Note that a restriction to the proper one-sided neighborhood is necessary if $c = a$ or $c = b$.

It has been shown in Theorem 8.4d that if $g(u)$ defines a continuous function at $u = A$, and if $f(x) \to A$ as $x \to a$, then for the composite function $g(f)$, we have

$$g[f(x)] \to g(A) \quad \text{as } x \to a.$$

This result can be extended by

Theorem 8.5b. If $u = f(x)$ defines a continuous function f on the domain $a \leq x \leq b$, and if $g(u)$ defines a continuous function on the range of f, then $g(f)$ is continuous on $a \leq x \leq b$.

PROOF: By Theorem 8.4d, if x_0 is any point in $a \leq x \leq b$,

$$\lim_{x \to x_0} g[f(x)] = g[\lim_{x \to x_0} f(x)] = g[f(x_0)].$$

Briefly, Theorem 8.5b states that *a continuous function of a continuous function is continuous*. The theorem allows us to conclude that certain functions are continuous without direct appeal to the definition of continuity. For example, the function defined by

$$y = \sqrt{x + 1}$$

is continuous for $x \geq -1$.

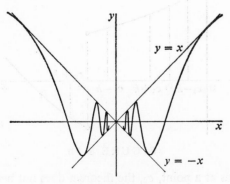

FIGURE 8.5a

A number of the properties of continuous functions seem to be intuitively obvious. However, an examination of the function f defined by

$$f(x) = \begin{cases} x \sin \dfrac{1}{x}, & x \neq 0, \\ 0, & x = 0, \end{cases}$$

in the neighborhood of $x = 0$ shows that it is easy to be misled by a preconceived notion of what the word *continuous* means. The function f is continuous at $x = 0$ and yet its graph (see Figure 8.5a) is so "crinkly" in every small neighborhood of the origin that we can only with difficulty imagine its appearance there and cannot draw it at all.

The following simple theorem is frequently used in advanced analysis.

Theorem 8.5c. Let f be defined on an interval $a \leq x \leq b$, and let f be continuous at an interior point c of this interval. If $f(c) > 0$, then there is a $\mathfrak{N}(c, h)$ such that $f(x) > 0$ for all $x \in \mathfrak{N}(c, h)$.

PROOF: Since f is continuous at $x = c$, then for any given ϵ there is a $\mathfrak{N}(c, h)$ such that

$$x \in \mathfrak{N}(c, h) \Rightarrow f(x) \in \mathfrak{N}[f(c), \epsilon]$$

or

$$f(c) - \epsilon < f(x) < f(c) + \epsilon.$$

Since this statement is true for every ϵ, it is true when $\epsilon = f(c)/2$, so that

$$\frac{f(c)}{2} < f(x) < \frac{3f(c)}{2}$$

when $x \in \mathfrak{N}(c, h)$. But $f(c) > 0$, so that $f(x) > 0$ for all $x \in \mathfrak{N}(c, h)$.

The proof of the corresponding theorem where $f(c) < 0$ can be carried out in a similar way, and is left for the reader. Figure 8.5b illustrates the fact that

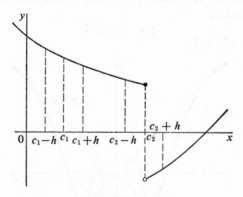

FIGURE 8.5b

if f is discontinuous at a point, c_2, the theorem does not necessarily hold, as it does at c_1, where f is continuous.

Another important property of continuous functions is related to the concept of a bounded function.

Definition 8.5a. A function f is said to be **bounded** if there is a positive number M such that $|f(x)| \leq M$ for all values of x in the domain of f.

This definition can be modified to describe boundedness over an interval by saying that if f is defined and if $|f(x)| \leq M$ on $a \leq x \leq b$, then f is bounded on the interval. As an illustration, the function defined by $y = 1/(x - 1)$ is unbounded on any interval containing 1, but it is bounded on any interval

$$a \leq x \leq b$$

such that $a < b < 1$ or $1 < a < b$.

The next theorem expresses an important property that is intuitively evident. An actual proof, however, is beyond the scope of this book.

Theorem 8.5d. If f is a continuous function on a closed interval $a \leq x \leq b$, then f is bounded on the interval.

To illustrate this result, consider the function defined by $y = 1/x$. On any closed interval $\delta \leq x \leq b$, where $\delta > 0$, the function is continuous and bounded. However, on the half-open interval $0 < x \leq b$, f is continuous and unbounded.

The next theorem expresses an important property that has a simple geometric interpretation. Suppose f is a function defined by $y = f(x)$ on an interval $a \leq x \leq b$, where $f(a) < f(b)$. Let $f(a) < k < f(b)$. Does there exist a point x_0 in the interval such that $f(x_0) = k$? This question is equivalent to asking if the graphs of $y = f(x)$ and $y = k$ intersect. As Figure 8.5c indicates, it is pos-

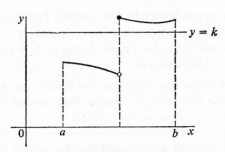

FIGURE 8.5c

sible for there to be no intersection if f is a discontinuous function. However, if f is continuous, then it seems "intuitively obvious" that there must be a point of intersection. As with the preceding theorem, the proof must be omitted.

Theorem 8.5e. *The Intermediate Value Theorem.* Let f be a continuous function on $a \leq x \leq b$. If k is a number between $f(a)$ and $f(b)$, then there is at least one point c in the interval at which $f(c) = k$.

This theorem plays a central role in many widely used methods for the approximate solution of equations. These methods depend on the following idea. Suppose we wish to solve an equation of the form $f(x) = 0$. If there are found two numbers x_1 and x_2 such that $f(x_1)$ and $f(x_2)$ are opposite in sign and if f is continuous on the interval $x_1 \leq x \leq x_2$, then there must be at least one root of $f(x) = 0$ between x_1 and x_2. This is an immediate consequence of the Intermediate Value Theorem. Why?

The concept of boundedness of a function which was introduced earlier in this section has an important refinement.

Definition 8.5b. A number M is called an *upper bound* for a function f on an interval $a \leq x \leq b$ if $f(x) \leq M$ for every x in the interval. A *lower bound* is defined in a similar manner.

Evidently, a function may have many upper or lower bounds (see Figures 8.5d and 8.5e).

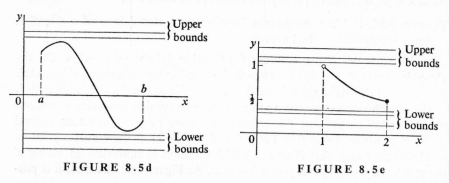

FIGURE 8.5d   **FIGURE 8.5e**

Definition 8.5c. If an upper bound U of a function f on an interval $a \leq x \leq b$ has the property that for every other upper bound M of f on the interval $U \leq M$, then U is called the *least upper bound* of f. A *greatest lower bound* can be defined in a similar fashion.

The reader should notice that these last two definitions can be modified for a function defined over any domain $\mathfrak{D}$ rather than over an interval.

An example will help to illustrate these ideas.

Example 8.5a. Find the least upper bound and the greatest lower bound of f if $f(x) = 1/x$, $1 < x \leq 2$ (see Figure 8.5e).

Any number greater than 1 is an upper bound and 1 is the least upper bound. The greatest lower bound is $\frac{1}{2}$. The function does not actually take on the value of its least upper bound, but it does take on the value of its greatest lower bound.

Example 8.5b. Discuss the function f defined by

$$f(x) = \sec x, \qquad 0 \leq x < \pi/3,$$

with respect to upper and lower bounds.

Since $\sec x = 1/\cos x$, and $\cos x$ decreases from the value 1 to the value $\frac{1}{2}$ as x increases from 0 to $\pi/3$, $\sec x$ increases from the value 1 to the value 2 for the same variation in the value of x. Thus 1 is a lower bound and is the greatest lower bound of f. In the same way, 2 is an upper bound and is the least upper bound of f. The fact that the domain of f is $0 \leq x < \pi/3$ means in this case that f takes on the value of its greatest lower bound (sec $0 = 1$) but does not take on the value of its least upper bound.

In the last examples it was assumed that a greatest lower bound and a least upper bound exist for the given functions. This assumption is justified by the next theorem, which is stated without proof.

Theorem 8.5f. If f is defined and bounded on $a \leq x \leq b$, then $f(x)$ has a least upper bound and a greatest lower bound.

It is sometimes easy to discover a least upper bound or a greatest lower bound from the graph of a simple function, but not every function can be graphed. However, it is possible to show that, under certain conditions, points exist where the function takes on a least upper bound or a greatest lower bound.

Theorem 8.5g. If M is the least upper bound of a continuous function f over an interval $a \leq x \leq b$, then there is a point x_0 in the interval such that $f(x_0) = M$.

PROOF: Suppose, on the contrary, that there is no point x_0 such that $f(x_0) = M$. Then let $g(x) = 1/(M - f(x))$, so that $g(x) > 0$ for all x in the interval. But $g(x)$ is a continuous function, and so must be bounded. (Why?) Let P be an upper bound on $g(x)$; that is,

$$\frac{1}{M - f(x)} < P.$$

Then

$$\frac{1}{P} < M - f(x)$$

and

$$f(x) < M - \frac{1}{P}$$

for all x in the interval. This shows that f has an upper bound $M - (1/P)$ that is less than M, which contradicts the supposition that M is the least upper bound. Hence, the theorem is proved.

The number M in Theorem 8.5g is the greatest or *maximum* value of f on the closed interval. The reader may prove a similar result for the greatest lower bound, say m, which is the least or *minimum* value of f on the closed interval.

We shall close this section with a basic theorem on inverse functions. Suppose a continuous function f, defined on the interval $a \leq x \leq b$, has a graph that rises as x increases, so that for all pairs of values x_1, x_2 in the interval such that $x_1 < x_2$, it is true that $f(x_1) < f(x_2)$. The graph will then have the appearance shown in Figure 8.5f. It looks extremely plausible, judging from the graph, that the inverse function f^{-1} exists and is of the same general character as the given function f. We shall prove that such is the case, but first we need a preliminary definition.

Definition 8.5d. A function f defined on an interval $a \le x \le b$ is said to be *strictly increasing* if, for x_1, x_2 in the interval, $x_1 < x_2 \Rightarrow f(x_1) < f(x_2)$. The function is said to be *strictly decreasing* if $x_1 < x_2 \Rightarrow f(x_1) > f(x_2)$.

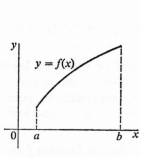

FIGURE 8.5f

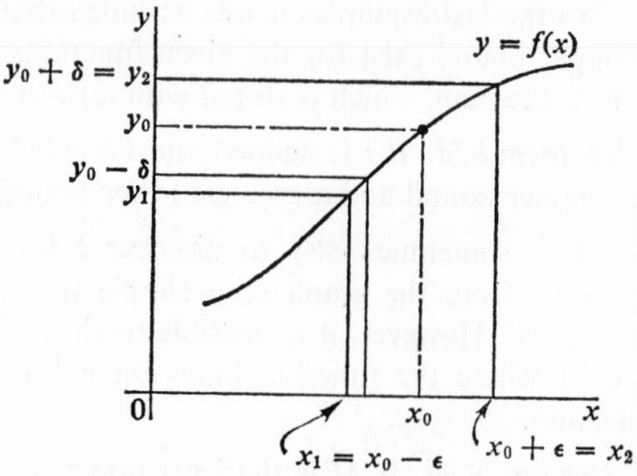

FIGURE 8.5g

The graph shown in Figure 8.5f is that of a strictly increasing function. If the graph falls steadily as x increases, then the function is strictly decreasing.

Theorem 8.5h. If a function f is continuous and strictly increasing on an interval $a \le x \le b$, then the inverse function f^{-1} exists on the interval $f(a) \le y \le f(b)$ and is also continuous and strictly increasing.

PROOF: Let us write $y = f(x)$ so that $f = \{(x, y)\}$. Consider the inverse relation $\{(y, x)\}$, and let us suppose that f is strictly increasing. Then there is one value of y for each value of x, and conversely. Hence, the inverse relation is a function. Moreover, if x_1 and x_2 are in the given interval and if $y_1 = f(x_1)$ and $y_2 = f(x_2)$, then, by hypothesis

$$x_1 < x_2 \Rightarrow y_1 < y_2.$$

Therefore,

$$y_1 < y_2 \Rightarrow x_1 < x_2;$$

otherwise, the strictly increasing character of f is contradicted. Accordingly,

$f = \{(x, y)\}$ is strictly increasing $\Leftrightarrow f^{-1} = \{(y, x)\}$ is strictly increasing.

With $c .= . f(a)$ and $d .= . f(b)$, the range of f is $f(a) \le y \le f(b)$. For each y_0 such that $f(a) < y_0 < f(b)$, there is a unique x_0 such that $a < x_0 < b$ and $y_0 = f(x_0)$.

Now let $\mathfrak{N}(x_0, \epsilon)$ be an arbitrary neighborhood (see Figure 8.5g) in the domain of f, and let $x_1 = x_0 - \epsilon$ and $x_2 = x_0 + \epsilon$, so that

$$y_1 = f(x_1) < y_0 < y_2 = f(x_2).$$

Since f and f^{-1} are strictly increasing, and since f is continuous, we have

$$x \in \mathfrak{N}(x_0, \epsilon) \Leftrightarrow y_1 < y < y_2.$$

Consequently, if $\delta = \min(y_0 - y_1, y_2 - y_0)$, then

$$y \in \mathfrak{N}(y_0, \delta) \Rightarrow x \in \mathfrak{N}(x_0, \epsilon),$$

which shows that $f^{-1} .=. \{(y, x)\}$ is continuous at y_0.

Since this argument holds for each point y_0 such that $f(a) < y_0 < f(b)$, then f^{-1} is a continuous function of y in this interval. A similar argument shows that f^{-1} has one-sided continuity at $f(a)$ and at $f(b)$, so that f^{-1} is continuous for all y in $f(a) \leq y \leq f(b)$. The reader may show that a corresponding result applies if f is a strictly decreasing function. A simple illustration of the preceding theorem is given by

$$f(x) = x^2, 0 \leq x \leq p, \quad \text{and} \quad f^{-1}(y) = \sqrt{y}, 0 \leq y \leq p^2.$$

Exercises 8.5

1. If $f(x) .=. x^2 + 2x + 1$ and $g(x) .=. \sqrt{x}$, where is $g[f(x)]$ continuous?
2. If $r(x) .=. x^2 - 4$ and $s(x) .=. \sqrt{x}$, where is $s[r(x)]$ continuous?

In Numbers 3 to 6, discuss the continuity of the function defined by the given equation. Indicate what theorems justify your conclusions.

3. $f(x) .=. x^5(x^2 - 7)^4$.

5. $g(x) .=. x^3[x^{-1} - (x^2 + 1)^{-1/2}]^3$.

4. $r(x) .=. \left[\dfrac{(x^2 - 1)}{(x^2 + 2x - 3)}\right]^{1/3}$.

6. $s(x) .=. \left[\dfrac{x^3}{(x^3 - 8)^2} - \dfrac{1}{x}\right]^{2/3}$.

7. Let $f(x) .=. \dfrac{x^2 - 4}{x - 2}$, $-4 \leq x \leq 4$ and $x \neq 2$, and let $f(2) .=. 4$. Does Theorem 8.5c apply to f on the interval $-4 \leq x \leq 4$? Explain.

In Numbers 8 to 13, find a number M (if one exists) such that $|f(x)| < M$ for the function defined by the given equation. (Be sure that you can demonstrate the validity of the inequality for the M you use.)

8. $f(x) .=. x^3 - 2x^2 + 3x - 4, -2 \leq x \leq 2$.

9. $f(x) .=. \dfrac{x^3 - 2x^2 - 1}{1 + x^4}, -1 \leq x \leq 4$.

10. $f(x) .=. \dfrac{2x^2 + x - 3}{x^2 + 2}, -3 \leq x \leq 4$.

11. $f(x) .=. x - [\![x]\!], 0 \leq x \leq 3$.
12. $f(x) .=. x[\![1/x]\!], 0 < x$.

13. $f(x) .=. \dfrac{4}{x + 1} \sin \dfrac{1}{x}, 0 < x$.

14. Let $f(x) .=. x/(x^2 + 1), 0 < x < 2$. What is the greatest lower bound and the least upper bound of $f(x)$ over its domain? At what points, if any, does $f(x)$ take on its least upper bound and its greatest lower bound?
15. For each of the following, find the greatest lower bound and the least upper bound for $f(x)$, and determine if the function actually takes on these values.

(a) $f(x) .=. x - [[x]], 0 \leq x \leq 3$.
(b) $f(x) .=. x[[1/x]], 0 < x$.
(c) $f(x) .=. x^2 + 4x + 5, -3 < x < 0$.

16. Let P be a point inside a circle C, and let s be the distance from P to a point on C nearest P, and let d be the distance from P to a point on C farthest from P. Can you prove that there is a point on C whose distance from P is $\frac{1}{2}(s + d)$?

17. Must a function be continuous in order to be bounded on an interval? Explain.

18. Is the function defined by $g(x) = 1/(1 + |x|)$ bounded? Explain.

19. Prove Theorem 8.5a (ii).

20. Prove Theorem 8.5a (iii).

21. State and prove the theorem corresponding to Theorem 8.5c for the case $f(c) < 0$.

22. Consider the function f, where

$$f(x) .=. \begin{cases} |x|, & -1 < x < 0, \\ x + 1, & 0 \leq x < 1. \end{cases}$$

This function is discontinuous at $x = 0$. But $f(0) > 0$, and $f(x) > 0$ on every $\mathfrak{N}(0, h)$. Does this result contradict Theorem 8.5c? Explain.

23. Consider the function f, where

$$f(x) .=. \begin{cases} 3, & -1 \leq x < 0, \\ 2 - x^2, & 0 \leq x \leq 4. \end{cases}$$

Here, $f(-1) = 3$ and $f(4) = -14$. Does the Intermediate Value Theorem guarantee that there is a point x_0 in $-1 \leq x \leq 4$ such that $f(x_0) = 0$? Is there actually such a point? Does this contradict the theorem? Why?

24. If $p(x) .=. x^3 - x^2 - 1$, show that there must be a value, say x_1, such that $p(x_1) = 0$. Use tables of squares and cubes to find an approximate value for x_1.

25. State whether the following propositions are true or false. Discuss.

(a) If f is defined on $a \leq x \leq b$, then $f(x)$ must have a least upper bound and a greatest lower bound.

(b) If f has a least upper bound M over an interval $a \leq x \leq b$, then there must exist a point x_0 in the interval such that $f(x_0) = M$.

(c) If f is a continuous function on an open interval, then f may or may not be bounded on the interval.

(d) If f is defined on $a \leq x \leq b$ and k is a number between $f(a)$ and $f(b)$, then there must exist a point c in the interval at which $f(c) = k$.

(e) If f is a continuous function on a closed interval $a \leq x \leq b$, then f has a least upper bound M and there is a point x_0 in the interval such that $f(x_0) = M$.

26. Explain why $f .=. \{(x, x^3)\}$ has a strictly increasing, continuous inverse on its entire domain $\mathfrak{R}$.

27. Show by means of a graph that the inverse of a function that is not strictly increasing (decreasing) is a relation but not a function.

28. You can't find an explicit formula for the inverse of the function defined by $y = x^5 + x$. Is the inverse a function? What are some of the properties of the inverse?

29. Explain why Theorem 8.5h does not apply to the function defined by $y = x^2 - x$. Can you restrict the domain of the function so that the theorem does apply?

Summary of Chapter 8

(1) The fundamental notion of calculus is the concept of limit. Calculus in the classical sense is concerned with "limiting processes," and it is therefore particularly important that the reader understand the *limit concept* on an intuitive basis, as well as on an analytical basis. That is, the meaning of "as $x \to a$, $y \to b$" must be clear, and the process for determining the relationship between h and ϵ in "$x \in \mathfrak{N}^*(a, h) \Rightarrow y \in \mathfrak{N}(b, \epsilon)$" is essential (Section 8.1) so that the definition of *limit* is clear (Section 8.2).

In addition, the following ideas are important:

(2) theorems on limits (Section 8.3);
(3) elementary techniques for finding limits (Section 8.3);
(4) continuity of a function at a point and on an interval (Section 8.4);
(5) the difference between the limit concept and continuity (Sections 8.1, 8.4);
(6) types of discontinuities (Section 8.4);
(7) properties of continuous functions and the Intermediate Value Theorem (Section 8.5);
(8) the concepts of least upper bound and greatest lower bound (Section 8.5).

Chapter 9　The Derivative and the Inverse Derivative

9.1 THE TANGENT PROBLEM

Many of the important problems of mathematical analysis can be translated into or made to depend on one basic problem that has been of interest to mathematicians since the Greeks (about 300–200 B.C.). This is the problem of constructing a tangent line to a given curve at a specified point on the curve.

This problem was solved by special methods in a number of isolated instances even in the early history of mathematics. For example, it is quite easy to solve the problem if the curve is a circle, and every student studies this solution in his high school geometry. However, it was not until the time of Isaac Newton (1642–1727) and Gottfried Wilhelm Leibniz (1646–1716) that a systematic general method for obtaining the solution was given. It is on this account that these two men are credited with the invention of the calculus.

Although the tangent problem may appear to be of only minor interest to nonmathematicians, the fact is that the techniques developed for the solution of this problem are the very backbone of much of the science and technology of today. For example, the direction of motion of an object along a curve at each instant is defined in terms of the direction of the tangent line to the path of motion. The paths of the planets around the sun and of artificial satellites around the earth are studied essentially by starting out with information about the tangent line to the path of the motion. A different type of problem is that of studying the decay of a radioactive substance such as radium when we know that the rate of decay at each instant is proportional to the amount of radium present. The key to this problem, as well as to the problem of motion, lies in an analysis of what we mean by the word *rate*. As we shall soon see, this concept is so closely related to the slope of the tangent line to a curve that the abstract mathematical formulation of a rate problem is indistinguishable from the formulation of the tangent problem.

We begin with the tangent problem, not only because of its historical and its practical significance, but also because the reader's geometric intuition will lend concreteness to an otherwise rather abstract notion. Figure 9.1a illustrates an intuitively plausible procedure for drawing a tangent line to a continuous curve, C, at a point, P. If a straight line is rotated about the point P, it generally will cross the curve at P and possibly at another point. A line that crosses the curve at P and at another point (such as Q) is called a **secant line** to the curve. As the point Q approaches the point P along the curve, the secant line rotates about P and appears to reach a limiting position, which is that of a line PT coincident in direction with the curve at P. In this sense, we regard the line PT as the limit of the secant line PQ. This apparently simple-minded idea motivates the next definition and is the origin of much of the important analysis that ensues.

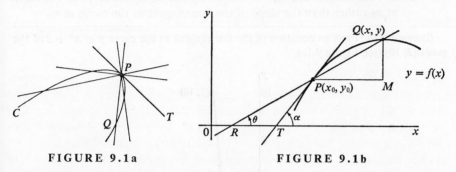

FIGURE 9.1a   FIGURE 9.1b

Definition 9.1a. Let PQ be a secant line through two points P and Q on a continuous curve C. The limit (if it exists) of the secant line as Q approaches P along the curve is called the **tangent line** to the curve at P.

Suppose that an equation of a curve is given in the form $y = f(x)$, where f is a specified continuous function and x and y are the usual rectangular coordinates. Let it be required to construct the tangent line at a point $P(x_0, y_0)$ on the curve (see Figure 9.1b). We wish to use Definition 9.1a and therefore we consider another point $Q(x, y)$ on the curve. The points P and Q determine a secant line whose slope is

$$\tan \theta = \frac{y - y_0}{x - x_0}.$$

Assuming that the curve has a tangent line PT, we find that as Q approaches P along the curve, the inclination θ of the secant line approaches the inclination α of the tangent line, that is,

$$\lim_{Q \to P} \theta = \alpha.$$

Furthermore, the slope of the secant line approaches the slope of the tangent line, so that

$$\lim_{Q \to P} \tan \theta = \tan \alpha.$$

Since for each point (x, y) on the curve, we have $y = f(x)$, the coordinates of P may be written $(x_0, f(x_0))$ and those of Q, $(x, f(x))$. Consequently,

$$Q \to P \Leftrightarrow x \to x_0$$

and

$$\lim_{Q \to P} \tan \theta = \lim_{x \to x_0} \frac{f(x) - f(x_0)}{x - x_0}.$$

Definition 9.1b. The slope $m(x_0)$ of the tangent to the curve with equation $y = f(x)$ at the point (x_0, y_0) is

$$m(x_0) .=. \lim_{x \to x_0} \frac{f(x) - f(x_0)}{x - x_0},$$

provided this limit exists.

Note: For the sake of brevity, we frequently call $m(x_0)$ the slope of the *curve* at x_0 rather than the slope of the line tangent to the curve at x_0.

Example 9.1a. Find an equation of the line tangent to the curve $y = x^3 + 2$ at the point $(2, 10)$ (see Figure 9.1c).

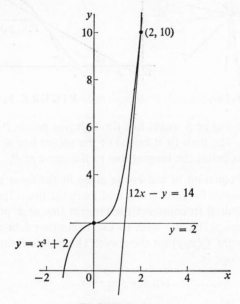

FIGURE 9.1c

Using Definition 9.1b, we first find the slope of the tangent line as follows:

$$\begin{aligned}
m(2) &= \lim_{x \to 2} \frac{f(x) - f(2)}{x - 2} \\
&= \lim_{x \to 2} \frac{(x^3 + 2) - 10}{x - 2} \\
&= \lim_{x \to 2} \frac{x^3 - 8}{x - 2} \\
&= \lim_{x \to 2} \frac{(x - 2)(x^2 + 2x + 4)}{x - 2} \\
&= \lim_{x \to 2} (x^2 + 2x + 4) = 12.
\end{aligned}$$

An equation of the tangent line may now be found by using the point-slope form of the straight line equation. This gives

$$y - 10 = 12(x - 2) \quad \text{or} \quad 12x - y = 14.$$

Example 9.1b. Find the points (if there are any) where the curve $y = x^3 + 2$ has its tangent line parallel to the x-axis.

Since this is equivalent to finding the points where the slope of the curve is zero, we must first find a general formula for the slope. Thus

$$
\begin{aligned}
m(x_0) &= \lim_{x \to x_0} \frac{f(x) - f(x_0)}{x - x_0} \\
&= \lim_{x \to x_0} \frac{(x^3 + 2) - (x_0^3 + 2)}{x - x_0} \\
&= \lim_{x \to x_0} \frac{x^3 - x_0^3}{x - x_0} \\
&= \lim_{x \to x_0} \frac{(x - x_0)(x^2 + xx_0 + x_0^2)}{x - x_0} \\
&= \lim_{x \to x_0} (x^2 + xx_0 + x_0^2) = 3x_0^2.
\end{aligned}
$$

It is now evident that the slope will be zero for $3x_0^2 = 0$ or $x_0 = 0$. Also if $x_0 = 0$, then $y_0 = f(x_0) = 2$. Thus the point $(0, 2)$ is a point on the curve where the tangent line is parallel to the x-axis (see Figure 9.1c).

A **normal** to a curve at a given point is a line perpendicular to the tangent line at that point. For instance, in examples 9.1a and b, the y-axis, or the line $x = 0$, is a normal to the curve $y = x^3 + 2$ at the point $(0, 2)$. The normal to this curve at the point $(2, 10)$ has a slope $-1/12$. (Why?)

Example 9.1c. At what point (if any) on the curve $y = \sqrt{x}$ is the normal parallel to the line $4x + y = 4$?

We shall first find a general expression for the slope of the tangent line to this curve. Thus,

$$
\begin{aligned}
m(x_0) &= \lim_{x \to x_0} \frac{f(x) - f(x_0)}{x - x_0} \\
&= \lim_{x \to x_0} \frac{\sqrt{x} - \sqrt{x_0}}{x - x_0} \\
&= \lim_{x \to x_0} \frac{\sqrt{x} - \sqrt{x_0}}{(\sqrt{x} - \sqrt{x_0})(\sqrt{x} + \sqrt{x_0})} \\
&= \lim_{x \to x_0} \frac{1}{\sqrt{x} + \sqrt{x_0}} = \frac{1}{2\sqrt{x_0}}.
\end{aligned}
$$

The slope of the normal at $x = x_0$ is $-2\sqrt{x_0}$ (why?), and the slope of the given line is -4. Hence, at the required point, or

$$-2\sqrt{x} = -4$$

$$\sqrt{x} = 2 \quad \text{and} \quad x = 4.$$

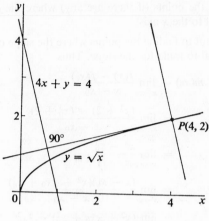

FIGURE 9.1d

Since $y = \sqrt{x}$, we have $y = 2$, and the required point is $(4, 2)$. See Figure 9.1d.

Exercises 9.1

In each of Numbers 1 to 10, find the equation of the tangent and the normal to the given curve at the indicated point.

1. $y = 2x^2 - 5$; $(1, -3)$.
2. $y = x^3 + 2x$; $(0, 0)$.
3. $y = x - 2x^3$; $(1, -1)$.
4. $y = 4/x$; $(2, 2)$.
5. $y = \sqrt{2x}$; $(8, 4)$.

6. $y = 2x^{3/2}$; $(4, 16)$.
7. $y = 1/(2 + x)$; $(-1, 1)$.
8. $y = 3/(2 + x^2)$; $(1, 1)$.
9. $y = 4/\sqrt{x}$; $(4, 2)$.

10. $y = x^{1/3}$; $(8, 2)$. *Hint:* $a - b = (a^{1/3} - b^{1/3})(a^{2/3} + a^{1/3}b^{1/3} + b^{2/3})$.

11. Find the equation of the line that is tangent to the parabola $y = x^2$ and is parallel to the line $y = 4x$.
12. A normal is drawn to the curve $y = x - x^2$ at the point $(1, 0)$. Where does this normal intersect the curve a second time?
13. At what points on the curve $y = x^3 + 2x - 1$ does the normal have a slope $-\frac{1}{5}$?
14. Find the equations of the lines drawn from the origin normal to the parabola $4y = 8x^2 - 9$.
15. Show that the x-intercept of the line tangent to the curve $cy = \sqrt{x}$ is always the negative of the x-coordinate of the point of tangency. Note that c is a constant.
16. A right triangle with its base on the x-axis is formed by the x-axis, a normal to the curve $y = 2\sqrt{x}$, and the ordinate through the point where the normal cuts the curve. Show that the length of the base of the triangle is a constant (independent of the point chosen on the curve).

9.2 THE VELOCITY PROBLEM

A second important problem involving limits is concerned with describing the velocity of a particle moving in a straight line. This is a problem that was of special interest to Isaac Newton.

Suppose a particle moves along a straight line in such a manner that its distance from a fixed point O is given by the formula

$$s(t) = t^2 + 1,$$

where s is measured in feet and t in seconds. When $t = 0$, the particle is 1 foot

FIGURE 9.2a

from O, and when $t = 3$ seconds, the particle is 10 feet from O (see Figure 9.2a). The average velocity for these three seconds is

$$v_{av} = \frac{10 - 1}{3 - 0} = 3 \text{ feet per second.}$$

We have used the fact that the average velocity for a given time interval is the ratio of the net distance traversed to the length of the time interval; that is, it is the average rate of change of distance with respect to time. In general, the average velocity for the preceding motion from time $t = 3$ to any other time t is given by

$$v_{av} = \frac{s(t) - s(3)}{t - 3} = \frac{s(t) - 10}{t - 3}.$$

Let it now be required to find the "velocity at the end of three seconds." The phrase in quotation marks is, of course, meaningless until we define it. It is clearly not possible to put $t = 3$ in the formula for the average velocity, since this would result in a zero denominator. However, we have an intuitive feeling that it is possible to come as close as we please to the "velocity at the end of three seconds" by choosing t sufficiently close to 3. Consequently, meaning can be given to the problem by the following definition.

Definition 9.2a. If a particle moves in a straight line in such a way that its directed distance s from a fixed point on the line is given in terms of the time t by a formula $s = s(t)$, the **velocity** *at any instant* t_1 is

$$v(t_1) .=. \lim_{t \to t_1} \frac{s(t) - s(t_1)}{t - t_1}$$

provided this limit exists. (The velocity $v(t_1)$ is frequently called the **instantaneous** velocity at t_1 and $|v(t_1)|$ is called the **speed** at t_1.)

We are now in a position to complete the original problem. Using the preceding definition, we have

$$v(3) = \lim_{t \to 3} \frac{s(t) - s(3)}{t - 3}$$

$$= \lim_{t \to 3} \frac{(t^2 + 1) - 10}{t - 3} = \lim_{t \to 3} \frac{t^2 - 9}{t - 3}$$

$$= \lim_{t \to 3} \frac{(t - 3)(t + 3)}{t - 3} = \lim_{t \to 3} (t + 3)$$

$$= 6.$$

Thus the instantaneous velocity at $t = 3$ is 6 feet per second in the positive direction.

Example 9.2a. A particle moves along the x-axis so that its distance from the origin is given by $x = 1/t$. Find a formula for the instantaneous velocity at time t_0.

We have

$$v(t_0) = \lim_{t \to t_0} \frac{s(t) - s(t_0)}{t - t_0}$$

$$= \lim_{t \to t_0} \frac{\dfrac{1}{t} - \dfrac{1}{t_0}}{t - t_0}$$

$$= \lim_{t \to t_0} \frac{t_0 - t}{t t_0 (t - t_0)}$$

$$= \lim_{t \to t_0} \frac{-1}{t t_0}$$

$$= -\frac{1}{t_0^2}.$$

What is the significance of the minus sign?

Example 9.2b. A particle moves in a straight line so that its distance s (feet) from the origin at time t (seconds) is given by $s = t^3 - 4t^2$, $t \geq 0$. At what instants is its speed (absolute value of its velocity) 3 feet per second?

We must first find a general expression for the velocity, as follows:

$$v(t_0) = \lim_{t \to t_0} \frac{s(t) - s(t_0)}{t - t_0}$$

$$= \lim_{t \to t_0} \frac{(t^3 - 4t^2) - (t_0^3 - 4t_0^2)}{t - t_0}$$

$$= \lim_{t \to t_0} (t^2 + t t_0 + t_0^2 - 4t - 4t_0)$$

$$= 3t_0^2 - 8t_0.$$

It is now necessary to find the solution set of the equation

$$|3t_0^2 - 8t_0| = 3, \qquad t_0 > 0.$$

This is done by solving the two equations

$$3t_0^2 - 8t_0 = 3 \quad \text{and} \quad 3t_0^2 - 8t_0 = -3.$$

The first of these gives $t_0 = 3$ and the second gives $t_0 = \frac{1}{3}(4 \pm \sqrt{7})$. The student should check to see that the speed is actually 3 feet per second at each of these three times.

Exercises 9.2

In Numbers 1 to 8, the given equation describes the motion of a particle in a straight line. The distance s from the origin is in feet and t is in seconds. Find the velocity at the given instant.

1. $s = 6 + 9t$; $t = 2$.
2. $s = t^2 + 2t$; $t = 3$.
3. $s = 8 - 4t^2$; $t = 3$.
4. $s = t^3 + 2t^2 - 4$; $t = 2$.

5. $s = 5 + 3t - t^3$; $t = 2$.
6. $s = 1/(4t + t^2)$; $t = 2$.
7. $s = \sqrt{2t}$; $t = 8$.
8. $s = 3/t^2$; $t = 2$.

9. A body thrown in a vertical direction near the surface of the earth moves so that its distance from the starting point is given by

$$s = -\tfrac{1}{2}gt^2 + v_0t,$$

where g is the gravitational acceleration (approximately 32 feet per second per second) and v_0 is the initial velocity. (The upward direction has been taken positive here.) Find a formula for the velocity at time t_1.

10. In Number 9, suppose the body is thrown upward with a speed of 96 feet per second. Take $g = 32$ feet per second per second and find at what instants the speed of the body will be 48 feet per second.

11. A particle P moves in a straight line in accordance with the equation $s = 15t - 3t^2$, where s (feet) is the distance from the starting point at time t (seconds). Find the distance of P from the starting point when the velocity is zero.

12. For the particle P of Number 11, what is the velocity of P at the instant it returns to the starting point?

13. A particle P moves in a straight line in accordance with the equation $s = t^3 - 9t^2 + 24t$, where s (feet) is the distance from the origin at time t (seconds). During what periods of time is P moving in a positive direction and during what periods of time is P moving in a negative direction?

14. Two particles P_1 and P_2 start from the same position on a line and move along that line in accordance with the equations

$$s_1 = t^2 - 4t \quad \text{and} \quad s_2 = 3t - t^2,$$

where s_1 and s_2 are in feet and t is in seconds. At what times will the two particles have the same speed?

15. Find the velocities of the particles in Number 14 at the times when they are at the same position on the line.

9.3 THE DERIVATIVE

The reader will certainly have noticed that the limit defining the slope of the curve $y = f(x)$ at x_0,

$$m(x_0) = \lim_{x \to x_0} \frac{f(x) - f(x_0)}{x - x_0},$$

and the limit defining the velocity at t_0 of a point moving on a straight line according to the formula $s = s(t)$,

$$v(t_0) = \lim_{t \to t_0} \frac{s(t) - s(t_0)}{t - t_0},$$

have exactly the same form. Furthermore, since many other problems involve this same type of limit, it is worthwhile to investigate such limits in more detail. In order to avoid any connection with a particular problem, these limits are given a name devoid of such a connotation.

Definition 9.3a. If

$$\lim_{x \to x_0} \frac{f(x) - f(x_0)}{x - x_0}$$

exists, it is called the **derivative** of f at x_0, and is denoted by $f'(x_0)$.

It is frequently somewhat simpler to write $x = x_0 + h$ so that $x \to x_0$ as $h \to 0$. Then the derivative is given in the form

$$f'(x_0) = \lim_{h \to 0} \frac{f(x_0 + h) - f(x_0)}{h}.$$

The fraction on the right side of this definition is called a **difference quotient**. Since the limit of the difference quotient is unique for each value x_0 for which it exists, it may be used to define a new function,

$$f' = \{(x, f'(x))\},$$

called the derivative of f. The formula for $f'(x)$ is, of course, the formula for $f'(x_0)$ with the x_0 replaced by x.

It is instructive to repeat the definitions of the slope of a curve and the velocity in a rectilinear motion in terms of the derivative.

(a) *The slope of the tangent to a curve $y = f(x)$ at the point x_0 is the derivative $f'(x_0)$.*

(b) *The velocity at time $t = t_0$ in a straight line motion where the distance from the origin is $s = f(t)$ is the derivative $f'(t_0)$.*

Velocity may be interpreted as a *rate of change* of distance with respect to time, and if $s = f(t)$ describes a straight line motion, this rate of change at any instant t_0 is represented by $f'(t_0)$. In a similar way we are often interested in a rate of change of one quantity with respect to some other quantity. Examples are the rate of change of the area of a circle with respect to its diameter, the rate of change of the length of a metal rod with respect to its temperature, and the rate of solution of a chemical in a solvent with respect to the time.

Such problems can frequently be analyzed in a manner exactly like that used for the tangent and the velocity problems. Thus, if u is given in terms of v by a formula

$$u = f(v)$$

we can discuss the rate of change of u with respect to v.

The average rate of change of u with respect to v from $v = v_1$ to $v = v_1 + h$ is

$$\frac{f(v_1 + h) - f(v_1)}{h}.$$

If this difference quotient has a limit as $h \to 0$, this limit meets our intuitive conception of an instantaneous rate of change of u with respect to v. Accordingly we make the following

Definition 9.3b. The *instantaneous rate of change* of $f(x)$ with respect to x at x_1 is the derivative $f'(x_1)$, whenever this derivative exists.

Example 9.3a. Find a formula for the instantaneous rate of change of the area of a circle with respect to its radius.

The formula

$$A = f(r) = \pi r^2$$

gives the area of a circle as a function of its radius. This example requires us to find $f'(r)$. Thus,

$$f'(r) = \lim_{h \to 0} \frac{f(r + h) - f(r)}{h}$$

$$= \lim_{h \to 0} \frac{\pi[(r + h)^2 - r^2]}{h}$$

$$= \lim_{h \to 0} \pi(2r + h) = 2\pi r.$$

Notice that the answer is exactly the formula for the circumference of the circle. In this connection, consider the very plausible fact that the increase in the area of a circle of radius r caused by increasing the radius by a small amount h is approximately $2\pi rh$.

In physics, the acceleration of a particle moving in a straight line is defined to be the instantaneous time rate of change of the velocity. This means that if the velocity is given by

$$v = v(t),$$

then the *acceleration at time* $t = t_1$ *is* $v'(t_1)$.

Example 9.3b. In Example 9.2b, we found the velocity in a certain straight line motion to be given by

$$v(t) = 3t^2 - 8t.$$

What is the acceleration at the end of 3 seconds?

We first calculate $v'(t)$ as follows:

$$v'(t) = \lim_{h \to 0} \frac{v(t + h) - v(t)}{h}$$

$$= \lim_{h \to 0} \frac{3(t + h)^2 - 8(t + h) - 3t^2 + 8t}{h}$$

$$\doteq \lim_{h \to 0} (6t + 3h - 8) = 6t - 8.$$

Therefore, $v'(3) = 18 - 8 = 10$ feet per second per second.

Exercises 9.3

1. Find the rate of change of the area of a square with respect to a side when the side is 5 inches long.

2. A metal disk expands when heated. Determine the rate of change of the area of a face of the disk with respect to the diameter when the diameter is 6 inches.

3. A right circular cylinder has a fixed height of 8 inches. Find the rate of change of the volume with respect to the radius when the radius is 4 inches.

4. Determine the rate of change of the volume of a spherical balloon with respect to the radius when the radius is 5 inches.

5. A cone has a fixed radius of 3 inches. Find the rate of change of the volume with respect to the height when the height is 4 inches and when the height is 8 inches.

6. The horsepower that can be transmitted by a shaft is proportional to the cube of the diameter of the shaft if the speed is constant. Find the rate of change of the horsepower with respect to the diameter when the diameter is 7 inches.

7. An engineering student discovered that the radius of a melting snowball was $(4 - 0.04t)$ inches, where t is the time in minutes. Find the rate of change of the volume with respect to time at the end of 60 minutes.

8. The formula $Q = a + bT + cT^2$, where a, b, and c are constants, determines the amount of heat Q in calories needed to raise the temperature of 1 gram of water from $0°$ to $T°C$. If the specific heat at any temperature is the rate of change of Q with respect to T at that temperature, find a formula for the specific heat at $20°C$.

9. If the equation of motion of a point along a straight line is $s = t^3 - 3t^2 + 7$ (s feet, t seconds), find the acceleration at the points where the speed is zero.

10. The pressure and volume of a gas at constant temperature are connected by the relation $pv = c$, where p is the pressure, v the volume, and c a constant. Determine the rate of change of p with respect to v when $v = v_1$.

11. Find the point (or points) on the parabola $y = x^2 + 2x$ where the rate of change with respect to x of the slope of the normal is 2 per linear unit.

12. If the equation of motion of a particle along a straight line is $s = 3t^2 - t^3$ (s feet, t seconds), find the speed at the point where the acceleration is zero. For what interval of time is v increasing?

13. If the radius and altitude of a cone are always equal, find the rate of change of the volume with respect to the radius.

14. A particle moving on a straight line is at distance $s = t^3 + 4t^2 - 1$ from the origin, where s is in feet and t in seconds. Find the speed when the acceleration is 14 feet per second per second.

9.4 THE DERIVATIVE OF A POLYNOMIAL

In order to facilitate the use of the derivative, we must develop formulas for the derivatives of the commonly occurring functions. In this section we shall show how this can be done for a power function and for a polynomial.

It will also be convenient to introduce another widely used notation for the derivative, namely,

$$D_x f(x) .=. f'(x).$$

Since a polynomial $P(x)$ is a sum of the type

$$a_0 x^n + a_1 x^{n-1} + \cdots + a_n,$$

the derivative will be built up by first considering derivatives of the separate terms and showing that $P'(x)$ is exactly the sum of these derivatives. This procedure results in the following basic theorems, in which it is assumed that all the functions involved actually possess derivatives. A function that possesses a derivative at a point is said to be **differentiable** at that point.

Theorem 9.4a. The derivative of a constant function is zero:

$$D_x c = 0.$$

PROOF: If $f(x) = c$, then $f(x + h) = c$ and

$$\lim_{h \to 0} \frac{f(x + h) - f(x)}{h} = \lim_{h \to 0} 0 = 0.$$

Notice that this agrees with the fact that a line $y = c$ has zero slope.

Theorem 9.4b. The derivative of a variable with respect to itself is unity:

$$D_x x = 1.$$

PROOF: If $f(x) = x$, then $f(x + h) = x + h$ and

$$\lim_{h \to 0} \frac{f(x + h) - f(x)}{h} = \lim_{h \to 0} \frac{h}{h} = 1.$$

Notice again the agreement with the graphical representation of the equation $y = x$ which is a line of slope 1.

Theorem 9.4c. The derivative of a constant times a differentiable function is the constant times the derivative of the function:

$$D_x[cf(x)] = c\, D_x f(x).$$

PROOF:
$$D_x[cf(x)] = \lim_{h \to 0} \frac{cf(x + h) - cf(x)}{h}$$

$$= c \lim_{h \to 0} \frac{f(x + h) - f(x)}{h}$$

$$= c\, D_x f(x).$$

Theorem 9.4d. The derivative of $F(x) .=. xf(x)$, where f is continuous and differentiable, is given by

$$D_x[xf(x)] = x\, D_x f(x) + f(x).$$

PROOF: $\displaystyle \lim_{h \to 0} \frac{F(x+h) - F(x)}{h} = \lim_{h \to 0} \frac{(x+h)f(x+h) - xf(x)}{h}$

$$= \lim_{h \to 0} \left\{ x \left[\frac{f(x+h) - f(x)}{h} \right] + f(x+h) \right\}$$

$$= xf'(x) + f(x).$$

By applying Theorem 9.4d with $f(x) = x$, we get

$$D_x x^2 = D_x(x \cdot x) = x \cdot 1 + x = 2x,$$

and again, by Theorem 9.4d,

$$D_x x^3 = D_x(x \cdot x^2) = x \cdot D_x x^2 + x^2 = x \cdot 2x + x^2 = 3x^2.$$

In each of these derivatives, the final coefficient is the original exponent, and the final exponent is obtainable by subtracting 1 from the original exponent. This pattern for the coefficient and exponent suggests the general result in

Theorem 9.4e. $D_x x^n = nx^{n-1}, \qquad n \in \mathfrak{N}.$

PROOF: It is easy to prove this result by mathematical induction. The formula is certainly correct for $n = 1$ since it gives

$$D_x x = 1x^0 = 1,$$

in agreement with Theorem 9.4b. Now suppose that the theorem is true for $n = k$; that is,

$$D_x x^k = kx^{k-1}.$$

Then

$$D_x x^{k+1} = D_x[x \cdot x^k],$$

which, upon application of Theorem 9.4d, becomes

$$x \cdot kx^{k-1} + x^k = kx^k + x^k$$
$$= (k+1)x^k.$$

This completes the proof by induction and the formula has been shown correct for all $n \in \mathfrak{N}$.

As illustrations of the preceding theorem, we may write

$$D_x x^{10} = 10x^9, \quad D_x x^{81} = 81x^{80}, \quad \text{and so on.}$$

Furthermore, by the use of Theorem 9.4c, we have

$$D_x(5x^{10}) = 50x^9, \quad D_x(-20x^{81}) = -1620x^{80}, \quad \text{and so on.}$$

These examples show that we can write by inspection the derivatives of the separate terms of a polynomial. The next theorem shows how to combine these separate derivatives.

Theorem 9.4f. If f and g are two differentiable functions, then the derivative of their sum is the sum of their derivatives; that is,

$$D_x[f(x) + g(x)] = D_x f(x) + D_x g(x).$$

PROOF: Write $F(x) = f(x) + g(x)$. Then

$$F'(x) = \lim_{h \to 0} \frac{F(x + h) - F(x)}{h}$$

$$= \lim_{h \to 0} \frac{f(x + h) + g(x + h) - f(x) - g(x)}{h}$$

$$= \lim_{h \to 0} \frac{f(x + h) - f(x)}{h} + \lim_{h \to 0} \frac{g(x + h) - g(x)}{h}$$

$$= f'(x) + g'(x).$$

Theorem 9.4f is easily extended to the sum of any finite number of different functions. This result, along with the other theorems so far obtained, allows the derivative of a polynomial to be written down essentially by inspection. Thus,

$$
\begin{aligned}
D_x P(x) &= D_x(a_0 x^n + a_1 x^{n-1} + \cdots + a_{n-1} x + a_n) \\
&= D_x(a_0 x^n) + D_x(a_1 x^{n-1}) + \cdots + D_x(a_{n-1} x) + D_x a_n \\
&= a_0 D_x x^n + a_1 D_x x^{n-1} + \cdots + a_{n-1} D_x x + D_x a_n \\
&= a_0 n x^{n-1} + a_1(n - 1) x^{n-2} + \cdots + a_{n-1} + 0 \\
&= n a_0 x^{n-1} + (n - 1) a_1 x^{n-2} + \cdots + a_{n-1}.
\end{aligned}
$$

Example 9.4a. Find $D_x(5x^3 - 6x^2 + 10x - 7)$.

Using the preceding result, we have

$$D_x(5x^3 - 6x^2 + 10x - 7) = 15x^2 - 12x + 10.$$

In Theorem 9.4e the formula for the derivative of a power was established for positive integral powers only. The formula itself holds, however, for all real exponents, a fact which will be demonstrated after a consideration of the logarithm function later in our work. For the present, we shall accept the following theorem without proof.

Theorem 9.4g. $\qquad D_x x^k = k x^{k-1}, \qquad k \in \mathcal{R}.$

Example 9.4b. Find $D_t\left(\sqrt{t} + \dfrac{1}{t}\right)$.

We write

$$D_t\left(\sqrt{t} + \frac{1}{t}\right) = D_t t^{1/2} + D_t t^{-1}$$

$$= \tfrac{1}{2} t^{-1/2} + (-1) t^{-2}$$

$$= \frac{1}{2\sqrt{t}} - \frac{1}{t^2}.$$

As a verification, the student should compare this result with those in Examples 9.1c and 9.2a.

Exercies 9.4

In Numbers 1 to 16, find the derivative by inspection.

1. $f(x) = 5x^2 - 7x^3$.
2. $f(t) = b_0 + b_1 t + b_2 t^2 + b_3 t^3$.
3. $f(x) = 2x^2 + 3x + 4$.
4. $G(u) = (u + 1)^2$.
5. $f(y) = y^3 + 2y^2 - 1$.
6. $g(\theta) = 3 - 5\theta^3 + \theta^4$.
7. $f(t) = (t - 1)^3$.
8. $F(y) = (y + 1)/\sqrt{y}$.
9. $F(x) = 1/(2x^2)$.
10. $U(z) = z^2 + 2z^{-4}$.

11. $g(x) = 1/\sqrt{3x}$.
12. $f(x) = 2x^{3/2} + 5x^{-3/5}$.
13. $W(t) = \dfrac{1}{t} - \dfrac{3}{t^2} + \dfrac{1}{3t^3}$.
14. $Y(x) = \sqrt[5]{5x} + \dfrac{5}{\sqrt[5]{5x}}$.
15. $H(u) = u^{-3/2} + a^{-3/2}$.
16. $G(x) = 2x^{-\pi} + x^{\sqrt{2}} + b^{-1/2}$.

In Numbers 17 to 20, find (a) the slope of the tangent line and (b) the rate of change of the slope with respect to x for the given value of x.

17. $y = x^2 + 2x$; $x = 0$.
18. $y = 5x^3 - 3x^5$; $x = 1$.
19. $y = 1/\sqrt{x} - 4/(x\sqrt{x})$; $x = 4$.
20. $y = \dfrac{1 + x}{x^2}$; $x = -1$.

In Numbers 21 to 24, s is distance in feet from the origin and t is time in seconds. The equations are for straight line motion. Find the distance, velocity, and acceleration at the indicated times.

21. $s = 16t - 16t^2$; $t = 0$ and $t = \frac{1}{2}$.
22. $s = t^4 - 4t^3 + 6t^2 - 4t$; $t = 1$.
23. $s = 2\sqrt{t}$; $t = 1$ and $t = 4$.
24. $s = 9 - 9/\sqrt{3t}$; $t = 3$.

25. Find the equations of the tangents to the curve $y = x^3 - 9x$ that are parallel to the x-axis.
26. Find the point on the curve $y = x^2 + 4x + 7$ where the angle of inclination of the normal is $\pi/6$.
27. Find the equations of the tangents to the curve $y = x^2 + 4x$ that pass through the point $(-1, -4)$.
28. Show that the tangent to the curve $xy = 1$ forms with the coordinate axes a triangle of constant area; that is, the area does not depend on the point of tangency.
29. Find the rate of change of the volume of a spherical balloon with respect to the surface area.
30. Obtain a formula for $D_x(ax + b)^n$, where a and b are constants and $n \in \mathfrak{N}$. *Hint:* You can do this easily for $n = 1, 2, 3$. Then make a conjecture and prove it by mathematical induction.
31. It was found experimentally that the quantity of heat Q (calories) required to raise the temperature of 1 gram of water from 0°C to t°C in the range 0°C to 100°C is given by

$$Q = t + 2 \cdot 10^{-5} t^2 + 3 \cdot 10^{-7} t^3.$$

The specific heat at any temperature is the rate of increase of the quantity of heat per degree rise in temperature. Find the specific heat of water at 50°C.

32. The kinetic energy E of a moving mass is given by the formula $E = \frac{1}{2}mv^2$, where m is the mass ($m = W/g$) and v is the velocity. A weight $W = 10$ pounds moves in a straight line according to the formula $s = 32t - 16t^2$, where s is in feet and t in seconds. Find the time rate of change of the kinetic energy when $t = 2$. Use $g = 32$ feet per second per second and give the units of your answer.

33. By repeated application of Theorem 9.4d, show that

$$D_x[x^n f(x)] = x^n f'(x) + n x^{n-1} f(x), \qquad n \in \mathfrak{N}.$$

9.5 THE INVERSE DERIVATIVE

It is frequently necessary to solve problems such as the tangent problem or the velocity problem in reverse. That is, a formula for the slope may be known and it is required to find a formula for the functional values, or a formula for the velocity may be known and it is required to find the distance. The simplest problems of this kind are essentially equivalent to the following: given $f(x)$, find a function F such that $F'(x) = f(x)$.

Definition 9.5a. An **inverse derivative** of a function f is a function F such that $F' = f$. The value of F at x is designated by $D_x^{-1} f(x)$.

Having seen, for instance, that $D_x x^2 = 2x$, we know that one inverse derivative of $2x$ is x^2. However, $D_x(x^2 + 3) = D_x(x^2 - 10) = D_x(x^2 + C) = 2x$, so that it would be correct to say

$$D_x^{-1}(2x) = x^2 + C,$$

where C is any constant. A proof that there is no other continuous function having the derivative formula $2x$ will appear in a later chapter when we show that two functions with the same derivative on an interval can differ only by a constant on that interval.

For the present, the truth of the theorem is to be assumed. We shall confine our attention here to the inverse derivative of a power and of a polynomial. Since $D_x(x^{n+1}) = (n+1)x^n$, it follows that

$$D_x\left(\frac{x^{n+1}}{n+1}\right) = x^n, \qquad n \neq -1,$$

or that

$$D_x^{-1}(x^n) = \frac{x^{n+1}}{n+1} + C, \qquad n \in \mathfrak{R}, \, n \neq -1.$$

(The exceptional case, $n = -1$, of the last formula is quite important, but must be postponed for consideration until we have studied some additional functions.)

As illustrations of the use of the formula, we have

$$D_x^{-1} x^5 = \frac{x^6}{6} + C,$$

$$D_x^{-1} x^{-3/2} = -2x^{-1/2} + C,$$

and

$$D_x^{-1}\left(\frac{1}{x^2}\right) = D_x^{-1} x^{-2} = -x^{-1} + C.$$

The reader should check any proposed inverse derivative by finding its derivative which must, of course, agree with the given formula.

Example 9.5a. Find $D_x^{-1}(x^3 + 5x^2 + 7x + 8)$.

We have

$$D_x^{-1}(x^3 + 5x^2 + 7x + 8) = \frac{x^4}{4} + \frac{5x^3}{3} + \frac{7x^2}{2} + 8x + C,$$

as may easily be verified by differentiation of the result.

Since the general form for the inverse derivative of a function involves an arbitrary constant C, the inverse derivative may be interpreted as a one-parameter family of functions. The graphs of these functions are called **integral curves.** If information is given that can be used to determine a particular value of C, then a particular member of the family is determined. A given condition of this type is called an "initial" condition. A problem in which a derivative and an initial condition are given is called an **initial value problem.** The following examples illustrate this type of problem.

Example 9.5b. The slope, m, of a curve at any point is given by the formula $m(x) = 2x - 2$. Find the equation of the curve if it passes through the point $(3, 2)$.

If the equation of the curve is $y = f(x)$, then

$$f'(x) = 2x - 2$$

and

$$f(x) = D_x^{-1}(2x - 2) = x^2 - 2x + c.$$

The curve must pass through the point $(3, 2)$ so the coordinates of this point must satisfy the equation. Thus,

$$2 = 3^2 - 2(3) + c$$

or

$$-1 = c.$$

Therefore, the equation of the curve is

$$y = x^2 - 2x - 1.$$

Example 9.5c. A body is thrown upward from the ground with an initial velocity of v_0 feet per second. If the acceleration due to gravity (considered constant) is g feet per second per second, find a formula for the distance, s, from the starting point at the end of t seconds.

Since velocity and acceleration are vectors, we must consider direction as well as magnitude. If upward directed distances are considered positive, then the initial velocity is positive and the gravitational acceleration is negative. Thus,

$$D_t v = -g$$

and

$$v = -D_t^{-1}g = -gt + c_1.$$

Furthermore,

$$v = D_t s,$$

so that

$$s = D_t^{-1}v = -\tfrac{1}{2}gt^2 + c_1 t + c_2.$$

Values for c_1 and c_2 may be determined from the initial conditions that $v = v_0$ and $s = 0$ when $t = 0$. Hence, we have

$$v_0 = 0 + c_1,$$

and

$$0 = 0 + 0 + c_2$$

Thus, $c_1 = v_0$ and $c_2 = 0$, so that

$$s = -\tfrac{1}{2}gt^2 + v_0t.$$

The preceding problems are typical of many initial value problems in which the value of the function and/or the derivative at certain points are known.

Note: An alternative notation which is quite commonly used for the inverse derivative is defined by

$$\int f(x)\, dx = D_x^{-1}f(x).$$

Exercises 9.5

In Numbers 1 to 15, find the indicated inverse derivative.

1. $D_x^{-1}(2x^3 - 3x^2 - 2x + 7)$.
2. $D_s^{-1}(5 + 4s^2 - 5s^3)$.

3. $D_x^{-1}\left(\dfrac{1}{2x^3} + \dfrac{3}{x^2} + 4\right)$.

4. $D_r^{-1}\left(5 - \dfrac{7}{2r^2} - \dfrac{1}{3r^3}\right)$.

5. $D_s^{-1}\left(\sqrt{2s} + \dfrac{1}{\sqrt{2s}}\right)$.

6. $D_x^{-1}\left(\sqrt[3]{x^2} - \dfrac{1}{\sqrt[3]{4x^2}}\right)$.

7. $D_x^{-1}(3 + 2x^2)^2$.
8. $D_t^{-1}(3t^3 + 2)^3$.

9. $D_x^{-1}\left(\dfrac{x^4 + 3x^3 + 4x^2 + 1}{x^2}\right)$.

10. $D_s^{-1}\left(\dfrac{s^4 + 3s^3 + 1}{\sqrt{s}}\right)$.

11. $D_t^{-1}\left(\dfrac{1 - 8t^3}{\sqrt[3]{t}}\right)$.

12. $D_x^{-1}[(2x^2 - 3)(x^3 + 1)]$.
13. $D_s^{-1}[s^2(2s^3 - 1)^3]$.

14. $D_t^{-1}\left[\dfrac{(1 - 2t^2)^2}{\sqrt{t}}\right]$.

15. $D_x^{-1}[\sqrt{x}(1 - 2x^2)^3]$.

In Numbers 16 to 21, find the equation of the curve that has the given slope and passes through the indicated point.

16. $D_x y = 3x - 2$; $(2, 2)$.
17. $D_x y = 6x^2 + 4x + 3$; $(-1, 1)$.
18. $D_x y = x - x^2$; $(2, -1)$.
19. $D_x y = x^3 - 4x + 1$; $(-2, 3)$.

20. $D_x y = 1 + \dfrac{1}{x^2}$; $(2, 3)$.
21. $D_x y = \sqrt{2x}$; $(2, 4)$.

22. A particle starts from rest at a point 15 feet from the origin. If it moves in a straight line away from the origin with a speed of $4t^3$ feet per second, at what time will the particle be 96 feet from the origin?

23. A particle starts from the origin with an initial velocity of 10 feet per second. If the particle moves away in a straight line with an acceleration of $2t^2 + 3t + 4$ feet per second per second, develop a formula for its distance from the origin at the end of t seconds.

24. Find the equation $y = f(x)$ of a curve that is tangent to the line $x + y = 4$ if $f'(x) = 2x + 3$.
25. If a ball is thrown vertically upward with an initial velocity of 64 feet per second from the top of a tower 100 feet high, find
    (a) the greatest height reached, and
    (b) the velocity with which the ball strikes the ground.
    Use the value $g = 32$ feet per second per second.
26. If a ball is thrown vertically upward with a velocity of v_0 feet per second from the top of a tower h feet high, develop a formula for the distance between the ball and the ground at time t.
27. The slope of a curve at each point is proportional to the square of the abscissa of the point. Find the equation of the curve if it passes through the point (2, 2) with a slope of 1.
28. The rate of change of the slope of a curve at each point is proportional to $1/x^3$. Find the equation of the curve if it passes through the points (1, 0) and $(-1, 0)$ with a slope of 1 at $(-1, 0)$.

Summary of Chapter 9

---

(1) The tangent problem and the velocity problem are important primitive illustrations of the fundamental ideas leading to the concept of the derivative of a function. A good understanding of the ideas illustrated by these two problems is essential to the succeeding material (Sections 9.1, 9.2).

(2) An understanding of the definition of the derivative of a function at a point in terms of the difference quotient and the interpretation of the derivative as an instantaneous rate of change are essential to an understanding of differential calculus (Section 9.3).

The reader must also have a thorough understanding of

(3) the meaning of "differentiability at a point" (Section 9.4);
(4) the theorems on derivatives (Section 9.4);
(5) the development of the derivative of a polynomial and the formula for the derivative of a power (Section 9.4);
(6) the inverse derivative (Section 9.5);
(7) the concept of an integral curve (Section 9.5);
(8) the meaning of "initial value problem" (Section 9.5).

Chapter 10 Theorems on Derivatives

10.1 CONTINUITY AND DIFFERENTIABILITY

In Chapter 9 it was shown how the derivative of a power function or a polynomial function can be found more efficiently by the use of special formulas than by the direct application of the definition of the derivative. In this chapter, we shall develop additional theorems and formulas in order to increase the efficiency with which the derivatives of more complicated functions can be found. There will also be introduced some new concepts that contribute toward a better understanding of the derivative and its role in mathematical analysis.

The reader should recall that a function is said to be differentiable at x_0 if its derivative exists at x_0. If the derivative exists at all points of an open interval, then f is said to be *differentiable on the interval*, and the value of the derivative at a point x in the interval is denoted by $f'(x)$. As the reader may have observed earlier, a function f may fail to have a derivative at some points of its domain. Consequently, the domain of f' is always a subset of the domain of f.

The assertion that a function is continuous over an interval means that the function has certain properties that are illustrated graphically by a kind of "connectedness." As we shall see later, the assertion that a function f is differentiable over an interval is related to certain properties of "smoothness" of the graph of f. Therefore, it is appropriate to ask if there is some connection between the continuity and differentiability of f at a point x_0. An answer to this question is contained in

Theorem 10.1a. If a function f is differentiable at a point x_0, then f is continuous at x_0.

PROOF: In order to show that f is continuous at x_0, it is sufficient to show that $\lim_{x \to x_0} [f(x) - f(x_0)] = 0$. We have

$$\lim_{x \to x_0} [f(x) - f(x_0)] = \lim_{x \to x_0} \left[\frac{f(x) - f(x_0)}{x - x_0} (x - x_0) \right].$$

Since f has a derivative at x_0, the limit defining $f'(x_0)$ exists; in fact,

$$\lim_{x \to x_0} \frac{f(x) - f(x_0)}{x - x_0} = f'(x_0).$$

Thus,

$$\lim_{x \to x_0} [f(x) - f(x_0)] = f'(x_0) \cdot 0 = 0,$$

which was to be shown.

We shall soon see that the converse of the preceding theorem is *not* true. That is, a function may be continuous at a point x_0 without being differentiable there. In this connection it is useful to have the notion of a *one-sided derivative*, which is obtained by considering a one-sided limit of the difference quotient, as in

Definition 10.1a. For a continuous function f defined at $x = a$, the *derivative from the right* is denoted by $f'_+(a)$ and

$$f'_+(a) .=. \lim_{x \to a^+} \frac{f(x) - f(a)}{x - a}.$$

Similarly, the *derivative from the left* is denoted by $f'_-(a)$ and

$$f'_-(a) .=. \lim_{x \to a^-} \frac{f(x) - f(a)}{x - a}.$$

Theorem 10.1b. If the function f is continuous at $x = a$, then

$$f'(a) \text{ exists} \Leftrightarrow f'_-(a) = f'_+(a).$$

PROOF: This follows immediately from the definitions, and details are left to the student.

Example 10.1a. Investigate the differentiability at $x = 0$ of the function

$$\{(x, y): y = x^{3/2}, 0 \leq x\}.$$

Since only the derivative from the right needs to be investigated, we have

$$f'_+(0) = \lim_{x \to 0^+} \frac{f(x) - f(0)}{x - 0}$$

$$= \lim_{x \to 0^+} \frac{x^{3/2} - 0}{x - 0}$$

$$= \lim_{x \to 0^+} x^{1/2} = 0.$$

Thus the function has a derivative from the right at $x = 0$, the value of this derivative being zero. What does this mean for the graph of f?

It should now be clear that if a function f is differentiable on a closed interval $a \leq x \leq b$, then f' exists on the open interval $a < x < b$ and $f'_+(a)$ and $f'_-(b)$ also exist. For example, the function defined by

$$f(x) = x^2, \quad 0 \leq x \leq 2,$$

is differentiable on its entire domain. In fact, the reader may easily obtain

$$f'(x) = 2x, \quad 0 \leq x \leq 2,$$

It is now possible to show by means of a simple example that the converse of Theorem 10.1a is not true—that is, to show that continuity of a function is not sufficient to guarantee differentiability.

Example 10.1b. Investigate the differentiability at $x = 0$ of the function defined by $f(x) = |x|$.

It is a direct consequence of the definition of $|x|$ that f is continuous for all real x. Since

$$|x| .=. \begin{cases} -x & \text{for } x < 0, \\ x & \text{for } x \geq 0, \end{cases}$$

a good procedure is to consider the one-sided derivatives at $x = 0$. Thus,

$$f'_-(0) = \lim_{x \to 0^-} \frac{f(x) - f(0)}{x - 0}$$

$$= \lim_{x \to 0^-} \frac{-x - 0}{x - 0} = -1,$$

and

$$f'_+(0) = \lim_{x \to 0^+} \frac{f(x) - f(0)}{x - 0}$$

$$= \lim_{x \to 0^+} \frac{x - 0}{x - 0} = 1.$$

Therefore, by Theorem 10.1b, $f'(0)$ does not exist. The reader should sketch the graph of $y = |x|$ to see that the result of this problem is geometrically obvious. (Why?)

Exercises 10.1

In each of Numbers 1 to 6, state the domain of f and the domain of f', where $f .=. \{(x, y)\}$.

1. $y = x^2 - 5x$.
2. $y = x^{-1}$.
3. $y = \sqrt{x}$.
4. $y = \sqrt{-x}$.
5. $y = |x|/x$.
6. $y = x - [\![x]\!]$.

In each of Numbers 7 to 13, find the points where $f'_-(x) \neq f'_+(x)$. Is the function continuous at each of these points?

7. $f(x) = |x - 1|$.

8. $f(x) = \begin{cases} 0, & x < 0. \\ x^2, & x \geq 0. \end{cases}$

9. $f(x) = \begin{cases} -x, & x < 0, \\ x^3, & x \geq 0. \end{cases}$

10. $f(x) = \begin{cases} 1 + x, & x < 0, \\ x, & x \geq 0. \end{cases}$

11. $f(x) = 2 + |x + 3|$.

12. $f(x) = \begin{cases} x^2, & x > 0, \\ -x^2, & x \leq 0. \end{cases}$

13. $f(x) = \begin{cases} x^2, & x > 0, \\ \sqrt{-x}, & x \leq 0. \end{cases}$

14. Prove Theorem 10.1b.

★15. Consider a set of functions with domain $0 \leq x \leq 1$, whose graphs are shown in Figure 10.1a. The graph of each of $f_2, f_3, \ldots$ is obtained from the preceding one by "folding" the figure about a line through the midpoints of the sides of the triangles. (This is the dashed line shown in the graphs of f_1, f_2, and f_3.)

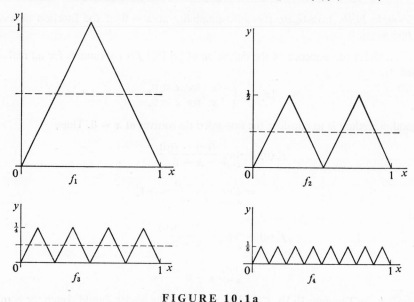

FIGURE 10.1a

(a) Is f_1 differentiable everywhere? If not, where is it differentiable?

(b) At what points does f_n fail to be differentiable? Is f_n continuous everywhere?

(c) Imagine letting $n \to \infty$, so that $f_n \to F$. Is F continuous? differentiable?

10.2 FURTHER GENERAL THEOREMS ON DERIVATIVES

In this section we shall derive general formulas for the derivatives of products and quotients of functions, and we shall introduce a somewhat more convenient notation for difference quotients.

The standard difference notation for the number $x_2 - x_1$ is Δx_1, read "delta x_1." Thus,

$$\Delta x_1 .=. x_2 - x_1,$$

so that Δx_1 must be regarded as a single symbol; the Δ is *not* a multiplier of x_1. It is helpful to think of Δx_1 as the change in x from x_1 to x_2. In a similar manner, the change in y from y_1 to y_2 is given by

$$\Delta y_1 = y_2 - y_1,$$

If $y = f(x)$, then

$$\Delta y_1 = \Delta f(x_1) = f(x_2) - f(x_1) = f(x_1 + \Delta x_1) - f(x_1).$$

In terms of the difference notation, we may rewrite the definition of the derivative at x_1 as follows:

$$f'(x_1) = \lim_{\Delta x_1 \to 0} \frac{\Delta f(x_1)}{\Delta x_1} = \lim_{\Delta x_1 \to 0} \frac{f(x_1 + \Delta x_1) - f(x_1)}{\Delta x_1}.$$

Since x_1 denotes any point in the domain of f, the subscripts may be dropped, so that the general formula for the derivative reads

$$f'(x) = \lim_{\Delta x \to 0} \frac{\Delta f(x)}{\Delta x} = \lim_{\Delta x \to 0} \frac{f(x + \Delta x) - f(x)}{\Delta x}.$$

Furthermore, if $y = f(x)$, so that $\Delta y = f(x + \Delta x) - f(x)$, then

$$D_x y = \lim_{\Delta x \to 0} \frac{\Delta y}{\Delta x}.$$

It must, of course, be understood that Δy is the y difference, or the change in the y value, corresponding to the x difference, Δx. The convenience of the difference notation will appear in the next theorems.

Theorem 10.2a. Let f and g be differentiable functions. Then, in the domain common to f' and g',

$$D_x[f(x)g(x)] = f(x)\, D_x g(x) + g(x)\, D_x f(x).$$

PROOF: Write $\qquad u = f(x), \quad v = g(x), \quad y = uv.$

Then
$$\Delta u = f(x + \Delta x) - f(x)$$

and
$$\Delta v = g(x + \Delta x) - g(x).$$

We also have
$$\Delta y = (u + \Delta u)(v + \Delta v) - uv$$
$$= u\,\Delta v + v\,\Delta u + \Delta u\,\Delta v$$

and
$$\frac{\Delta y}{\Delta x} = u\,\frac{\Delta v}{\Delta x} + v\,\frac{\Delta u}{\Delta x} + \frac{\Delta u}{\Delta x}\,\Delta v,$$

so that
$$D_x y = \lim_{\Delta x \to 0} \left(u\,\frac{\Delta v}{\Delta x} + v\,\frac{\Delta u}{\Delta x} + \frac{\Delta u}{\Delta x}\,\Delta v \right).$$

Since f and g were assumed to be differentiable,

$$\lim_{\Delta x \to 0} \frac{\Delta u}{\Delta x} = D_x u, \quad \lim_{\Delta x \to 0} \frac{\Delta v}{\Delta x} = D_x v,$$

and
$$\lim_{\Delta x \to 0} \Delta v = \lim_{\Delta x \to 0} \left[g(x + \Delta x) - g(x) \right] = 0.$$

Hence,
$$D_x y = u \lim_{\Delta x \to 0} \frac{\Delta v}{\Delta x} + v \lim_{\Delta x \to 0} \frac{\Delta u}{\Delta x} + \left(\lim_{\Delta x \to 0} \frac{\Delta u}{\Delta x} \right) \left(\lim_{\Delta x \to 0} \Delta v \right)$$
$$= u\, D_x v + v\, D_x u,$$

which is the required formula.

As an aid to the reader in remembering the content of Theorem 10.2a, we restate it as

The Product Rule for Differentiation. The derivative of the product of two functions is the first function times the derivative of the second, plus the second function times the derivative of the first. Symbolically,

$$(fg)' = f'g + fg'.$$

Example 10.2a. Find $D_x y$ if

$$y = (x^2 + 5)(x^3 - 9x + 2).$$

We use Theorem 10.2a to obtain

$$\begin{aligned}
D_x y &= (x^2 + 5) D_x(x^3 - 9x + 2) + (x^3 - 9x + 2) D_x(x^2 + 5) \\
&= (x^2 + 5)(3x^2 - 9) + (x^3 - 9x + 2)(2x) \\
&= 5x^4 - 12x^2 + 4x - 45.
\end{aligned}$$

The reader should check this by first multiplying out the expression for y and then finding the derivative of the resulting polynomial.

Example 10.2b. Find $D_t s$ if $s = (t^2 + 2t)\sqrt{t}$.

Writing $s = (t^2 + 2t)t^{1/2}$, we have

$$\begin{aligned}
D_t s &= (t^2 + 2t)D_t t^{1/2} + t^{1/2} D_t(t^2 + 2t) \\
&= (t^2 + 2t)\tfrac{1}{2}t^{-1/2} + t^{1/2}(2t + 2) \\
&= \tfrac{5}{2}t^{3/2} + 3t^{1/2}.
\end{aligned}$$

Again, this result can be checked by first multiplying out the factors of s and then finding $D_t s$.

Theorem 10.2b. Let f and g be differentiable functions. Then, in the domain common to f', g', and f/g,

$$D_x \left[\frac{f(x)}{g(x)} \right] = \frac{g(x) D_x f(x) - f(x) D_x g(x)}{[g(x)]^2}.$$

PROOF: Write $u = f(x)$, $v = g(x)$, and $y = u/v$.

Then,

$$\Delta y = \frac{u + \Delta u}{v + \Delta v} - \frac{u}{v}$$

$$= \frac{v\Delta u - u\Delta v}{v(v + \Delta v)},$$

$$\frac{\Delta y}{\Delta x} = \frac{v\dfrac{\Delta u}{\Delta x} - u\dfrac{\Delta v}{\Delta x}}{v(v + \Delta v)}.$$

As in the proof of Theorem 10.2a, the differentiability of f and g implies that

$$\lim_{\Delta x \to 0} \frac{\Delta u}{\Delta x} = D_x u, \quad \lim_{\Delta x \to 0} \frac{\Delta v}{\Delta x} = D_x v,$$

and

$$\lim_{\Delta x \to 0} \Delta v = \lim_{\Delta x \to 0} [g(x + \Delta x) - g(x)] = 0.$$

Therefore,

$$D_x y = \frac{v\,D_x u - u\,D_x v}{v^2},$$

the required formula.

The formula of Theorem 10.2b may be described as
The Quotient Rule for Differentiation. The derivative of the quotient of two functions is the denominator times the derivative of the numerator, minus the numerator times the derivative of the denominator, all divided by the square of the denominator. Symbolically,

$$\left(\frac{f}{g}\right)' = \frac{f'g - fg'}{g^2}.$$

Example 10.2c. Find

$$D_z\left(\frac{z^2 - 1}{z^2 + 1}\right).$$

Theorem 10.2b gives

$$D_z\left(\frac{z^2 - 1}{z^2 + 1}\right) = \frac{(z^2 + 1)D_z(z^2 - 1) - (z^2 - 1)D_z(z^2 + 1)}{(z^2 + 1)^2}$$

$$= \frac{(z^2 + 1)(2z) - (z^2 - 1)(2z)}{(z^2 + 1)^2}$$

$$= \frac{4z}{(z^2 + 1)^2}.$$

Example 10.2d. Find

$$D_m\left(\frac{m^2}{1 + m^{1/2}}\right).$$

Again, the formula of Theorem 10.2b gives

$$D_m\left(\frac{m^2}{1 + m^{1/2}}\right) = \frac{(1 + m^{1/2})D_m m^2 - m^2 D_m(1 + m^{1/2})}{(1 + m^{1/2})^2}$$

$$= \frac{(1 + m^{1/2})(2m) - m^2(\tfrac{1}{2}m^{-1/2})}{(1 + m^{1/2})^2}$$

$$= \frac{4m + 3m^{3/2}}{2(1 + m^{1/2})^2}.$$

It should be noted that the product rule can be extended in an obvious way if there are more than two factors.

Example 10.2e. If $y = (x + 1)(x^2 + 2)(x - 9)$, find $D_x y$.

$$D_x y = (x - 9)D_x[(x + 1)(x^2 + 2)] + (x + 1)(x^2 + 2)D_x(x - 9)$$
$$= (x - 9)[(x^2 + 2)D_x(x + 1) + (x + 1)D_x(x^2 + 2)]$$
$$+ (x + 1)(x^2 + 2)D_x(x - 9)$$
$$= (x - 9)(x^2 + 2)D_x(x + 1) + (x + 1)(x - 9)D_x(x^2 + 2)$$
$$+ (x + 1)(x^2 + 2)D_x(x - 9)$$
$$= (x - 9)(x^2 + 2)(1) + (x + 1)(x - 9)(2x) + (x + 1)(x^2 + 2)(1)$$
$$= 4x^3 - 24x^2 - 14x - 16.$$

Exercises 10.2

In each of Numbers 1 to 10, find $D_x y$.

1. $y = (x - 1)(x + 1)$.
2. $y = (x + 10)(x^2 - 9)^2$.
3. $y = x(x + 1)(x + 2)(x + 3)$.
4. $y = (3x - 9)(x^2 + 18)$.

5. $y = \dfrac{x + 1}{x - 1}$.

6. $y = \dfrac{1}{x^2 + 2}$.

7. $y = \dfrac{x}{x + 1}$.

8. $y = \dfrac{x^2}{x^2 - 1}$.

9. $y = \dfrac{x}{\sqrt{x} + 1}$.

10. $y = \dfrac{\sqrt{x} + 1}{\sqrt{x} - 1}$.

In each of Numbers 11 to 14, s is the distance in feet and t the time in seconds in a straight line motion. Find the time where the velocity is zero.

11. $s = \dfrac{2t}{t^2 + 4}$, $t \geq 0$.

12. $s = \dfrac{t^2 - 1}{t^2 + 1}$, $t \geq 0$.

13. $s = \dfrac{\sqrt{t}}{t + 1}$, $t > 0$.

14. $s = \dfrac{t^2}{\sqrt{t} - 1}$, $t > 0$.

In each of Numbers 15 to 18, find an equation of the tangent line at the indicated point for the curve whose equation is given.

15. $y = \dfrac{1}{x^2 + 4}$; $(1, \frac{1}{5})$.

16. $y = \dfrac{x}{x - 1}$; $(2, 2)$.

17. $y = \dfrac{x}{x^2 - 1}$; $(0, 0)$.

18. $y = \dfrac{x^4 - 1}{x^2 + 4}$; $(1, 0)$.

19. Suppose a function F is the product of n differentiable functions $f_1, f_2, \ldots, f_n$, so that

$$F(x) = f_1(x)f_2(x)\cdots f_n(x).$$

Prove that $F'(x)$ is the sum of all the terms that can be formed by differentiating $f_1, f_2, \cdots, f_n$ one at a time, each time multiplying by all the remaining functions.
20. Using the result of Number 19, find a formula for $F'(x)$, where $F(x) = [f(x)]^n$, with $n \in \mathfrak{N}$.
21. Write $u/v = uv^{-1}$ and use Theorem 10.2a to obtain the formula of Theorem 10.2b.
22. Is the set of all differentiable functions on an open interval $a < x < b$ a group under addition? under multiplication? Explain.

10.3 COMPOSITE FUNCTIONS

It is frequently desirable to break down the consideration of a complicated function into steps involving simpler functions. For this purpose, it is convenient to use the notation of a composite function as given by Definition 5.7b. It should be noted that many authors call a composite function a *function of a function*. Clearly, there is no unique way of expressing a given function as a composite of other functions. For instance, for the function defined by $y = \sqrt{1 - x^2}$, we may write $y = f[g(x)]$, where $f(u) = \sqrt{u}$, and $g(x) = 1 - x^2$, with $|x| \leq 1$, or we may write

$$y = f\{h[w(x)]\},$$

where

$$f(u) = u^{1/2},$$
$$h(v) = 1 - v, \qquad v \leq 1,$$

and

$$w(x) = x^2, \qquad |x| \leq 1.$$

In this last illustration, the domain of f is $u \geq 0$, so that the domain of h must be $v \leq 1$ in order that $h(v) \geq 0$. Similarly, the domain of w must be $|x| \leq 1$, so that the range of w falls into the domain of h.

Before obtaining a formula for the derivative of a composite function, we return to the definition of the derivative in the form

$$D_x y = \lim_{\Delta x \to 0} \frac{\Delta y}{\Delta x}$$

and rewrite it as

$$\frac{\Delta y}{\Delta x} = D_x y + \eta, \quad \text{where } \lim_{\Delta x \to 0} \eta = 0.$$

A moment's reflection shows that these two forms of the definition are completely equivalent. For, whenever the derivative exists, it is true that

$$\lim_{\Delta x \to 0} \left(\frac{\Delta y}{\Delta x} - D_x y \right) = 0,$$

and we have merely designated the difference between $\Delta y/\Delta x$ and $D_x y$ by η.

The second form of the definition leads to the following result:

$$\Delta y = (D_x y) \, \Delta x + \eta \, \Delta x, \quad \text{where } \lim_{\Delta x \to 0} \eta = 0.$$

This is a useful formula that expresses the change Δy in the functional value in terms of the derivative and the change Δx, and it indicates that for sufficiently small values of Δx, the change Δy is given as closely as desired by the product $(D_x y) \, \Delta x$. This fact is, of course, clear from the definition of the derivative

We are now ready to consider the problem of finding the derivative of a composite function. Let f and g be differentiable functions and write

$$y = f(u), \quad u = g(x).$$

Then f may be regarded as a composite function F of the argument x; that is,

$$y = f[g(x)] = F(x).$$

Furthermore, Δy may be expressed in terms of Δu, and Δu in terms of Δx as follows:

$$\Delta y = (D_u y)\, \Delta u + \epsilon_1\, \Delta u, \quad \text{where } \lim_{\Delta u \to 0} \epsilon_1 = 0,$$

and

$$\Delta u = (D_x u)\, \Delta x + \epsilon_2\, \Delta x, \quad \text{where } \lim_{\Delta x \to 0} \epsilon_2 = 0.$$

Upon substituting for Δu from the second equation into the first term of the first equation, there results

$$\Delta y = (D_u y)(D_x u)\, \Delta x + (D_u y)\, \epsilon_2\, \Delta x + \epsilon_1\, \Delta u,$$

which, after division by Δx, becomes

$$\frac{\Delta y}{\Delta x} = (D_u y)(D_x u) + (D_u y)\, \epsilon_2 + \epsilon_1\, \frac{\Delta u}{\Delta x}.$$

Since f and g were both assumed differentiable, it follows that $\lim_{\Delta x \to 0} (\Delta u / \Delta x)$ exists. Furthermore, $\Delta u \to 0$ as $\Delta x \to 0$, so that

$$\lim_{\Delta x \to 0} \epsilon_1 = \lim_{\Delta u \to 0} \epsilon_1 = 0.$$

We also had $\lim_{\Delta x \to 0} \epsilon_2 = 0$, so that the limit as $\Delta x \to 0$ of each of the last two terms in the formula for $\Delta y / \Delta x$ is zero, and we obtain

$$D_x y = (D_u y)(D_x u).$$

This formula for the derivative of a function of a function is frequently called the **chain rule.** By deriving it we have proved the following theorem.

Theorem 10.3a. If f and g are differentiable functions so that $f'(u_0)$ exists, where $u_0 = g(x_0)$ and $g'(x_0)$ exists, then the derivative of the composite function $F = f(g)$ exists at x_0 and is given by the formula

$$F'(x_0) = f'(u_0)g'(x_0).$$

Note: The derivation of the chain rule assumes that there is a neighborhood about $\Delta x = 0$ for which $\Delta u \neq 0$ since ϵ_1 is undefined if $\Delta u = 0$. In order to avoid this assumption, we may define $\epsilon_1 = 0$ for $\Delta u = 0$ so that, for each value of u, ϵ_1 is a continuous function of Δu. With this additional definition, the derivation of the formula is satisfactory even if there are zero values of Δu in every neighborhood of $\Delta x = 0$.

As an example of the use of Theorem 10.3a, let us return to our first illustration of a composite function.

Example 10.3a. Find $D_x\sqrt{1 - x^2}$.

We write $y = u^{1/2}$ and $u = 1 - x^2$. Then

$$\begin{aligned}
D_x y &= (D_u y)(D_x u) \\
&= (\tfrac{1}{2} u^{-1/2})(-2x) \\
&= \tfrac{1}{2}(1 - x^2)^{-1/2}(-2x) \\
&= -x(1 - x^2)^{-1/2}.
\end{aligned}$$

The next theorem follows immediately as an application of the chain rule. The details are left to the student.

Theorem 10.3b. Let $u = f(x)$ define a differentiable function. Then, in the domain common to f' and the $(n - 1)$th power of f,

$$D_x u^n = nu^{n-1} D_x u.$$

Example 10.3b. Find $D_x(2x^2 + 3x)^{10}$.

We use Theorem 10.3b to get

$$D_x(2x^2 + 3x)^{10} = 10(2x^2 + 3x)^9 D_x(2x^2 + 3x)$$
$$= 10(2x^2 + 3x)^9(4x + 3).$$

Example 10.3c. Find $D_x y$ if

$$y = \sqrt{\frac{x^2 + 1}{x^2 - 1}}.$$

Let us write

$$y = \left(\frac{x^2 + 1}{x^2 - 1}\right)^{1/2}.$$

Then we have

$$D_x y = \frac{1}{2}\left(\frac{x^2 + 1}{x^2 - 1}\right)^{-1/2} D_x\left(\frac{x^2 + 1}{x^2 - 1}\right)$$

$$= \frac{1}{2}\left(\frac{x^2 - 1}{x^2 + 1}\right)^{1/2} \frac{(x^2 - 1)(2x) - (x^2 + 1)(2x)}{(x^2 - 1)^2}$$

$$= \frac{-2x}{(x^2 + 1)^{1/2}(x^2 - 1)^{3/2}}.$$

Notice that the quotient rule as well as the power rule is used in this example.

The chain rule is easily extended to longer chains of functions than that considered in Theorem 10.3a. For example, in the case of three functions, we have

$$D_x y = (D_u y)(D_v u)(D_x v).$$

The reader may derive this result by making two applications of the chain rule.

Example 10.3d. Find $D_x y$ if

$$y = \sqrt{1 - \frac{1}{x^2 + 1}}.$$

Consider the following chain of functions:

$$\{(u, y): y = u^{1/2}\},$$

$$\left\{(v, u): u = 1 - \frac{1}{v}\right\},$$

$$\{(x, v): v = x^2 + 1\}.$$

Then, $D_xy = (D_uy)(D_vu)(D_xv)$, where $D_uy = \frac{1}{2}u^{-1/2}$, $D_vu = v^{-2}$, and $D_xv = 2x$. Hence,

$$D_xy = \frac{1}{2}u^{-1/2}\frac{1}{v^2}(2x) = \frac{x}{(x^2+1)^2}\left(1 - \frac{1}{x^2+1}\right)^{-1/2}$$

$$= \frac{x}{(x^2+1)^2}\frac{\sqrt{x^2+1}}{|x|}.$$

Notice that D_xy is discontinuous at $x = 0$. Is the function defined by the given formula discontinuous at $x = 0$? Explain.

Exercises 10.3

In Numbers 1 to 10, write out a chain of functions and find the indicated derivative.

1. $y = \sqrt{x+2}$; D_xy.

2. $y = \sqrt[3]{1+2x^2}$; D_xy.

3. $s = \dfrac{1}{\sqrt{2-t}}$; D_ts.

4. $y = |x|$; D_xy.
   Hint: $|x| = \sqrt{x^2}$.

5. $u = \left(\dfrac{2s-1}{2s+1}\right)^{1/2}$; D_su.

6. $y = \sqrt[3]{\dfrac{x^2+4}{x^2-4}}$; D_xy.

7. $v = \sqrt{1 + \dfrac{4}{4+u^3}}$; D_uv.

8. $y = [1 + \sqrt{x}]^{3/2}$; D_xy.

9. $s = \dfrac{1}{1 - \dfrac{1}{1-t}}$; D_ts.

10. $y = \dfrac{t}{\sqrt{1-t^2}}$; D_ty.

11. Find $f'(x)$ for $f(x) = |x^2 - 9|$. *Hint*: See Number 4.
12. Derive a general formula for finding D_xy if $y = |f(x)|$. *Hint*: See Number 4.

In Numbers 13 to 18, find the indicated derivative.

13. $f(x) = x\sqrt{x^2-1}$; $f'(x)$.

14. $y = \left(\dfrac{x}{x^2-1}\right)^{3/2}$; D_xy.

15. $w = \dfrac{z^2}{\sqrt{z^2+1}}$; D_zw.

16. $z = \left(1 + \dfrac{2a}{w}\right)^{3/2}$; D_wz.

17. $y = (a^{1/2} - x^{1/2})^2$; D_xy.

18. $y = (a^{2/3} - x^{2/3})^{3/2}$; D_xy.

19. Find the point (or points) on the graph of $y = 1/(x + \sqrt{x^2+1})$ where the tangent line has a slope of -1.
20. Find the points on the circle $x^2 + y^2 = 25$ where the tangent line is inclined $30°$. (When solving for y be sure to get both halves of the circle.)
21. Examine $y = \sqrt{|x|}$ to find values of x for which the graph has a vertical tangent. *Hint*: If the tangent is vertical at $x = a$, then $|f'(x)| \to \infty$ as $x \to a$.
22. Find the points (if there are any) where $y = \sqrt{x^2 + 4x + 3}$ has a horizontal tangent. (Caution!)
23. Prove Theorem 10.3b.
24. Derive the formula $D_xy = (D_uy)(D_vu)(D_xv)$ for a chain of three differentiable functions.

25. Show that if $y = f(x)$ has a horizontal tangent at any point, then $y = [f(x)]^n$, $n \in \mathfrak{N}$, has a horizontal tangent for the same value of x. Is the converse necessarily true?

26. Write equations for the tangent lines to the graph of the equation $y = 1/(\sqrt{x^2 - 9})$ at the points for which $|x| = 5$.

In Numbers 27 and 28, s is measured in feet and t in seconds.

27. A certain motion of a point in a straight line is described by

$$s = \sqrt{t^2 + 1} - 1.$$

Find the times when the velocity is zero. Are there any times when the velocity is 1 ft./sec.?

28. The motion of a point in a straight line is given by

$$s = t\sqrt{1 - t^2}, \qquad 0 < t < 1.$$

At what time is the velocity zero?

29. Is the set of all differentiable functions on an open interval $a < x < b$ closed with respect to composition—that is, does $g[f(x)]$ always define a differentiable function on $a < x < b$ if f and g are differentiable there?

10.4 HIGHER ORDER DERIVATIVES

We have seen that we may look upon the function

$$f' .=. \{(x, y'): y' = f'(x) = D_x y\}$$

as a new function derived from the function

$$f .=. \{(x, y): y = f(x)\}.$$

It is natural to consider the possibility of differentiating the derived function to obtain a second derived function and perhaps even to continue this sequence of differentiations.

The derivative (if it exists) of the function f' is called the **second derivative** of f and is denoted by f''. Also, the value of f'' at x may be written in one of the following equivalent ways:

$$f''(x) .=. D_x(D_x y) .=. D_x^2 y .=. y''.$$

Thus, we have

$$f'' = \{(x, y''): y'' = D_x^2 y\}.$$

The *third, fourth*, ..., *n*th, ..., *derivatives* are all defined in a similar manner, and are denoted by f''', $f^{(4)}$, ..., $f^{(n)}$, ..., respectively. The corresponding functional values at x are written

$$f'''(x) = D_x^3 y, \quad f^{(4)}(x) = D_x^4 y, \quad \text{and so on,}$$

the upper index on the f or the D indicating the order of the derivative.

If we wish to distinguish f' from the higher order derivatives, we call it the *first derivative*.

Example 10.4a. Find $D_x^2(1 + x^2)^{3/2}$.

We first find

$$D_x(1 + x^2)^{3/2} = \tfrac{3}{2}(1 + x^2)^{1/2}(2x) = 3x(1 + x^2)^{1/2}.$$

Then,

$$D_x^2(1 + x^2)^{3/2} = 3[(1 + x^2)^{1/2} + (x)(\tfrac{1}{2})(1 + x^2)^{-1/2}(2x)]$$
$$= 3(1 + x^2)^{-1/2}(1 + 2x^2).$$

Example 10.4b. If $z = (1 - x)^n$, find $D_x^k z$, where n and k are positive integers and $k < n$.

First, we find

$$D_x z = n(1 - x)^{n-1}(-1) = -n(1 - x)^{n-1}.$$

Next,

$$D_x^2 z = -n(n - 1)(1 - x)^{n-2}(-1) = n(n - 1)(1 - x)^{n-2}.$$

Continuing in the same manner, we see that

$$D_x^k z = (-1)^k n(n - 1)\cdots(n - k + 1)(1 - x)^{n-k}.$$

If s is the distance from the origin and t is the time in a straight line motion with $s = f(t)$, we know that the derivative of s with respect to t is the velocity at time t; also, the derivative of the velocity with respect to t is the acceleration at time t. Thus,

$$v = D_t s \quad \text{and} \quad a = D_t v,$$

so that

$$a = D_t^2 s.$$

That is, *the acceleration is the second derivative of the distance with respect to the time.*

If x and y are interpreted as the rectangular coordinates of a point on a curve $y = f(x)$, then $D_x y$ gives the slope of the curve at the point (x, y), and $D_x^2 y$ is the *rate of change of the slope* with respect to x. We shall discuss some important geometrical implications of this interpretation in Chapter 11.

Derivatives of order higher than the second are not susceptible of any such simple physical or geometrical interpretations. However, as we shall see at a later time, these derivatives are of considerable importance in both theoretical and practical investigations.

Exercises 10.4

Find the indicated derivative in each of Numbers 1 to 8.

1. $y = \dfrac{x + 1}{x - 1}$; $D_x^2 y$.

2. $y = \sqrt{x^2 + 2x + 3}$; y''.

3. $f(x) = \dfrac{x}{\sqrt{x + 1}}$; $f''(x)$.

4. $g(s) = s(s^2 + 1)$; $g'''(s)$.

5. $h(t) = (1 + 3t)^{1/3}$; $h'''(t)$.

6. $x = v^{4/5}$; $D_v^3 x$.

7. $y = x^{1/2}$; $D_x^n y$.

8. $w = \dfrac{1}{1 + 2u}$; $D_u^n w$.

In Numbers 9 to 14, s (feet) is the distance at time t (seconds) of a particle from the origin in a straight line motion. Find the time, the distance, and the velocity at each instant when the acceleration is zero.

9. $s = t^2 - \dfrac{1}{t}, t > 0.$

10. $s = 6t^{1/2} + t^{3/2}, t > 0.$

11. $s = t^4 - 24t^2 + 12t - 12, t \geq 0.$

12. $s = t^3 - 3t^2 + 2t - 1, t \geq 0.$

13. $s = \dfrac{32}{t^2 + 12}, t \geq 0.$

14. $s = t^2 + \sqrt{t - 1}, t > 1.$

15. Find the slope at each point on the following curve where the rate of change of the slope is zero:

$$y = 3x^5 - 40x^3 + x.$$

16. Compare the behavior of f'' at $x = 0$ for the three functions defined by

$$\text{(a) } f(x) = \frac{x^2}{|x|}, \quad \text{(b) } f(x) = \frac{x^3}{|x|}, \quad \text{(c) } f(x) = \frac{x^4}{|x|}$$

if $f(0) .=. 0$ in all three cases.

17. Find the rate of change of the slope at $(3, 27)$ for the curve $y = (2x - 3)^3$.

18. If u and v are functions of x, and $y = uv$, derive the formula

$$y'' = uv'' + 2u'v' + u''v.$$

Develop a similar formula for y'''.

19. If $f(x) = x|x|$, find the values of x for which $f'(x)$ and $f''(x)$ exist. Sketch the graphs of f, f', f''.

20. Show that if $y = x^2 - 3x$, then $x^2y'' - 2xy' + 2y = 0$.

21. If $f(x)$ and $g(x)$ are differentiable functions of x, determine which of the following statements are true.

(a) If $f'(x) = g'(x)$ for all x, then $f(x) = g(x)$ for all x.
(b) If $f(x) = g(x)$ for all x, then $f'(x) = g'(x)$ for all x.
(c) The domain of $f'' \subset$ the domain of f'.
(d) $(f^{(3)})^{(4)} = f^{(12)}$.
(e) $(f^{(4)})^{(3)} = f^{(7)}$.

10.5 EXPLICIT AND IMPLICIT FUNCTIONS

Most of the functions that we have met up to this point have been described by a statement of the form

$$f .=. \{(x, y): y = f(x)\},$$

where the equation $y = f(x)$ represents a formula or rule telling how to compute the value of the dependent variable y directly in terms of the value of the independent variable x. Such a function is generally called an **explicit function.**

Let us represent an expression involving both x and y by the symbol $F(x, y)$ so that an equation involving both x and y but not solved for y may be put into the form

$$F(x, y) = 0.$$

For example, the equation

$$x^2 + xy = 3 - y^2$$

may be written in the form $F(x, y) = 0$, where

$$F(x, y) .= . x^2 + xy + y^2 - 3.$$

In this last example, we may think of the equation

$$x^2 + xy + y^2 - 3 = 0$$

as a quadratic equation in y,

$$y^2 + xy + (x^2 - 3) = 0,$$

with the solutions for y,

$$y = \tfrac{1}{2}(-x \pm \sqrt{12 - 3x^2}).$$

Since there are two values of y for each value of x such that $|x| < 2$, the set of pairs $\{(x, y)\}$ is a relation but not a function. However, if we specify which sign to use before the radical, then the relation implies the existence of a function, either

$$f_1 = \{(x, y): y = \tfrac{1}{2}(-x + \sqrt{12 - 3x^2})\}$$

or

$$f_2 = \{(x, y): y = \tfrac{1}{2}(-x - \sqrt{12 - 3x^2})\},$$

depending upon which square root is specified. In either case, the domain of the function is $|x| \leq 2$.

It is because of examples such as the preceding one that we have an "intuitive" feeling that an equation $F(x, y) = 0$ generally implies one or more functional relationships. Actually, however, this is not always true. For instance, the equation

$$x^2 + y^2 + 1 = 0$$

is true for no real values of x and y, so that it does not imply the existence of any real function.

The exact situation is beyond the scope of this book to describe. Instead, we accept the fact that, under circumstances usually met in the applications, an equation $F(x, y) = 0$ defines one or more differentiable functions, a particular one of which may be chosen by making additional specifications. A function whose existence is implied by an equation $F(x, y) = 0$ is called an **implicit function.**

Since it frequently happens that the equation $F(x, y) = 0$ cannot conveniently be solved for y, it becomes desirable to find $D_x y$ directly from the given equation. We may argue as follows

$$F(x, y) = 0 \Rightarrow y = f(x),$$

where $f(x)$ is such that substitution of it for y in the equation $F(x, y) = 0$ reduces this equation to an identity; that is,

(1) $$F[x, f(x)] = 0$$

for all x in the domain of f. For example, if the expression for y in the preceding definition of f_1 is substituted into the left member of the original equation

$$x^2 + xy + y^2 - 3 = 0,$$

we get

$$x^2 + x\left(\frac{-x + \sqrt{12 - 3x^2}}{2}\right) + \left(\frac{-x + \sqrt{12 - 3x^2}}{2}\right)^2 - 3$$

$$= x^2 - \tfrac{1}{2}x^2 + \tfrac{1}{2}x\sqrt{12 - 3x^2} + \tfrac{1}{4}x^2 - \tfrac{1}{2}x\sqrt{12 - 3x^2} + \frac{12 - 3x^2}{4} - 3,$$

which simplifies to zero as Equation (1) indicates.

As a consequence of Equation (1), it follows that

$$D_x F[x, f(x)] = 0.$$

The next example illustrates how this result can be used to find $D_x y$.

Example 10.5a. Find $D_x y$ from the equation

$$x^2 + xy + y^2 - 3 = 0.$$

The preceding discussion shows that

$$D_x(x^2 + xy + y^2 - 3) = 0$$

if $y = f(x)$ is implied by the given equation. Thus, we have

$$2x + D_x(xy) + D_x(y^2) = 0.$$

The term xy may now be differentiated by the product rule and the term y^2 by the general power rule, keeping in mind that y stands for the value at x of one of the implicit functions determined by the given equation. Accordingly,

$$2x + (y + x\,D_x y) + 2y\,D_x y = 0.$$

This equation may now be solved for $D_x y$ by first collecting terms as follows:

$$(x + 2y)\,D_x y = -(2x + y).$$

Then

$$D_x y = -\frac{2x + y}{x + 2y}, \qquad x \neq -2y.$$

In order to evaluate $D_x y$ for any given value of x, it is necessary to find the value of y such that $F(x, y) = 0$. Thus, in the preceding problem let it be required to evaluate $D_x y$ for $x = 1$. Since, for $x = 1$ the given equation,

$$x^2 + xy + y^2 - 3 = 0,$$

becomes

$$y^2 + y - 2 = 0,$$

we have $y = -2$ or $y = 1$. Thus, $(1, 1)$ and $(1, -2)$ are points on the graph of the given equation. Notice that $(1, 1) \in f_1$ and $(1, -2) \in f_2$, where f_1 and f_2 are the designations we gave the two functions implied by the equation. Then at the point $(1, 1)$,

$$D_x y = -\frac{2 + 1}{1 + 2} = -1,$$

and at the point $(1, -2)$,

$$D_x y = -\frac{2-2}{1-4} = 0.$$

These results are illustrated in Figure 10.5a.

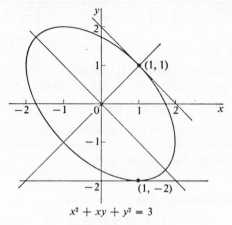

$$x^2 + xy + y^2 = 3$$

FIGURE 10.5a

Even though it may be impossible to solve the equation $F(x, y) = 0$ for y explicitly in any simple form in terms of x, it is usually possible to obtain accurate numerical approximations to the solutions of $F(x_0, y) = 0$ for a specified numerical value of x_0. The existence of more than one such solution generally indicates that $F(x, y) = 0$ implies the existence of more than one function.

The process of taking the derivative with respect to x of both members of $F(x, y) = 0$, while regarding y as the value of the function implied by the equation, is called *implicit differentiation*. We can employ implicit differentiation to find higher derivatives, as in the next example.

Example 10.5b. Find $D_x^2 y$ for $x = 1$ if

$$x^2 + xy + y^2 - 3 = 0.$$

In Example 10.5a, we had

$$2x + y + x\, D_x y + 2y\, D_x y = 0.$$

We regard this equation along with the given equation as defining the value of y and the value of $D_x y$, and we differentiate both members of the last equation with respect to x to get

$$2 + D_x y + (D_x y + x\, D_x^2 y) + 2[(D_x y)^2 + y\, D_x^2 y] = 0.$$

Notice carefully the way in which the product terms are handled:

$$D_x(x\, D_x y) = (D_x x)(D_x y) + x\, D_x(D_x y)$$

and

$$D_x(y\, D_x y) = (D_x y)(D_x y) + y\, D_x(D_x y).$$

Note that $(D_x y)^2$ and $D_x^2 y$ are entirely different!

By collecting terms and solving for D_x^2y, we find

$$D_x^2y = -\frac{2 + 2\,D_xy + 2(D_xy)^2}{x + 2y}, \qquad x \neq -2y.$$

The simplest procedure to follow next is to substitute the values we found previously for y and D_xy. Thus, at $(1, 1)$, where $D_xy = -1$,

$$D_x^2y = -\frac{2 - 2 + 2}{1 + 2} = -\frac{2}{3},$$

and at $(1, -2)$, where $D_xy = 0$,

$$D_x^2y = -\frac{2}{1 - 4} = \frac{2}{3}.$$

An alternative procedure for finding D_x^2y is to differentiate directly the expression found for D_xy. Thus,

$$D_x^2y = -D_x\left(\frac{2x + y}{x + 2y}\right)$$

$$= -\frac{(x + 2y)\,D_x(2x + y) - (2x + y)\,D_x(x + 2y)}{(x + 2y)^2}$$

$$= -\frac{(x + 2y)(2 + D_xy) - (2x + y)(1 + 2\,D_xy)}{(x + 2y)^2}$$

$$= -\frac{3y - 3x\,D_xy}{(x + 2y)^2}.$$

The expression for D_xy may be substituted into the preceding result to obtain D_x^2y in terms of x and y alone. This gives

$$D_x^2y = -\frac{3y + 3x\dfrac{2x + y}{x + 2y}}{(x + 2y)^2}$$

$$= -\frac{6(x^2 + xy + y^2)}{(x + 2y)^3}.$$

But for all points (x, y) on the graph of the given equation we have $x^2 + xy + y^2 = 3$. Hence,

$$D_x^2y = \frac{-18}{(x + 2y)^3}, \qquad x \neq -2y.$$

Although the two expressions we found for D_x^2y are different in appearance, it is easy to show that substitution of the formula for D_xy into the first expression reduces it to the second.

Exercises 10.5

In each of Numbers 1 to 4, find whether or not the given equation describes one or more implicit functions. *Hint*: Complete the squares in x and y.

1. $x^2 + y^2 - 2x + 4y + 6 = 0$.
2. $x^2 + y^2 - y + 1 = 0$.
3. $4x^2 + 9y^2 + 8x - 18y + 25 = 0$.
4. $4x^2 - 9y^2 + 8x + 18y - 17 = 0$.

In each of Numbers 5 to 10, use implicit differentiation to find the indicated derivative.

5. $4x^2 + y^2 = 16$; $D_x y$. Check by solving for y first.
6. $x^2 - y^2 = 10$; $D_y x$. Check by solving for x first.

7. $x^2 + y^2 - 10x + 4y = 0$; $D_x y$. 9. $x^3 - t^3 + 3t = 0$; $D_x t$.
8. $x^2 - y^2 + 2xy = 10$; $D_y x$. 10. $u + v + u^2 v^2 = 3$; $D_u v$.

In each of Numbers 11 to 16, find the slope of the curve at the given point.

11. $x^3 + y^3 - 2xy = 5$; $(1, 2)$.
12. $x^2 + y^2 - 4x - 6y = 0$; $(0, 0)$.
13. $(x + y)^2 - 3x - 2y = 0$; $(-1, 2)$.
14. $bx^2 = y^2(b - y)$, with $b > 0$; at the point where $y = b/2$, with $x > 0$.

15. $x = \dfrac{2a^3}{2a^2 - y^2}$; $(2a, -a)$.

16. $x^2 = \dfrac{b^3}{b - y}$; $(-b, 0)$.

In each of Numbers 17 to 22, use implicit differentiation to find the indicated derivative.

17. $x^2 - 2y^2 = 4$; $D_x^2 y$. 20. $x^2 + y^2 = 3 - 2xy$; $D_x^2 y$.
18. $xy = 50$; $D_x^2 y$. 21. $x^{2/3} + y^{2/3} = a^{2/3}$; $D_x^2 y$.
  22. $u^{1/2} + s^{1/2} = a^{1/2}$; $D_s^2 u$.
19. $\dfrac{w}{z} - \dfrac{z}{w} = 1$; $D_z^2 w$.

In each of Numbers 23 to 26, find the value of $D_x^2 y$ at the points where $D_x y = 0$.

23. $x^3 + y^3 = a^3$. 25. $x^2 + 2xy - y^2 + 8 = 0$.
24. $2\sqrt{x} + 3\sqrt{y} = 8$. 26. $x^2 = y^4 - y^2$.

10.6 PARAMETRIC EQUATIONS

In Section 6.1, we discussed briefly the parametric equations of a straight line passing through a given point and having a given direction. Thus

$$x = 2 + 2t, \quad y = -1 + 6t$$

are parametric equations of the line passing through the point $(2, -1)$ and having direction numbers $[2, 6]$. Compare Example 6.1a.

In this section we shall discuss more general parametric representations, which will usually have graphs more complicated than a straight line. Suppose that f and g are two real-valued functions whose domains are δ_f and δ_g, respectively, and suppose that $\delta_f \cap \delta_g$ is not empty. Then

$$S .=. \ \{(x, y): x = f(t), y = g(t), t \in \delta_f \cap \delta_g\}$$

is a set of points with a graph in the xy plane. The equations

$$x = f(t), \quad y = g(t), \quad t \in \delta_f \cap \delta_g,$$

are called *parametric* equations of the graph and t is called the **parameter.**

For example,

$$x = t, \quad y = \sqrt{1 - t^2}, \quad |t| \leq 1,$$

are parametric equations of the upper half of the circle $x^2 + y^2 = 1$. This follows at once, since

$$(x^2 + y^2 = 1, x = t, |t| \leq 1, y \geq 0) \Rightarrow y = \sqrt{1 - t^2}.$$

Parametric equations occur most commonly in the discussion of curvilinear motion, where x and y may be considered to be the usual distances from the coordinate axes and the parameter t is the time. Frequently, the equations $x = f(t)$ and $y = g(t)$ are called the **equations of motion.** The graph of the set of points $\{(x, y)\}$ is the **path** of the motion.

We often employ parametric equations to simplify the calculation of the coordinates of points on a given curve. For instance, points on the curve $4y^3 = 27x^2$ are easily found by putting $x = 2t^3$, which gives $y^3 = 27t^6$ and thus $y = 3t^2$, since $t, y \in \mathfrak{R}$. A three-column table with headings t, x, y and a table of squares and cubes enable us to write down quite rapidly and in an obvious way the coordinates of points on the curve.

We shall postpone further discussion of curves represented in parametric form until Chapter 11. For the present, we wish to consider the calculation of $D_x y$ and $D_x^2 y$ when x and y are given in terms of a parameter, say t. We assume that the parametric equations

$$x = f(t), \quad y = g(t), \quad t \in \delta_f \cap \delta_g,$$

imply the existence of at least one differentiable function F such that $y = F(x)$. This would be true, for example, if g were a differentiable function and f had a differentiable inverse, so that $t = f^{-1}(x)$ and thus $y = g[f^{-1}(x)]$. Generally, we are faced with the same problems that occur in the discussion of implicit functions.

This discussion suggests the following theorem.

Theorem 10.6a. Let f and g be differentiable functions on an interval $t_1 < t < t_2$ and let f have a differentiable inverse on this interval. Then at each point where $f'(t) \neq 0$, the equations

$$x = f(t), \quad y = g(t)$$

imply that there exists a differentiable function F such that

$$y = F(x) \quad \text{and} \quad D_x y = \frac{g'(t)}{f'(t)} = \frac{D_t y}{D_t x}.$$

PROOF: Suppose that $t_1 < t_0 < t_2$ and $f'(t_0) \neq 0$. Then

$$x_0 = f(t_0) \quad \text{and} \quad y_0 = g(t_0)$$

are values of x and y corresponding to the value t_0. Also, we assumed that f has an inverse, so that

$$t_0 = f^{-1}(x_0)$$

and thus

$$y_0 = g[f^{-1}(x_0)].$$

This procedure may be followed for each value t_0 in the given interval. From the assumption that f^{-1} is a function, it follows that for each x value corresponding to a t value in the interval $t_1 < t < t_2$, there is exactly one value $f^{-1}(x)$, so that $g[f^{-1}(x)]$ furnishes one value of y. Thus,

$$F(x) = g[f^{-1}(x)]$$

defines a function.

At t_0 the equation $y = g(t)$ gives

$$D_x y = g'(t_0) \, D_x t$$

by the chain rule (Theorem 10.3a). Suppose further that $f'(t_0) \neq 0$. Then the equation $x = f(t)$ gives, upon differentiation with respect to x,

$$1 = f'(t_0) \, D_x t,$$

and we may solve for $D_x t$ to obtain

$$D_x t = 1/f'(t_0).$$

Therefore, at t_0,

$$D_x y = \frac{g'(t_0)}{f'(t_0)}.$$

Since t_0 is any value between t_1 and t_2 such that $f'(t_0) \neq 0$, the proof of the theorem is complete.

Another useful result is given in Theorem 10.6b. Let $y = f(x)$ define a strictly increasing (decreasing) function on an interval $a < x < b$, where $f'(x) \neq 0$. Then the inverse function f^{-1} is differentiable and

$$D_y x = \frac{1}{D_x y}, \quad a < x < b.$$

PROOF: The theorem follows from the fact that for $\triangle y \neq 0$,

$$\frac{\triangle x}{\triangle y} = \frac{1}{\triangle y / \triangle x}.$$

Example 10.6a. Verify that Theorem 10.6a applies to the following equations and find $D_x y$ in terms of t.

$$x = t^2 + 2, \quad y = t + 1/t.$$

Writing $x \,.=.\, f(t) = t^2 + 2$ and $y \,.=.\, g(t) = t + 1/t$, we see that

$$\delta_f \cap \delta_g = \mathfrak{R} - \{0\}$$

(or all values of t except $t = 0$) and that f and g are both differentiable on the common domain. Furthermore, the first equation has the solutions

$$t = \sqrt{x - 2} \quad \text{and} \quad t = -\sqrt{x - 2},$$

each of which defines a differentiable function for $x > 2$. Thus, either of the functions

$$f_1^{-1} = \{(x, t): t = \sqrt{x - 2}, x > 2\},$$

or

$$f_2^{-1} = \{(x, t): t = -\sqrt{x - 2}, x > 2\}$$

may be chosen as a differentiable inverse of f. (The particular choice would have to be dictated by another condition such perhaps as a requirement that $t \geq 0$.) This completes the verification that the hypotheses of Theorem 10.6a are satisfied.

Accordingly, the theorem assures us that the two given equations do define a differentiable function with the value at x,

$$y = g[f_1^{-1}(x)] \quad \text{for } t > 0$$

and

$$y = g[f_2^{-1}(x)] \quad \text{for } t < 0.$$

Furthermore, whichever of the two functions is chosen, we have

$$D_x y = \frac{g'(t)}{f'(t)} = \frac{1 - 1/t^2}{2t}$$

$$= \frac{1}{2t} - \frac{1}{2t^3}.$$

As a check, we take the case where $t > 0$. Then

$$t = \sqrt{x - 2} \quad \text{and} \quad y = \sqrt{x - 2} + \frac{1}{\sqrt{x - 2}}$$

$$= (x - 2)^{1/2} + (x - 2)^{-1/2}.$$

Thus

$$D_x y = \tfrac{1}{2}(x - 2)^{-1/2} - \tfrac{1}{2}(x - 2)^{-3/2}$$

$$= \frac{1}{2t} - \frac{1}{2t^3},$$

as before.

If it is desired to find $D_x^2 y$ for x and y given in parametric form, the following scheme may be used. Theorem 10.6a showed that

$$D_x y = \frac{D_t y}{D_t x},$$

so $D_x^2 y$ may be found by replacing y in this formula by $D_x y$ to obtain

$$D_x(D_x y) = \frac{D_t(D_x y)}{D_t x}.$$

Example 10.6b. Find $D_x^2 y$ for $x = t^2 + 2$ and $y = t + (1/t)$.

In Example 10.6a, we found that

$$D_x y = \frac{1}{2t} - \frac{1}{2t^3}.$$

Hence

$$D_x^2 y = \frac{D_t\left(\dfrac{1}{2t} - \dfrac{1}{2t^3}\right)}{D_t x} = \frac{-\dfrac{1}{2t^2} + \dfrac{3}{2t^4}}{2t}$$

$$= \frac{3}{4t^5} - \frac{1}{4t^3}.$$

Higher order derivatives may also be found in this manner. In general,

$$D_x^n y = \frac{D_t(D_x^{n-1} y)}{D_t x}.$$

It is frequently impossible for us to verify in an elementary fashion (say by solving for t) that $x = f(t)$ defines a function with a differentiable inverse. We shall assume (unless the contrary is stated) that this portion of the hypothesis of Theorem 10.6a is satisfied in the problems we consider. A more practical statement must await a deeper consideration of implicit functions than is possible at this point.

Example 10.6c. Find the points where the curve described by the following equations has a zero slope:

$$x = 3t/(1 + t^3), \quad y = 3t^2/(1 + t^3).$$

We have

$$D_t x = \frac{3[(1 + t^3) - 3t^3]}{(1 + t^3)^2} = \frac{3(1 - 2t^3)}{(1 + t^3)^2},$$

$$D_t y = \frac{3[2t(1 + t^3) - 3t^4]}{(1 + t^3)^2} = \frac{3(2t - t^4)}{(1 + t^3)^2},$$

so that

$$D_x y = \frac{D_t y}{D_t x} = \frac{2t - t^4}{1 - 2t^3}.$$

Then

$$D_x y = 0 \quad \text{for } t = 0 \text{ and for } t = 2^{1/3}.$$

For $t = 0$, we find $x = 0$, $y = 0$ and for $t = 2^{1/3}$ we find $x = 2^{1/3}$, $y = 4^{1/3}$. So the points where there is a zero slope are $(0, 0)$ and $(2^{1/3}, 4^{1/3})$.

Exercises 10.6

In Numbers 1 to 6, show that $D_x y = 1/D_y x$ for all points at which the two derivatives are defined and $D_y x \neq 0$.

1. $y^2 = x$.
2. $y = x^2 - 3$.
3. $x^3 + y^3 = 3xy$.

4. $2x^5 y - y^3 + 27xy = 17$.
5. $y = (x^2 - 2)^{1/2}$.
6. $x^2 + y^2 = a^2$.

In Numbers 7 to 12, find the coordinates of the point or points (if there are any) on the given curve where the slope of the curve is zero.

7. $x = 2t^2 - 9, y = t + \dfrac{1}{t}.$

8. $x = \dfrac{t^2}{t^2 - 1}, y = \dfrac{t}{t^2 - 1}.$

9. $x = \sqrt{t^2 - 1}, y = \sqrt{t^2 + 1}.$

10. $x = \dfrac{1}{t + 1}, y = \dfrac{1}{t - 1}.$

11. $x = t^{1/2} - 2t^{-1/2}, y = t^{1/2} + 2t^{-1/2}.$

12. $x = \dfrac{3}{1 + t^3}, y = \dfrac{3t}{1 + t^3}.$

In Numbers 13 to 16, find an equation of the line tangent to the curve at the indicated point.

13. $x = t^2 - 1, y = t^3 + 1; t = 2.$
14. $x = at, y = bt - ct^2; t = 0.$
15. $x = u/(1 + u^2), y = u^2/(1 + u^2); u = 1/2.$
16. $x = r^2 - 8r, y = r^{2/3}; r = 8.$

In Numbers 17 to 20, find $D_x y$ and $D_x^2 y$ in terms of the given parameter.

17. $x = 2u^2, y = 3u^3.$
18. $x = \sqrt{1 - v^2}, y = \sqrt{1 + v^2}.$

19. $x = at^{1/2}, y = bt + ct^2.$
20. $x = t/(t^2 - 1), y = t^2/(t^2 - 1).$

In each of the following problems, find the interval over which the hypotheses of Theorem 10.6a are satisfied. (The numbers refer to the preceding problems.)

21. Number 7.
22. Number 9.

23. Number 10.
24. Number 11.

10.7 DIFFERENTIALS

Whenever the derivative of a function f exists, we have

$$D_x y = \lim_{\Delta x \to 0} \frac{\Delta y}{\Delta x} \Rightarrow \frac{\Delta y}{\Delta x} = D_x y + \eta,$$

where $\lim\limits_{\Delta x \to 0} \eta = 0$. Hence,

(1) $$\Delta y = (D_x y)\, \Delta x + \eta\, \Delta x.$$

As we saw in Section 10.3, the right side of Equation (1) is an expression for the change or *increment* Δy in y corresponding to the increment Δx in x. For example, if $y = x^3$, so that $D_x y = 3x^2$, then

$$\Delta y = (x + \Delta x)^3 - x^3 = 3x^2\, \Delta x + 3x(\Delta x)^2 + (\Delta x)^3$$
$$= (D_x y)\, \Delta x + [3x\, \Delta x + (\Delta x)^2]\, \Delta x.$$

Hence, for $y = x^3$, the η of Equation (1) is given by

$$\eta = 3x\, \Delta x + (\Delta x)^2,$$

and it is clear that for any fixed value of x, η can be made arbitrarily small by keeping Δx sufficiently small.

In general, we may consider the increment in y for any value of x and any increment Δx. The fact that $\lim\limits_{\Delta x \to 0} \eta = 0$ means that for any arbitrary $\epsilon > 0$, there is an h such that

$$\Delta x \in \mathfrak{N}^*(0, h) \Rightarrow \eta \in \mathfrak{N}(0, \epsilon).$$

At a point (x, y), we have $y = f(x)$, and

$$\Delta y = f'(x)\,\Delta x + \eta\,\Delta x.$$

If $f'(x) \neq 0$, then for each given $\theta > 0$, we can find a corresponding h small enough that $|\eta| < \theta|f'(x)|$. In this sense, we can make the term $\eta\,\Delta x$ remain negligible in comparison with $f'(x)\,\Delta x$; that is, we can make $f'(x)\,\Delta x$ as good an approximation to the increment Δy as we like by restricting Δx to a sufficiently small neighborhood of zero.

For instance, in the preceding illustration, where $y = x^3$, at the point where $x = 3$, we have

$$f'(3) = 27 \quad \text{and} \quad \eta = 9\Delta x + (\Delta x)^2.$$

If it is required to have

$$|\eta| < (0.001)|f'(3)| = 0.027$$

or

$$|9\Delta x + (\Delta x)^2| < 0.027,$$

we can display a neighborhood of zero to which Δx should be restricted. First, let us agree to keep $|\Delta x| < 1$ so that

$$|9\Delta x + (\Delta x^2)^2| = |\Delta x||9 + \Delta x| < 10|\Delta x|.$$

Then surely

$$|\eta| < 0.027 \quad \text{if} \quad |\Delta x| < 0.0027.$$

The preceding discussion serves as the basis for

Definition 10.7a. Let f be a differentiable function. At any point x, where $f'(x) \neq 0$, the product $f'(x)\,\Delta x$ is called the **principal part** with respect to x of the increment $\triangle y$, and is denoted by the symbol "dy." Thus,

$$dy .=. f'(x)\,\Delta x.$$

It is important to notice that the increments of the functional values so far considered have been with respect to the independent variable of the function. The treatment in the case of an intermediate variable is exemplified in the next discussion.

Suppose that we consider a composite function $F = f(g)$ defined by the chain

$$y = f(x), \quad x = g(t).$$

where t is the final independent variable, x is an intermediate variable, and

$$y = F(t).$$

We may apply Definition 10.7a to both y and x to get

$$dy = F'(t)\,\Delta t$$

and

$$dx = g'(t)\,\Delta t.$$

The chain rule applied to $F = f(g)$ gives

$$F'(t) = f'(x)g'(t),$$

so that

$$dy = f'(x)g'(t)\,\Delta t.$$

Consequently, since

$$dx = g'(t)\,\Delta t,$$

it follows that

$$dy = f'(x)\,dx.$$

In order to handle the independent variable itself, let us apply this definition to the identity function f, defined by $y = x$. The result is

$$dy = \Delta x.$$

However, since $y = x$, it is desirable to be able to substitute x for y and thus to have $dy = dx$, so that in this case we are led to write

$$dx .=. \Delta x.$$

The symbols dx, dy, and so on are called **differentials.** For dy we may read the "differential of y." The entire discussion of the differential up to this point is summarized in the following definition.

Definition 10.7b. Let a differentiable function f be defined by $y = f(x)$. The differential of y is always

$$dy .=. f'(x)\,dx,$$

and, if x is the final independent variable, then

$$dx .=. \Delta x.$$

A geometric interpretation of Definition 10.7b appears in Figure 10.7a. Since

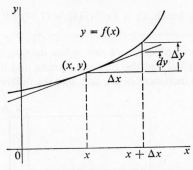

FIGURE 10.7a

the slope of the tangent line to the graph of f at x is $f'(x)$, the quantity $f'(x)\,\Delta x$ (or $f'(x)\,dx$) is the increment up to the tangent line corresponding to the increment Δy up to the curve itself. The figure gives a visual indication that dy becomes a better and better approximation to Δy as Δx is taken smaller and smaller.

Example 10.7a. What is the increment in y and the differential of y for an increment $\Delta x = 1$ at $x = 2$, if $y = x^2$? For an increment $\Delta x = 0.01$?

If $y = x^2$, $x = 2$, and $\Delta x = 1$, then

$$y + \Delta y = (x + \Delta x)^2,$$

so that

$$\Delta y = (x + \Delta x)^2 - x^2 = (2 + 1)^2 - (2)^2 = 9 - 4 = 5.$$

Furthermore, by Definition 10.7a,

$$dy = 2x\, dx = (2)(2)(1) = 4.$$

If $y = x^2$, $x = 2$, and $\Delta x = 0.01$, then

$$\Delta y = (x + \Delta x)^2 - x^2 = (2.01)^2 - 2^2 = 0.0401$$

and

$$dy = 2x\, dx = (2)(2)(0.01) = 0.0400.$$

Example 10.7b. A large, rubber weather balloon is 4 feet in diameter at sea level. After rising a certain distance in the atmosphere it swells to 4 feet, 2 inches in diameter. What is (a) the exact, (b) the approximate change in volume of the enclosed gas?

(a) The volume at sea level is $\frac{4}{3}\pi(24)^3$ cubic inches, and at the higher altitude it is $\frac{4}{3}\pi(25)^3$ cubic inches. The exact increase in volume is

$$\frac{4}{3}\pi(25)^3 - \frac{4}{3}\pi(24)^3 = \frac{4}{3}\pi(25 - 24)(25^2 + 25\cdot24 + 24^2)$$

$$= \frac{4}{3}\pi(1801) = (7.54)(10^3) \text{ cubic inches.}$$

(b) The approximate increase in volume can be obtained by finding the differential of the volume:

$$dv = 4\pi r^2\, dr.$$

For $r = 24$ inches, $dr = 1$ inch, $dv = 4\pi(24)^2(1) = (7.24)(10^3)$ cubic inches.

Example 10.7c. Suppose a square of side x has its side increased by an amount $dx = \Delta x$. Draw the original and the enlarged squares and interpret the increases in the area in terms of the increment of the area and the differential (see Figure 10.7b).

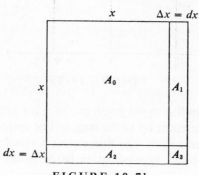

FIGURE 10.7b

For the original area, we have $A_0 = x^2$. The enlarged area is

$$A = (x + \Delta x)^2 = x^2 + 2x\,\Delta x + (\Delta x)^2.$$

The term x^2 is, of course, A_0. The term $2x\,\Delta x$ corresponds to the two areas A_1 and A_2. The term $(\Delta x)^2$ corresponds to A_3. The *increment*, $A_1 + A_2 + A_3$, is equivalent to $2x\,\Delta x + (\Delta x)^2$, and the differential of the area, $dA = 2x\,dx$, corresponds to $A_1 + A_2$.

It cannot be emphasized too strongly that the differential is defined for arbitrary Δx or dx. It is only when the differential is to be used for approximating increments that dx is required to be reasonably small.

As a consequence of the differential notation,

$$dy = f'(x)\,dx,$$

it is natural to divide by dx and to write

$$\frac{dy}{dx} = f'(x).$$

This notation, which is due to Leibniz, is commonly used to designate the derivative and we shall employ it often in the future. This notation may also be used for higher ordered derivatives. For example, by applying the definition of the differential to f', we get

$$\frac{df'}{dx} = f''(x),$$

which may be written

$$\frac{d\left(\dfrac{dy}{dx}\right)}{dx} = f''(x).$$

The symbol $d\left(\dfrac{dy}{dx}\right)/dx$ is usually written as d^2y/dx^2, where it is to be understood that the symbols d^2y and dx^2 do not have individual meanings in this notation. Similarly, we may write

$$\frac{d^n y}{dx^n} = f^{(n)}(x) = \frac{d\left(\dfrac{d^{n-1}y}{dx^{n-1}}\right)}{dx}$$

to denote the nth derivative of f.

It is sometimes convenient to have a basic derivative formula restated in differential form, as in the next example.

Example 10.7d. Suppose $u = f(x)$ and $v = g(x)$, where f and g are differentiable functions on a common domain. Express the differential of the product uv in terms of the differentials of u and v.

By the definition of the differential we have

$$\begin{aligned}
d(uv) &= D_x(uv)\,dx \\
&= (u\,D_x v + v\,D_x u)\,dx \\
&= u(D_x v)\,dx + v(D_x u)\,dx.
\end{aligned}$$

But

$$dv = (D_x v)\, dx \quad \text{and} \quad du = D_x u\, dx,$$

so that

$$d(uv) = u\, dv + v\, du.$$

Example 10.7e. Use differentials to find $D_x y$ from the equation $x^2 + xy + y^2 = 3$.

We make use of the fact that the derivative may be regarded as the quotient of the differentials dy and dx by finding the differentials of both members of the given equation and then solving for the ratio dy/dx. Thus,

$$d(x^2 + xy + y^2) = 0,$$

or

$$2x\, dx + x\, dy + y\, dx + 2y\, dy = 0,$$

or

$$(x + 2y)\, dy + (2x + y)\, dx = 0.$$

Hence,

$$D_x y = \frac{dy}{dx} = -\frac{2x + y}{x + 2y}.$$

Notice in Example 10.7e that the product xy was differentiated by making use of the result of Example 10.7d. The verb "to differentiate" means to find either the differential or the derivative. It is usually clear from the context which of these is intended.

Exercises 10.7

In each of Numbers 1 to 4, calculate the increment and the differential of y.

1. $y = x^2$; $x = 3$, $\Delta x = dx = 0.5$.
2. $y = x - 3$; $x = 5$, $\Delta x = dx = 0.1$.
3. $y = \sqrt{x}$; $x = 4$, $\Delta x = dx = 0.04$.
4. $y = 3x^3 - 9x$; $x = 1$, $\Delta x = dx = 1$.

In each of Numbers 5 to 10, use differentials to find $D_x y$.

5. $x^2 + y^2 = 4$.
6. $x^2 y + y^2 = 2x$.
7. $x^3 + 3xy + y^3 = 5$.
8. $x^4 - x^2 y^2 + y = 13$.
9. $x = t/(t^2 - 1)$, $y = (t^2 + 1)/(t^2 - 1)$.
10. $x = 3u$, $y = \sqrt{4 - u^2}$.

11. Use the differential to find an approximate value of s for $t = 2.01$ if $s = t/(t^2 + 1)$.
12. Use the differential to find an approximate value of y for $x = 10.01$ if

$$y = x^3 - 2x^2 + 1000.$$

13. Use the differential to find an approximate value of $\sqrt{9.04}$. *Hint*: Let $y = \sqrt{x}$. Then take $x = 9$, $\Delta x = 0.04$.

14. Find an approximate value of $\sqrt[3]{1027}$. See Number 13
15. Find an approximate value of $(99)^{-1}$. See Number 13.
16. Find an approximate value of $\sqrt[3]{1004} - \sqrt[3]{996}$.
17. The length of a metal rod as a function of temperature is given by $L = L_0(1 + \alpha t)$, where L_0 is the initial length of the rod and t is the temperature. Assuming that all three dimensions depend on the temperature in the same way, find a formula for the volume of a rectangular metal bar as a function of the temperature. Find the differential of the volume.
18. In Number 17, if the volume of the metal bar is increased by 0.1% when the temperature is changed from 100° to 110°, find the approximate value of α.
19. A man contracts to dip-paint 10,000 circular metal signs each 2 feet in diameter. When they are delivered he discovers they are 1 inch in diameter oversize. Approximately what percentage of additional paint will be required?
20. A cone-shaped tank, vertex down, is 4 feet in diameter and 6 feet deep. If it is filled to a depth of 3 feet with water, approximately how much additional water will be required to raise the water level 2 inches?
21. What is the approximate percentage increase in the volume of wood per foot of log if the circumference of a tree increases from 12 feet to 12 feet 6 inches?
22. The image distance q and the object distance p of a simple thin lens are related by the equation

$$\frac{1}{p} + \frac{1}{q} = \frac{1}{f},$$

where f is the focal length of the lens. Suppose a slide projector with a focal length of 3 inches, 10 feet away from the screen, is moved to 12 feet away from the screen. How far must the slide be moved in relation to the lens? (To simplify the problem, consider that focusing is accomplished by moving the slide, rather than the lens—as is usually done.)
23. Archimedes' principle states that a floating body displaces a volume of liquid equal in weight to the weight of the body. Suppose a hollow ball 10 centimeters in diameter sinks to a depth of 2 centimeters in water (1 gram per cubic centimeter). Now suppose 5 grams of lead is introduced into the interior of the ball. To what depth will it now sink? *Note*: If the sphere is submerged to a depth $h \leq 2r$, the volume of the submerged portion is

$$V = \tfrac{1}{3}\pi h^2(3r - h).$$

24. The formula for the period (time in seconds for a complete swing) of a simple pendulum is given by the formula $T = 2\pi\sqrt{L/g}$, where L is the length of the pendulum in feet and $g = 32.16$ feet per second per second. The pendulum on a certain clock was intended to make one complete swing every 2 seconds, but the clock gains 2 minutes per day. Find the approximate change in the length of the pendulum that is necessary to correct the inaccuracy.
25. Express the differential of a sum $u + v$, where u and v are differentiable functions on a common domain, in terms of the differentials of u and v.
26. Express the differential of the quotient u/v, where u and v are as in Number 25, in terms of the differentials of u and v.

Summary of Chapter 10

It is very important that the student develop a facility with techniques of differentiation in order that he be able to proceed into studies in which the ideas or concepts are of primary concern. Without this facility, he is likely to get bogged down in mechanical details and consequently miss the importance of the fundamental concepts. It is, therefore, appropriate that he understand clearly the following important results:

(1) what is meant by saying that a function is differentiable over an interval (Section 10.1);
(2) the relationship between the differentiability and continuity of a function (Section 10.1);
(3) the meaning of "derivative from the right (or left)" (Section 10.1);
(4) the product and quotient rules for differentiation (Section 10.2);
(5) the chain rule for the differentiation of a composite function (Section 10.3);
(6) the meaning of the second and higher order derivatives (Section 10.4);
(7) the interpretation of the second derivative as acceleration and rate of change of slope (Section 10.4);
(8) the differentiation of implicit functions (Section 10.5);
(9) the differentiation of functions defined by parametric equations (Section 10.6);
(10) the differentiation of the inverse of a function and the relationship of this derivative to the derivative of the original function (Section 10.6);
(11) the concept of the differential and its use in approximating increments (Section 10.7).

Chapter 11　Further Applications of the Derivative

11.1 INCREASING AND DECREASING FUNCTIONS

It has already been noted several times that an important aspect of scientific investigation is the study of the way in which one quantity depends on another. For example, if $s = 16t^2$ gives the distance passed over by an object falling under the influence of gravity, then it is of interest to study exactly the manner in which s increases as t increases. We shall find that the derivative is an invaluable aid in many problems of this type.

More generally, we shall be concerned with the behavior of a function f with values $y = f(x)$ as x increases. Geometrically, this means that we shall be interested in the behavior of the curve given by the equation $y = f(x)$ as we view it from left to right.

In order to sketch a curve without plotting a great many points, it is desirable to obtain as much information about the curve as possible from the function. One important piece of information that can frequently be obtained tells us whether the curve is rising or falling over a particular interval.

Suppose that at a point (x_0, y_0), the derivative $f'(x_0)$ is positive. Then the tangent line at the point slopes *up* from left to right as at the points A and C in Figure 11.1a. If the value of x is slightly increased, it appears from the figure that the curve rises and that the value of y increases.

Similarly, if $f'(x_0)$ is negative, the tangent line at (x_0, y_0) slopes down from left to right as at B in Figure 11.1a. If the value of x is slightly increased, the curve falls and the value of y decreases.

This discussion suggests the following definitions and theorems.

Definition 11.1a. A function f is said to be *increasing on an open interval* if, for every pair of points x_1 and x_2 of the interval

$$x_1 < x_2 \Rightarrow f(x_1) < f(x_2).$$

The student should formulate for himself the definition of a function *decreas-*

ing on an open interval. Figure 11.1a illustrates the graph of a decreasing function on the interval $p < x < q$ and an increasing function in the interval $q < x < r$.

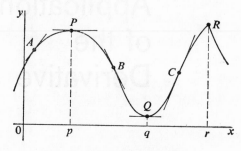

FIGURE 11.1a

A function that does not decrease (or does not increase) on an interval $a < x < b$ is said to be **monotonic** on that interval. If the function is always increasing (or decreasing) on the interval, then it is called a **strictly monotonic** function on that interval. For example, a function with a graph such as that in Figure 11.1b is monotonic but not strictly monotonic on the interval $a < x < b$.

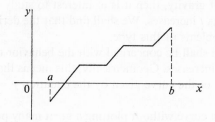

FIGURE 11.1b

Theorem 11.1a. Let x_0 be a point where f has a nonzero derivative. Then there exists no neighborhood of x_0 such that $f(x_0)$ is either the least or the greatest value of f on the neighborhood; that is, every neighborhood (no matter how small) of x_0 contains a point, say x_1, such that $f(x_1) < f(x_0)$ and also a point, say x_2, such that $f(x_2) > f(x_0)$.

PROOF: By the definition of the derivative, we have

$$f'(x_0) = \lim_{x \to x_0} \frac{f(x) - f(x_0)}{x - x_0},$$

so that there must be some $\mathfrak{N}^*(x_0, h)$ such that the value of the difference quotient itself is arbitrarily close to $f'(x_0)$ for all $x \in \mathfrak{N}^*(x_0, h)$.

Thus, if $f'(x_0) > 0$, then

$$x \in \mathfrak{N}^*(x_0, h) \Rightarrow \frac{f(x) - f(x_0)}{x - x_0} > 0.$$

But this neighborhood extends both to the left and to the right of x_0. Let $x_1 \in \mathfrak{N}^*(x_0^-, h)$. Then $x_1 - x_0 < 0$ and the preceding inequality implies that

$$f(x_1) < f(x_0).$$

Similarly, if $x_2 \in \mathfrak{N}^*(x_0^+, h)$, then $x_2 - x_0 > 0$ and so

$$f(x_2) > f(x_0).$$

The proof for the case where $f'(x) < 0$ is effected simply by a reversal of the inequality signs.

The points A, B, C in Figure 11.1a illustrate Theorem 11.1a.

Theorem 11.1b. Let x_0 be a point such that $f(x_0)$ is either the least or the greatest value of f on some neighborhood of x_0. Then $f'(x_0) = 0$ or else f has no derivative at x_0.

PROOF: If f has a derivative at x_0, then, in order not to contradict Theorem 11.1a, we must have $f'(x_0) = 0$. If f has no derivative at x_0, then the conclusion of the theorem is, of course, satisfied.

Points P, Q, and R in Figure 11.1a furnish illustrations of the preceding theorem. At P and Q, the curve has horizontal tangents so that the derivative is zero, and at R the derivative fails to exist.

Theorem 11.1c. Let f be a differentiable function on an open interval $a < x < b$. Then $f'(x) > 0$ on the interval implies f is increasing on the interval, and $f'(x) < 0$ on the interval implies f is decreasing on the interval.

PROOF: Let x_1 and x_2 be any two points in the interval such that $x_1 < x_2$, and suppose $f'(x) > 0$. Then we must show that

$$f(x_1) < f(x_2).$$

Consider the closed interval $x_1 \leq x \leq x_2$. Since f is differentiable, it must be continuous, and hence, by Theorem 8.5g, must have a maximum value on this closed interval. Furthermore, $f'(x) > 0$, so that by Theorem 11.1a this maximum cannot occur at any interior point.

Suppose that the maximum is at x_1. Then for all x in the interior of the interval, $x - x_1 > 0$ and $f(x) - f(x_1) \leq 0$, so that

$$\frac{f(x) - f(x_1)}{x - x_1} \leq 0,$$

which implies that $f'(x_1) \leq 0$. (Why?) But $f'(x_1) > 0$ by hypothesis. This contradiction shows that the maximum must occur at x_2; that is,

$$f(x_1) < f(x_2).$$

The proof for the case $f'(x) < 0$ is quite similar to that for $f'(x) > 0$ and is therefore left to the reader.

Example 11.1a. Find the intervals on which $y = x^2 + 1$ is increasing or decreasing.

Since $y' = 2x$, y is increasing for $x > 0$ and decreasing for $x < 0$, by Theorem 11.1c.

Example 11.1b. Discuss the graph of

$$y = \frac{x}{1 - x^2}.$$

Since

$$y' = \frac{1 + x^2}{(1 - x^2)^2} > 0 \quad \text{for all } x, \ |x| \neq 1,$$

we conclude, by Theorem 11.1c, that the graph is rising everywhere. The given equation shows that $x = 1$ and $x = -1$ are vertical asymptotes, and $y = 0$ is a horizontal asymptote. The equation also shows that $(0, 0)$ is the only intercept (see Figure 11.1c).

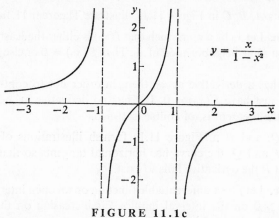

$$y = \frac{x}{1 - x^2}$$

FIGURE 11.1c

Example 11.1c. The motion of a particle in a straight line is given by the formula

$$s = t + \frac{1}{t},$$

where s is in feet and t in seconds. For what values of t is s increasing (the particle moving to the right)?

Since

$$D_t s = 1 - \frac{1}{t^2} = \frac{t^2 - 1}{t^2},$$

we see that

$$\frac{t^2 - 1}{t^2} > 0 \quad \text{for } t^2 > 1,$$

that is, for $t < -1$ or $1 < t$. Thus, s increases for $t < -1$ and for $t > 1$.

Exercises 11.1

In Numbers 1 to 10, determine the open intervals of the domain for which f is an increasing function; a decreasing function. In each case $f . =. \ \{(x, y)\}$.

1. $y = \sqrt{|x|}$.
2. $y = x^2 - 5x + 6$.

3. $y = \dfrac{x + 1}{x - 1}$.

4. $f(x) = x^2 + \dfrac{1}{x^2}$.

5. $y = x^3$.
6. $f . =. \ \{(x, y) : x^2 + y^2 = a^2, y \geqq 0\}$.
7. $y = x^3 + x^2 - x - 2$.

8. $y = |x|^3$.

9. $f . = . \{(x, y): x = t - 2, y = t^2 + 1\}$. (Check by eliminating t.)

10. $f . = . \left\{(x, y): x = t + \dfrac{1}{t}, y = t - \dfrac{1}{t}\right\}$.

11. Choose $x_0 = 0$ and show that the function defined in Number 1 illustrates Theorem 11.1b.

12. Find the vertex of the parabola described by the equation in Number 2. Use this point to illustrate Theorem 11.1b.

13. Show that the points where $x = \pm a$ in Number 6 furnish an illustration of Theorem 11.1b.

14. Apply Theorem 11.1a to show that the function f defined by $f(x) = 1/x^3$ can have no greatest or least value

15. Find the greatest and least values of y if

$$y = \frac{x}{x^2 + 4}, \qquad 0 \leq x \leq 1.$$

16. Suppose the domain of f is the set $\mathcal{R}$ of all real numbers and

$$f(x) = \frac{x}{x^2 + 4}.$$

At what points might f have its greatest or least values? Can you determine what actually does occur?

11.2 CONCAVITY AND THE SIGN OF THE SECOND DERIVATIVE

Let us consider the curve shown in Figure 11.2a. In a neighborhood of such points as A and B, the curve lies below its tangent line, and in going from A

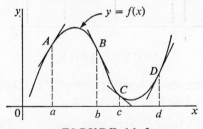

FIGURE 11.2a

to B the tangent line turns in the clockwise direction. Similarly, in a neighborhood of C or D, the curve lies above its tangent line, and in going from C to D the tangent line turns in the counterclockwise direction. Furthermore, if the tangent line turns counterclockwise as we go to the right, the slope of the tangent line increases, and if the tangent line turns clockwise, the slope decreases. Since the slope of the tangent line at any point (x, y) is given by $f'(x)$, it appears that the sign of $D_x f'(x) = f''(x)$, provided f'' exists, may be used to distinguish the behavior of the curve at a point such as A from that at a point such as C.

Theorem 11.2a. Let f be a twice differentiable function on the interval $a < x < b$.

(i) If $f''(x) > 0$ for $a < x < b$, then the slope of the graph of f is an increasing function and the tangent to the graph turns counterclockwise as x increases.

(ii) If $f''(x) < 0$ for $a < x < b$, then the slope of the graph of f is a decreasing function and the tangent of the graph turns clockwise as x increases.

PROOF: The proof follows at once from the discussion in Section 11.1.

Suppose that f is a twice differentiable function on an interval $a < x < b$. Then f' is a continuous function on this interval and the graph of f has a tangent line at each of its points. If (x_1, y_1) is such a point, then the equation of the tangent line is, as we have seen,

$$y - y_1 = f'(x_1)(x - x_1)$$

or

$$y = f(x_1) + f'(x_1)(x - x_1),$$

since $y_1 = f(x_1)$. The equation of the tangent defines a linear function, say t, such that

$$t(x) = f(x_1) + f'(x_1)(x - x_1)$$

is the directed distance from the x-axis to the tangent line measured parallel to the y-axis (see Figure 11.2b).

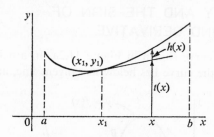

FIGURE 11.2b

The following theorem shows how the sign of $f''(x)$ determines whether the graph of f lies above or below its tangent line.

Theorem 11.2b. Let f be a twice differentiable function on the interval $a < x < b$. Let x_1 be a point in this interval, and let t be the linear function defined by

$$t(x) = f(x_1) + f'(x_1)(x - x_1).$$

(i) If $f''(x) > 0$ on the interval, then for each x_1 there is a $\mathfrak{N}^*(x_1, k)$ such that $x \in \mathfrak{N}^*(x_1, k) \Rightarrow f(x) > t(x)$.

(ii) If $f''(x) < 0$ on the interval, then for each x_1 there is a $\mathfrak{N}^*(x_1, k)$ such that $x \in \mathfrak{N}^*(x_1, k) \Rightarrow f(x) < t(x)$.

Note that in (i) the geometric interpretation of the final inequality is that the curve given by $y = f(x)$ lies above its tangent line over the $\mathfrak{N}^*(x_1, k)$ and in (ii) the curve lies below its tangent line.

PROOF: Consider the function $h = f - t$, where $h(x) = f(x) - t(x)$. (Geometrically, this is the directed distance *from* the tangent line *to* the graph of f measured parallel to the y-axis. See Figure 11.2b.)

From the definition of t, we have

$$h(x) = f(x) - f(x_1) - f'(x_1)(x - x_1),$$

where $f(x_1)$ and $f'(x_1)$ are the constants obtained by evaluating f and f' at x_1. Clearly, $h(x_1) = 0$, and

$$h'(x) = f'(x) - f'(x_1).$$

Since $f''(x) > 0$ means that $f'(x)$ is increasing with increasing x, it is true that, for all x in the interval,

$$x > x_1 \Rightarrow f'(x) > f'(x_1) \Rightarrow h'(x) > 0$$

and

$$x < x_1 \Rightarrow f'(x) < f'(x_1) \Rightarrow h'(x) < 0.$$

But $h'(x) > 0$ implies that $h(x)$ is increasing with x, so that

$$x > x_1 \Rightarrow h(x) > h(x_1) = 0.$$

Similarly, $h'(x) < 0$ implies $h(x)$ is decreasing with x, so that

$$x < x_1 \Rightarrow h(x) > h(x_1) = 0.$$

This completes the proof of (i). The proof of (ii) differs from this only in minor details and is left for the reader.

Definition 11.2a. The graph of a function is said to be *concave up* over an interval if the graph lies above its tangent line in the sense of Theorem 11.2b. The graph is said to be *concave down* if it lies below its tangent line.

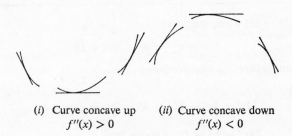

(i) Curve concave up (ii) Curve concave down
$f''(x) > 0$ $f''(x) < 0$

FIGURE 11.2c

In view of this definition, Theorem 11.2b may be restated as follows:
(i) *Over any interval where $f''(x) > 0$, the graph of f is concave up.*
(ii) *Over any interval where $f''(x) < 0$, the graph of f is concave down.*
Figure 11.2c illustrates schematically the possibilities for (i) and (ii).

Example 11.2a. Examine the concavity of the graph of the function *f*, where $f(x) .=. x^2 - 4x^{1/2}$.

We first find

$$f'(x) = 2x - 2x^{-1/2},$$

and

$$f''(x) = 2 + x^{-3/2}.$$

The domain of *f* is $x \geq 0$ (why?) and the domains of *f'* and *f''* are both $x > 0$. For $x > 0$, it is clear that $f''(x) > 0$. Hence, the graph is concave upward for $x > 0$. The reader may examine the function in more detail near $x = 0$ to see that as $x \to 0^+$, the curve approaches tangency to the *y* axis at the origin. Since $f(0) = 0$, the origin is on the curve, but the curve does not extend to the left of the origin. (See Figure 11.2d.)

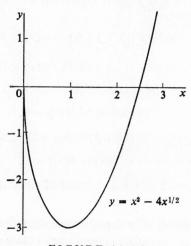

$$y = x^2 - 4x^{1/2}$$

FIGURE 11.2d

Example 11.2b. Find where the curve

$$24y = x^3 - 6x^2 - 36x + 16$$

is concave up and where it is concave down.

We first find

$$24y' = 3x^2 - 12x - 36 = 3(x + 2)(x - 6),$$

and

$$24y'' = 6x - 12 = 6(x - 2).$$

Hence,

$$y'' > 0 \quad \text{for } x > 2,$$

so that the curve is concave up for $x > 2$.

Similarly, $y'' < 0$ for $x < 2$, so that the curve is concave down for $x < 2$ (see Figure 11.2e).

In Example 11.2b, we find that $y'' = 0$ for $x = 2$ and the point $(2, -3)$ on the curve separates a portion of the curve that is concave up from a portion that is concave down. At such a point, the tangent line must cross the curve, as Figure 11.2e illustrates. Points of this kind are useful guides in curve sketching.

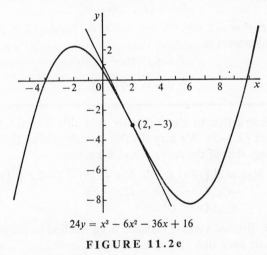

$$24y = x^3 - 6x^2 - 36x + 16$$

FIGURE 11.2e

Definition 11.2b. A point on a curve at which there exists a unique tangent line and which separates a portion of the curve that is concave up from a portion that is concave down is called an **inflection point**. The tangent to the curve at an inflection point is called an **inflectional tangent**.

Definition 11.2c. If there is a deleted neighborhood of a point x_0 such that a given function is positive on one half of the neighborhood and negative on the other half, then the function is said to *change sign* at x_0.

For example, the quadratic function q, defined by

$$q(x) = (x - 1)(x + 2)$$

changes sign at $x = -2$ and at $x = 1$.

Theorem 11.2c. On a curve $y = f(x)$, let (x_0, y_0) be a point where the curve has a unique tangent line. The point (x_0, y_0) is an inflection point of the curve if f has a continuous second derivative in some $\mathfrak{N}^*(x_0)$ and f'' changes sign at x_0.

PROOF: The reader should note that the hypothesis of this theorem is satisfied only if $f''(x_0) = 0$ or else $f''(x_0)$ does not exist. The proof of the theorem follows directly from Definition 11.2b and the connection between the sign of $f'(x)$ and the concavity of the graph of f. The details are left for the exercises.

Example 11.2c. Find an equation of the inflectional tangent to the curve in Example 11.2b.

The discussion preceding Definition 11.2b shows that $(2, -3)$ is the inflection point. In Example 11.2b, we found

$$24y' = 3(x + 2)(x - 6),$$

or

$$8y' = (x + 2)(x - 6)$$

For $x = 2$, we get $y' = -2$, which is the slope of the required line. Thus, an equation of the inflectional tangent is

$$y + 3 = -2(x - 2),$$

or

$$y = -2x + 1.$$

Note: It is instructive to show directly that this line actually crosses the curve at $(2, -3)$. We may do this by subtracting the ordinate of the line from that of the curve. Thus, we get

$$\begin{aligned} h(x) &= \tfrac{1}{24}(x^3 - 6x^2 - 36x + 16) - (-2x + 1) \\ &= \tfrac{1}{24}(x^3 - 6x^2 + 12x - 8) \\ &= \tfrac{1}{24}(x - 2)^3 \end{aligned}$$

for the directed vertical distance from the line to the curve. The result shows at once that $h(x)$ changes sign at $x = 2$.

Example 11.2d. Examine the curve $y = (x - 2)^{1/3}$ for inflection points.

We first find the derivatives

$$D_x y = \tfrac{1}{3}(x - 2)^{-2/3}$$

and

$$D_x^2 y = -\tfrac{2}{9}(x - 2)^{-5/3}.$$

In this example, there is no value of x such that $D_x^2 y = 0$; however, $D_x^2 y$ fails to exist

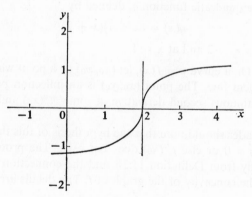

FIGURE 11.2f

for $x = 2$. The point $(2, 0)$ is on the curve (why?), and it is evident from the formula for $D_x^2 y$ that the second derivative function is continuous except at $x = 2$. Furthermore,

$$D_x^2 y > 0 \quad \text{for } x < 2,$$

and

$$D_x^2 y < 0 \quad \text{for } x > 2.$$

Accordingly, the curve is concave up for $x < 2$ and concave down for $x > 2$, so that $(2, 0)$ is an inflection point. We see also that

$$D_x y \to \infty \quad \text{as } x \to 2$$

so that the inflectional tangent is vertical (see Figure 11.2f).

Exercises 11.2

For each of Numbers 1 to 8, find the intervals in which the curve is concave up and those in which it is concave down. Also find the inflection points.

1. $y = 3x^5 - 10x^3$.
2. $y = 3x^5 + 30x^4 + 110x^3 + 180x^2$.
3. $y = 4x^3 - x^4$.
4. $y = 4x^3 - 3x^5$.
5. $y = x - x^{-1}$.

6. $y = 3x^2 - 4x^{5/2}$.
7. $y = a^2 x/(x^2 + a^2)$, $a > 0$.
8. $y = \left(\dfrac{x}{x+1}\right)^2$.

9. Let the equation of a "cubic curve" be

$$y = ax^3 + bx^2 + cx + d.$$

Prove that this curve always has one inflection point and that this point is a point of symmetry of the curve. *Hint:* If (h, k) is the inflection point, the substitution

$$x = x' + h, \quad y = y' + k,$$

will yield the equation of the curve referred to a new set of axes with the origin at the inflection point. Then the usual test for symmetry with respect to the origin may be used.

10. Find conditions on the coefficients so that

$$y = ax^4 + bx^3 + cx^2 + dx + e$$

has no inflection point (if possible).

★11. Construct an equation $y = ax^4 + bx^3 + cx^2 + dx + e$ so that the corresponding curve is concave down for $-1 < x < 2$, is concave up everywhere else, and that passes through the points $(0, 1)$, $(2, 0)$, and $(-1, 0)$. *Hint:* Start by writing $f''(x) = A(x - x_1)(x - x_2)$, with x_1 and x_2 chosen to satisfy the concavity conditions.

In each of Numbers 12 to 20, assume that f has a continuous second derivative. Sketch a curve showing the behavior of the graph of f over a $\mathfrak{N}(a, h)$, if the prescribed behavior is possible. If not possible, explain why.

12. $f''(a) = 0$; $f'(a) = 0$; $x \in \mathfrak{N}^*(a, h) \Rightarrow f'(x) > 0$.
13. $f''(a) = 0$; $f'(a) = 0$; $x \in \mathfrak{N}^*(a, h) \Rightarrow f'(x) < 0$.
14. $f''(a) > 0$; $x \in \mathfrak{N}(a, h) \Rightarrow f'(x) > 0$.
15. $f''(a) < 0$; $x \in \mathfrak{N}(a, h) \Rightarrow f'(x) > 0$.
16. $f''(a) = 0$; $f'(a) > 0$; $x \in \mathfrak{N}^*(a^-, h) \Rightarrow f''(x) < 0$; $x \in \mathfrak{N}^*(a^+, h) \Rightarrow f''(x) > 0$.
17. $f''(a) = 0$; $f'(a) < 0$; $x \in \mathfrak{N}^*(a^-, h) \Rightarrow f''(x) < 0$; $x \in \mathfrak{N}^*(a^+, h) \Rightarrow f''(x) > 0$.
18. $f''(a) = 0$; $x \in \mathfrak{N}^*(a^-, h) \Rightarrow f'(x) < 0$; $x \in \mathfrak{N}^*(a^+, h) \Rightarrow f'(x) > 0$.

19. $f''(a) = 0; f'(a) = 1, x \in \mathfrak{N}^*(a, h) \Rightarrow f'(x) < 0.$
20. $f''(a) > 0; x \in \mathfrak{N}^*(a, h) \Rightarrow f''(x) < 0.$
21. Show that the curve $y = (x^2 + a^2)^{k/2}$, $k \neq 0$, has two inflection points for $k < 1$ and no inflection points for $k \geq 1$.

11.3 MAXIMA AND MINIMA

Many mathematical problems are concerned with finding the maximum (greatest) or the minimum (least) value of a function, and the derivative is often a useful tool in such problems. It also frequently happens that we are concerned with the greatest or least value over a certain neighborhood in the domain of the function rather than with the absolutely greatest or least value over the entire domain. The next definition makes this idea more precise.

Definition 11.3a. A function f is said to have a **relative maximum** at a point x_0 of the domain of f if there is a neighborhood $\mathfrak{N}(x_0)$ such that $f(x_0) \geq f(x)$ for each $x \in \mathfrak{N}(x_0)$.

A **relative minimum** is defined in a similar manner. The greatest value (if there is one) of a function on its entire domain is sometimes called an *absolute maximum*. The least value is called an *absolute minimum*. We shall frequently use the terms maximum and minimum to refer to either a relative or an absolute maximum or minimum since it will be clear from the context which is intended. The maxima and minima of a function are called the **extremes** of the function. Note that the existence of a relative maximum (or minimum) at x_0 implies that the function is defined in some neighborhood of x_0. If x_0 is an end point of the domain of f, then the neighborhood is a left or a right neighborhood, and the extreme is sometimes called an *end point extreme*. Figure 11.3a illustrates some of the ways in which extremes can occur.

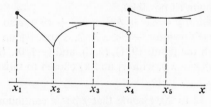

FIGURE 11.3a

The graph shown in Figure 11.3a is that of a function with a relative maximum at each of the points where $x = x_1$, x_3, and x_4, and with a relative minimum for each of $x = x_2$ and x_5. The extreme at x_1 is an end point maximum. The extreme at x_2 is an absolute minimum. There is no absolute maximum as the curve is indicated to be rising indefinitely for $x > x_5$.

The figure also suggests that if $f(x_0)$ is an extreme and $f'(x_0)$ exists, then $f'(x_0) = 0$. This seems to be so at $x = x_3$ and at $x = x_5$. At x_1, x_2, and x_4, the derivative apparently does not exist. (Only one-sided derivatives can exist at such points.) The following theorem covers these conjectures.

Theorem 11.3a. If a function has an extreme $f(x_0)$, then either
  (i) $f'(x_0) = 0$, or else
  (ii) $f'(x_0)$ does not exist.

PROOF: If $f(x_0)$ is an end point extreme, then f can have only a one-sided derivative at x_0; the derivative itself does not exist. Suppose that x_0 is in the interior of the domain. By Theorem 11.1a, if $f'(x_0)$ exists and is different from zero, then $f(x_0)$ is not an extreme, which is contrary to the hypothesis. Accordingly, either $f'(x_0) = 0$ or else $f'(x_0)$ does not exist.

It is important to realize that the converse of Theorem 11.3a is not true. For example, the function f defined by $f(x) = x^3$ has a zero derivative for $x = 0$, since $f'(x) = 3x^2$. Yet f has no extreme at $x = 0$ as $f'(x) > 0$ for $x \neq 0$, so that f is an increasing function over its entire domain, the set of all real numbers. The student may easily verify that the curve $y = x^3$ has a point of inflection with a horizontal tangent at $(0, 0)$. As an illustration of an instance where the nonexistence of the derivative does not imply an extreme, the reader may refer to Example 11.2d.

In summary, the preceding paragraph shows that neither $f'(x_0) = 0$ nor the failure of $f'(x_0)$ to exist is a sufficient condition for $f(x_0)$ to be an extreme. However, it does follow from Theorem 11.3a that an extreme of a function can occur only (i) at an end point of its domain or (ii) at an interior point where the derivative either is zero or else fails to exist. Accordingly, points where $f'(x) = 0$, or where $f'(x)$ fails to exist, and end points of the domain are called **critical points of the domain** of f.

A direct consequence of the preceding discussion is stated in

Theorem 11.3b. If the function f is continuous on a closed interval $a \leq x \leq b$ and if $f(a) = f(b)$, then there exists at least one critical point x_c in the open interval $a < x < b$.

PROOF: If f is a constant function, then $f'(x) = 0$ for all x in the open interval. In this case, any such point may be taken as the x_c of the theorem. If f is not a constant function, then, as a consequence of the continuity of f, it must attain both a maximum and a minimum value on the closed interval (see Theorem 8.5g). But since $f(a) = f(b)$ and $f(x)$ is not a constant, one of these extremes must occur at a point inside the interval. By Theorem 11.3a this point is a critical point of the domain, and the proof is complete.

If, in addition to the continuity of f on the closed interval $a \leq x \leq b$, it is known that f' exists on the open interval, then for the x_c of Theorem 11.3b, we have $f'(x_c) = 0$. We state this result as

Theorem 11.3c. *Rolle's Theorem.* If the function f is continuous on the closed interval $a \leq x \leq b$, with $f(a) = f(b)$, and if $f'(x)$ exists everywhere on the open interval $a < x < b$, then there is at least one number x_c, $a < x_c < b$, such that $f'(x_c) = 0$.

PROOF: This is a direct consequence of the preceding two theorems. The details are left to the reader.

Example 11.3a. Show that the function f defined by

$$f(x) = |1 - x^2|, \qquad -2 \leqq x \leqq 2,$$

illustrates Theorems 11.3b and 11.3c.

Since

$$f(x) = \begin{cases} 1 - x^2 & \text{for } |x| \leqq 1, \\ x^2 - 1 & \text{for } 1 \leqq |x| \leqq 2, \end{cases}$$

it follows that f is continuous on $-2 \leqq x \leqq 2$. Moreover,

$$f'(x) = \begin{cases} -2x & \text{for } |x| < 1, \\ 2x & \text{for } 1 < |x| < 2. \end{cases}$$

Hence,

$$f'(x) = 0 \quad \text{for } x = 0,$$

and $f'(x)$ does not exist at $x = -1$ or at $x = 1$. (Why?)

Thus, we have an example in which both types of critical points occur. This illustrates Theorem 11.3b. Furthermore, since $f(1) = f(-1)$ and $f'(x)$ exists for $-1 < x < 1$, we may regard the function on the interval $-1 \leqq x \leqq 1$ as an illustration of Rolle's Theorem (see Figure 11.3b).

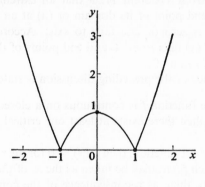

FIGURE 11.3b

We shall next give conditions that are sufficient for a continuous function to have an extreme at a critical point in the interior of the domain. The first set of conditions is an easy consequence of the interpretation of the sign of the derivative.

Theorem 11.3d. Let f be a continuous function over a $\mathfrak{N}(x_c, h)$, where x_c is a critical point of the domain of f, and let $f'(x)$ exist for $x \in \mathfrak{N}^*(x_c, h)$. Then

    (i) $f'(x) > 0$ for $x \in \mathfrak{N}^*(x_c^-, h)$ and $f'(x) < 0$ for $x \in \mathfrak{N}^*(x_c^+, h) \Rightarrow f(x_c)$ is a maximum;

(ii) $f'(x) < 0$ for $x \in \mathfrak{N}^*(x_c^-, h)$ and $f'(x) > 0$ for $x \in \mathfrak{N}^*(x_c^+, h) \Rightarrow f(x_c)$
   is a minimum;

(iii) $f'(x)$ of constant sign for $x \in \mathfrak{N}^*(x_c, h) \Rightarrow f(x_c)$ is not an extreme.

PROOF: For (i), the given conditions imply that f is an increasing function over the left neighborhood of x_c and a decreasing function over the right neighborhood. Hence $f(x_c)$ must be the greatest value that the function assumes over $\mathfrak{N}(x_c, h)$. Thus, $f(x_c)$ is a maximum.

The argument for (ii) and (iii) is similar to that for (i) and is consequently left to the reader.

Theorem 11.3d is frequently called the **first derivative test** for maxima and minima. Its use is illustrated in the next three examples.

Example 11.3b. Find the extremes of the function defined by

$$f(x) = 2x^3 + 3x^2 - 12x.$$

For this function,

$$f'(x) = 6x^2 + 6x - 12 = 6(x^2 + x - 2) = 6(x + 2)(x - 1).$$

If $f'(x) = 0$, then $x = -2$ or 1. Since f' is continuous for all x, the only possible extremes are at these critical values of x.

We also find that

$$f'(x) > 0 \quad \text{for } x < -2 \text{ and for } x > 1$$

and

$$f'(x) < 0 \quad \text{for } -2 < x < 1.$$

Consequently, there is a left neighborhood $\mathfrak{N}^*(-2^-)$ such that $f'(x) > 0$ for $x \in \mathfrak{N}^*(-2^-)$, and there is a right neighborhood $\mathfrak{N}^*(-2^+)$ such that $f'(x) \leq 0$ for $x \in \mathfrak{N}^*(-2^+)$. This means that $f(-2) = 20$ is a relative maximum of f (see Figure 11.3c).

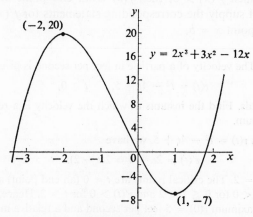

FIGURE 11.3c

Similarly, there is a left neighborhood $\mathfrak{N}^*(1^-)$ such that $f'(x) < 0$ for $x \in \mathfrak{N}^*(1^-)$ and there is a right neighborhood $\mathfrak{N}^*(1^+)$ such that $f'(x) > 0$ for $x \in \mathfrak{N}^*(1^+)$. This shows that $f(1) = -7$ is a relative minimum of the function (see Figure 11.3c).

To summarize, we see that $f'(-2) = 0$, and $f'(x)$ changes sign from plus to minus as x increases through the value -2. The point $(-2, 20)$ is a maximum point on the graph of f. Also $f'(1) = 0$, and $f'(x)$ changes sign from minus to plus as x increases through the value 1. The point $(1, -7)$ is a minimum point on the graph.

Example 11.3c. Find the extremes of the function defined by $f(x) = x^{2/3}$.

In this example,

$$f'(x) = \tfrac{2}{3}x^{-1/3}, \qquad x \neq 0.$$

The domain of the function is all $x \in \mathcal{R}$, yet there is no value of x for which $f'(x) = 0$. The only possible critical value of x is $x = 0$, for which $f'(x)$ does not exist. Since $f'(x) < 0$ for $x < 0$, and $f'(x) > 0$ for $x > 0$, $f(0) = 0$ is a relative minimum of the function. The graph of the function is shown in Figure 11.3d.

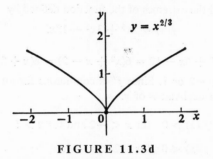

FIGURE 11.3d

An obvious modification of the first derivative test applies in the case of end point extremes. For example, if the interval is $a \leq x \leq b$, and there is a $\mathcal{R}^*(a^+, h)$ over which $f'(x) > 0$, then $f(a)$ is an end point minimum. Why? The reader should supply the corresponding statements for $f'(x) < 0$ and also for the right end point $x = b$.

Example 11.3d. The velocity of a particle in feet per second is given by

$$v(t) = t^2 - 4t + 5, \qquad t \geq 0,$$

where t is in seconds. Find the instants at which the velocity is a relative maximum or a relative minimum.

For the equation $v(t) = t^2 - 4t + 5$, we have

$$v'(t) = 2t - 4 = 2(t - 2).$$

If $v'(t) = 0$, then $t = 2$. The critical points are $t = 0$ (an end point) and $t = 2$.

We see that $v'(t) < 0$ for $0 \leq t < 2$ and $v'(t) > 0$ for $t > 2$. Hence, it follows that v has an end point maximum $v(0) = 5$ feet per second and a relative minimum $v(2) = 1$ foot per second. Explain. The graph of the function v is shown in Figure 11.3e.

Before considering a second test for maxima and minima, we need the following refinement of Theorem 11.1c on increasing and decreasing functions.

Theorem 11.3e. Let f be defined on an open interval $a < x < b$ and let f have a continuous first derivative at the point x_0 in this interval Then,

(i) $f'(x_0) > 0 \Rightarrow$ there exists a $\mathfrak{N}(x_0, h)$ over which f is an increasing function;

(ii) $f'(x_0) < 0 \Rightarrow$ there exists a $\mathfrak{N}(x_0, h)$ over which f is a decreasing function.

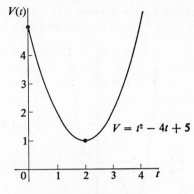

FIGURE 11.3e

PROOF: Since the derivative f' is by hypothesis continuous at x_0, it follows from Theorem 8.5c that

$f'(x_0) > 0 \Rightarrow$ there exists a $\mathfrak{N}(x_0, h)$ such that $f'(x) > 0$ for all $x \in \mathfrak{N}(x_0, h)$.

Hence, by Theorem 11.1c, f is an increasing function on this neighborhood. This completes the proof of (i). The modification of this argument needed to prove (ii) is left for the reader.

The next theorem is the **second derivative test** for maxima and minima.

Theorem 11.3f. Let f be defined on the open interval $a < x < b$ and let $f'(x_c) = 0$, where x_c is a point in the interval. Then, if f has a continuous second derivative at x_c,

(i) $f''(x_c) > 0 \Rightarrow f(x_c)$ is a minimum;

(ii) $f''(x_c) < 0 \Rightarrow f(x_c)$ is a maximum.

PROOF: The hypothesis $f''(x_c) > 0$ in (i) implies the existence of a neighborhood of x_c over which f' is an increasing function (by Theorem 11.3e). Since $f'(x_c) = 0$, then over the left neighborhood it must be that $f'(x) < 0$ and over the right neighborhood $f'(x) > 0$. Thus the first derivative test shows that $f(x_c)$ is a minimum.

The proof of (ii) is similar and so is left for the reader.

Example 11.3e. Find the extremes of the function f defined by $f(x) = 3x^4 + 4x^3$.

For this function, we find

$$f'(x) = 12x^3 + 12x^2 = 12x^2(x + 1).$$

If $f'(x) = 0$, then $x = -1$ or $x = 0$. Since f' is continuous for all x, there can be no other critical points. We also have

$$f''(x) = 36x^2 + 24x = 12x(3x + 2),$$

which shows that f'' is continuous for all x.

At $x = -1$, we find $f''(-1) = (-12)(-1) > 0$ so that $f(-1) = -1$ is a minimum.

At $x = 0$, we have $f''(0) = 0$ so that the second derivative test does not apply. However, $f''(x)$ changes sign as x passes through the value zero. Therefore, $(0, 0)$ is an inflection point. The fact that $f'(0) = 0$ means that the inflectional tangent is parallel to the x-axis. The graph of the function is shown in Figure 11.3f.

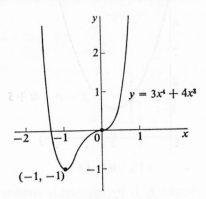

FIGURE 11.3f

Example 11.3f. Find the extremes of the function $f .=. \{(x, y)\}$, where x and y are given by the parametric equations

$$x = t^3 - 1, \qquad y = t^2 + t.$$

Using the procedure of Section 10.6 for finding derivatives of functions defined by parametric equations, we obtain

$$D_x y = \frac{D_t y}{D_t x} = \frac{2t + 1}{3t^2} = \tfrac{2}{3}t^{-1} + \tfrac{1}{3}t^{-2},$$

and, letting y' denote $D_x y$, we get

$$D_x^2 y = \frac{D_t y'}{D_t x} = \frac{-\tfrac{2}{3}t^{-2} - \tfrac{2}{3}t^{-3}}{3t^2} = -\tfrac{2}{9}(t^{-4} + t^{-5}).$$

These results show that $D_x y$ and $D_x^2 y$ are both continuous for all nonzero values of t. Furthermore,

$$D_x y = 0 \Leftrightarrow \tfrac{2}{3}t^{-1} + \tfrac{1}{3}t^{-2} = 0$$
$$\Leftrightarrow \tfrac{1}{3}t^{-2}(2t + 1) = 0 \Leftrightarrow t = -\tfrac{1}{2}.$$

For $t = -\tfrac{1}{2}$, $D_x^2 y = -\tfrac{2}{9}(16 - 32) > 0$. Therefore, by Theorem 11.3f, the function f has a minimum for this value of t. Since $x = -\tfrac{9}{8}$ and $y = -\tfrac{1}{4}$, then $(-\tfrac{9}{8}, -\tfrac{1}{4})$ is a minimum point on the graph of f and $-\tfrac{1}{4}$ is the minimum value of f.

At $t = 0$, $D_x y$ and $D_x^2 y$ do not exist. However, the fact that

$$D_x y = \tfrac{1}{3}t^{-2}(2t + 1)$$

shows that $D_x y$ does not change sign at $t = 0$, so that the function f has neither a maximum nor a minimum value at $t = 0$.

Exercises 11.3

In each of Numbers 1 to 4, use the first derivative test and find the extremes of the function defined by the given formula.

1. $f(x) = 1 - 2x - x^2, \; -3 \leq x \leq 3$.   3. $F(x) = 4/(x^2 + 4)$.
2. $g(x) = x^2 - x^4, \; -2 \leq x \leq 2$.   4. $H(x) = x^{1/2} + x^{-1/2}$.

In each of Numbers 5 to 8, use the second derivative test and find the extremes of the function defined by the given formula.

5. $h(x) = x^3 - 6x^2 + 12x - 8$.   7. $f(x) = x^2/\sqrt{x^2 + 4}$.
6. $A(x) = 12x^5 + 45x^4 + 40x^3$.   8. $g(x) = a^2x/(x^2 + a^2)$.

In each of Numbers 9 to 20, use any convenient test and find the maximum and minimum points on the given curve.

9. $y = x^{2/3} + 4, \; -2 \leq x \leq 3$.   15. $y = x - (x - 1)^{3/2}$.
10. $y = x^3 - 5x^5$.   16. $y = 4x - 3(x + 1)^{4/3}$.
11. $y = |x^3 - 1|$.   17. $x = 1 - 3t, \; y = 9t^2 - 12t + 6$.
12. $y = x^2 - |3x - 2| + 1$.   18. $x = t^{-2}, \; y = t^2 + t$.
13. $y = x^3/(x^2 + 4)$.   19. $x = t^{-2}, \; y = t^2 - t + 1$.
14. $x = 1 + (y - 2)^{1/2}$.   20. $x = 1 + t, \; y = t^2 - 4t + 5$.

21. Determine conditions on a, b, c, and d so that the function defined by

$$f(x) = ax^3 + bx^2 + cx + d$$

will have a minimum at $x = 0$ and a maximum at $x = 1$.

22. Show that the function defined by $f(x) = x^k - kx, \; k \neq 1$, always has a maximum at $x = 1$ for $0 < k < 1$ and a minimum at $x = 1$ for $k > 1$.

23. Discuss the maximum and minimum points of the curve $y = x^m(1 - x)^n$, where m and n are positive integers greater than 1. Consider various combinations such as m and n both even, both odd, and so on.

★24. Let f be a function that is differentiable at every point of an interval $a \leq x \leq b$ and let $f'(a)$ and $f'(b)$ have opposite signs. Prove that there is a critical point of the domain in the open interval $a < x < b$. *Hint:* Use an indirect proof.

★25. Let f be a continuous function on $a \leq x \leq b$ with just one critical point x_c in $a < x < b$. Suppose that $f(a)$ and $f(b)$ are both less than $f(x_c)$. Prove that $f(x_c)$ is a maximum. *Hint:* Consider the two intervals $a < x < x_c$ and $x_c < x < b$. Can f have an extreme in either of these intervals?

26. If $f'(a) = 0$, $f''(a) = 0$, and $f''(x) > 0$ for x in some deleted neighborhood of a, prove that $f(a)$ is a minimum of the function f.

★27. For each of the following sets of conditions make a sketch of the graph of a continuous function f near the point where $x = a$, if possible. If the information is not consistent, explain.

(a) $f'(a), f''(a)$ both fail to exist;

$$x \in \mathfrak{N}^*(a^-, h) \Rightarrow f''(x) > 0;$$
$$x \in \mathfrak{N}^*(a^+, h) \Rightarrow f''(x) < 0.$$

(b) $f'(a), f''(a)$ both fail to exist;

$$x \in \mathfrak{N}^*(a^-, h) \Rightarrow f'(x) > 0, f''(x) < 0;$$
$$x \in \mathfrak{N}^*(a^+, h) \Rightarrow f'(x) > 0, f''(x) > 0.$$

11.4 THE MEAN VALUE THEOREM FOR DERIVATIVES

A geometric interpretation of Rolle's Theorem (Theorem 11.3c) is as follows. Let $y = f(x)$ be the equation of a curve with f continuous on the closed interval $a \leq x \leq b$ and having a derivative everywhere on the open interval $a < x < b$. If $f(a) = f(b)$, then there is at least one point $(\xi, f(\xi))$, with $a < \xi < b$, where the tangent to the curve is horizontal (see Figure 11.4a).

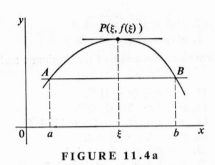

FIGURE 11.4a

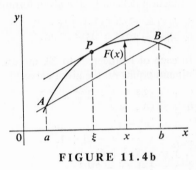

FIGURE 11.4b

Clearly, if the curve APB were turned so that the line AB became not parallel to the x-axis, the geometric content of Rolle's Theorem would still be true; that is, the tangent line through P would still be parallel to the secant line AB. This apparently evident result has an important analytic formulation which is given in

Theorem 11.4a. *The Mean Value Theorem for Derivatives.* Let f be a continuous function on the closed interval $a \leq x \leq b$, and let f' exist everywhere on the open interval $a < x < b$. Then there is at least one point ξ in the open interval such that

(1)
$$f'(\xi) = \frac{f(b) - f(a)}{b - a}.$$

PROOF: The geometric discussion of the preceding paragraphs gives a good hint for the proof of this theorem. Consider Figure 11.4b; let $F(x)$ be the directed distance, measured parallel to the y-axis, from the secant AB to the curve. Since the distance from the x-axis to the curve is $y = f(x)$, and that to the secant line is

$$y = f(a) + \frac{f(b) - f(a)}{b - a}(x - a),$$

$F(x)$ is the difference between these and is given by

$$F(x) = f(x) - f(a) - \frac{f(b) - f(a)}{b - a}(x - a).$$

But $F(a) = 0$ and $F(b) = 0$. Also, because of the conditions on f, F is a continuous function on $a \leq x \leq b$ and F' exists on $a < x < b$. Thus, Rolle's

Theorem applies to F, and so there is a number ξ in $a < x < b$ such that $F'(\xi) = 0$. Hence, by differentiating F, we find

$$F'(\xi) = 0 = f'(\xi) - \frac{f(b) - f(a)}{b - a},$$

so that

$$f'(\xi) = \frac{f(b) - f(a)}{b - a},$$

as was to be shown.

Equation (1) is often written in the form obtained by solving for $f(b)$

(2) $\qquad f(b) = f(a) + (b - a)f'(\xi), \qquad a < \xi < b.$

Furthermore, the same theorem clearly applies to any closed interval from a to x on which f is continuous if f is differentiable (at least on the open interval). Therefore,

(3) $\qquad f(x) = f(a) + (x - a)f'(\xi),$

where ξ is between a and x.

Replacing a by x and x by $x + h$, we get $h = x - a$, and Equation (3) becomes

(4) $\qquad f(x + h) = f(x) + hf'(x + \theta h), \quad \text{where } 0 < \theta < 1.$

Note that the last formula simply replaces the ξ of the preceding formulas by $x + \theta h$, which is between x and $x + h$ for $0 < \theta < 1$ regardless of the sign of h.

Example 11.4a. Find the value (or values) of ξ which the Mean Value Theorem predicts if

$$f(x) = x^3 - x, \qquad a = 0, b = 3.$$

We find

$$f(a) = 0, \quad f(b) = 24, \quad \text{and} \quad f'(x) = 3x^2 - 1.$$

Therefore, for the required value ξ, we must have

$$3\xi^2 - 1 = \frac{24 - 0}{3 - 0} = 8,$$

so that

$$\xi^2 = 3.$$

Since the number ξ must lie in the interval $0 < x < 3$, the positive root of this equation must be used. Hence $\xi = \sqrt{3}$.

Example 11.4b. Use the Mean Value Theorem to estimate the value of $\sqrt{110}$.

Let $f(x) = . \sqrt{x}$ and use the Mean Value Theorem in the form

$$f(x + h) = f(x) + hf'(x + \theta h), \qquad 0 < \theta < 1.$$

Then, since

$$f'(x) = \frac{1}{2\sqrt{x}} \quad \text{and} \quad f'(x + \theta h) = \frac{1}{2\sqrt{x + \theta h}},$$

we have

$$\sqrt{x+h} = \sqrt{x} + \frac{h}{2\sqrt{x+\theta h}}.$$

With $x = 100$ and $h = 10$, this formula gives

(5) $$\sqrt{110} = 10 + \frac{5}{\sqrt{100 + 10\theta}}.$$

Since $f(x)$ increases with x (why?), we have

(6) $$\sqrt{100} < \sqrt{100 + 10\theta} < \sqrt{110}.$$

Accordingly, the left portion of (6) along with (5) shows that

$$\sqrt{110} < 10 + \frac{5}{\sqrt{100}} = 10.5.$$

Similarly, the right portion of (6) along with (5) gives

$$\sqrt{110} > 10 + \frac{5}{\sqrt{110}} = 10 + \frac{\sqrt{110}}{22}$$

or

$$\frac{21}{22}\sqrt{110} > 10,$$

so that

$$\sqrt{110} > \frac{220}{21} = 10.476^{+}.$$

A combination of the two results now shows that

$$10.476 < \sqrt{110} < 10.5.$$

The following basic theorem is an easy but quite important consequence of the Mean Value Theorem.

Theorem 11.4b. If two functions are both continuous on the closed interval $a \leqq x \leqq b$ and have the same derivative on the open interval $a < x < b$, then the difference of the two functions is a constant function.

PROOF: Let the two functions be denoted by F and G, respectively. By hypothesis

$$F'(x) = G'(x) \quad \text{on } a < x < b.$$

Write $H(x) = F(x) - G(x)$, so that

$$H'(x) = 0 \quad \text{on } a < x < b.$$

Then, by the Mean Value Theorem in the form given by (3), we have

$$H(x) = H(a) + (x - a)H'(\xi)$$
$$= H(a), \text{ a constant,}$$

since H' has the value zero at every point of the interval. This completes the proof.

Note that this theorem guarantees the uniqueness to within an additive constant of the inverse derivative (when it exists) of a given function. We have already used this result repeatedly in Section 9.5.

Exercises 11.4

In each of Numbers 1 to 4, find the value of ξ that is guaranteed by the Mean Value Theorem, Equation (1):

1. $f(x) = 1 - x^2$, $a = 0$, $b = 2$.
2. $f(x) = \sqrt{x}$, $a = 1$, $b = 9$.
3. $f(x) = x^3 - 3x^2$, $a = 1$, $b = 4$.
4. $f(x) = x/(x - 4)$, $a = 5$, $b = 8$.

In each of Numbers 5 to 8, find the value of θ that is guaranteed by the Mean Value Theorem, Equation (4):

5. $f(x) = x^3$, $x = 1$, $h = 2$.
6. $f(x) = 1/x$, $x = 1$, $h = 3$.
7. $f(x) = \sqrt{1 - x^2}$, $x = 0$, $h = 1$.
8. $f(x) = x + \sqrt{x}$, $x = 1$, $h = 8$.

9. If $f(x) = ax^2 + bx + c$, show that the value of θ guaranteed by the Mean Value Theorem, Equation (4), is $\frac{1}{2}$ for all values of x and h. Give a geometric interpretation of this fact.
10. Does the Mean Value Theorem apply if $f(x) = 1/x$, $a = -1$, $b = 3$? Explain.
11. Does the Mean Value Theorem apply if $f(x) = x^{1/3}$, $a = -1$, $b = 1$? Explain.
12. Use the Mean Value Theorem to estimate

$$\text{(a) } \sqrt{40}; \quad \text{(b) } \sqrt{66}; \quad \text{(c) } \sqrt[3]{27.2}; \quad \text{(d) } \sqrt[5]{35}.$$

13. If $f(x) = x^{1/3}$, $x = 0$, $h > 0$, show that the value of θ guaranteed by the Mean Value Theorem, Equation (4), is independent of the value of h.
14. Does the result of Number 13 apply to other powers of x? Explain.

11.5 APPLICATIONS TO CURVE SKETCHING

In Chapter 5 we discussed a number of techniques and ideas useful in making a rapid sketch of the graph of an equation. With the additional techniques available, since we have studied the properties of the derivative, it is now possible to extend the discussion of curve sketching. It is desirable to minimize the plotting of points other than crucial points on the graph. With practice it is possible to produce accurate sketches using only a few plotted points.

The techniques of Chapter 5 were limited to the following items.

(1) Finding where the curve cuts the axes.
(2) Determining if any simple symmetry exists.
(3) Finding horizontal and vertical asymptotes if there are any.

We shall add three items to this list.

(4) Finding the extent of the curve—that is, the set of values of x for which y is real and the set of values of y for which x is real.

(5) Investigating maximum and minimum points and determining intervals over which the curve rises or falls.

(6) Investigating concavity and inflection points.

The following examples show how these techniques can be employed.

Example 11.5a. Discuss and sketch the graph of

$$y = \frac{x}{x^2 + 1}.$$

The first line of the following items may be determined by inspection.

(1) Intercepts: $x = 0 \Leftrightarrow y = 0$.

(2) Symmetry: the graph possesses symmetry with respect to the origin; replacement of (x, y) by $(-x, -y)$ yields the original equation, and hence $(-x, -y)$ satisfies the equation if (x, y) does.

(3) Asymptotes: $y = 0$ is a horizontal asymptote.

(4) There are no restrictions on the values of x. However, if we solve for y, we obtain

$$x = \frac{1 \pm \sqrt{1 - 4y^2}}{2y}.$$

This formula shows that for x to be real we must have

$$1 - 4y^2 \geqq 0 \quad \text{or} \quad 4y^2 \leqq 1.$$

Hence $|2y| \leqq 1$, and

$$|y| \leqq \tfrac{1}{2} \quad \text{or} \quad -\tfrac{1}{2} \leqq y \leqq \tfrac{1}{2}.$$

This is the interval of permissible values of y.

(5) Since

$$y' = \frac{1 - x^2}{(x^2 + 1)^2},$$

it is easy to see that the curve has a tangent with slope 1 at the origin. Furthermore, since $y' = 0$ for $x = \pm 1$, the curve has horizontal tangents at $(-1, -\tfrac{1}{2})$ and $(1, \tfrac{1}{2})$. The denominator of y' is positive, so that the sign of y' is the same as the sign of $1 - x^2$. We find

$$y' > 0 \quad \text{for } -1 < x < 1,$$

and

$$y' < 0 \quad \text{for } x < -1 \text{ and } x > 1.$$

Thus, the curve is falling in the interval $x < -1$, rising in the interval $-1 < x < 1$, and falling in the interval $x > 1$. Therefore $(-1, -\tfrac{1}{2})$ is a minimum point and $(1, \tfrac{1}{2})$ is a maximum point.

(6) The second derivative is calculated, after simplification, to be

$$y'' = \frac{2x(x^2 - 3)}{(x^2 + 1)^3}.$$

Points where $y'' = 0$ are found to be $(0, 0)$, $(\sqrt{3}, \tfrac{1}{4}\sqrt{3})$, and $(-\sqrt{3}, -\tfrac{1}{4}\sqrt{3})$. That these are points of inflection may be shown by investigating the sign changes in y''. In fact, $y'' > 0$ for $2x(x^2 - 3) > 0$, or for $x(x - \sqrt{3})(x + \sqrt{3}) > 0$. The solution of this inequality is $-\sqrt{3} < x < 0$ and $\sqrt{3} < x$. Also, $y'' < 0$ for $x < -\sqrt{3}$ and $0 < x < \sqrt{3}$. The curve is thus concave down for $x < -\sqrt{3}$ and $0 < x < \sqrt{3}$, and concave up for $-\sqrt{3} < x < 0$ and $\sqrt{3} < x$.

Before sketching the curve, we try to display all of the preceding information at once, as in Figure 11.5a.

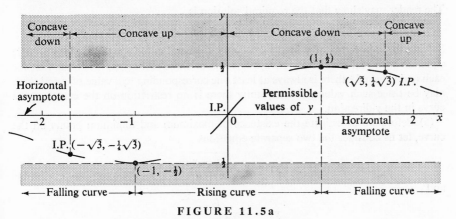

FIGURE 11.5a

With this much information given, it should be clear how the graph must appear. The desired curve, which is shown in Figure 11.5b, is known as a *serpentine*.

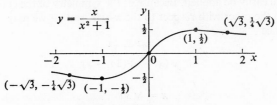

FIGURE 11.5b

Example 11.5b. Discuss and sketch the curve

$$x^3 + xy^2 + ay^2 - 3ax^2 = 0, \qquad a > 0.$$

(1) From the equation it follows that if $x = 0$, then $y = 0$, and if $y = 0$, then $x^3 - 3ax^2 = 0$ so that $x = 0$ or $x = 3a$. Hence the curve crosses the axes at $(0, 0)$ and at $(3a, 0)$.

(2) Since y appears to even powers only, the curve must be symmetric to the x-axis. This is the only simple symmetry that the curve has.

(3) We solve for y to obtain

$$y = \pm x \sqrt{\frac{3a - x}{x + a}},$$

which shows that there is a vertical asymptote at $x = -a$, provided that $x = -a$ is within or on the boundary of the extent of the curve. As we shall see in (4), the extent of the curve is $-a < x \leq 3a$, so that the curve lies to the right of and is asymptotic to the line $x = -a$.

(4) To determine the extent of the curve—that is, the set of values of x for which y is real—it is necessary to solve the inequality

$$\frac{3a - x}{x + a} \geq 0.$$

The reader may show that the required solution is

$$-a < x \leq 3a.$$

Solving for x in terms of y involves solving a general cubic equation. Since a cubic equation with real coefficients always has one or three real roots, it is clear that for each real value of y there is always at least one corresponding real value of x and there may be three such values. Consequently there is no restriction on the extent of the curve in the y-direction.

(5) Before we investigate the existence of maximum and minimum points on the curve, let us consider the two separate equations

$$y_1 = x \sqrt{\frac{3a - x}{x + a}},$$

and

$$y_2 = -x \sqrt{\frac{3a - x}{x + a}}.$$

These two formulas represent two "branches" of the curve. The two equations can now be properly associated with functions rather than relations and the theorems of calculus can more easily be applied. Because of the symmetry of the curve, one branch is symmetrical to the other with respect to the x-axis, so that we may restrict the discussion to y_1. Since

$$y_1' = \frac{3a^2 - x^2}{\sqrt{(x + a)^3 (3a - x)}},$$

we see that

$$x = \sqrt{3}a$$

is a critical value of x. (Why is $x = -\sqrt{3}a$ not a critical value?) The nature of the point at $x = \sqrt{3}a$ can be investigated easily by determining the intervals over which the curve is rising or falling. The reader may show that for

$$-a < x < \sqrt{3}a, \qquad y_1' > 0,$$

and for

$$\sqrt{3}a < x < 3a, \qquad y_1' < 0,$$

so that the curve is rising and falling, respectively, over these intervals. This shows, of course, that the point $x = \sqrt{3}a$, $y = 1.2a$ (approx.) is a maximum point.

It has already been shown that $x = -a$ is a vertical asymptote. The fact that $|y_1'| \to \infty$ as $x \to -a^+$ is consistent with this result. However, at $x = 3a$ something new shows up; namely, as $x \to 3a^-$, $y_1' \to -\infty$. This indicates that there is a vertical tangent at $(3a, 0)$ or that the curve approaches the x-axis vertically as $x \to 3a^-$.

(6) The reader may show that

$$y_1'' = -\frac{12a^3}{(3a - x)^{3/2}(x + a)^{5/2}}.$$

From this we see that no points of inflection occur and that the curve is concave down everywhere.

Figure 11.5c displays all of the preceding information for y_1. In Figure 11.5d we see the completed graph. The curve is known as a *trisectrix* because of the property that

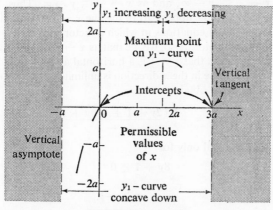

FIGURE 11.5c

the angle α shown in the figure is one-third of angle β if $x > 0$, $y > 0$ for $P(x, y)$. The concave down portion of the curve corresponds to y_1 and the concave up portion, which is obtained by symmetry, corresponds to y_2.

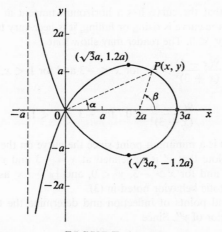

FIGURE 11.5d

Example 11.5c. Discuss and sketch the graph of

$$y = \frac{x(x - 3)}{(x + 3)^2}.$$

(1) When $x = 0$, then $y = 0$, and when $y = 0$, then $x(x - 3) = 0$, so that $x = 0$ or $x = 3$. The intercepts are 0 on both axes and 3 on the x-axis.

(2) There is no simple type of symmetry. (Why?)

(3) Since for positive h sufficiently small,

$$x \in \mathfrak{N}(-3, h) \Rightarrow x(x - 3) > 0,$$

we see that as $x \to -3^-$, $y \to \infty$, and as $x \to -3^+$, $y \to \infty$. Thus, both portions of the curve are asymptotic to the upper part of the line $x = -3$. This kind of asymptotic behavior is characteristic of equations in which a factor such as $x + 3$ appears to an even power in the denominator. Also, we see that as $x \to \infty$, $y \to 1^-$, and as $x \to -\infty$, $y \to 1^+$. (Why?) This shows that $y = 1$ is a horizontal asymptote.

(4) The extent of the curve in the x-direction is unlimited since y is real for all real x, $x \ne -3$. Solving for x, we obtain

$$x = -\frac{3}{2}\left\{\frac{2y + 1 \pm \sqrt{8y + 1}}{y - 1}\right\},$$

which indicates that x is real only for

$$8y + 1 \geqq 0$$

or

$$y \geqq -\tfrac{1}{8}.$$

The extent of the curve in the y-direction is thus $y \geqq -\tfrac{1}{8}$.

(5) In order to search for maximum and minimum points, we need to find the derivative of y with respect to x. The reader may show that

$$y' = \frac{9(x - 1)}{(x + 3)^3},$$

from which we see that the curve has a horizontal tangent at $(1, -\tfrac{1}{8})$. To find the intervals over which the curve is rising or falling, it is necessary to find the values of x for which $y' > 0$ or $y' < 0$. The reader may show that

$$\frac{9(x - 1)}{(x + 3)^3} > 0 \quad \text{for } x < -3 \text{ and for } 1 < x,$$

and that

$$\frac{9(x - 1)}{(x + 3)^3} < 0 \quad \text{for } -3 < x < 1.$$

Therefore, $(1, -\tfrac{1}{8})$ is a minimum point since the curve on the left is falling and on the right is rising. Note that y' is undefined at $x = -3$ and y' changes sign there; for $x < -3$, $y' > 0$ and for $x > -3$, $y' < 0$, and $|y'| \to \infty$ as $x \to -3$. This substantiates the asymptotic behavior noted in (3).

(6) In order to find points of inflection and determine the type of concavity we investigate the behavior of y''. Since

$$y'' = 18\frac{3 - x}{(x + 3)^4},$$

we see that there is an inflection point at $(3, 0)$. In fact, it is easy to see that

$$y'' > 0 \quad \text{for } x < -3 \text{ and for } -3 < x < 3,$$

and that

$$y'' < 0 \quad \text{for } 3 < x,$$

from which we further deduce that the curve is concave up for $x < -3$ and $-3 < x < 3$, and is concave down for $3 < x$.

It is sometimes helpful in sketching a curve to find the slope of the curve at crucial points such as points where the curve cuts the axes and points of inflection. In this example we find

$$y' = -\tfrac{1}{3} \quad \text{at } (0, 0),$$

and

$$y' = +\tfrac{1}{12} \quad \text{at } (3, 0).$$

We now display the preceding information in Figure 11.5e.

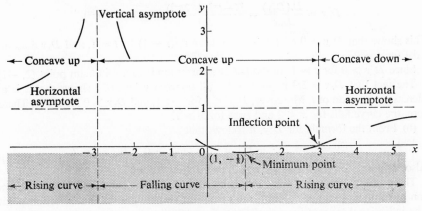

FIGURE 11.5e

The completed graph is shown in Figure 11.5f.

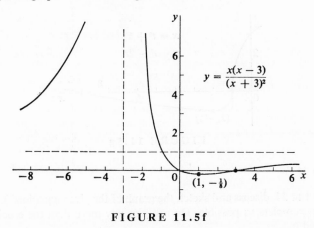

FIGURE 11.5f

Example 11.5d. Discuss and sketch the curve defined by the parametric equations

$$x = t^3 + 1, \qquad y = t^2 - 2t.$$

(1) For $y = 0$, we have $t = 0$ or $t = 2$, so that $x = 1$ or $x = 9$. For $x = 0$, we have $t = -1$, so that $y = 3$. Thus the curve cuts the axes at $(1, 0)$, $(9, 0)$, and $(0, 3)$.

(2) There is no simple symmetry.

(3) and (4) Since x and y are continuous functions of t for all real values of t and the range of x consists of all real numbers, there can be no vertical asymptotes. Moreover, $y \to \infty$ as $|t| \to \infty$, so that there can be no horizontal asymptotes. In the formula for y, we complete the square in t to get $y = (t - 1)^2 - 1$, which shows that $y \geq -1$.

(5) We have

$$D_x y = \frac{D_t y}{D_t x} = \frac{2t - 2}{3t^2} = \tfrac{2}{3}(t^{-1} - t^{-2})$$

and

$$D_x^2 y = \frac{D_t(D_x y)}{D_t x} = \frac{\tfrac{2}{3}(-t^{-2} + 2t^{-3})}{3t^2} = \tfrac{2}{9}(2t^{-5} - t^{-4}).$$

This shows that $D_x y = 0 \Leftrightarrow t^{-1} - t^{-2} = 0 \Leftrightarrow t^{-2}(t - 1) \Leftrightarrow t = 1$, and $D_x y$ does not exist for $t = 0$.

Since $D_x^2 y > 0$ for $t = 1$, this value of t corresponds to a minimum point $(2, -1)$.

The fact that $D_t x = 3t^2$ is positive for all nonzero values of t shows that x is an increasing function of t. Moreover, $D_x y < 0$ for $t < 1$, and $D_x y > 0$ for $t > 1$. Therefore, the curve falls for $x < 2$ and rises for $x > 2$.

(6) From the formula for $D_x^2 y$, it follows that

$$D_x^2 y = 0 \Leftrightarrow 2t^{-5} - t^{-4} = 0 \Leftrightarrow t^{-5}(2 - t) = 0 \Leftrightarrow t = 2.$$

Also, $D_x^2 y < 0$ for $t < 0$ and for $t > 2$, and $D_x^2 y > 0$ for $0 < t < 2$.

These results mean that the curve is concave down for $x < 1$ and for $x > 9$, and concave up for $1 < x < 9$. Thus, the point $(1, 0)$ where $t = 0$ is an inflection point. The inflectional tangent is vertical there since $|D_x y| \to \infty$ as $t \to 0$. The point $(9, 0)$, where $t = 2$, is an inflection point with the tangent having a slope $1/6$.

The curve is shown in Figure 11.5g.

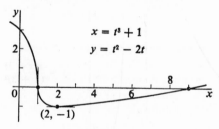

$$x = t^3 + 1$$
$$y = t^2 - 2t$$

FIGURE 11.5g

Exercises 11.5

In Numbers 1 to 24, discuss and sketch the graph of the given equation(s). Make your discussion as complete as possible. Do not plot any more than the crucial points if you can avoid it.

1. $y = x^4 - 8x^2$.
2. $y = 3x^5 - 5x^3$.
3. $y = \sqrt{x^2 - 9}$.
4. $y = -\sqrt{9 - x^2}$.
5. $y = x^2 + |x|$.
6. $y = |x| + |x^2 - 1|$.

7. $y = \dfrac{x - 1}{x + 1}$.

8. $y = \dfrac{x}{\sqrt{x - 9}}$.

9. $y = x\sqrt{x^2 - 4}$.

10. $xy^2 + 4x = y$.

11. $y = \dfrac{|x|}{x^2 + 1}$.

15. $y = \dfrac{x(5 - x)}{(x + 2)^2}$.

12. $y = \dfrac{x^2}{\sqrt{x^2 + 2}}$.

16. $y = \dfrac{x(x + 2)}{(x - 2)^2}$.

13. $y = (2x + 10)(x - 3)^{2/3}$.

★14. $x^2y + xy^2 = 16$.

17. $y = \dfrac{8a^3}{x^2 + 4a^2}$ (the Witch of Agnesi).

★18. $x^3 + y^3 = 6xy$ (the Folium of Descartes). *Hint:* Let $y = tx$, and get parametric equations $x = f(t)$, $y = g(t)$.

19. $x^3 + ax^2 + xy^2 - ay^2 = 0$, $a > 0$ (the strophoid). *Hint:* Let $y = tx$, and get parametric equations $x = f(t)$, $y = g(t)$.

20. $(x - 3)y^2 = x^2(x + 6)$.

21. $x = t - 2$, $y = t^2 + 1$.

22. $x = t^2 + 1$, $y = t^3 - 1$.

23. $x = \frac{1}{2}t^2 - 6$, $y = \frac{1}{2}t^3 - 6t$.

24. $x = t^{-2}$, $y = t^2 + 1$.

★25. Let $y_1 = f(x)$ and $y_2 = g(x)$ be the equations of two curves symmetric to each other with respect to the x-axis.
   (a) How are the functions f and g related?
   (b) Prove that a maximum value of y_1 is a minimum value of y_2.
   (c) Prove that if $y_1 = f(x)$ is concave down for $a < x < b$, then $y_2 = g(x)$ is concave up for the same interval.

26. For what value of a will the curve $y = 9x^{-1} + a(x - 3)$ have a minimum point at $x = 3$?

11.6 APPLICATIONS OF MAXIMA AND MINIMA

One of the important reasons for studying the calculus is its usefulness in applications. The scientist and the engineer may appreciate the inherent beauty of the subject, but for them its principal attraction lies in its use as a tool for furthering the study of natural phenomena. In any such application, the user of mathematics attempts to build what is sometimes called a "mathematical model" of the phenomenon under consideration. Often this takes the form of an equation involving the observable quantities, or variables. The interpretation of this equation may yield new insight into the phenomenon under investigation or the equation may be used to predict results under certain combinations of values of the variables.

Almost always the phenomenon, when examined closely, is too complex to be accurately described in any simple way, but sometimes simplifying or "idealizing" the problem still gives worthwhile results. For instance, the exact equations describing the flight of a stone would be virtually impossible to write and solve if one were to account for such things as air drag caused by the shape and surface conditions of the stone, the rotation of the stone, the variations in the earth's gravitational field, the rotation of the earth beneath the flying stone, stray winds, or the attraction of the moon. However, for most purposes, all such effects, including air friction, can be neglected without seriously affecting the accuracy of prediction of the trajectories of thrown stones. In general, the degree of idealization permitted usually depends upon the accuracy desired.

In this section the discussion will be restricted to simple applications that do not require extensive background in the sciences. Furthermore, the problems to be considered are generally simplified to a greater degree than is desirable in actual practice. A few are obviously contrived for the benefit of the reader, but these should not be thought of as any the less valuable, since the main purpose of these problems is to give experience in constructing and interpreting mathematical models from given information.

These exercises concern the finding of maxima or minima of physically meaningful quantities. Although it is difficult to give detailed, universal rules for the solution of such problems, a few general remarks on procedure are in order.

(1) Determine the quantity to be maximized or minimized.

(2) Express this quantity in terms of a single independent variable, using any constraint equations connecting the variables to eliminate unwanted variables in favor of the chosen variable. This procedure will lead to an equation that defines a function. Be sure to specify the domain of this function.

(3) Find the derivative of the function described in (2), and then find the critical points of the domain. Do not omit the end points or the points where the derivative fails to exist.

(4) Determine the nature of suspected extremes by appropriate tests.

(5) Check the results in all possible ways to see that every condition of the problem is satisfied. In particular, make sure that domain restrictions are observed.

The following examples illustrate the procedures for solving problems of this type.

Example 11.6a. Find the area of the largest rectangle that can be inscribed in a right triangle of sides 5, 12, and 13 inches, respectively, if one vertex of the rectangle is on the longest side of the triangle (see Figure 11.6a).

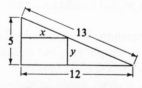

FIGURE 11.6a

It seems intuitively evident that the rectangle has maximum area for some configuration near that in the figure, for as $x \to 12$, $y \to 0$ and $A \to 0$, and as $y \to 5$, $x \to 0$ and $A \to 0$. Moreover, the area of the rectangle shown is far from being zero.

With the variables x and y shown in the figure, we can express the area as $A = xy$. To express A as a function of only one of these variables we must find an equation involving x and y from which we can substitute for one variable in terms of the other. By using similar triangles, we may write the proportion

$$\frac{y}{5} = \frac{12 - x}{12},$$

from which it follows that

$$y = \tfrac{5}{12}(12 - x).$$

Thus,

$$A = \tfrac{5}{12}(12 - x)x = \tfrac{5}{12}(12x - x^2), \qquad 0 \leq x \leq 12.$$

Hence

$$\frac{dA}{dx} = \tfrac{5}{12}(12 - 2x),$$

and the critical value $x = 6$ results from the equation $dA/dx = 0$. This critical value yields a maximum for A because

$$\frac{d^2 A}{dx^2} = -\tfrac{5}{6} < 0.$$

For $x = 6$, we find

$$y = \tfrac{5}{12}(12 - 6) = \tfrac{5}{2} \text{ inches}$$

and

$$A = (6)(\tfrac{5}{2}) = 15 \text{ square inches.}$$

It is evident that the end point values $x = 0$ and $x = 12$ give the minimum value $A = 0$.

An alternative way of handling dA/dx is to employ the ideas of implicit differentiation. Thus, from $A = xy$, it follows that

$$\frac{dA}{dx} = y + x\frac{dy}{dx}.$$

But the equation defining the relationship between x and y may be written as

$$5x + 12y = 60,$$

and differentiated to obtain

$$5 + 12\frac{dy}{dx} = 0.$$

By solving this equation for dy/dx and substituting the result into the formula for dA/dx, we get

$$\frac{dA}{dx} = y + x(-\tfrac{5}{12}).$$

Thus, if $dA/dx = 0$, then

$$y = \tfrac{5}{12}x,$$

which may be substituted into the equation $5x + 12y = 60$ to give

$$5x + 12(\tfrac{5}{12}x) - 60 = 0,$$

an equation which leads to the same critical value, $x = 6$, we obtained before.

A more difficult example, in which the existence of a maximum at other than an end point depends upon the parameters of the problem, follows next.

Example 11.6b. Find the point on the ellipse

$$\frac{x^2}{a^2} + \frac{y^2}{b^2} = 1, \qquad a > 0, b > 0,$$

that is farthest from $(0, -b)$ (see Figure 11.6b).

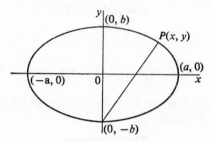

FIGURE 11.6b

The distance from $P(x, y)$ to $(0, -b)$ is

$$d = \sqrt{x^2 + (y + b)^2}.$$

Since $d \geq 0$, then d and d^2 must have extreme values for the same values of x and y. (Why?) Hence, let us try to find the maximum of

$$z .=. d^2 = x^2 + (y + b)^2.$$

We can eliminate x by using the fact that $P(x, y)$ is a point on the ellipse. Thus, $b^2x^2 + a^2y^2 = a^2b^2$, and upon solving this equation for x^2 and substituting the result into the expression for z, we get

$$z = f(y) = a^2 - \frac{a^2}{b^2} y^2 + (y + b)^2, \qquad -b \leq y \leq b.$$

Consequently,

$$D_y z = -2\frac{a^2}{b^2} y + 2(y + b),$$

and

$$D_y z = 0 \Rightarrow y = \frac{b^3}{a^2 - b^2}.$$

Let us next investigate this critical value. If $a > b > 0$, then

$$\frac{b^3}{a^2 - b^2} > 0.$$

Furthermore,

$$D_y^2 z = -2\frac{a^2}{b^2} + 2.$$

This result indicates that we have a maximum if $-(a^2/b^2) + 1 < 0$ or $a > b$. Everything appears to be in order until we ask whether the value of y for the indicated maximum is an element of the set of permissible values of y; that is, $-b \leq y \leq b$. Since

$$y = \frac{b^3}{a^2 - b^2} > 0,$$

we must determine whether

$$\frac{b^3}{a^2 - b^2} \leqq b.$$

If this last inequality is true, then, since $0 < b < a$, we may divide by b to obtain

$$\frac{b^2}{a^2 - b^2} \leqq 1$$

or

$$b^2 \leqq a^2 - b^2.$$

This inequality yields

$$a \geqq \sqrt{2}b, \qquad a > 0, b > 0.$$

By retracing our steps, we can show that if $a \geqq \sqrt{2}b$, $a > 0$, and $b > 0$, then

$$\frac{b^3}{a^2 - b^2} \leqq b.$$

That is, the critical value of y is in the range of y, provided that $a > \sqrt{2}b$, $a > 0$, $b > 0$.

Hence no maximum value of z with $D_y z = 0$ occurs unless the ellipse is sufficiently elongated. If the ellipse is nearly circular, the point of maximum distance from $(0, -b)$ is at $(0, +b)$, which is an end point of the domain of f. The same is true if the ellipse degenerates into a circle ($a = b$), or if it is elongated in the y direction ($b > a$). In summary, we may say that a maximum distance from $(0, -b)$ to $P(x, y)$ occurs when P is at the points for which $y = b^3/(a^2 - b^2)$ when $a \geqq \sqrt{2}b$, or at $(0, b)$ for $a < \sqrt{2}b$.

A type of problem to which the foregoing procedures do not apply directly is one which involves a function whose domain is a set of discrete values rather than an interval. In some cases, it is possible to approximate the behavior of such a function by means of a differentiable function on which the methods of calculus may be used. After finding the extremes of the new function, it is necessary only to check a few values of the independent variable in the neighborhoods of the critical values to determine which ones actually locate the desired extremes. These remarks are illustrated in

---

Example 11.6c. A manufacturer of boxes produces and sells them in unbroken lots of 1000 at \$4.98 per box with \$0.05 per box reduction in price for each thousand ordered (provided two or more lots are ordered). If the boxes cost him \$3.66 each to make, find the number of thousands in an order that will yield the maximum gross profit.

Let n be the number of thousands of boxes ordered. Then the price per box is \$$(4.98 - 0.05n)$, and the total number of dollars received is

$$1000(4.98 - 0.05n)n.$$

The manufacturer's gross profit is

$$P = 1000(4.98 - 0.05n)n - 3.66n(1000)$$
$$= 1320n - 50n^2, \qquad n \in \mathfrak{N}.$$

We now replace n, the discrete variable, by x, a continuous variable, and differentiate

$$P = 1320x - 50x^2$$

to get

$$D_x P = 1320 - 100x.$$

For $D_x P = 0$, we have $x = 13.2$, which yields a maximum for P as may be verified by calculating $D_x^2 P$. This answer indicates that we should investigate $n = 13$ and $n = 14$. Since $P = \$8710$ for $n = 13$ and $P = \$8680$ for $n = 14$, and P increases with increasing x for $x < 13.2$ and decreases with increasing x for $x > 13.2$, we see that $n = 13$ gives the maximum profit.

Exercises 11.6

1. Find two numbers whose sum is 12 and whose product is a maximum.
2. Find two positive numbers whose sum is 12 and the product of whose squares is a maximum.
3. A line segment A units long joins the points $P(0, y)$ and $Q(x, 0)$. Find x and y such that the line segment, the x-axis, and the y-axis form a triangle of maximum area.
4. Show that a square is the rectangle of largest area with a specified (constant) perimeter.
5. Show that a square is the rectangle of minimum perimeter for a specified (constant) area.
6. Find the largest rectangle with one side on the x-axis and inscribed in the area bounded by the x-axis and the curve whose equation is $y = 27 - x^2$.
7. A sheet of tin 16 inches wide by 21 inches long is to be used to make an open rectangular box by cutting a square from each corner of the sheet and folding up the sides. What should be the length of the side of the cut-out square to furnish a box of maximum volume?
8. Find the point on the parabola $y^2 = 4x$ that is nearest the point $(0, -3)$.
9. An open rectangular box with a square base is to have a fixed volume V. What must be the relation between the inside dimensions if the inside surface area is to be a minimum?
10. What is the area of the largest isosceles triangle that can be inscribed in a circle of radius a?
11. What is the altitude of the circular cylinder of greatest volume that can be inscribed in a circular cone of radius a and height h?
12. Find the rectangle of maximum perimeter that can be inscribed in the ellipse $x^2/a^2 + y^2/b^2 = 1$.
13. A window consists of a rectangle surmounted by a semicircle. Find the shape that would give the most light for a fixed perimeter.
14. A container manufacturer wishes to design a closed cylindrical can with a specified fixed volume V, but of such radius r and height h that the amount of tinplate used in making the container is a minimum. Find the ratio of the height to the radius that he should use.
15. Work Number 14 if the can is to have an open top.

16. Find the area of the rectangle of maximum area that can be inscribed in the ellipse $4x^2 + 9y^2 = 36$.

17. The electromotive force of a battery is E volts and the internal resistance is r ohms. The formula $I = E/(R + r)$ gives the current I (amperes) that will flow when a resistor of R ohms is connected across the battery terminals. If the formula $P = I^2R$ gives the power P (watts) developed in the resistor, find the value of R for which the power will be a maximum.

18. A rancher wishes to build a small corral against the side of a steep, straight cliff in order to save on fencing. Determine the proportions of the rectangular corral that will require the least amount of fence for a given area.

19. The strength of a wooden beam of rectangular cross section is proportional to the width of the beam and the square of its depth. Determine the proportions of the strongest beam that can be sawed from a round log.

20. The amplitude I of the alternating current flowing in an electric circuit with inductance L, capacitance C, and resistance R in series is given by

$$I = \frac{V}{\sqrt{R^2 + \left(L\omega - \dfrac{1}{\omega C}\right)^2}},$$

where V is the amplitude of the alternating voltage and ω is $2\pi f$, where f (cycles per second) is the frequency of the voltage. Show that I is a maximum when

$$f = \frac{1}{2\pi\sqrt{LC}} \text{ cycles per second.}$$

21. A loan shark, whose monthly interest charge is limited by law to 3%, finds that the amount of money people will invest with him is proportional to the interest rate that he will pay them. If he can lend out all the money that people will invest with him, find the interest rate that he should pay them in order to maximize his monthly profit.

★22. A manufacturer of electronic assemblies finds that for no more than 1000 assemblies per week the cost for labor and parts is $\$A$ per assembly. In addition he has fixed costs (overhead) of $\$C$ regardless of the number assembled. If he exceeds 1000 assemblies per week, then overtime and inefficiencies due to crowding, and so on, raise the price per assembly by $\$B$ for each assembly over one thousand. (If he produces 1003 assemblies, the cost for the 1001st unit is $\$A + \$B$, the cost for the 1002nd unit is $\$A + \$2B$, and the cost for the 1003rd unit is $\$A + \$3B$. One would expect B to be very small, of course.) If he can sell all that he can produce at a fixed price of $\$P$ per assembly, $P > A$, find the number per week that he should try to produce to maximize his gross profit F. *Hint:* Set up expressions for F, for $n \leq 1000$, and $n \geq 1000$. For the case of $n \geq 1000$, see what conditions must be satisfied in order to have a solution. Investigate carefully what happens at $n = 1000$.

23. In connecting a water line to a building at A (see Figure 11.6c), the contractor finds that he must connect to a certain point C on the water main which lies under the paved parking lot of a shopping center. It will cost him $20.00 per foot to dig, lay pipe, fill, and resurface the parking lot, but only $12.00 per foot to lay pipe along the edge. Find the distance from the store water inlet (point A) to the

point *B*, where he should turn the water line and go directly to point *C* in order to minimize his cost.

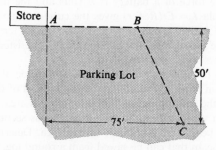

FIGURE 11.6c

★24. Work Number 23 with the dimensions 50 feet by 75 feet replaced by *a* feet by *b* feet.

11.7 TIME-RATE PROBLEMS

A number of applications of the derivative are concerned with the rate of change of one or more related quantities with respect to time. The relationship between these quantities ordinarily may be expressed by means of one or more equations, and differentiation of both members of each such equation with respect to time gives an equation relating the time-rates of change. This procedure is illustrated in the following examples.

Example 11.7a. Car *A* is traveling east at 30 miles per hour and car *B* is traveling north at 22.5 miles per hour. Both cars are traveling toward a junction *O* of two roads as indicated in Figure 11.7a. (a) At what rate are the cars approaching each other at

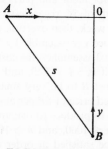

FIGURE 11.7a

the instant when car *A* is 300 feet and car *B* is 400 feet from the junction? (b) What is the rate of change of the speed of one car with respect to the other?

(a) Let *s* be the distance between the two cars so that the value of $D_t s$ will be the answer to this question. We have (see Figure 11.7a)

$$s^2 = x^2 + y^2,$$

so that, by differentiation with respect to t, we get

$$s\, D_t s = x\, D_t x + y\, D_t y.$$

For $x = 300$ and $y = 400$, $s = 500$. Also

$$D_t x = -44 \text{ feet per second}$$

and

$$D_t y = -33 \text{ feet per second.}$$

Hence,

$$D_t s = \frac{(300)(-44) + (400)(-33)}{500}$$

$$= -52.8 \text{ feet per second.}$$

The minus sign indicates that s is decreasing with the time.

(b) By differentiating both members of the equation

$$s\, D_t s = x\, D_t x + y\, D_t y$$

with respect to t, we obtain

$$s\, D_t^2 s + (D_t s)^2 = x\, D_t^2 x + (D_t x)^2 + y\, D_t^2 y + (D_t y)^2.$$

But $D_t x$ and $D_t y$ are both constant in this problem, so that $D_t^2 x = 0$ and $D_t^2 y = 0$. Accordingly, for $x = 300$ and $y = 400$, we have

$$500\, D_t^2 s + (-52.8)^2 = (-44)^2 + (-33)^2,$$

and

$$D_t^2 s = -0.47 \text{ (approx.) foot per second per second.}$$

The negative sign indicates that the speed of one car relative to the other is decreasing algebraically at the instant in question. However, since by (a) the relative speed is negative, the absolute value of the speed must be increasing.

Example 11.7b. An optical tracking device has a lens of focal length 6 inches that forms the image of a moving object on a small screen. If the object is moving away at a speed of 20 feet per second, how fast must the lens be moving and in what direction in order to keep the object in focus at the instant when it is 50 feet away from the lens? The simple lens equation is

$$\frac{1}{u} + \frac{1}{v} = \frac{1}{f},$$

where u is the object distance, v the image distance, and f the focal length, all measured in the same units.

By differentiation with respect to t, we get from the lens equation

$$-\frac{1}{u^2}\, D_t u - \frac{1}{v^2}\, D_t v = 0$$

or

$$D_t v = -\frac{v^2}{u^2}\, D_t u.$$

With $f = \frac{1}{2}$ (foot) and $u = 50$ (feet), the lens equation becomes

$$\frac{1}{50} + \frac{1}{v} = 2,$$

so that

$$v = \frac{50}{99}.$$

Since $D_t u = 20$, we get

$$D_t v = -\left(\frac{50}{99}\right)^2 \left(\frac{1}{50}\right)^2 (20)$$

$$= -\frac{20}{9801} \text{ foot per second}$$

$$= -0.024 \text{ (approx.) inch per second.}$$

Thus the lens must be moving toward the screen at the rate of approximately 0.024 inch per second.

Exercises 11.7

1. As a spherical rubber balloon is being inflated, its volume increases at the rate of 2π cubic inches per second. At what rate is the surface area changing?

2. A storage tank is in the shape of an inverted circular cone with a diameter of 8 feet and a height of 6 feet. At what rate is water running out of the tank when the depth is 3 feet and is decreasing at the rate of 6 inches per minute?

3. A man 6 feet tall walks at the rate of 4 miles per hour toward a street light that hangs 16 feet directly above the sidewalk. At what rate is the end of his shadow moving? Is the end of his shadow accelerating?

4. In number 3, if the light is located at a height of 16 feet above the street and 20 feet from the walk, find the rate at which the end of the man's shadow moves. At what rate is the man's shadow becoming shorter?

5. A rope 32 feet long is attached to a weight and passed over a pulley 16 feet above the ground. The other end of the rope is pulled away along the ground at the rate of 3 feet per second. At what rate does the weight rise at the instant when the other end of the rope is 12 feet from its initial point?

6. A plane 2 miles above the ground is flying due south at a speed of 600 miles per hour. It flies directly over a car going due east at 60 miles per hour. How fast is the distance between the plane and the car increasing 1 minute later?

7. A swimming pool is 100 feet long, 30 feet wide, 12 feet deep at one end and 2 feet deep at the other. If water is being let into the pool at the rate of 500 cubic feet per minute, at what rate is the surface rising when the greatest depth is 6 feet? 10 feet?

8. One end of a spring is fastened to a point 10 inches up on the y-axis and the lower end just reaches the origin. The lower end is then pulled along the x-axis at the rate of 2 inches per minute. At what rate is the spring being stretched at the instant when the lower end reaches the point 8 inches from the origin?

9. The two ends of a rubber strip are fastened at the points $(-3, 0)$ and $(3, 0)$, respectively. If the midpoint of the strip is moved up the y-axis at the rate of 4 inches per minute, at what rate is the strip being stretched at the end of 2 minutes?

10. Two stones are dropped from the edge of a cliff, one 5 seconds after the other. At what rate does the subsequent distance between the stones increase before the first stone hits the ground? *Hint:* The formula $s = \frac{1}{2}gt^2$ gives the distance passed through in t seconds by a freely falling body.

11. Two ships leave from the same point. The first leaves at 9 A.M. and sails due east at a speed of 10 miles per hour. The second leaves at 10 A.M. and sails 30° east of north at a speed of 15 miles per hour. At what rate are the ships separating at noon?

12. A mass of air is expanding isothermally in accordance with Boyle's Law, $pv = C$, where p is the pressure, v is the volume, and C is a constant. At a certain instant the pressure is 50 pounds per square inch and the volume is 100 cubic inches. If the volume is decreasing at the rate of 4 cubic inches per second, how is the pressure changing?

13. A train leaves a station at a certain time and travels north at the rate of 60 miles per hour. A second train leaves the same station one hour later and goes east at a rate of 40 miles per hour. At what rate are the trains separating 3 hours after the second train leaves the station? Is the rate of change of distance between the two trains a constant? Explain.

Summary of Chapter 11

The important ideas in this chapter are not so much the methods used in solving particular problems as the general principles that are illustrated by the various methods used in those problems. These general principles and the fundamental ideas relating to them are

(1) the definition of increasing and decreasing functions over an open interval, and of monotonic functions (Section 11.1);

(2) the condition that a function be increasing or decreasing expressed mathematically in terms of the derivative (Section 11.2);

(3) concavity of a curve and its relationship to the second derivative (Section 11.2);

(4) points of inflection and conditions that a point be a point of inflection expressed in terms of the derivatives (Section 11.2);

(5) maximum and minimum points, relative extremes, and conditions for an extreme (Section 11.3);

(6) critical points of a curve (Section 11.3);

(7) the first derivative test and the second derivative test for maxima and minima (Section 11.3);

(8) the Mean Value Theorem for Derivatives, and the application of this important theorem in proving that two functions having the same derivative over an interval differ by a constant (Section 11.4);

(9) the use of the first and second derivatives in curve sketching (Section 11.5);

(10) applications of maxima and minima and the use of implicit differentiation for cases involving a side condition (Section 11.6);

(11) applications of the derivative to time-rate problems (Section 11.7)

Chapter 12 The Definite Integral

12.1 THE SUMMATION NOTATION

Two fundamental geometric problems, which eventually led to the development of many important mathematical concepts, are those of finding the circumference of a circle and the area enclosed by a circle. Similar problems arise in connection with finding the area of any plane figure bounded by a curved line, or in finding the volume of any solid bounded by a curved surface. When mathematical techniques were developed to handle these problems, it was found that these same techniques could be used to solve a variety of physical problems, such as that of finding the work done by a force acting through a given distance, or that of finding the force exerted on a dam by the water contained by the dam.

In this chapter, we shall develop the mathematical techniques for solving such problems. In order to do this, we must constantly be concerned with sums of quantities, such as the sum of areas of rectangles, expressed in the form

$$a_1 + a_2 + \cdots + a_n.$$

Since such expressions occur so frequently and are clumsy to use extensively, mathematicians have developed a more compact and efficient notation for them.

Definition 12.1a. Let $\{a_1, a_2, \ldots, a_n\}$ be a set of n numbers. Then

$$\sum_{k=1}^{n} a_k .=. a_1 + a_2 + \cdots + a_n.$$

The notation $\sum_{k=1}^{n} a_k$ is simply a shorthand form for the sum indicated by the symbol

$$a_1 + a_2 + \cdots + a_n$$

and is read "the sum of a_k from $k = 1$ to $k = n$." This notation is called the *summation notation*. The symbol Σ is the Greek letter capital sigma. The subscript k on the sigma is called the *index* of the summation, and the subscript 1 and the superscript n indicate the range of the index.

For example, we may write

(a) $\displaystyle\sum_{k=1}^{n} k^2 = 1^2 + 2^2 + 3^2 + \cdots + n^2,$

(b) $\displaystyle\sum_{k=1}^{5} x^k = x + x^2 + x^3 + x^4 + x^5,$ or

(c) $\displaystyle\sum_{k=1}^{n} \frac{2k}{1+k} = 1 + \frac{4}{3} + \frac{3}{2} + \frac{8}{5} + \cdots + \frac{2n}{1+n}.$

The reader should note the basic properties

$$\sum_{k=1}^{n} (a_n + b_n) = \sum_{k=1}^{n} a_n + \sum_{k=1}^{n} b_n$$

and

$$\sum_{k=1}^{n} ca_n = c \sum_{k=1}^{n} a_n,$$

which result directly from the basic laws of addition and multiplication.

Any convenient letter may be used for the index of a summation. For example, the expressions

$$\sum_{k=1}^{n} k^2, \quad \sum_{p=1}^{n} p^2, \quad \sum_{\sigma=1}^{n} \sigma^2$$

all represent

$$1^2 + 2^2 + 3^2 + \cdots + n^2.$$

It is also convenient on occasion to have the range of the index begin with 0 or some integer other than 1. The definition can be modified accordingly. Ordinarily the index does not include negative integers in its range, but there is no reason why negative integers need be excluded. Expressions in which the index may take on negative integral values simply do not occur as frequently as expressions with the index having positive integral values. For example, we may have

$$\sum_{k=5}^{7} \frac{1}{k} = \frac{1}{5} + \frac{1}{6} + \frac{1}{7},$$

$$\sum_{k=0}^{5} a^k = a^0 + a^1 + a^2 + a^3 + a^4 + a^5,$$

or

$$\sum_{k=-2}^{2} 2^k = 2^{-2} + 2^{-1} + 2^0 + 2^1 + 2^2$$
$$= \tfrac{1}{4} + \tfrac{1}{2} + 1 + 2 + 4.$$

Some additional examples will help to illustrate this notation.
(a) The equation $1 + 2 + 3 + \cdots + n = \frac{1}{2}n(n+1)$ becomes

$$\sum_{k=1}^{n} k = \tfrac{1}{2}n(n+1).$$

(b) The expression

$$\sqrt{1 - \frac{1}{n^2}} + \sqrt{1 - \frac{2^2}{n^2}} + \sqrt{1 - \frac{3^2}{n^2}} + \cdots + \sqrt{1 - \frac{n^2}{n^2}}$$

may be written as

$$\sum_{k=1}^{n} \sqrt{1 - \frac{k^2}{n^2}}.$$

(c) The expression

$$\frac{1}{10} + \frac{1}{14} + \frac{1}{18} + \frac{1}{22} + \frac{1}{26}$$

becomes

$$\sum_{k=0}^{4} \frac{1}{10 + 4k} \quad \text{or} \quad \sum_{p=2}^{6} \frac{1}{2 + 4p}.$$

This last illustration shows that a given expression may be represented in more than one way by the summation notation.

(d) $\displaystyle\sum_{k=1}^{n} (A_k + 4) = (A_1 + 4) + (A_2 + 4) + \cdots + (A_n + 4)$

$$= 4n + \sum_{k=1}^{n} A_k.$$

(e) $\displaystyle\sum_{k=-n}^{n} (k^2 + kn) = \sum_{k=-n}^{n} k^2 = 2 \sum_{k=1}^{n} k^2.$

(f) $\displaystyle\sum_{k=1}^{n} \frac{1}{k} = \sum_{k=0}^{n-1} \frac{1}{k + 1} = \sum_{k=0}^{n-1} \frac{1}{n - k}.$

The second summation in (f) amounts only to a renumbering of the terms, beginning with $k = 0$ rather than with $k = 1$; the last summation is the same as the second with the terms written in reverse order.

As a further illustration of the use of the summation notation, we shall prove the binomial theorem by means of mathematical induction.

Theorem 12.1a. *The Binomial Theorem.* Let $n \in \mathfrak{N}$. Then

$$(a + b)^n = \sum_{k=0}^{n} \binom{n}{k} a^{n-k} b^k,$$

where

$$\binom{n}{k} \doteq \frac{n(n - 1) \cdots (n - k + 1)}{k!}, \qquad k = 1, 2, \ldots, n,$$

and

$$\binom{n}{0} \doteq 1.$$

PROOF: For $n = 1$, the preceding formula becomes

$$a + b = \sum_{k=0}^{1} \binom{1}{k} a^{1-k} b^k = \binom{1}{0} a + \binom{1}{1} b = a + b,$$

which is of course correct.

Now assuming that the formula is valid for a particular value of n, say s, we have

$$(a + b)^{s+1} = (a + b)(a + b)^s = (a + b) \sum_{k=0}^{s} \binom{s}{k} a^{s-k}b^k$$

$$= a \sum_{k=0}^{s} \binom{s}{k} a^{s-k}b^k + b \sum_{k=0}^{s} \binom{s}{k} a^{s-k}b^k$$

$$= \sum_{k=0}^{s} \binom{s}{k} a^{s+1-k}b^k + \sum_{k=0}^{s} \binom{s}{k} a^{s-k}b^{k+1}.$$

In the first of these summations, let us write the first term separately, and in the second summation let us write the last term separately. Thus,

(1) $\quad (a + b)^{s+1} = a^{s+1} + \sum_{k=1}^{s} \binom{s}{k} a^{s+1-k}b^k + \sum_{k=0}^{s-1} \binom{s}{k} a^{s-k}b^{k+1} + b^{s+1}.$

Next, the second summation can be rewritten by replacing the index k by $k - 1$ to get

$$\sum_{k=0}^{s-1} \binom{s}{k} a^{s-k}b^{k+1} = \sum_{k=1}^{s} \binom{s}{k-1} a^{s+1-k}b^k.$$

This allows the two summations in Equation (1) to be combined in the form

$$\sum_{k=1}^{s} \left[\binom{s}{k} + \binom{s}{k-1} \right] a^{s+1-k}b^k = \sum_{k=1}^{s} \binom{s+1}{k} a^{s+1-k}b^k,$$

since

$$\binom{s}{k} + \binom{s}{k-1} = \frac{s(s-1) \cdots (s-k+1)}{k!} + \frac{s(s-1) \cdots (s-k+2)}{(k-1)!}$$

$$= \frac{s(s-1) \cdots (s-k+2)}{(k-1)!} \left(\frac{s-k+1}{k} + 1 \right)$$

$$= \frac{s(s-1) \cdots (s-k+2)}{(k-1)!} \left(\frac{s+1}{k} \right)$$

$$= \frac{(s+1)(s)(s-1) \cdots (s+1-k+1)}{k!} = \binom{s+1}{k}.$$

Accordingly, we use the fact that

$$\binom{s+1}{0} = 1 \quad \text{and} \quad \binom{s+1}{s+1} = 1$$

to write Equation (1) with a single summation on the right:

$$(a + b)^{s+1} = \sum_{k=0}^{s+1} \binom{s+1}{k} a^{s+1-k}b^k.$$

This shows that the validity of the binomial formula for $(a + b)^s$ implies its validity for $(a + b)^{s+1}$, and, since the formula has been shown to hold for $n = 1$, the proof by mathematical induction is complete.

Exercises 12.1

1. Write each of the following expressions in the summation notation.

   (a) $2 + 4 + 8 + \cdots + 2^n$.

   (b) $7 + 8 + 10 + \cdots + \left[7 + \dfrac{n(n+1)}{2} \right]$.

   (c) $a_1 + 2a_2 + 3a_3 + \cdots + na_n$.

   (d) $\dfrac{1}{n+1} + \dfrac{1}{n+2} + \cdots + \dfrac{1}{n+n}$.

2. If $a_1 .=. 6$ and $a_{k+1} .=. a_k + k$, show that

$$\sum_{k=1}^{n} a_k = 6n + \sum_{k=1}^{n} \frac{(k-1)k}{2}.$$

3. Write out the expressions represented by

   (a) $\displaystyle\sum_{\alpha=1}^{4} a_\alpha$;

   (d) $\displaystyle\sum_{\alpha=1}^{4} \frac{\alpha}{n-\alpha}$;

   (b) $\displaystyle\sum_{\beta=1}^{5} 2^\beta$;

   (e) $\displaystyle\sum_{k=1}^{4} \frac{(-1)^k + 1}{2}$;

   (c) $\displaystyle\sum_{k=1}^{5} \frac{1}{(n-k)}$;

   (f) $\displaystyle\sum_{k=5}^{10} \frac{1}{k}$.

4. Show that $\displaystyle\sum_{k=p}^{n} a_k = \sum_{k=1}^{n} a_k - \sum_{k=1}^{p-1} a_k, \quad p < n$.

5. Show that $\displaystyle\sum_{\alpha=1}^{n} a_\alpha = \sum_{\beta=p}^{n+p-1} a_{\beta-p+1}$.

6. Show that $\displaystyle\sum_{k=-n}^{n} k^2 = 2 \sum_{k=1}^{n} k^2$.

7. Show that $\displaystyle\sum_{k=-n}^{n} \frac{k}{n} = 0$.

8. Show that $\displaystyle\sum_{k=-n}^{n} \sqrt{1 - \left(\frac{k}{n}\right)^2} = 1 + 2 \sum_{k=1}^{n} \sqrt{1 - \left(\frac{k}{n}\right)^2}$.

9. Choose $a = b = 1$ in the binomial theorem and evaluate $\displaystyle\sum_{k=0}^{n} \binom{n}{k}$. Can you evaluate $\displaystyle\sum_{k=0}^{n} (-1)^k \binom{n}{k}$?

10. Use the results of Number 9 to evaluate $\displaystyle\sum_{k=0}^{[\![n/2]\!]} \binom{n}{2k}$.

11. Expand the following expressions using the binomial theorem:

   (a) $(2a - 3b^2)^6$;

   (c) $\left(\dfrac{x}{3} - \dfrac{3y}{2}\right)^6$;

   (b) $\left(\dfrac{a}{2} - \dfrac{2}{a^2}\right)^7$;

   (d) $(x^2 - x + 1)^4$.

12. Evaluate each of the following to five significant digits, using the binomial theorem:

$$\text{(a) } (1.02)^5; \quad \text{(b) } (1.01)^8; \quad \text{(c) } (0.98)^7.$$

13. In each of the following find the indicated term of the expansion without writing all the preceding terms:

(a) $(2a^{-1} + a^2)^{11}$; 7th term;

(b) $\left(3x + \dfrac{2}{x^2}\right)^{13}$; 8th term;

(c) $(x - \tfrac{1}{2}y^2)^{17}$; 9th term.

14. Find the coefficient of x^{14} in $\left(x^3 + \dfrac{1}{x^2}\right)^{13}$.

15. Find the coefficient of y^{-8} in $\left(\dfrac{1}{4y^3} - \dfrac{2y^2}{3}\right)^{14}$.

16. Find the term that involves no u in $\left(\dfrac{2}{u^4} + \dfrac{u^2}{4}\right)^{12}$.

17. The coefficients in the binomial theorem for successive values of n starting with $n = 1$ may be written in the form of an interesting array called Pascal's triangle. This array is

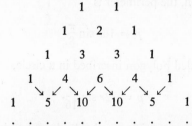

Note that, after the first line, every coefficient except the 1's in a given line may be obtained by adding the two coefficients on the preceding line on either side of the required coefficient as is indicated by the arrows in the array. This is a consequence of what formula that was obtained in this section? Notice that the second number in each line is the value of the exponent for that line. Complete the triangle through the eighth line.

⋆18. If you did Number 17, you may have observed that the coefficients in lines 1, 3, and 7 are all odd numbers. It is an interesting problem to conjecture for which lines this is so and then to prove that your conjecture is correct.

⋆19. Find a closed formula in terms of n for the value of

$$\sum_{k=1}^{n} k(k!), \quad n = 2, 3, 4, \ldots.$$

12.2 SEQUENCES

Over two thousand years ago the Greek mathematicians became interested in the problem of finding the circumference of a circle having a given radius.

At that time the exact formula, $C = 2\pi r$, which is so familiar to us today, was unknown. For that matter, even though the formula is now well known, very few persons who are not mathematicians understand the profound reasoning underlying its discovery. What is the number denoted by π? What do we mean when we speak of the "circumference of" or "distance around" a circle?

These are the questions the ancient Greeks attempted to answer. Even though they did not have the benefit of many of the mathematical tools that we use today, they were able to discover the formula $C = 2\pi r$ by reasoning in a manner essentially equivalent to that discussed in the next paragraphs.

Since it was apparently easy to assign a length to a straight line segment, the Greeks hit upon the idea of approximating the circumference of a circle by means of a sum of lengths of straight line segments, and they were able to do this with any desired degree of accuracy. Knowing how to find the perimeter of a regular polygon of 2^n sides inscribed in the circle, they simply considered perimeters of polygons of a successively greater number of sides. Thus, for a square inscribed in a circle of radius r, the perimeter is

$$p = 8r \sin \frac{\pi}{4}.$$

For an inscribed octagon, the perimeter is

$$p = 16r \sin \frac{\pi}{8}.$$

For a regular sixteen-sided polygon inscribed in a circle,

$$p = 32r \sin \frac{\pi}{16},$$

and in general, for a polygon of 2^n equal sides inscribed in a circle of radius r,

$$p = 2^{n+1}r \sin \frac{\pi}{2^n}, \qquad n = 2, 3, 4, \ldots.$$

The idea is that as n gets larger, p becomes more nearly equal to the circumference of the circle. Of course, this idea is based on the assumption that the expression $2^{n+1}r \sin (\pi/2^n)$ has a limit as $n \to \infty$. If this limit exists, it would naturally be called the circumference of the circle. It seems intuitively evident that the limit does exist. In fact, we shall show later that

$$\lim_{n \to \infty} \frac{\sin (\pi/2^n)}{\pi/2^n} = 1,$$

from which it follows that $\lim_{n \to \infty} p = 2\pi r$.

The set of numbers $\{2^{n+1}r \sin (\pi/2^n), n = 1, 2, 3, \ldots\}$ is in a one-to-one correspondence with the natural numbers, and thus the elements of the set may be regarded as having a definite order. In fact, these numbers may be considered as values in the range of a function whose domain is $\mathfrak{N}$.

Definition 12.2a. An *infinite sequence* is a function whose domain is the set $\mathfrak{N}$ of natural numbers. If s_n denotes the value of the function for the number $n \in \mathfrak{N}$, then s_n is called the *nth term* of the sequence. A sequence is usually denoted by the set of its *terms*, $\{s_n\}$.

A sequence is characterized by the fact that its elements are ordered, that is, its elements occur in a definite succession, a consequence of the order properties of the natural numbers. The term s_n is said to *precede* the term s_{n+1}, and s_{n+1} is called the *successor* of s_n, so that the sequence has a first term, a second term, and a third term, and so on. Accordingly, the notation $\{s_n\}$ is to be interpreted as a symbol for the *ordered* set of numbers

$$\{s_1, s_2, \ldots, s_n, s_{n+1}, \ldots\},$$

which is analogous to the concept of an ordered pair of numbers.

In order to specify a sequence, it is necessary that some rule of formation for its terms be given. Some examples of sequences are:

(a) $\left\{1, \frac{1}{2}, \frac{1}{3}, \frac{1}{4}, \ldots, \frac{1}{n}, \ldots\right\}$ or $\left\{s_n = \frac{1}{n}, n \in \mathfrak{N}\right\}$;

(b) $\left\{1, 0, 1, 0, \ldots, \frac{1-(-1)^n}{2}, \ldots\right\}$ or $\left\{s_n = \frac{1-(-1)^n}{2}, n \in \mathfrak{N}\right\}$;

(c) $\left\{1, \frac{1}{2}, -1, \frac{1}{3}, 1, \frac{1}{4}, -1, \ldots s_n, \ldots\right\}$, where

$$s_{2k-1} = (-1)^{k+1}, \quad s_{2k} = \frac{1}{k+1}, \quad k \in \mathfrak{N}.$$

Notice in the third example that the terms of the sequence are described by means of two formulas.

Since the terms of a sequence constitute a set of "points," it proves useful to restate the definition of a "cluster point."

Definition 12.2b. A number a is called a **cluster point of a sequence** $\{s_n\}$ if every arbitrary neighborhood $\mathfrak{N}(a, \epsilon)$ contains infinitely many terms of the sequence.

In Example (a), 0 is a cluster point. This is seen from the fact that if $n > 1/\epsilon$, then all terms $1/n, 1/(n+1), \ldots$, lie in $\mathfrak{N}(0, \epsilon)$. In Example (b), both 0 and 1 are cluster points of $\{s_n\}$; in (c), the cluster points of the sequence are -1, 0, and 1.

The last two examples illustrate the fact that an infinite sequence can have more than one cluster point. However, certain special sequences having only one cluster point are particularly important in many mathematical considerations.

Definition 12.2c. If $\{s_n\}$ is an infinite sequence having a cluster point S such that for each neighborhood of S, $\mathfrak{N}(S, \epsilon)$, there is some integer N_0 for which $s_n \in \mathfrak{N}(S, \epsilon)$ for all $n \geq N_0$, then we say that $\{s_n\}$ **converges** to the limit S and write

$$\lim_{n \to \infty} s_n = S,$$

or

$$s_n \to S \quad \text{as } n \to \infty.$$

To illustrate, consider the following example.

Example 12.2a. What is the limit, if it exists, of each of the following sequences?

(a) $\left\{1, \dfrac{3}{2}, \dfrac{7}{4}, \dfrac{15}{8}, \ldots, \dfrac{2^{n+1} - 1}{2^n}, \ldots\right\}, n = 0, 1, 2, \ldots.$

(b) $\{s_n\}$ where $s_n = (-1)^n\left(1 - \dfrac{1}{n}\right), n = 1, 2, \ldots.$

(c) $\{s_n\}$ where $s_n = 1 + \dfrac{(-1)^n}{n}, n = 1, 2, \ldots.$

In (a) it appears that 2 is a limit. To verify this conjecture, let $\mathfrak{N}(2, \epsilon)$ be an arbitrary neighborhood of 2. We want to know if there is some integer N_0 for which $s_n \in \mathfrak{N}(2, \epsilon)$ for all $n \geq N_0$. Hence, let us consider

$$|s_n - 2| = \left|\frac{2^{n+1} - 1}{2^n} - 2\right| = \frac{1}{2^n}.$$

In order to have $s_n \in \mathfrak{N}(2, \epsilon)$ we need $|s_n - 2| < \epsilon$, and this will indeed be the case if n is large enough to have $1/2^n < \epsilon$. For example, if $\epsilon = 1/1000$, N_0 can be taken as 10, since $1/2^{10} = 1/1024 < 1/1000$, and for $n > 10$, $1/2^n < 1/2^{10}$.

In (b) the sequence has two cluster points, $+1$ and -1, so that it has no limit in the sense of Definition 12.2c, and therefore the sequence does not converge. In (c) it appears that $s_n \to 1$ as $n \to \infty$. To verify this, consider

$$|s_n - 1| = \left|\frac{(-1)^n}{n}\right| = \frac{1}{n}.$$

Since $1/n < \epsilon$ if $n > N_0$, where

$$N_0 = [\![1/\epsilon]\!],$$

it follows that

$$\lim_{n \to \infty} s_n = 1.$$

If the terms of an infinite sequence do not decrease as n increases, that is, if $s_{n+1} \geq s_n$ for all n, the sequence is said to be *nondecreasing*. Similarly. if $s_{n+1} \leq s_n$ for all n, then the sequence is said to be *nonincreasing*. Nondecreasing and nonincreasing sequences will be of particular interest to us in the succeeding sections of this chapter. Furthermore, we shall be concerned for the most part with bounded infinite sequences—that is, with sequences having the property that there exist two numbers, a and b, such that

$$a \leq s_n \leq b \quad \text{for all } n.$$

As in the case of functions in general, a is called a *lower bound* and b is called an *upper bound* of the sequence (see Section 8.5).

We state without proof the following basic theorem, which should appear highly plausible to the reader.

Theorem 12.2a. A bounded infinite sequence has a least upper bound, and a greatest lower bound.

As illustrations, we refer to the sequences given in Example 12.2a. These illustrations show that the greatest lower bound and the least upper bound need not themselves be elements of the sequence.

(a) Since

$$s_n = \frac{2^{n+1} - 1}{2^n} = 2 - \frac{1}{2^n},$$

and $1/2^n$ is arbitrarily small for all sufficiently large values of n, the sequence has the least upper bound 2. It also has the greatest lower bound 1, since the greatest value of $1/2^n$ occurs for $n = 0$.

(b) Since

$$s_n = (-1)^n \left(1 - \frac{1}{n}\right), \qquad n = 1, 2, \ldots,$$

and $1/n$ is arbitrarily small for all sufficiently large values of n, the sequence has the least upper bound 1 and the greatest lower bound -1.

(c) Since

$$s_n = 1 - \frac{1}{n}, \qquad n = 1, 2, \ldots,$$

the sequence has the least upper bound 1 and the greatest lower bound 0.

For bounded nondecreasing (nonincreasing) sequences we have the following major results which are indispensable tools in the succeeding discussions.

Theorem 12.2b. A bounded nondecreasing infinite sequence converges to its least upper bound. That is, if B is the least upper bound of $\{s_n\}$, then $\lim_{n\to\infty} s_n = B$.

PROOF: Consider an arbitrary left neighborhood of B, say $\mathfrak{N}(B^-, \epsilon)$. There must be at least one element, say s_m, of the sequence $\{s_n\}$ in this neighborhood, otherwise $B - \epsilon$ is an upper bound of the sequence, contrary to the hypothesis that B is the *least* upper bound. However, the sequence is nondecreasing, so that

$$s_m \leq s_{m+1} \leq s_{m+2} \leq \cdots.$$

Consequently, $s_n \in \mathfrak{N}(B^-, \epsilon)$ for all $n \geq m$, which, by Definition 12.2c, means that

$$\lim_{n\to\infty} s_n = B.$$

Theorem 12.2c. A bounded nonincreasing infinite sequence converges to its greatest lower bound. That is, if A is the greatest lower bound of $\{s_n\}$, then $\lim_{n\to\infty} s_n = A$.

PROOF: The proof is left as an exercise for the reader.

Example 12.2b. Show that the sequence $\{s_n\}$, where

$$s_n = \sum_{k=n}^{2n} \frac{1}{k} = \frac{1}{n} + \frac{1}{n+1} + \frac{1}{n+2} + \cdots + \frac{1}{2n},$$

converges to a limit A such that $A \geq \frac{1}{2}$.

We first show that the sequence $\{s_n\}$ has a lower bound $a \geq \frac{1}{2}$. For this purpose, we observe that

$$s_n = \frac{1}{n} + \frac{1}{n+1} + \frac{1}{n+2} + \cdots + \frac{1}{2n}$$

is the sum of $n + 1$ terms, the smallest of which is $1/(2n)$. Accordingly, for all n, the sum of these terms must be greater than the number of terms times the smallest of them; that is,

$$s_n > (n+1)\left(\frac{1}{2n}\right) = \frac{1}{2} + \frac{1}{2n} > \frac{1}{2}.$$

Next, it can be shown that the sequence is a decreasing one. Consider the difference

$$s_n - s_{n+1} = \sum_{k=n}^{2n} \frac{1}{k} - \sum_{k=n+1}^{2n+2} \frac{1}{k}$$

$$= \frac{1}{n} + \sum_{k=n+1}^{2n} \frac{1}{k} - \left(\sum_{k=n+1}^{2n} \frac{1}{k} + \frac{1}{2n+1} + \frac{1}{2n+2}\right)$$

$$= \frac{1}{n} - \frac{1}{2n+1} - \frac{1}{2n+2} = \frac{3n+2}{n(2n+1)(2n+2)}.$$

Since this last fraction is positive for all $n \in \mathfrak{N}$, it follows that $s_n > s_{n+1}$.

We have thus demonstrated that $\{s_n\}$ is a decreasing sequence with a lower bound $\frac{1}{2}$ (not necessarily the greatest lower bound). Hence, by Theorems 12.2a and 12.2c, the sequence converges to a number A which is not less than $\frac{1}{2}$; that is,

$$\lim_{n \to \infty} s_n = A \geq \frac{1}{2}.$$

Exercises 12.2

In each of Numbers 1 to 12, write out the first five terms, find the cluster points, and find the limit, if it exists, for the sequence whose general term is given.

1. $s_n = \dfrac{n}{n+3}$.

2. $s_n = \dfrac{n^2 + 2n + 1}{2n^2 - 2n + 1}$.

3. $s_n = (-1)^n 2^{-n}$.

4. $s_n = \cos n\pi$.

5. $s_n = (-1)^n \left(1 - \dfrac{(-1)^n}{2^n}\right)$.

6. $s_n = \dfrac{1 + (-1)^n}{2} 2^n$.

7. $s_n = a^n$, $a \in \mathfrak{R}$.

8. $s_{2k-1} = \dfrac{1}{2} \sin \dfrac{k\pi}{2}$, $s_{2k} = (-1)^k \left(1 - \dfrac{1}{k}\right)$, $k = 1, 2, 3, \ldots$.

9. $s_n = \dfrac{2^{-n} - 2^n}{2^{-n} + 2^n}$.

10. $s_n = \sin \dfrac{n\pi}{2} + \cos \dfrac{n\pi}{2}$.

11. $s_n = \dfrac{(n-1)^3 - (n+1)^3}{n^2}$.

12. $s_{2k-1} = k$, $s_{2k} = \dfrac{(-1)^k}{2}$, $k = 1, 2, 3, \ldots$

In each of Numbers 13 and 14, find how many terms of the given sequence are *not* included in the neighborhood of the limit of the sequence, for the given ϵ.

13. $\left\{ s_n = \dfrac{(-1)^n}{2^n} \right\}$, $\epsilon = \dfrac{1}{1000}$.

14. $\left\{ s_n = \dfrac{n+1}{2n+3} \right\}$, $\epsilon = \dfrac{1}{100}$.

Use Theorem 12.2b or Theorem 12.2c to show, in Numbers 15 to 18, that the given sequence converges.

15. $\left\{ s_n = \dfrac{2n+1}{2n+3} \right\}$.

16. $\left\{ s_n = \dfrac{3^n + 1}{3^n} \right\}$.

17. $\left\{ s_n = \displaystyle\sum_{k=1}^{n} \dfrac{1}{2^k} \right\}$.

18. $\left\{ s_n = \displaystyle\sum_{k=n+1}^{2n} \dfrac{1}{k} \right\}$.

12.3 AREA AS THE LIMIT OF AN APPROXIMATION

Archimedes (287–212 B.C.) was an outstanding person in many different respects. In addition to being the discoverer of a number of important principles in mechanics and the inventor of many ingenious devices, he was a profound mathematician. So advanced were some of his mathematical inventions that they lay forgotten or not understood for over 1800 years. The method devised by Archimedes to measure the area of a parabolic segment, for example, was not revitalized until about 1650 A.D. Apparently, Archimedes was the first person to use "limiting processes" in mathematical work. (See E. T. Bell, *The Development of Mathematics*, McGraw-Hill, New York, 1940, pages 69–72.)

Suppose we consider the problem of finding the "area" of a circle. There are really two distinct ideas associated with this problem. One is concerned with explaining what is meant by the "area" of a circle. The other deals with devising a method for finding the area.

Perhaps the concept of the "area" of a circle is clear on an intuitive basis. However, it is not necessarily evident what one means when he says "the area of a circle of radius 2 inches is 4π square inches." It is not possible to fit together squares of any size, no matter how small, that will exactly cover the area bounded by a closed curved line. There will always be overlapping (see Figure 12.3a) or there will be portions of area that are not covered by the squares. A clarification of both of these problems is provided by the following discussion.

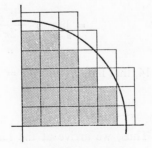

FIGURE 12.3a

Since we can easily determine the area of a triangle, let us inscribe a regular polygon of n sides in a circle of radius r, and then calculate the area of the

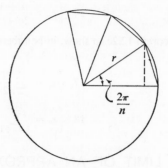

FIGURE 12.3b

polygon by partitioning it into n congruent triangles (see Figure 12.3b). The area of one of the triangles is given by

$$T_n = \frac{1}{2} r^2 \sin \frac{2\pi}{n}.$$

Hence, the area of the polygon is

$$A_n = nT_n = \frac{n}{2} r^2 \sin \frac{2\pi}{n}.$$

Although this expression does not give an "area" that satisfies our intuitive concept of the area enclosed by the circle, it does give an "approximation" to that "intuitive area." Evidently, the larger the value of n, the more closely the approximation fits the "intuitive area." Consequently, if the sequence of approximations $\{A_n\}$ has a limit as n increases without bound, it seems reasonable to *define* the area of the circle to be that limit number. Thus,

$$\text{area of the circle} = \lim_{n \to \infty} A_n$$

$$= \lim_{n \to \infty} \frac{n}{2} r^2 \sin \frac{2\pi}{n}$$

$$= \lim_{n \to \infty} \pi r^2 \frac{\sin \dfrac{2\pi}{n}}{\dfrac{2\pi}{n}}.$$

We shall prove, in Chapter 14, that $\lim_{x \to 0} (\sin x)/x = 1$, which implies that

$$\lim_{n \to \infty} \frac{\sin 2\pi/n}{2\pi/n} = 1,$$

since $2\pi/n \to 0$ as $n \to \infty$. Thus, we arrive at the familiar formula $A = \pi r^2$ for the area of a circle.

The delightful result of this approximation process immediately suggests a number of entertaining possibilities. For instance, perhaps this method can be used to define the "area" enclosed by any closed curve. Perhaps a similar process can be used in defining the volume of a solid having curved faces, such as a cone or sphere. However, a certain amount of caution is needed. How do we know that different approximation methods will always lead to the same limit? If the method of approximation is of any value at all, it must lead to unambiguous results.

For example, the area of the circle could be approximated in an entirely different way by means of rectangular strips. Will the use of such strips lead to the same formula for the area of a circle? In order to attempt an answer to this question we consider the first quadrant portion of a circle whose center is at the origin (see Figure 12.3c).

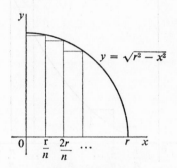

FIGURE 12.3c

Let us partition the radius along the x-axis into n equal parts each of length r/n units. The points of the partition are then $0, r/n, 2r/n, 3r/n, \ldots, nr/n = r$. Now, construct rectangles over each of the subintervals of the partition, as shown in Figure 12.3c. Since the points on the circle are described by the formula $f(x) = \sqrt{r^2 - x^2}$, the height of each rectangle can be determined by finding the value of $f(x)$ at the right hand end of each subinterval. Thus, the height of the first rectangle is $f(r/n)$, of the second, $f(2r/n)$, of the third $f(3r/n)$, and the height of the kth rectangle is $f(kr/n)$. Hence the area of the kth rectangle is

$$R_k = \frac{r}{n} f\left(\frac{kr}{n}\right) = \frac{r}{n}\sqrt{r^2 - \frac{k^2 r^2}{n^2}}.$$

The sum of all these areas gives

$$A_n = \sum_{k=1}^{n} R_k = \sum_{k=1}^{n} \frac{r}{n} f\left(\frac{kr}{n}\right) = \sum_{k=1}^{n} \frac{r}{n}\sqrt{r^2 - \frac{k^2 r^2}{n^2}}$$

as the nth approximation to the area of the quarter circle.

As before, it appears that the larger the value of n, the better will be the approximation to the "intuitive area" which is defined as $\lim_{n \to \infty} A_n$. Hence, the desired area is

$$A = \lim_{n \to \infty} \sum_{k=1}^{n} \frac{r}{n} f\left(k\frac{r}{n}\right) = \lim_{n \to \infty} \sum_{k=1}^{n} \frac{r}{n} \sqrt{r^2 - \frac{k^2 r^2}{n^2}}.$$

Unfortunately, we are not in a position to try to evaluate the limit, even if it exists, at this time. Indeed, this result illustrates the fact that this method of approximation may lead to a serious and difficult problem in evaluating limits, a problem that must be solved if the method is to be of any value to us.

However, let us continue exploring the idea of approximating area by applying the rectangular strip method to an area bounded by a simple type of curve such as $f(x) = x^2$, the x-axis, and the line $x = 1$, as shown in Figure 12.3d.

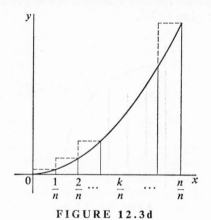

FIGURE 12.3d

The interval between 0 and 1 is partitioned into n equal parts by the points $1/n, 2/n, 3/n, \ldots, (n-1)/n$. Rectangles are constructed to cover the area being considered as shown in the figure. The width of each rectangle is $1/n$ units, and the height of the kth rectangle can be found by evaluating the function f at the point k/n, $k = 1, 2, \ldots, n$. The area of the kth rectangle is then

$$R_k = \frac{1}{n} f\left(\frac{k}{n}\right),$$

and the approximation of the area by the n rectangles is given by

$$A_n = \sum_{k=1}^{n} R_k = \sum_{k=1}^{n} \frac{1}{n} f\left(\frac{k}{n}\right) = \sum_{k=1}^{n} \frac{1}{n} \left(\frac{k}{n}\right)^2.$$

Evidently the quantity we visualize as the "area" enclosed by the given curves is the limit of A_n as $n \to \infty$. Hence we may write

$$\text{area} = \lim_{n \to \infty} \sum_{k=1}^{n} \frac{1}{n} f\left(\frac{k}{n}\right) = \lim_{n \to \infty} \sum_{k=1}^{n} \frac{1}{n} \left(\frac{k}{n}\right)^2,$$

provided the indicated limit exists. Although the last expression may appear difficult to evaluate, it can be handled very nicely with the aid of a simple formula in algebra. First, observe that

$$A_n = \sum_{k=1}^{n} \frac{1}{n} \frac{k^2}{n^2} = \frac{1}{n^3} \sum_{k=1}^{n} k^2 = \frac{1}{n^3} [1^2 + 2^2 + 3^2 + \cdots + n^2].$$

Now the expression in the brackets can be simplified since

$$1^2 + 2^2 + 3^2 + \cdots + n^2 = \frac{n}{6}(n+1)(2n+1).$$

(See Exercises 2.2, Number 6.) Hence,

$$A_n = \frac{1}{n^3} \left[\frac{n}{6}(n+1)(2n+1) \right]$$

$$= \frac{1}{3} + \frac{1}{2n} + \frac{1}{6n^2},$$

and

$$\lim_{n\to\infty} A_n = \lim_{n\to\infty} \left(\frac{1}{3} + \frac{1}{2n} + \frac{1}{6n^2} \right) = \frac{1}{3}.$$

Thus we have actually obtained a number representing the number of units of area enclosed by the given curves.

As a summary of the results of our investigation so far, we have found that in some cases the method of approximation yields complete results, whereas in other cases it may lead to a difficult limit problem. Furthermore, although we have obtained some concrete results, we have not yet demonstrated that the results obtained by the approximation process are unique—that is, that they do not depend upon the way in which the approximations are set up. Finally, although we have considered only problems involving areas, the approximation method is valuable in the investigation of volumes and in a number of other practical problems of a similar nature, some of which will be considered in the next section.

One other point worthy of mention in the last two illustrations is that in the first we used rectangles enclosed entirely within the area, as illustrated in Figure 12.3c, and in the second we used rectangles that extended beyond the confines of the area, as illustrated in Figure 12.3d. When an approximation is formed as in the first case, it is called an **inner sum** and is denoted by s_n. In the second case the approximation is called an **outer sum** and is denoted by S_n.

Exercises 12.3

1. Find the area enclosed by the lines $y = 2x + 3$, $x = 0$, $x = 2$, and the x-axis by the method of approximations.
2. Use the method of approximations to obtain the area enclosed by the curves $y = \frac{1}{4}x^2$, $x = 2$, $x = 4$, and the x-axis.
3. Use the method of approximations to find the area enclosed by the parabola $x^2 + y - 9 = 0$ and the lines $x = 0$, $x = 2$, and $y = 0$.

4. Use the method of approximations to find the area enclosed by the curves $y = \sqrt{x}$, $y = 1$, $y = 3$, and the y-axis.

5. In Figure 12.3d, the approximations were obtained by using outer sums. Use inner sums to approximate the area shown and show that as $n \to \infty$ the same result is obtained for the area as was obtained previously.

6. For the area in Number 2, show that inner sums and outer sums lead to the same value.

7. Assuming that the two methods discussed in this section for finding the area of a circle will lead to the same formula, show that

$$\lim_{n \to \infty} \sum_{k=1}^{n} \frac{1}{n} \sqrt{1 - \frac{k^2}{n^2}} = \frac{\pi}{4}.$$

8. (a) Obtain an approximation for the area bounded by $f(x) = x^3$ and the x-axis between $x = 0$ and $x = 2$ by using an outer sum S_n and an inner sum s_n.

(b) Show that $s_n < \frac{2^4}{4} < S_n$. See the hint in Part (d).

(c) If the area in (a) is between $x = 0$ and $x = b$, show that $s_n < \frac{b^4}{4} < S_n$.

(d) From (b) or (c) try to deduce the limit of s_n and S_n as $n \to \infty$, and thus obtain the area. *Hint:*

$$\sum_{\alpha=1}^{n} \alpha^3 = \frac{n^2(n+1)^2}{4}$$

(See Exercises 2.2, Numbers 1 and 16.)

12.4 OTHER APPLICATIONS OF THE LIMIT OF AN APPROXIMATION

The process used to define an area by the method of Section 12.3 is not confined to areas. It may be used in connection with a number of physical problems. The process is characterized by four distinct steps whenever the problem is in some way associated with a function f defined on an interval.

(1) The interval is partitioned into subintervals.

(2) Each term of the approximating sum is determined by evaluating the function f at an appropriate point and multiplying this value by the length of the corresponding subinterval.

(3) The approximation is obtained by adding together the values of the products so formed.

(4) The limit of the sum is found, provided the limit exists.

The next examples will illustrate this process applied to several different types of problems.

Example 12.4a. Determine the volume of a cone by the method of approximation. Suppose the height of the cone is h units and the radius of the base is r units. We shall assume that the volume of a cylinder is known and approximate the volume by a set of cylinders as shown in Figure 12.4a.

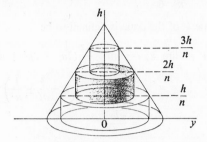

FIGURE 12.4a

The altitude of the cone is partitioned into n equal parts by the points

$$\frac{h}{n}, \frac{2h}{n}, \frac{3h}{n}, \ldots, \frac{(n-1)h}{n}.$$

The radius R_k of the kth cylinder can be found by using proportional parts of similar triangles. This gives

$$\frac{R_k}{r} = \frac{h - \dfrac{kh}{n}}{h}.$$

Hence, the volume of the kth cylinder is

$$C_k = \frac{h}{n} \cdot \pi R_k^2 = \frac{\pi h}{n} \cdot \left[\frac{h - \dfrac{kh}{n}}{h} \right]^2 \cdot r^2 = \frac{\pi h r^2}{n} \left(1 - \frac{k}{n} \right)^2$$

$$= \frac{h}{n} f\left(\frac{k}{n} \right),$$

where

$$f\left(\frac{k}{n} \right) = \pi r^2 \left(1 - \frac{k}{n} \right)^2.$$

Thus the nth approximation to the volume of the cone is

$$V_n = \sum_{k=1}^{n} C_k = \sum_{k=1}^{n} \frac{\pi h r^2}{n} \left(1 - \frac{k}{n} \right)^2,$$

$$= \frac{\pi h r^2}{n^3} \sum_{k=1}^{n} (n - k)^2.$$

Since

$$\sum_{k=1}^{n} (n - k)^2 = (n-1)^2 + (n-2)^2 + \cdots + 2^2 + 1^2 + 0^2$$

$$= 1^2 + 2^2 + 3^2 + \cdots + (n-1)^2 = \sum_{\alpha=1}^{n-1} \alpha^2$$

$$= \frac{1}{6} (n-1)(n)(2n-1) \qquad \text{(Exercises 2.2, Number 6),}$$

then

$$V_n = \frac{\pi h r^2}{n^3} \frac{n}{6} (n - 1)(2n - 1).$$

Hence the exact volume V of the cone is defined to be

$$V = \lim_{n \to \infty} V_n = \lim_{n \to \infty} \frac{\pi h r^2}{6n^3} (2n^3 - 3n^2 + n)$$

$$= \lim_{n \to \infty} \frac{\pi h r^2}{6} \left(2 - \frac{3}{n} + \frac{1}{n^2} \right)$$

$$= \frac{\pi h r^2}{3},$$

which is the usual formula for the volume of a cone.

The next example illustrates the use of the method of approximation in a problem that is not entirely geometrical.

Example 12.4b. What is the total force acting on one side of a rectangular gate a units wide and b units high, if the gate is submerged vertically in a lake so that its upper edge is H units below the surface of the lake (Figure 12.4b)?

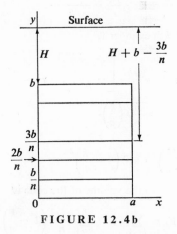

FIGURE 12.4b

It is an accepted experimental fact that the force acting on a submerged object depends on the depth of the object. In this case, since different portions of the gate are at different depths, the problem does not have an immediately obvious solution. However, the force on one side of the gate can be approximated by partitioning the gate into horizontal strips of equal width and considering all portions of a particular strip to be at the same depth.

In order to describe the problem easily, let us choose an origin at a lower corner of the gate, as shown in Figure 12.4b. The points of division along the y-axis are b/n, $2b/n, \ldots, (n - 1)b/n$. The length of each strip is a, so that the area of the kth strip is ab/n.

The force F acting on a *horizontal* area A submerged h units below the surface of a liquid of specific weight ρ is given by

$$F = \rho h A.$$

This force is simply the weight of the column of liquid standing above the area, and is obtained by multiplying the density ρ by the volume hA. This formula can be used to approximate the force on the kth strip by assuming all points of the strip to be at nearly the same depth as its upper edge. The resulting force on the strip is

$$f_k = \rho \frac{ba}{n} \left(H + b - \frac{kb}{n} \right).$$

Accordingly, the total force on the gate is approximately

$$F_n = \sum_{k=1}^{n} f_k = \sum_{k=1}^{n} \rho \frac{ba}{n} \left(H + b - \frac{kb}{n} \right)$$

$$= \rho \frac{ba}{n^2} \sum_{k=1}^{n} [(H + b)n - kb]$$

$$= \rho \frac{ba}{n^2} \left[n^2(H + b) - b \sum_{k=1}^{n} k \right]$$

$$= \rho \frac{ba}{n^2} \left[n^2(H + b) - b \frac{n}{2} (n + 1) \right].$$

It seems intuitively clear that this approximation to the total force is better and better for narrower and narrower strips. Hence, the exact force acting on one side of the gate may be defined as

$$\lim_{n\to\infty} F_n = \lim_{n\to\infty} \rho \frac{ba}{n^2} \left[n^2(H + b) - b \left(\frac{n^2}{2} + \frac{n}{2} \right) \right]$$

$$= \rho b a \left(H + b - \frac{b}{2} \right)$$

$$= \rho b a \left(H + \frac{b}{2} \right).$$

It is interesting to consider the same problem using a circular gate instead of a rectangular one.

Example 12.4c. Find the force on one side of a circular gate of radius a submerged so that its center is H units, $H > a$, below a liquid surface.

Figure 12.4c shows a coordinate system and strips introduced in order to set up the expressions for the force acting on a typical strip. The vertical axis has been labeled the x-axis simply to show that the choice of axes is arbitrary. The vertical diameter of the circle is partitioned into $2n$ parts by the points

$$\pm \frac{a}{n}, \pm \frac{2a}{n}, \pm \frac{3a}{n}, \cdots, \pm \frac{ka}{n}, \cdots, \pm \frac{(n-1)a}{n}.$$

In this case the length of each rectangular strip may be expressed as twice the value of $f(x)$ at the point on the upper edge of the strip for the portion of the area above the y-axis and at the point on the lower edge of the strip for the portion of the area below the y-axis.

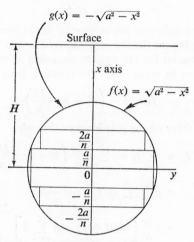

FIGURE 12.4c

Thus, for the kth strip, we get an area of

$$2\frac{a}{n}f\left(\frac{ka}{n}\right), \qquad \text{where } f(x) = \sqrt{a^2 - x^2}.$$

This time, in order to take into account the negative values of x, we let k take on values from $-n$ to n, and get for the nth approximation of the force on the gate

$$F_n = 2 \sum_{k=-n}^{n} \rho \frac{a}{n} f\left(\frac{k}{n}a\right)\left(H - \frac{ka}{n}\right)$$

$$= 2 \sum_{k=-n}^{n} \rho \frac{a}{n}\left(H - \frac{ka}{n}\right)\sqrt{a^2 - \frac{k^2 a^2}{n^2}}.$$

Although the evaluation of the limit of this expression poses a formidable looking problem, it can be resolved with the aid of Exercises 12.3, Number 7. We may write

$$F = \lim_{n\to\infty} 2 \sum_{k=-n}^{n} \frac{a\rho}{n}\left[H - \frac{ka}{n}\right]\sqrt{a^2 - \frac{k^2}{n^2}a^2}$$

$$= \lim_{n\to\infty}\left[2a^2\rho H \sum_{k=-n}^{n} \frac{1}{n}\sqrt{1 - \frac{k^2}{n^2}} - 2a^3\rho \sum_{k=-n}^{n} \frac{k}{n^2}\sqrt{1 - \frac{k^2}{n^2}}\right]$$

$$= 2a^2\rho H \lim_{n\to\infty} \sum_{k=-n}^{n} \frac{1}{n}\sqrt{1 - \frac{k^2}{n^2}},$$

since the second sum in the brackets is always zero. Thus, $F = \pi\rho a^2 H$ is obtained by using the fact that

$$\lim_{n\to\infty} \sum_{k=-n}^{n} \frac{1}{n}\sqrt{1 - \frac{k^2}{n^2}} = \frac{\pi}{2}.$$

In the preceding examples, the expression for each term in the nth approximation may be interpreted as the product of an interval length and the value of some function at a point in the interval. Thus, in Example 12.4a, the term

$$C_k = \frac{\pi h r^2}{n} \left(1 - \frac{k}{n}\right)^2$$

may be considered as the product of the interval length h/n and the functional value

$$f(x) = \pi r^2 (1 - x)^2$$

evaluated at $x = k/n$. A similar statement also applies in Examples 12.4b and 12.4c.

Exercises 12.4

1. Use the method of approximations to develop the formula for the volume of a right circular cylinder by using prisms inscribed in the cylinder.
2. Set up an approximation for the volume of a sphere, and then use a limiting process to find the volume.
3. Use outer sums to approximate the volume of a cone and show that in the limit the same result is obtained as in Example 12.4a.
4. If a square of side b is submerged vertically in a liquid with the top edge of the square at the surface of the liquid, find the force on one side of the square.
5. Find the force on one side of the square of Number 4 if the square is submerged with a diagonal parallel to the surface of the liquid and the top vertex at the surface.
6. Determine the force on one side of a triangle of height h units and having a base b units, if it is submerged vertically in a liquid so that its vertex is above its base and is H units below the surface, and its base is parallel to the surface.
7. Work Number 6 if the base of the triangle is H units below the surface and the vertex is below the base.
8. The amount of work done by a constant force F acting over a distance s is defined to be

$$W = Fs,$$

where F is in pounds, s in inches, and W in inch-pounds. Suppose the amount of force required to compress a spring s inches is $F = 12s$ pounds. Determine an approximation for the amount of work done in compressing the spring 3 inches, and find its limit.
9. Express the approximations in Examples 12.4b and 12.4c in the form

$$F_n = \sum_{k=1}^{n} f(x_k)\, \Delta x_k,$$

where Δx_k represents the width of the kth strip and $f(x_k)$ is the value of an appropriately chosen function at a point in the kth interval.

12.5 THE DEFINITE INTEGRAL

In each of the examples in the two preceding sections, we have been concerned with the same four steps. Namely, an interval was partitioned into n parts or subintervals, a function was evaluated at a point in each subinterval, the sum of the products of the functional value and the length of the corresponding subinterval was formed, and when possible, the limit of this sum was determined. Since this process has occurred in connection with a number of practical problems, it appears worthwhile to try to express these ideas in as general a way as possible, and, in order for the results to be useful, we must eventually show that the end result does not depend on the particular subdivision that is chosen. Furthermore, we should hope to discover some methods or techniques that will enable us to "short cut" much of the work associated with finding the limit of an approximating sum.

With the idea of making the approximating process as general as possible, let us restate the four steps used in the process in purely mathematical form for an arbitrary function f, defined on a closed interval $a \leq x \leq b$. The first essential generalization that is possible is to allow subdivisions having unequal subintervals. The only reason for our having used equal subintervals was to have reasonable simplicity for the algebraic manipulations. However, if the approximating process is to be meaningful, we should expect to obtain the same end result regardless of the partitioning scheme. Consequently, let f be defined for all x such that $a \leq x \leq b$, and let an arbitrary subdivision of the interval $a \leq x \leq b$ be given by the distinct points

$$a = x_0 < x_1 < x_2 < x_3 < \cdots < x_{n-1} < x_n = b,$$

as in Figure 12.5a.

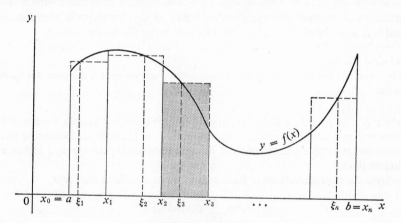

FIGURE 12.5a

Another place where considerable generalization is possible occurs in connection with the point in a particular subinterval at which the function is evaluated. In the examples in the two previous sections, the function was always evaluated at an end point of the subinterval. Actually, there is no reason, other than simplifying the calculations, why the function cannot be evaluated at any point within the interval. This statement is clearly supported by the geometric interpretation of the limit of the approximation as the number of units of area bounded by the curve, the x-axis and the ordinates $x = a$ and $x = b$. Again, if the approximation process is of any value, the final result should not depend on the points at which $f(x)$ is evaluated. Indeed, there are some instances in which it is simpler to evaluate $f(x)$ at an interior point rather than at an end point of a subinterval. Hence, let ξ_α, where $x_{\alpha-1} \leqq \xi_\alpha \leqq x_\alpha$, denote the chosen value of x in the αth subinterval at which f is to be evaluated, as illustrated in Figure 12.5a.

For an approximation, we have the expression

$$A_n = \sum_{\alpha=1}^{n} f(\xi_\alpha)(x_\alpha - x_{\alpha-1}),$$

where $x_\alpha - x_{\alpha-1}$ denotes the length of the αth subinterval. In order to simplify the expression for A_n, it is convenient to write

$$\Delta x_\alpha = x_\alpha - x_{\alpha-1}.$$

Then we have

$$A_n = \sum_{\alpha=1}^{n} f(\xi_\alpha) \, \Delta x_\alpha.$$

Although a geometric interpretation of A_n is given in Figure 12.5a, A_n in no way depends on the geometry; A_n can be calculated independently of any geometrical interpretation, as we shall see.

The final step is to investigate the limit of the approximating sum. If the limit exists, it is given a special name, and is denoted by a special symbol.

Definition 12.5a. Let $\delta .=.\max \Delta x_\alpha$. If

$$\lim_{\delta \to 0} \sum_{\alpha=1}^{n} f(\xi_\alpha) \, \Delta x_\alpha$$

exists, and is the same for every sequence of subdivisions, it is called the **definite integral** of f from a to b, and is denoted by the symbol

$$\int_a^b f(x) \, dx.$$

Notice that the condition $\delta \to 0$ implies that every Δx_α must approach zero; this condition is necessary, since otherwise it would be possible to obtain different limits by holding one subinterval fixed and partitioning only the remaining ones. It is evident that the number of subintervals increases without bound as $\delta \to 0$.

All that has been done thus far is simply to give a name and a symbolic notation to the process discussed and illustrated in Sections 12.3 and 12.4. In order to illustrate the notation, we recast some of the examples in those sections in this symbolic notation.

Example 12.5a. Express the area enclosed by the curves $f(x) = x^2$, the x-axis, and the line $x = 1$ (Figure 12.3d) in terms of a definite integral.

Using the notation of Definition 12.5a with $f(x) = x^2$, $a = 0$, and $b = 1$, we have

$$A = \lim_{\delta \to 0} \sum_{\alpha=1}^{n} f(\xi_\alpha) \, \Delta x_\alpha = \lim_{\delta \to 0} \sum_{\alpha=1}^{n} \xi_\alpha^2 \, \Delta x_\alpha = \int_0^1 x^2 \, dx.$$

From the result of the evaluation carried out for $f(x) = x^2$ in Section 12.3, we must have

$$\int_0^1 x^2 \, dx = \tfrac{1}{3}.$$

It is instructive to consider a variation of this problem.

Example 12.5b. Evaluate $\displaystyle\int_a^b x^2 \, dx$. (Assume that the limit exists.)

Since

$$\int_a^b x^2 \, dx = \lim_{\delta \to 0} \sum_{\alpha=1}^{n} f(\xi_\alpha) \, \Delta x_\alpha,$$

where $f(x) = x^2$, let us choose a subdivision of the interval from a to b into n equal subintervals. (We may choose any particular subdivision we wish; if the limit exists, it must be the same regardless of what particular subdivision is used.) The points of subdivision are then

$$a + \frac{b-a}{n}, \; a + 2\left(\frac{b-a}{n}\right), \; a + 3\left(\frac{b-a}{n}\right), \dots,$$

$$a + k\left(\frac{b-a}{n}\right), \dots, a + (n-1)\left(\frac{b-a}{n}\right),$$

where the length of each subinterval is $(b-a)/n$. Then, choosing

$$\xi_\alpha = a + \frac{\alpha(b-a)}{n},$$

we have

$$\int_a^b x^2 \, dx = \lim_{n \to \infty} \sum_{\alpha=1}^{n} \frac{b-a}{n} \left[a + \alpha \frac{(b-a)}{n} \right]^2.$$

But

$$\sum_{\alpha=1}^{n} \frac{b-a}{n} \left[a + \alpha \frac{b-a}{n} \right]^2 = \sum_{\alpha=1}^{n} \left[a^2 \left(\frac{b-a}{n} \right) + 2a\alpha \left(\frac{b-a}{n} \right)^2 + \alpha^2 \left(\frac{b-a}{n} \right)^3 \right]$$

$$= na^2 \left(\frac{b-a}{n} \right) + 2a \left(\frac{b-a}{n} \right)^2 \sum_{\alpha=1}^{n} \alpha + \left(\frac{b-a}{n} \right)^3 \sum_{\alpha=1}^{n} \alpha^2$$

$$= a^2(b-a) + 2a \left(\frac{b-a}{n} \right)^2 \frac{n(n+1)}{2} + \left(\frac{b-a}{n} \right)^3 \frac{n}{6} (n+1)(2n+1),$$

and, taking the limit as $n \to \infty$, we get

$$\int_a^b x^2 \, dx = a^2(b-a) + 2a(b-a)^2 \left(\frac{1}{2} \right) + (b-a)^3 \left(\frac{1}{3} \right)$$

$$= a^2 b - a^3 + ab^2 - 2a^2 b + a^3 + \frac{b^3}{3} - ab^2 + a^2 b - \frac{a^3}{3}$$

$$= \frac{b^3}{3} - \frac{a^3}{3}.$$

As is to be expected, even these simple problems lead to a considerable amount of work. It would be desirable to find some method of evaluating definite integrals that would circumvent the work of the direct evaluation. In fact, in many cases a direct evaluation of a definite integral appears to be impossible.

Example 12.5c. Express the formula for F in Example 12.4c in terms of a definite integral.

We had

$$F = \lim_{n \to \infty} 2\sum_{k=-n}^{n} \frac{a\rho}{n}\left(H - \frac{ka}{n}\right)\sqrt{a^2 - \frac{k^2 a^2}{n^2}}$$

By taking $x_k = ka/n$, $\Delta x_k = a/n$, and $f(x) = 2\rho(H - x)\sqrt{a^2 - x^2}$, so that $-a \le x \le a$, we may write

$$F = \int_{-a}^{a} 2\rho(H - x)\sqrt{a^2 - x^2}\, dx.$$

In order to investigate the feasibility of devising some procedure for handling definite integrals, it is necessary that we develop systematically whatever properties of the definite integral we can see easily, and to study the conditions under which the limit of a sum actually exists. This will be the major effort in the next three sections of this chapter.

Exercises 12.5

Evaluate each of the definite integrals of Numbers 1 to 6 by using the definition in terms of the limit of a sum.

1. $\int_{0}^{1} c\, dx.$

2. $\int_{a}^{b} x\, dx.$

3. $\int_{0}^{2} mx\, dx.$

4. $\int_{a}^{b} (cx + e)\, dx.$

5. $\int_{0}^{2} 3x^2\, dx.$

6. $\int_{0}^{1} (x - x^2)\, dx.$

7. Evaluate $\int_{0}^{1} x\, dx$ by using a partitioning of the interval from 0 to 1 into unequal parts by the points

$$x_0 = 0, \quad x_\alpha = \frac{\alpha^2}{n^2}, \quad \alpha = 1, 2, \ldots, n.$$

Note:

$$\sum_{\alpha=1}^{n} \alpha^3 = \frac{n^2(n+1)^2}{4}, \quad \sum_{\alpha=1}^{n} \alpha^2 = \frac{n}{6}(n+1)(2n+1).$$

8. Express $\int_{1}^{2} \frac{1}{x}\, dx$ as the limit of a sum.

9. Express $\lim_{n \to \infty} \sum_{k=1}^{n} \frac{1}{n+k}$ as a definite integral. *Hint:* Consider the function f where $f(x) = \frac{1}{x}.$

10. Express $\lim\limits_{n \to \infty} \sum\limits_{k=1}^{n} \dfrac{k^2 b^3}{n^3}$ as a definite integral. *Hint:* Consider the function for which $y = x^2$.

11. Show that $\int_a^b k \, dx = k(b - a)$, where k is a nonzero constant.

12.6 UPPER AND LOWER SUMS

The use of inner and outer sums as approximations to the definite integral was discussed briefly in Section 12.3. That discussion suggests the following general treatment of the definite integral. In order to clarify the ideas, we shall resort to a geometric interpretation of the discussion in terms of areas, although the concepts actually depend in no way upon this geometric interpretation.

Definition 12.6a. Let $\mathfrak{D}$ be the interval $\{x : a \leq x \leq b\}$. The set of points

$$\mathcal{P}_n .=. \{x_0, x_1, \ldots, x_n\},$$

where $x_0 = a$, $x_n = b$, $x_{\alpha-1} < x_\alpha$, $\alpha = 1, 2, \ldots, n$, is called a **partition** of the interval $\mathfrak{D}$.

Clearly, a partition $\mathcal{P}_n$ of an interval divides the interval into n subintervals

$$x_{\alpha-1} \leq x \leq x_\alpha, \qquad \alpha = 1, 2, \ldots, n.$$

Suppose that f is defined and bounded on $\mathfrak{D}$, and let $\mathcal{P}_n$ be a partition of $\mathfrak{D}$. Let us consider a typical subinterval $x_{\alpha-1} \leq x \leq x_\alpha$ (see Figure 12.6a).

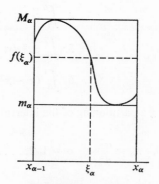

FIGURE 12.6a

In setting up the expression for the definite integral of f, we choose an arbitrary point, ξ_α, in the subinterval, and form the product

$$f(\xi_\alpha) \, \Delta x_\alpha.$$

Since f is bounded on $a \leq x \leq b$, it is bounded on every subinterval. Hence f has a greatest lower bound and a least upper bound on the αth subinterval.

If these bounds are denoted by m_α and M_α, respectively, then it follows that, for any ξ_α, where $x_{\alpha-1} \leq \xi_\alpha \leq x_\alpha$,

$$m_\alpha \leq f(\xi_\alpha) \leq M_\alpha$$

and

$$m_\alpha \, \Delta x_\alpha \leq f(\xi_\alpha) \, \Delta x_\alpha \leq M_\alpha \, \Delta x_\alpha.$$

(See Figure 12.6a.) Hence, we have the inequality

(1) $$\sum_{\alpha=1}^{n} m_\alpha \, \Delta x_\alpha \leq \sum_{\alpha=1}^{n} f(\xi_\alpha) \, \Delta x_\alpha \leq \sum_{\alpha=1}^{n} M_\alpha \, \Delta x_\alpha.$$

The quantity

$$s_n \;.=.\; \sum_{\alpha=1}^{n} m_\alpha \, \Delta x_\alpha$$

is called a **lower sum** of $f(x)$ over the interval $a \leq x \leq b$, and the quantity

$$S_n \;.=.\; \sum_{\alpha=1}^{n} M_\alpha \, \Delta x_\alpha$$

is called an **upper sum** of $f(x)$ over $a \leq x \leq b$. Inequality (1) is equivalent to the statement that, based on a given partition, every approximating sum

$$A_n = \sum_{\alpha=1}^{n} f(\xi_\alpha) \, \Delta x_\alpha$$

must satisfy the inequality

(2) $$s_n \leq A_n \leq S_n.$$

Notice that for a given n, infinitely many different pairs of s_n's and S_n's can be formed by varying the points of subdivision. However, we can show that under certain conditions on $f(x)$, and for every sequence of lower and upper sums,

$$\lim_{\delta \to 0} s_n, \quad \text{where } \delta = \max \Delta x_\alpha,$$

exists and is independent of the particular sequence of sums considered; and, similarly, that for every sequence of upper sums (not necessarily corresponding to the preceding lower sums)

$$\lim_{\delta \to 0} S_n$$

exists in the same sense. Then if

$$\lim_{\delta \to 0} s_n = \lim_{\delta \to 0} S_n,$$

we may conclude that the definite integral, $\int_a^b f(x) \, dx$, exists and is independent of both the mode of subdivision and the choice of the points ξ_α at which $f(x)$ is evaluated in each subinterval. This discussion is summarized in

Theorem 12.6a. $\quad \int_a^b f(x) \, dx$ exists $\Leftrightarrow \displaystyle\lim_{\delta \to 0} s_n = \lim_{\delta \to 0} S_n.$

PROOF: The proof follows from the definition of the definite integral and the fact that every approximating sum A_n must satisfy Inequality (1).

It may appear that $\int_a^b f(x)\,dx$ exists for almost any function that is defined and bounded on the interval $a \leq x \leq b$, but a simple example will show that this is not the case.

Example 12.6a. Let

$$f(x) .=. \begin{cases} 0 & \text{if } 0 \leq x \leq 1 \text{ and } x \text{ is a rational number,} \\ 1 & \text{if } 0 \leq x \leq 1 \text{ and } x \text{ is an irrational number.} \end{cases}$$

Prove that $\int_0^1 f(x)\,dx$ does not exist.

For any mode of subdivision it follows that, in each subinterval, $m_\alpha = 0$ and $M_\alpha = 1$. Hence, for every lower sum we have $s_n = 0$, and for every upper sum, $S_n = 1$, so that

$$\lim_{\delta \to 0} s_n \neq \lim_{\delta \to 0} S_n.$$

In view of this example, one is tempted to ask for what type of functions does $\int_a^b f(x)\,dx$ exist? In general, the problem of demonstrating the conditions under which the existence of the definite integral is guaranteed is a complex and difficult one. One of the simplest conditions is given in the following theorem.

Theorem 12.6b. Let f be a continuous function on the interval $a \leq x \leq b$. Then

$$\int_a^b f(x)\,dx \text{ exists.}$$

Because the proof of this theorem is involved and requires a number of preliminary results, it is presented after Theorem 12.7d in the next section.

★12.7 THE EXISTENCE OF $\int_a^b f(x)\,dx$

It is convenient to introduce a number of additional concepts in order to facilitate the discussion of the proof of Theorem 12.6b. The first of these is given in

Definition 12.7a. Let $\mathcal{P}_n$ be a partition of the interval $a \leq x \leq b$, and let $\mathcal{Q}_k .=. \{q_1, q_2, \ldots, q_k\}$ be a different partition of the same interval, that is, such that at least one q_i is not an x_j. Then the set $\mathcal{P}_n \cup \mathcal{Q}_k$, which is also a partition of $a \leq x \leq b$, is called a **refinement** of the partition $\mathcal{P}_n$.

The upper and lower sums of a refinement of a partition $\mathcal{P}_n$ have an important relationship to the upper and lower sums of $\mathcal{P}_n$, as shown in

Theorem 12.7a. Let f be a function defined and bounded on the interval $a \leq x \leq b$. Let $\mathcal{P}_n$ be a partition of $a \leq x \leq b$, and let $\mathcal{R}_p = \mathcal{P}_n \cup \mathcal{Q}_k$ be a refinement of $\mathcal{P}_n$. Then

$$s_n \leq s_p \quad \text{and} \quad S_p \leq S_n.$$

PROOF: We shall prove that $s_n \leqq s_p$, and leave the proof that $S_p \leqq S_n$ for the reader. Since $\mathcal{R}_p$ is a partition of $a \leqq x \leqq b$, and one or more of the points of $\mathcal{Q}_k$ are distinct from those in $\mathcal{P}_n$, let us consider a typical subinterval $x_{\alpha-1} \leqq x \leqq x_\alpha$ that contains one or more points, q_i of $\mathcal{Q}_k$. The greatest lower bound, m_{α_1}, of $f(x)$ on the interval $x_{\alpha-1} \leqq x \leqq q_1$ is not less than the greatest lower bound, m_α of $f(x)$ on $x_{\alpha-1} \leqq x \leqq x_\alpha$. That is,

$$m_{\alpha_1} \geqq m_\alpha.$$

(See Figure 12.7a.) Similarly, on the interval $q_1 \leqq x \leqq q_2$, $m_{\alpha_2} \geqq m_\alpha$. For each subinterval of the interval $x_{\alpha-1} \leqq x \leqq x_\alpha$ formed by the points q_i of $\mathcal{Q}_k$ a

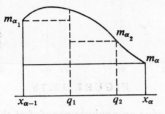

FIGURE 12.7a

similar statement may be made. Hence, if q_1 is the only point of $\mathcal{Q}_k$ in the αth subinterval, then

$$\begin{aligned}
m_\alpha(x_\alpha - x_{\alpha-1}) &= m_\alpha(x_\alpha - q_1 + q_1 - x_{\alpha-1})\\
&= m_\alpha(x_\alpha - q_1) + m_\alpha(q_1 - x_{\alpha-1})\\
&\leqq m_{\alpha_2}(x_\alpha - q_1) + m_{\alpha_1}(q_1 - x_{\alpha-1}).
\end{aligned}$$

If there are additional points of $\mathcal{Q}_k$ in the αth interval, a similar partition of the αth interval into subintervals can be made.

In any case, each term in

$$s_n = \sum_{\alpha=1}^{n} m_\alpha(x_\alpha - x_{\alpha-1})$$

either is unaltered or else is replaced by a sum of terms greater than or equal to it, so that

$$\sum_{\alpha=1}^{n} m_\alpha(x_\alpha - x_{\alpha-1}) \leqq \sum_{\beta=1}^{p} \overline{m}_\beta(\overline{x}_\beta - \overline{x}_{\beta-1}),$$

where the $\overline{x}_\beta$'s are points in the partition $\mathcal{R}_p$. Hence

$$s_n \leqq s_p.$$

This result shows that for a sequence of refinements, the lower sums form a sequence of nondecreasing numbers. Furthermore, we show in the next theorem that every upper sum is greater than or equal to any lower sum.

Theorem 12.7b. For a given function f defined and bounded on the interval $a \leqq x \leqq b$, and for any two positive integers m and n,

$$s_m \leqq S_n.$$

PROOF: Geometrically, the result appears evident (see Figure 12.7b).

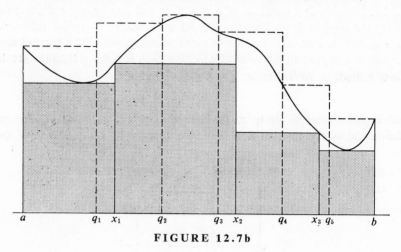

FIGURE 12.7b

However, it is easy to give an analytic proof. Let the partition for the lowei sum s_m be

$$\mathcal{P}_m .=. \{x_0, x_1, \ldots, x_m\},$$

and for the upper sum S_n let the partition be

$$\mathcal{Q}_n .=. \{q_0, q_1, \ldots, q_n\}.$$

The set of points $\mathcal{P}_m \cup \mathcal{Q}_n$ forms a partition that either is the same as or is a refinement of each of the partitions $\mathcal{P}_m$ and $\mathcal{Q}_n$. Let s_p and S_p be the sums corresponding to the partition $\mathcal{P}_m \cup \mathcal{Q}_n$. By Theorem 12.7a and Inequality (2) of Section 12.6, it follows that

$$s_m \leqq s_p \leqq S_p \leqq S_n.$$

In order to arrive at the main result of this section, we need the following rather more sophisticated property of continuous functions.

Theorem 12.7c. If f is a continuous function on a closed interval $a \leqq x \leqq b$, then for any given $\epsilon > 0$, no matter how small, there is a partition $\mathcal{P}_n$ such that for n sufficiently large,

$$M_\alpha - m_\alpha < \epsilon$$

on each subinterval of the partition.

PROOF: Since f is continuous on a closed interval $a \leqq x \leqq b$, M_α and m_α exist on any closed subinterval of $a \leqq x \leqq b$. Choose any partition. Suppose there is a subinterval for which $M_\alpha - m_x \geqq \epsilon$. Partition the subinterval into two equal parts. If $M_\alpha - m_\alpha \geqq \epsilon$ on either of these new subintervals, divide the subinterval into two equal parts again, and repeat this process until $M_\alpha - m_\alpha < \epsilon$ on all resulting subintervals, if possible. Otherwise, consider the process continued indefinitely. In the latter case, there is obtained a sequence of intervals having a point c in common. It follows that every sub-interval containing c has the property $M_\alpha - m_\alpha \geqq \epsilon$. But, since f is continuous at c, there is a $\mathfrak{N}(c, h)$ such that

$$x \in \mathfrak{N}(c, h) \Rightarrow f(x) \in \mathfrak{N}[f(c), \epsilon/2].$$

That is, for all x such that $c - h < x < c + h$,

$$f(c) - \epsilon/2 < f(x) < f(c) + \epsilon/2,$$

and over this interval $M_\alpha - m_\alpha < \epsilon$, which contradicts the conclusion that $M_\alpha - m_\alpha \geqq \epsilon$. Hence the process cannot continue indefinitely, and a partition can be found such that $M_\alpha - m_\alpha < \epsilon$ over every subinterval.

The preceding theorem is fundamental in the proof of the next two results, which complete this section.

Theorem 12.7d. If f is a continuous function on $a \leqq x \leqq b$, then

$$\lim_{\delta \to 0} s_n \quad \text{and} \quad \lim_{\delta \to 0} S_n$$

both exist.

PROOF: Choose a sequence of lower sums, $\{s_n\}$, such that

$$s_1 \leqq s_2 \leqq s_3 \leqq \cdots \leqq s_n \leqq \cdots.$$

Such a choice is always possible through the use of refinements. Since every $s_n \leqq S_m$, the set

$$\{s_1, s_2, \ldots, s_n, \ldots\}$$

is a bounded nondecreasing infinite sequence, and by Theorem 12.2b it must have a limit, say s.

Suppose $\{\sigma_n\}$ is any other sequence of lower sums with $\{\Sigma_n\}$ as the corresponding sequence of upper sums. Then, by Theorem 12.7b, we have $\sigma_n \leqq S_n$ and $s_n \leqq \Sigma_n$. Consequently, for each n, either

$$0 \leqq \sigma_n - s_n \leqq S_n - s_n = \sum_{\alpha=1}^{n} (M_\alpha - m_\alpha)\,\Delta x_\alpha$$

or else

$$0 \leqq s_n - \sigma_n \leqq \Sigma_n - \sigma_n = \sum_{\beta=1}^{n} (M_\beta - m_\beta)\,\Delta x_\beta.$$

In either case, if n is sufficiently large,

$$M_\alpha - m_\alpha < \frac{\epsilon}{b - a} \quad \text{and} \quad M_\beta - m_\beta < \frac{\epsilon}{b - a}$$

for every α or β, by Theorem 12.7c, with ϵ replaced by $\epsilon/(b - a)$. Hence,

$$|\sigma_n - s_n| < \sum_{\alpha=1}^{n} \frac{\epsilon}{b - a}\,\Delta x_\alpha = \frac{\epsilon}{b - a} \sum_{\alpha=1}^{n} \Delta x_\alpha,$$

or

$$|\sigma_n - s_n| < \epsilon.$$

This means that the sequence $\{\sigma_n\}$ must also have the limit s.

The proof that $\lim_{\delta \to 0} S_n$ exists is similar and is left for the reader.

We can now prove Theorem 12.6b, which stated that if f is continuous on the interval $a \leqq x \leqq b$, then

$$\int_a^b f(x)\, dx \text{ exists.}$$

To show this, we need only demonstrate that

$$\lim_{\delta \to 0} s_n = \lim_{\delta \to 0} S_n.$$

Consider

$$S_n - s_n = \sum_{\alpha=1}^n (M_\alpha - m_\alpha)\, \Delta x_\alpha$$

$$\leqq \frac{\epsilon}{b-a} \sum_{\alpha=1}^n \Delta x_\alpha = \epsilon,$$

since, by Theorem 12.7c,

$$M_\alpha - m_\alpha < \frac{\epsilon}{b-a}$$

on every subinterval of the partition for n sufficiently large and the Δx_α's sufficiently small. Thus, for this partition,

$$S_n \leqq s_n + \epsilon,$$

and by Theorem 12.7d, $\lim_{\delta \to 0} S_n$ and $\lim_{\delta \to 0} s_n$ both exist, so that

$$s_n \leqq S_n \leqq s_n + \epsilon$$

implies that

$$\lim_{\delta \to 0} S_n = \lim_{\delta \to 0} s_n.$$

Exercises 12.7

1. Prove the second part of Theorem 12.7a.
2. In the proof of Theorem 12.7c, under the assumption that the subdivision process must be continued indefinitely, explain why every subinterval containing c must have the property $M_\alpha - m_\alpha \geqq \epsilon$.
3. Prove the second part of Theorem 12.7d.
4. Let $f(x)$ be continuous on $a \leqq x \leqq b$ except at the point c, where it has a finite jump h; that is,

$$\lim_{x \to c^+} f(x) - \lim_{x \to c^-} f(x) = h.$$

   Prove that the definite integral from a to b of f exists.
5. Prove that if $\lim_{\delta \to 0} s_n$ exists, then $s_p \leqq \lim_{\delta \to 0} s_n$ for any partition $\mathcal{P}_p$.

12.8 PROPERTIES OF THE DEFINITE INTEGRAL

When the definite integral of a function f exists over an interval, the function is said to be **integrable**. We have shown in the preceding section that functions continuous on closed intervals are integrable, but we have not yet given any simple way to evaluate such integrals. In order to arrive at such a means of evaluation, it is necessary first to investigate some elementary properties of the integral.

The definition of the definite integral has been stated for the case where $a < b$. It is desirable to extend the definition to include the case where $a > b$. In order to make such an extension, it is sufficient simply to change the order of the points in the partitions that are used.

Definition 12.8a. Let $\mathfrak{D}$ be the interval $\{x: b \leq x \leq a\}$. The set of points

$$\mathcal{P}_n .=. \{x_0, x_1, \ldots, x_n\},$$

where $x_0 = a$, $x_n = b$, $x_{\alpha-1} > x_\alpha$, $\alpha = 1, 2, \ldots, n$, is a **partition** of the interval from a to b.

Definition 12.8b. If $b < a$, then $\int_a^b f(x)\,dx$ is defined as in Definition 12.5a except that all partitions are to be from a to b and $\delta .=. \max |\Delta x_\alpha|$, where $\Delta x_\alpha = x_\alpha - x_{\alpha-1}$.

Crudely speaking, these conventions indicate that one always starts with the lower end point indicated on the symbol $\int_a^b$ and progresses to the upper end point in choosing partition points.

The preceding definitions allow us to establish an important elementary property of the definite integral.

Theorem 12.8a. If the function f is integrable on the interval $a \leq x \leq b$, then

$$\int_a^b f(x)\,dx = -\int_b^a f(x)\,dx.$$

PROOF: Let $\mathcal{P}_n$ be a partition for $\int_a^b f(x)\,dx$ for which

$$a = x_0 < x_1 < x_2 < \cdots < x_n = b.$$

The same partition may be used for $\int_b^a f(x)\,dx$ if the points are properly relabeled. We have

$$b = \bar{x}_0 > \bar{x}_1 > \bar{x}_2 > \cdots > \bar{x}_n = a,$$

where $\bar{x}_k = x_{n-k}$, $k = 0, 1, 2, \ldots, n$. Thus, in an approximating sum for $\int_a^b f(x)\,dx$, the interval lengths are of the form

$$\Delta x_\alpha = x_\alpha - x_{\alpha-1}$$

and for $\int_b^a f(x)\,dx$, the interval lengths are of the form

$$\Delta \bar{x}_\alpha = \bar{x}_\alpha - \bar{x}_{\alpha-1} = x_{n-\alpha} - x_{n-\alpha+1},$$

which is the negative of one of the Δx_α's. Hence, for a given partition, the Δx_α in an approximating sum A_n for $\int_a^b f(x)\,dx$ is simply the negative of the corresponding $\Delta \bar{x}_\alpha$ in an approximating sum for $\int_b^a f(x)\,dx$. The theorem follows directly as a consequence of this reversal in sign.

With the relationship between the symbols $\int_a^b$ and $\int_b^a$ established by Theorem 12.8a for the case $a \neq b$, it is appropriate to ask about a symbol such as $\int_a^a$. In none of the preceding definitions has the interval been allowed to degenerate to zero length. However, it turns out later that it is most desirable to have a definition for this case. From the geometric point of view, it is appropriate to have $\int_a^a f(x)\,dx$ equal to zero, since, if the integral can be interpreted as an area, then as $b \to a$ the area must approach zero. Accordingly, we make the following definition.

Definition 12.8c. $\qquad\qquad \int_a^a f(x)\,dx\; .=. \;0.$

The next four theorems are simple consequences of the definition of the definite integral and their proofs are left for the reader.

Theorem 12.8b. If f is integrable on the interval $a \leq x \leq b$, then for each ξ such that $a < \xi < b$,

$$\int_a^b f(x)\,dx = \int_a^\xi f(x)\,dx + \int_\xi^b f(x)\,dx.$$

Theorem 12.8c. If k is a constant and f is integrable on the interval $a \leq x \leq b$, then

$$\int_a^b k f(x)\,dx = k \int_a^b f(x)\,dx.$$

Theorem 12.8d. If f and g are integrable on the interval $a \leq x \leq b$, then

$$\int_a^b [f(x) + g(x)]\,dx = \int_a^b f(x)\,dx + \int_a^b g(x)\,dx.$$

Theorem 12.8e. If $f(x) \leq g(x)$ on $a \leq x \leq b$ and if f and g are integrable on this interval, then

$$\int_a^b f(x)\,dx \leq \int_a^b g(x)\,dx.$$

There is one additional property of the definite integral that is of fundamental importance in the development of some of the most significant results in the theory of integration. Although this property has a simple geometric interpretation in terms of area, the reader is again cautioned not to assume that every definite integral arises from an area, since it may not. As has been indicated earlier—and it is repeated here for emphasis—the definite integral can be used to *define* areas, volumes, work done by a variable force, and many other geometric and physical concepts.

Theorem 12.8f. *The Mean Value Theorem for Integrals.* Let f be continuous on $a \leq x \leq b$. Then there is a value of x, say ξ, such that $a < \xi < b$, and

$$\int_a^b f(x)\,dx = f(\xi)(b-a).$$

PROOF: Before proceeding with the proof, it is useful to consider a geometric interpretation of the theorem. If the integral can be interpreted as an area enclosed by $y = f(x)$, $x = a$, $x = b$, and the x-axis, the theorem simply asserts that there is a rectangle of width $b - a$ and height $f(\xi)$ that has the same area. The diagram in Figure 12.8a illustrates a case in which each of

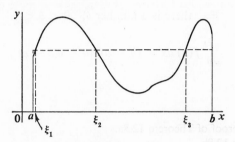

FIGURE 12.8a

three different values, ξ, in the interval $a \leq x \leq b$ satisfies the requirements of the theorem. However, the theorem asserts only that there is *at least* one such point.

Since $f(x)$ is continuous over a closed interval, it has a least value, m, and a greatest value M. Thus, for all x such that $a \leq x \leq b$,

$$m \leq f(x) \leq M.$$

It follows by Theorem 12.8e that

$$\int_a^b m\,dx \leq \int_a^b f(x)\,dx \leq \int_a^b M\,dx,$$

or that

$$m(b-a) \leq \int_a^b f(x)\,dx \leq M(b-a).$$

Hence,

$$m \leq \frac{1}{b-a}\int_a^b f(x)\,dx \leq M.$$

The last inequality says that the number

$$\frac{1}{b-a}\int_a^b f(x)\,dx$$

has a value between the least value and the greatest value of $f(x)$ on the closed interval. It follows by the Intermediate Value Theorem that there is a point ξ, $a < \xi < b$, at which $f(x)$ takes on this value, so that

$$f(\xi) = \frac{1}{b-a}\int_a^b f(x)\,dx,$$

and

$$\int_a^b f(x)\,dx = (b-a)f(\xi).$$

Note: If $a > b$, then, by virtue of Theorem 12.8a, the Mean Value Theorem is still valid, but $a > \xi > b$. This statement of the theorem may conveniently be combined with the original statement as follows.

Theorem 12.8g. f is continuous on the interval of integration

$$\Rightarrow \quad \text{there is a number } \theta, \quad 0 < \theta < 1,$$

such that

$$\int_a^b f(x)\,dx = (b-a)f[a + \theta(b-a)].$$

Exercises 12.8

1. Complete the proof of Theorem 12.8a.
2. Prove Theorem 12.8b.
3. Verify Theorem 12.8b for $f(x) = x^2$, $a = 2$, $b = 7$, and $\xi = 5$.
4. In Theorem 12.8b, prove that the point ξ need not be between a and b for the theorem to hold if all three integrals exist.
5. Verify the statement of Number 4 for $f(x) = x^2$, $a = 2$, $b = 7$, and $\xi = 9$.
6. Prove Theorem 12.8c.
7. Prove Theorem 12.8d.
8. Verify Theorem 12.8d for $f(x) = x$, $g(x) = x^2$, $a = 2$, and $b = 6$.
9. Prove Theorem 12.8e.
10. Find the ξ of Theorem 12.8f if $f(x) = x^2$, $a = 2$, and $b = 5$.

12.9 THE INDEFINITE INTEGRAL

The reader should realize that the letter denoting the variable of integration in a definite integral is immaterial to the evaluation of the integral. In other words, the integrals

$$\int_a^b f(x)\,dx \quad \text{and} \quad \int_a^b f(u)\,du$$

have exactly the same value. Hence, we may freely change the letter used for the variable of integration if it is convenient to do so.

It is clear that the value of the definite integral of a function ordinarily depends on the end points of the interval of integration. In particular, if the value of the upper limit is changed, we would expect the value of the integral to be changed. Geometrically, this is clear whenever the integral can be interpreted as an area (see Figure 12.9a).

This observation suggests that the concept of the definite integral can be used to describe a function by considering one of the end points of the interval of integration as a variable.

Theorem 12.9a. If f is an integrable function on the interval

$$\mathfrak{D} .=. \{x: a \leq x \leq b\},$$

and if t is an arbitrary point in the interval, then

$$\int_a^t f(x)\, dx$$

describes a function of t with domain $\mathfrak{D}$.

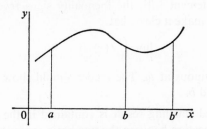

FIGURE 12.9a

PROOF: Since f is integrable, then for a given value of $t \in \mathfrak{D}$, say t_0, $\int_a^{t_0} f(x)\, dx$ exists. Thus to each t in $\mathfrak{D}$, there corresponds a unique value $\int_a^t f(x)\, dx$. Hence, the set of ordered pairs,

$$\left\{ \left(t, \int_a^t f(x)\, dx \right) \right\},$$

is, by definition, a function with domain $\mathfrak{D}$.

Definition 12.9a. The integral $\int_a^t f(x)\, dx$ is called the **indefinite integral** of the function f, and the expression $f(x)$ is called the **integrand** of the integral.

Since the indefinite integral of a function f describes another function, say F, it is reasonable to inquire as to the nature of this second function. The next theorem states one of the simplest properties of F.

Theorem 12.9b. Let f be a bounded integrable function on the interval

$$\mathfrak{D} .=. \{x: a \leq x \leq b\}.$$

If

$$F(t) .=. \int_a^t f(x)\, dx, \qquad t \in \mathfrak{D},$$

then F is continuous on $\mathfrak{D}$.

PROOF: To show that F is continuous, we need only show that, for $a < t_0 < b$,

$$\lim_{t \to t_0} F(t) = F(t_0).$$

Hence let us consider

$$F(t) - F(t_0) = \int_a^t f(x)\, dx - \int_a^{t_0} f(x)\, dx$$

$$= \int_{t_0}^t f(x)\, dx \qquad \text{(by Theorem 12.8a).}$$

Since f is bounded, it has a greatest lower bound, say m, and a least upper bound, say M, and, on the entire interval, it is true that

$$m \leq f(x) \leq M.$$

Thus, by Theorem 12.8e, if $t > t_0$, then

$$(t - t_0)m \leq \int_{t_0}^{t} f(x)\, dx \leq (t - t_0)M,$$

and the same statement with the inequality signs reversed holds if $t_0 < t$. These inequalities make it clear that

$$\lim_{t \to t_0} \int_{t_0}^{t} f(x)\, dx = 0.$$

Hence, F is continuous at t_0. The reader should show that F has one-sided continuity at a and b.

A more subtle and startling result is contained in the next theorem, which shows the close connection between the two basic concepts, the integral and the derivative.

Theorem 12.9c. *The Fundamental Theorem of Integral Calculus.* Let f be continuous on the interval $a \leq x \leq b$. If

$$F(t) .=. \int_{a}^{t} f(x)\, dx, \qquad a \leq t \leq b,$$

then

$$D_t F(t) = f(t).$$

(In other words, the theorem states that the derivative of a function defined by an indefinite integral of a continuous function is the integrand function.)

PROOF: We may determine the derivative of F directly from the definition. We have

$$F(t + h) - F(t) = \int_{a}^{t+h} f(x)\, dx - \int_{a}^{t} f(x)\, dx$$

$$= \int_{t}^{t+h} f(x)\, dx \qquad \text{(by Theorems 12.8a and b)}$$

$$= hf(t + \theta h), \quad 0 < \theta < 1 \quad \text{(by Theorem 12.8g)},$$

or

$$\frac{F(t + h) - F(t)}{h} = f(t + \theta h).$$

Since

$$D_t F(t) = \lim_{h \to 0} \frac{F(t + h) - F(t)}{h} = \lim_{h \to 0} f(t + \theta h),$$

and since f is continuous, we obtain

$$\lim_{h \to 0} f(t + \theta h) = f(t),$$

which completes the proof of the theorem.

This tremendously important relation between the two distinct concepts—the derivative on the one hand and the integral on the other—first of all demonstrates the essential unity of the calculus. As a most profitable by-product, it often provides a simple method for the evaluation of a definite integral without direct recourse to the definition of the integral. This method is essentially contained in

Theorem 12.9d. Let G be an inverse derivative of a continuous function f. Then

$$\int_a^b f(x)\, dx = G(b) - G(a).$$

PROOF: Let

(1) $$F(t) .=. \int_a^t f(x)\, dx.$$

Then

$$D_t F(t) = f(t) = D_t G(t).$$

Since the derivatives of F and G are the same, then, by Theorem 11.4b, $F(t)$ and $G(t)$ can differ only by a constant; that is,

(2) $$F(t) = G(t) + C.$$

From (1) and (2), we have

$$\int_a^b f(x)\, dx = F(b) = G(b) + C.$$

It also follows from (1) that

$$F(a) = \int_a^a f(x)\, dx = 0,$$

so that from (2),

$$0 = G(a) + C,$$

or

$$C = -G(a).$$

Consequently,

$$\int_a^b f(x)\, dx = G(b) - G(a).$$

In connection with the evaluation of the definite integral by means of Theorem 12.9d, it is customary to use the notation

$$[G(x)]_a^b .=. G(b) - G(a).$$

As illustrations of the use of Theorem 12.9d, consider the following examples.

Example 12.9a. Evaluate $\int_2^3 (x^2 - 2x)\, dx$.

If $f(x) = x^2 - 2x$, then an inverse derivative of $f(x)$ is

$$G(x) = \frac{x^3}{3} - x^2.$$

Therefore, by Theorem 12.9d,

$$\int_2^3 (x^2 - 2x)\, dx = \left[\frac{x^3}{3} - x^2\right]_2^3$$

$$= \left(\frac{3^3}{3} - 3^2\right) - \left(\frac{2^3}{3} - 2^2\right) = \frac{4}{3}.$$

Notice that $G(x)$ could have been taken as $\frac{1}{3}x^3 - x^2 + C$, where C is an arbitrary constant. However, the specific value of this constant will never affect the value of the definite integral. (Why?)

Example 12.9b. Evaluate $\int_{-2}^3 |x + 1|\, dx$.

Here, it is not convenient to try to find $D_x^{-1}|x + 1|$ directly. Instead, $f(x) = |x + 1|$ is rewritten as

$$f(x) = \begin{cases} x + 1, & x \geq -1, \\ -x - 1, & x < -1. \end{cases}$$

Then, by Theorem 12.8b,

$$\int_{-2}^3 |x + 1|\, dx = \int_{-2}^{-1} (-x - 1)\, dx + \int_{-1}^3 (x + 1)\, dx,$$

where the point of division is taken as the point at which the formula for $f(x)$ is changed. The two integrals on the right are evaluated as follows:

$$\int_{-2}^{-1} (-x - 1)\, dx = \left[\frac{-x^2}{2} - x\right]_{-2}^{-1} = \frac{1}{2},$$

$$\int_{-1}^3 (x + 1)\, dx = \left[\frac{x^2}{2} + x\right]_{-1}^3 = 8.$$

Consequently,

$$\int_{-2}^3 |x + 1|\, dx = 8 + \frac{1}{2} = \frac{17}{2}.$$

It is because of Theorem 12.9c that the integral sign without any indicated limits is so widely used to denote an inverse derivative. We shall yield to this almost universal custom and shall hereafter usually employ the integral sign notation, with the explicit understanding that

$$\int f(x)\, dx .=. D_x^{-1} f(x).$$

This means that $\int f(x)\, dx$ is simply a symbol to denote the general inverse derivative of $f(x)$; that is,

$$\int f(x)\, dx .=. G(x) + C,$$

where $G'(x) = f(x)$ and C is an arbitrary constant, the so-called **constant of integration.**

The primary problem in evaluating a definite integral is finding, when possible, an inverse derivative of the integrand. As we shall see later, it is not uncommon to encounter a function that has no "elementary" function as an inverse derivative. However, in many of the simpler cases it is possible to find an inverse derivative with the aid of the chain rule,

$$D_x f(u) = D_u f(u) D_x u = f'(u) D_x u,$$

from which we get

$$f(u) = \int f'(u) D_x u \, dx = \int f'(u) \, du.$$

This formula presents the possibility of sometimes grouping terms in an appropriate way so that the integral appears in the form $\int f'(u) \, du$. The following examples illustrate this idea.

Example 12.9c. Evaluate

$$F(t) .=. \int_0^t x\sqrt{a^2 - x^2} \, dx, \qquad |t| \le a.$$

We note that $D_x(a^2 - x^2) = -2x$, so that, by letting $u = a^2 - x^2$, we get $du = -2x \, dx$ and

$$\int x\sqrt{a^2 - x^2} \, dx = \int -\frac{1}{2} u^{1/2} \, du = -\frac{1}{2} \int u^{1/2} \, du$$

$$= -\frac{1}{2} \frac{u^{3/2}}{3/2} + C = -\frac{1}{3} (a^2 - x^2)^{3/2} + C.$$

The first term of this result may be taken as the desired inverse derivative, say $G(x)$, of the given integrand. Hence,

$$\int_0^t x\sqrt{a^2 - x^2} \, dx = \left[-\frac{1}{3} (a^2 - x^2)^{3/2} \right]_0^t = -\frac{(a^2 - t^2)^{3/2}}{3} + \frac{a^3}{3}.$$

Example 12.9d. Evaluate

$$p(t) .=. \int_a^t \frac{1}{\sqrt{x} (1 - \sqrt{x})^2} \, dx, \qquad 1 < a < t.$$

Since $D_x(-\sqrt{x}) = -\frac{1}{2} x^{-1/2}$, the grouping $-2(1 - \sqrt{x})^{-2}(-\frac{1}{2} x^{-1/2})$ is suggested. This form can be treated by letting $u = 1 - \sqrt{x}$ and using the fact that

$$\int u^{-2} \, du = -u^{-1} + C,$$

so that an inverse derivative is seen to be

$$G(x) = \frac{2}{1 - \sqrt{x}}.$$

Hence,

$$p(t) = [G(x)]_a^t = \frac{2}{1 - \sqrt{t}} - \frac{2}{1 - \sqrt{a}}.$$

Exercises 12.9

Evaluate the given definite integral in each of Numbers 1 to 16.

1. $\int_0^2 (x^2 - 2x)\, dx.$

2. $\int_0^1 (x^3 - \frac{1}{2}x)\, dx.$

3. $\int_1^2 (x^2 - \sqrt{x})\, dx.$

4. $\int_0^4 \sqrt{5u}\, du.$

5. $\int_1^4 (s - 1)(\sqrt{s} + 2)\, ds.$

6. $\int_{-4}^{-1} \sqrt{x^4 + x^2}\, dx.$

7. $\int_0^4 \frac{dx}{\sqrt{1 + 2x}}.$

8. $\int_0^{2a} \frac{x\, dx}{\sqrt{a^2 + x^2}}.$

9. $\int_0^a (a^{2/3} - x^{2/3})^3\, dx.$

10. $\int_{2b}^{3b} \frac{x\, dx}{(x^2 - b^2)^3}.$

11. $\int_0^1 \frac{x^3}{(1 + x^4)^2}\, dx.$

12. $\int_0^{\sqrt{3}} \frac{x\, dx}{(4 - x^2)^{3/2}}.$

13. $\int_{-2}^4 |x - 2|\, dx.$

14. $\int_{-2}^2 \sqrt{2 + |x|}\, dx.$

15. $\int_{-1}^1 \sqrt{|x| - x}\, dx.$

16. $\int_2^4 \frac{6s^2 + 4}{\sqrt{s^3 + 2s}}\, ds.$

In each of Numbers 17 to 22, evaluate the given indefinite integral.

17. $\int_4^t \sqrt{2|x| + 1}\, dx.$

18. $\int_1^t \frac{(x - 1)^2}{\sqrt{x}}\, dx,\ t > 0.$

19. $\int_1^x \frac{t^{1/2} + t^{1/4}}{t}\, dt,\ 0 < x.$

20. $\int_0^t (x^4 + 2)^3 x^3\, dx.$

21. $\int_0^t (|2x| + x)\, dx.$

22. $\int_0^t (|x - 1| + |x|)\, dx.$

Use the Fundamental Theorem of Integral Calculus to obtain the desired derivative in each of Numbers 23 to 28.

23. $D_x \int_0^x \sqrt{1 + t^4}\, dt.$

24. $D_t \int_0^t \cos \theta\, d\theta.$

25. $D_s \int_s^a \frac{a - u}{a + u}\, du.$

26. $D_x \int_x^{\pi/2} \sin 2u\, du.$

27. $D_x \int_{-x}^x \frac{dt}{1 + t}.$

28. $D_x \int_0^{x^2} \frac{dt}{1 + t}.$

29. If $D_x f(x) = G(x)$, show that, for $n \neq -1$,

$$\int [f(x)]^n G(x)\, dx = \frac{[f(x)]^{n+1}}{n + 1} + C$$

and

$$\int_a^b [f(x)]^n G(x)\, dx = \frac{[f(b)]^{n+1} - [f(a)]^{n+1}}{n + 1}.$$

30. If $\int_a^b f(t)\,dt = G(b) - G(a)$, find $\int_a^b f(ct)\,dt$, where c is a nonzero constant.

31. Consider the set of all integrable functions on an interval $a \leq x \leq b$. Is this set closed with respect to addition? Explain.

12.10 APPLICATIONS TO AREAS

The concept of the definite integral was strongly motivated by the problem of finding areas bounded by curves. This application of the definite integral will be discussed in detail now, and other applications will be discussed in the following section.

Example 12.10a. Calculate the area enclosed by the curve $y = 2/x^2$, the x-axis, and the ordinates $x = 1$ and $x = 4$.

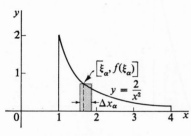
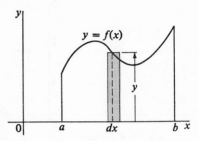

FIGURE 12.10a   FIGURE 12.10b

From our earlier discussion we know that the desired area is defined by an expression of the form

$$\lim_{\delta \to 0} \sum_{\alpha=1}^n f(\xi_\alpha)\,\Delta x_\alpha = \int_a^b f(x)\,dx.$$

(See Figure 12.10a.) Hence we may go directly to the definite integral and write, for the area A,

$$A = \int_1^4 \frac{2}{x^2}\,dx.$$

An inverse derivative of $2/x^2$ is $-2/x$. Hence

$$A = \left[-\frac{2}{x} \right]_1^4 = -\frac{1}{2} + 2 = \frac{3}{2} \text{ (l.u.)}^2.$$

(The abbreviation "l.u." will be used for *linear units*.)

The integral needed for calculating an area is often set up by considering a typical subinterval of "width" dx, as shown in Figure 12.10b. The area of a rectangular strip of height $f(x) = y$ and "width" dx is denoted by

$$dA = f(x)\,dx \quad \text{or} \quad y\,dx.$$

The process of forming the sum of the elements of area and taking the limit is summarized by simply writing

$$A = \int_a^b y\,dx \quad \text{or} \quad \int_a^b f(x)\,dx.$$

Thus, the definite integral for the area can be set up directly without actually having to go through all the intermediate steps.

If a curve crosses the x-axis, some care must be taken in setting up an integral to find an area, as is illustrated in the following example.

Example 12.10b. Find the area enclosed by the curve $f(x) = x^2 - x - 2$, the x-axis, and the lines $x = 0$, $x = 3$.

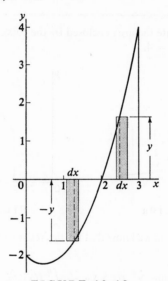

FIGURE 12.10c

The problem is illustrated in Figure 12.10c. For that portion of the graph of f that lies below the x-axis, a typical "element of area," dA, is given by

$$dA = -f(x)\,dx.$$

Because $f(x)$ is negative, it is necessary to represent the length of the element by $-f(x)$ in order to get a positive quantity as a measure of area. Thus the area A can be expressed as

$$A = \int_0^2 [-f(x)]\,dx + \int_2^3 f(x)\,dx$$

$$= \int_0^2 [-(x^2 - x - 2)]\,dx + \int_2^3 (x^2 - x - 2)\,dx$$

$$= \left[-\left(\frac{x^3}{3} - \frac{x^2}{2} - 2x \right) \right]_0^2 + \left[\frac{x^3}{3} - \frac{x^2}{2} - 2x \right]_2^3$$

$$= \frac{10}{3} + \frac{11}{6} = \frac{31}{6} \text{ (l.u.)}^2.$$

The reader should observe that

$$\int_0^3 (x^2 - x - 2)\, dx = \left[\frac{x^3}{3} - \frac{x^2}{2} - 2x\right]_0^3 = -\frac{3}{2},$$

being negative, does not properly represent an area. If an area is bounded by a curve $y = f(x)$ and the x-axis from $x = a$ to $x = b$, $a < b$, then the area is always given by

$$A \; . = . \; \int_a^b |f(x)|\, dx.$$

The problem of finding an area need not be restricted to an area bounded, in part, by the x-axis. The technique used in the preceding examples can be extended to areas enclosed by any simple curves.

Example 12.10c. Find the area enclosed by the curves $f(x) = x + 1$ and $g(x) = (x - 1)^2$ (see Figure 12.10d).

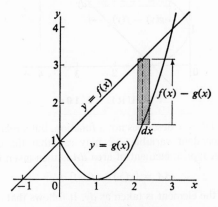

FIGURE 12.10d

In this case, a typical element of area dA of "width" dx extends from one curve to the other. Hence, the length of the element is given by

$$f(x) - g(x).$$

[The length must be positive; that is, $g(x) - f(x)$ *cannot* be used as a measure of the length of the element when $g(x) < f(x)$.]

The process of summing over elements of this type and taking the proper limit of the sum leads to the integral

$$A = \int_0^3 [f(x) - g(x)]\, dx$$

for the area. Thus,

$$A = \int_0^3 [(x + 1) - (x - 1)^2]\, dx$$

$$= \int_0^3 [3x - x^2]\, dx$$

$$= \left[\frac{3x^2}{2} - \frac{x^3}{3}\right]_0^3 = \frac{9}{2}\ (\text{l.u.})^2.$$

Although each of the three preceding examples has illustrated the definite integral when the partitioning is carried out along the x-axis, there is no reason why the same process cannot be used along the y-axis. In that case the roles of the variables are interchanged. In some problems, it is more convenient to use this procedure.

Example 12.10d. Find the area enclosed by the curves

$$(y - 1)^2 = x, \quad y = x - 1.$$

(See Figure 12.10e.)

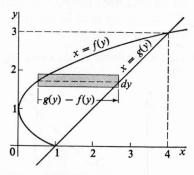

FIGURE 12.10e

The equation $(y - 1)^2 = x$ describes not a function, but a relation. However, if y is regarded as the independent variable, we may say that the equation describes a function $\{(y, f(y))\}$. A typical element of area dA is then given by

$$dA = [g(y) - f(y)] \, dy,$$

where the "width" of the element is taken as dy. It follows that

$$A = \int_0^3 [(y + 1) - (y - 1)^2] \, dy,$$

which, except for the use of y rather than x for the variable of integration, is exactly the same integral as occurred in Example 12.10c.

Suppose we attempt to calculate the area in Example 12.10d by using elements of area of width dx. What difficulties would we encounter? (See Exercises 12.10, Number 17.)

Exercises 12.10

In each of Numbers 1 to 12, find the area enclosed by the given curves. Make a sketch and show a typical element of area.

1. $y = 9 - x^2$; $x = -3$; $x = 3$; $y = 0$.
2. $y = x^3 + 2x$; $x = -2$; $y = 0$.
3. $y = x^{1/2} - x^{-1/2}$; $x = 1$; $x = 4$; $y = 0$.
4. $x^{1/2} + y^{1/2} = a^{1/2}$; $x = 0$; $y = 0$.

5. $y = \dfrac{x}{(x^2 + 1)^2}$; $x = -2$; $x = 3$; $y = 0$.

6. $y = x(x^2 - 1)$; $x = -2$; $x = 3$; $y = 0$.
7. $4y = x^3$; $y = x$, $x \geq 0$.
8. $4y = x^3$; the tangent to this curve at $x = -2$.
9. $4x = 4 - y^2$; $2x = 4 - y^2$.
10. $x = y^3 - 4y$; $x = 5y$, $y \geq 0$.
11. $y = x(x^2 - 1)$; $y = 3x$.
12. $y = x\sqrt{4 - x^2}$, $y = 0$.

In each of Numbers 13 to 16, find in two ways the area enclosed by the given curves.

13. $2x = 2 + y^3$; $x = -3$; $y = 2$.
14. $2y = (x - 1)^3$; $y = 4$; $x = -2$.
15. $27y = 2x^3$; the tangent to the curve at $x = 3$.
16. $y^2 = x^3$, $y = x$.
17. In Example 12.10d, use elements of area of width dx and try to calculate the area.
18. Find m in terms of a so that the segment of the parabola $y = ax - x^2$ cut off by the line $y = mx$ has an area one-eighth that of the segment cut off by the x-axis.

12.11 APPLICATIONS TO VOLUMES

The techniques used to calculate areas can also frequently be used to calculate volumes, forces, work, and other quantities that often arise in physical problems. A few of the simpler applications to volume will be considered at this time; other applications will be deferred to a later section.

Example 12.11a. Find the volume of a right pyramid having a height of h units and a square base a units on a side (see Figure 12.11a).

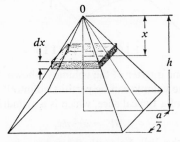

FIGURE 12.11a

The volume can be approximated by means of square slabs as indicated in the figure. If the origin is taken at the vertex 0, and the x-axis is along the altitude of the pyramid, then the element of volume dV of a typical slab of side s is given by

$$dV = s^2 \, dx.$$

The volume of the pyramid is therefore

$$V = \int_0^h s^2 \, dx.$$

In order to evaluate the integral, we must be able to express s in terms of x. By considering similar triangles as indicated in the diagram, we may write

$$\frac{s/2}{x} = \frac{a/2}{h},$$

or

$$s = \frac{a}{h} x.$$

Hence,

$$V = \int_0^h \frac{a^2}{h^2} x^2 \, dx$$

$$= \left[\frac{a^2 x^3}{3h^2} \right]_0^h = \frac{1}{3} a^2 h \text{ (l.u.)}^3.$$

The success of the procedure in the preceding example depends upon our being able to establish a functional relationship between the variables used to measure the element of volume. The same technique works easily for volumes of revolution—that is, for volumes generated by revolving an area about an axis.

Example 12.11b. Find the volume of the solid obtained by revolving the area enclosed by $y = x^2$, $x = 1$, and $y = 0$ about the x-axis (see Figure 12.11b).

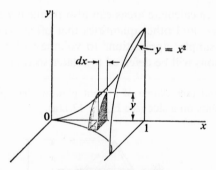

FIGURE 12.11b

In the diagram, only one quarter of the volume is shown in order to keep the figure as simple as possible. The volume can be partitioned into "slices," as indicated in the figure. The volume, dV, of a typical slice, which is a cylindrical disk, is

$$dV = \pi r^2 \, dx,$$

where r is the radius of the disk. Evidently the radius r is actually measured by the y-coordinate of the curve in this case, so that

$$dV = \pi y^2 \, dx$$

and

$$V = \pi \int_0^1 x^4 \, dx$$

$$= \frac{\pi}{5} \text{ (l.u.)}^3.$$

In order to illustrate a variation of this problem, we consider the same area revolved about a different line.

Example 12.11c. Find the volume of the solid generated by revolving the area in Example 12.11b about the line $x = 1$ (see Figure 12.11c).

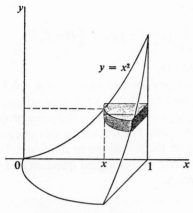 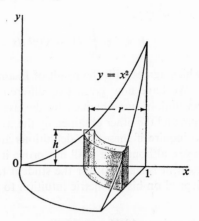

FIGURE 12.11c   **FIGURE 12.11d**

The typical element of volume, dV, is taken parallel to the plane of the base of the solid, so that

$$dV = \pi r^2 \, dy.$$

The radius of the element is the length $1 - x$. Since $x = \sqrt{y}$,

$$dV = \pi(1 - \sqrt{y})^2 \, dy.$$

Thus,

$$V = \pi \int_0^1 (1 - \sqrt{y})^2 \, dy = \frac{\pi}{6} \, (\text{l.u.})^3.$$

In general, it appears that the definite integral is useful in finding the volume of any solid having a cross section whose area can be expressed in terms of the perpendicular distance of the section from some fixed plane. In any such case, the integral can be set up by using the "slice" method illustrated in the preceding three examples.

In the case of volumes of revolution, it is sometimes convenient to set up an integral using cylindrical shell elements rather than cylindrical disk elements, such as were used in Examples 12.11b and 12.11c. Thus, consider once again the volume described in Example 12.11c, but regard the volume as the limit of the sum of cylindrical shells of which a portion of a typical one is shown in Figure 12.11d. In order to simplify the computational details, let r be the radius from the line $x = 1$, which is the axis of the cylindrical shell, to the midpoint of the wall of the shell. Then, if the division along the x-axis is of length Δx, the volume of the shell is

$$\pi(r + \tfrac{1}{2} \Delta x)^2 h - \pi(r - \tfrac{1}{2} \Delta x)^2 h = 2\pi r h \, \Delta x.$$

Thus, the volume of the solid is

$$V = \int_0^1 2\pi r h\, dx,$$

where

$$r = 1 - x \quad \text{and} \quad h = y = x^2.$$

Accordingly,

$$V = 2\pi \int_0^1 (1 - x)x^2\, dx = 2\pi \int_0^1 (x^2 - x^3)\, dx = \frac{\pi}{6}\,(\text{l.u.})^3,$$

which agrees with the result of Example 12.11c.

We have now given two different definitions for the volume of a solid of revolution, one obtained by the use of cylindrical disks in the approximation sum and the other obtained by the use of cylindrical shells. It is therefore proper to inquire if these two definitions are consistent. The answer to this question is yes, although we shall not prove it here. At the present point in his development, it is sufficient for the student to be aware of this logical question and to depend on his geometric intuition to answer it.

Exercises 12.11

1. Use a definite integral to obtain the formula for the volume of a regular tetrahedron (a triangular pyramid with equilateral triangles for its faces).

2. The base of a certain solid is the parabolic segment enclosed between the parabola $y^2 = 4x$ and the line $x = 4$. Every section of the solid perpendicular to the x-axis is an isosceles right triangle with its hypotenuse in the plane of the base. Find the volume of the solid.

3. The base of a certain solid is the portion of the xy-plane for which $x^2 + y^2 \leqq 1$. If every section of the solid perpendicular to the y-axis is a square, find the volume of the solid.

4. A horn-shaped solid has the xy-plane for a plane of symmetry and the section of the solid in the xy-plane is bounded by the two parabolic arcs $y = \sqrt{x}$ and $y = 2\sqrt{x}$ and by the line $x = 4$. If every section of the solid perpendicular to the xy-plane and parallel to the y-axis is a circle, find the volume of the solid.

5. Use the method of cylindrical disks to obtain the formula for the volume of a sphere of radius b.

6. Use the method of cylindrical shells to obtain the formula for the volume of a right circular cone of radius b and height h.

7. Find the volume formed by revolving the area bounded by the x-axis and the elliptic arc

$$\frac{x^2}{a^2} + \frac{y^2}{b^2} = 1, \qquad y \geqq 0,$$

about the x-axis.

8. Find the volume of the solid obtained by revolving the area enclosed by $y = 2\sqrt{x}$, $x = 1$, and $y = 0$ about

    (a) the x-axis; (b) the line $x = 1$; (c) the line $x = 0$.

9. Find the volume of the solid obtained by revolving the area enclosed by $x^2 = 4ay$, $y = 0$, and $x = 2a$ about

   (a) the x-axis;
   (b) the line $y = a$;

   (c) the line $x = 2a$;
   (d) the line $y = 4a$.

10. Find the volume of the wedge-shaped solid formed by passing two planes through the center of a sphere if the planes intersect at an angle α.

11. Find the volume of a pyramid having a cross section that is a regular polygon of n sides.

12. Find the volume of the intersection of two cylinders of equal radii when their axes intersect at right angles.

13. The area bounded by the line $y = x$ and the parabola $y^2 = 4x$ is revolved about the y-axis. Find the volume that is generated.

14. The first quadrant area formed by the two curves $y^2 = x$ and $y^2 = x^3$ is revolved about the x-axis. Find the volume that is generated.

15. Find the volume generated by revolving the area in Number 14 about (a) the line $x = 1$; (b) the line $y = 2$.

★16. Find the volume generated by revolving the area in Number 13 about the line $y = x$.

12.12 AVERAGES

The concept of an average or a weighted mean is important in many statistical and physical problems. For example, a weighted average is often used to compute the average grade on an examination. Suppose there are 5 grades of 70, 10 grades of 75, 8 grades of 80, 6 grades of 85, and 4 grades of 90. Then the average grade g is given by

$$g = \frac{5(70) + 10(75) + 8(80) + 6(85) + 4(90)}{5 + 10 + 8 + 6 + 4}.$$

This kind of average is called a **weighted average** and the number of occurrences of each grade is called a **weight factor**.

In general, if the numbers $x_1, x_2, x_3, \ldots, x_n$ have weight factors $w_1, w_2, \ldots, w_n$, respectively, then the number

$$\bar{x} .=. \frac{\sum\limits_{\alpha=1}^{n} w_\alpha x_\alpha}{\sum\limits_{\alpha=1}^{n} w_\alpha}$$

is called the weighted average of the numbers x_α. This concept of weighted average can easily be generalized to define the concept of the average value of a quantity u with respect to a variable t, where u is a continuous function of t. The definite integral is an ideal tool for accomplishing this generalization.

For instance, suppose the temperature u of a furnace is regulated so that $u = f(t)$, where t is time in hours. Is it possible to find a number that can reasonably be called an average temperature for the period $a \leq t \leq b$? An approximate average temperature can be obtained by partitioning the time interval into subintervals $\Delta t_1, \Delta t_2, \ldots, \Delta t_n$, and making spot temperature checks at times $t_1^*, t_2^*, \ldots, t_n^*$ in each of the time periods, respectively. (see Figure 12.12a).

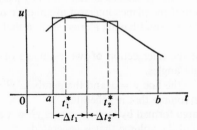

FIGURE 12.12a

Using the value $f(t_\alpha^*)$ as the temperature over the time interval Δt_α, an approximate average temperature $\bar{u}_n$ is given by

$$\bar{u}_n = \frac{\sum\limits_{\alpha=1}^{n} f(t_\alpha^*) \Delta t_\alpha}{\sum\limits_{\alpha=1}^{n} \Delta t_\alpha} = \frac{\sum\limits_{\alpha=1}^{n} f(t_\alpha^*) \Delta t_\alpha}{b - a}.$$

Evidently, if $\lim_{n\to\infty} \bar{u}_n$ exists, it would be suitable as an average value of $f(t)$ over the interval in question. But the limit of the numerator of $\bar{u}_n$ defines $\int_a^b f(t)\, dt$, so that the following definition is suggested.

Definition 12.12a. The average value of a function $f(t)$ with respect to t, over the interval $a \leq t \leq b$, is $\bar{y}$, where

$$\bar{y} .=. \frac{\int_a^b f(t)\, dt}{b - a}.$$

Example 12.12a. Find the average height above the x-axis of the curve described by $y = x^2(2 - x)$, $0 \leq x \leq 2$.

From the definition of average value, we get

$$\bar{y} = \frac{\int_0^2 x^2(2 - x)\, dx}{2 - 0}$$

$$= \frac{1}{2}\left[\frac{2x^3}{3} - \frac{x^4}{4}\right]_0^2 = \frac{2}{3}.$$

The average of a quantity $f(x)$ may also be defined with respect to any variable t for which $x = g(t)$.

Definition 12.12b. The average of the functional values $f(x)$ with respect to a variable t, where $x = g(t)$, over the interval $a \leq t \leq b$ is

$$\bar{y} . = . \frac{\int_a^b f(x)\, dt}{b - a} = \frac{\int_a^b f[g(t)]\, dt}{b - a}.$$

Example 12.12b. Find the average value of $y = x^2(2 - x)$, $0 \leq x \leq 2$, with respect to the quantity x^2.

By letting $x = \sqrt{t}$, so that $y = t(2 - \sqrt{t})$, we reduce the problem to that of finding the average value of y with respect to t for $0 \leq t \leq 4$. Thus,

$$\bar{y} = \frac{\int_0^4 y\, dt}{4 - 0} = \frac{1}{4} \int_0^4 t(2 - \sqrt{t})\, dt = \frac{4}{5}.$$

An important application of the concept of average value occurs in physics and engineering in connection with the concepts of **center of mass** and **centroid.** To illustrate these ideas let us consider a simple physical problem, in which a weight w is suspended on a rigid horizontal rod that is supported at a point P (Figure 12.12b).

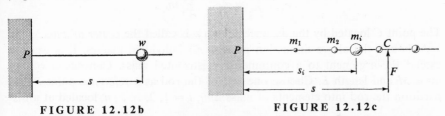

FIGURE 12.12b   **FIGURE 12.12c**

Experience indicates that the farther away the weight is from the support point P, the greater will be the tendency of the rod to turn about P. This "turning tendency" was first expressed in mathematical form by Archimedes, who enunciated the idea in connection with the law of the lever. The turning effect of the weight is called a turning *moment*, and is defined as the product of the weight and its distance from the reference point or reference axis. That is, the *moment M* due to a force F acting at a distance s from a reference point P is

$$M = Fs.$$

A fundamental law of mechanics states that if a plane system of parallel forces acting on a rigid body is in equilibrium, then
(1) the vector sum of all of the forces must be zero, and
(2) the algebraic sum of the moments relative to an arbitrary reference point in the plane of all the forces must be zero.
Consider a system of n particles of mass m_i on a rod of negligible weight, with the ith particle located at a distance s_i from a reference point P, and suppose the rod is hinged to a rigid support at P (see Figure 12.12c). Suppose we

wish to find the distance, s, from P, at which a vertical force of magnitude F should be applied on the rod in order to prevent the rod from turning down due to the weight of the masses m_i, and to keep the system in equilibrium. It is known from physics that the weight of a mass m is proportional to the mass and that the constant of proportionality is the gravitational constant g (approximately 32 feet per second per second). Hence, the force due to the ith mass is $F_i = m_i g$, and the preceding laws of mechanics yield the two equations

$$\sum_{i=1}^{n} m_i g - F = 0 \quad \text{and} \quad \sum_{i=1}^{n} m_i g s_i - Fs = 0.$$

The distance s is a kind of weighted average, since the first of the preceding equations states, in effect, that the force F must equal the sum of the forces due to the masses m_i. That is,

$$F = \sum_{i=1}^{n} g m_i,$$

so that the second equation yields the result

$$s = \frac{\displaystyle\sum_{i=1}^{n} m_i g s_i}{\displaystyle\sum_{i=1}^{n} m_i g} = \frac{\displaystyle\sum_{i=1}^{n} m_i s_i}{\displaystyle\sum_{i=1}^{n} m_i}.$$

The point C located by the distance s from p is called the *center of mass*.

Although the above discussion pertains to individual masses, it is easy to extend the argument to a continuously distributed mass. Consider a rod of mass M and length L. Choose one end of the rod as a reference point P and partition the rod into elements of mass Δm_i, $i = 1, 2, \ldots, n$, located at a dis-

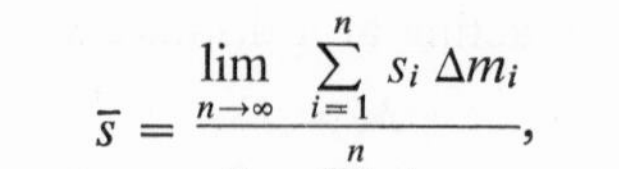

FIGURE 12.12d

tance s_i from P (Figure 12.12d). Then the center of mass of the rod is at the point $\bar{s}$ units distant from P, where

$$\bar{s} = \frac{\displaystyle\lim_{n \to \infty} \sum_{i=1}^{n} s_i \Delta m_i}{\displaystyle\lim_{n \to \infty} \sum_{i=1}^{n} \Delta m_i},$$

or

$$\bar{s} = \frac{\displaystyle\int_{s=0}^{s=L} s \, dm}{\displaystyle\int_{s=0}^{s=L} dm}.$$

If the rod is of uniform density k (mass units per unit length), then

$$dm = k \, ds$$

and

$$\bar{s} = \frac{k \int_0^L s \, ds}{k \int_0^L ds} = \frac{k \dfrac{L^2}{2}}{kL} = \frac{L}{2}.$$

Thus, the center of mass of the rod is at the center of the rod, as is to be expected.

A further extension of these ideas to two (or even three) dimensions is reasonable. Consider a plate of uniform density ρ (mass units per unit volume) and thickness h, as indicated in Figure 12.12e. It is assumed that the plate has

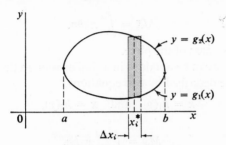

FIGURE 12.12e

a shape that can be described in terms of simple functions. There are two averages to be found in order to locate the center of mass: an average x value, $\bar{x}$, and an average y value, $\bar{y}$. To find the average x value, partition the plate into vertical strips. The mass of the ith strip is approximately $\rho \, \Delta V_i$, where ΔV_i is the volume of the ith strip. Now suppose that the edge of the plate can be described by the equations

$$y = g_1(x) \quad \text{and} \quad y = g_2(x),$$

as shown in the figure. Then

$$\Delta V_i = h \, \Delta x_i [g_2(x_i^*) - g_1(x_i^*)],$$

and the moment of the ith mass with respect to the y-axis is

$$M_i = x_i^* \, \Delta m_i$$
$$= x_i^* \rho h [g_2(x_i^*) - g_1(x_i^*)] \, \Delta x_i.$$

In this case the y-axis is used as a reference line since it is parallel to the strip, a fact that allows us to use a fixed measurement of distance between the axis and the strip. The approximate average x value, $\bar{x}_n$, is given by

$$\bar{x}_n = \frac{\displaystyle\sum_{i=1}^{n} M_i}{\displaystyle\sum_{i=1}^{n} \Delta m_i}$$

$$= \frac{\displaystyle\sum_{i=1}^{n} x_i^* \rho h [g_2(x_i^*) - g_1(x_i^*)] \, \Delta x_i}{\displaystyle\sum_{i=1}^{n} \rho h [g_2(x_i^*) - g_1(x_i^*)] \, \Delta x_i}.$$

In the limit this expression becomes

$$\bar{x} = \frac{\int_a^b x\rho h[g_2(x) - g_1(x)]\, dx}{\int_a^b \rho h[g_2(x) - g_1(x)]\, dx}$$

$$= \frac{\int_a^b x\, dm}{\int_a^b dm},$$

or

$$M\bar{x} = \int_a^b x\, dm,$$

where M is the total mass of the plate.

An average y value can be obtained in a similar way. In that case the boundary of the plate must be described by two equations,

$$x = h_1(y) \quad \text{and} \quad x = h_2(y),$$

so that

$$M\bar{y} = \int_{y=c}^{y=d} y\, dm.$$

If the density ρ and the thickness h are constants, the equations for $\bar{x}$ and $\bar{y}$ may be written as

$$A\bar{x} = \int_{x=a}^{x=b} x\, dA \quad \text{and} \quad A\bar{y} = \int_{y=c}^{y=d} y\, dA,$$

where A is the area of the face of the plate. In this case, a physical problem has been expressed in terms of a purely geometric problem—that of finding average x- and y-coordinates, $\bar{x}$ and $\bar{y}$, respectively, for a geometric area. The point $(\bar{x}, \bar{y})$ is called the *centroid* of the area. Thus, we shall speak of finding moments of areas just as we speak of finding moments of masses.

The succeeding examples in this section will illustrate the preceding discussion.

Example 12.12c. Find the centroid of a rectangular area (Figure 12.12f).

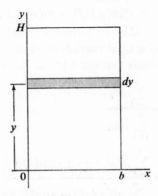

FIGURE 12.12f

Suppose the rectangle is H units high and b units wide. Let 0 be an origin at the lower left corner. To find the average y value, $\bar{y}$, choose a rectangular strip parallel to the x-axis. Then

$$dA = b\,dy$$

and

$$A\bar{y} = \int_0^H yb\,dy = \left[\frac{by^2}{2}\right]_0^H = \frac{bH^2}{2}.$$

Since $A = bH$, we have

$$\bar{y} = \frac{bH^2}{2bH} = \frac{H}{2}.$$

Similarly, the average x value is found to be $b/2$. Hence the centroid is at the point $(b/2, H/2)$.

In general, it appears that the centroid of an area must be on a line of symmetry of the area, if such a line exists. This conjecture is easy to prove.

Theorem 12.12a. Let the line L be a line of symmetry of an area A. Then the centroid of the area lies on L.

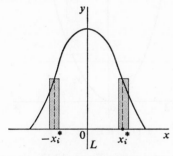

FIGURE 12.12g

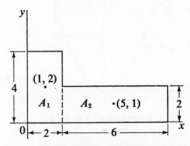

FIGURE 12.12h

PROOF: Choose an origin on L as in Figure 12.12g. We want to show that $\bar{x} = 0$. Consider a vertical element of area ΔA_i at an approximate distance x_i^* from the y-axis. Because the curve is symmetric, there is a corresponding element of area at $-x_i^*$. Hence the moments due to these elements are

$$x_i^* \,\Delta A_i \quad \text{and} \quad -x_i^* \,\Delta A_i.$$

The sum of these terms is 0. It follows that $\bar{x} = 0$. (Why?)

The information contained in the preceding theorem considerably simplifies the problem of finding the centroid of an area that can be partitioned into areas having lines of symmetry.

Example 12.12d. Find the centroid of the area shown in Figure 12.12h.

The area is divided into two rectangles as indicated in the figure, and the total area is

$$A = A_1 + A_2 = 8 + 12 = 20 \text{ (l.u.)}^2.$$

The centroid, $(\bar{x}_1, \bar{y}_1)$, of rectangle A_1 is at the point $(1, 2)$, as indicated by the preceding example. Similarly, the centroid of A_2 is $(\bar{x}_2, \bar{y}_2) = (5, 1)$. Since the moment of a plane area with respect to any axis is the product of the area and the perpendicular distance of the centroid of the area from the axis, the sum of the moments with respect to the y-axis is

$$A\bar{x} = A_1\bar{x}_1 + A_2\bar{x}_2 = (8)(1) + (12)(5) = 68 \text{ (l.u.)}^3.$$

Similarly, the sum of the moments with respect to the x-axis is

$$A\bar{y} = A_1\bar{y}_1 + A_2\bar{y}_2 = (8)(2) + (12)(1) = 28 \text{ (l.u.)}^3.$$

Therefore, the required coordinates are

$$\bar{x} = \frac{68}{20} = \frac{17}{5} \quad \text{and} \quad \bar{y} = \frac{28}{20} = \frac{7}{5}.$$

Example 12.12e. Find the centroid of the area bounded by the parabola $y = x^2$ and the line $y = 4$.

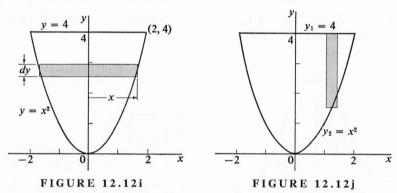

FIGURE 12.12i   FIGURE 12.12j

If the rectangular strip is taken parallel to the x-axis, as in Figure 12.12i, then the moment of the strip with respect to the x-axis is $y \, dA = y(2x \, dy)$ and

$$A\bar{y} = \int_0^4 (2x)y \, dy.$$

Since $x = y^{1/2}$,

$$A\bar{y} = \int_0^4 2y^{3/2} \, dy$$

$$= \left[\frac{4}{5} y^{5/2}\right]_0^4$$

$$= \frac{128}{5} \text{ (l.u.)}^3.$$

Also,

$$A = 2 \int_0^4 y^{1/2} \, dy = 2\left[\frac{2}{3} y^{3/2}\right]_0^4 = \frac{32}{3} \text{ (l.u.)}^2,$$

so that

$$\bar{y} = \left(\frac{128}{5}\right)\left(\frac{3}{32}\right) = \frac{12}{5}.$$

The y-axis is a line of symmetry, and therefore $\bar{x} = 0$.

Example 12.12f. Find the centroid of the area described in Example 12.12e by using vertical strips.

The *y*-coordinate of the centroid of the rectangular strip shown in Figure 12.12j is $\frac{1}{2}(y_1 + y_2)$, where $y_1 = 4$ and $y_2 = x^2$. The area of the strip is $(y_1 - y_2)\,dx$ and the moment with respect to the *x*-axis is therefore

$$\frac{1}{2}(y_1 + y_2)(y_1 - y_2)\,dx = \frac{1}{2}(y_1^2 - y_2^2)\,dx.$$

Thus

$$A\bar{y} = 2\int_0^2 \frac{1}{2}(y_1^2 - y_2^2)\,dx.$$

Use is made of symmetry so that the limits on the definite integrals are 0 to 2 and each integral is multiplied by a factor of 2. Since $y_1 = 4$ and $y_2 = x^2$, the expression for $A\bar{y}$ becomes

$$A\bar{y} = \int_0^2 (16 - x^4)\,dx = \frac{128}{5}\ (\text{l.u.})^3.$$

It follows that

$$\bar{y} = \left(\frac{128}{5}\right)\left(\frac{3}{32}\right) = \frac{12}{5}.$$

Exercises 12.12

1. Find the average ordinate (*y* value) of the parabola $ay = 2ax - x^2$ from $x = 0$ to $x = 2a$, with respect to *x*.
2. Find the average width parallel to the *x*-axis of the area bounded by the curves $y^2 = x^3$ and $y = x$, with respect to *y*.
3. Find the average *y* value of the curve $y^2 = x^3$ with respect to x^3 from $x = 0$ to $x = 2$.
4. Find the average value of y^2 with respect to *x* for the upper half of the circle $x^2 + y^2 = r^2$.
5. Find the average value of y^2 with respect to x^2 for the upper half of the circle $x^2 + y^2 = r^2$.
6. Find the centroid of the area shown in Figure 12.12k.

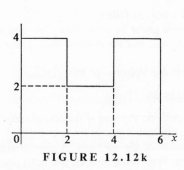

FIGURE 12.12k

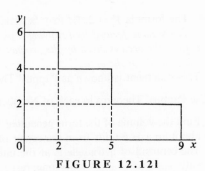

FIGURE 12.12l

7. Find the centroid of the area shown in Figure 12.12l.
8. Show that the centroid of any triangle is at the intersection of the medians.

In each of Numbers 9 to 20, find the centroid of the area bounded by the given curves.

9. $x^2 + y^2 = a^2$, $y = 0$ (upper half).

10. $x^2 + y^2 = a^2$, $x = 0$, $y = 0$ (first quadrant). Compare the result with that of Number 9.

11. $y = x$, $y = x^2$.

12. $y^2 = 6y + 3x$, $x = 0$.

13. $y^3 = x$, $y = x^2$.

14. $x^2 - y - 4x = 0$, $y = 0$.

15. $y = x^2$, $y = x + 2$.

16. $y^2 + 4x = 0$, $x^2 + 4y = 0$.

17. $x^2 = 4y$, $2y = x + 4$.

18. $y = x^4$, $y + x^2 - 2 = 0$.

19. $y = x^3 - 8x$, $y = x$ (to the right of the y-axis).

20. $y + x = 0$, $y = x + x^2$.

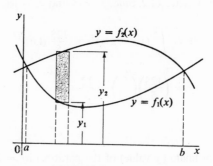

FIGURE 12.12m

21. In Figure 12.12m, the area A bounded by the two curves $y = f_1(x)$ and $y = f_2(x)$ is to be revolved about the x-axis to generate a volume. Show that this volume is given by

$$V = 2\pi \bar{y} A,$$

where $\bar{y}$ is the y-coordinate of the centroid of the area. *Hint:*

$$V = \pi \int_a^b (y_2^2 - y_1^2)\, dx = 2\pi \int_a^b \left(\frac{y_2 + y_1}{2}\right)(y_2 - y_1)\, dx.$$

The formula $V = 2\pi \bar{y} A$ may be stated in words as follows:

The volume formed by revolving a plane area about an axis in its plane and not cutting the area is given by the product of the area and the distance passed over by the centroid of the area.

This statement is known as Pappus' Theorem for Volumes of Revolution.

Use Pappus' Theorem in each of Numbers 22 to 26.

22. Find the volume of the torus generated by revolving the area of a circle of radius a about an axis b units from the center of the circle, $b > a$.

23. The centroid of a triangle is at the intersection of the medians. A right triangle with legs 3 units and 4 units long, respectively, is revolved about a line in its plane. This line is parallel to its hypotenuse and 6 units from the hypotenuse on the side opposite the vertex of the right angle. Find the volume generated.

24. Locate the centroid of the area of a semicircle of radius a.

25. The cross section of a solid metal ring is a square that is $\frac{1}{2}$ inch on a side. The radius of the ring measured from its axis to the center of the square is 2 inches. Find the volume of material in the ring.
26. Find the volume of a right circular cone of radius a and altitude h.

12.13 APPLICATIONS TO PHYSICAL PROBLEMS

A basic concept in mechanics that lends itself to analysis by means of the limit of a sum is that of the work done by a force F that is directed along an axis and that moves an object through a distance s on this axis. If F is a constant force, then the work done is given by $W = Fs$. However, if F is not constant, then the problem of calculating the work done leads to the employment of the definite integral.

Let $F(x)$ describe the force acting on an object at the point x in moving the object from a point a to a point b on the x-axis, where $a \leq x \leq b$. The work done by the force in moving the object through a small interval $\Delta x_i = x_i - x_{i-1}$, $a \leq x_{i-1} < x_i \leq b$, may be approximated by $F(x_i^*) \Delta x_i$, where $x_{i-1} \leq x_i^* \leq x_i$. Consequently, if we form a partition of the interval from a to b into n subintervals by the points

$$a = x_0, x_1, x_2, \ldots, x_n = b,$$

then the total work done is approximated by the sum

$$W_n = \sum_{i=1}^{n} F(x_i^*) \Delta x_i.$$

It is therefore appropriate to *define* the total work done by a force $F(x)$ acting over the interval from a to b by

$$W = \lim_{\delta \to 0} \sum_{i=1}^{n} F(x_i^*) \Delta x_i = \int_a^b F(x) \, dx.$$

A simple example of work done by a varying force is provided by the stretching or compressing of a spring. According to Hooke's Law, the force F required to stretch or compress a spring is proportional to the amount of extension or compression, x, of the spring; that is,

$$F(x) = kx.$$

The constant k is called the spring constant and has dimensions of pounds per foot.

Example 12.13a. A force of 10 pounds is required to compress a spring 20 inches long to 19 inches. What is the work done in stretching the spring from a length of 24 inches to a length of 30 inches?

Since the foot-pound is an appropriate unit of work to use here, we convert measurements in inches to feet, and, from Hooke's Law, we have

$$F(\tfrac{1}{12}) = 10 = \tfrac{1}{12}k.$$

Hence the spring constant is $k = 120$ pounds per foot, and the work done in stretching the spring from 24 inches to 30 inches is given by the integral

$$W = \int_{1/3}^{5/6} 120x \, dx,$$

where the appropriate conversion of inches to feet has been made. It follows that

$$W = [60x^2]_{1/3}^{5/6} = 135 \text{ foot-pounds.}$$

Another type of work problem occurs in finding the work done in pumping water out of a tank.

Example 12.13b. A tank in the shape of an inverted right circular cone 12 feet high and with a base radius of 6 feet is filled with water. Find the work done in pumping the water to the top of the tank. (Water weighs approximately 62.5 pounds per cubic foot.)

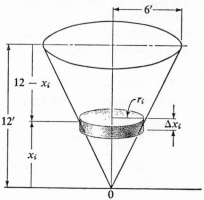

FIGURE 12.13a

The work done in pumping the water to the top of the tank may be approximated by considering the volume to consist of n thin disk-shaped elements, and finding the work done in pumping the water in each element to the top of the tank. Let the origin be chosen at the vertex of the cone (Figure 12.13a) and let x measure the upward distance along the axis of the tank. Then the work done in pumping the water in the ith disk to the top of the tank is given by

$$\Delta W_i = (12 - x_i)(62.5\pi r_i^2 \, \Delta x_i),$$

where r_i is the radius of the ith disk.

We can express r_i in terms of x_i by considering the ratios of corresponding sides of similar triangles. Thus,

$$r_i = \tfrac{1}{2}x_i,$$

so that

$$\Delta W_i = (62.5\pi)\tfrac{1}{4}(12 - x_i)x_i^2 \, \Delta x_i.$$

The sum of such contributions will provide an approximation for the work done. Hence

$$W_n = \sum_{i=1}^{n} \frac{62.5\pi x_i^2}{4} (12 - x_i) \, \Delta x_i.$$

By using the limit of this sum, we obtain a suitable definition for the work done in terms of a definite integral, which gives

$$W = \int_0^{12} \frac{62.5\pi}{4} (12 - x)x^2 \, dx = 27,000\pi \text{ foot-pounds.}$$

The complete details of finding an approximating sum and then passing to the limit are not necessary once the fundamental ideas are grasped. Instead, the definite integral may be set up directly by considering a typical element, as illustrated in the next example.

Example 12.13c. A plate in the form of a parabolic segment is submerged vertically in water with the axis vertical. The base of the plate is 12 feet across and is at a depth of 10 feet, while the vertex is at a depth of 30 feet. Find the force exerted on one face of the plate (see Figure 12.13b).

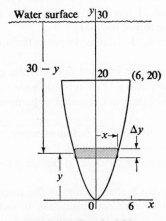

FIGURE 12.13b

If the origin and axes are chosen as in the figure, then a typical element of area on the face of the plate has dimensions $2x$ by Δy. An approximation to the force on this element is given by

$$\Delta F = 62.5(30 - y)2x \, \Delta y.$$

In order to express x in terms of y, we need to know the equation of the parabola. For the chosen axes, the equation must be of the form $x^2 = ay$ and the curve passes through the point $(6, 20)$; therefore we find $a = 9/5$ and $x = (3/\sqrt{5})y^{1/2}$. It follows that

$$\Delta F = 62.5(30 - y) \frac{6}{\sqrt{5}} y^{1/2} \, \Delta y,$$

and the total force on the face of the plate is given by

$$F = \int_0^{20} \frac{6}{\sqrt{5}} (62.5)(30 - y)y^{1/2} \, dy$$

$$= \frac{375}{\sqrt{5}} \int_0^{20} (30y^{1/2} - y^{3/2}) \, dy = 180,000 \text{ pounds.}$$

(The reader should compare this abbreviated setup of the integral with the treatment of that in Example 12.3b.)

Exercises 12.13

1. A spring is stretched 3 inches by a force of 25 pounds. How much work is required to stretch the spring an additional 3 inches?

2. A spring 8 feet long is stretched to a length of 10 feet by a force of 120 pounds. What is the work done in stretching the spring from a length of 9 feet to a length of 12 feet?

3. A force of 10 pounds stretches a spring 1 inch. What is the percentage increase in the work done in stretching the spring from 10 inches to 12 inches over the work done in stretching it from its natural length of 8 inches to 10 inches?

4. A tank in the shape of a vertical right circular cylinder with a base radius of 8 feet and a height of 24 feet is filled with water. Find the work required to pump the water to the top of the tank.

5. In Number 4, find the work required to pump the water to a point 6 feet above the top of the tank.

6. A tank is in the shape of an inverted right circular cone of base radius 10 feet and a height of 20 feet, with its axis vertical. If the tank is filled with a liquid of specific gravity 0.9, find the work required to pump the liquid to a point 10 feet above the tank.

7. A spherical tank of radius 20 feet is full of water. What is the work done in pumping the water to the top of the tank?

8. In Number 7, what is the work done in pumping the water to a point 20 feet above the tank?

9. A trough 20 feet long has a cross section in the shape of an isosceles trapezoid with a lower base 4 feet long, an upper base 10 feet long, and an altitude of 4 feet. How much work is done in filling the trough with water if the bottom of the trough is located 20 feet above the pump and the water is pumped in through a valve in the bottom of the tank?

10. A tank is in the form of a right circular cylinder with a horizontal axis and has a base radius r feet and a length L feet. Set up an integral for the work done in filling the tank with water from a point a feet ($a > r$) below the center of the tank, if the water is pumped in through a valve in the bottom of the tank.

11. Set up an integral for the force exerted on the circular end of a cylindrical tank with its axis horizontal if the tank is filled with water, and if the radius of the tank is 4 feet.

12. A vertical dam in the shape of a parabolic segment with its vertex down is 100 feet deep and 100 feet across the top. Find the force on the face of the dam if the water level is at the top of the dam.

13. A triangular gate of altitude h feet and base b feet is submerged vertically in water so that the base is below the vertex and parallel to the surface of the water. If the vertex is h feet below the surface, find the force exerted on one side of the gate.

14. A plate in the shape of a parabolic segment is submerged vertically in water with the axis parallel to the surface. If the plate has a base 8 feet long and a vertex

4 feet from the base, and is submerged so that its highest point is at the surface, find the force exerted on one side of the plate.

15. In Number 14, suppose the plate is submerged vertically with its vertex at the surface and the base below it. What is the force exerted on one side of the plate?

16. Prove that the force exerted on one side of a plane surface entirely submerged vertically in a fluid is equal to the product of the area of the surface, the depth of the centroid, and the specific weight of the fluid.

17. A particle on the x-axis is attracted toward the origin by a force of magnitude

$$F = \frac{kx}{(a^2 + x^2)^{3/2}}.$$

Find the work done by the force if it moves the particle from a distance $2a$ to a distance a from the origin.

18. Two masses attract each other with a force that is proportional to the product of their masses and inversely proportional to the square of the distance between them. A rod of length a units is located on the x-axis between the origin and the point where $x = a$. If the rod has a uniform density μ mass units per unit length, find the force of attraction of the rod on a particle of unit mass located at the point $(2a, 0)$.

19. The weight of an object varies inversely as the square of its distance from the center of the earth. How much work is done in propelling a space capsule weighing 2000 pounds to a height of 400 miles? Take the radius of the earth to be 4000 miles and disregard the resistance of the atmosphere.

20. Find the work done in lifting a mine bucket weighing 500 pounds from a depth of 500 feet to a depth of 300 feet if the hoist cable weighs 3 pounds per foot.

21. A piston compresses a gas in a cylinder from an initial volume of 100 cubic inches to a volume of 40 cubic inches. If the initial pressure is 80 pounds per square inch and if the process is such that the pressure p and the volume v obey the equation $pv^{1.4} = C$, find the work done by the piston. *Hint*: If the piston moves a small distance Δx, show that the work done is approximately $p \, \Delta v$.

22. A rod extends along the x-axis from $x = 1$ to $x = 3$. If the mass per unit length is proportional to the distance from the origin, calculate the total mass of the rod.

23. If it takes 50% more work to stretch a spring from 11 inches to 12 inches than it does to stretch it from 10 inches to 11 inches, what is the natural length of the spring?

24. If a constant force F (pounds) acts during time t (seconds), the impulse is defined to be Ft (pound-seconds).
    (a) Define the impulse if the force is a variable, say $F(t)$.
    (b) A freight car backs slowly into a heavy spring bumper and comes to rest after compressing the springs 2 inches. The speed of the car is $\frac{1}{12}(2 - t)$ feet per second, where $t = 0$ at the instant of contact with the bumper. If the modulus of the spring bumper is 72,000 pounds per inch, find the total impulse that the car delivers to the bumper.

25. The force of attraction between two mass particles is proportional to the product of their masses and inversely proportional to the square of the distance between them. Let a mass m be distributed uniformly along the portion of the x-axis between x_1 and x_2, $x_2 > x_1$. What is the force of attraction of this mass on a particle of mass m placed at the point x_3 on the axis with $x_3 > x_2$?

★26. The dimensions of a parabolic dam are shown in Figure 12.13c. At what depth on the axis of the parabola would a single force have to be placed in order to be

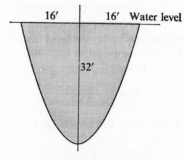

FIGURE 12.13c

mechanically equivalent to the total force on the dam? *Hint*: Consider the equilibrium conditions for a system of parallel forces.

12.14 SECTIONALLY CONTINUOUS FUNCTIONS

Although most of the discussion of the preceding few sections has been devoted to functions that are continuous on a closed interval, there are a number of physics and engineering problems in which it is important to consider functions with certain types of discontinuities. In the simpler applications, these discontinuities are finite and the functions are continuous except for a finite number of finite discontinuities on a closed interval.

Definition 12.14a. A function f is said to be **sectionally** (or **piecewise**) **continuous** on a closed interval $a \leq x \leq b$ if

(i) it is discontinuous at only a finite number of points in the interval,

(ii) at each point x_1 of discontinuity (interior to the interval) $\lim_{x \to x_1^-} f(x)$ and $\lim_{x \to x_1^+} f(x)$ both exist, and

(iii) $\lim_{x \to a^+} f(x)$ and $\lim_{x \to b^-} f(x)$ both exist.

For example, the graph of the function f defined by

$$f(x) = U(x) - U(x - 1), \qquad 0 \leq x \leq 2,$$

where U is the unit step function (Definition 5.4a), is shown in Figure 12.14a.

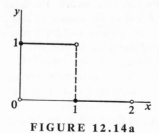

FIGURE 12.14a

This function has two finite discontinuities, one at $x = 0$ and the other at $x = 1$. Since f is defined at every point of the interval, $0 \leq x \leq 2$, and $\lim_{x \to 0^+} f(x) = 1$, $\lim_{x \to 1^-} f(x) = 1$, $\lim_{x \to 1^+} f(x) = 0$, and $\lim_{x \to 2^-} f(x) = 0$, the function is sectionally continuous on the interval.

On the other hand, the function f defined by

$$f(x) = (x - 1)^{-2}, \quad 0 \leq x < 1, \quad 1 < x \leq 2,$$
$$f(1) = 0,$$

is *not* sectionally continuous. Although this function is continuous in the half-open intervals $0 \leq x < 1$ and $1 < x \leq 2$, neither $\lim_{x \to 1^-} f(x)$ nor $\lim_{x \to 1^+} f(x)$ exists. In fact, the function has an infinite discontinuity at $x = 1$.

In order to examine the definite integral of a function that is sectionally continuous on an interval $a \leq x \leq b$, let us first consider a specific example. Let

$$f(x) .=. \begin{cases} x^2 & \text{for } 0 \leq x < 1, \\ \frac{3}{2} & \text{for } x = 1, \\ 2 & \text{for } 1 < x \leq 2. \end{cases}$$

(See Figure 12.14b.) It appears clear intuitively from the geometric interpretation of the integral as an area that $\int_0^2 f(x)\, dx$ ought to exist, since it would measure the area below the curve $y = f(x)$ and above the x-axis from $x = 0$ to $x = 2$.

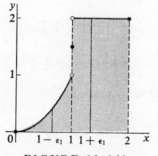

FIGURE 12.14b

Let us divide the interval $0 \leq x \leq 2$ into three parts by choosing a number $\epsilon_1, 0 < \epsilon_1 < 1$, and inserting the points $1 - \epsilon_1$ and $1 + \epsilon_1$. (The choice of ϵ_1 will be made more specific later.) Then f is continuous on $0 \leq x \leq 1 - \epsilon_1$ and on $1 + \epsilon_1 \leq x \leq 2$. For any partition of the respective intervals taken in order from left to right, let the lower approximation sums be s_1, s_2, s_3, and the upper sums be S_1, S_2, S_3. For the entire interval, we have

$$s = s_1 + s_2 + s_3 \quad \text{and} \quad S = S_1 + S_2 + S_3.$$

For every $\epsilon_1, 0 < \epsilon_1 < 1$, the given function is continuous on the two intervals $0 \leq x \leq 1 - \epsilon$ and $1 + \epsilon \leq x \leq 2$. Hence, if the norm of the partition is $\delta = \max \Delta x_i$, then

$$\lim_{\delta \to 0} s_1 = \lim_{\delta \to 0} S_1 \quad \text{and} \quad \lim_{\delta \to 0} s_3 = \lim_{\delta \to 0} S_3.$$

This means that for every $\epsilon > 0$ there is a partition fine enough that

$$S_1 - s_1 < \frac{\epsilon}{3} \quad \text{and} \quad S_3 - s_3 < \frac{\epsilon}{3}.$$

Consequently,

$$S - s \leq \frac{\epsilon}{3} + \frac{\epsilon}{3} + S_2 - s_2.$$

Since f is continuous on the interval $1 - \epsilon_1 \leq x \leq 1 + \epsilon_1$ except at the one point $x = 1$, and $f(1) = \frac{3}{2}$, the difference between the maximum value and the minimum value of $f(x)$ in this interval is bounded. In this example, this difference is not greater than 2. Therefore, $S_2 - s_2$ is not greater than 2 times the length of the interval; that is,

$$S_2 - s_2 \leq 4\epsilon_1.$$

This shows that if ϵ_1 is chosen less than $\epsilon/12$, then

$$S - s \leq \epsilon,$$

and thus the definite integral $\int_0^2 f(x)\, dx$ exists.

It is important to note that the preceding discussion indicates that

$$\int_0^2 f(x)\, dx = \lim_{\epsilon \to 0^+} \left[\int_0^{1-\epsilon} x^2\, dx + \int_{1+\epsilon}^2 2\, dx \right]$$

$$= \lim_{\epsilon \to 0} \left\{ \left[\frac{x^3}{3} \right]_0^{1-\epsilon} + [2x]_{1+\epsilon}^2 \right\}$$

$$= \lim_{\epsilon \to 0^+} \left[\frac{1}{3}(1 - \epsilon)^3 + 4 - 2(1 + \epsilon) \right] = \frac{7}{3}.$$

Furthermore, it is easy to verify that

$$\lim_{\epsilon \to 0^+} \int_0^{1-\epsilon} x^2\, dx = \int_0^1 x^2\, dx = \frac{1}{3},$$

and

$$\lim_{\epsilon \to 0^+} \int_{1+\epsilon}^2 2\, dx = \int_1^2 2\, dx = 2,$$

so that

$$\int_0^2 f(x)\, dx = \int_0^1 x^2\, dx + \int_1^2 2\, dx = \frac{7}{3}.$$

Notice that the value of the integral is independent of the value of $f(1)$. Thus, even if f were undefined at $x = 1$, it would still be reasonable to define the definite integral of f on the basis of the preceding three equations.

Every function that is sectionally continuous on a finite interval and has only one discontinuity there can be treated in exactly the same manner as that of the preceding discussion. Consequently, we are led to the following extension of the definite integral.

Definition 12.14b. Let f be a sectionally continuous function on the closed interval $a \leq x \leq b$ with a single discontinuity at c, $a < c < b$. Let

$$g(x) .=. f(x) \quad \text{for } a \leq x < c,$$
$$g(c) .=. \lim_{x \to c^-} f(x),$$

and

$$h(x) .=. f(x) \quad \text{for } c < x \leq b,$$
$$h(c) .=. \lim_{x \to c^+} f(x).$$

Then the definite integral of $f(x)$ from $x = a$ to $x = b$ is

$$\int_a^b f(x)\, dx .=. \int_a^c g(x)\, dx + \int_c^b h(x)\, dx.$$

The discussion preceding Definition 12.14b applies equally well to a sectionally continuous function having more than one discontinuity. We shall therefore omit a formal general definition of the integral of a function that is sectionally continuous on a finite closed interval, but shall illustrate by the following examples how such integrals may be treated.

Example 12.14a. A particle moves along the x-axis with an acceleration $a = f(t)$ feet per second per second, where $f(t) = t - k$, $k \leq t < k + 1$, $k = 0, 1, 2, \ldots$. If the particle starts from rest at the origin, find its velocity after T seconds.

Using the fact that $a = dv/dt$, we have

$$v = \int_0^T f(t)\, dt + C.$$

This form of the indefinite integral is convenient, since we have the initial condition that $v = 0$ when $T = 0$. This gives

$$0 = \int_0^0 f(t)\, dt + C \Rightarrow C = 0,$$

so that

$$v = \int_0^T f(t)\, dt.$$

To evaluate this integral, let us suppose that

$$k \leq T < k + 1.$$

Then,

$$v = \int_0^1 t\, dt + \int_1^2 (t - 1)\, dt + \int_2^3 (t - 2)\, dt + \cdots + \int_k^T (t - k)\, dt$$

$$= \sum_{p=0}^{k-1} \int_p^{p+1} (t - p)\, dt + \int_k^T (t - k)\, dt.$$

A typical integral in the sum is

$$\int_p^{p+1} (t - p)\, dt = \left[\frac{(t - p)^2}{2} \right]_p^{p+1}$$

$$= \frac{1}{2}(1 - 0) = \frac{1}{2}.$$

Therefore,

$$v = \sum_{p=0}^{k-1} \frac{1}{2} + \left[\frac{(t-k)^2}{2} \right]_k^T$$

$$= \left[\frac{k}{2} + \frac{(T-k)^2}{2} \right] \text{ feet per second.}$$

Example 12.14b. Suppose a force F directed along the x-axis moves an object from the origin to a point 3 feet to the right. Calculate the work done if the force F (in pounds) is given by

$$F(x) = \sum_{k=0}^{n} (-1)^k x U(x-k), \qquad n > 3,$$

where U is the unit step function and x is in feet. A graph of F is shown in Figure 12.14c.

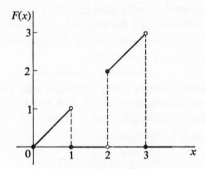

FIGURE 12.14c

The work done by the force F (see Section 12.13) is

$$W = \int_0^3 F(x)\, dx = \int_0^3 x[U(x) - U(x-1) + U(x-2)]\, dx$$

$$= \int_0^1 x\, dx + \int_1^2 0\, dx + \int_2^3 x\, dx$$

$$= \left[\frac{x^2}{2} \right]_0^1 + \left[\frac{x^2}{2} \right]_2^3 = 3 \text{ foot-pounds.}$$

Exercises 12.14

In each of Numbers 1 to 4, find the value of the given integral.

1. $\int_{-2}^{2} f(x)\, dx$, where $f(x) .=. \begin{cases} -1, & -2 \leq x \leq 0, \\ x, & 0 < x \leq 2. \end{cases}$

2. $\int_{-2}^{2} f(x)\, dx$, where $f(x) .=. \begin{cases} 1/x^2, & -2 \leq x \leq -1, \\ 2-x, & -1 < x \leq 2. \end{cases}$

3. $\int_{0}^{6} g(x)\, dx$, where $g(x) .=. \begin{cases} 4-x^2, & 0 \leq x < 2, \\ x, & 2 \leq x \leq 6. \end{cases}$

4. $\displaystyle\int_0^4 g(x)\,dx$, where $g(x)\,.=.\begin{cases} -x, & 0 \le x \le 1, \\ 1 - x^2, & 1 < x < 2, \\ 6 - x, & 2 \le x \le 4. \end{cases}$

5. Find the value of $\displaystyle\int_0^n f(x)\,dx$ if

$$f(x) = \sqrt{x - n + 1}, \qquad n - 1 \le x < n, n = 1, 2, 3, \ldots.$$

6. Find the value of $\displaystyle\int_0^{x_1} f(x)\,dx$ where $f(x)$ is given in Number 5.

7. If $U(x)$ is the unit step function, find the value of

$$\int_0^n f(x)\,dx, \qquad \text{where } f(x) = \sum_{p=0}^n U(x - p).$$

8. In Example 12.14b, find the work done if the object moves from the origin to a point n feet away.

9. A particle, starting from rest at the origin, moves along the x-axis. Its acceleration is given by

$$f(t) = U(t) + \sum_{p=1}^n (-1)^p 2U(t - p), \qquad 0 \le t \le n,$$

where n is a positive integer and U is the unit step function. Make a graph of the acceleration, and find the velocity of the particle at time $T \le n$. Make a graph of the velocity function.

10. An elevator weighing 2000 pounds is suspended by cables weighing a total of 10 pounds per foot. If the elevator starts from the ground floor with 10 passengers of average weight of 160 pounds each, and two passengers get off at the 5th floor, 3 at the 8th floor, 4 at the 12th floor, and 1 at the 20th floor, find the work done. Assume that each floor is 10 feet above the next lower floor. (Express the work done as an integral of a function that is expressible in terms of the unit step function.)

Summary of Chapter 12

The first fundamental concept of calculus is the derivative and the associated limit process. This chapter is concerned with the second fundamental concept of calculus, the definite integral, and the limit process associated with it. The following concepts are essential preparation for a study of the definite integral:

   (1) the summation notation (Section 12.1);
   (2) an infinite sequence (Section 12.2);
   (3) cluster point of a sequence (Section 12.2);
   (4) convergence and divergence of a sequence (Section 12.2);
   (5) nonincreasing and nondecreasing sequences (Section 12.2);
   (6) upper and lower bounds of a sequence (Section 12.2);
   (7) theorems pertaining to bounded sequences (Section 12.2).

The concept of an nth approximation to a physical or geometrical quantity (Sections 12.3, 12.4) dates as far back as the ancient Greek mathematicians. Although the concept of the *limit* of a sequence of approximations was evidently known to Archimedes, it was not seriously considered again until the late 16th and early 17th centuries. The definite integral, as the limit of a sequence of approximating sums, is the culmination of those ideas (Section 12.5). In this connection, the concept of upper and lower sums is important (Section 12.6).

The following ideas are also essential to a proper understanding of the definite integral:

(8) the definition of area by means of the definite integral (Section 12.5);

(9) conditions on a function f for the existence of the definite integral (Section 12.7);

(10) properties of the definite integral (Section 12.8);

(11) the Mean Value Theorem (Section 12.8);

Stemming from the concept of the definite integral is the extremely important and closely allied concept of the indefinite integral and its properties (Section 12.9). Associated with this concept is the Fundamental Theorem of Integral Calculus, which expresses a relationship between the two distinct concepts of the derivative and the indefinite integral (Section 12.9).

In view of the importance of the definite and indefinite integrals, a student must develop an understanding of the applications to

(12) areas (Section 12.10);

(13) volumes of revolution by using "shells" and "disks" (Section 12.11);

(14) averages, moments, and centroids (Section 12.12);

(15) physical problems such as those involving work (Section 12.13);

(16) sectionally continuous functions (Section 12.14).

Chapter 13

Exponential and Logarithmic Functions

13.1 THE EXPONENTIAL FUNCTION AND THE LOGARITHMIC FUNCTION

The meaning of the symbol a^x, where a is a given positive number, has previously been defined for rational but not for irrational values of x. We know, for example, the meaning of $2^{3/5}$, but we have not defined $2^{\sqrt{2}}$ or 2^π. Since it is desirable in many applications to have 2^x defined for every real value of x, if possible, and even to have 2^x define a differentiable function, we now raise the question as to whether it is possible to define a^x if x is an irrational number. That the answer is in the affirmative can be shown with the help of the concept of the limit of a sequence.

An irrational number was defined to be a number with an infinite nonrepeating decimal representation. Consequently, let

$$x = x_0.x_1x_2x_3 \ldots x_n \ldots$$

be such a decimal, where x_0 is a positive integer and each x_k, $k = 1, 2, 3, \ldots$, is a digit. Now, let $a > 1$, and consider the sequence $\{b_n\}$, where

$$b_1 = a^{x_0}, \quad b_2 = a^{x_0.x_1}, \quad \ldots, \quad b_n = a^{x_0.x_1x_2 \cdots x_{n-1}}, \quad \ldots.$$

We shall show that this sequence has a limit, and shall define this limit to be the value of a^x for the irrational number x.

For any rational number $p \geq 0$, it is true that

$$a > 1 \Rightarrow a^p \geq 1 \qquad \text{(Theorem 3.8g)}.$$

Accordingly,

$$b_n \geq b_{n-1}, \qquad n = 2, 3, \ldots,$$

since

$$b_n = a^{x_0.x_1x_2 \cdots x_{n-2}x_{n-1}}$$

$$= a^{x_0.x_1x_2 \cdots x_{n-2}}(a^{x_{n-1}/10^{n-1}})$$

and

$$a^{x_{n-1}/10^{n-1}} \geq 1.$$

Furthermore,

$$x = x_0.x_1x_2 \ldots x_n \ldots < x_0 + 1,$$

so that

$$b_n < a^{x_0+1} \quad \text{for } n = 1, 2, 3, \ldots.$$

Thus, the sequence $\{b_n\}$ is a bounded nondecreasing sequence, and therefore, by Theorem 12.2b, has a limit. This limit will be denoted by a^x.

A similar discussion applies for $0 < a < 1$, since the corresponding sequence would be bounded and nonincreasing. As a consequence of these results, we see that to each number $x > 0$ there corresponds exactly one real number a^x for any given a such that $0 < a < 1$ or $a > 1$. For example, the number 2^π is the limit of the sequence

$$2^3, \ 2^{3.1}, \ 2^{3.14}, \ 2^{3.141}, \ 2^{3.1415}, \ 2^{3.14159}, \ \ldots,$$

where the exponents are the successive "partial" decimals in the infinite decimal representation of the number π. Similar results hold for $x < 0$.

We may summarize the preceding discussion by saying that for each fixed value of a such that $0 < a < 1$ or $a > 1$, the formula $f(x) = a^x$ describes a function with the domain $\mathcal{R}$.

Definition 13.1a. The function f for which

$$f(x) = a^x, \qquad a > 1 \quad \text{or} \quad 0 < a < 1,$$

is called the **exponential function** to the base a.

Another notation, which is frequently used in dealing with the exponential function, is

$$\exp_a(x) = a^x.$$

Thus, one might write $\exp_2(\pi)$ for 2^π. This notation is particularly useful whenever the exponent is a complicated expression that is difficult to print in the customary exponent position.

It can be shown that the usual rules for rational exponents also hold for irrational exponents. However, we shall not undertake to show this at the present time but shall use these rules without proof. We shall also need some elementary inequalities involving exponents in order to investigate the properties of the exponential function.

Theorem 13.1a. $\qquad a > 1 \quad \text{and} \quad x > 0 \Rightarrow a^x > 1.$

PROOF: This theorem has already been proved for rational values of x (see Theorem 3.8g). Now consider x irrational and, as before, let

$$x = x_0.x_1x_2 \ldots.$$

Suppose $y = x_0.x_1x_2 \ldots x_k$ is any nonzero "partial" decimal in the infinite decimal representation of x. Then y is a rational number and

$$a^y > 1 \qquad \text{(by Theorem 3.8g)}.$$

The proof of the existence of

$$\lim_{n\to\infty} \exp_a (x_0.x_1x_2 \ldots x_n)$$

showed that as we take more and more digits from the representation of x, the corresponding sequence of powers of a is nondecreasing. Thus it follows that if

$$a^x .=. \lim_{n\to\infty} \exp_a (x_0.x_1x_2 \ldots x_n),$$

then

$$a^x > 1.$$

Theorem 13.1b. $a > 1$ and $x < 0 \Rightarrow 0 < a^x < 1.$

PROOF: This theorem follows from the preceding theorem and the fact that if $x = -y$, then

$$a^x = a^{-y} .=. \frac{1}{a^y}.$$

The details are left to the reader.

Theorem 13.1c. $0 < x < y$ and $a > 1 \Rightarrow a^x < a^y.$

PROOF: If $x < y$, there is a positive number s such that

$$x + s = y.$$

Also,

$$a > 1 \Rightarrow a^s > 1 \qquad \text{(by Theorem 13.1a).}$$

Hence

$$a^{x+s} = a^x a^s > a^x,$$

or

$$a^y > a^x.$$

This result shows that if $f(x) = a^x$, $a > 1$, then f is an increasing function on its entire domain.

As an aid toward visualizing the preceding results, Figure 13.1a shows the

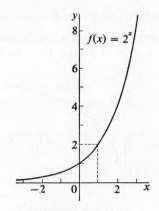

FIGURE 13.1a

graph of the function defined by $f(x) = 2^x$. The smooth appearance of the curve will be justified by the later work of this chapter, which in part deals with the derivative of the exponential function.

Figure 13.1a illustrates the following properties which are consequences of the definition of the exponential function given by $f(x) = a^x, a > 1$:

(1) $f(0) = 1$;
(2) $f(1) = a$;
(3) $\lim\limits_{x \to -\infty} f(x) = 0$;

(4) as $x \to +\infty, f(x) \to +\infty$.

Since for $a > 1$ the exponential function, $f .=. \{(x, a^x)\}$, is an increasing function on its entire domain, it must have an inverse that is also a function. (Why?) The inverse function, f^{-1}, is the set of number pairs $\{(a^x, x)\}$. In the usual functional notation, we let $u = a^x$ and denote the same set of number pairs by $\{(u, f^{-1}(u))\}$.

Definition 13.1b. If $f .=. \{(x, a^x)\}$ and if $u = a^x$, then the inverse function, f^{-1}, which is the set of pairs $\{(u, f^{-1}(u))\}$, is called the **logarithm function** to the base a and is denoted by $\log_a$.

In particular, if $u = a^x$, then $\log_a u .=. f^{-1}(u) = x$, and x is called the **logarithm** of u to the base a. The reader should keep in mind that the exponential function, $\exp_a$, is defined only when $0 < a < 1$ or $1 < a$, so that the inverse function, $\log_a$, is also defined only for such values of a. Furthermore, since $a^x > 0$ for all x, $\log_a u$ is defined only if $u > 0$.

The concept of the logarithm may be expressed by saying that *the logarithm of a number u to the base a is the exponent of that power of a which equals the number u.* Thus, if $2^4 = 16$, then $\log_2 16 = 4$. Similarly, if

$$\log_3 N = 2,$$

then N must be 9, since $3^2 = N = 9$. Again

$$\log_a 8 = \tfrac{3}{2} \Rightarrow a^{3/2} = 8 \Rightarrow a = 4.$$

The graph of the equation $y = \log_2 x$, which is shown in Figure 13.1b, can be obtained from that of $y = 2^x$ in Figure 13.1a by reflecting the curve with

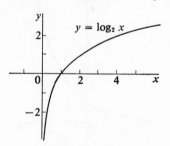

FIGURE 13.1b

respect to the line $y = x$. The general appearance of the graph of $y = \log_a x$, $a > 1$, is the same as that for the base 2.

Corresponding to the properties of the exponential function, we have for $f(x) = \log_a x$, $a > 1$:

$$(1)\ f(1) = 0;$$
$$(2)\ f(a) = 1;$$
$$(3)\ \text{as } x \to 0^+, f(x) \to -\infty;$$
$$(4)\ \text{as } x \to +\infty, f(x) \to +\infty.$$

Logarithms of numbers were first used by John Napier, a Scottish mathematician (1550–1617), as a computational aid. Using 10 as a base, he laboriously and without mechanical aids compiled the first table of logarithms, which was published in 1614.

The following elementary theorems establish those properties of logarithms of numbers that make the logarithms useful in computational as well as theoretical problems.

Theorem 13.1d. $\qquad \log_a MN = \log_a M + \log_a N.$

That is, *the logarithm of the product of two numbers is the sum of logarithms of the factors.*

PROOF: Let $\qquad x = \log_a N, \quad y = \log_a M.$

Then, by definition,

$$a^x = N \quad \text{and} \quad a^y = M,$$

so that

$$a^x a^y = a^{x+y} = MN$$

and

$$\log_a MN = x + y.$$

If x and y are replaced by the appropriate expressions, then we have

$$\log_a MN = \log_a M + \log_a N.$$

Theorem 13.1e. $\qquad \log_a \dfrac{M}{N} = \log_a M - \log_a N.$

PROOF: Left as an exercise.

Theorem 13.1f. $\qquad \log_a M^p = p \log_a M.$

PROOF: Left as an exercise.

Theorem 13.1g. $\qquad a^{\log_a N} = N.$

PROOF: Left as an exercise.

Theorem 13.1h. $\qquad (\log_a b)(\log_b a) = 1.$

PROOF: Left as an exercise.

The next theorem is commonly known as the Rule for Change of Base.

Theorem 13.1i. $\qquad \log_b N = \dfrac{\log_a N}{\log_a b}.$

PROOF: Left for the reader with the hint: $N = a^x = b^y$. What is $\log_a N$?

Although logarithms originally were introduced as an aid in computational problems, they are no longer so important in this respect because most computational problems can be handled more efficiently by desk calculators or modern computers. Of considerably greater importance are the fundamental properties of logarithms as expressed in the preceding theorems. The following examples illustrate how those properties may be used in a noncomputational manner as well as in a computational manner.

Example 13.1a. Prove that

$$\log_a \sqrt{\frac{MN^3}{P}} = \tfrac{1}{2}(\log_a M + 3 \log_a N - \log_a P).$$

The procedure is a straightforward application of the first three theorems:

$$\log_a \sqrt{\frac{MN^3}{P}} = \log_a \left(\frac{MN^3}{P}\right)^{1/2} = \tfrac{1}{2} \log_a \frac{MN^3}{P}$$

$$= \tfrac{1}{2}(\log_a MN^3 - \log_a P)$$
$$= \tfrac{1}{2}(\log_a M + \log_a N^3 - \log_a P)$$
$$= \tfrac{1}{2}(\log_a M + 3 \log_a N - \log_a P).$$

In computational practice, we use decimal approximations, usually obtained from a book of tables, for the logarithms of numbers. For example, we may have

$$\log_{10} 20 \approx 1.30103,$$

where the sign $\approx$ is used to emphasize the fact that $\log_{10} 20$ is approximately equal to 1.30103. The next example illustrates the idea.

Example 13.1b. If $\log_{10} 2 \approx 0.30103$ and $\log_{10} 3 \approx 0.47712$, find (a) $\log_{10} 24$; (b) $\log_{10} 1/5$; (c) $\log_{10} \sqrt{6}$.

Using the preceding theorems, we obtain

(a)
$$\log_{10} 24 = \log_{10} 2^3 \cdot 3 = 3 \log_{10} 2 + \log_{10} 3$$
$$\approx 3(0.30103) + 0.47712 = 1.38021.$$

(b)
$$\log_{10} \tfrac{1}{5} = \log_{10} \tfrac{2}{10}$$
$$= \log_{10} 2 - \log_{10} 10$$
$$\approx 0.30103 - 1 = -0.69897.$$

(c)
$$\log_{10} \sqrt{6} = \tfrac{1}{2} \log_{10} 6$$
$$= \tfrac{1}{2}(\log_{10} 2 + \log_{10} 3)$$
$$\approx \tfrac{1}{2}(0.30103 + 0.47712) = 0.38908.$$

Example 13.1c. Show that

$$\log_a \frac{-1 + \sqrt{x^2 + 1}}{x} = -\log_a \frac{1 + \sqrt{x^2 + 1}}{x}.$$

To do this, we rationalize the numerator of the argument of the logarithm to obtain

$$\log_a\left(\frac{-1+\sqrt{x^2+1}}{x}\cdot\frac{1+\sqrt{x^2+1}}{1+\sqrt{x^2+1}}\right)=\log_a\frac{-1+x^2+1}{x(1+\sqrt{x^2+1})}$$

$$=\log_a\frac{x}{1+\sqrt{x^2+1}}=\log_a\left(\frac{1+\sqrt{x^2+1}}{x}\right)^{-1}$$

$$=-\log_a\frac{1+\sqrt{x^2+1}}{x}.$$

Exercises 13.1

Solve for x in Numbers 1 to 8.

1. $2^x = 3$.
2. $3(3^x) = 6$.
3. $2^{x+1} = 3^x$.
4. $\log_{1/2} 8 = x$.

5. $\log_3 x = -2$.
6. $\log_x 81 = -4$.
7. $3(3^x) = 27^{2x}$.
8. $(2^{2x+1})(4^{x+3}) = 8^{2x}$.

9. Prove Theorem 13.1e.
10. Prove Theorem 13.1f.

11. Prove Theorem 13.1g.
12. Prove Theorem 13.1h.

Solve for x in terms of y in Numbers 13 to 16.

13. $y = 5^{-x}$.
14. $3y = 3^x$.

15. $3^y = 2^{3x+1}$.
16. $y = \frac{1}{2}(10^{2x} + 10^{-2x})$.

In Numbers 17 to 20, transform the left side of the equation into the right.

17. $\log_a \sqrt{x^5} + \log_a \sqrt[3]{x^2} + \log_a \sqrt[4]{x} + \log_a \sqrt{x^3} + \log_a \sqrt[12]{x} = \log_a x^5$.

18. $\log_{10} \dfrac{x^3 \cdot 10^{2x}}{10^{x^2}} = 3 \log_{10} x + 2x - x^2$.

19. $\log_a \sqrt[3]{2\sqrt{x}} = \frac{1}{3} \log_a 2 + \frac{1}{6} \log_a x$.
20. $\log_a 9 + \log_a 8 + \log_a 2 - \log_a 16 - \log_a 3 = \log_a 3$.

In Numbers 21 to 30, find the value of each logarithm. Use $\log_{10} 2 \approx 0.30103$ and $\log_{10} 3 \approx 0.47712$.

21. $\log_{10} 5$.
22. $\log_{10} \sqrt{18}$.
23. $\log_{10} \frac{1}{5}$.
24. $\log_{10} 900$.
25. $\log_{10} 150$.

26. $\log_{10} 12$.
27. $\log_{10} \sqrt{45}$.
28. $\log_{10} \frac{1}{54}$.
29. $\log_{10} \sqrt[3]{60}$.
30. $\log_{10} 24$.

Sketch the graph of each equation in Numbers 31 to 34.

31. $y = 2^{-x}$.
32. $y = \log_{1/2} x$.

33. $y = (2^x + 2^{-x})/2$.
34. $y = \log_3 (x - 3)$.

13.2 THE DERIVATIVE OF THE LOGARITHM FUNCTION

A number of questions concerning the exponential and the logarithm functions remain unanswered. For example, we tacitly assumed that $y = a^x$ and $y = \log_a x$ each describe continuous functions, but we have yet to prove it. Furthermore, if the functions are continuous, are they differentiable? The problem of answering these questions turns out to be more formidable than might be expected.

For instance, if we want to investigate the differentiability of the logarithm function, we naturally appeal to the definition of the derivative. Thus, if

$$f(x) = \log_a x, \qquad x > 0,$$

then

$$\frac{f(x + h) - f(x)}{h} = \frac{1}{h} \left[\log_a (x + h) - \log_a x \right]$$

$$= \frac{1}{h} \log_a \left(\frac{x + h}{x} \right)$$

$$= \frac{1}{h} \log_a \left(1 + \frac{h}{x} \right).$$

It appears that we are faced with the difficult problem of investigating the limit as $h \to 0$. The form of the problem can be changed slightly by writing

$$\frac{f(x + h) - f(x)}{h} = \frac{1}{x} \cdot \frac{x}{h} \log_a \left(1 + \frac{h}{x} \right)$$

$$= \frac{1}{x} \log_a \left(1 + \frac{h}{x} \right)^{x/h}.$$

Assuming that the logarithm is a continuous function, we now get

$$\lim_{h \to 0} \frac{1}{x} \log_a \left(1 + \frac{h}{x} \right)^{x/h} = \frac{1}{x} \log_a \left[\lim_{h \to 0} \left(1 + \frac{h}{x} \right)^{x/h} \right],$$

so that the limit to be evaluated is essentially

$$\lim_{h \to 0} \left(1 + \frac{h}{x} \right)^{x/h}.$$

The replacement of h/x by t and the fact that $t \to 0$ as $h \to 0$ for every fixed $x > 0$ leads to the result

$$\lim_{h \to 0} \left(1 + \frac{h}{x} \right)^{x/h} = \lim_{t \to 0} (1 + t)^{1/t},$$

and shows that the limit (if it exists) does not depend on the value of x.

If, indeed, $\lim_{t \to 0} (1 + t)^{1/t}$ does exist and is $A \neq 1$, we could then write

$$D_x \log_a x = \frac{1}{x} \log_a A, \qquad \log_a A \neq 0,$$

and we could also obtain an inverse derivative,

$$\frac{\log_a x}{\log_a A} = D_x^{-1}\left(\frac{1}{x}\right).$$

Unfortunately, this is all speculation. However, the last result does strongly suggest that there may be some connection between $\log_a x$ and $D_x^{-1}(1/x)$, or between $\log_a x$ and the indefinite integral

$$\int_1^x \frac{dt}{t}.$$

From the results in Section 12.9, we know that the indefinite integral

$$L(x) .=. \int_1^x \frac{dt}{t}, \qquad x > 0$$

describes a continuous function that has a derivative,

$$D_x L(x) = \frac{1}{x}.$$

This result shows that $L(x)$ fills the gap left by the inverse derivative formula

$$\int x^n \, dx = \frac{x^{n+1}}{n+1} + C, \qquad n \neq -1,$$

with the new formula

$$\int x^{-1} \, dx = L(x) + C.$$

The fact that $L'(x) = 1/x$ indicates that L is an increasing function for $x > 0$ and that the tangent to the graph of L approaches a vertical position as $x \to 0^+$ and becomes more and more nearly horizontal as $x \to \infty$. Indeed, the definition of $L(x)$ must describe the function L completely, and further investigation should reveal its connection with the logarithm function.

For example, if c is a constant, we have

$$L(cx) = \int_1^{cx} \frac{dt}{t}.$$

By using the chain rule for differentiation, we get

$$D_x L(cx) = \frac{1}{cx} D_x(cx) = \frac{1}{x},$$

or,

$$D_x L(cx) = D_x L(x).$$

Hence, $L(cx)$ and $L(x)$ differ by a constant (why?), so that

$$L(cx) = L(x) + k.$$

From the integral expression for $L(x)$, it follows that $L(1) = 0$. Hence, the preceding equation gives

$$L(c) = L(1) + k \quad \text{and} \quad k = L(c).$$

Therefore, the function defined by the indefinite integral $\int_1^x \frac{dt}{t}$ has the property

(1) $$L(cx) = L(x) + L(c),$$

which is one of the basic properties of the logarithm function. Of course, we have no guarantee that a function having this property is necessarily a logarithm function, so we must not yet draw a conclusion in this respect.

Another important property of $L(x)$ can be obtained from (1) by putting $x = c$ to get

$$L(c^2) = 2L(c).$$

In general, we may conclude, by mathematical induction, that

$$L(c^n) = nL(c), \qquad n \in \mathfrak{N}.$$

Now suppose that $c > 1$. Then $L(c) > 0$, and evidently, as $n \to \infty$, $L(c^n) \to \infty$. Since $L(1) = 0$ and since $L(c^n)$ can be made arbitrarily large, $L(x)$ must take on every positive real value because it is a continuous function. For instance, from the Intermediate Value Theorem in Section 8.5 on continuous functions, we know that there exists a value of x for which $L(x) = 1$. This value of x is important enough to deserve special recognition.

Definition 13.2a. The number e is that number for which $L(e) = 1$.

It will be left as an exercise for the reader to show that for $0 < x < 1$, $L(x) < 0$ and as $x \to 0^+$, $L(x) \to -\infty$. This, along with the preceding results, shows that the range of L is the set of all real numbers.

It has been shown that

(2) $$L(c^p) = pL(c)$$

holds when p is a positive integer. The reader can extend the result to include values of p that are negative integers. The next theorem generalizes the result further.

Theorem 13.2a. If $q \in \mathfrak{N}$, and if $c > 0$, then

$$L(c^{1/q}) = \frac{1}{q} L(c).$$

PROOF: Let $x = c^{1/q}$, so that $c = x^q$. Then

$$L(c) = L(x^q) = qL(x),$$

so that

$$L(x) = \frac{1}{q} L(c),$$

or

$$L(c^{1/q}) = \frac{1}{q} L(c).$$

The reader should extend this result to include any rational number p/q.

Continuing this line of exploration, we can try to extend the Relation (2) to hold when p is an irrational number, say r. Since $L(x)$ is an increasing function that takes on every real value, there is some number a for which

$$L(a) = rL(c).$$

Now, let r have the usual decimal form

$$r = x_0.x_1x_2 \ldots x_n \ldots,$$

where x_0 is an integer and each x_i is a digit. Then, with

$$r_n = x_0.x_1x_2 \ldots x_n,$$

we have

$$\lim_{n\to\infty} r_n L(c) = rL(c) = L(a).$$

Since r_n is a rational number,

$$r_n L(a) = L(a^{r_n}),$$

so that

$$\lim_{n\to\infty} r_n L(c) = \lim_{n\to\infty} L(c^{r_n}).$$

Thus,

$$rL(c) = L(c^r) = L(a),$$

follows from the definition of the exponential c^r and the fact that the function L is continuous.

From the last equations, we have

$$a = c^r, \quad \text{or} \quad r = \log_c a = \frac{L(a)}{L(c)},$$

which identifies L as a logarithm function. In particular, if c is the number e for which $L(e) = 1$, then $L(a) = r$, and

$$r = \log_e a.$$

Hence

$$L(a) = \log_e a.$$

We have now identified the function L as the logarithm function defined by

$$L(x) = \log_e x.$$

The properties of L as determined by the integral definition show that the logarithm function is a continuous, increasing function on its entire domain, the set of positive real numbers. As a consequence, the inverse function exists and is the exponential function f, where

$$f(x) .=. e^x.$$

It follows (see Theorem 8.5h) that the exponential function is *continuous* on its entire domain $\mathfrak{R}$, the range of the logarithm function.

We now have the tools necessary for the solution of one of the problems raised but not solved earlier in this chapter and thereby to prove the following theorem.

Theorem 13.2b. $$\lim_{t\to 0} (1 + t)^{1/t} = e.$$

PROOF: We may write, by Theorems 13.1f and 13.1g,

$$(1 + t)^{1/t} = \exp_e \left[\frac{1}{t} \log_e (1 + t) \right].$$

Hence, by reason of the continuity of the exponential function,

$$\lim_{t \to 0} (1 + t)^{1/t} = \lim_{t \to 0} \exp_e \left[\frac{1}{t} \log_e (1 + t) \right]$$

$$= \exp_e \left\{ \lim_{t \to 0} \left[\frac{1}{t} \log_e (1 + t) \right] \right\}.$$

Since $\log_e 1 = 0$, we have

$$\lim_{t \to 0} \frac{1}{t} \log_e (1 + t) = \lim_{t \to 0} \frac{\log_e (1 + t) - \log_e 1}{t},$$

which is exactly the definition of $L'(1)$. But

$$L'(x) = 1/x \Rightarrow L'(1) = 1,$$

so that

$$\lim_{t \to 0} (1 + t)^{1/t} = \exp_e 1 = e^1 = e,$$

and the proof of the theorem is complete.

It can be shown that

$$e \approx 1 + \frac{1}{1!} + \frac{1}{2!} + \frac{1}{3!} + \cdots + \frac{1}{n!},$$

and that the larger the value of n, the more accurate is the approximation for e. We shall discuss this fact more fully in our work with infinite series. The value of e to 12 decimal places is given by

$$e \approx 2.718281828459.$$

With the knowledge that $\lim_{t \to 0} (1 + t)^{1/t} = e$, we are able to justify the conjectures entertained at the beginning of this section. The number e is, of course, the number that we earlier called A.

Theorem 13.2c. $\qquad D_x \log_a x = \frac{1}{x} \log_a e.$

PROOF: By Theorem 13.1i,

$$\log_a x = (\log_a e)(\log_e x).$$

Therefore,

$$D_x(\log_a x) = (\log_a e) D_x(\log_e x)$$

$$= \frac{1}{x} \log_a e.$$

It has already been shown that if the base of the logarithm function is taken to be e, then the expression for the derivative of the function is in its simplest form. This is important enough to bear repetition:

$$D_x \log_e x = \frac{1}{x}.$$

It is because of this simplicity that e is called the **natural base** for logarithms and that logarithms to this base are called **natural logarithms.** In order to indicate a logarithm to the base e, we shall henceforth use the symbol "ln," which has received wide acceptance in recent years.

An easy application of the chain rule suffices to prove the next result. The details are left for the reader.

Theorem 13.2d. If $u = f(x)$ defines a differentiable function such that $f(x) > 0$ on some domain, then on this domain

$$D_x \ln u = \frac{1}{u} D_x u.$$

Example 13.2a. Find $F'(x)$ if $F(x) = \ln \sqrt{1 - x^2}$, $|x| < 1$.

First, let us write

$$F(x) = \ln (1 - x^2)^{1/2} = \frac{1}{2} \ln (1 - x^2).$$

Thus,

$$F'(x) = \frac{1}{2} D_x \ln (1 - x^2)$$

$$= \frac{1}{2} \cdot \frac{1}{1 - x^2} D_x(1 - x^2) \qquad \text{(Theorem 13.2d)}$$

$$= \frac{-x}{1 - x^2}.$$

Example 13.2b. Find $f'(x)$ if $f(x) = \log_{10} (x^3 \sqrt{1 - x^2})$.

Using the properties of logarithms, we first write

$$f(x) = 3 \log_{10} x + \frac{1}{2} \log_{10} (1 - x^2).$$

Thus,

$$f'(x) = \frac{3}{x} \log_{10} e + \frac{1}{2} \left(\frac{1}{1 - x^2} \right)(-2x) \log_{10} e$$

$$= (\log_{10} e)\left(\frac{3}{x} - \frac{x}{1 - x^2} \right).$$

Example 13.2c. If $x > 0$ is the thickness of the insulation of a submarine cable, it is found that the speed with which a signal can be transmitted along the cable varies directly as $(\ln x)/x^2$. Find the value of x that would give the maximum speed.

Let $V(x) = k(\ln x)/x^2$, where k is the constant of proportionality. Then

$$V'(x) = k \frac{x^2 \left(\dfrac{1}{x} \right) - (\ln x)(2x)}{x^4}$$

$$= \frac{k(1 - 2 \ln x)}{x^3}.$$

For $V'(x) = 0$, we have

$$1 - 2 \ln x = 0,$$

or

$$x = e^{1/2}.$$

The student may check by either the first derivative test or the second derivative test to show that this value of x actually yields a maximum value for $V(x)$.

Exercises 13.2

Find y' in Numbers 1 to 15.

1. $y = \dfrac{\ln x}{x^3}$.

2. $y = \log_{10} x^2$.
3. $y = (\ln x^3)^2$.
4. $y = \log_{10} x^2\sqrt{1 + x^3}$.

5. $y = \dfrac{x^2}{\ln x^3}$.

6. $y = \sqrt{x} \log_{10} x^3$.
7. $xy + \ln xy = 3$.

8. $y = \ln (\ln x)$.

9. $y = \ln \dfrac{x}{4 + x^2}$.

10. $3xy^2 - \ln x = 5$.
11. $x = t + t \ln t,\ y = t - t \ln t$.
12. $y = \ln (x \ln x)$.
13. $y = \ln (x + \sqrt{x^2 + 1})$.
14. $x = s^2 \ln s,\ y = s + \ln s$.

15. $y = \ln \dfrac{x^2 - 1}{x^2 + 1}$.

Find y' and y'' in Numbers 16 to 19.

16. $y = \ln (x^2 - 4)$.
17. $y = x^2 \ln 3x$.

18. $xy + \ln x = 1$.
19. $x = \ln s,\ y = s^2$.

Discuss and sketch the curves in Numbers 20 to 26.

20. $y = \log_{1/2} x$.
21. $y = x \ln x$.
22. $y = \ln (x^2 + 1)$.
23. $y + 2 = \log_3 x$.

24. $y = \ln |x|$.

25. $y = \dfrac{3 \ln x}{x}$.

26. $y = \ln |x^2 - 1|$.

27. If $\ln y = kt$, where k is a constant and t is the time, show that the instantaneous rate of change of y is proportional to y itself. This is an important law of variation in many physical problems such as that of radioactive decay.

28. For values of x that are large in comparison with the value of h, show that the difference between $\ln (x + h)$ and $\ln x$ is approximately h/x. What would be the approximate percentage error made in using $\ln 1000$ in place of $\ln 1002$?

29. Show that $(1/101) < \ln 1.01 < (1/100)$. *Hint*: Apply the Mean Value Theorem for Derivatives to $f(x) = \ln x$.

30. The capacitance of a certain type of coaxial cylindrical condenser is given by the formula

$$C = \frac{kL}{\ln (r_o/r_i)},$$

where k is a constant, L is the length, and r_o and r_i are the outside and inside radii, respectively, of the condenser. The radii of a certain condenser are 4 centimeters and 2 centimeters, respectively. What approximate percentage change would occur in the capacitance if the outside radius were increased to 4.02 centimeters, all other dimensions remaining unaltered?

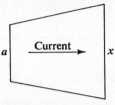

FIGURE 13.2a

★31. For a wedge-shaped electrical conductor (see Figure 13.2a) the resistance is given by

$$R = k \frac{\ln (x/a)}{x - a},$$

where k is a constant depending on the length and width of the wedge and the physical properties of the material. Show that R decreases with x for $x > a$.

13.3 THE DERIVATIVE OF THE EXPONENTIAL FUNCTION

As we already know, the fact that a function is continuous does not guarantee it to be differentiable. Our investigation of the exponential function leads next to the question of differentiability.

Let $f(x) = a^x$ and let us try to find $f'(x)$ directly from the definition. First, the difference quotient is

$$\frac{f(x + h) - f(x)}{h} = \frac{a^{x+h} - a^x}{h} = a^x \left(\frac{a^h - 1}{h} \right).$$

Hence

$$f'(x) = \lim_{h \to 0} a^x \left(\frac{a^h - 1}{h} \right) = a^x \lim_{h \to 0} \left(\frac{a^h - 1}{h} \right).$$

The evaluation of the last limit, if it exists at all, is the entire key to the problem. It is interesting to note that if the limit does exist, it is $f'(0)$.

It is, of course, not surprising that there is a close connection between the preceding limit and the limit that arose in the problem of differentiating the logarithm function. In the expression

$$\frac{a^h - 1}{h},$$

let $a^h - 1 = k$. Then $h = \log_a (1 + k)$, and we obtain

$$\frac{a^h - 1}{h} = \frac{k}{\log_a (1 + k)}$$

$$= \frac{1}{\frac{1}{k} \log_a (1 + k)}$$

$$= \frac{1}{\log_a (1 + k)^{1/k}}.$$

Since $h \to 0 \Leftrightarrow k \to 0$, we have

$$\lim_{h \to 0} \frac{a^h - 1}{h} = \lim_{k \to 0} \frac{1}{\log_a (1 + k)^{1/k}}$$

$$= \frac{1}{\log_a e} = \ln a.$$

We have thus proved

Theorem 13.3a. $\qquad D_x a^x = a^x \ln a, \qquad a > 0, a \neq 1.$

By putting $a = e$, we have the following important special case.

Theorem 13.3b. $\qquad\qquad D_x e^x = e^x.$

Notice that the function $\{(x, e^x)\}$ is unaltered by differentiation.

By a direct application of the chain rule, we can easily prove

Theorem 13.3c. If $u = f(x)$ defines a differentiable function, then

$$D_x e^u = e^u D_x u.$$

Example 13.3a. Find $D_x e^{x^2}$.

Using Theorem 13.3c, we obtain

$$D_x e^{x^2} = e^{x^2} D_x x^2$$
$$= 2x e^{x^2}.$$

Example 13.3b. Find $D_x \exp_{10} \sqrt{1 - x^2}$.

With the aid of Theorem 13.3a, we find

$$D_x \exp_{10} \sqrt{1 - x^2} = (\exp_{10} \sqrt{1 - x^2})(\ln 10) D_x \sqrt{1 - x^2}$$

$$= (\exp_{10} \sqrt{1 - x^2})(\ln 10)\left(\frac{-x}{\sqrt{1 - x^2}}\right).$$

Example 13.3c. Find $D_t \ln (1 + e^{-t})$.

We have

$$D_t \ln (1 + e^{-t}) = \frac{1}{1 + e^{-t}} D_t(1 + e^{-t})$$

$$= \frac{-e^{-t}}{1 + e^{-t}}$$

$$= -\frac{1}{e^t + 1}.$$

Theorem 13.3d. If $x > 0$ and k is real, then

$$D_x(x^k) = k x^{k-1}.$$

PROOF: It has already been shown under milder restrictions on x that this formula holds if the exponent is a positive integer. In the present case, we have

$$x^k = e^{k \ln x},$$

so that, by Theorem 13.3c,

$$D_x x^k = e^{k \ln x} D_x(k \ln x)$$

$$= (x^k)\left(\frac{k}{x}\right) = kx^{k-1}.$$

This completes the proof of a formula that we have used many times.

Exercises 13.3

Find the indicated derivative in Numbers 1 to 20.

1. $y = e^{x^3}$; y'.

2. $s = \dfrac{e^x}{x}$; $D_x s$.

3. $x = 3^{2y}y$; $D_y x$.
4. $xy + e^{xy} = 4$; $D_x y$.
5. $t = \exp_5 \sqrt{4 + u^2}$; $D_u t$.
6. $x = e^{t+1}$; $y = e^{t^2}$; $D_x y$.
7. $\ln xy + e^{xy} = x$; $D_x y$.
8. $e^{2t} + e^{2s} = e^{ts}$; $D_s t$.
9. $w = e^{u + \ln u}$; $D_u w$.
10. $x = e^{2t}$, $y = \ln t$; $D_x y$.
11. $y = e^{x \ln x}$; $D_x y$.

12. $s = \dfrac{e^u}{u^2 + 1}$; $D_u s$.

13. $y = e^2$; $D_x y$.
14. $x = e^{y^e}$; $D_y x$.
15. $v = e^w \ln w$; $D_w v$.
16. $y = e^{1/\ln x}$; $D_x y$.

17. $y = \ln \dfrac{e^{3x} + 1}{e^{3x} - 1}$; $D_x y$.

18. $w = e^{e^s}$; $D_s w$.
19. $y = \log_{10}(e^x + e^{-x})$; $D_x y$.
20. $s = x \exp_4 \sqrt{1 + x^2}$; $D_x s$.

Find y' and y'' in Numbers 21 to 24.

21. $y = x^3 e^{-x^2}$.
22. $y = e^x \ln x$.

23. $y = e^{x^2 - x}$.
24. $e^{xy} = x$.

In each of Numbers 25 to 32, discuss and sketch the graph of the given equation.

25. $y = e^{-x^2}$.

26. $y = \dfrac{e^x + e^{-x}}{2}$.

27. $y = \dfrac{e^x - e^{-x}}{2}$.

28. $y = \dfrac{e^x - e^{-x}}{e^x + e^{-x}}$.

29. $y + 1 = 2^x$.
30. $y = 2(2^x)$.
31. $y = 2^{|x|}$.
32. $y = xe^{-x}$.

In Numbers 33 to 36, use the differential to find the approximate value of the given expression.

33. $e^{1.03}$.
34. $e^{-1.98}$.

35. $8^{1.98}$.
36. $(\frac{1}{2})^{2.03}$.

37. Use the Mean Value Theorem for Derivatives in the form of Equation (4), Theorem 11.4a, to show that $2.7726 < e^{1.02} < 2.7737$.
38. If k is a fraction in lowest terms with an odd integer for its denominator, then $f(x) = x^k$ defines a real function whose domain is all real values of x except possibly $x = 0$. Show that, even if $x < 0$,

$$D_x(x^k) = kx^{k-1}.$$

Hint: Write $x = -z$ so that $x^k = (-1)^k z^k$.

39. Find an equation of the line that is tangent to the curve $y = e^{-2x}$ and that is parallel to the line $x + y = 2$.
40. A rectangle has its base on the x-axis and two vertices on the curve $y = e^{-x^2}$. Show that the rectangle has a maximum area when the two vertices on the curve are at the inflection points.

13.4 INVERSE DERIVATIVES LEADING TO EXPONENTIAL AND LOGARITHMIC FUNCTIONS

Formulas for the inverse derivatives of the exponential and logarithmic functions follow immediately from the work of the preceding two sections. From the formula $D_u \ln u = 1/u$, we have

Theorem 13.4a. $\qquad \displaystyle\int \frac{du}{u} = \ln u + C, \qquad u > 0.$

This formula fills a gap by taking care of the exceptional case $n = -1$ in the formula for $D_x^{-1} x^n$.

Example 13.4a. Find $\displaystyle\int \frac{x\,dx}{x^2 - 1}$, $x > 1$.

If we let $u = x^2 - 1$, then $du = 2x\,dx$. Thus,

$$\int \frac{x\,dx}{x^2 - 1} = \frac{1}{2} \int \frac{2x\,dx}{x^2 - 1} = \frac{1}{2} \ln(x^2 - 1) + C.$$

In the next example we shall find the area bounded by the x-axis, the lines $x = -3$ and $x = -2$, and the curve $xy = 1$. This is a meaningful problem, but Theorem 13.4a is not applicable. Let us see if we can modify the theorem so that it will be applicable.

Since the result of Theorem 13.4a applies only for $u > 0$, we now consider the case $u < 0$. We let $u = -w$ so that $w > 0$ and

$$\int \frac{du}{u} = \int \frac{-dw}{-w} = \int \frac{dw}{w} = \ln w + C = \ln(-u) + C.$$

This result, which may be written $\ln |u| + C$, is combined with that of Theorem 13.4a in

Theorem 13.4b. $\qquad \displaystyle\int \frac{du}{u} = \ln |u| + C, \qquad u > 0 \quad \text{or} \quad u < 0.$

Example 13.4b. Find the area bounded by the x-axis, the lines $x = -3$ and $x = -2$, and the curve $xy = 1$ (see Figure 13.4a).

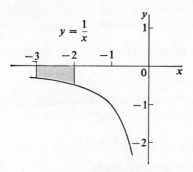

FIGURE 13.4a

Since the area lies below the x-axis, we have

$$\text{area} = -\int_{-3}^{-2} \frac{dx}{x}$$

$$= -[\ln |x|]_{-3}^{-2}$$

$$= -[\ln 2 - \ln 3]$$

$$= (\ln \tfrac{3}{2}) \, (\text{l.u.})^2.$$

Example 13.4c. The rate of decrease of mass of a radioactive substance is proportional to the mass present. If the half-life (the time for half of the mass to decompose) is 10 minutes, how much of a given sample of x_0 grams will remain undecomposed at the end of t minutes?

Let $x =$ amount of mass present at time t (minutes). Then the rate of change of the mass is $D_t x$, so that, by the hypothesis,

$$D_t x = -kx,$$

or, by Theorem 10.6b,

$$-D_x t = \frac{1}{kx}.$$

Notice that we have regarded k as a positive physical constant and have written $-kx$ since x is supposed to be decreasing. We thus find

$$-kt = \int \frac{dx}{x},$$

and

$$-kt = \ln x + C.$$

We can now evaluate the constant C by using the fact that $x = x_0$ when $t = 0$. Hence,

$$0 = \ln x_0 + C,$$

or

$$C = -\ln x_0.$$

Thus, we obtain

$$-kt = \ln x - \ln x_0,$$

or

$$-kt = \ln \frac{x}{x_0}.$$

We can now find k by using the known half-life, which tells us that when

$$t = 10, \quad x = \tfrac{1}{2}x_0.$$

Therefore,

$$-10k = \ln \frac{\frac{1}{2}x_0}{x_0} = -\ln 2,$$

so that

$$-\frac{t}{10} \ln 2 = \ln \frac{x}{x_0}.$$

By solving for x, we get the desired formula

$$x = x_0 \exp\left[-(t/10) \ln 2\right] = x_0 \exp_2(-t/10).$$

Another inverse derivative formula arises from the result

$$D_u e^u = e^u,$$

which gives the next theorem.

Theorem 13.4c. $$\int e^u \, du = e^u + C.$$

Example 13.4d. Find

$$\int x^2 e^{x^3} \, dx.$$

If $u = x^3$, then $D_x u = 3x^2$. Hence

$$\int x^2 e^{x^3} \, dx = \frac{1}{3} \int 3x^2 e^{x^3} \, dx = \frac{1}{3} e^{x^3} + C.$$

In a similar manner, since $D_u a^u = a^u \ln a$, $a > 0$, we have

Theorem 13.4d. $$\int a^u \, du = \frac{a^u}{\ln a} + C, \qquad a > 0, a \neq 1.$$

Example 13.4e. Find the volume formed by revolving about the x-axis the area bounded by the x-axis, the line $x = 1$, and the curve $y = \sqrt{x}e^{-x^2}$.

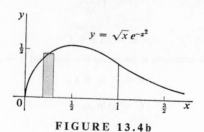

$$y = \sqrt{x}\, e^{-x^2}$$

FIGURE 13.4b

This curve touches the y-axis at the origin and lies above the x-axis (see Figure 13.4b). Using the cylindrical disk method of Example 12.11b, we find

$$V = \pi \int_0^1 y^2 \, dx = \pi \int_0^1 xe^{-2x^2} \, dx$$

$$= -\frac{\pi}{4} \int_0^1 -4xe^{-2x^2} \, dx = -\frac{\pi}{4} [e^{-2x^2}]_0^1$$

$$= \frac{\pi}{4} (1 - e^{-2}) \text{ (l.u.)}^3.$$

Example 13.4f. Find

$$\int \frac{x \, dx}{x + 1}.$$

A problem of this type, in which the integrand is a rational fraction, with the degree of its numerator equal to or greater than the degree of its denominator, can always be handled by first dividing numerator by denominator. Thus

$$\frac{x}{x + 1} = 1 - \frac{1}{x + 1}$$

and

$$\int \frac{x \, dx}{x + 1} = \int \left(1 - \frac{1}{x + 1}\right) dx = x - \ln |x + 1| + C.$$

Exercises 13.4

In each of Numbers 1 to 20, find the indicated inverse derivative.

1. $\displaystyle\int \frac{x^2 \, dx}{1 + x^3}.$

2. $\displaystyle\int \frac{dt}{2t + 3}.$

3. $\displaystyle\int \frac{x \, dx}{\sqrt{1 - x^2}}.$

4. $\displaystyle\int \frac{2x \, dx}{4x + 3}.$

5. $\displaystyle\int xe^{-x^2} \, dx.$

6. $\displaystyle\int \sqrt{3^x} \, dx.$

7. $\displaystyle\int \frac{e^x - e^{-x}}{e^x + e^{-x}} \, dx.$

8. $\displaystyle\int \frac{s \, ds}{1 - s^2}.$

9. $\displaystyle\int \frac{t^3 + t}{t^2 - 1} \, dt.$

10. $\displaystyle\int \frac{e^w \, dw}{(e^w + 1)^2}.$

11. $\displaystyle\int \frac{e^{1/x}}{x^2} \, dx.$

12. $\displaystyle\int \frac{\ln t \, dt}{t}.$

13. $\displaystyle\int 3^{3x} \, dx.$

14. $\displaystyle\int e^{y3-y} \, dy.$

15. $\displaystyle\int \frac{1}{1 + e^t} \, dt.$

16. $\displaystyle\int \frac{e^x \, dx}{e^x + 1}.$

17. $\int e^{2+3x}\, dx.$

19. $\int \frac{y\, dy}{(1+y^2)^2}.$

18. $\int \frac{e^{2x}+1}{e^{2x}}\, dx.$

20. $\int \frac{2x+3}{2x-3}\, dx.$

Evaluate the definite integrals in Numbers 21 to 30.

21. $\int_{-4}^{-2} \frac{3x\, dx}{1+x^2}.$

26. $\int_{1}^{4} \frac{\ln x}{x}\, dx.$

22. $\int_{0}^{2} \frac{v\, dv}{2v^2+1}.$

27. $\int_{-3}^{-1} xe^{x^2}\, dx.$

23. $\int_{0}^{1} \frac{dx}{\sqrt{1+x}}.$

28. $\int_{2}^{6} xe^{-3\ln x}\, dx.$

24. $\int_{1}^{3} e^2\, dx.$

29. $\int_{-5}^{-3} \frac{dx}{2x+3}.$

25. $\int_{-1}^{0} \frac{t\, dt}{t-1}.$

30. $\int_{0}^{1} 2^{3x}\, dx.$

Find the area bounded by the x-axis and the given curves in Numbers 31 to 34.

31. $y = \frac{x}{1+x^2},\ x = 1,\ x = 3.$

33. $y = \frac{1}{x+1},\ x = -4,\ x = -2.$

32. $y = 3^{-x},\ x = -4,\ x = -2.$

34. $y = xe^{-x^2},\ x = 1,\ x = 3.$

35. The number of bacteria in a culture increases at a rate proportional to the number present. If it takes 20 minutes for the original number to double, when will the colony be five times its original size?

36. A cubical tank 10 feet on an edge is filled with water. A slow leak in the bottom of the tank allows the water to escape, and a reasonable assumption is that the rate of leakage at each instant is proportional to the depth of the water remaining in the tank at that instant. Suppose that 5% of the water leaks out in 2 hours; how much will leak out in 6 hours?

37. If four percent of a given amount of radium decomposes in 100 years, find the half-life.

38. When a gas expands from a volume v_1 to a volume v_2, the work W done by the gas is given by the formula

$$W = \int_{v_1}^{v_2} p\, dv,$$

where p is the pressure. If $pv = c$ (a constant), find the work done.

39. Find the centroid of the area bounded by

$$xy = 4, \quad y = 0, \quad x = 1, \quad x = 2.$$

40. Find the volume generated by revolving about the x-axis the area bounded by

$$y = e^{-x}, \quad y = 0, \quad x = 0, \quad x = 1.$$

13.5 LOGARITHMIC DIFFERENTIATION

Logarithms may frequently be used to good advantage in differentiating complicated products, quotients, or exponential expressions. This idea is illustrated in the following examples.

Example 13.5a. Find $D_x x^x$.

Notice that the exponent here is not a constant, so that the formula for $D_x x^n$ does not apply. However, we may write $y = x^x$, take the logarithms of both sides, and then differentiate implicitly. Thus,

$$\ln y = x \ln x,$$

$$\frac{1}{y}(y') = 1 + \ln x,$$

$$y' = y(1 + \ln x) = x^x(1 + \ln x).$$

Example 13.5b. Find

$$D_x \left[\frac{\sqrt{1 - x^2}(1 + x^3)^2}{(1 + x^2)^4} \right].$$

In this example it would be possible to differentiate the expression in its present form but the work can be greatly simplified by using logarithms. Let

$$y = \frac{\sqrt{1 - x^2}(1 + x^3)^2}{(1 + x^2)^4}.$$

Then

$$\ln y = \tfrac{1}{2} \ln(1 - x^2) + 2 \ln(1 + x^3) - 4 \ln(1 + x^2)$$

and

$$\frac{1}{y}(y') = \frac{-x}{1 - x^2} + \frac{6x^2}{1 + x^3} - \frac{8x}{1 + x^2},$$

or

$$y' = \frac{\sqrt{1 - x^2}(1 + x^3)^2}{(1 + x^2)^4} \left[-\frac{x}{1 - x^2} + \frac{6x^2}{1 + x^3} - \frac{8x}{1 + x^2} \right].$$

Exercises 13.5

Find the indicated derivative in Numbers 1 to 12.

1. $y = x^{\ln x}$; $D_x y$.
2. $s = r^{r^2}$; $D_r s$.
3. $y = x e^{e^{-x}}$; $D_x y$.
4. $y = (w^2 + 2)^3(1 - w^4)^{1/3}$; $D_w y$.
5. $x = \dfrac{y^5 \sqrt[3]{1 - y^2}}{\sqrt{1 + 3y}}$; $D_y x$.
6. $y = \dfrac{e^{2x}\sqrt{1 - x^2}}{x^4}$; $D_x y$.
7. $u = (\ln 2v)^v$; $D_v u$.
8. $r = x^{\ln 2x}$; $D_x r$.
9. $y = \sqrt[4]{\dfrac{x^2 + 4}{\sqrt{1 + x^2}(x^3 + 2)}}$; $D_x y$.
10. $y = x^{\sqrt[y]{x}}$; $D_x y$.
11. $w = u^{1/u}$; $D_u w$.
12. $s = r^{\exp(-r^2)}$; $D_r s$.

13. If $y = u^v$, where u and v are differentiable functions of x, find a formula for $D_x y$.

14. The period of a simple pendulum is given quite accurately for small oscillations by the formula $T = 2\pi\sqrt{L/g}$, where T is the number of seconds taken for a complete oscillation, L is the length of the pendulum in feet, and g is the gravitational acceleration in feet per second per second. A pendulum clock is adjusted to keep accurate time when its pendulum is 12 inches long. Approximately how much time would the clock lose per day if the pendulum were set $\frac{1}{24}$ inch too long? *Hint:* The number of seconds lost per second is approximately dT/T.

$\star$15. Since $D_x \ln f(x) = f'(x)/f(x)$, the latter fraction is frequently called the *logarithmic derivative* of $f(x)$. Suppose $f(x)$ is a polynomial of degree n with the zeros $\alpha_1, \alpha_2, \ldots, \alpha_n$. Show that

$$\sum_{k=1}^{n} \lim_{x \to \alpha_k} (x - \alpha_k) D_x \ln f(x) = n.$$

Hint: Use Theorem 3.6d.

Summary of Chapter 13

Chapter 13 is concerned with the introduction of the exponential and logarithmic functions and their properties. The student should understand the method of defining a^x, $a > 0$, $a \neq 1$, for any real number x by means of the limit of a sequence (Section 13.1). The logarithm function is defined as the inverse of the exponential function (Section 13.1). Of course, the student must know the fundamental properties of the two functions (Section 13.1).

Finding the derivative of the logarithm function poses a particularly difficult limit problem, whose solution leads to the number e. It is desirable to understand how the number e arises and its importance in mathematics (Section 13.2). Also, the derivative of the exponential and logarithmic functions should be firmly implanted in the student's mind (Sections 13.2, 13.3). There are many functions whose inverse derivatives lead to exponential or logarithmic functions and it is necessary to have considerable facility with these forms (Section 13.4).

Logarithms may frequently be used to good advantage in differentiating complicated products, quotients, or exponential expressions (Section 13.5).

Chapter 14

The Calculus of Trigonometric and Hyperbolic Functions

14.1 CONTINUITY OF THE SINE FUNCTION

Although the trigonometric functions were introduced in Chapter 7, very little study of their properties was made there. For example, it seems intuitively evident that the sine and cosine functions are continuous everywhere, but it has not yet been demonstrated that these functions satisfy the definition of continuity.

Since $\cos x = \pm\sqrt{1 - \sin^2 x}$, the continuity of the cosine function can be deduced from that of the sine function. Hence, it suffices to investigate the continuity of the sine function.

Theorem 14.1a. If $f(x) = \sin x$, then f is continuous at $x = 0$.

PROOF: By Theorem 7.2b, we know for $0 < x < \pi/2$ that

$$0 < \sin x < x.$$

Since $\sin(-x) = -\sin x$, it follows from the inequality that

$$\lim_{x \to 0} \sin x = 0$$

Furthermore, $\sin 0 = 0$, so that the sine function is continuous at $x = 0$.

Using this result we can prove

Theorem 14.1b. The cosine function is continuous at $x = 0$.

PROOF: Since $\cos x = \sqrt{1 - \sin^2 x}$, $-\pi/2 \leq x \leq \pi/2$, we may regard $\cos x$ as a composite of

$$y = f(x) .=. 1 - \sin^2 x \quad \text{and} \quad g(y) .=. \sqrt{y}.$$

We have previously proved (Example 8.2b) that $\lim_{x \to a} \sqrt{x} = \sqrt{a}$ for $a > 0$, which means that the square root function is continuous for $x > 0$. It has just been shown that $\lim_{x \to 0} \sin x = 0$, so that an application of Theorem

8.4d, which concerns the interchange of taking a limit and the formation of a functional value, gives

$$\lim_{x \to 0} \cos x = \lim_{x \to 0} \sqrt{1 - \sin^2 x}$$

$$= \sqrt{\lim_{x \to 0} (1 - \sin^2 x)}$$

$$= 1.$$

Since $\cos 0 = 1$, we have proved that the cosine function is continuous at $x = 0$.

We are now in a position to show quite simply that the sine function is continuous for all values of x.

Theorem 14.1c. The sine function is continuous at $x = a$, where a is any real number.

PROOF: Consider $\sin (a + h) = \sin a \cos h + \cos a \sin h$. Then

$$\lim_{h \to 0} \sin (a + h) = \lim_{h \to 0} \sin a \cos h + \lim_{h \to 0} \cos a \sin h$$

$$= \sin a. \qquad \text{(Why?)}$$

Hence, the sine function is continuous at $x = a$.

Example 14.1a. Evaluate $\lim_{x \to 0} (\csc x - \cot x)$.

We write

$$\lim_{x \to 0} (\csc x - \cot x) = \lim_{x \to 0} \left(\frac{1}{\sin x} - \frac{\cos x}{\sin x} \right)$$

$$= \lim_{x \to 0} \frac{1 - \cos x}{\sin x} = \lim_{x \to 0} \frac{(1 - \cos x)(1 + \cos x)}{\sin x(1 + \cos x)}$$

$$= \lim_{x \to 0} \frac{\sin^2 x}{\sin x(1 + \cos x)} = \lim_{x \to 0} \frac{\sin x}{1 + \cos x} = 0.$$

The continuity of the other trigonometric functions may be determined from theorems concerning continuous functions. For example, since the tangent function is described by

$$\tan x = \frac{\sin x}{\cos x},$$

it follows that this function is continuous everywhere except at the points where the cosine is zero, that is, at the odd multiples of $\pi/2$. Explain.

It is now possible to obtain a result that is basic in the investigation of derivatives of the trigonometric functions.

Theorem 14.1d. $\qquad\qquad \lim_{x \to 0} \dfrac{\sin x}{x} = 1.$

PROOF: Since the denominator has a limit zero, Theorem 8.3e on the limit of a quotient does not apply. Consequently, it is necessary to investigate the limit from another point of view.

From $\sin(-x) = -\sin x$, we get

$$\frac{\sin(-x)}{(-x)} = \frac{\sin x}{x},$$

so that it is sufficient to consider the fraction $(\sin x)/x$ for $x > 0$ only. According to Theorem 7.2b,

$$0 < x < \frac{\pi}{2} \Rightarrow 0 < \sin x < x < \tan x,$$

and since $\sin x > 0$ for this set of values of x, we may divide by $\sin x$ to get

$$1 < \frac{x}{\sin x} < \frac{1}{\cos x}.$$

Thus, by taking reciprocals, we obtain

$$1 > \frac{\sin x}{x} > \cos x.$$

By Theorem 14.1b, $\lim_{x \to 0} \cos x = 1$. Hence the preceding inequality shows that

$$\lim_{x \to 0} \frac{\sin x}{x} = 1,$$

as was to be proved.

Using the results of this theorem, we can evaluate limits of many expressions that involve a quotient of a sine function and the variable argument.

Example 14.1b. Evaluate

$$\lim_{x \to 0} \frac{\sin 2x}{x}.$$

If $u = 2x$, then $u \to 0$ as $x \to 0$, and

$$\lim_{x \to 0} \frac{\sin 2x}{x} = \lim_{u \to 0} \frac{\sin u}{u/2} = 2 \lim_{u \to 0} \frac{\sin u}{u} = 2.$$

Exercises 14.1

In Numbers 1 to 6, find the limit if it exists.

1. $\lim\limits_{x \to 0} \dfrac{\cos 2x}{x}$.

2. $\lim\limits_{x \to 0} \dfrac{\sin 2x}{3x}$.

3. $\lim\limits_{x \to 0} \dfrac{\tan x}{x}$.

4. $\lim\limits_{x \to \pi/2} \dfrac{\cot x}{x - \pi/2}$.

5. $\lim\limits_{x \to \pi/2} (\sec x - \tan x)$.

6. $\lim\limits_{x \to \pi} \dfrac{\sin x}{\pi - x}$.

7. Prove that the cosine function is continuous at every point.

For the function described by each of the following equations, determine the points of continuity and discontinuity and describe the discontinuities.

8. $y = \dfrac{\sin x}{1 - \cos x}$.

9. $u = \cot v$.

10. $u = \dfrac{\sin v}{|\sin v|}$.

11. $y = \csc x$.

12. $g(x) = \begin{cases} \dfrac{\sin 2x}{x}, & x \neq 0, \\ 1, & x = 0. \end{cases}$

13. $r = \sec s$.

14. $f(x) = \dfrac{x}{\sin x}$.

14.2 DERIVATIVES OF THE TRIGONOMETRIC FUNCTIONS

Although the sine and cosine functions are continuous on their entire domain, this is no guarantee that they are differentiable. However, that they are differentiable is easily established.

Theorem 14.2a. $\qquad D_x \sin u = \cos u \, D_x u.$

PROOF: $\qquad\qquad D_x \sin x = \lim_{h \to 0} \dfrac{\sin(x + h) - \sin x}{h}$.

By the formula in Number 22 of Exercises 7.5, we have

$$\sin(x + h) - \sin x = 2 \cos(x + h/2) \sin h/2,$$

so that

$$\lim_{h \to 0} \frac{\sin(x + h) - \sin x}{h} = \lim_{h \to 0} \cos(x + h/2) \frac{\sin h/2}{h/2} = \cos x$$

or

$$D_x \sin x = \cos x.$$

The chain rule then yields the more general form

$$D_x \sin u = \cos u \, D_x u.$$

The derivatives of the other trigonometric functions can be obtained from Theorem 14.2a with the aid of some of the fundamental trigonometric identities.

Theorem 14.2b. $\qquad D_x \cos u = -\sin u \, D_x u.$

PROOF: $\qquad\qquad D_x \cos x = D_x \sin(\pi/2 - x)$
$$= D_v \sin v \, D_x v = \cos v \, D_x v,$$

where $v = \pi/2 - x$. Hence

$$D_x \cos x = [\cos(\pi/2 - x)](-1)$$
$$= -\sin x,$$

as was to be shown. Again, application of the chain rule gives

$$D_x \cos u = -\sin u \, D_x u.$$

Theorem 14.2c. $\qquad D_x \tan u = \sec^2 u \, D_x u.$

PROOF: $D_x \tan u = D_x \dfrac{\sin u}{\cos u} = \dfrac{\cos u \cos u \, D_x u - \sin u(-\sin u) \, D_x u}{\cos^2 u}$

$$= \frac{(\cos^2 u + \sin^2 u)}{\cos^2 u} D_x u$$

$$= \sec^2 u \, D_x u.$$

Theorem 14.2d. $\qquad\qquad D_x \cot u = -\csc^2 u \, D_x u.$

PROOF: The proof of this result is left for the reader.

Theorem 14.2e. $\qquad\qquad D_x \sec u = \sec u \tan u \, D_x u.$

PROOF: $\qquad D_x \sec u = D_x (\cos u)^{-1}$

$$= -(\cos u)^{-2} (-\sin u) \, D_x u$$

$$= \sec u \tan u \, D_x u.$$

Theorem 14.2f. $\qquad\qquad D_x \csc u = -\csc u \cot u \, D_x u.$

PROOF: The proof is left for the reader.

The following examples illustrate the application of some of the derivative formulas to composite functions involving trigonometric functions.

Example 14.2a. If $y = (\tan x^2)^3$, find $D_x y$.

The quantity $(\tan x^2)^3$ may be treated like u^3, so that

$$\begin{aligned} D_x y &= 3(\tan x^2)^2 \, D_x(\tan x^2) \\ &= 3(\tan x^2)^2(\sec^2 x^2) \, D_x x^2 \\ &= 6x(\tan x^2)^2 \sec^2 x^2. \end{aligned}$$

Example 14.2b. If $y = 1/(1 + \cos \theta)$, find $D_\theta y$.

We may write

$$y = (1 + \cos \theta)^{-1},$$

so that

$$\begin{aligned} D_\theta y &= (-1)(1 + \cos \theta)^{-2} \, D_\theta(1 + \cos \theta) \\ &= (-1)(1 + \cos \theta)^{-2}(-\sin \theta) \\ &= \frac{\sin \theta}{(1 + \cos \theta)^2}. \end{aligned}$$

Example 14.2c. Find $D_x \ln \tan 3x$.

We have

$$\begin{aligned} D_x \ln \tan 3x &= \frac{1}{\tan 3x} D_x \tan 3x \\[2mm] &= \frac{1}{\tan 3x} (\sec^2 3x)(D_x 3x) \\[2mm] &= \frac{3}{\tan 3x} (\sec^2 3x) \\[2mm] &= \frac{3}{\sin 3x \cos 3x}. \end{aligned}$$

Example 14.2d. Find $D_x^2 y$ if $x = \sin^4 t$, $y = \cos^4 t$.

Using the formula $D_x y = D_t y / D_t x$, we obtain

$$D_x y = \frac{-4 \cos^3 t \sin t}{4 \sin^3 t \cos t} = -\cot^2 t, \qquad t \neq \frac{n\pi}{2}, n \in \mathcal{I}.$$

The second derivative of y with respect to x is given by

$$D_x^2 y = \frac{D_t(D_x y)}{D_t x}$$

$$= \frac{2 \cot t \csc^2 t}{4 \sin^3 t \cos t} = \frac{1}{2} \csc^6 t, \qquad t \neq \frac{n\pi}{2}, n \in \mathcal{I}.$$

Exercises 14.2

1. Prove Theorem 14.2d.
2. Prove Theorem 14.2f.
3. Derive the formula for $D_x \cos x$ by direct use of the definition of the derivative.
4. Derive the formula for $D_x \tan x$ by direct use of the definition of the derivative.

In each of Numbers 5 to 14, the indicated derivative should be read off by inspection.

5. $y = \cos 5x$; $D_x y$.
6. $y = \tan (2 + 3x)$; $D_x y$.
7. $u = \sin t^2$; $D_t u$.
8. $v = \cot (1 + s^2)$; $D_s v$.
9. $w = \ln \tan \theta$; $D_\theta w$.
10. $s = \sin (1/t^2)$; $D_t s$.
11. $z = \csc e^w$; $D_w z$.
12. $x = \csc 3y$; $D_y x$.
13. $y = e^{\sin x}$; $D_x y$.
14. $r = \cot e^u$; $D_u r$.

Find the indicated derivative in each of Numbers 15 to 38.

15. $y = \sin^4 3x$; $D_x y$.
16. $y = \sin^2 x \cos^3 x$; $D_x y$.
17. $r = \tan^2 4x$; $D_x r$.
18. $s = \cot^2 (1 - x)$; $D_x s$.
19. $u = \ln \cos 3w$; $D_w^2 u$.
20. $y = \tan 5x$; $D_x^2 y$.
21. $w = \sin^2 (1 - 2z)$; $D_z^2 w$.
22. $s = e^{-t} \sin 3t$; $D_t^2 s$.
23. $x = \cos mt \sin nt$; $D_t^2 x$.
24. $v = \ln \tan e^t$; $D_t v$.
25. $y = \sqrt{\sin t^2}$; $D_t y$.
26. $r = \sec^2 3\theta$; $D_\theta^2 r$.
27. $y + x \sec y = \pi$; $D_x y$.
28. $y = (\sin x)^{\cos x}$; $D_x y$.
29. $\cos x + \cos y = 1$; $D_x^2 y$.
30. $x \sin y - y \sin x = 1$; $D_x y$.

31. $x = \sin 2t$, $y = 1 + \cos t$; $D_x y$.
32. $x = \tan t$, $y = \sin^2 t$; $D_x y$.
33. $x = a(u - \sin u)$,
    $y = a(1 - \cos u)$; $D_x y$.
34. $x = a(\sin \theta - \theta \cos \theta)$,
    $y = a(\cos \theta + \theta \sin \theta)$; $D_x^2 y$.
35. $x = a \sin^3 t$,
    $y = a \cos^3 t$; $D_x y$.
36. $x = a \cos t$,
    $y = b \sin t$; $D_x^2 y$.
37. $y = \sin x$; $D_x^{35} y$.
38. $y = \cos^2 x$; $D_x^{10} y$.

39. Show that $D_x^n \cos x = \cos \left(x + \dfrac{n\pi}{2} \right)$.

40. Show that $D_x^n \sin x = \sin \left(x + \dfrac{n\pi}{2} \right)$.

14.3 APPLICATIONS OF THE DERIVATIVES OF THE TRIGONOMETRIC FUNCTIONS

With the aid of the derivative formulas of the preceding section, it is frequently possible to give an analysis of the salient features of the graph of an equation involving trigonometric functions. Such equations occur frequently in electric circuit analysis, in mechanical vibration analysis, and in other applications. The first two of these applications will be discussed later in connection with the subject of differential equations, and we shall illustrate the application to maximum and minimum problems in this section.

Example 14.3a. Determine the maxima and minima and the points of inflection of the curve described by

$$y = A \sin(ax + b), \quad A > 0, \quad a > 0$$

We already have discussed the fact that the sine and cosine are periodic functions. Thus, we know that

$$\sin(ax + b) = \sin(ax + b + 2\pi),$$

so that $\sin(ax + b) = \sin[a(x + 2\pi/a + b/a)]$. Thus,

$$f\left(x + \frac{2\pi}{a}\right) = f(x),$$

which shows the period to be $2\pi/a$.

To find relative maxima and minima, we have

$$D_x y = Aa \cos(ax + b),$$

which is zero if

$$ax + b = \frac{(2n + 1)\pi}{2}, \quad n \in \mathcal{G}$$

or if

$$x = \frac{2n + 1}{2a}\pi - \frac{b}{a}.$$

It is clear that the maximum values of y occur for

$$x = \frac{\pi}{2a} - \frac{b}{a}, \frac{5\pi}{2a} - \frac{b}{a}, \quad \cdots,$$

and are all equal to A. Similarly, the minimum values of y occur when

$$x = \frac{3\pi}{2a} - \frac{b}{a}, \frac{7\pi}{2a} - \frac{b}{a}, \quad \cdots,$$

and are all equal to $-A$. The quantity

$$\tfrac{1}{2}(y_{max} - y_{min})$$

is called the **amplitude** of a periodic function. Another term often associated with a periodic function is the **frequency** $\mu \doteq 1/T$, where T is the period. The factor a in $A \sin(ax + b)$ is often called the **angular frequency** which will be discussed later. The quantity b/a is called the **phase shift** of the function. It measures the amount by which the curve

$$y = A \sin(ax + b)$$

is "shifted" from the curve

$$y = A \sin ax,$$

as illustrated in Figure 14.3a.

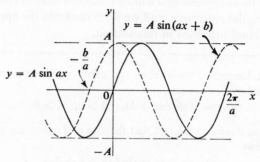

$y = A \sin (ax + b)$

$y = A \sin ax$

FIGURE 14.3a

Points of inflection are determined from

$$D_x^2 y = -Aa^2 \sin (ax + b),$$

which is zero if

$$ax + b = n\pi, \qquad n \in \mathcal{G},$$

or if

$$x = \frac{n\pi - b}{a}.$$

Each of these values actually corresponds to a point of inflection. Why?

Example 14.3b. Discuss and sketch the curve

$$y = \sin^2 x + 2 \cos x, \qquad -\pi \leq x \leq \pi.$$

This curve is symmetric with respect to the y-axis. Explain.

Since

$$y' = 2 \sin x \cos x - 2 \sin x$$
$$= 2 \sin x(\cos x - 1),$$

and

$$y'' = 2 \cos^2 x - 2 \sin^2 x - 2 \cos x$$
$$= 4 \cos^2 x - 2 \cos x - 2$$
$$= 2(2 \cos x + 1)(\cos x - 1),$$

we find

$$y'' = 0 \Rightarrow x = \pm 2\pi/3, \qquad x = 0.$$

Also,

$$y'' > 0 \quad \text{for } -\pi < x < -2\pi/3 \text{ and } 2\pi/3 < x < \pi,$$

and

$$y'' < 0 \quad \text{for } -2\pi/3 < x < 2\pi/3, \ x \neq 0.$$

Thus, the curve is concave up for $-\pi < x < -2\pi/3$ and for $2\pi/3 < x < \pi$. The curve is concave down for $-2\pi/3 < x < 2\pi/3$. Since $y' = 0$ for $x = 0$, $\pm\pi$, the concavity indicates that $(0, 2)$ is a maximum point and that $(\pm\pi, -2)$ are end point minima. The points $(\pm 2\pi/3, -1/4)$ are inflection points. The sketch is shown in Figure 14.3b.

In this example, if x were unrestricted, it would be quite easy to extend the curve by making use of the periodicity of the trigonometric functions. The curve in Figure 14.3b is actually one complete cycle.

The next example illustrates an important type of physical application of the trigonometric functions.

Example 14.3c. A ray of light, emitted from a source S in a medium in which the velocity of light is v_1, reaches a point P in a second medium in which the velocity of light is v_2 (Figure 14.3c). Suppose that the media are separated by a plane interface

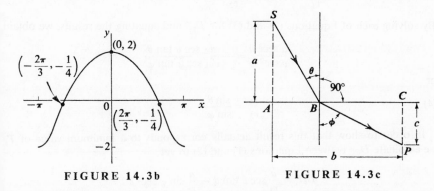

FIGURE 14.3b   FIGURE 14.3c

and that the time taken by the light to go from S to P is a minimum. Show that the angle of incidence θ is related to the angle of refraction φ by the equation

$$\frac{\sin \theta}{\sin \varphi} = \frac{v_1}{v_2}.$$

This is known as Snell's law of refraction. Principles of *least time* and *least action* are of great importance in many physical problems.

Let the interface between the two media be ABC, where B is the point where the ray passes through the interface. Then, with the labeling in the figure, we have

$$SB = a \sec \theta, \quad BP = c \sec \varphi,$$

and

$$AB + BC = a \tan \theta + c \tan \varphi = b.$$

The time T taken for the ray to pass from S to P is

$$T = \frac{SB}{v_1} + \frac{BP}{v_2},$$

or

$$T = \frac{a}{v_1} \sec \theta + \frac{c}{v_2} \sec \varphi,$$

which is the quantity to be minimized.

Since it seems clear that the elimination of φ or θ will result in a quite unwieldy expression in the remaining variable, we shall use implicit differentiation. Upon choosing θ as the independent variable, we have

(1)
$$D_\theta T = \frac{a}{v_1} \sec \theta \tan \theta + \frac{c}{v_2} \sec \varphi \tan \varphi \, D_\theta \varphi.$$

From the equation relating a, b, c, we get the condition

(2)
$$a \sec^2 \theta + c \sec^2 \varphi \, D_\theta \varphi = 0,$$

since a, b, c are all constant.

To find the value of θ for minimum T, we put $D_\theta T = 0$ to get

(3)
$$\frac{a}{v_1} \sec \theta \tan \theta + \frac{c}{v_2} \sec \varphi \tan \varphi \, D_\theta \varphi = 0.$$

By solving each of Equations (2) and (3) for $D_\theta \varphi$ and equating the results, we obtain

$$-\frac{a \sec^2 \theta}{c \sec^2 \varphi} = -\frac{a v_2 \sec \theta \tan \theta}{c v_1 \sec \varphi \tan \varphi},$$

or

(4)
$$\frac{v_1}{v_2} = \frac{\sin \theta}{\sin \varphi}.$$

In order to show that this result actually corresponds to a minimum value of T, we eliminate $D_\theta \varphi$ between Equations (1) and (2) to get

$$D_\theta T = \frac{a}{v_1} \sec \theta \tan \theta - \frac{a}{v_2} \sin \varphi \sec^2 \theta$$

$$= a \sec^2 \theta \left(\frac{\sin \theta}{v_1} - \frac{\sin \varphi}{v_2} \right).$$

From this equation, it is evident that

$$D_\theta T < 0 \quad \text{for } \sin \theta < \frac{v_1}{v_2} \sin \varphi$$

and

$$D_\theta T > 0 \quad \text{for } \sin \theta > \frac{v_1}{v_2} \sin \varphi.$$

Accordingly, $D_\theta T$ changes sign from minus to plus as θ passes through the critical value given by (4) and the condition

$$a \tan \theta + c \tan \varphi = b.$$

Therefore, this critical value corresponds to a minimum value of T.

Although it seems physically evident that there always exists such a critical value of θ, the more mathematically inclined reader may assure himself of this fact by writing $x = \tan \theta$, $y = \tan \varphi$, so that $\sin \theta = x/\sqrt{x^2 + 1}$ and $\sin \varphi = y/\sqrt{y^2 + 1}$. It is then not difficult to show that the resulting equations have graphs that always intersect at exactly one point in the first quadrant.

Exercises 14.3

In each of Numbers 1 to 10, discuss and sketch the curve described by the given equation.

1. $y = 2 \cos \frac{1}{2}x, \ 0 \leq x \leq 4\pi$.
2. $y = \frac{1}{2} \tan 4x, \ 0 \leq x \leq \pi$.
3. $y = 4 \sin (2x - \pi), \ 0 \leq x \leq \pi$.
4. $y = \begin{cases} \cos x, & 0 < x < \pi, \\ \cos (x - \pi), & \pi < x < 2\pi. \end{cases}$
5. $y = \begin{cases} \sin x, \ 0 < x < \pi, \\ \cos x, \ \pi < x < 2\pi. \end{cases}$

6. $y = 5|\sin 4x|, \ 0 \leq x \leq \pi$.
7. $y = 5 \sin |2x|, \ -\pi \leq x \leq \pi$.
8. $y = |\cos 2x|, \ 0 \leq x \leq \pi$.
9. $y = 2 - \cos 2x$.
10. $y = 1 + \sin \pi(x - 1)$.

The graph of an equation of the form

$$y = f(x) + g(x)$$

may be conveniently obtained by the method of *composition of ordinates*. For example, the graph of

$$y = \sin 2x + 2 \cos x$$

may be obtained by first sketching the two curves

$$y = \sin 2x \quad \text{and} \quad y = 2 \cos x$$

on the same set of axes. Points on the required curve may then be found by adding geometrically the ordinates of the two component curves for the same value of x. In each of Numbers 11 to 16, use this method to sketch the curve described by the given equation. Find the maximum, minimum, and inflection points for each curve.

11. $y = 2x - \sin x$.
12. $y = x + \cos x; \ 0 \leq x \leq 2\pi$.
13. $y = \sin x + \cos x; \ 0 \leq x \leq 2\pi$.

14. $y = \sin 2x + 2 \cos x$.
15. $y = x - 2 + \sin 2x$.
16. $y = \cos^2 x - 2 \cos x; \ 0 \leq x \leq 2\pi$.

In each of Numbers 17 to 19, use composition of ordinates to sketch the given curve. Find the maximum and minimum points.

17. $y = \frac{1}{2} \cos 2x - \cos x$.
★18. $y = \frac{4}{3} \sin 3x + 3 \cos 2x$.
★19. $y = 2 \cos 3x - 3 \cos 2x$.

20. What is the period of the curve $y = 2 \cos 2x + \sin 3x$? Is a curve of the form $y = a \cos mx + b \sin nx$, $m, n \in \mathfrak{N}$, necessarily periodic? Explain.
★21. Is the curve $y = \sin x + \sin \sqrt{2}x$ periodic? Explain.
22. A line segment of length 20 units is to lie in the first quadrant and is to be terminated by the coordinate axes. Locate the line so that its perpendicular distance from the origin is a maximum.
23. Given a circle of radius r, what is the altitude of the isosceles triangle with least area that can be circumscribed about the circle?
24. An irrigation ditch is to have a cross section in the shape of an isosceles trapezoid with the equal sides and the bottom each of length L. What should be the width across the top for maximum carrying capacity—that is, for maximum cross-sectional area? *Hint:* Let θ be the angle of inclination of one of the sloping sides.

25. A metal solid of revolution consists of two cylinders with a common axis. Figure 14.3d shows a cross section of the solid through its axis. Suppose the solid is to be put into a lathe and turned down to a cone with the elements of the cone passing through the edge of the base of the upper cylinder as indicated in the figure. Find the dimensions of the cone of largest volume and the dimensions of the cone of smallest volume that can be turned from the solid.

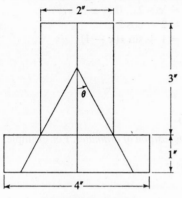

FIGURE 14.3d

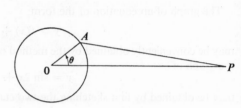

FIGURE 14.3e

26. A steel ball bearing of radius b is to fit into a hollow conical bearing so that the ball is barely but entirely inside the cone. Find the dimensions of the cone of smallest volume for which this is possible.

27. A thin rod of length $4b$ and with perfectly smooth ends passes through the center of a small heavy ball that is fixed on the rod a distance b from one end. The rod is placed in a smooth hollow hemisphere of radius $4b$ and is allowed to come to its equilibrium position. Find the angle that the rod makes with the horizontal when it finally comes to rest. Assume that the weight of the rod is negligible in comparison with that of the ball. *Hint:* The center of the ball will be as low as possible.

28. A perfectly smooth cable is passed over two smooth pegs in the same horizontal plane and $2b$ units apart. One end of the cable is then passed through a loop in the other end and is attached to a weight W. If the weight is assumed to pull the cable taut, find the angle between the two portions of the cable where it passes over one of the pegs. *Hint:* The weight will hang as low as possible.

29. A particle P starts at $A(a, 0)$ and moves counterclockwise on a circle of radius a and with center at the origin. If P makes one complete revolution every 12 seconds, find the rate at which the length of the segment AP is changing at the end of 2 seconds; at the end of 4 seconds; at the end of 8 seconds.

30. The crankshaft of an engine is turning at the rate of 30 revolutions per second. At what rate is the piston P (Figure 14.3e) moving if the arm OA is 1.5 inches long and the connecting rod AP is 6 inches long? What is the rate at the instant when $\theta = 150°$?

31. The hour hand of a watch is 10 millimeters long and the minute hand is 12 millimeters long. At what rate are the ends of the hands approaching each other at 4 o'clock?

14.4 INVERSE DERIVATIVES OF TRIGONOMETRIC FUNCTIONS

It follows directly from the corresponding differentiation formulas that

(1) $$\int \sin x \, dx = -\cos x + C,$$

(2) $$\int \cos x \, dx = \sin x + C.$$

Example 14.4a. Find $\int \sin 3x \, dx$.

We note that $\int \sin 3x \, dx$ is $\cos 3x$ except for a constant factor. Since $D_x \cos 3x = -3 \sin 3x$, the constant factor is $-\frac{1}{3}$. Consequently,

$$\int \sin 3x \, dx = -\tfrac{1}{3} \cos 3x + C.$$

Example 14.4b. Find the area bounded by the curve $y = \sin 2x$, the line $x = \pi/4$, and that portion of the x-axis between 0 and $\pi/4$.

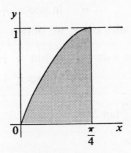

FIGURE 14.4a

The area lies entirely above the x-axis, as Figure 14.4a indicates. Thus we have

$$A = \int_0^{\pi/4} \sin 2x \, dx.$$

Since,

$$D_x^{-1} \sin 2x = -\tfrac{1}{2} \cos 2x,$$

it follows that

$$A = -\tfrac{1}{2}[\cos 2x]_0^{\pi/4}$$
$$= -\tfrac{1}{2}[\cos \pi/2 - 1]$$
$$= \tfrac{1}{2} \text{ (l.u.)}^2.$$

By reading the corresponding derivative formulas in reverse, we have the following additional inverse derivative formulas:

(3) $$\int \sec^2 x \, dx = \tan x + C,$$

(4)
$$\int \csc^2 x \, dx = -\cot x + C,$$

(5)
$$\int \sec x \tan x \, dx = \sec x + C,$$

(6)
$$\int \csc x \cot x \, dx = -\csc x + C.$$

The preceding six formulas include the inverse derivatives of only two of the six simple trigonometric functions. It is, however, not difficult to obtain the remaining desired formulas.

The definition of $\tan x$ in terms of $\sin x$ and $\cos x$ is the clue to the inverse derivative of $\tan x$. Since

$$\tan x = \frac{\sin x}{\cos x} = \frac{-D_x(\cos x)}{\cos x},$$

we may use the formula

$$D_x^{-1}\left(\frac{D_x u}{u}\right) = \ln |u| + C$$

to obtain

(7)
$$\int \tan x \, dx = -\ln |\cos x| + C$$
$$= \ln |\sec x| + C.$$

Using the same approach with $\cot x$, we obtain

(8)
$$\int \cot x \, dx = \ln |\sin x| + C$$
$$= -\ln |\csc x| + C.$$

Example 14.4c. Evaluate $\int_{3\pi/8}^{\pi/2} \tan 2\theta \, d\theta$.

We use Formula (7) to obtain

$$\int_{3\pi/8}^{\pi/2} \tan 2\theta \, d\theta = \frac{1}{2} \int_{3\pi/8}^{\pi/2} \tan 2\theta \, (2d\theta)$$

$$= -\frac{1}{2} \left[\ln |\cos 2\theta|\right]_{3\pi/8}^{\pi/2}$$

$$= -\frac{1}{2} \ln |\cos \pi| + \frac{1}{2} \ln \left|\cos \frac{3\pi}{4}\right|$$

$$= \frac{1}{2} \ln \frac{1}{\sqrt{2}} = -\frac{1}{4} \ln 2.$$

In order to derive a formula for the inverse derivative of $\sec x$, we examine the two derivative formulas that involve $\sec x$; that is,

$$D_x \sec x = \sec x \tan x,$$
$$D_x \tan x = \sec^2 x.$$

We note that if the corresponding members of these two equations are added, the expression sec x + tan x appears on both sides of the resulting equation. Thus,

$$D_x(\tan x + \sec x) = \sec x(\sec x + \tan x),$$

so that

$$\sec x = \frac{D_x(\sec x + \tan x)}{\sec x + \tan x}.$$

Therefore,

(9)
$$\int \sec x \, dx = \ln |\sec x + \tan x| + C.$$

In a similar manner we may obtain the result

(10)
$$\int \csc x \, dx = \ln |\csc x - \cot x| + C$$
$$= \ln |\tan \tfrac{1}{2}x| + C.$$

Example 14.4d. Evaluate

$$\int_{\pi/4}^{\pi/2} \frac{dx}{\sin x/2}.$$

Since $1/\sin u = \csc u$, Formula (10) may be used to get

$$\int_{\pi/4}^{\pi/2} \frac{dx}{\sin x/2} = 2 \int_{\pi/4}^{\pi/2} \tfrac{1}{2} \csc \tfrac{1}{2}x \, dx$$

$$= 2[\ln |\csc \tfrac{1}{2}x - \cot \tfrac{1}{2}x|]_{\pi/4}^{\pi/2}$$
$$= 2 \ln (\sqrt{2} - 1) - 2 \ln (\csc \pi/8 - \cot \pi/8).$$

Exercises 14.4

In Numbers 1 to 20, find the indicated inverse derivatives.

1. $\int \cos \dfrac{2x}{3} \, dx.$

2. $\int s \sin s^2 \, ds.$

3. $\int \dfrac{dx}{\tan 2x}.$

4. $\int e^{3x} \cot e^{3x} \, dx.$

5. $\int \dfrac{\sin 3r}{\cos^2 3r} \, dr.$

6. $\int \dfrac{dy}{\sec 2y}.$

7. $\int \sin (2 - 3t) \, dt.$

8. $\int \sec 2x \tan 2x \, dx.$

9. $\int \dfrac{dw}{\sin^2 2w}.$

10. $\int \tan (3y + 4) \, dy.$

11. $\int \dfrac{dx}{\cos 3x}.$

12. $\int \dfrac{du}{\cos^2 2u}.$

13. $\int e^{\sin y} \cos y \, dy.$

14. $\int \dfrac{\sin \omega x}{\sqrt{1 + \cos \omega x}} \, dx.$

15. $\int \csc 4y \cot 4y \, dy.$

18. $\int \dfrac{\cos 3w - \sin 3w}{\cos 3w} \, dw.$

16. $\int \sin^3 2z \cos 2z \, dz.$

19. $\int \dfrac{\sin 3\theta}{1 + \cos 3\theta} \, d\theta.$

17. $\int x \sin (1 + x^2) \, dx.$

20. $\int \dfrac{x}{\sin x^2} \, dx.$

Evaluate the definite integrals in Numbers 21 to 30.

21. $\int_0^{\pi/2} (w^2 + \sin 2w) \, dw.$

26. $\int_0^{2\pi} |\sin t - \cos t| \, dt.$

22. $\int_{\pi/8}^{\pi/6} \tan 2\theta \, d\theta.$

27. $\int_0^{2\pi} |\sin 2t| \, dt.$

23. $\int_0^{1/3} \sin \pi w \, dw.$

28. $\int_{\pi/6}^{\pi/3} \sin^2 2s \cos 2s \, ds.$

24. $\int_0^{\sqrt{\pi/2}} x \cos x^2 \, dx.$

29. $\int_{\pi}^{4\pi/3} \sin (\pi - x) \, dx.$

25. $\int_0^{\pi/2} \sec \dfrac{x}{2} \tan \dfrac{x}{2} \, dx.$

30. $\int_0^{\pi/3} \dfrac{du}{\cos^2 u/2}.$

31. Derive Formula 10.
32. Find the area bounded by the x-axis and one arch of the curve $y = \sin x/3$.
33. Find the area bounded by the x-axis and the curve $y = |\cos x/2|$ from $x = 0$ to $x = 2\pi$.
34. Find the first quadrant area under the curve $y = \cos x - \sin x$ from $x = 0$ to the first point where the curve cuts the positive x-axis.
35. Find the area bounded by the x-axis and one arch of the curve $y = a \sin bx$.
36. Find the area in the first quadrant enclosed by the x-axis and the curves $y = \tan x$ and $y = \cot x$, between $x = 0$ and $x = \pi/2$.
37. Find the volume of revolution formed by revolving the curve $y = \csc x$ between $x = \pi/4$ and $x = \pi/2$ about the x-axis.
38. Find the volume formed by revolving the curve $y = \cot 2x$ between $x = \pi/8$ and $x = \pi/4$ about the x-axis. *Hint:* Use the formula $\cot^2 u = \csc^2 u - 1$.
39. The area bounded by $y = 1$, the y-axis, and $y = \tan 3x$ is revolved about the line $y = 1$ to generate a solid. Find the volume of this solid. (See the hint in Number 38.)
40. The area bounded by $y = 2$ and the portion of $y = \sec 2x$ for which $|x| < \pi/4$ is revolved about the line $y = 2$. Find the volume of the solid of revolution so generated.
41. In a certain type of "nonlinear" spring (not obeying Hooke's Law), the force F necessary to produce a deflection x is

$$F = A \sin kx,$$

where A and k are constants dependent upon the particular spring, and where $|kx| < \pi/2$. Find the work done in compressing such a spring from its natural length by an amount ξ, where $0 \le \xi < \pi/2k$.

14.5 INVERSE TRIGONOMETRIC FUNCTIONS

In studying the inverses of the trigonometric functions, we encounter a practical difficulty that did not arise in the case of the exponential function $\{(x, a^x)\}$, where the inverse relation $\{(x, \log_a x)\}$ is also a function. Let the inverse of the sine function $\{(x, \sin x)\}$ be designated by $\{(x, \sin^{-1} x)\}$, where $\{\sin^{-1} x\}$ is the set of numbers that satisfy the equation $x = \sin y$. Then it follows, for instance, that $\sin^{-1}(\frac{1}{2})$ must satisfy the equation $\frac{1}{2} = \sin y$ so that y can have any one of the values $\pi/6, 5\pi/6, 2\pi + \pi/6, 2\pi + 5\pi/6, \ldots$. Obviously, $\sin^{-1} x$ is not single-valued, and hence describes a relation rather than a function.

In order to avoid the ambiguity arising from the multiple-valued relations, we define what are sometimes called the **principal-valued** inverse trigonometric functions. These definitions simply eliminate all but a small portion of the range of the inverse trigonometric relations, so that the remaining parts yield functions.

In order to make the inverse functions as useful as possible, it is desirable to choose, as part of the definition, the set of values corresponding to the usually tabulated values. This requirement dictates that the range of the principal inverse sine function, for example, include the values from 0 to $\pi/2$. As a second desirable property, continuity of the inverse function should be attained. In Figure 14.5a, there appears the graph of $y = \sin^{-1} x$ with the heavy portion of the

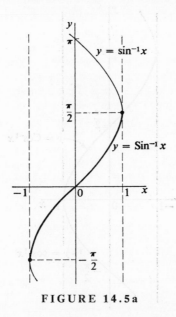

FIGURE 14.5a

curve corresponding to the customary principal value portion of the inverse sine. The inverse function whose range is $-\pi/2 \leqq y \leqq \pi/2$ is designated with a capital letter $\{(x, \operatorname{Sin}^{-1} x)\}$. Thus, we make the following definition.

Definition 14.5a. The **principal inverse sine** function is the function

$$\{(x, y): x = \sin y, \ -\pi/2 \leqq y \leqq \pi/2\}.$$

The value of this function at x is denoted by $\mathrm{Sin}^{-1} x$.

(In many books, especially the older ones, the archaic notations, arcsin x and Arcsin x are used in place of $\sin^{-1} x$ and $\mathrm{Sin}^{-1} x$.)

Example 14.5a. Find $\sin^{-1}(-\tfrac{1}{2})$ and $\mathrm{Sin}^{-1}(-\tfrac{1}{2})$.

If we let $y = \sin^{-1}(-\tfrac{1}{2})$, then we may write

$$\sin y = -\tfrac{1}{2},$$

and thus

$$y = n\pi + \frac{(-1)^{n+1}\pi}{6}, \qquad n \in \mathcal{J}.$$

For

$$y = \mathrm{Sin}^{-1}(-\tfrac{1}{2}),$$

we have only

$$y = -\frac{\pi}{6}.$$

It has already been shown that the sine function is continuous on its entire domain, and, since the sine function is a strictly increasing function on the

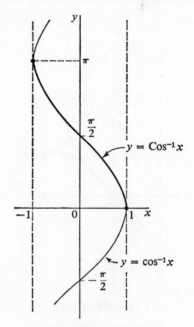

FIGURE 14.5b

interval $-\pi/2 \leqq x \leqq \pi/2$, it follows, by Theorem 8.5h, that the principal inverse sine function is also a continuous strictly increasing function on its domain $-1 \leq x \leq 1$. These characteristics are, of course, verified by the graph in Figure 14.5a. Note that the domain of $\{(x, \text{Sin}^{-1} x)\}$ is exactly the same as that of $\{(x, \sin^{-1} x)\}$.

The inverse relation for $\{(x, \cos x)\}$ is denoted by $\{(x, \cos^{-1} x)\}$, where $\cos^{-1} x$ is the set of real numbers y that satisfy the equation $x = \cos y$. The domain of the inverse relation is $-1 \leq x \leq 1$, and the range is the set of all real numbers. The graph is shown in Figure 14.5b.

In choosing a subset of $\{(x, \cos^{-1} x)\}$ that will be a function, we adopt the convention of restricting the range so that $0 \leq y \leq \pi$. As in the case of the inverse sine, the criteria used for making this choice are that, if possible, the function should be continuous and should include the points where $0 \leq y \leq \pi/2$ (that is, the customarily tabulated portion of the function), and that the function should have the same domain as the relation. With this in mind, we make the following definition.

Definition 14.5b. The **principal inverse cosine** function is the function

$$\{(x, y): x = \cos y, 0 \leq y \leq \pi\}.$$

The value of this function at x is denoted by $\text{Cos}^{-1} x$.

Example 14.5b. Find $\cos^{-1}(-\tfrac{1}{2})$ and $\text{Cos}^{-1}(-\tfrac{1}{2})$.

Let $y = \cos^{-1}(-\tfrac{1}{2})$, so that

$$\cos y = -\tfrac{1}{2}$$

and

$$y = 2n\pi \pm \tfrac{2}{3}\pi, \qquad n \in \mathcal{I}$$

For

$$y = \text{Cos}^{-1}(-\tfrac{1}{2}),$$

we have only

$$y = \tfrac{2}{3}\pi.$$

Example 14.5c. Find $\sin(\text{Cos}^{-1} \tfrac{1}{3})$.

If we let $\theta = \text{Cos}^{-1} \tfrac{1}{3}$, the problem is to find $\sin \theta$. Since $\text{Cos}^{-1} \tfrac{1}{3}$ is the inverse function, it follows that θ must be between 0 and $\pi/2$, and thus

$$\sin \theta = \sqrt{1 - \cos^2 \theta}$$
$$= \sqrt{1 - \tfrac{1}{9}}$$
$$= \tfrac{2}{3}\sqrt{2}.$$

As is indicated by the heavy portion of the curve in Figure 14.5b, the principal inverse cosine function is a strictly decreasing continuous function on its domain. This is assured by Theorem 8.5h. (Why?)

The inverse relation for $\{(x, \tan x)\}$ is denoted by $\{(x, \tan^{-1} x)\}$, where $\tan^{-1} x$ is the set of real numbers such that $x = \tan y$. The domain of the inverse relation is the set of all real numbers and the range is the set of all real numbers except those values of y for which $\cos y = 0$. The graph of the inverse relation is shown in Figure 14.5c.

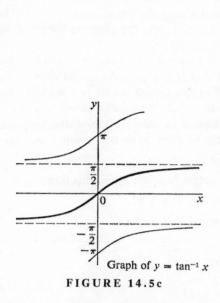

Graph of $y = \tan^{-1} x$

FIGURE 14.5c

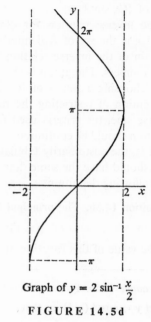

Graph of $y = 2 \sin^{-1} \dfrac{x}{2}$

FIGURE 14.5d

The same criteria as those used for the inverse sine and cosine functions lead to the following definition for the inverse tangent function.

Definition 14.5c. The **principal inverse tangent** function is the function
$$\{(x, y): x = \tan y, \; -\pi/2 < y < \pi/2\}.$$

The value of this function at x is denoted by $\mathrm{Tan}^{-1} x$.

Example 14.5d. Find $\mathrm{Tan}^{-1}(\tan 3\pi/4)$.

Since $\tan 3\pi/4 = -1$,
$$\mathrm{Tan}^{-1}(\tan 3\pi/4) = \mathrm{Tan}^{-1}(-1) = -\pi/4.$$

The construction of the graphs of the inverse relations for the remaining three trigonometric functions is left for the exercises.

Example 14.5e. Sketch $y = 2 \sin^{-1} \tfrac{1}{2}x$.

We have
$$\tfrac{1}{2}y = \sin^{-1} \tfrac{1}{2}x,$$
so that
$$\tfrac{1}{2}x = \sin \tfrac{1}{2}y,$$
and
$$x = 2 \sin \tfrac{1}{2}y.$$

The graph is a sine curve along the y-axis with an amplitude of 2 and a period of $2\pi/\tfrac{1}{2} = 4\pi$. See Figure 14.5d.

Exercises 14.5

In each of Numbers 1 to 12, evaluate the given expression.

1. $\sin^{-1}(-\sqrt{3}/2)$.
2. $\tan^{-1}\sqrt{3}$.
3. $\cos^{-1}1/\sqrt{2}$.
4. $\cos^{-1}(-1)$.
5. $\text{Tan}^{-1}(-1)$.
6. $\text{Sin}^{-1}(-1)$.

7. $\text{Cos}^{-1}(-\sqrt{3}/2)$.
8. $\text{Tan}^{-1}(-1/\sqrt{3})$.
9. $\text{Sin}^{-1}(\cos \pi/2)$.
10. $\text{Cos}^{-1}(\cos 5\pi/3)$.
11. $\text{Cos}^{-1}[\sin(-\pi/4)]$.
12. $\text{Sin}^{-1}(\tan \pi/4)$.

In each of Numbers 13 to 15, define and sketch the *inverse relation* of the given function.

13. $\{(x, \cot x)\}$.
14. $\{(x, \sec x)\}$.
15. $\{(x, \csc x)\}$.

16. Make restrictions on the range of each of the relations in Numbers 13 to 15 so that the relation will be a function.
17. Is it true that $\text{Sin}^{-1}(-x) = -\text{Sin}^{-1}x$? Explain.
18. Is it true that $\text{Cos}^{-1}(-x) = \text{Cos}^{-1}x$? Explain.

In each of Numbers 19 to 22, solve for x in terms of y.

19. $y = \frac{1}{2}\tan^{-1}2x$.
20. $y = 5\sin^{-1}2/x$.

21. $y + 1 = 2\cos^{-1}(x + 1)$.
22. $y = \frac{1}{2}\text{Sin}^{-1}\sqrt{2x}$.

In each of Numbers 23 to 26, discuss and sketch the graph of the given equation.

23. $y = \frac{1}{2}\sin^{-1}3x$.
24. $y = 2\cos^{-1}x/3$.

25. $y = 3\text{Tan}^{-1}(x - 1)$.
26. $y = \text{Sin}^{-1}\sqrt{x}$.

In each of Numbers 27 to 34, simplify the given expression.

27. $\tan(\text{Sin}^{-1}x)$.
28. $\sec(\text{Tan}^{-1}1/x)$.
29. $\sec(\text{Sin}^{-1}\sqrt{4 - x^2})$.
30. $\sin(\text{Tan}^{-1}3/\sqrt{x^2 - 9})$.

31. $\sin(2\text{Cos}^{-1}21/29)$.
32. $\cos(2\text{Sin}^{-1}3/5)$.
33. $\tan(\frac{1}{2}\text{Sin}^{-1}24/25)$.
34. $\sin(\frac{1}{2}\text{Tan}^{-1}5/12)$.

In each of Numbers 35 to 40, find (a) $\sin \theta$, (b) $\cos \theta$, (c) $\tan \theta$. Do not use tables.

35. $\theta = \text{Sin}^{-1}(\frac{1}{3}) + \text{Cos}^{-1}(\frac{2}{3})$.
36. $\theta = \text{Tan}^{-1}1 + \text{Cos}^{-1}(\frac{1}{2})$.
37. $\theta = \text{Tan}^{-1}(\frac{3}{4}) - \text{Sin}^{-1}(\frac{1}{2})$.

38. $\theta = \text{Tan}^{-1}(\frac{1}{2}) - 2\text{Tan}^{-1}(\frac{1}{3})$.
39. $\theta = 2\text{Sin}^{-1}(\frac{3}{5}) - \text{Cos}^{-1}(\frac{12}{13})$.
40. $\theta = \text{Cos}^{-1}(\frac{3}{5}) + 2\text{Tan}^{-1}(\frac{5}{12})$.

Solve for x in each of Numbers 41 to 48. Do not use tables.

41. $\text{Tan}^{-1}x + \text{Tan}^{-1}(\frac{3}{5}) = \pi/4$.
42. $\text{Sin}^{-1}(\frac{3}{5}) + \text{Sin}^{-1}x = \text{Tan}^{-1}(\frac{56}{33})$.
43. $\text{Tan}^{-1}(\frac{1}{3}) + \text{Tan}^{-1}x = \text{Tan}^{-1}(-1)$.
44. $2\text{Tan}^{-1}(\frac{1}{3}) + \text{Tan}^{-1}x = \pi/4$.

45. $\text{Tan}^{-1}(\frac{1}{2}) + \text{Tan}^{-1}(\frac{1}{3}) = \text{Tan}^{-1}x$.
46. $\text{Sin}^{-1}x = \text{Cos}^{-1}(\frac{1}{5}) + \text{Cos}^{-1}(\frac{2}{5})$.
47. $\text{Tan}^{-1}x = \text{Tan}^{-1}h + \text{Tan}^{-1}k$.
48. $\text{Sin}^{-1}x = 2\text{Sin}^{-1}a - \text{Sin}^{-1}b$.

14.6 THE CALCULUS OF THE
INVERSE TRIGONOMETRIC FUNCTIONS

To find the derivative of the inverse sine function $\{(x, y): y = \text{Sin}^{-1} x\}$, let us write

$$x = \sin y, \qquad -\pi/2 \leqq y \leqq \pi/2,$$

and use implicit differentiation to obtain

$$1 = (\cos y) D_x y, \qquad -\pi/2 < y < \pi/2.$$

This equation leads to the result

$$D_x y = \frac{1}{\cos y}, \qquad -\pi/2 < y < \pi/2.$$

To avoid division by zero, we must exclude the end points $y = \pm\pi/2$ from the set of permissible values in the last equation. With this additional restriction, $\cos y > 0$, and we have

$$\cos y = \sqrt{1 - \sin^2 y} = \sqrt{1 - x^2}, \qquad |x| < 1.$$

Thus,

$$D_x \text{Sin}^{-1} x = \frac{1}{\sqrt{1 - x^2}}, \qquad |x| < 1.$$

Furthermore, an application of the chain rule yields the formula

(1)
$$D_x \text{Sin}^{-1} u = \frac{1}{\sqrt{1 - u^2}} D_x u, \qquad |u| < 1.$$

The inverse differential formula corresponding to (1) is

(2)
$$\int \frac{du}{\sqrt{1 - u^2}} = \text{Sin}^{-1} u + C, \qquad |u| < 1.$$

Formula (2) may be replaced by the following more general formula, which may be verified by differentiation:

(3)
$$\int \frac{du}{\sqrt{a^2 - u^2}} = \text{Sin}^{-1} \frac{u}{a} + C, \qquad |u| < a.$$

The only other inverse trigonometric function of particular interest in differentiation and integration techniques is the inverse tangent function given by $\{(x, y): y = \text{Tan}^{-1} x\}$. Here we may write

$$x = \tan y, \qquad -\pi/2 < y < \pi/2,$$

and use implicit differentiation to obtain

$$1 = \sec^2 y \, D_x y, \qquad -\pi/2 < y < \pi/2,$$

or

$$D_x y = \frac{1}{\sec^2 y}, \qquad -\pi/2 < y < \pi/2.$$

Since $\sec^2 y = 1 + \tan^2 y = 1 + x^2$, we have the formula

$$D_x \operatorname{Tan}^{-1} x = \frac{1}{1 + x^2}.$$

This result is generalized by use of the chain rule to give

(4) $$D_x \operatorname{Tan}^{-1} u = \frac{1}{1 + u^2} D_x u.$$

The following inverse differential formula may now be verified by direct differentiation:

(5) $$\int \frac{du}{a^2 + u^2} = \frac{1}{a} \operatorname{Tan}^{-1} \frac{u}{a} + C, \qquad a \neq 0.$$

Example 14.6a. Find

$$\int \frac{dx}{\sqrt{4 - 9x^2}} \quad \text{and} \quad \int \frac{x\,dx}{\sqrt{4 - 9x^2}}.$$

In the first case, we have

$$\int \frac{dx}{\sqrt{4 - 9x^2}} = \frac{1}{3} \int \frac{3\,dx}{\sqrt{(2)^2 - (3x)^2}}$$

$$= \frac{1}{3} \operatorname{Sin}^{-1} \frac{3x}{2} + C.$$

In the second case, the formula for $\int u^n\,du$ must be used (why?), and we obtain

$$\int \frac{x\,dx}{\sqrt{4 - 9x^2}} = -\frac{1}{18} \int (4 - 9x^2)^{-1/2}(-18x\,dx)$$

$$= -\frac{1}{9} \sqrt{4 - 9x^2} + C.$$

Example 14.6b. Find

$$\int \frac{dx}{4 + 9x^2} \quad \text{and} \quad \int \frac{x\,dx}{4 + 9x^2}.$$

In the first case, we have

$$\int \frac{dx}{4 + 9x^2} = \frac{1}{3} \int \frac{3\,dx}{(2)^2 + (3x)^2}$$

$$= \frac{1}{6} \operatorname{Tan}^{-1} \frac{3x}{2} + C.$$

In the second case, the formula for $\int du/u$ must be used (why?), and we have

$$\int \frac{x\,dx}{4 + 9x^2} = \frac{1}{18} \int \frac{18x\,dx}{4 + 9x^2}$$

$$= \frac{1}{18} \ln (4 + 9x^2) + C.$$

The student should study the preceding two examples carefully and be able to distinguish among the cases where the different formulas apply.

Exercises 14.6

1. Verify Formula (3).
2. Verify Formula (5).
3. Obtain a formula for $D_x \text{Cos}^{-1} u$, where $0 < \text{Cos}^{-1} u < \pi$.
4. Show that

$$D_x \text{Sec}^{-1} u = \frac{1}{u\sqrt{u^2 - 1}} D_x u,$$

where $0 < \text{Sec}^{-1} u < \frac{\pi}{2}$ for $u > 1$, and $-\pi < \text{Sec}^{-1} u < -\frac{\pi}{2}$ for $u < -1$.

Find the indicated derivative in each of Numbers 5 to 16.

5. $r = \text{Tan}^{-1}(s/2); \; D_s r.$
6. $y = \text{Sin}^{-1} 2x; \; D_x y.$
7. $w = \text{Sin}^{-1} \sqrt{2u}; \; D_u w.$
8. $y = \text{Tan}^{-1} e^x; \; D_x y.$
9. $y = e^{2x} \text{Tan}^{-1} e^{2x}; \; D_x y.$
10. $s = \text{Sin}^{-1} \ln u; \; D_u s.$
11. $y = 3x \text{Sin}^{-1} 2x; \; D_x y.$
12. $w = x \text{Tan}^{-1}(1/x); \; D_x w.$

13. $t = \ln \text{Tan}^{-1} \frac{1}{2}s; \; D_s t.$

14. $x = \dfrac{\text{Sin}^{-1} t}{t}; \; D_t x.$

15. $u = \dfrac{v}{\text{Tan}^{-1} 2v}; \; D_v u.$

16. $y = \text{Sin}^{-1} \dfrac{x}{1 + x^2}; \; D_x y.$

In each of Numbers 17 to 26, find the indicated inverse derivative.

17. $\displaystyle\int \frac{4}{4 + s^2}\, ds.$

22. $\displaystyle\int \frac{u^3\, du}{4 + u^4}.$

18. $\displaystyle\int \frac{t\, dt}{9 + t^4}.$

23. $\displaystyle\int \frac{t\, dt}{1 + t}.$

19. $\displaystyle\int \frac{x\, dx}{\sqrt{1 - 4x^2}}.$

24. $\displaystyle\int \frac{x^2\, dx}{x^2 + 1}.$

20. $\displaystyle\int \frac{dx}{\sqrt{9 - 16x^2}}.$

25. $\displaystyle\int \frac{\cos u\, du}{1 + \sin^2 u}.$

21. $\displaystyle\int \frac{e^v\, dv}{1 + 4e^{2v}}.$

26. $\displaystyle\int \frac{s\, ds}{\sqrt{16 - 9s^4}}.$

In each of Numbers 27 to 30, evaluate the given definite integral.

27. $\displaystyle\int_0^1 \frac{dx}{\sqrt{4 - x^2}}.$

29. $\displaystyle\int_0^1 \frac{dx}{e^x + e^{-x}}.$

28. $\displaystyle\int_{-3}^3 \frac{du}{9 + u^2}.$

30. $\displaystyle\int_0^{1/2} \frac{x\, dx}{\sqrt{1 - 4x^4}}.$

31. Find the area bounded by the curve $y = 1/(4 + x^2)$, the x-axis, and the lines $x = -2$ and $x = 0$,

32. Find the area bounded by the curve $y = 8/(4 + 9x^2)$, the x-axis, the y-axis, and the line $x = 2/3$.
33. Discuss and sketch the graph of $y = \text{Sin}^{-1} \sqrt{2x - x^2}$.
34. Discuss and sketch the graph of $y = \text{Sin}^{-1} (1/\sqrt{2x})$.
35. Show that

$$D_x \text{Tan}^{-1} \left(\frac{1 + x}{1 - x}\right) = \frac{1}{1 + x^2}.$$

Explain how to reconcile this with the fact that

$$\int \frac{dx}{1 + x^2} = \text{Tan}^{-1} x + C.$$

36. Show that

$$D_x \left[\frac{1}{2} \text{Sin}^{-1} \left(\frac{1 - x^2}{1 + x^2}\right)\right] = \begin{cases} -(1 + x^2)^{-1} & \text{for } x \geq 0, \\ (1 + x^2)^{-1} & \text{for } x < 0. \end{cases}$$

Explain how to reconcile this with the fact that

$$\int \frac{dx}{1 + x^2} = \text{Tan}^{-1} x + C.$$

37. Find $D_x y$ if $\text{Tan}^{-1}(y/x) - \ln \sqrt{x^2 + y^2} = 1$, and determine for what values of x, if any, the derivative function is discontinuous.
38. Show that the area under the curve $y = a/(b^2 + c^2 x^2)$ from $x = 0$ to $x = t$ is bounded as $t \to \infty$.
39. Find the area enclosed by $x = 0$, $y = 0$, $y = 1/\sqrt{9 - 4x^2}$, and $x = 3\sqrt{3}/4$.
40. Find the volume generated by revolving the area bounded by $x = 0$, $y = 0$, $x = 4/5$, and $y = 1/\sqrt{16 + 25x^2}$ about the x-axis.
41. A flagpole 15 feet high stands at the edge of the roof of a building so that the foot of the pole is 60 feet above an observer's eye level. How far from the building should the observer stand so that the pole subtends the maximum possible angle at his eye?
42. A line is drawn from the point $(-1, 0)$ to a point (x, y) on the curve $y = 2\sqrt{x}$. Find the maximum inclination that this line can have.
43. Use the Mean Value Theorem for Derivatives to show that

$$0.7952 < \text{Tan}^{-1} 1.02 < 0.7954.$$

44. Use the Mean Value Theorem for Derivatives to show that

$$0.1 < \text{Sin}^{-1} 0.1 < 0.10051.$$

45. In Example 11.7a, find the rate at which the angle OAB is changing.
46. In Exercises 11.7, Number 5, find the rate at which the angle between the rope and the ground is changing.
47. In Exercises 11.7, Number 9, find the rate at which the angle between the two parts of the strip is changing.
48. A balloon is released 500 feet away from an observer. If the balloon rises at the rate of 100 feet per minute, what is the rate at which the angle of elevation of the observer's line of sight is increasing, 6 minutes after the balloon is released?

49. In Number 48, suppose that while the balloon is rising a wind carries it directly away from the observer at a rate of 75 feet per minute. At what rate is the angle of elevation of the observer's line of sight increasing, 6 minutes after the balloon is released?

50. A searchlight is trained on a plane that flies directly above the light at an altitude of 2 miles and at a speed of 400 miles per hour. How fast must the light be turning 2 seconds after the plane passes directly overhead?

14.7 THE HYPERBOLIC FUNCTIONS

Certain combinations of the exponential functions occur frequently enough in engineering and physics that they have been given special names. The two most important such combinations are called the **hyperbolic sine** (sinh) and the **hyperbolic cosine** (cosh). They are

(1)
$$\sinh u .=. \frac{e^u - e^{-u}}{2},$$

and

(2)
$$\cosh u .=. \frac{e^u + e^{-u}}{2}.$$

These functions are called hyperbolic functions because they are related geometrically to the hyperbola in much the same way that the trigonometric functions are related to a circle. It is easily shown from Equations (1) and (2) that

$$\cosh^2 u - \sinh^2 u = 1.$$

This fundamental identity suggests that the hyperbola

$$x^2 - y^2 = 1$$

may be represented in parametric form by the equations

$$x = \cosh u, \quad y = \sinh u.$$

The relationship between the parameter u, $\cosh u$, $\sinh u$, and the hyperbola may then be given a geometric interpretation similar to that given to the relationship between θ, $\cos \theta$, $\sin \theta$, and the unit circle. For the unit circle in Figure 14.7a, the area of the sector AOP, where A is the point $(1, 0)$, O is the origin,

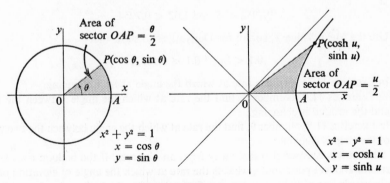

FIGURE 14.7a

and P is the point $(\cos \theta, \sin \theta)$, is $\theta/2$ (l.u.)^2. For the hyperbola $x^2 - y^2 = 1$, if A is the point $(1, 0)$ and P the point $(\cosh u, \sinh u)$, then the area of the sector AOP is $u/2$ (l.u.)^2. (The proof that the area of the hyperbolic sector AOP is $u/2$ is deferred to Exercises 15.3, Number 41.)

The other hyperbolic functions are defined with reference to the hyperbolic sine and hyperbolic cosine by analogy with the definitions of the trigonometric functions; that is,

$$(3) \qquad \tanh u \overset{.}{=} \frac{\sinh u}{\cosh u} = \frac{e^u - e^{-u}}{e^u + e^{-u}},$$

$$(4) \qquad \coth u \overset{.}{=} \frac{\cosh u}{\sinh u} = \frac{e^u + e^{-u}}{e^u - e^{-u}},$$

$$(5) \qquad \operatorname{sech} u \overset{.}{=} \frac{1}{\cosh u} = \frac{2}{e^u + e^{-u}},$$

$$(6) \qquad \operatorname{csch} u \overset{.}{=} \frac{1}{\sinh u} = \frac{2}{e^u - e^{-u}}.$$

The graph of $y = \sinh x$ can be obtained by sketching the curves $y = e^x/2$ and $y = e^{-x}/2$ and then subtracting the ordinates (see Figure 14.7b). The graph of $y = \cosh x$ can be obtained in a similar manner by adding ordinates (see Figure 14.7c).

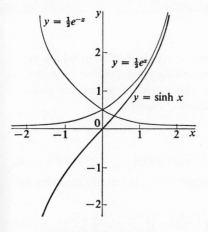

FIGURE 14.7b

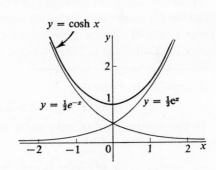

FIGURE 14.7c

If a uniform, perfectly flexible, and inextensible cable is suspended between two points, under its own weight the cable forms a curve called a *catenary*. A close approximation to a catenary is the curve formed by an electric transmission cable suspended between two poles, and the calculations for the length of wire needed for a given project are based on the length of the catenary. If the origin is taken at a distance a below the lowest point of the curve, then it can be shown that the equation of the curve is

$$y = a \cosh \frac{x}{a}.$$

Thus, Figure 14.7c illustrates the catenary for $a = 1$.

To obtain the graph of $y = \tanh x$, note that

$$\lim_{x \to \infty} \tanh x = \lim_{x \to \infty} \frac{e^x - e^{-x}}{e^x + e^{-x}} = \lim_{x \to \infty} \frac{1 - e^{-2x}}{1 + e^{-2x}} = 1,$$

and also that

$$\lim_{x \to -\infty} \tanh x = \lim_{x \to -\infty} \frac{e^{2x} - 1}{e^{2x} + 1} = -1.$$

The graph is shown in Figure 14.7d. Notice that the range of the hyperbolic tangent function is $-1 < y < 1$.

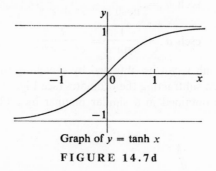

Graph of $y = \tanh x$

FIGURE 14.7d

There are numerous identities involving the hyperbolic functions which are quite similar to the corresponding identities involving trigonometric functions. These identities for the hyperbolic functions can easily be proved by direct use of the definitions of the functions, as in the next example.

Example 14.7a. Prove that

$$\sinh (x + y) = \sinh x \cosh y + \cosh x \sinh y.$$

In this problem, we may make use of the definitions of the hyperbolic functions to write $\sinh x \cosh y + \cosh x \sinh y$

$$= \left(\frac{e^x - e^{-x}}{2} \right)\left(\frac{e^y + e^{-y}}{2} \right) + \left(\frac{e^x + e^{-x}}{2} \right)\left(\frac{e^y - e^{-y}}{2} \right)$$
$$= \tfrac{1}{4}(e^{x+y} - e^{-x+y} + e^{x-y} - e^{-x-y} + e^{x+y} + e^{-x+y} - e^{x-y} - e^{-x-y})$$
$$= \tfrac{1}{2}(e^{x+y} - e^{-x-y})$$
$$= \sinh (x + y).$$

Similar expressions may be obtained for $\sinh (x - y)$, $\cosh (x + y)$, and $\cosh (x - y)$. (See Exercises 14.7, Numbers 4 and 5.) Identities such as these are occasionally helpful in simplifying more cumbersome expressions involving the hyperbolic functions, as will be illustrated later.

The derivatives of the hyperbolic sine and hyperbolic cosine are easily obtained from their definitions. Thus,

(7)
$$D_x \sinh x = D_x \frac{e^x - e^{-x}}{2} = \frac{e^x + e^{-x}}{2} = \cosh x,$$

and

(8)
$$D_x \cosh x = D_x \frac{e^x + e^{-x}}{2} = \frac{e^x - e^{-x}}{2} = \sinh x.$$

The derivation of the formulas for the derivatives of the other hyperbolic functions is left for the exercises.

The following example illustrates the application of some of these ideas.

Example 14.7b. Find the maximum, minimum, and inflection points, and sketch the curve $y = 5 \cosh x - 4 \sinh x$.

We have
$$y' = 5 \sinh x - 4 \cosh x$$
and
$$y'' = 5 \cosh x - 4 \sinh x = y$$

It follows from the first of these equations that
$$y' = 0 \Rightarrow \tanh x = \frac{4}{5},$$

and a book of tables gives the value $x = 1.1$ (approximately). Also, since
$$\tanh x = \frac{\sinh x}{\cosh x} \quad \text{and} \quad 1 + \sinh^2 x = \cosh^2 x,$$

we find
$$\tanh x = \frac{4}{5} \Rightarrow \sinh x = \frac{4}{3} \quad \text{and} \quad \cosh x = \frac{5}{3}.$$

Hence, at the critical point, where $x = 1.1$, we obtain $y'' = 3 > 0$, so that the curve is concave up and the point $(1.1, 3)$ is a minimum point.

Since $\cosh x \geqq 1$ and $\cosh x > \sinh x$, it follows that $y'' > 0$ for all values of x, and the curve is concave upward everywhere with no inflection points. It can be shown (see Exercises 14.7, Number 5) that

$$\cosh (a - b) = \cosh a \cosh b - \sinh a \sinh b.$$

This result suggests that we write

$$5 \cosh x - 4 \sinh x = k \cosh x \cosh b - k \sinh x \sinh b.$$

Then,
$$k \cosh b = 5 \quad \text{and} \quad k \sinh b = 4 \Rightarrow k^2 \cosh^2 b - k^2 \sinh^2 b = k^2 = 9$$
$$\Rightarrow k = 3,$$

since $\cosh b > 0$. Thus, $\cosh b = 5/3$, $\sinh b = 4/3$, and

$$5 \cosh x - 4 \sinh x = 3 \cosh (x - b).$$

It follows that the given curve is simply a hyperbolic cosine curve with its minimum point at $(b, 3) = (1.1, 3)$ (see Figure 14.7e).

The inverse of the function $\{(x, y): y = \sinh x\}$ is the relation described by $\{(x, y): y = \sinh^{-1} x\}$. Since to each value of the range of the hyperbolic sine function there corresponds only one value of the domain, this inverse is also a function (see Figure 14.7f).

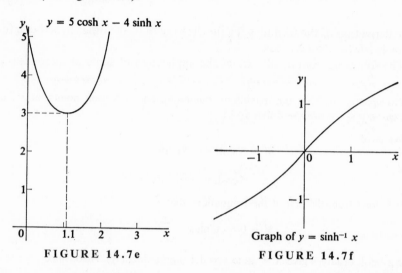

FIGURE 14.7e

FIGURE 14.7f

It would seem that $\sinh^{-1} x$ might be expressed as a logarithmic function, since $\sinh x$ is defined in terms of the exponential function. This conjecture is easily verified by writing

$$y = \sinh^{-1} x$$

in the form

$$x = \sinh y = \frac{e^y - e^{-y}}{2}$$

and solving for y. Upon multiplying each side by e^y and solving the resulting quadratic equation in e^y, we get

$$2xe^y = e^{2y} - 1,$$
$$e^{2y} - 2xe^y - 1 = 0.$$

and

$$e^y = x + \sqrt{x^2 + 1}.$$

Only the positive sign is used in front of the radical, since $e^y > 0$. Thus, by taking logarithms, we find $y = \ln (x + \sqrt{x^2 + 1})$, or

(9) $$\sinh^{-1} x = \ln (x + \sqrt{x^2 + 1}).$$

The inverse of the hyperbolic cosine function is not a function but may be made one by restricting the range so that $y \geq 0$, as is indicated by the heavy portion of the curve in Figure 14.7g.

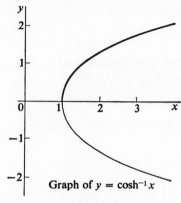

Graph of $y = \cosh^{-1} x$

FIGURE 14.7g

If $\cosh^{-1} x$ is expressed in terms of logarithms, the result is

$$(10) \qquad \cosh^{-1} x = \ln(x \pm \sqrt{x^2 - 1}), \qquad x \geq 1.$$

The inverse hyperbolic cosine *function* is obtained by choosing the positive sign in front of the radical. Thus,

$$(10') \qquad \operatorname{Cosh}^{-1} x = \ln(x + \sqrt{x^2 - 1}), \qquad x \geq 1.$$

By differentiating Formulas (9) and (10'), we obtain

$$(11) \qquad D_x \sinh^{-1} u = \frac{D_x u}{\sqrt{u^2 + 1}}$$

and

$$(12) \qquad D_x \operatorname{Cosh}^{-1} u = \frac{D_x u}{\sqrt{u^2 - 1}}, \qquad u > 1.$$

Example 14.7c. Find

$$\int \frac{dx}{\sqrt{9x^2 + 4}}.$$

It follows from Formula (11) that

$$\int \frac{dx}{\sqrt{9x^2 + 4}} = \frac{1}{2} \int \frac{dx}{\sqrt{(3x/2)^2 + 1}}$$

$$= \frac{1}{3} \int \frac{3/2 \, dx}{\sqrt{(3x/2)^2 + 1}}$$

$$= \frac{1}{3} \sinh^{-1} \frac{3x}{2} + C.$$

Exercises 14.7

In each of Numbers 1 to 13, verify the given identity.

1. $\cosh^2 x - \sinh^2 x = 1$.
2. $1 - \tanh^2 x = \text{sech}^2 x$.
3. $\coth^2 x - 1 = \text{csch}^2 x$.
4. $\sinh (x - y) = \sinh x \cosh y - \cosh x \sinh y$.
5. $\cosh (x - y) = \cosh x \cosh y - \sinh x \sinh y$.
6. $\sinh 2x = 2 \sinh x \cosh x$.
7. $\cosh 2x = \cosh^2 x + \sinh^2 x$.

8. $\sinh \dfrac{x}{2} = \pm \sqrt{\dfrac{\cosh x - 1}{2}}$.

9. $\cosh \dfrac{x}{2} = \sqrt{\dfrac{\cosh x + 1}{2}}$.

10. $\tanh \dfrac{x}{2} = \dfrac{\sinh x}{1 + \cosh x}$.

11. $\sinh x + \sinh y = 2 \sinh \frac{1}{2}(x + y) \cosh \frac{1}{2}(x - y)$.
12. $\cosh x + \cosh y = 2 \cosh \frac{1}{2}(x + y) \cosh \frac{1}{2}(x - y)$.

13. $\tanh (x + y) = \dfrac{\tanh x + \tanh y}{1 + \tanh x \tanh y}$.

In each of Numbers 14 to 21, verify the differentiation formula.

14. $D_x \tanh u = \text{sech}^2 u \, D_x u$.
15. $D_x \coth u = -\text{csch}^2 u \, D_x u$.
16. $D_x \text{sech} \, u = -\text{sech} \, u \tanh u \, D_x u$.
17. $D_x \text{csch} \, u = -\text{csch} \, u \coth u \, D_x u$.
18. Formula (11).

19. Formula (12).

20. $D_x \tanh^{-1} u = \dfrac{D_x u}{1 - u^2}$, $|u| < 1$.

21. $D_x \coth^{-1} u = \dfrac{D_x u}{1 - u^2}$, $|u| > 1$.

In each of Numbers 22 to 25, sketch the graph of the function defined by the given equation.

22. $y = \coth x$.
23. $y = \text{sech} \, x$.

24. $y = \text{csch} \, x$.
25. $y = 2 \sinh (x - 3)$.

In each of Numbers 26 to 39, find the indicated inverse derivative.

26. $\displaystyle \int x \cosh \tfrac{1}{2}x^2 \, dx$.

27. $\displaystyle \int \sinh 3x \cosh 3x \, dx$.

28. $\displaystyle \int \sinh^2 x \, dx$.

29. $\displaystyle \int \tanh 2x \, dx$.

30. $\displaystyle \int \text{sech} \, x \, dx$.

31. $\displaystyle \int \tanh^3 x \, dx$.

32. $\displaystyle \int \sinh^3 3u \, du$.

33. $\displaystyle \int \dfrac{dx}{\sqrt{4x^2 - 9}}$.

34. $\displaystyle \int \dfrac{4 \, dx}{\sqrt{4x^2 + 9}}$.

35. $\displaystyle\int \frac{dx}{4 - x^2},\ |x| < 2.$

36. $\displaystyle\int \frac{x\,dx}{\sqrt{4x^2 - 9}}.$

37. $\displaystyle\int \frac{dx}{9x^2 - 16},\ |3x| > 4.$

38. $\displaystyle\int \frac{x^2\,dx}{x^2 - 4},\ |x| > 2.$

39. $\displaystyle\int \frac{x\,dx}{4 - 9x^2},\ |3x| < 2.$

40. Derive Formula (10).

41. Find the volume formed by revolving about the x-axis the area under the catenary $y = a \cosh x/a$ from $x = 0$ to $x = a$.

42. Find the maximum and minimum points of the curve
$$y = a \cosh x + b \sinh x, \qquad a > 0,\ b > 0.$$

43. Sketch the curve $x = 3 \cosh t,\ y = 4 \sinh t$.

14.8 COMPLEX-VALUED FUNCTIONS

The domain and range of a function have thus far been restricted to subsets of the field of real numbers. However, the definition of a function can be extended so that the range is a subset of the field of complex numbers.

Definition 14.8a. A function f whose domain is a subset of $\mathcal{R}$ and whose range is a subset of $\mathcal{C}$ and is such that
$$f(t) = g(t) + ih(t),$$
where g and h are real-valued functions of the real variable t, is called a **complex-valued function** of the real variable t.

That is, a complex-valued function f is a set of ordered pairs $\{(t, w)\}$, for which $t \in \mathcal{R}$ and $w \in \mathcal{C}$ such that $(t_0, w_1) \in f$ and $(t_0, w_2) \in f \Rightarrow w_1 = w_2$.

In general, a complex number $a + ib$ may be interpreted geometrically as a vector from the origin to the point (a, b). Therefore, a complex-valued function

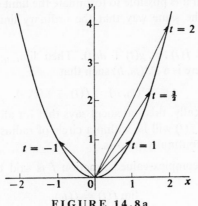

FIGURE 14.8a

has a range that is a collection of vectors whose x- and y-components are $g(t)$ and $h(t)$, respectively. Thus, the function f defined by $f(t) = g(t) + ih(t)$ may be regarded as having for its graph a curve in the xy-plane whose equations are given in parametric form by

(1) $$x = g(t), \quad y = h(t).$$

The curve is traced by the end of the vector $f(t)$.

For example, if

$$f(t) = t + it^2,$$

then we may let $x = t$ and $y = t^2$ to obtain $y = x^2$, which is the equation of the parabola shown in Figure 14.8a.

In order to discuss limits and continuity of a complex-valued function, we must extend the neighborhood concept.

Definition 14.8b. A neighborhood, $\mathfrak{N}(P, \epsilon)$, of a complex number $P = a + ib$, is the set of points

$$\{(x + iy): (x - a)^2 + (y - b)^2 < \epsilon^2\}.$$

That is, a neighborhood of P is the set of points inside a circle of radius ϵ and center at P (see Figure 14.8b).

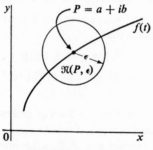

FIGURE 14.8b

With this extension it is possible to formulate the limit concept for a complex-valued function in the same way that the ordinary limit concept was formulated.

Definition 14.8c. Let $f(t) .=. g(t) + ih(t)$. Then $\lim_{t \to t_0} f(t) = P$ means that given an $\epsilon > 0$, there is a $\mathfrak{N}^*(t_0, h)$ such that

$$t \in \mathfrak{N}^*(t_0, h) \Rightarrow f(t) \in \mathfrak{N}(P, \epsilon).$$

Interpreted geometrically, this statement says that for all values of t sufficiently near t_0, the graph of $f(t)$ will lie within a circle of radius ϵ about P.

The definition of continuity follows.

Definition 14.8d. A complex-valued function f is said to be continuous at a point t_0 if

$$\lim_{t \to t_0} f(t) = f(t_0).$$

A complex-valued function is continuous on $a \leq t \leq b$ if it is continuous at every point in the interval.

Theorem 14.8a. A complex-valued function f, where $f(t) .=. g(t) + ih(t)$, is continuous at a point $t_0 \Leftrightarrow g$ and h are continuous at t_0.

PROOF: First, if f is continuous at t_0, then for each $\epsilon > 0$ there is a $\mathfrak{N}(t_0, h)$ such that

$$t \in \mathfrak{N}(t_0, h) \Rightarrow f(t) \in \mathfrak{N}[f(t_0), \epsilon].$$

That is,

$$[g(t) - g(t_0)]^2 + [h(t) - h(t_0)]^2 < \epsilon^2.$$

It follows that

$$[g(t) - g(t_0)]^2 < \epsilon^2$$

or that

$$|g(t) - g(t_0)| < \epsilon.$$

Therefore, if f is continuous at t_0, then g is continuous at t_0. A similar argument holds for the function h.

For the second part of the proof, we show that if g and h are continuous at t_0, then f is continuous at t_0. For a given ϵ there is an h_1 such that

$$t \in \mathfrak{N}(t_0, h_1) \Rightarrow g(t) \in \mathfrak{N}[g(t_0), \epsilon/\sqrt{2}],$$

and there is an h_2 such that

$$t \in \mathfrak{N}(t_0, h_2) \Rightarrow h(t) \in \mathfrak{N}[h(t_0), \epsilon/\sqrt{2}].$$

Let

$$\mathfrak{N}(t_0, h) = \mathfrak{N}(t_0, h_1) \cap \mathfrak{N}(t_0, h_2).$$

Then, for $t \in \mathfrak{N}(t_0, h)$,

$$|g(t) - g(t_0)| < \epsilon/\sqrt{2}$$

or

$$[g(t) - g(t_0)]^2 < \epsilon^2/2$$

and

$$|h(t) - h(t_0)| < \epsilon/\sqrt{2}$$

or

$$[h(t) - h(t_0)]^2 < \epsilon^2/2,$$

so that

$$t \in \mathfrak{N}(t_0, h) \Rightarrow [g(t) - g(t_0)]^2 + [h(t) - h(t_0)]^2 < \epsilon^2$$
$$\Rightarrow f(t) \in \mathfrak{N}[f(t_0), \epsilon],$$

which shows that f is continuous at t_0

The derivative of a complex-valued function f is easily defined.

Definition 14.8e. If $f(t) .=. g(t) + ih(t)$, then

$$D_t f .=. g'(t) + ih'(t),$$

provided the latter two derivatives exist.

Thus, if $f(t) = \cos 4t + i\sqrt{t}$, $t \geq 0$, then

$$f'(t) = -4 \sin 4t + i/(2\sqrt{t}), \qquad t > 0.$$

The importance of the derivative concept for a complex-valued function will become apparent a little later.

It is not difficult to show that all the usual rules for derivatives hold for complex-valued functions. For example, if p and q are complex-valued functions, then

$$D_t[p(t)q(t)] = p(t) \, D_t q(t) + q(t) \, D_t p(t).$$

Suppose

$$p(t) = u(t) + iv(t) = u + iv$$

and

$$q(t) = w(t) + iz(t) = w + iz.$$

Then

$$p(t)q(t) = [uw - vz] + i[vw + uz]$$

and

$$
\begin{aligned}
D_t[p(t)q(t)] &= uw' + u'w - vz' - v'z + i(vw' + wv' + uz' + zu') \\
&= (u + iv)w' + i(u + iv)z' + (w + iz)u' + i(w + iz)v' \\
&= (u + iv)(w' + iz') + (w + iz)(u' + iv') \\
&= p(t) \, D_t q(t) + q(t) \, D_t p(t).
\end{aligned}
$$

The inverse derivative of a complex-valued function is also defined in a manner similar to that for a real-valued function.

Definition 14.8f. If there is a complex-valued function F such that $F'(t) = f(t)$, then F is an inverse derivative of f, and we write

$$D_t^{-1} f(t) = F(t) + C \quad \text{or} \quad \int f(t)\,dt = F(t) + C.$$

As a consequence of this definition, if $f(t) = g(t) + ih(t)$, then

$$\int f(t)\,dt = \int g(t)\,dt + i \int h(t)\,dt.$$

Toward the end of the 18th century, the Swiss mathematician Euler discovered that he could extend the definition of the exponential function in a highly useful manner. Consider the complex-valued function φ defined by

$$\varphi(\alpha) = \cos \alpha + i \sin \alpha.$$

We have

$$
\begin{aligned}
\varphi(\alpha)\varphi(\beta) &= (\cos \alpha + i \sin \alpha)(\cos \beta + i \sin \beta) \\
&= (\cos \alpha \cos \beta - \sin \alpha \sin \beta) + i(\cos \alpha \sin \beta + \cos \beta \sin \alpha) \\
&= \cos (\alpha + \beta) + i \sin (\alpha + \beta)
\end{aligned}
$$

or

$$(2) \qquad \varphi(\alpha)\varphi(\beta) = \varphi(\alpha + \beta).$$

The functional property expressed by the last equation is characteristic of the ordinary exponential function. For if

$$f(x) = e^{ax}, \qquad a, x \in \Re,$$

then

$$f(x)f(y) = e^{ax}e^{ay} = e^{a(x+y)},$$

or

$$f(x)f(y) = f(x + y).$$

Does this similarity of properties imply that φ is an exponential type function? In seeking the answer to this question, we first compare other properties of $\varphi(\alpha)$ and $f(x)$. For example, we know that

$$D_x e^{ax} = ae^{ax},$$

or, in functional form,

$$D_x f(x) = af(x).$$

But

$$D_\alpha \varphi(\alpha) = -\sin \alpha + i \cos \alpha$$

or $D_\alpha \varphi(\alpha) = i[\cos \alpha + i \sin \alpha]$, so that

(3) $$D_\alpha \varphi(\alpha) = i\varphi(\alpha).$$

This relationship resembles in a remarkable way the relationship expressed in $D_x f(x) = af(x)$ with $a = i$. Indeed, if we wrote

$$\varphi(\alpha) = e^{i\alpha},$$

and agreed to apply to $e^{i\alpha}$ the rules of exponents and the derivative formula which are valid for the ordinary real exponential function, then it would appear that Equations (2) and (3) are satisfied. Thus, it looks as if a meaning can be given to the exponential form $e^{i\alpha}$ in terms of the complex-valued function defined by $\cos \alpha + i \sin \alpha$.

We have just shown that φ is a complex-valued function that satisfies properties (2) and (3). Can we be sure there is no other function satisfying these same properties? In other words, is $\varphi(\alpha)$ *uniquely* determined by properties (2) and (3)?

Suppose g is another complex-valued function with these properties. That is, let g be a function for which

$$g(\alpha)g(\beta) = g(\alpha + \beta)$$

and

$$D_\alpha g(\alpha) = ig(\alpha).$$

Then

$$\frac{D_\alpha g(\alpha)}{g(\alpha)} = \frac{D_\alpha \varphi(\alpha)}{\varphi(\alpha)},$$

or

$$\frac{D_\alpha g(\alpha)}{g(\alpha)} - \frac{D_\alpha \varphi(\alpha)}{\varphi(\alpha)} = 0$$

and

$$\varphi(\alpha) \, D_\alpha g(\alpha) - g(\alpha) \, D_\alpha \varphi(\alpha) = 0.$$

Hence

$$\frac{\varphi(\alpha)\, D_\alpha g(\alpha) - g(\alpha)\, D_\alpha \varphi(\alpha)}{\varphi(\alpha)^2} = 0,$$

or

$$D_\alpha \left(\frac{g(\alpha)}{\varphi(\alpha)} \right) = 0,$$

so that

$$\frac{g(\alpha)}{\varphi(\alpha)} = c, \qquad c \text{ a constant.}$$

Thus,

$$g(\alpha) = c\varphi(\alpha)$$

and, in particular,

$$g(0) = c\varphi(0).$$

From (2), we have $\varphi(\alpha)\varphi(0) = \varphi(\alpha)$ when $\beta = 0$, so that $\varphi(0) = 1$. Similarly, since g obeys the same functional relationship as φ does, $g(0) = 1$. Hence $c = 1$, and it follows that

$$g(\alpha) = \varphi(\alpha).$$

This result shows that the complex-valued function φ satisfying Equations (2) and (3) is unique. Accordingly, the preceding discussion strongly suggests the following extension of the meaning of the exponential function to imaginary exponents.

Definition 14.8g. $\qquad e^{i\alpha} .=. \cos \alpha + i \sin \alpha.$

This remarkable relationship, which is credited to Euler, serves as an important unifying link between the exponential and hyperbolic functions and the trigonometric functions. Through this definition, these apparently unrelated functions will soon appear simply as different combinations of exponential functions.

According to this definition, $e^{i\alpha}$ is a complex number with $\cos \alpha$ as its real part and $\sin \alpha$ as the coefficient of its imaginary part. With an additional definition, it is possible to extend the meaning of the exponential to the field of complex numbers.

Definition 14.8h. $\qquad e^{x+iy} .=. e^x e^{iy}, \qquad x, y \in \mathfrak{R}.$

With the last two definitions, it can be shown that e^z, $z \in \mathfrak{C}$, obeys all the usual rules of algebra developed for real numbers. For instance, it is a direct consequence of Equation (2) that

$$e^{i\alpha} e^{i\beta} = e^{i(\alpha+\beta)}.$$

This result may be used to show that

$$e^{z_1} e^{z_2} = e^{z_1 + z_2},$$

where $z_1 = x_1 + iy_1$ and $z_2 = x_2 + iy_2$.

Since, by Definition 14.8g,

$$e^{i2\pi} = \cos 2\pi + i \sin 2\pi = 1,$$

it follows that

$$e^{z+i2\pi} = e^z e^{i2\pi} = e^z.$$

Thus, the exponential function satisfies the functional equation

$$f(z + i2\pi) = f(z);$$

that is, the function is periodic with period $i2\pi$.

There are a number of other interesting consequences of the preceding definitions. For example, if $\alpha = \pi$, we get

$$e^{i\pi} + 1 = 0,$$

a simple statement that encompasses in one result the five most important numbers in mathematics. Furthermore, since every complex number may be written in polar form (see Section 7.7), we have

$$a + ib = \sqrt{a^2 + b^2}\left[\frac{a}{\sqrt{a^2 + b^2}} + i\,\frac{b}{\sqrt{a^2 + b^2}}\right]$$
$$= r(\cos\theta + i\sin\theta) = re^{i\theta},$$

where $r = \sqrt{a^2 + b^2}$, and where θ is the smallest nonnegative angle such that $\cos\theta = a/r$, and $\sin\theta = b/r$. For example,

$$-\sqrt{3} + i = 2(-\sqrt{3}/2 + i\,1/2) = 2[\cos 5\pi/6 + i\sin 5\pi/6]$$
$$= 2e^{i5\pi/6}.$$

As we shall see later, the exponential form for complex numbers will simplify considerably some of the work involving complex quantities.

Another interesting relationship is obtained as follows. Since

$$e^{i\alpha} = \cos\alpha + i\sin\alpha,$$

it follows that

$$e^{-i\alpha} = \cos\alpha - i\sin\alpha.$$

(Why?) By adding, and dividing by 2, we get

$$\cos\alpha = \frac{e^{i\alpha} + e^{-i\alpha}}{2}.$$

Similarly,

$$\sin\alpha = \frac{e^{i\alpha} - e^{-i\alpha}}{2i}.$$

Upon comparing these expressions with the exponential forms for $\sinh\alpha$ and $\cosh\alpha$, we get

$$\cos\alpha = \cosh i\alpha,$$
$$i\sin\alpha = \sinh i\alpha.$$

It is customary to base the definitions of the trigonometric and hyperbolic functions of complex numbers on the preceding results. Thus, for $z \in \mathcal{C}$, we have

$$\cos z .=. \frac{e^{iz} + e^{-iz}}{2}, \qquad \sin z .=. \frac{e^{iz} - e^{-iz}}{2i},$$

$$\cosh z .=. \frac{e^z + e^{-z}}{2}, \qquad \sinh z .=. \frac{e^z - e^{-z}}{2}.$$

Exercises 14.8

1. Sketch the graph associated with each of the following complex-valued functions.

   (a) $f(t) = t^2 + it^2$.

   (b) $f(s) = \cos s + i \sin s$.

   (c) $G(u) = \dfrac{u}{1 + u^2} + i\dfrac{u^2}{1 + u^2}$.

   (d) $p(s) = (s^2 - s) + i(s^2 + s)$.

2. For what real values of the variable is each of the following complex-valued functions continuous?

   (a) $f(t) = t + i(t^2 - 1)$.

   (b) $f(s) = \dfrac{1}{s} + i\dfrac{1}{s - 1}$.

   (c) $f(t) = \sec t + i \cot t$.

   (d) $g(t) = \coth t + i \tanh t$.

   (e) $h(s) = \mathrm{Sin}^{-1} s + i\, \mathrm{Cos}^{-1} s, \; |s| \leq 1$.

3. Find the derivative of each of the following.

   (a) $f(s) = \cos 2s + i \sin 2s$.

   (b) $f(t) = \dfrac{t}{1 - t^2} + i\dfrac{1}{1 - t^2}$.

   (c) $g(u) = \cos^2 u + i \sin^2 u$.

   (d) $h(s) = \mathrm{Sin}^{-1} s + i\, \mathrm{Cos}^{-1} s, \; |s| \leq 1$.

4. If p and q are differentiable complex-valued functions, prove that

   (a) $D_t[p + q] = D_t p + D_t q$.

   (b) $D_t p^n = np^{n-1} D_t p, \; n \in \mathcal{I}$. *Hint:* Let $p(t) = r(t)e^{i\theta(t)}$.

   (c) $D_t\left(\dfrac{p}{q}\right) = \dfrac{q\, D_t p - p\, D_t q}{q^2}$. *Hint:* Show first that $D_t\left(\dfrac{1}{q}\right) = -\dfrac{D_t q}{q^2}$.

   (d) $D_t\left\{\displaystyle\int_a^t p(u)\, du\right\} = p(t)$.

5. Write each of the following numbers in the exponential form $re^{i\theta}$.

   (a) $-2\sqrt{3} - 2i$.

   (b) $\sqrt{2} - \sqrt{2}i$.

   (c) $6 + 8i$.

   (d) $\dfrac{1}{1 + \sqrt{3}i}$.

6. Deduce that $\displaystyle\int \sin\theta\, d\theta = -\cos\theta + C$ and $\displaystyle\int \cos\theta\, d\theta = \sin\theta + C$ by considering $\displaystyle\int e^{i\theta}\, d\theta$ and equating the real and imaginary parts of the resulting expression.

7. Evaluate $\displaystyle\int e^{s+is}\, ds$, and then deduce expressions for

$$\int e^s \cos s\, ds \quad \text{and} \quad \int e^s \sin s\, ds.$$

8. Show that $\cosh (x + iy) = \cosh x \cos y + i \sinh x \sin y$.
9. Show that $\sin (x + iy) = \sin x \cosh y + i \cos x \sinh y$.
10. The logarithmic function is defined as the inverse of the exponential function. That is, if $z = e^w$, then $w .=. \ln z$. Every complex number can be written in exponential form, so that

$$z = x + iy = re^{i\theta},$$

where $r = \sqrt{x^2 + y^2}$, $\theta = \tan^{-1} y/x$. Hence we make this definition:

$$\text{Ln } z .=. \text{Ln } r + i\theta, \qquad -\pi < \theta \le \pi,$$

where Ln r is the logarithm of the real number r. Thus,

$$\text{Ln } (1 + i) = \text{Ln } [\sqrt{2} (\cos \pi/4 + i \sin \pi/4)]$$
$$= \text{Ln } \sqrt{2} + i\pi/4.$$

Find each of the following as a complex number in the form $a + ib$.

(a) Ln (-1).   (c) Ln i.
(b) Ln $(2 - 2i)$.

11. In each of the following, determine a complex number of the form $a + ib$, with a and b real, equivalent to the given number.

(a) $\sin i$.   (f) e^{3+4i}.
(b) $\cos (1 - i)$.   (g) Ln $2i$.
(c) $\sin (-\pi/4 - i)$.   (h) Ln $(1 + i)$.
(d) $\sinh 2i$.   (i) Ln (-3).
(e) $e^{i\pi/4}$.   (j) $\cosh (2 + i\pi/2)$.

⋆12. On the basis of the definition in Number 10, is it necessarily true that

$$\text{Ln } z_1z_2 = \text{Ln } z_1 + \text{Ln } z_2,$$

where z_1 and z_2 are complex numbers? Explain.

14.9 ROOTS OF COMPLEX NUMBERS

From De Moivre's Theorem, established in Section 7.7, we have

$$[r(\cos \theta + i \sin \theta)]^n = r^n(\cos n\theta + i \sin n\theta), \qquad n \in \mathcal{I}.$$

By making use of the relationship

$$\cos \theta + i \sin \theta = e^{i\theta},$$

we may write the preceding result in the more compact form

(1) $$\qquad\qquad (re^{i\theta})^n = r^n e^{in\theta}.$$

This equation makes it possible for us to define the nth root of a complex number in a relatively simple way. As in the case of real numbers, we define the nth root of a complex number $r(\cos \theta + i \sin \theta)$ to be a complex number $R(\cos \varphi + i \sin \varphi)$ such that

$$[R(\cos \varphi + i \sin \varphi)]^n = r(\cos \theta + i \sin \theta)$$

or, in exponential form,

$$[Re^{i\varphi}]^n = re^{i\theta}.$$

It follows from Equation (1) that

$$R^n e^{in\varphi} = re^{i\theta},$$

which implies

$$R^n = r \quad \text{and} \quad n\varphi = \theta.$$

Since both R and r are real and nonnegative and $0 \leq \theta < 2\pi$, it follows that

$$R = \sqrt[n]{r} \quad \text{and} \quad \varphi = \theta/n.$$

Thus, an nth root of the complex number $re^{i\theta}$ is given by

$$\sqrt[n]{re^{i\theta/n}} = \sqrt[n]{r}(\cos \theta/n + i \sin \theta/n).$$

However, further investigation reveals that the nth root of a complex number given in this way is not the only nth root, an observation that may be verified in either of two ways. If we make use of the Fundamental Theorem of Algebra, and related theorems appearing in Section 3.6, we find that the problem of determining an nth root z of a given complex number α is equivalent to solving the equation

$$z^n - \alpha = 0.$$

According to the theory of equations, this equation must have n roots (not necessarily distinct) in the field of complex numbers. Consequently, we may expect to find values for z other than

$$\sqrt[n]{r}(\cos \theta/n + i \sin \theta/n).$$

A second verification consists in finding the other nth roots of the complex number, which is easily done by making use of the periodicity of the exponential function. Since

$$e^{i\theta} = e^{i(\theta + 2\pi k)}, \qquad k \in \mathcal{I},$$

we may write for the nth roots of a complex number $\alpha = re^{i\theta}$ the more general form

$$z = \sqrt[n]{r}e^{i(\theta + 2\pi k)/n}.$$

It follows further from the periodicity of the exponential function that $k = 0, 1, 2, \ldots, n - 1$ will yield the only distinct values of

$$\exp [i(\theta + 2k\pi)/n],$$

so that there are exactly n different roots. Furthermore, since all of these roots have the same modulus $\sqrt[n]{r}$, they will, if plotted on the plane of complex numbers, correspond to a set of n equally spaced points on a circle of radius $\sqrt[n]{r}$. This is illustrated in the next example.

Example 14.9a. Solve the equation $z^5 + 2\sqrt{3} - 2i = 0$.

If we write this equation in the form

$$z^5 = -2\sqrt{3} + 2i = 4 \exp\left[i\left(\frac{5\pi}{6} + 2k\pi\right)\right],$$

we have

$$z = \left\{4 \exp i\left(\frac{5\pi}{6} + 2k\pi\right)\right\}^{1/5}$$

$$= \sqrt[5]{4} \exp\left[i\left(\frac{\pi}{6} + \frac{2k\pi}{5}\right)\right].$$

The five distinct roots may be obtained by letting $k = 0, 1, 2, 3, 4$ to get

$$z_0 = \sqrt[5]{4} \exp\frac{i\pi}{6} = \sqrt[5]{4} \,(\cos 30° + i \sin 30°),$$

$$z_1 = \sqrt[5]{4} \exp\frac{i17\pi}{30} = \sqrt[5]{4} \,(\cos 102° + i \sin 102°),$$

$$z_2 = \sqrt[5]{4} \exp\frac{i29\pi}{30} = \sqrt[5]{4} \,(\cos 174° + i \sin 174°),$$

$$z_3 = \sqrt[5]{4} \exp\frac{i41\pi}{30} = \sqrt[5]{4} \,(\cos 246° + i \sin 246°),$$

$$z_4 = \sqrt[5]{4} \exp\frac{i53\pi}{30} = \sqrt[5]{4} \,(\cos 318° + i \sin 318°).$$

These roots are represented geometrically in Figure 14.9a.

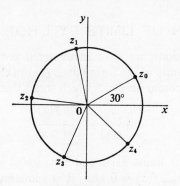

FIGURE 14.9a

It is left to the reader to verify that with the preceding result for the nth roots of $re^{i\theta}$, we obtain

$$(re^{i\theta})^{p/n} = \sqrt[n]{r^p} \exp\left[i\left(\frac{p\theta}{n} + \frac{2kp\pi}{n}\right)\right], \qquad k = 0, 1, 2, \ldots, n - 1,$$

where p is any integer and n is any positive integer.

Exercises 14.9

In Numbers 1 to 16, solve the given equation and make a sketch to show the roots graphically.

1. $x^3 - 8 = 0$.
2. $y^5 + 32i = 0$.
3. $x^3 + i = 0$.
4. $y^3 + 27 = 0$.
5. $x^4 + 16 = 0$.
6. $w^6 - 1 = 0$.
7. $z^3 - 8i = 0$.
8. $x^6 + 1 = 0$.

9. $z^2 = 1 - i\sqrt{3}$.
10. $x^4 = 2(-1 + i\sqrt{3})$.
11. $x^3 = -3 + 4i$.
12. $y^5 = 1$.
13. $w^2 = -4(1 + i)$.
14. $x^3 = 2(1 + i)$.
15. $w^8 = 1$.
16. $x^5 + 2\sqrt{3} + 2i = 0$.

17. Solve the equation $w^4 + w^2 + 1 = 0$.
18. Solve the equation $x^6 + x^3 + 1 = 0$.
19. If $w^4 + 2w^3 + 4w^2 + 8w + 16 = 0$, what are the possible values of w?
20. Find the integer of smallest absolute value of which $-\sqrt{2} + i\sqrt{2}$ is a root.
21. Find the integer of smallest absolute value of which $\sqrt{3} + i$ is a root.

The n distinct solutions of the equation $z^n = 1$ are called the nth *roots of unity*. Numbers 22 to 25 are concerned with certain nth roots of unity.

22. Find the sixth roots of unity and show that they form a multiplicative group.
23. Find the fifth roots of unity and show that they form a multiplicative group.
24. Show that, for each n, the nth roots of unity form a multiplicative group.
25. If ω is an imaginary fifth root of unity, and if $u = \omega + 1/\omega$, show that $u^2 + u = 1$.

14.10 EVALUATION OF LIMITS BY L'HÔPITAL'S RULE

On a number of occasions, we have encountered problems in which it was necessary to evaluate limits of the form $\lim_{x \to a} f(x)/g(x)$. In some cases we have been able to use the theorem on limits which states that

$$\lim_{x \to a} \frac{f(x)}{g(x)} = \frac{\lim_{x \to a} f(x)}{\lim_{x \to a} g(x)}$$

provided the latter two limits exist and $\lim_{x \to a} g(x) \neq 0$. In the event that $\lim_{x \to a} g(x) = 0$ and $\lim_{x \to a} f(x) = 0$ also, it is sometimes possible to evaluate $\lim_{x \to a} f(x)/g(x)$. For example, it has already been shown that

$$\lim_{x \to 2} \frac{x^2 - 4}{x - 2} = 4 \quad \text{and} \quad \lim_{x \to 0} \frac{\sin x}{x} = 1.$$

However, there are many examples of expressions of the form $f(x)/g(x)$ for which a limit exists but for which we have not yet developed a technique for finding the limit. For instance, does $\lim_{x \to 1} [(\ln x)/(x - 1)]$ exist, and, if it does, what is the limit?

In order to develop a general method for evaluating limits of this form, we find it convenient first to refer back to Rolle's Theorem and the Mean Value Theorem for Derivatives and to derive from those ideas a somewhat more generalized version of the Mean Value Theorem.

The Mean Value Theorem for Derivatives was given for functions described by an equation of the form $y = f(x)$. If a function is described in parametric form, then the theorem assumes the following somewhat different aspect.

Theorem 14.10a. Suppose that $x = f(t)$ and $y = g(t)$ define two functions on the interval $a \leqq t \leqq b$ such that

(1) f and g are continuous on $a \leqq t \leqq b$,
(2) f and g are differentiable over $a < t < b$,
(3) $g(a) \neq g(b)$,
(4) $g'(t) \neq 0$ for $a < t < b$.

Then there is a value of t, say t_1, in $a < t < b$ such that

$$\frac{f(b) - f(a)}{g(b) - g(a)} = \frac{f'(t_1)}{g'(t_1)}.$$

PROOF: The proof of the theorem is based on Rolle's Theorem and is similar to the proof of the original Mean Value Theorem. Let

$$\varphi(t) = f(t) - f(a) - \left[\frac{f(b) - f(a)}{g(b) - g(a)}\right] [g(t) - g(a)].$$

It is then easy to verify that $\varphi(a) = \varphi(b) = 0$, so that Rolle's Theorem may be used. Hence, there is a point, t_1, such that $\varphi'(t_1) = 0$. Thus

$$0 = f'(t_1) - \left[\frac{f(b) - f(a)}{g(b) - g(a)}\right] g'(t_1),$$

and the theorem follows.

The preceding theorem provides a simple way of proving the next theorem, which can frequently be used for the evaluation of limits.

Theorem 14.10b. *L'Hôpital's Rule.* Let two functions f and g have continuous derivatives on some $\mathfrak{N}^*(a, h)$, where $g'(x) \neq 0$, and let $f(a) = g(a) = 0$. Then,

(i)
$$\lim_{x \to a} \frac{f'(x)}{g'(x)} \text{ exists} \Rightarrow \lim_{x \to a} \frac{f(x)}{g(x)} = \lim_{x \to a} \frac{f'(x)}{g'(x)}$$

and

(ii)
$$\frac{f'(x)}{g'(x)} \to \infty \text{ as } x \to a \Rightarrow \frac{f(x)}{g(x)} \to \infty \text{ as } x \to a.$$

PROOF: The proof will be given for (i). The details of (ii) are left for the reader.

In $\mathfrak{N}^*(a^+, h)$, $g'(x) \neq 0$, so that Theorem 14.10a may be applied for the interval $a < x < a + h$. In this interval, there is an x_1 such that $a < x_1 < x$, and

$$\frac{f(x) - f(a)}{g(x) - g(a)} = \frac{f'(x_1)}{g'(x_1)} \quad \text{or} \quad \frac{f(x)}{g(x)} = \frac{f'(x_1)}{g'(x_1)},$$

and, since $\lim_{x \to a} f'(x)/g'(x)$ exists,

$$\lim_{x \to a^+} \frac{f'(x_1)}{g'(x_1)} = \lim_{x \to a^+} \frac{f'(x)}{g'(x)} = \lim_{x \to a^+} \frac{f(x)}{g(x)}.$$

In a similar way, the limit from the left can be shown to exist, and consequently

$$\lim_{x \to a} \frac{f'(x)}{g'(x)} = \lim_{x \to a} \frac{f(x)}{g(x)}.$$

The following examples illustrate the use of L'Hôpital's Rule.

Example 14.10a. Find

$$\lim_{x \to 0} \frac{x \cos x - \sin x}{x}.$$

If $f(x) = x \cos x - \sin x$ and $g(x) = x$, it follows that $f(0) = 0$ and $g(0) = 0$. Also, we have

$$f'(x) = \cos x - x \sin x - \cos x = -x \sin x,$$

and

$$g'(x) = 1.$$

The conditions of Theorem 14.10b are satisfied, so that

$$\lim_{x \to 0} \frac{x \cos x - \sin x}{x} = \lim_{x \to 0} \frac{-x \sin x}{1} = \frac{0}{1} = 0,$$

a result that makes use of the continuity of the derivatives.

Example 14.10b. Evaluate

$$\lim_{x \to 0^+} \frac{\sin x}{\sqrt{x}}.$$

If $f(x) = \sin x$ and $g(x) = \sqrt{x}$, then $f(0) = g(0) = 0$, and

$$f'(x) = \cos x, \quad g'(x) = \frac{1}{2\sqrt{x}}.$$

Again the conditions of Theorem 14.10b are satisfied, so that

$$\lim_{x \to 0^+} \frac{\sin x}{\sqrt{x}} = \lim_{x \to 0^+} \frac{\cos x}{1/(2\sqrt{x})} = \lim_{x \to 0^+} 2\sqrt{x} \cos x = 0.$$

If an application of L'Hôpital's Rule should lead to a form $\lim_{x \to a} f'(x)/g'(x)$, where both $f'(a)$ and $g'(a)$ are 0, then the rule may be applied to the ratio $f'(x)/g'(x)$, provided that the functions f' and g' satisfy the conditions of the theorem.

Example 14.10c. Evaluate

$$\lim_{x \to 0} \frac{xe^x - x}{\sin^2 2x}.$$

Since the conditions of Theorem 14.10b are satisfied, we have

$$\lim_{x \to 0} \frac{xe^x - x}{\sin^2 2x} = \lim_{x \to 0} \frac{e^x + xe^x - 1}{4 \sin 2x \cos 2x} = \lim_{x \to 0} \frac{e^x + xe^x - 1}{2 \sin 4x}.$$

The numerator and denominator of the last expression are both 0 when $x = 0$, so that the limit cannot yet be determined. However, the expressions $e^x + xe^x - 1$ and $2 \sin 4x$ both satisfy the conditions of Theorem 14.10b. Hence, a further application of this theorem yields

$$\lim_{x \to 0} \frac{e^x + xe^x - 1}{2 \sin 4x} = \lim_{x \to 0} \frac{2e^x + xe^x}{8 \cos 4x} = \frac{1}{4}.$$

It is clear that Theorem 14.10b may be used successively as often as is necessary, provided the appropriate conditions are satisfied at each stage of the application.

The following extension of L'Hôpital's Rule is stated without proof.

Theorem 14.10c. If f and g both have continuous derivatives for all sufficiently large values of x, and $f(x) \to 0$, $g(x) \to 0$ as $x \to \infty$, then

(i) $$\lim_{x \to \infty} \frac{f'(x)}{g'(x)} \text{ exists} \Rightarrow \lim_{x \to \infty} \frac{f(x)}{g(x)} = \lim_{x \to \infty} \frac{f'(x)}{g'(x)},$$

and

(ii) $$\frac{f'(x)}{g'(x)} \to \infty \text{ as } x \to \infty \Rightarrow \frac{f(x)}{g(x)} \to \infty \text{ as } x \to \infty.$$

Example 14.10d. Evaluate

$$\lim_{x \to \infty} \frac{1/x^2}{\sin^2 (2/x)}.$$

Since the conditions of Theorem 14.10c are satisfied, we have

$$\lim_{x \to \infty} \frac{1/x^2}{\sin^2 (2/x)} = \lim_{x \to \infty} \frac{-2/x^3}{-(4/x^2) \sin (2/x) \cos (2/x)}$$

$$= \lim_{x \to \infty} \frac{1/x}{\sin (4/x)}$$

$$= \lim_{x \to \infty} \frac{-1/x^2}{-(4/x^2) \cos (4/x)}$$

$$= \lim_{x \to \infty} \frac{1}{4 \cos (4/x)} = \frac{1}{4}.$$

(Notice that in addition to the algebraic simplifications, L'Hôpital's Rule has been applied twice. This limit can be evaluated without L'Hôpital's Rule. Do you see how to do it?)

The following case of L'Hôpital's Rule is also given without proof.

Theorem 14.10d. Suppose that $f(x)$ and $g(x)$ both increase without limit as x approaches a and that f' and g' are both continuous on some $\mathfrak{N}^*(a, h)$. Then

(i) $$\lim_{x \to a} \frac{f'(x)}{g'(x)} \text{ exists} \Rightarrow \lim_{x \to a} \frac{f(x)}{g(x)} = \lim_{x \to a} \frac{f'(x)}{g'(x)},$$

and

(ii) $$\frac{f'(x)}{g'(x)} \to \infty \text{ as } x \to a \Rightarrow \frac{f(x)}{g(x)} \to \infty \text{ as } x \to a.$$

Furthermore, the same rule applies without other changes as $x \to \infty$, provided f' and g' are continuous for all sufficiently large values of x.

Example 14.10e. Evaluate

$$\lim_{x \to \infty} \frac{\ln x}{\ln (a + x)}.$$

Using L'Hôpital's Rule, we get

$$\lim_{x \to \infty} \frac{\ln x}{\ln (a + x)} = \lim_{x \to \infty} \frac{1/x}{1/(a + x)} = \lim_{x \to \infty} \frac{a + x}{x} = 1.$$

Exercises 14.10

Evaluate each of the following limits, if the limit exists. Make algebraic simplifications when possible before using L'Hôpital's Rule.

1. $\lim\limits_{x \to 0} \dfrac{\sin kx}{x}$.

2. $\lim\limits_{x \to \pi/2} \dfrac{\frac{1}{2}\pi - x}{\cos 3x}$.

3. $\lim\limits_{x \to 0} \dfrac{e^x - e^{-x}}{x^2}$.

4. $\lim\limits_{t \to 0} \dfrac{1 - \cos t}{\sin t}$.

5. $\lim\limits_{x \to a^-} \dfrac{a - x}{\ln (a - x)}$.

6. $\lim\limits_{x \to 0^+} \dfrac{e^{-1/x}}{x}$.

7. $\lim\limits_{t \to \infty} \dfrac{t}{\ln t}$.

8. $\lim\limits_{u \to \infty} \dfrac{e^u}{u^2}$.

9. $\lim\limits_{y \to \infty} \dfrac{y^3}{e^y}$.

10. $\lim\limits_{s \to \infty} \dfrac{\ln (as + b)}{\ln (cs + d)}$.

11. $\lim\limits_{\varphi \to 0} \dfrac{\sin \varphi - \varphi}{\tan \varphi - \varphi}$.

12. $\lim\limits_{x \to 0} \dfrac{1 - x}{\cos x}$.

13. $\lim\limits_{x \to \infty} \dfrac{\ln x}{\sqrt{x}}$.

14. $\lim\limits_{x \to \pi/2} \dfrac{\tan 3x}{\tan 5x}$.

15. $\lim\limits_{x \to 0} \dfrac{a^x - b^x}{x}$.

16. $\lim\limits_{x \to 0^-} \dfrac{\ln (1 - x)}{\sin x}$.

17. $\lim\limits_{t \to 0} \dfrac{\operatorname{Sin}^{-1} t}{t}$.

18. $\lim\limits_{y \to a} \dfrac{y^n - a^n}{y - a}$.

19. $\lim\limits_{\theta \to 0} \dfrac{\theta - \theta \cos \theta}{\sin^3 2\theta}$.

20. $\lim\limits_{x \to 0} \dfrac{e^{2x^2} - 1}{\sin^2 x}$.

21. $\lim\limits_{u \to 0} \dfrac{e^x - \sin x - 1}{1 - \cos 2x}$.

22. $\lim\limits_{t \to 0} \dfrac{t - \sin^2 t}{1 - \cos 2t}$.

14.11 FURTHER EVALUATION OF LIMITS

In the preceding section we saw that the limit of a fraction $f(x)/g(x)$, where both $f(x)$ and $g(x) \to 0$ or else increase without limit, can be evaluated with the aid of L'Hôpital's Rule. These limits are conveniently referred to as $0/0$ or ∞/∞ forms. There are a number of other forms that can be changed algebraically into one of these forms so that L'Hôpital's Rule may be applied.

Suppose $f(x) \to 0$ and $g(x) \to \infty$ as $x \to a$. Then, $\lim_{x \to a} f(x)g(x)$ may be designated as a $0 \cdot \infty$ form. Such a form is easily changed into a $0/0$ form or an ∞/∞ form by writing

$$f(x)g(x) = \frac{f(x)}{1/g(x)} \quad \text{or} \quad f(x)g(x) = \frac{g(x)}{1/f(x)},$$

and then L'Hôpital's Rule may often be used.

Example 14.11a. Evaluate $\lim_{x \to 0^+} x \ln \sin x$.

Since

$$x \ln \sin x = \frac{\ln \sin x}{1/x},$$

we have a form to which L'Hôpital's Rule applies. Hence,

$$\lim_{x \to 0^+} \frac{\ln \sin x}{1/x} = \lim_{x \to 0^+} \frac{\cos x / \sin x}{-1/x^2}$$

$$= \lim_{x \to 0^+} (-x) \frac{x}{\sin x} \cos x = 0.$$

Another form that can be changed algebraically into one to which L'Hôpital's Rule may be applied is $f(x) - g(x)$, where $f(x)$ and $g(x)$ both $\to \infty$ as $x \to a$. The procedure is illustrated in the following example.

Example 14.11b. Evaluate

$$\lim_{x \to 0} \left[\frac{1}{x} - \frac{1}{\sin x} \right].$$

Since

$$\frac{1}{x} - \frac{1}{\sin x} = \frac{\sin x - x}{x \sin x},$$

L'Hôpital's Rule may be applied to give

$$\lim_{x \to 0} \frac{\sin x - x}{x \sin x} = \lim_{x \to 0} \frac{\cos x - 1}{\sin x + x \cos x}$$

$$= \lim_{x \to 0} \frac{-\sin x}{2 \cos x - x \sin x} = 0.$$

Exponential forms may also be analyzed, as in the following example, by first taking logarithms to obtain a form of one of the types already discussed

Example 14.11c. Evaluate $\lim_{x \to 0^+} (\cos 2x)^{1/x}$.

Let $y = (\cos 2x)^{1/x}$, so that $\ln y = (1/x) \ln \cos 2x$. Then, by L'Hôpital's Rule, we get

$$\lim_{x \to 0^+} \ln y = \lim_{x \to 0^+} \frac{\ln \cos 2x}{x}$$

$$= \lim_{x \to 0^+} \frac{-2 \sin 2x}{\cos 2x} = 0.$$

Since $\ln y \to 0$ as $x \to 0^+$, then $y \to 1$, so that

$$\lim_{x \to 0^+} (\cos 2x)^{1/x} = 1.$$

The reader is cautioned against falling into the trap of saying that since $\cos 2x \to 1$ as $x \to 0$, then

$$(\cos 2x)^{1/x} \to 1$$

because "any power of 1 is 1." Since we are concerned only with values of x in a *deleted* neighborhood of 0, $\cos 2x$ is never actually equal to 1 for values of $x \in \mathfrak{N}^*(0, \epsilon)$, if $\epsilon < \pi/4$.

An expression of the type $\lim_{x \to a} [f(x)]^{g(x)}$, for which one of the following is true,

$$\text{(a)} \quad g(x) \to 0, \quad f(x) \to 0, \quad \text{as } x \to a,$$
$$\text{(b)} \quad g(x) \to 0, \quad f(x) \to \infty, \quad \text{as } x \to a,$$
$$\text{(c)} \quad g(x) \to \infty, \quad f(x) \to 1, \quad \text{as } x \to a,$$

can often be evaluated by the process described in the preceding example.

Exercises 14.11

Evaluate each of the following limits, if possible.

1. $\lim_{x \to \infty} x e^{1/x}$.

2. $\lim_{x \to 0^+} x \ln x$.

3. $\lim_{x \to 0^+} x^x$.

4. $\lim_{y \to \infty} y^2 e^{-y}$.

5. $\lim_{x \to \pi/2} (\sec x - \tan x)$.

6. $\lim_{x \to 0} (\csc 2x - \cot x)$.

7. $\lim_{x \to 0^+} x \ln \sin x$.

8. $\lim_{\theta \to 0} \theta \csc 3\theta$.

9. $\lim_{t \to 0} \left(\frac{1}{t^2} - \frac{1}{\sin^2 t} \right)$.

10. $\lim_{u \to 0^+} \left(\frac{1}{u} + \ln u \right)$.

11. $\lim_{x \to 1} \left(\frac{1}{x - 1} - \frac{1}{\ln x} \right)$.

12. $\lim_{\theta \to \pi/2} \left(2 \sec^2 \theta - \frac{1}{1 - \sin \theta} \right)$.

13. $\lim_{x \to 0^+} (1 - \sin x)^{1/x}$.

14. $\lim_{\varphi \to 0} (\cos 2\varphi)^{1/\varphi^2}$.

15. $\lim_{t \to \pi/2} (\sin t)^{\tan t}$.

16. $\lim_{x \to \infty} (1 + e^{-x^2})^x$.

17. $\lim_{x \to 0} (1/x)^{\sin x}$.

18. $\lim_{h \to \infty} \left(1 + \frac{b}{h} \right)^h$.

19. $\lim_{x \to 0} (x + e^x)^{a/x}$.

20. $\lim_{x \to 1^-} x^{1/(1-x)}$.

14.12 THE NEWTON-RAPHSON METHOD OF SOLVING EQUATIONS

It is quite common in mathematics and in its applications to be required to find a root of an equation $f(x) = 0$, where there is no elementary method for solving the equation in an exact form. For instance, although quadratic equations can be solved by means of the quadratic formula, there are no corresponding formulas for polynomial equations of degree higher than the fourth. Even the third and fourth degree equations are usually solved more conveniently by approximation methods rather than by the use of the complicated general formulas that are available. Equations involving trigonometric, inverse trigonometric, logarithmic, or exponential functions may be deceptively simple in appearance without being amenable to any practical method of exact solution. One example will suffice to illustrate the truth of this statement.

Example 14.12a. A wire 10 inches long is to be bent into a circular arc with a chord 8 inches long. Find the radius of the arc (see Figure 14.12a).

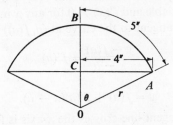

FIGURE 14.12a

From the geometry of the figure, we see that the length of arc AB is given by $r\theta$, and that the half-chord AC is given by $r \sin \theta$. Hence,

$$r\theta = 5 \quad \text{and} \quad r \sin \theta = 4,$$

so that, by eliminating r, we obtain the equation

$$4\theta = 5 \sin \theta.$$

Once this equation is solved, the radius r can easily be found from the equation $r\theta = 5$. However, at this stage of our discussion we can solve this equation only by trial and error methods using a table of trigonometric functions for angles in radians. From such a table, we find for $\theta = 1.13$ that $\sin \theta = 0.9044$, which is very nearly $\frac{4}{5}(1.13)$. Consequently, θ is approximately 1.13 radians and $r = 5/1.13 = 4.42$ inches.

A better method than simply guessing and verifying the guess by means of a table is desirable even in as easy a problem as the preceding one, and it is quite necessary in more complicated problems. A simple and often effective procedure for approximating a root of an equation is known as the **Newton-Raphson method,** which we shall discuss next.

Suppose we wish to find a root of $f(x) = 0$. Then, as was pointed out in Section 6.3, an equivalent problem is that of finding where the graph of the function f crosses the x-axis (see Figure 14.12b). If f is a continuous function, then, by

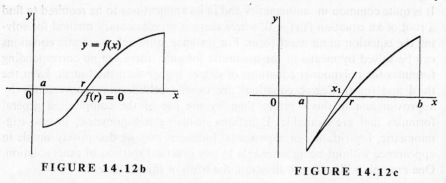

FIGURE 14.12b   **FIGURE 14.12c**

the Intermediate Value Theorem, at least one root r of the equation must be located between every two numbers a and b for which $f(a)$ and $f(b)$ have opposite signs. For simplicity, let us assume that $f(a) < 0$ and $f(b) > 0$. Suppose further that f is differentiable and $f'(x) \neq 0$ for any x in the interval $a \leq x \leq b$. The equation of a line tangent to the curve at $(a, f(a))$ is easily found to be

$$\frac{y - f(a)}{x - a} = f'(a)$$

or

$$y = f(a) + f'(a)(x - a).$$

The point where this tangent line crosses the x-axis is found by putting $y = 0$, and the corresponding value of x is

$$x_1 = a - \frac{f(a)}{f'(a)}.$$

Now, if the curve $y = f(x)$ is concave down over the interval $a \leq x \leq b$, so that the tangent line lies above the curve, and if $f(a) < 0$, then x_1 is between a and the root r; that is, x_1 is *nearer* than a is to the root r. This situation is illustrated in Figure 14.12c. Thus, the number x_1 may be taken as an approximation to the root r of the equation. By repeating this procedure with x_1 in place of a, a second approximation x_2 may be obtained, where

$$x_2 = x_1 - \frac{f(x_1)}{f'(x_1)}.$$

This process may be repeated as many times as is necessary in order to obtain an approximation to r to any desired degree of accuracy.

In order to be assured that the successive points $x_1, x_2, \ldots$, approach r, we must impose certain conditions on the function f in the neighborhood of the root r. In the preceding discussion, one of four possible cases was illustrated. A complete statement is given in the following theorem.

Theorem 14.12a. Let f be a function with a continuous second derivative on an interval $a \leq x \leq b$ and such that $f(a)$ and $f(b)$ have opposite signs and neither $f'(x)$ nor $f''(x)$ is zero for any x in the interval.

  (i) If the sign of $f''(x)$ is the same as that of $f(a)$, and $x_1 = a - [f(a)/f'(a)]$, then $a < x_1 < r$.
  (ii) If the sign of $f''(x)$ is opposite to that of $f(a)$, and $x_1 = b - [f(b)/f'(b)]$, then $r < x_1 < b$.

PROOF: The proof, which depends simply on the interpretation of the sign of $f''(x)$, is left to the reader.

By the use of the appropriate part of Theorem 14.12a, we may show that a sequence of approximations $\{x_n\}$, where

$$x_{n+1} = x_n - \frac{f(x_n)}{f'(x_n)},$$

approaches the root r as $n \to \infty$. Frequently, only a few steps are needed to obtain a good approximation to the root.

We can even show that, under fairly simple conditions, the number of accurate decimal places is at least doubled at each successive step. Thus, suppose that r is a root of $f(x) = 0$, where $a < r < b$, and suppose that $f(a) < 0$, $f(b) > 0$, $f'(x) \neq 0$, and $f''(x) < 0$. Then the conditions of (i) of Theorem 14.12a are met. Let x_{n+1} be the $(n + 1)$th approximation to r obtained by using the Newton-Raphson formula, so that

$$x_1 = a - \frac{f(a)}{f'(a)},$$

and

$$x_{n+1} = x_n - \frac{f(x_n)}{f'(x_n)}, \qquad n \in \mathfrak{N}.$$

By Theorem 14.12a, $x_n < x_{n+1} < r$, and the difference $r - x_n$ is a positive number, say h. We have

$$r - x_{n+1} = r - x_n + \frac{f(x_n)}{f'(x_n)} = h + \frac{f(x_n)}{f'(x_n)}.$$

Also, by the Mean Value Theorem for Derivatives,

$$f(r) = f(x_n) + hf'(x_n + \theta_1 h), \qquad 0 < \theta_1 < 1,$$

and, since $f(r) = 0$,

$$f(x_n) = -hf'(x_n + \theta_1 h).$$

By applying the Mean Value Theorem to f', we obtain

$$f'(x_n + \theta_1 h) = f'(x_n) + \theta_1 hf''(x_n + \theta_2 \theta_1 h), \qquad 0 < \theta_2 < 1.$$

Hence

$$f(x_n) = -h[f'(x_n) + \theta_1 hf''(x_n + \theta_1 \theta_2 h)],$$

so that

$$\frac{f(x_n)}{f'(x_n)} = -h - \theta_1 h^2 \cdot \frac{f''(x_n + \theta_1 \theta_2 h)}{f'(x_n)}.$$

Accordingly,

$$r - x_{n+1} = -\theta_1 h^2 \frac{f''(x_n + \theta_1\theta_2 h)}{f'(x_n)},$$

and, since $0 < \theta_1 < 1$,

$$|r - x_{n+1}| < Mh^2,$$

where $M = \max |f''(x)|/\min |f'(x)|$ for x_2 between x_n and r.

The final result can be obtained in the same way if any one of the other sets of conditions in Theorem 14.12a is assumed.

It follows that if we have a root r in an interval of length h for which $M < 1$, then the error in each approximation after the first is less than the square of the error in the preceding approximation. Now suppose that at some stage of the procedure we get the root correct to $k \geq 1$ decimal places, so that the error is not greater than $5 \times 10^{-k-1}$. Then the error in the next step will be not greater than

$$25 \times 10^{-2k-2} < 5 \times 10^{-2k-1}.$$

That is, the number of correct decimal places is doubled. In practice, it is convenient to choose for h the length of any interval which contains r and one of whose end points is x_n.

Example 14.12b. Find, correct to three decimal places, the real root of the equation

$$\ln x + x - 2 = 0.$$

If $f(x) .=. \ln x + x - 2$, then f is a continuous function with continuous derivatives for $x > 0$. Using tables, we find

$$f(1) = -1 \quad \text{and} \quad f(2) = 0.69315,$$

indicating that the root lies between 1 and 2. Furthermore,

$$f'(x) = \frac{1}{x} + 1 \quad \text{and} \quad f''(x) = -\frac{1}{x^2}.$$

Since $f''(x) < 0$ for all x, the curve is concave down and Case (i) of Theorem 14.12a applies. Hence, an approximation to the root is

$$x_1 = 1 - \frac{f(1)}{f'(1)} = 1.5.$$

By Theorem 14.12a, we know that the root r is greater than 1.5, and less than 2. A second approximation is

$$x_2 = 1.5 - \frac{f(1.5)}{f'(1.5)} = 1.5 - \frac{(-0.09453)}{5/3}$$

$$= 1.5567 \text{ (approx.)}.$$

In order to obtain an idea of the accuracy of this result, we make use of the fact that $r - x_2 < Mh^2$, where

$$M = \frac{\max |f''(x)|}{\min |f'(x)|} \quad \text{for } 1.5 \leq x \leq 2,$$

and

$$h = r - x_1.$$

For values of x from 1.5 to 2, we find that

$$\max |f''(x)| = \frac{1}{(1.5)^2} = \frac{4}{9}$$

and

$$\min |f'(x)| = \frac{1}{2} + 1 = \frac{3}{2}.$$

Hence, $M = 8/27 < 0.3$. This bound on the value of M may be used from this point on, since the value of M can only decrease if the interval containing the root is diminished. To get an estimate for h so that h is reasonably small, we need to determine a value of x near r such that $f(x) > 0$. Because the second approximation is less than 1.6, the latter value may prove to be satisfactory. In fact, with the aid of tables, we find that $f(1.6) = 0.07 > 0$. Therefore, we may take $h = 1.6 - 1.5 = 0.1$, and get

$$r - x_2 < Mh^2 < (0.3)(0.1)^2 = 0.003,$$

so that $r < 1.5597 < 1.56$. Since, by Theorem 14.12a, $x_2 < r$, we have

$$1.5567 < r < 1.56.$$

A third approximation is found to be

$$x_3 = 1.556 - \frac{f(1.556)}{f'(1.556)}$$

$$= 1.556 - \frac{-0.001882}{1.64267} = 1.557145.$$

An estimate for the error of this approximation is given by

$$r - x_3 < (0.3)(0.0033)^2 < 0.0000033,$$

where the value of h is taken as the difference between the two previously given bounds on r.

Thus, we may say with certainty that

$$1.557145 < r < 1.5571483,$$

and to three decimals, we have $r = 1.557$. As this example illustrates, the accuracy of the approximation increases rapidly after the root has been located in an interval of length 0.1 or less.

A second example will illustrate the method further.

Example 14.12c. Find the real root of

$$x^3 - 2x - 5 = 0$$

to four decimal places.

If $f(x) = x^3 - 2x - 5$, then $f(2) = -1$ and $f(3) = 16$, so that a root lies between 2 and 3, since f is continuous. Also,

$$f'(x) = 3x^2 - 2 \quad \text{and} \quad f''(x) = 6x.$$

Since, $f''(x) > 0$ over the interval between 2 and 3, and since $f'(x) \neq 0$ over this interval, we may use Theorem 14.12a, Case (ii). However, rather than using $b = 3$, it appears that we ought to choose a value for b nearer 2—because $f(3)$ is so much larger than $|f(2)|$. Substitution of $x = 2.1$ into $f(x)$ shows that $f(2.1) > 0$, so that we may take $b = 2.1$. Then,

$$x_1 = 2.1 - \frac{f(2.1)}{f'(2.1)} = 2.095 \text{ (approx.).}$$

For the interval $2 \leq x \leq 2.1$, max $|f''(x)| = 12.6$, and min $|f'(x)| = 10$, and we have

$$|r - 2.095| < \left(\frac{1}{10}\right)^2 \left(\frac{12.6}{10}\right) < 0.013,$$

so that

$$2.082 < r < 2.095.$$

Since it is awkward to round off 2.095 any further, let us make a second approximation using this value. Then,

$$x_2 = 2.095 - \frac{f(2.095)}{f'(2.095)} = 2.095 - \frac{0.005075}{11.167075} = 2.094552 \text{ (approx.).}$$

Furthermore, $f(2.094) < 0$, so that $2.094 < r < 2.095$. Therefore,

$$|r - 2.094552| < (0.001)^2 (1.26) = 0.00000126,$$

where the value of h in this case is taken as 0.001, since r is in the interval from 2.094 to 2.095. Hence the approximation $x_2 = 2.09455$ is accurate to the fifth decimal place. Calculations show that

$$f(2.094552) = 0.00000578,$$

and

$$f(2.094550) = -0.000016,$$

so that the root $r > 2.09455$ and thus $r = 2.0946$, correct to four decimal places.

In the preceding example, the reader should observe that in rounding off an approximation x_n, he must round off to a larger number in order to assure that $f(x_n)$ will be of the same sign as $f(x_{n-1})$. Rounding off to a smaller number may lead to an "overcorrection." When an approximation x_n is an overcorrection, then $f(x_n)$ will be of opposite sign from that of $f(x_{n-1})$. Normally, however, the overcorrection will cause no trouble. In general, in rounding off an approximation x_n, when x_n is greater than the root r, we should round off to a larger value, and when x_n is less than the root r, we should round off to a smaller value.

Exercises 14.12

For each of Numbers 1 to 10, use the Newton-Raphson Method to find the indicated root of the given equation to three decimal places.

1. $2 \ln x + x = 0$; the real root.
2. $x^4 + 4x + 1 = 0$; the negative root of smaller absolute value.
3. $x^3 - 3x - 3 = 0$; the real root.
4. $2 \sin x = x$; the positive root.
5. $e^x + x - 2 = 0$; the real root.
6. $\theta + \cos 2\theta = 0$; the real root.
7. $e^x = \tan x$; the smallest positive root.
8. $3 \sin x = x^2$; the positive root.
9. $x^4 + x^3 + x^2 = 1$; the smallest positive root.

10. $x + \text{Tan}^{-1} x - 1 = 0$; the smallest positive root.
11. In a certain circle, a chord 9 inches long subtends an arc 12 inches long. Find, in radians correct to three decimal places, the central angle which the chord subtends.
12. The area of one end of a tank in the form of a right circular cylinder is 75 square feet. The axis of the tank is horizontal and the tank is partially filled with water. Find the depth of the water if one-third of the area of the end of the tank is covered with water.
13. A wire 12 inches long is bent into a circular arc whose chord is 10 inches. What is the radius of the arc?
14. Two buildings are on opposite sides of an alley. A ladder 16 feet long extends from the foot of one building to the wall of the second building. Another ladder 20 feet long extends from the foot of the second building to the wall of the first building. If the ladders cross at a point 4 feet above the alley, find the width of the alley. *Hint:* You should get a fourth degree polynomial equation to solve for the height to which a ladder reaches up the side of the building. Use this distance to calculate the width of the alley.
15. A sector of a circle is cut from a piece of paper and rolled up without overlapping to form a right circular cone. What should be the central angle of the sector so that this angle is 1.5 times the vertex angle of the cone?
16. Find the maximum point on the curve $y = x \sin x$, $x > 0$, that is closest to the origin.

Summary of Chapter 14

The trigonometric and hyperbolic functions and their inverses play an important role in many mathematical studies. It is therefore important that the student have a thorough knowledge of and facility with them, as well as an understanding of the general techniques, in regard to the following points:

(1) the continuity of the sine and cosine functions (Section 14.1);
(2) the derivatives of the trigonometric functions and their applications (Sections 14.2, 14.3);
(3) the inverse derivatives of the trigonometric functions (Section 14.4);
(4) the inverse trigonometric functions (Section 14.5);
(5) the derivatives of the inverse trigonometric functions (Section 14.6);
(6) the hyperbolic and inverse hyperbolic functions and their derivatives (Section 14.7);
(7) the definition of complex-valued functions and their geometric interpretation as vector functions (Section 14.8);
(8) the definition of e^{x+iy} and the relationships involving this expression (Section 14.8);
(9) finding roots of complex numbers (Section 14.9);
(10) L'Hôpital's Rule for the evaluation of limits and its applications (Sections 14.10, 14.11);
(11) the Newton-Raphson Method for the approximation of roots of equations (Section 14.12).

Chapter 15 Formal Integration and Applications

15.1 REVIEW OF BASIC INVERSE DERIVATIVES

The definite integral has been shown to be of fundamental importance in the mathematical analysis of many practical problems. The evaluation of definite integrals has been based upon the Fundamental Theorem of Integral Calculus, which requires a knowledge of the appropriate inverse derivatives. Thus far, inverse derivatives have been found by inspection or by a simple inversion of a derivative formula. For example, from

$$D_x \sin x = \cos x$$

it follows that

$$\int \cos x \, dx = \sin x + C.$$

However, it should not be expected that every definite integral can be handled simply by finding an inverse derivative in the form of a familiar elementary type of function. For example, the integral

$$\int_1^3 e^{-x^2} \, dx$$

cannot be evaluated in this way because there is no simpler form for the inverse derivative of e^{-x^2} than

$$\int_1^x e^{-t^2} \, dt.$$

(The proof of this is beyond the scope of our work here.)

Meanwhile, we must develop additional techniques for finding inverse derivatives when they can be expressed in terms of the simple functions with which we are already familiar. Most of these techniques are based upon the inverse derivatives that have been obtained in the preceding chapters. Accordingly, it is important for the student to be familiar with the following basic list which summarizes the pertinent inverse derivative formulas that have been discussed previously. The exercises that follow provide a review of the skills associated with the use of these formulas.

(1) $\int u^n\, du = \dfrac{u^{n+1}}{n+1} + C,\, n \neq -1.$

(2) $\int \dfrac{du}{u} = \ln |u| + C.$

(3) $\int e^u\, du = e^u + C.$

(4) $\int a^u\, du = \dfrac{a^u}{\ln a} + C,\, a > 0,\, a \neq 1.$

(5) $\int \sin u\, du = -\cos u + C.$

(6) $\int \cos u\, du = \sin u + C.$

(7) $\int \sec^2 u\, du = \tan u + C.$

(8) $\int \csc^2 u\, du = -\cot u + C.$

(9) $\int \sec u \tan u\, du = \sec u + C.$

(10) $\int \csc u \cot u\, du = -\csc u + C.$

(11) $\int \tan u\, du = \ln |\sec u| + C = -\ln |\cos u| + C.$

(12) $\int \cot u\, du = \ln |\sin u| + C = -\ln |\csc u| + C.$

(13) $\int \sec u\, du = \ln |\sec u + \tan u| + C.$

(14) $\int \csc u\, du = \ln |\csc u - \cot u| + C = \ln |\tan \tfrac{1}{2}u| + C.$

(15) $\int \dfrac{du}{\sqrt{a^2 - u^2}} = \text{Sin}^{-1} \dfrac{u}{a} + C,\, 0 < |u| < a.$

(16) $\int \dfrac{du}{a^2 + u^2} = \dfrac{1}{a} \text{Tan}^{-1} \dfrac{u}{a} + C,\, a \neq 0.$

(17) $\int \dfrac{du}{\sqrt{u^2 + a^2}} = \sinh^{-1} \dfrac{u}{a} + C,\, a > 0.$

(18) $\int \dfrac{du}{\sqrt{u^2 - a^2}} = \text{Cosh}^{-1} \dfrac{u}{a} + C,\, u > a > 0.$

Exercises 15.1

In each of Numbers 1 to 34, find the inverse derivative.

1. $\displaystyle\int (4x^3 + 8x^2 + 7)\,dx.$

2. $\displaystyle\int \sqrt{2x + 3}\,dx.$

3. $\displaystyle\int \cos t \sin^2 t\,dt.$

4. $\displaystyle\int x \cos x^2\,dx.$

5. $\displaystyle\int w\sqrt{w^2 + 1}\,dw.$

6. $\displaystyle\int v^2(2 + v^3)^{1/2}\,dv.$

7. $\displaystyle\int \frac{x}{x + 1}\,dx.$

8. $\displaystyle\int \frac{t^3\,dt}{t^2 + 9}.$

9. $\displaystyle\int e^{3u}\,du.$

10. $\displaystyle\int (2^s + s^2)\,ds.$

11. $\displaystyle\int \frac{\sin v}{\cos^2 v}\,dv.$

12. $\displaystyle\int \csc 5w\,dw.$

13. $\displaystyle\int \frac{\tan \sqrt{x}}{\sqrt{x}}\,dx.$

14. $\displaystyle\int x \sec x^2 \tan x^2\,dx.$

15. $\displaystyle\int \frac{w\,dw}{\sqrt{w^2 + 4}}.$

16. $\displaystyle\int \frac{dw}{\sqrt{w^2 + 4}}.$

17. $\displaystyle\int \frac{t\,dt}{t^2 - 9}.$

18. $\displaystyle\int \frac{r^3}{4r^4 + 9}\,dr.$

19. $\displaystyle\int x\,2^{x^2}\,dx.$

20. $\displaystyle\int xe^{x^2}\,dx.$

21. $\displaystyle\int \frac{u\,du}{\sqrt{u^2 - 4}}.$

22. $\displaystyle\int \frac{du}{\sqrt{u^2 - 4}}.$

23. $\displaystyle\int \frac{dx}{4x^2 + 25}.$

24. $\displaystyle\int \frac{u^2\,du}{u^2 + 4}.$

25. $\displaystyle\int \frac{dy}{\sqrt{4 - y^2}}.$

26. $\displaystyle\int \frac{dx}{\sqrt{3 - 4x^2}}.$

27. $\displaystyle\int u^2 \csc u^3\,du.$

28. $\displaystyle\int \sec^3 \theta \tan \theta\,d\theta.$

29. $\displaystyle\int (\sqrt{2w} + 1)^2\,dw.$

30. $\displaystyle\int \frac{ds}{\sqrt{4s + 9}}.$

31. $\displaystyle\int \sin^3 2x \cos 2x\,dx.$

32. $\displaystyle\int \csc 2w \cot 2w\,dw.$

33. $\displaystyle\int 2^w\,dw.$

34. $\displaystyle\int e^2\,dx.$

In each of Numbers 35 to 44, evaluate the given definite integral.

35. $\displaystyle\int_0^1 \frac{3x\,dx}{\sqrt{x^2+8}}$.

36. $\displaystyle\int_2^{2\sqrt{3}} \frac{dt}{4+t^2}$.

37. $\displaystyle\int_0^{\pi/2} \sin 2t\,dt$.

38. $\displaystyle\int_0^{\pi/2} (\sin x)e^{\cos x}\,dx$.

39. $\displaystyle\int_0^2 3se^{s^2}\,ds$.

40. $\displaystyle\int_0^4 \frac{dx}{\sqrt{2x+1}}$.

41. $\displaystyle\int_{-1/4}^{1/4} \sec^2 \pi x \tan \pi x\,dx$.

42. $\displaystyle\int_{-3\pi/4}^0 \tan \tfrac{1}{3}t\,dt$.

43. $\displaystyle\int_0^{\sqrt{2}/2} \frac{dw}{\sqrt{1-w^2}}$.

44. $\displaystyle\int_0^{\pi/6} \tan^2 2w \sec^2 2w\,dw$.

15.2 ADDITIONAL INTEGRALS INVOLVING TRIGONOMETRIC FUNCTIONS

The inverse derivatives of the trigonometric functions were discussed in Section 14.4. By the use of trigonometric identities, many integrals involving products and powers of the trigonometric functions may be reduced to a standard form. Several examples will illustrate the procedure.

Example 15.2a. Evaluate

$$\int_0^{\pi/2} \tan^2 \frac{x}{2}\,dx.$$

Replacing $\tan^2 x/2$ by its equivalent, $\sec^2 (x/2) - 1$, we obtain

$$\int_0^{\pi/2} \tan^2 \frac{x}{2}\,dx = \int_0^{\pi/2} \left(\sec^2 \frac{x}{2} - 1\right) dx$$

$$= \left[2 \tan \frac{x}{2} - x\right]_0^{\pi/2} = 2 - \frac{\pi}{2}.$$

It is frequently possible to rewrite the integrand as the sum of powers of a trigonometric function multiplied by the differential of that function, as in the next examples.

Example 15.2b. Find $\displaystyle\int \cos^3 x\,dx$.

Using the fact that $d \sin x = \cos x\,dx$, we write

$$\int \cos^3 x\,dx = \int (\cos^2 x) \cos x\,dx$$

$$= \int (1 - \sin^2 x) \cos x\,dx$$

$$= \int \cos x\,dx - \int \sin^2 x\,d(\sin x)$$

$$= \sin x - \tfrac{1}{3} \sin^3 x + C.$$

Example 15.2c. Find $\int \tan^5 3x \, dx$.

In this problem, we make use of the identity $\tan^2 3x = \sec^2 3x - 1$, and proceed as follows:

$$\int \tan^5 3x \, dx = \int \tan^3 3x \tan^2 3x \, dx$$

$$= \int \tan^3 3x(\sec^2 3x - 1) \, dx$$

$$= \tfrac{1}{3} \int \tan^3 3x(\sec^2 3x)(3 \, dx) - \int \tan^3 3x \, dx$$

$$= \tfrac{1}{3} \int \tan^3 3x \, d(\tan 3x) - \int \tan 3x(\sec^2 3x - 1) \, dx$$

$$= \tfrac{1}{12} \tan^4 3x - \tfrac{1}{3} \int \tan 3x \, d(\tan 3x) + \int \tan 3x \, dx$$

$$= \tfrac{1}{12} \tan^4 3x - \tfrac{1}{6} \tan^2 3x + \tfrac{1}{3} \ln |\sec 3x| + C.$$

Even powers of $\sin u$ and $\cos u$ may be integrated by means of the identities

$$\sin^2 u = \tfrac{1}{2}(1 - \cos 2u),$$
$$\cos^2 u = \tfrac{1}{2}(1 + \cos 2u),$$

as in the following example.

Example 15.2d. Find $\int \cos^4 5y \, dy$.

We proceed as follows:

$$\int \cos^4 5y \, dy = \int \left(\frac{1 + \cos 10y}{2}\right)^2 dy$$

$$= \tfrac{1}{4} \int (1 + 2 \cos 10y + \cos^2 10y) \, dy$$

$$= \tfrac{1}{4} \int (1 + 2 \cos 10y + \tfrac{1}{2} + \tfrac{1}{2} \cos 20y) \, dy$$

$$= \tfrac{3}{8}y + \tfrac{1}{20} \sin 10y + \tfrac{1}{160} \sin 20y + C.$$

Although techniques similar to the preceding ones enable us to find the inverse derivatives of many combinations of trigonometric functions, the reader should recognize that such a procedure will not always suffice. For example, $\int \sec^3 x \, dx$ cannot be handled by any of the preceding schemes. However, a method of finding this inverse derivative will be discussed in Section 15.5 on Integration by Parts.

Exercises 15.2

In each of Numbers 1 to 32, find the inverse derivative.

1. $\int \sin^3 3x \, dx.$

2. $\int \cot^2 2y \, dy.$

3. $\int \frac{\tan^2 \theta}{\sin^2 \theta} \, d\theta.$

4. $\int \frac{\cos 2x}{\sin x} \, dx.$

5. $\int \frac{\tan 2r}{\cos^2 2r} \, dr.$

6. $\int \cos^3 (w/2) \, dw.$

7. $\int \sec^3 3y \tan^5 3y \, dy.$

8. $\int \sin^2 5r \, dr.$

9. $\int \tan^3 2s \, ds.$

10. $\int \sin 2x \tan x \, dx.$

11. $\int \sin^2 y \cos^3 y \, dy.$

12. $\int \tan^4 (s/2) \, ds.$

13. $\int \cos^5 2w \, dw.$

14. $\int \sec^4 3y \, dy.$

15. $\int \frac{\cos x}{\sin^3 x} \, dx.$

16. $\int \sin^5 3r \cos^2 3r \, dr.$

17. $\int \sin^2 2x \cos^2 2x \, dx.$

18. $\int \cos^2 2x \sin 4x \, dx.$

19. $\int (\cos x - \cos x \cos 2x) \, dx.$

20. $\int \cos^4 4x \, dx.$

21. $\int \frac{\cos 3y \, dy}{1 + \sin 3y}.$

22. $\int \frac{dy}{1 + \sin 5y}.$

23. $\int \cot^5 2r \, dr.$

24. $\int \sin^3 (s/2) \cos^2 (s/2) \, ds.$

25. $\int \sqrt{1 + \cos 2x} \, dx.$

26. $\int \sqrt{1 - \cos (w/3)} \, dw.$

27. $\int \frac{1 + \cos 2\theta}{\sin 2\theta} \, d\theta.$

28. $\int \frac{\cos 2y}{\sin^2 2y} \, dy.$

29. $\int \frac{dw}{1 + \sec (w/2)}.$

30. $\int \frac{dw}{1 - \cos 7w}.$

31. $\int \cot^6 2u \, du.$

32. $\int \sin^3 3y \cos^5 3y \, dy.$

In each of Numbers 33 to 42, evaluate the definite integral.

33. $\int_0^{\pi/4} \tan^3 x \, dx.$

34. $\int_0^{\pi/2} \sqrt{\cos x} \sin^3 x \, dx.$

35. $\int_0^{\pi/2} \cos^4 3y \, dy.$

36. $\int_0^{\pi/4} (\cos y + \cos^2 y)^2 \, dy.$

37. $\displaystyle\int_0^{\pi/3} \frac{dw}{1 + \sin w}.$

40. $\displaystyle\int_0^{\pi/2} \frac{1 - \sin x}{x + \cos x}\, dx.$

38. $\displaystyle\int_0^{\pi/4} (\sin y - \cos y)^2\, dy.$

41. $\displaystyle\int_{\pi/4}^{\pi/2} \csc^6 u\, du.$

39. $\displaystyle\int_0^{\pi/2} \sin^3 2v\, dv.$

42. $\displaystyle\int_0^{\pi/6} \tan^4 2z\, dz.$

By using the fact that

$$a \cos \theta + b \sin \theta = \sqrt{a^2 + b^2}\, \cos (\theta - \alpha),$$

where $\alpha = \text{Tan}^{-1} b/a$ for $a > 0$, $b > 0$, integrals such as those in Numbers 43 to 46 can be evaluated.

43. $\displaystyle\int_0^t \frac{dx}{4 \cos x + 3 \sin x}.$

45. $\displaystyle\int_0^x \frac{dy}{(4 \sin y - 3 \cos y)^2}.$

44. $\displaystyle\int_0^x \frac{d\varphi}{5 \cos \varphi - 12 \sin \varphi}.$

46. $\displaystyle\int_0^t \frac{d\varphi}{(5 \cos \varphi + 12 \sin \varphi)^2}.$

If the integrand is a product of two sines or two cosines or a sine and a cosine of different multiples of the same variable, the inverse differentiation can be performed by using the appropriate one of the following trigonometric identities (see Theorems 7.5g, 7.5h, and 7.5i).

$$\sin \alpha \cos \beta = \tfrac{1}{2} \sin (\alpha + \beta) + \tfrac{1}{2} \sin (\alpha - \beta),$$
$$\cos \alpha \cos \beta = \tfrac{1}{2} \cos (\alpha + \beta) + \tfrac{1}{2} \cos (\alpha - \beta),$$
$$\sin \alpha \sin \beta = -\tfrac{1}{2} \cos (\alpha + \beta) + \tfrac{1}{2} \cos (\alpha - \beta).$$

Use these results to evaluate the integrals in Numbers 47 to 50.

47. $\displaystyle\int_0^{\pi/2} \sin 2x \cos 3x\, dx.$

49. $\displaystyle\int_0^{\pi/6} \cos \tfrac{1}{2}x \cos \tfrac{7}{2}x\, dx.$

48. $\displaystyle\int_0^{\pi/4} \sin \theta \sin 3\theta\, d\theta.$

50. $\displaystyle\int_0^{\pi} \cos 2u \sin 4u\, du.$

51. Show that

$$\int \tan^n x\, dx = \frac{\tan^{n-1} x}{n - 1} - \int \tan^{n-2} x\, dx, \qquad n \neq 1.$$

52. Show that

$$\int \cot x \csc^n x\, dx = -\frac{\csc^n x}{n} + C, \qquad n \neq 0.$$

53. Find the area bounded by the curve $y = \tan^2 x$, the x-axis, and the line $x = \pi/4$.

54. Find the area bounded by the curve $y = |\sin^3 x|$ and the x-axis from $x = 0$ to $x = 2\pi$.

55. Find the area bounded by the curve $y = (\cos 2x - \sin 2x)^2$, the y-axis, and the x-axis from $x = 0$ to the first point where the curve touches the positive x-axis.

56. Find the area bounded by the curve $y = \sec^4 x$ and the lines $x = 0$, $y = 4$, $x = \pi/3$.

57. Calculate the volume formed by revolving the area bounded by $y = \tan x$, $x = 0$, $y = 0$, $x = \pi/4$ about the x-axis.

58. Find the volume formed by revolving the area bounded by one arch of the curve $y = \sin \frac{1}{2}x$ and the x-axis about the x-axis.
59. The quantity of heat (joules) generated by a constant current I (amperes) in a resistance R (ohms) in time t_0 (seconds) is $Q = RI^2 t_0$. If the current is not constant but is 60-cycle per second current, so that $I = I_0 \sin 120\pi t$, what quantity of heat is generated in 1 minute?
60. A variable force directed along the positive x-axis has a magnitude in pounds $F = F_0 \cos^2 \omega x$. How much work is done by this force in moving a body from $x = 0$ to $x = 2\pi/\omega$ (feet) on the x-axis?

15.3 THE METHOD OF SUBSTITUTION

In the preceding work, we have often found an inverse derivative of a given function by means of a substitution method based on the chain rule. For instance, in the integral

$$\int x\sqrt{x^2 + 4}\, dx,$$

we observe that $d(x^2 + 4) = 2x\, dx$ and rewrite the integral in the form

$$\frac{1}{2} \int \sqrt{x^2 + 4}\,(2x\, dx).$$

If we let $u = x^2 + 4$, then the integral becomes

$$\frac{1}{2} \int \sqrt{u}\, du = \frac{1}{3}u^{3/2} + C,$$

so that

$$\int x\sqrt{x^2 + 4}\, dx = \frac{1}{3}(x^2 + 4)^{3/2} + C.$$

This procedure is justified by considering two differentiable functions defined by $y = F(u)$ and $u = g(x)$ and applying the chain rule to get

$$D_x F(u) = D_u F(u)\, D_x u = D_u F(u)\, g'(x).$$

If $f(u) .=. D_u F(u)$, so that

$$D_x F(u) = f[g(x)]g'(x),$$

then the corresponding inverse derivative formula is

(1)
$$\int f[g(x)]g'(x)\, dx = F[g(x)] + C,$$

which may be put in the form

(2)
$$\int f(u)\, du = F(u) + C$$

since $u = g(x)$.

The foregoing discussion suggests that a substitution of the type $x = g(u)$ might be used to transform an integral

$$\int f(x)\, dx$$

into the form

$$\int f[g(u)]g'(u)\, du,$$

where the inverse derivative is known, say

$$\int f[g(u)]g'(u)\, du = H(u) + C.$$

If the function g has a corresponding inverse function, then under the appropriate hypotheses, we can justify the result

$$\int f(x)\, dx = H[g^{-1}(x)] + C,$$

which would be obtained by replacing u by $g^{-1}(x)$.

Theorem 15.3a. Let $x = g(u)$ be a differentiable function having a differentiable inverse function $u = g^{-1}(x)$. Then, on any interval where $g'(x) \neq 0$,

$$(3) \qquad \int f[g(u)]g'(u)\, du = H(u) + C \Rightarrow \int f(x)\, dx = H[g^{-1}(x)] + C.$$

PROOF: By the chain rule we have

$$D_x H(u) = D_u H(u)\, D_x g^{-1}(x) = D_u H(u)\, \frac{1}{g'(u)},$$

and since $D_u H(u) = f[g(u)]g'(u)$, it follows that

$$D_x H[g^{-1}(x)] = f[g(u)]g'(u)\, \frac{1}{g'(u)} = f[g(u)] = f(x).$$

In other words, we have shown that $H[g^{-1}(x)]$ is an inverse derivative of $f(x)$ and that the process of substitution is justified under the appropriate conditions.

The replacement of the variable of integration x in an integral $\int f(x)\, dx$ by means of an equation $x = g(u)$ and the application of Theorem 15.3a to the resulting integral is called the **method of substitution**. This method may be used successfully whenever a substitution $u = g(x)$, $du = g'(x)\, dx$ transforms an integral into a known inverse derivative as in the preceding example. The ability needed to determine useful substitutions comes only with practice and experience.

The example of the first paragraph is a special case of the integral

$$(4) \qquad \int (a + bx^n)^{p/q} x^m\, dx.$$

Before reading further, make a guess as to a good substitution and try it.

The substitution should be one that transforms the integrand into a rational algebraic expression, so an obvious conjecture is

$$(5) \qquad a + bx^n = y^q.$$

Differentiation of both members of this equation gives

(6) $$nbx^{n-1} \, dx = qy^{q-1} \, dy,$$

and the result of substituting from these two equations into (4) is

$$\frac{q}{nb} \int \left(\frac{y^q - a}{b}\right)^{(m-n+1)/n} y^{p+q-1} \, dy.$$

Thus it appears that if $(m - n + 1)/n$ is an integer, then the new integrand is a rational expression in y.

Example 15.3a. Integrate $\int x^3 \sqrt{1 + 2x^2} \, dx$.

Here we have $m = 3$ and $n = 2$, so that $(m - n + 1)/n = 1$. Hence, let $y^2 = 1 + 2x^2$, so that $2y \, dy = 4x \, dx$. Then,

$$\int x^3 \sqrt{1 + 2x^2} \, dx = \int x^2 \sqrt{1 + 2x^2} \, x \, dx$$

$$= \int [\tfrac{1}{2}(y^2 - 1)](y)(\tfrac{1}{2}y \, dy)$$

$$= \tfrac{1}{4} \int (y^4 - y^2) \, dy$$

$$= \tfrac{1}{4}(\tfrac{1}{5}y^5 - \tfrac{1}{3}y^3) + C$$

$$= \tfrac{1}{60}y^3(3y^2 - 5) + C$$

$$= \tfrac{1}{60}(1 + 2x^2)^{3/2}(6x^2 - 2) + C.$$

If $n = 1$ in the general integral (4), then $(m - n + 1)/n$ is an integer and the substitution $a + bx = y^q$ will always yield a rational integrand.

Frequently an integral involving $ax^2 + bx + c$ may be transformed into one of the standard forms by completing the square in x and then making a substitution.

Example 15.3b. Integrate

$$\int \frac{dx}{\sqrt{x^2 + 6x}}.$$

We first complete the square under the radical to get

$$\int \frac{dx}{\sqrt{x^2 + 6x}} = \int \frac{dx}{\sqrt{x^2 + 6x + 9 - 9}} = \int \frac{dx}{\sqrt{(x + 3)^2 - 9}}.$$

Then let $u = x + 3$, so that the integral becomes

$$\int \frac{du}{\sqrt{u^2 - 3^2}} = \mathrm{Cosh}^{-1} \frac{u}{3} + C$$

$$= \mathrm{Cosh}^{-1} \frac{x + 3}{3} + C.$$

Example 15.3c. Integrate

$$\int \frac{x+3}{x^2+2x+2} \, dx.$$

By completing the square in the denominator of the integrand, we get

$$x^2 + 2x + 2 = (x+1)^2 + 1.$$

Accordingly, let $x + 1 = v$ so that $dx = dv$, and

$$\int \frac{(x+3)\,dx}{x^2+2x+2} = \int \frac{(v+2)\,dv}{v^2+1}$$

$$= \int \frac{v\,dv}{v^2+1} + \int \frac{2\,dv}{v^2+1}$$

$$= \tfrac{1}{2} \ln (v^2 + 1) + 2 \operatorname{Tan}^{-1} v + C$$

$$= \tfrac{1}{2} \ln (x^2 + 2x + 2) + 2 \operatorname{Tan}^{-1} (x + 1) + C.$$

The evaluation of a definite integral can often be made by substitution on the basis of the next theorem.

Theorem 15.3b. Let f be a continuous function of x on the closed interval $a \leq x \leq b$, and let $x = g(t)$, where $t = c$ when $x = a$, $t = d$ when $x = b$, and t is in the interval from c to d when x is in the interval $a \leq x \leq b$. Let g' be continuous on the interval from c to d. Then

$$\int_a^b f(x)\,dx = \int_c^d f[g(t)]g'(t)\,dt = \int_c^d h(t)\,dt,$$

where $h(t) = f[g(t)]g'(t)$.

PROOF: Let $F(x) = \int_a^x f(y)\,dy$ and $H(t) = \int_c^t h(s)\,ds$. Then

$$F(b) = \int_a^b f(y)\,dy \quad \text{and} \quad H(d) = \int_c^d h(s)\,ds,$$

so that we need only show that $F(b) = H(d)$. By the Fundamental Theorem of Integral Calculus, we have

$$F'(x) = f(x) \quad \text{and} \quad H'(t) = h(t).$$

Next, using $x = g(t)$, we get

$$F[g(t)] = \int_a^{g(t)} f(y)\,dy$$

and

$$D_t F[g(t)] = F'[g(t)]g'(t)$$
$$= f[g(t)]g'(t)$$
$$= h(t)$$
$$= H'(t).$$

Thus

$$F[g(t)] = H(t) + C.$$

If we substitute $t = c$, then

$$F[g(c)] = H(c) + C.$$

But $g(c) = a$, so that

$$F(a) = H(c) + C.$$

However,

$$F(a) = \int_a^a f(y)\, dy = 0 \quad \text{and} \quad H(c) = \int_c^c h(s)\, ds = 0,$$

so that

$$C = 0 \quad \text{and} \quad F(x) = H(t).$$

Hence, if we let $x = b$, then $t = d$, and we obtain

$$F(b) = H(d),$$

which completes the proof.

Example 15.3d. Evaluate

$$\int_0^4 \frac{x}{\sqrt{1 + 2x}}\, dx.$$

If $y = \sqrt{1 + 2x}$, then $y^2 = 1 + 2x$, $dx = y\, dy$, and $x = 0 \Rightarrow y = 1$, $x = 4 \Rightarrow y = 3$. Thus,

$$\int_0^4 \frac{x}{\sqrt{1 + 2x}}\, dx = \frac{1}{2} \int_1^3 \frac{(y^2 - 1)y\, dy}{y}$$

$$= \frac{1}{2}\left[\frac{y^3}{3} - y\right]_1^3$$

$$= \frac{10}{3}.$$

Another way in which Theorem 15.3b is useful is illustrated by the next example, which involves parametric equations.

Example 15.3e. Find the area bounded by the x-axis and the curve $x = t + t^2$, $y = t - t^2$ from $t = 0$ to $t = 1$.

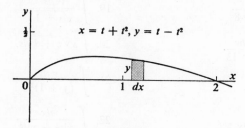

FIGURE 15.3a

From the given equations, it is seen that $t = 0$ corresponds to the point $(0, 0)$ and $t = 1$ to the point $(2, 0)$. Figure 15.3a shows that the required area is given by

$$A = \int_0^2 y\, dx.$$

Since it is inconvenient to substitute for y in terms of x, we substitute for y and x both in terms of t. From the equation $x = t + t^2$, it follows that $dx = (1 + 2t)\, dt$, which we use along with the limits on t to obtain

$$A = \int_0^2 y\, dx = \int_0^1 (t - t^2)(1 + 2t)\, dt$$

$$\int_0^1 (t + t^2 - 2t^3)\, dt = \tfrac{1}{3} \text{ (l.u.)}^2.$$

Exercises 15.3

In each of Numbers 1 to 22, find the inverse derivative.

1. $\displaystyle\int \frac{x\, dx}{\sqrt{x + 4}}.$

2. $\displaystyle\int \frac{dy}{y - \sqrt{y}}.$

3. $\displaystyle\int s^3\sqrt{9 - s^2}\, ds.$

4. $\displaystyle\int \frac{\sqrt{r - 4}}{r}\, dr.$

5. $\displaystyle\int \frac{dx}{\sqrt{8 + 2x - x^2}}.$

6. $\displaystyle\int \frac{dt}{t^2 - 6t + 12}.$

7. $\displaystyle\int \frac{u\, du}{\sqrt{u^2 - 4u + 8}}.$

8. $\displaystyle\int \frac{(x + 7)\, dx}{x^2 + 4x + 8}.$

9. $\displaystyle\int \frac{(w - 2)\, dw}{w^2 - 4w + 13}.$

10. $\displaystyle\int \frac{dx}{x\sqrt{x^2 - 4}}.$

11. $\displaystyle\int \frac{\sqrt{x^2 - 9}}{3x}\, dx.$

12. $\displaystyle\int \frac{dy}{\sqrt{y^2 - 6y + 5}}.$

13. $\displaystyle\int \frac{dt}{t^2 + 2t + 3}.$

14. $\displaystyle\int \frac{x\, dx}{4 + \sqrt{x + 4}}.$

15. $\displaystyle\int \frac{y^3\, dy}{(4 + y^2)^{3/2}}.$

16. $\displaystyle\int t(1 + t)^{3/2}\, dt.$

17. $\displaystyle\int \frac{x + 3}{\sqrt[5]{x}}\, dx.$

18. $\displaystyle\int \frac{s\, ds}{\sqrt{s^2 + s}}.$

19. $\displaystyle\int \frac{s^2\, ds}{\sqrt{s + 1}}.$

20. $\displaystyle\int s\sqrt[3]{s + 1}\, ds.$

21. $\displaystyle\int \frac{y\, dy}{(y + 1)^{2/3}}.$

22. $\displaystyle\int \frac{dx}{x^{1/2} + x^{1/3}}.$

Evaluate the definite integral in each of Numbers 23 to 34.

23. $\displaystyle\int_0^7 \frac{s\,ds}{\sqrt[3]{s+1}}$.

24. $\displaystyle\int_0^{2\sqrt{3}} \frac{x^3\,dx}{\sqrt{4+x^2}}$.

25. $\displaystyle\int_4^7 \frac{dx}{x^2-8x+25}$.

26. $\displaystyle\int_0^5 \frac{3y\,dy}{\sqrt{y+4}}$.

27. $\displaystyle\int_0^3 t^5\sqrt{9-t^2}\,dt$.

28. $\displaystyle\int_2^3 \frac{dy}{\sqrt{4y-y^2}}$.

29. $\displaystyle\int_1^{\sqrt{2}} \frac{t^3\,dt}{\sqrt{4-t^2}}$.

30. $\displaystyle\int_4^9 \frac{3\,dx}{x+\sqrt{x}}$.

31. $\displaystyle\int_0^3 y^2(1+y)^{-3/2}\,dy$.

32. $\displaystyle\int_1^4 \frac{x\,dx}{x+\sqrt{x}}$.

33. $\displaystyle\int_1^2 \frac{dx}{x^2\sqrt{1+x^2}}$. $\left(\text{Let } x = \dfrac{1}{z}.\right)$

34. $\displaystyle\int_{4/\sqrt{3}}^4 \frac{dz}{z^2\sqrt{z^2-4}}$.

35. Find the area bounded by the curve $y = x/\sqrt{1+3x}$ and the lines $y = 0$, $x = 5$.
36. Find the area within the loop of the curve $y^2 + x^3 = x^2$.
37. Find the area bounded by the curve $y = x/(1+\sqrt{x})$ and the lines $y = 0$, $x = 9$.
38. Find the x-coordinate of the centroid of the area of Number 37.
39. Find the volume formed by revolving about the y-axis the area of Number 37.
40. Find the area bounded by the y-axis and the curve $x = t - t^3$, $y = t + t^3$ from $t = 0$ to $t = 1$.
41. Refer to Figure 14.7a and show that the area of the hyperbolic sector *AOP* is $\frac{1}{2}u$ (l.u.)². *Hint:* Use the parametric equations $x = \cosh u$, $y = \sinh u$.
42. Find the area enclosed by the ellipse $x = a\cos\theta$, $y = b\sin\theta$.

15.4 TRIGONOMETRIC AND HYPERBOLIC SUBSTITUTIONS

Formulas (15), (16), (17), and (18) of Section 15.1 express certain integrals in terms of inverse trigonometric or inverse hyperbolic functions. These formulas may be derived using the method of substitution and some of the trigonometric or hyperbolic identities. These substitutions not only furnish a handy method of developing the formulas, but are useful in integrating many other expressions.

Example 15.4a. Use a trigonometric substitution to derive a formula for

$$\int \frac{du}{\sqrt{a^2-u^2}}, \qquad a > 0.$$

Here it would be advantageous to find a substitution that would remove the radical in the denominator. This suggests the use of the identity

$$1 - \sin^2\theta = \cos^2\theta,$$

since if we let

$$u = a\sin\theta, \qquad \theta = \text{Sin}^{-1}(u/a),$$

then

$$\sqrt{a^2 - u^2} = \sqrt{a^2 - a^2 \sin^2 \theta} = a \cos \theta.$$

Notice that $\cos \theta \geq 0$ since we have employed the principal inverse sine function. This agrees with the understanding that the radical sign signifies the principal square root. Furthermore,

$$du = a \cos \theta \, d\theta,$$

so that the integral is transformed as follows:

$$\int \frac{du}{\sqrt{a^2 - u^2}} = \int \frac{a \cos \theta \, d\theta}{a \cos \theta} = \int d\theta$$

$$= \theta + C = \mathrm{Sin}^{-1} (u/a) + C.$$

Since $1 - \tanh^2 \theta = \mathrm{sech}^2 \theta$, the substitution $u = a \tanh \theta$ could also have been used although not as conveniently, as the reader may verify.

Example 15.4b. Integrate

$$\int \frac{dx}{x^2 \sqrt{4 - x^2}}.$$

Let $x = 2 \sin \theta$, with $\theta = \mathrm{Sin}^{-1} (x/2)$. Then $dx = 2 \cos \theta \, d\theta$, so that

$$\int \frac{dx}{x^2 \sqrt{4 - x^2}} = \int \frac{2 \cos \theta \, d\theta}{4 \sin^2 \theta (2 \cos \theta)}$$

$$= \frac{1}{4} \int \csc^2 \theta \, d\theta$$

$$= -\frac{1}{4} \cot \theta + C.$$

From Figure 15.4a, it is apparent that if $\sin \theta = x/2$, then

$$\cot \theta = \frac{\sqrt{4 - x^2}}{x}.$$

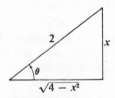

FIGURE 15.4a

The specification of the principal inverse sine value for θ justifies the use of the triangle. Thus we find

$$\int \frac{dx}{x^2 \sqrt{4 - x^2}} = \frac{-\sqrt{4 - x^2}}{4x} + C.$$

Note: The student should keep in mind that any inverse derivative can always be checked by differentiation.

Example 15.4c. Use a trigonometric substitution to derive a formula for

$$\int \frac{du}{a^2 + u^2}.$$

The form of the denominator suggests using the identity $1 + \tan^2 \theta = \sec^2 \theta$. Thus we let

$$u = a \tan \theta, \quad \theta = \text{Tan}^{-1}(u/a).$$

Then $du = a \sec^2 \theta \, d\theta$, and the result is

$$\int \frac{du}{a^2 + u^2} = \int \frac{a \sec^2 \theta \, d\theta}{a^2 + a^2 \tan^2 \theta} = \int \frac{a \sec^2 \theta \, d\theta}{a^2 \sec^2 \theta}$$

$$= \frac{1}{a} \int d\theta = \frac{1}{a} \theta + C = \frac{1}{a} \text{Tan}^{-1} \frac{u}{a} + C.$$

The next example illustrates the substitution of a hyperbolic function to simplify the form of an inverse derivative, and brings in an important subtlety pertaining to the form of an inverse derivative.

Example 15.4d. Integrate

$$\int \frac{du}{\sqrt{u^2 - a^2}}.$$

We may let $u = a \cosh x$, and make use of the identity $\cosh^2 x - \sinh^2 x = 1$ to obtain

$$\int \frac{du}{\sqrt{u^2 - a^2}} = \int \frac{a \sinh x \, dx}{\sqrt{a^2 \cosh^2 x - a^2}}$$

$$= \int dx = x + C$$

$$= \text{Cosh}^{-1} \frac{u}{a} + C.$$

Or, we could let $u = a \sec \theta$ to obtain

$$\int \frac{du}{\sqrt{u^2 - a^2}} = \int \frac{a \sec \theta \tan \theta \, d\theta}{\sqrt{a^2 \sec^2 \theta - a^2}}$$

$$= \int \sec \theta \, d\theta$$

$$= \ln [\sec \theta + \tan \theta] + C_1$$

$$= \ln [u + \sqrt{u^2 - a^2}] + C_2.$$

This last result is indeed rather startling because it apparently has no resemblance whatsoever to $\text{Cosh}^{-1}(u/a) + C$. Indeed, it appears that we may have obtained a contradiction to Theorem 11.4b, which states that two functions having the same derivative differ at most by a constant. However, let us see if these apparently different expressions are really equivalent. The work in Section 14.7 included a derivation of the formula

$$\text{Cosh}^{-1} x = \ln \left[x + \sqrt{x^2 - 1} \right], \qquad 1 \leq x,$$

so that upon replacing x by u/a in this expression, we can show the equivalence of the two seemingly different results. The reader should find the difference between the two constants C and C_2.

The point to be emphasized here is simply that the form obtained for an inverse derivative may very well depend upon the method by which the result was obtained. The fact that a particular result does not agree with a given solution or with a solution obtained by another method does not necessarily imply that the result is not a correct solution. For example, the two expressions

$$2 \text{Sin}^{-1} \left(\frac{\sqrt{x}}{2} \right) \quad \text{and} \quad \text{Sin}^{-1} \left(\frac{x - 2}{2} \right)$$

differ only by a constant. (Can you show this?)

Example 15.4e. Integrate

$$\int \frac{dx}{x^2 \sqrt{x^2 + 4}}.$$

Let $x = 2 \tan \theta$, with $\theta = \text{Tan}^{-1} (x/2)$. Then $dx = 2 \sec^2 \theta \, d\theta$, and

$$\int \frac{dx}{x^2 \sqrt{x^2 + 4}} = \int \frac{2 \sec^2 \theta \, d\theta}{(4 \tan^2 \theta)(2 \sec \theta)}$$

$$= \frac{1}{4} \int \frac{1}{\cos \theta} \left(\frac{\cos^2 \theta}{\sin^2 \theta} \right) d\theta$$

$$= \frac{1}{4} \int \csc \theta \cot \theta \, d\theta$$

$$= -\frac{1}{4} \csc \theta + C$$

$$= -\frac{\sqrt{x^2 + 4}}{4x} + C.$$

To obtain the final step, we may refer to Figure 15.4b, from which it follows that if $\theta = \text{Tan}^{-1} (x/2)$, then $\csc \theta = (\sqrt{x^2 + 4}/x)$.

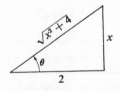

FIGURE 15.4b

As in the preceding section, the student should not be limited to the specific substitutions suggested, but should try to develop other substitutions to fit special cases. Some of these are suggested in the hints for certain problems.

Exercises 15.4

1. Use a hyperbolic substitution to derive Formula (17) of Section 15.1.
2. Use a hyperbolic substitution to derive Formula (18) of Section 15.1.

Find the inverse derivative in each of Numbers 3 to 18.

3. $\displaystyle\int \frac{x^2}{\sqrt{9-x^2}}\,dx.$

4. $\displaystyle\int \frac{dy}{9-y^2}.$

5. $\displaystyle\int \sqrt{1-t^2}\,dt.$

6. $\displaystyle\int \frac{dx}{\sqrt{4+x^2}}.$

7. $\displaystyle\int \frac{ds}{s^2\sqrt{4-s^2}}.$

8. $\displaystyle\int y^3\sqrt{y^2-4}\,dy.$

9. $\displaystyle\int \frac{y^3\,dy}{4+y^2}.$

10. $\displaystyle\int \frac{w^2\,dw}{\sqrt{2-3w^2}}.$

11. $\displaystyle\int \frac{dx}{(4+x^2)^{3/2}}.$

12. $\displaystyle\int \frac{dw}{w\sqrt{w^2-2}}.$

13. $\displaystyle\int \frac{dx}{x\sqrt{x^2+4}}.$

14. $\displaystyle\int \frac{dt}{\sqrt{4t+t^2}}.$ (Let $t = 4\tan^2\theta.$)

15. $\displaystyle\int \frac{x^3\,dx}{\sqrt{9-x^2}}.$

16. $\displaystyle\int \frac{dy}{\sqrt{y^2-4y+8}}.$

17. $\displaystyle\int \frac{dy}{\sqrt{4y-y^2}}.$ (Let $y = 4\sin^2\theta.$)

18. $\displaystyle\int \frac{\sqrt{s^2-16}}{s^4}\,ds.$

Evaluate the definite integral in each of Numbers 19 to 26.

19. $\displaystyle\int_0^1 \frac{u^2\,du}{\sqrt{4-u^2}}.$

20. $\displaystyle\int_{\sqrt{3}}^3 \frac{x^2\,dx}{9+x^2}.$

21. $\displaystyle\int_4^8 \frac{dy}{(y^2-4)^{3/2}}.$

22. $\displaystyle\int_{\sqrt{3}}^3 \frac{dx}{x^2\sqrt{x^2+9}}.$

23. $\displaystyle\int_4^6 \frac{dw}{w\sqrt{w^2-4}}.$

24. $\displaystyle\int_2^{2\sqrt{3}} \frac{t^3\,dt}{\sqrt{t^2+4}}.$

25. $\displaystyle\int_{\sqrt{2}/2}^{\sqrt{3}/2} x^2\sqrt{1-x^2}\,dx.$

26. $\displaystyle\int_1^3 x^3\sqrt{3+x^2}\,dx.$

27. Use integration to find the area enclosed by the ellipse $4x^2 + 9y^2 = 36$.
28. Use integration to find the area enclosed by the circle $x^2 + y^2 = 9$.
29. Find the volume of the solid formed by rotating about the x-axis the area bounded by the x-axis and the curve $y = x(1-x^3)^{1/3}$.
30. Find the area enclosed by the curve $x^{2/3} + y^{2/3} = a^{2/3}$.
31. Find the area bounded by the x-axis, the line $x = 4$, and the curve

$$y = (\sqrt{x^2-4})/x^2.$$

32. Find the volume formed when the area of Number 31 is revolved about the y-axis.
33. Find the area enclosed by one loop of the curve $x^2 = y^4(1 - y^2)$.
34. Find the area bounded by the x-axis and one arch of the cycloid $x = b(t - \sin t)$, $y = b(1 - \cos t)$.
35. Find the area of Number 30 by using the parametric equations $x = a \cos^3 \varphi$, $y = a \sin^3 \varphi$.
36. Find the volume of a spherical segment of one base and of altitude h if the radius of the sphere is b.

15.5 INTEGRATION BY PARTS

One of the most important techniques frequently used to transform an integral into a more manageable form is based on the formula for the derivative of a product of two differentiable functions, say u and v:

$$D_x(uv) = u\, D_x v + v\, D_x u.$$

If we solve this formula for the term $u\, D_x v$ and take inverse derivatives, we obtain, in succession,

$$u\, D_x v = D_x(uv) - v\, D_x u$$

and

$$(1) \qquad \int u\, D_x v\, dx = uv - \int v\, D_x u\, dx.$$

Formula (1) is frequently written in terms of the differentials du and dv as follows:

$$(2) \qquad \int u\, dv = uv - \int v\, du.$$

Integration by means of (1) or (2) is called **integration by parts.**

Whenever the integrand is regarded as the product of a function u and the derivative of a second function v, the formula expresses the integral in terms of a second integral in which the roles of the two factors are interchanged, the function u being replaced by its derivative and the derivative $D_x v$ by the function v. Some examples will indicate the possibilities stemming from the use of this formula.

Example 15.5a. Integrate $\int x \sin x\, dx$.

We let

$$u = x \quad \text{and} \quad D_x v = \sin x,$$

so that

$$D_x u = 1 \quad \text{and} \quad v = -\cos x.$$

Thus, Formula (1) gives

$$\int x \sin x\, dx = -x \cos x - \int -\cos x\, dx$$

$$= -x \cos x + \sin x + C.$$

Notice in the preceding example that the constant of integration C was added after the last integration was performed. It is usually convenient to follow this procedure, which is justified because we may regard the problem at the start as that of obtaining *an* inverse derivative, the general result then being obtained by adding the arbitrary constant. (The student may easily verify the fact that omission of a constant of integration in the intermediate step of finding v from dv makes no difference in the final result.)

Example 15.5b. Integrate $\int x^2 \cos x \, dx$.

In this example, we use the notation of Formula (2) and let

$$dv = \cos x \, dx \quad \text{and} \quad u = x^2,$$

so that

$$v = \sin x, \quad du = 2x \, dx,$$

and

$$\int x^2 \cos x \, dx = x^2 \sin x - 2 \int x \sin x \, dx.$$

Since the last integral is exactly that of Example 15.5a, we obtain

$$\int x^2 \cos x \, dx = x^2 \sin x + 2x \cos x - 2 \sin x + C.$$

This example illustrates the possibility of removing a factor x^n by integrating by parts n times, each time taking the power of x as the factor to be differentiated. This scheme is often successful in handling inverse derivatives of the type

$$\int x^n f(x) \, dx.$$

The next example illustrates another type of integral for which repeated integration by parts is useful.

Example 15.5c. Integrate $\int e^{-x} \sin 2x \, dx$.

Letting

$$u = e^{-x} \quad \text{and} \quad D_x v = \sin 2x,$$

so that

$$D_x u = -e^{-x} \quad \text{and} \quad v = -\tfrac{1}{2} \cos 2x,$$

we get

$$\int e^{-x} \sin 2x \, dx = -\tfrac{1}{2} e^{-x} \cos 2x - \tfrac{1}{2} \int e^{-x} \cos 2x \, dx.$$

In this last integral, we let

$$u = e^{-x} \quad \text{and} \quad D_x v = \cos 2x,$$

so that

$$D_x u = -e^{-x} \quad \text{and} \quad v = \tfrac{1}{2} \sin 2x.$$

Then

$$\int e^{-x} \sin 2x \, dx = -\tfrac{1}{2} e^{-x} \cos 2x - \tfrac{1}{4} e^{-x} \sin 2x - \tfrac{1}{4} \int e^{-x} \sin 2x \, dx.$$

Since the last integral in this equation is the same as the one with which we started, we may solve for it and then complete the problem by adding an arbitrary constant. The final result is

$$\int e^{-x} \sin 2x \, dx = -\tfrac{2}{5} e^{-x} \cos 2x - \tfrac{1}{5} e^{-x} \sin 2x + C.$$

It should be noted that Formula (1) can be put into definite integral form by use of the Fundamental Theorem of Integral Calculus. Thus, we have

(3) $$\int_a^b u \, D_x v \, dx = [uv]_a^b - \int_a^b v \, D_x u \, dx.$$

Example 15.5d. Evaluate $\int_0^2 x^2 e^x \, dx$.

We let

$$u = x^2 \quad \text{and} \quad D_x v = e^x,$$

so that

$$D_x u = 2x \quad \text{and} \quad v = e^x.$$

Then,

$$\int_0^2 x^2 e^x \, dx = [x^2 e^x]_0^2 - 2 \int_0^2 x e^x \, dx$$

$$= 4e^2 - 2 \int_0^2 x e^x \, dx.$$

In the last integral, write $u = x$, $D_x v = e^x$, to get $D_x u = 1$, $v = e^x$, and then

$$\int_0^2 x^2 e^x \, dx = 4e^2 - 2[xe^x]_0^2 + 2 \int_0^2 e^x \, dx$$

$$= 4e^2 - 4e^2 + [2e^x]_0^2 = 2(e^2 - 1).$$

Exercises 15.5

In each of Numbers 1 to 24, find the inverse derivative.

1. $\int w \cos 3w \, dw.$

2. $\int y e^{-y} \, dy.$

3. $\int x^2 \sin x \, dx.$

4. $\int \ln x \, dx.$

5. $\int \text{Tan}^{-1} w \, dw.$

6. $\int s^2 e^{2s} \, ds.$

7. $\int x^3 \cos 2x \, dx.$

8. $\int \text{Sin}^{-1} (y/2) \, dy.$

9. $\int y \ln y \, dy.$

10. $\int e^u \sin 2u \, du.$

11. $\int y \, \text{Sin}^{-1} y \, dy.$

12. $\int \cos t \sin 3t \, dt.$

13. $\int x \csc^2 x \, dx.$

14. $\int t \sqrt{t + 1} \, dt.$

15. $\int e^{2x} \cos 3x \, dx.$

19. $\int \theta \sec^2 \theta \, d\theta.$

16. $\int t^2 \ln t \, dt.$

20. $\int x^2 \sqrt{x-2} \, dx.$

17. $\int x^3 \operatorname{Tan}^{-1} x \, dx.$

21. $\int y^{3/2} \ln 3y \, dy.$

18. $\int \ln^2 y \, dy.$

22. $\int x \sin^2 2x \, dx.$

23. $\int \sec^3 t \, dt.$ *Hint:* Let $dv = \sec^2 t \, dt$ and in the resulting integral use the formula $\tan^2 t = \sec^2 t - 1.$

24. $\int \csc^3 2t \, dt.$ *Hint:* See Number 23.

In Numbers 25 to 32, evaluate the definite integrals.

25. $\int_0^{\pi/2} y \sin y \, dy.$

29. $\int_0^{\pi/4} e^x \sin 2x \, dx.$

26. $\int_0^1 u e^{3u} \, du.$

30. $\int_{-\pi/2}^{\pi/2} w \cos w \, dw.$

27. $\int_0^1 \operatorname{Tan}^{-1} x \, dx.$

31. $\int_0^5 x\sqrt{x+4} \, dx.$

28. $\int_0^{\pi/2} x^2 \cos 2x \, dx.$

32. $\int_0^{1/2} \operatorname{Sin}^{-1} x \, dx.$

33. Find the area bounded by the x-axis, the curve $y = xe^{-x}$, and the ordinate drawn to the maximum point of the curve.
34. Find the volume formed by revolving about the x-axis the area of Number 33.
35. Calculate the area bounded by the x-axis, the curve $y = \operatorname{Sin}^{-1} 2x$, and the line $x = \sqrt{3}/4.$
36. Calculate the area below the curve $y = \ln x$ and above the x-axis from $x = 1$ to $x = 5.$
37. Locate the centroid of the area in Number 36.
38. Find the area bounded by the x-axis, the curve $y = xe^{-x}$, and the ordinate drawn to the inflection point of the curve.
39. Find the x-coordinate of the centroid of the area bounded by the curve $y = \sin x$ and the lines $y = 0$, $x = \pi/2.$
★40. Calculate $\int xe^x \cos x \, dx.$

15.6 WALLIS' FORMULAS

The reader has undoubtedly noticed the frequent occurrence of integrals of the type

$$\int_0^{\pi/2} \cos^m \theta \, d\theta, \quad \int_0^{\pi/2} \sin^m \theta \, d\theta, \quad \text{and} \quad \int_0^{\pi/2} \cos^m \theta \sin^n \theta \, d\theta,$$

where m and n are positive integers. For such integrals there is a set of efficient formulas named after the English mathematician John Wallis (1616–1703).

Although we shall find it not difficult to derive Wallis' formulas, his own derivation exhibited remarkable ingenuity, being obtained without the aid of the symbolism of modern calculus.

Let us apply integration by parts to the integral

$$\int \cos^m \theta \, d\theta, \qquad m = 2, 3, 4, \ldots,$$

by setting

$$dv = \cos \theta \, d\theta, \quad u = \cos^{m-1} \theta,$$
$$v = \sin \theta, \quad du = -(m-1) \cos^{m-2} \theta \sin \theta \, d\theta.$$

Then

$$\int \cos^m \theta \, d\theta = \cos^{m-1} \theta \sin \theta + (m-1) \int \cos^{m-2} \theta \sin^2 \theta \, d\theta.$$

If we replace the factor $\sin^2 \theta$ by $1 - \cos^2 \theta$ in the last integrand, we get

$$\int \cos^m \theta \, d\theta = \cos^{m-1} \theta \sin \theta + (m-1) \int \cos^{m-2} \theta \, d\theta - (m-1) \int \cos^m \theta \, d\theta.$$

Hence, by adding $(m-1) \int \cos^m \theta \, d\theta$ to both members and then dividing by m, we obtain the formula

$$(1) \qquad \int \cos^m \theta \, d\theta = \frac{1}{m} \cos^{m-1} \theta \sin \theta + \frac{m-1}{m} \int \cos^{m-2} \theta \, d\theta.$$

Because this equation expresses the original integral in terms of an integral in which the exponent of $\cos \theta$ is 2 less than its original value, Formula (1) is called a **reduction formula**. Many other examples of such formulas appear in tables of integrals (see Section 15.11).

We next consider the two definite integrals

$$\int_0^{\pi/2} \cos^m x \, dx \quad \text{and} \quad \int_0^{\pi/2} \sin^m x \, dx.$$

In the second integral we make the substitution $x = \pi/2 - v$, to obtain

$$\int_0^{\pi/2} \sin^m x \, dx = \int_{\pi/2}^0 \cos^m v \, (-dv) = \int_0^{\pi/2} \cos^m v \, dv.$$

Thus

$$\int_0^{\pi/2} \cos^m x \, dx = \int_0^{\pi/2} \sin^m x \, dx.$$

Next, from Formula (1), it follows that

$$\int_0^{\pi/2} \cos^m x \, dx = \left[\frac{1}{m} \cos^{m-1} x \sin x \right]_0^{\pi/2} + \frac{m-1}{m} \int_0^{\pi/2} \cos^{m-2} x \, dx,$$

or

$$(2) \qquad \int_0^{\pi/2} \cos^m x \, dx = \frac{m-1}{m} \int_0^{\pi/2} \cos^{m-2} x \, dx,$$

since the term in brackets is zero at both $x = 0$ and $x = \pi/2$.

If $m - 2 \geq 2$, the preceding result may be applied as a reduction formula to the integral on the right to get

$$\int_0^{\pi/2} \cos^m x \, dx = \frac{(m-1)(m-3)}{m(m-2)} \int_0^{\pi/2} \cos^{m-4} x \, dx.$$

By successive applications of Formula (2), the exponent of cos x may be reduced to 0 if m is even or to 1 if m is odd. Thus

(3)
$$\int_0^{\pi/2} \cos^m x \, dx = \int_0^{\pi/2} \sin^m x \, dx$$

$$= \frac{(m-1)(m-3)\cdots(1) \text{ or } (2)}{m(m-2)\cdots(2) \text{ or } (3)} M,$$

where if m is even and ≥ 2,

$$M = \int_0^{\pi/2} dx = \frac{\pi}{2},$$

and, if m is odd and ≥ 3,

$$M = \int_0^{\pi/2} \cos x \, dx = 1.$$

Notice in Formula (3) that the denominator begins with m, the original exponent, and the numerator begins with 1 less than the denominator. The remaining factors both above and below are each obtained by subtracting 2 from the preceding factor. This subtraction is stopped when the next factor so constructed would be zero or negative. The factor 2 in the denominator of $\pi/2$ should suggest that this factor comes in when m is even.

Example 15.6a. Evaluate $\int_0^{\pi/2} \cos^5 x \, dx$.

Formula (3) immediately yields

$$\int_0^{\pi/2} \cos^5 x \, dx = \frac{(4)(2)}{(5)(3)} = \frac{8}{15}.$$

Example 15.6b. Evaluate $\int_0^{\pi/2} \sin^6 x \, dx$.

In this instance m is even, so that

$$\int_0^{\pi/2} \sin^6 x \, dx = \frac{(5)(3)(1)}{(6)(4)(2)} \left(\frac{\pi}{2}\right) = \frac{5\pi}{32}.$$

A formula corresponding to Formula (3) can be found for

$$\int_0^{\pi/2} \cos^m x \sin^n x \, dx.$$

The derivation is left for the exercises (see Exercises 15.6, Number 40).
If m, n are both positive integers ≥ 2, then

(4)
$$\int_0^{\pi/2} \cos^m x \sin^n x \, dx$$

$$= \frac{[(m-1)(m-3)\cdots(1) \text{ or } (2)][(n-1)(n-3)\cdots(1) \text{ or } (2)]}{(m+n)(m+n-2)\cdots(2) \text{ or } (3)} N,$$

where

$$N = \begin{cases} 1 \text{ unless both } m \text{ and } n \text{ are even,} \\ \pi/2 \text{ if both } m \text{ and } n \text{ are even.} \end{cases}$$

Example 15.6c. Evaluate $\int_0^{\pi/2} \cos^3 x \sin^2 x \, dx$.

Using Formula (4), we get

$$\int_0^{\pi/2} \cos^3 x \sin^2 x \, dx = \frac{(2)(1)}{(5)(3)} = \frac{2}{15}.$$

Example 15.6d. Evaluate $\int_0^{\pi/2} \cos^4 x \sin^2 x \, dx$.

Again, by the use of Formula (4), we obtain

$$\int_0^{\pi/2} \cos^4 x \sin^2 x \, dx = \frac{(3)(1)(1)}{(6)(4)(2)} \left(\frac{\pi}{2}\right) = \frac{\pi}{32}.$$

Although the limits are 0 and $\pi/2$ in Wallis' formulas, simple considerations allow us to use the formulas if the limits are integral multiples of $\pi/2$. Thus, Formula (4) applies immediately to

$$\int_{k\pi/2}^{(k+1)\pi/2} \cos^m x \sin^n x \, dx$$

if the interval $k\pi/2$ to $(k + 1)\pi/2$ is one on which the integrand $\cos^m x \sin^n x$ is positive. If the integrand is negative, only a minus sign needs to be supplied before the right hand side of the formula. It is left to the reader to verify these statements (see Exercises 15.6, Number 41). If the integral extends over more than one interval of length $\pi/2$, it may be written as a sum of integrals of the type of the preceding one and handled as in the next examples.

Example 15.6e. Evaluate $\int_0^{5\pi/2} \cos^4 x \sin^2 x \, dx$.

In this integral both exponents are even, so the integrand is always nonnegative. Since the interval 0 to $5\pi/2$ is equivalent to 5 intervals of length $\pi/2$, we have

$$\int_0^{5\pi/2} \cos^4 x \sin^2 x \, dx = (5) \frac{(3)(1)(1)}{(6)(4)(2)} \left(\frac{\pi}{2}\right) = \frac{5\pi}{32}.$$

Example 15.6f. Evaluate $\int_{-3\pi/2}^{0} \cos^5 x \sin^3 x \, dx$.

In this problem, we have for the interval

$$\begin{array}{ll} -3\pi/2 < x < -\pi, & \text{the integrand is negative,} \\ -\pi < x < -\pi/2, & \text{the integrand is positive,} \\ -\pi/2 < x < 0, & \text{the integrand is negative.} \end{array}$$

Accordingly, it follows that

$$\int_{-3\pi/2}^{0} \cos^5 x \sin^3 x \, dx = -\frac{(4)(2)(2)}{(8)(6)(4)(2)} = -\frac{1}{24}.$$

It frequently happens that a change of the variable of integration allows us to use Wallis' formulas, as in the following examples.

Example 15.6g. Evaluate $\int_0^\pi \cos^4 3\theta \, d\theta$.

Let $3\theta = x$ or $\theta = x/3$. Then

$$d\theta = 1/3 \, dx,$$
$$\theta = 0 \Rightarrow x = 0 \quad \text{and} \quad \theta = \pi \Rightarrow x = 3\pi.$$

Hence

$$\int_0^\pi \cos^4 3\theta \, d\theta = \frac{1}{3} \int_0^{3\pi} \cos^4 x \, dx$$

$$= 2 \int_0^{\pi/2} \cos^4 x \, dx = \frac{3\pi}{8}.$$

Example 15.6h. Evaluate $\int_0^a x^2 \sqrt{a^2 - x^2} \, dx$.

Let $x = a \sin \theta$ and $\theta = \text{Sin}^{-1} x/a$. Then

$$dx = a \cos \theta \, d\theta,$$
$$x = 0 \Rightarrow \theta = 0 \quad \text{and} \quad x = a \Rightarrow \theta = \pi/2.$$

Thus

$$\int_0^a x^2 \sqrt{a^2 - x^2} \, dx = a^4 \int_0^{\pi/2} \sin^2 \theta \cos^2 \theta \, d\theta$$

$$= \frac{\pi a^4}{16}.$$

Exercises 15.6

In each of Numbers 1 to 32, evaluate the given integral.

1. $\int_0^{\pi/2} \cos^3 x \, dx$.

2. $\int_0^{\pi/2} \sin^{10} x \, dx$.

3. $\int_0^{\pi/2} \sin^4 \varphi \, d\varphi$.

4. $\int_0^{\pi/2} \cos^7 y \, dy$.

5. $\int_0^{\pi/2} \cos^2 \theta \sin^3 \theta \, d\theta$.

6. $\int_0^{\pi/2} \cos^2 u \sin^2 u \, du$.

7. $\int_0^{\pi/2} \cos^3 w \sin^4 w \, dw$.

8. $\int_0^{\pi/2} \cos^4 t \sin^6 t \, dt$.

9. $\int_0^\pi \sin^2 z \, dz$.

10. $\int_0^{3\pi/2} \cos^4 \theta \, d\theta$.

11. $\int_{-\pi/2}^\pi \sin^3 u \, du$.

12. $\int_{-\pi/2}^\pi \cos^5 y \, dy$.

13. $\int_0^{2\pi} |\cos^3 x| \, dx.$

23. $\int_0^\pi \sin^6 4\theta \, d\theta.$

14. $\int_{-\pi}^\pi |\sin^5 \theta| \, d\theta.$

24. $\int_{-\pi}^\pi \cos^4 (\theta/2) \sin^2 (\theta/2) \, d\theta.$

15. $\int_0^{2\pi} \cos^2 v \sin^4 v \, dv.$

25. $\int_0^{2\pi} \cos^2 \theta \sin^2 2\theta \, d\theta.$

16. $\int_{-\pi}^{\pi/2} \cos^3 x \sin^3 x \, dx.$

26. $\int_0^{2\pi} \sin^2 \theta \cos^2 2\theta \, d\theta.$

17. $\int_0^\pi \cos^2 t \sin^3 t \, dt.$

27. $\int_0^4 \sqrt{16 - x^2} \, dx.$

18. $\int_0^{2\pi} \cos^4 u \sin^5 u \, du.$

28. $\int_0^3 (9 - t^2)^{3/2} \, dt.$

19. $\int_{-\pi/2}^{\pi/2} \cos^2 t \sin^6 t \, dt.$

29. $\int_0^2 \sqrt{2y - y^2} \, dy.$

20. $\int_{-\pi/2}^\pi \cos^5 x \sin^2 x \, dx.$

30. $\int_0^a u\sqrt{au - u^2} \, du.$

21. $\int_0^{\pi/4} \sin^7 2\theta \, d\theta.$

31. $\int_0^a (a^{2/3} - x^{2/3})^{3/2} \, dx.$

22. $\int_0^{\pi/2} \cos^3 5\theta \, d\theta.$

32. $\int_0^a w^3\sqrt{a^2 - w^2} \, dw.$

33. Find the area bounded by one arch of the curve $y = \sin^3 3x$ and the x-axis.
34. Find the area bounded by one arch of the curve $y = \sin^6 2x$ and the x-axis.
35. Find the volume formed by revolving about the x-axis the area bounded by the curve $y = \cos^2 x$, the y-axis, and the x-axis from $x = 0$ to $x = \pi/2$.
36. Find the volume formed by revolving about the x-axis the area bounded by one arch of the curve $y = \sin^2 2x$ and the x-axis.
37. Find the area enclosed by one loop of the curve $y^2 = x^4(1 - x^2)^3$.
38. Find the area enclosed by the curve $b^8 x^2 = (b^2 - y^2)^5$.
39. Find a formula for the area enclosed by the loop of the curve $x^2 = y^{2m}(1 - y)^{2n-1}$, where m and n are positive integers.
40. (a) By integration by parts with $dv = \cos^m x \sin x \, dx$, show that

$$\int_0^{\pi/2} \cos^m x \sin^n x \, dx = \frac{n - 1}{m + n} \int_0^{\pi/2} \cos^m x \sin^{n-2} x \, dx, \qquad n \geq 2.$$

(b) Let m be an even integer ≥ 2 and show that repeated application of the preceding formula gives the result of Wallis' formula.
(c) Repeat the procedure in (b) for m an odd integer ≥ 3.
41. By use of the substitution $x = y + k\pi/2$, show that

$$\int_{k\pi/2}^{(k+1)\pi/2} \cos^m x \sin^n x \, dx$$

can be evaluated by Formula (4).
42. If $k, m, n \in \mathfrak{N}$, evaluate the integral

$$\int_{k\pi/4}^{(k+1)\pi/4} \cos^{2m} 2x \sin^{2n} 4x \, dx.$$

15.7 INTEGRATION OF RATIONAL FRACTIONS

An expression of the type $P(x)/Q(x)$, where $P(x)$ and $Q(x)$ are polynomials, is called a **rational fraction.** The inverse derivatives of several types of rational fractions have already been discussed.

For example, the inverse derivative of $A/(x - a)^n$ is easily written, since this fraction is the derivative of the constant A times a power of $x - a$, for $n \neq 1$, and of $\ln |x - a|$, if $n = 1$. The inverse derivative of a rational fraction of the type

$$\frac{Ax + B}{x^2 + bx + c},$$

where $x^2 + bx + c$ is irreducible in $\mathcal{R}$ (that is, has no real linear factors) was found in Example 15.3c.

To find the inverse derivative of a fraction of the type

$$\frac{Ax + B}{(x^2 + bx + c)^n},$$

where $x^2 + bx + c$ is again irreducible, the same procedure as in Example 15.3c may be used. This leads in part to an integral of the form

$$\int \frac{du}{(a^2 + u^2)^n},$$

which may be handled by using the substitution

$$u = a \tan \theta, \quad \theta = \text{Tan}^{-1} u/a,$$

or by means of Formula 22 in the table of integrals in the appendix of this book. This formula is another example of a reduction formula, since it reduces the exponent in the integral from n to $n - 1$.

Example 15.7a. Integrate

$$\int \frac{(4x + 9) \, dx}{(x^2 + 4x + 13)^2}.$$

Since $D_x(x^2 + 4x + 13) = 2x + 4$, we rewrite the numerator in the form

$$4x + 9 = 2(2x + 4) + 1,$$

and thus obtain

$$\int \frac{(4x + 9) \, dx}{(x^2 + 4x + 13)^2} = \int \frac{2(2x + 4) \, dx}{(x^2 + 4x + 13)^2} + \int \frac{dx}{[(x + 2)^2 + 9]^2}.$$

The first integral on the right is of the form $2 \int u^{-2} \, du$ and so gives $-2u^{-1}$; that is

$$-\frac{2}{x^2 + 4x + 13}.$$

In the second integral, let

$$x + 2 = 3 \tan \theta, \quad \theta = \text{Tan}^{-1} \left(\frac{x + 2}{3} \right),$$

so that $dx = 3 \sec^2 \theta \, d\theta$. Then

$$\int \frac{dx}{[(x+2)^2 + 9]^2} = \int \frac{3 \sec^2 \theta \, d\theta}{81 \sec^4 \theta} = \frac{1}{27} \int \cos^2 \theta \, d\theta$$

$$= \frac{1}{27} \int \frac{1 + \cos 2\theta}{2} \, d\theta = \frac{1}{54} \left(\theta + \frac{1}{2} \sin 2\theta \right)$$

$$= \frac{1}{54} \theta + \frac{1}{54} \sin \theta \cos \theta$$

$$= \frac{1}{54} \mathrm{Tan}^{-1} \left(\frac{x+2}{3} \right) + \frac{1}{54} \left(\frac{x+2}{\sqrt{x^2 + 4x + 13}} \right) \left(\frac{3}{\sqrt{x^2 + 4x + 13}} \right)$$

$$= \frac{1}{54} \mathrm{Tan}^{-1} \left(\frac{x+2}{3} \right) + \frac{x+2}{18(x^2 + 4x + 13)}.$$

The final result is now written as

$$\int \frac{(4x+7) \, dx}{(x^2 + 4x + 13)^2} = \frac{x - 34}{18(x^2 + 4x + 13)} + \frac{1}{54} \mathrm{Tan}^{-1} \left(\frac{x+2}{3} \right) + C.$$

The preceding discussion suggests that it is possible to find the inverse derivative of any rational fraction *if* the denominator can be factored into linear factors and/or quadratic factors which are irreducible in the field of real numbers, and *if* the fraction can then be "decomposed" into a sum of fractions whose denominators are of the types mentioned earlier in this section.

In order to investigate this possibility, it is necessary to digress briefly to consider the factorization of a polynomial,

$$p(x) .=. a_0 x^n + a_1 x^{n-1} + \cdots + a_{n-1} x + a_n,$$

where the coefficients are real numbers. The essential theorems for the present purposes were discussed in Section 3.6. Theorems 3.6b, 3.6d, 3.6e, and 3.6f state the basic facts that we need here.

(1) The remainder upon dividing a polynomial $p(x)$ by $x - c$ is a constant $p(c)$ (The Remainder Theorem, Theorem 3.6b). An important consequence of this theorem is that $x - c$ is a factor of $p(x)$ if, and only if, $p(c) = 0$.

(2) A polynomial $p(x)$ of degree n in $\mathcal{C}$ is reducible to a product of exactly n linear factors in $\mathcal{C}$ (Theorem 3.6d).

(3) If the value of a polynomial $p(x)$ of degree n is equal to the value of a polynomial $q(x)$ of degree m, $m \le n$, for at least $n + 1$ values of x, then the polynomials are identical and have equal values for all values of x (Theorem 3.6e).

(4) If $p(x)$ is a polynomial in the field $\mathcal{R}$, then

$$p(a + ib) = 0 \Rightarrow p(a - ib) = 0 \qquad \text{(Theorem 3.6f)}.$$

It follows from Statement (4) that if a polynomial $p(x)$ in the field $\mathcal{R}$ has a zero $a + ib$, then

$$(x - a - ib)(x - a + ib) = x^2 - 2ax + a^2 + b^2$$

is a factor of the polynomial. Consequently, the preceding facts show that every polynomial in the field $\mathcal{R}$ can theoretically be factored into linear and/or quadratic factors with real coefficients. Of course, it may not be possible to find the factors in any practical fashion, but if $p(x)$ has numerical coefficients, the factors can always be approximated as accurately as is desired, even if they cannot be found exactly. Thus, the first of the two problems suggested earlier—factoring the denominator of the rational fraction—may be regarded as solved. Let us then consider the second problem—decomposing a rational fraction into a sum of simpler rational fractions, which are customarily called **partial fractions**.

In some of the earlier work in finding inverse derivatives of rational fractions, we encountered fractions in which the degree of the numerator was equal to or greater than the degree of the denominator. In such cases the first operation was to divide and obtain a polynomial plus a "proper" fraction (that is, a fraction in which the numerator is of lower degree than the denominator). In this work we shall assume that this division has been done and also that all common factors have been removed from numerator and denominator.

Let us first consider the case of a linear factor $x - a$ to the power k in the denominator. The next theorem shows that an expansion into partial fractions can be made.

Theorem 15.7a. Let $P(x)/Q(x)$ be a proper rational fraction in lowest terms, and let

$$\frac{P(x)}{Q(x)} = \frac{P(x)}{(x - a)^k Q_1(x)},$$

where $Q_1(a) \neq 0$, so that $Q_1(x)$ does not have $x - a$ as a factor. Then there exist k unique constants $A, B, \ldots$, such that

$$\frac{P(x)}{(x - a)^k Q_1(x)} = \frac{A}{(x - a)^k} + \frac{B}{(x - a)^{k-1}} + \cdots + \frac{P_k(x)}{Q_1(x)}, \qquad A \neq 0.$$

PROOF: The first step will be to show that we can get an expansion of the form

(1) $$\frac{P(x)}{(x - a)^k Q_1(x)} = \frac{A}{(x - a)^k} + \frac{P_1(x)}{(x - a)^{k-1} Q_1(x)},$$

where A is a constant. With this in mind, consider the difference

$$\frac{P(x)}{(x - a)^k Q_1(x)} - \frac{A}{(x - a)^k} = \frac{P(x) - A Q_1(x)}{(x - a)^k Q_1(x)}.$$

If we can find a value for A such that

$$P(x) - A Q_1(x) = (x - a) P_1(x),$$

then

$$\frac{P(x) - A Q_1(x)}{(x - a)^k Q_1(x)} = \frac{P_1(x)}{(x - a)^{k-1} Q_1(x)},$$

which would lead to the desired form. Since $P(x)$ and $Q_1(x)$ are polynomials, it follows from the Remainder Theorem (Theorem 3.6b) that $x - a$ is a factor of $P(x) - A Q_1(x)$ if, and only if,

$$P(a) - AQ_1(a) = 0.$$

This equation and the inequality $Q_1(a) \neq 0$ imply that

$$A = \frac{P(a)}{Q_1(a)},$$

and thus a unique A exists such that Equation (1) holds. Furthermore, $A \neq 0$ because $P(a) \neq 0$, since $P(x)$ and $Q(x)$ have no common factors.

Notice also that the new numerator $P_1(x)$ is obtained by dividing $P(x) - AQ_1(x)$ by $x - a$, so that the degree of $P_1(x)$ is at least one less than the degree of $P(x)$. This means that the new fraction is also a proper one. Consequently, the preceding argument may be repeated with

$$\frac{P_1(x)}{(x - a)^{k-1}Q_1(x)}$$

to find the constant B, and repeated application will determine the other constants.

Example 15.7b. Integrate

$$\int \frac{x^2 + 2}{(x + 2)(x - 1)(x + 3)}\, dx.$$

Using the preceding theorem, we write

$$\frac{x^2 + 2}{(x + 2)(x - 1)(x + 3)} = \frac{A}{(x + 2)} + \frac{B}{x - 1} + \frac{D}{x + 3}.$$

The constant A is $P(-2)/Q_1(-2)$, where $P(x)$ is the numerator and $Q_1(x)$ is that portion of the denominator of the original fraction that multiplies the factor $(x + 2)$—that is, the denominator with the factor $x + 2$ deleted. Thus,

$$A = \frac{P(-2)}{Q_1(-2)} = \left[\frac{x^2 + 2}{(x - 1)(x + 3)}\right]_{x=-2} = \frac{6}{(-3)(1)} = -2.$$

In determining B, we use $a = 1$ and $Q_1(x) = (x + 2)(x + 3)$ to get

$$B = \left[\frac{x^2 + 2}{(x + 2)(x + 3)}\right]_{x=1} = \frac{3}{(3)(4)} = \frac{1}{4}.$$

Finally, we use $a = -3$ and $Q_1(x) = (x + 2)(x - 1)$, to find

$$D = \left[\frac{x^2 + 2}{(x + 2)(x - 1)}\right]_{x=-3} = \frac{11}{(-1)(-4)} = \frac{11}{4}.$$

Substituting the values of the constants into the assumed expansion, we have

$$\int \frac{x^2 + 2}{(x + 2)(x - 1)(x + 3)}\, dx = \int \frac{-2}{x + 2}\, dx + \int \frac{1/4}{x - 1}\, dx + \int \frac{11/4}{x + 3}\, dx$$

$$= -2 \ln |x + 2| + \frac{1}{4} \ln |x - 1| + \frac{11}{4} \ln |x + 3| + C.$$

For a repeated linear factor, such as $(x - a)^k$, $k > 1$, it is frequently a good idea to use a general procedure called the **method of undetermined coefficients,** since, if the preceding method is used, the constants would have to be determined one at a time and the process could become excessively laborious. In order to use the method of undetermined coefficients we need to rely on Theorem 3.6e (the identity theorem for polynomials). The following example illustrates the manner in which this theorem enters the discussion.

Example 15.7c. Integrate

$$\int \frac{x-1}{(x-2)^2(x+3)}\,dx.$$

Theorem 15.7a guarantees that there exist unique constants A, B, D such that

$$\frac{x-1}{(x-2)^2(x+3)} = \frac{A}{(x-2)^2} + \frac{B}{x-2} + \frac{D}{x+3}$$

is an identity in x. After multiplying each side by the lowest common denominator (the denominator of the original fraction), we get

(2) $$x-1 = A(x+3) + B(x-2)(x+3) + D(x-2)^2.$$

Since both members of this equation are polynomials of degree two or less and must be equal for more than two values of x, it follows from Theorem 3.6e that they are equal for all values of x. Accordingly, we may choose three arbitrary values of x to substitute into Equation (2) to obtain three equations in the three unknowns A, B, and D. The values of A, B, and D may be found from these equations.

Usually we choose values for x that will lead to the simplest possible equations. For example, if $x = 2$, we get

$$1 = A(2+3) \quad \text{or} \quad A = \tfrac{1}{5}.$$

Similarly, for $x = -3$, we find

$$-4 = D(-5)^2 \quad \text{or} \quad D = -\tfrac{4}{25}.$$

After this method has been used to determine as many of the constants as possible, the coefficients of corresponding powers of x may be equated to determine the other constants. In this case, the coefficient of x^2 on the left side is zero and on the right side is $B + D$. Thus,

$$B + D = 0,$$

and since $D = -4/25$, we have

$$B = \frac{4}{25}.$$

Substituting the values of the constants into the assumed expansion, we obtain

$$\int \frac{x-1}{(x-2)^2(x+3)}\,dx = \frac{1}{5}\int \frac{dx}{(x-2)^2} + \frac{4}{25}\int \frac{dx}{x-2} - \frac{4}{25}\int \frac{dx}{x+3}$$

$$= \frac{-1}{5(x-2)} + \frac{4}{25}\ln|x-2| - \frac{4}{25}\ln|x+3| + C.$$

Quadratic factors in the denominator will be discussed in the next section.

Exercises 15.7

In each of Numbers 1 to 18, find the indicated inverse derivative.

1. $\displaystyle \int \frac{dx}{x^2 - 4}.$

2. $\displaystyle \int \frac{y^2\, dy}{y^2 + y - 6}.$

3. $\displaystyle \int \frac{5w - 2}{w^2 - 4}\, dw.$

4. $\displaystyle \int \frac{1 - t}{t^2 + t}\, dt.$

5. $\displaystyle \int \frac{2x^2 + 3x - 3}{x^3 - x}\, dx.$

6. $\displaystyle \int \frac{-14y + 20}{y^3 + 4y^2 - 5y}\, dy.$

7. $\displaystyle \int \frac{2w^2 + 11w + 8}{w^3 + 4w^2 + 4w}\, dw.$

8. $\displaystyle \int \frac{x^2 + x - 2}{x^3 - 2x^2}\, dx.$

9. $\displaystyle \int \frac{t^2\, dt}{t^2 - 3t + 2}.$

10. $\displaystyle \int \frac{s^3 + s^2 - 6s - 14}{s^2 - s - 6}\, ds.$

11. $\displaystyle \int \frac{x^2 + 5x + 1}{x(x + 1)^2}\, dx.$

12. $\displaystyle \int \frac{y^2 + 15y + 2}{(y - 2)(y + 1)(y + 3)}\, dy.$

13. $\displaystyle \int \frac{24w^2 - 3w - 3}{9w^3 - w}\, dw.$

14. $\displaystyle \int \frac{x^3 + 2x^2 - 4x - 6}{x^2 - 4}\, dx.$

15. $\displaystyle \int \frac{5t^2 + 6t + 2}{t(t + 1)^2}\, dt.$

16. $\displaystyle \int \frac{4t^2 - 30}{t^3 + 3t^2 - 10t}\, dt.$

17. $\displaystyle \int \frac{6w^2 - 5w - 9}{w^3 - 2w^2 - w + 2}\, dw.$

18. $\displaystyle \int \frac{3x^2 - 10x + 6}{x^3 - 7x^2 + 16x - 12}\, dx.$

In each of Numbers 19 to 26 evaluate the given definite integral.

19. $\displaystyle \int_0^2 \frac{-x + 1}{x^2 + 3x + 2}\, dx.$

20. $\displaystyle \int_2^5 \frac{4t + 5}{t^2 + t - 2}\, dt.$

21. $\displaystyle \int_1^4 \frac{2w^2 + 13w + 18}{w(w + 3)^2}\, dw.$

22. $\displaystyle \int_1^3 \frac{2x^2 - x - 3}{x^3 + 3x^2}\, dx.$

23. $\displaystyle \int_0^2 \frac{2w^2 + 6w + 2}{w^3 + 6w^2 + 11w + 6}\, dw.$

24. $\displaystyle \int_0^3 \frac{2x^2 + 9x + 11}{x^3 + 7x^2 + 16x + 12}\, dx.$

25. $\displaystyle \int_1^2 \frac{2x^2 + x + 4}{x^3 + 4x^2}\, dx.$

26. $\displaystyle \int_0^3 \frac{t^2 + 6t + 7}{(t + 2)^2(t + 1)}\, dt.$

27. Find the area bounded by the curve $y = (x - 1)/(x^2 - 5x + 6)$ and the lines $x = 4$, $x = 6$, $y = 0$.

28. Find the area bounded by the curve $y = (x - 2)/(2x^2 + 7x + 3)$ and the lines $x = 0$, $x = 4$, $y = 0$.

29. Find the area bounded by the curve $y = \sqrt{9 + x}/x^2$ and the lines $x = 7$, $x = 16$, $y = 0$.

30. Find the area bounded by the curve $y = \sqrt{x + 4}/[x(x + 3)]$ and the lines $x = 5$, $x = 12$, $y = 0$.
31. Find the x-coordinate of the centroid of the area of Number 27.
32. Find the x-coordinate of the centroid of the area of Number 28.
33. Calculate the volume formed by revolving about the y-axis the area of Number 27.
34. Calculate the volume formed by revolving about the y-axis the area of Number 28.

15.8 RATIONAL FRACTIONS WITH QUADRATIC FACTORS

Suppose the denominator $Q(x)$ of the rational fraction $P(x)/Q(x)$ has the imaginary number $a + ib$ as a zero. Then from Theorem 3.6f it is known that $a - ib$ is also a zero. The product of the corresponding factors is

$$[x - (a + ib)][x - (a - ib)] = x^2 - 2ax + a^2 + b^2,$$

and if these are simple factors, the partial fractions expansion is

(1) $$\frac{P(x)}{(x^2 - 2ax + a^2 + b^2)Q_1(x)} = \frac{A}{x - a - ib} + \frac{B}{x - a + ib} + \frac{P_1(x)}{Q_1(x)}.$$

From the proof of Theorem 15.7a, we know that

$$A = \left[\frac{P(x)}{(x - a + ib)Q_1(x)}\right]_{x=a+ib} = \frac{P(a + ib)}{(2ib)Q_1(a + ib)}$$

and

$$B = \left[\frac{P(x)}{(x - a - ib)Q_1(x)}\right]_{x=a-ib} = \frac{P(a - ib)}{(-2ib)Q_1(a - ib)}.$$

Thus,

(2) $$\frac{A}{x - a - ib} + \frac{B}{x - a + ib} = \frac{\dfrac{P(a + ib)}{(2ib)Q_1(a + ib)}}{x - a - ib} + \frac{\dfrac{P(a - ib)}{(-2ib)Q_1(a - ib)}}{x - a + ib}.$$

The numerator of the last fraction is the same as the numerator of the preceding fraction with the exception that each imaginary number has been replaced by its conjugate. To appreciate how this fact can be used, we need two preliminary theorems. The notation $\bar{z}$, introduced in Section 7.7, will be used for the conjugate of the number z, so that $z = a + ib \Rightarrow \bar{z} = a - ib$.

Theorem 15.8a. If $P(x)$ is a polynomial over $\mathcal{R}$ and z is an imaginary number, then

$$P(\bar{z}) = \overline{P(z)}.$$

PROOF: To prove this theorem, we first use the fact that

$$z = r(\cos \theta + i \sin \theta) = re^{i\theta} \Rightarrow \bar{z} = r(\cos \theta - i \sin \theta) = re^{-i\theta}.$$

Hence (see Section 14.9),

$$z^n = r^n e^{in\theta} \Rightarrow \overline{(z^n)} = r^n e^{-in\theta}.$$

Since $(\bar{z})^n = (re^{-i\theta})^n = r^n e^{-in\theta}$, it follows that

$$\overline{(z^n)} = (\bar{z})^n.$$

Thus, for the polynomial

$$P(x) = a_0 x^n + a_1 x^{n-1} + \cdots + a_n,$$

we have

$$
\begin{aligned}
P(\bar{z}) &= a_0(\bar{z})^n + a_1(\bar{z})^{n-1} + \cdots + a_n \\
&= a_0 \overline{z^n} + a_1 \overline{z^{n-1}} + \cdots + a_n, \\
&= \overline{P(z)},
\end{aligned}
$$

since the a's are real numbers.

As a simple example of this theorem, let $P(x) = x^2 - x + 3$, and let $z = 1 + i$. Then

$$P(z) = P(1 + i) = (1 + i)^2 - (1 + i) + 3 = 2 + i$$

and

$$\overline{P(z)} = 2 - i.$$

But

$$P(\bar{z}) = P(1 - i) = (1 - i)^2 - (1 - i) + 3 = 2 - i,$$

and thus

$$\overline{P(z)} = P(\bar{z}).$$

Another theorem that is needed here is

Theorem 15.8b. If z_1 and z_2 are imaginary numbers, then

$$\overline{\left(\frac{z_1}{z_2}\right)} = \frac{\bar{z_1}}{\bar{z_2}}.$$

PROOF: This theorem can be proved quite simply by making use of the exponential form of the numbers z_1 and z_2. Thus, let

$$z_1 = r_1 e^{i\theta_1} \quad \text{and} \quad z_2 = r_2 e^{i\theta_2}.$$

Then

$$\frac{z_1}{z_2} = \frac{r_1 e^{i\theta_1}}{r_2 e^{i\theta_2}} = \frac{r_1}{r_2} e^{i(\theta_1 - \theta_2)}$$

and

$$\overline{\left(\frac{z_1}{z_2}\right)} = \frac{r_1}{r_2} e^{-i(\theta_1 - \theta_2)}.$$

Also, we have

$$
\begin{aligned}
\frac{\bar{z_1}}{\bar{z_2}} &= \frac{r_1 e^{-i\theta_1}}{r_2 e^{-i\theta_2}} = \frac{r_1}{r_2} e^{-i(\theta_1 - \theta_2)} \\
&= \overline{\left(\frac{z_1}{z_2}\right)}.
\end{aligned}
$$

We now return to Equation (2) and let

$$\frac{P(a + ib)}{2ib Q_1(a + ib)} = A_1 + iB_1.$$

Then, by Theorems 15.8a and 15.8b, the numerator of the last fraction in Equation (2) must be the conjugate of this expression; that is,

$$\frac{P(a - ib)}{(-2ib)Q_1(a - ib)} = A_1 - iB_1.$$

Equation (2) may now be written

$$\frac{A}{x - a - ib} + \frac{B}{x - a + ib} = \frac{A_1 + iB_1}{x - a - ib} + \frac{A_1 - iB_1}{x - a + ib}$$

$$= \frac{2A_1(x - a) - 2b\,B_1}{x^2 - 2ax + a^2 + b^2}.$$

Consequently, we have proved the following theorem.

Theorem 15.8c. Let $P(x)/Q(x)$ be a proper rational fraction in lowest terms with real coefficients, and let $Q(x)$ have a simple quadratic factor

$$ax^2 + bx + c$$

with imaginary zeros. Then

$$\frac{P(x)}{Q(x)} = \frac{P(x)}{(ax^2 + bx + c)Q_1(x)} = \frac{Ax + B}{ax^2 + bx + c} + \frac{P_1(x)}{Q_1(x)},$$

where A and B are real.

For the case where the quadratic factor appears with an exponent $k \geqq 2$, the proof follows along the same lines as the preceding proof, but is rather more complicated and will not be given. The theorem is as follows.

Theorem 15.8d. Let $P(x)/Q(x)$ be a proper rational fraction in lowest terms and let

$$\frac{P(x)}{Q(x)} = \frac{P(x)}{(ax^2 + bx + c)^k Q_1(x)},$$

where $ax^2 + bx + c$ and $Q_1(x)$ are relatively prime. Then,

$$\frac{P(x)}{(ax^2 + bx + c)^k Q_1(x)} = \frac{A_1 x + B_1}{(ax^2 + bx + c)^k} + \frac{A_2 x + B_2}{(ax^2 + bx + c)^{k-1}} + \cdots$$

$$+ \frac{A_k x + B_k}{ax^2 + bx + c} + \frac{P_1(x)}{Q_1(x)},$$

where the degree of $P_1(x)$ is less than the degree of $Q_1(x)$, A_1 and B_1 are not both zero, and all of the A's and B's are real.

Example 15.8a. Integrate

$$\int \frac{3x + 7}{(x^2 + 2x + 2)(x^2 + 4)}\, dx.$$

Using the theorems on partial fractions, we first write

$$\frac{3x + 7}{(x^2 + 2x + 2)(x^2 + 4)} = \frac{Ax + B}{x^2 + 2x + 2} + \frac{Dx + E}{x^2 + 4}.$$

Then, multiplying each side by the denominator on the left, we get

(3) $\qquad 3x + 7 = (Ax + B)(x^2 + 4) + (Dx + E)(x^2 + 2x + 2).$

Equating coefficients of corresponding powers of x in Equation (3), we obtain the set of equations

$$x^3: \quad\quad A + D = 0,$$
$$x^2: \quad\quad B + 2D + E = 0,$$
$$x: \quad 4A + 2D + 2E = 3,$$
$$x^0: \quad\quad\quad 4B + 2E = 7.$$

The preceding four equations are sufficient to determine the values of the four coefficients, and we find

$$A = 1, \quad B = \frac{3}{2}, \quad D = -1, \quad E = \frac{1}{2}.$$

Consequently,

$$\int \frac{3x + 7}{(x^2 + 2x + 2)(x^2 + 4)}\, dx = \frac{1}{2}\int \frac{2x + 3}{x^2 + 2x + 2}\, dx - \frac{1}{2}\int \frac{2x - 1}{x^2 + 4}\, dx.$$

Since the derivative of $x^2 + 2x + 2$ is $2x + 2$, we write the numerator of the first fraction as

$$2x + 3 = [(2x + 2) + 1]$$

and then split each of the fractions into two fractions to obtain

$$\int \frac{3x + 7}{(x^2 + 2x + 2)(x^2 + 4)}$$

$$= \frac{1}{2}\int \frac{2x + 2}{x^2 + 2x + 2}\, dx + \frac{1}{2}\int \frac{dx}{(x + 1)^2 + 1} - \frac{1}{2}\int \frac{2x\, dx}{x^2 + 4} + \frac{1}{2}\int \frac{dx}{x^2 + 4}$$

$$= \frac{1}{2}\ln(x^2 + 2x + 2) + \frac{1}{2}\mathrm{Tan}^{-1}(x + 1) - \frac{1}{2}\ln(x^2 + 4) + \frac{1}{4}\mathrm{Tan}^{-1}\frac{x}{2} + C.$$

Example 15.8b. Integrate

$$\int \frac{3x^4 + 5x^3 - 2x + 2}{(x^2 + 1)^2(x - 1)}\, dx.$$

Using the theorems on partial fractions, we write

$$\frac{3x^4 + 5x^3 - 2x + 2}{(x^2 + 1)^2(x - 1)} = \frac{Ax + B}{(x^2 + 1)^2} + \frac{Dx + E}{x^2 + 1} + \frac{F}{x - 1}.$$

Multiplying by the denominator on the left, we have

$$3x^4 + 5x^3 - 2x + 2 = (Ax + B)(x - 1) + (Dx + E)(x^2 + 1)(x - 1) + F(x^2 + 1)^2.$$

For $x = 1$, we find

$$8 = 4F \quad \text{or} \quad 2 = F.$$

If we now equate coefficients of corresponding powers of x, the resulting equations are

$$D + F = 3,$$
$$-D + E = 5,$$
$$A + D - E + 2F = 0,$$
$$-A + B - D + E = -2,$$
$$-B - E + F = 2.$$

Again, the preceding five equations are sufficient to obtain the five unknowns, but we can make use of the value of F obtained earlier to simplify the work.

Since $F = 2$, then $D = 1$, and $D = 1$ gives $E = 6$. With these results, we get $A = 1$, and finally, $B = -6$. Now the original integral may be written as

$$\int \frac{3x^4 + 5x^3 - 2x + 2}{(x^2 + 1)^2(x - 1)}\, dx$$

$$= \int \frac{x\, dx}{(x^2 + 1)^2} - 6 \int \frac{dx}{(x^2 + 1)^2} + \int \frac{x\, dx}{x^2 + 1} + 6 \int \frac{dx}{x^2 + 1} + 2 \int \frac{dx}{x - 1}$$

$$= -\frac{1}{2(x^2 + 1)} - \left(\frac{3x}{x^2 + 1} + 3\, \text{Tan}^{-1}\, x \right) + \frac{1}{2} \ln\,(x^2 + 1)$$

$$\qquad\qquad\qquad\qquad\qquad + 6\, \text{Tan}^{-1}\, x + 2 \ln\,|x - 1| + C$$

$$= -\frac{6x + 1}{2(x^2 + 1)} + 3\, \text{Tan}^{-1}\, x + \frac{1}{2} \ln\,[(x^2 + 1)(x - 1)^4] + C.$$

Exercises 15.8

In Numbers 1 to 22, find the inverse derivative.

1. $\displaystyle\int \frac{3y^2 + 2y + 1}{(y + 1)(y^2 + 1)}\, dy.$

2. $\displaystyle\int \frac{4w^2 - 3w + 6}{(w^2 + 4)(w - 2)}\, dw.$

3. $\displaystyle\int \frac{(4t^2 + 7t + 30)\, dt}{(t + 3)(t^2 + 4t + 8)}.$

4. $\displaystyle\int \frac{3x^2 + 14x + 12}{(x + 4)(x^2 + 6x + 10)}\, dx.$

5. $\displaystyle\int \frac{2w^2 + 3w + 8}{w(w^2 + 4)}\, dw.$

6. $\displaystyle\int \frac{5s^2 + 4}{s^3 + 8}\, ds.$

7. $\displaystyle\int \frac{3x^2 + 7x - 8}{(x - 2)(x^2 + 2x + 10)}\, dx.$

8. $\displaystyle\int \frac{2t^2 - 1}{t^2(t^2 + 1)}\, dt.$

9. $\displaystyle\int \frac{s^2 + 1}{s^4 + s^2 - 2}\, ds.$

10. $\displaystyle\int \frac{2w^2 - 2w + 18}{w^3 + 9w}\, dw.$

11. $\displaystyle\int \frac{-x^2 + 5x - 2}{x^3 - 2x^2 + 2x}\, dx.$

12. $\displaystyle\int \frac{3t^2 + 3t + 8}{t^3 + 2t^2 + 3t + 6}\, dt.$

13. $\displaystyle\int \frac{3w^2 + 4w + 5}{w^3 + 2w^2 + 5w - 8}\, dw.$

14. $\displaystyle\int \frac{3t^2 + 24}{t^3 + 6t + 20}\, dt.$

15. $\displaystyle\int \frac{2w^3 + 3w^2 + 11w + 15}{(w + 1)(w^2 + 4)}\, dw.$

16. $\displaystyle\int \frac{dy}{y^3 - 8}.$

17. $\displaystyle\int \frac{7x^2 + 11x + 15}{x^3 + 4x^2 + 5x}\, dx.$

18. $\displaystyle\int \frac{5y^2 - 3y + 1}{y^3 + y}\, dy.$

19. $\displaystyle\int \frac{3x^4 + x^2 - 5x + 3}{(x + 1)(x^2 + 1)^2}\, dx.$

20. $\displaystyle\int \frac{2w^4 + 7w^2 - 6w + 2}{(w^2 + 1)^2(w - 2)}\, dw.$

21. $\displaystyle\int \frac{x\, dx}{x^4 + 4}.$

22. $\displaystyle\int \frac{dx}{x^4 + 4}.$

Evaluate the definite integrals in Numbers 23 to 32.

23. $\int_0^3 \dfrac{3y^2 + 2y + 15}{(y + 3)(y^2 + 9)}\, dy.$

28. $\int_0^1 \dfrac{5y^3 + y^2 + 20y + 12}{y^4 - 16}\, dy.$

24. $\int_1^{\sqrt{3}} \dfrac{4x^3 + 3x^2 + 2x + 2}{x^3 + x}\, dx.$

29. $\int_0^2 \dfrac{5w^2 + 12w + 1}{(w + 3)(w^2 + 2w + 2)}\, dw.$

25. $\int_{1/\sqrt{3}}^1 \dfrac{4w^2 - 4w + 2}{w^3 + w}\, dw.$

30. $\int_1^2 \dfrac{x^2 + 1}{(x + 1)(x^2 + 2x + 3)}\, dx.$

26. $\int_{\sqrt{3}/3}^{\sqrt{3}} \dfrac{3x^3 + 3x^2 + 2}{x^4 + x^2}\, dx.$

31. $\int_1^{\sqrt{3}} \dfrac{t^4 + 4t^2 + 6}{t^2(t^2 + 3)}\, dt.$

27. $\int_0^1 \dfrac{3y^2 + 2y - 13}{(y^2 + 1)(y + 5)}\, dy.$

32. $\int_1^2 \dfrac{-2x - 8}{x^3 + 4x^2 + 8x}\, dx.$

33. Find the area bounded by the curve $y = 1/[x^2(x^2 + 4)]$ and the lines $x = 2$, $x = 2\sqrt{3}$, and $y = 0$.
34. Find the area bounded by the curve $x = 2/[(y^2 + 1)(y^2 + 3)]$ and the lines $y = 0$, $y = \sqrt{3}$, and $x = 0$.
35. Find the area bounded by the curve $y = 12/(8 + x^3)$ and the lines $x = 0$, $x = 2$, $y = 0$.
36. Find the volume obtained by revolving about the y-axis the area of Number 35.

15.9 IMPROPER INTEGRALS

The definite integral, $\int_a^b f(x)\, dx$, was introduced in Chapter 12 under the assumption that the function f was defined at every point of a finite interval $a \leq x \leq b$. It is possible to relax this restriction on f and on the interval to obtain extensions of the definite integral that are often useful in practical applications.

For example, a fundamental concept in electromagnetic field theory is that of the electric potential at a point in an electromagnetic field due to an electric charge distribution. It is known that two like electric charges, q_1 and q_2, repel each other with a force F given by

$$F = k\,\frac{q_1 q_2}{r^2},$$

where r is the distance between the charges and k is a constant of proportionality. The electric potential V_P at a point P in an electromagnetic field due to a charge q is defined by the physicist as the work done in bringing a unit charge from "infinity" to the point P. Using the definition of work, and letting r be the distance from the charge q, we may express the potential at P by the "integral"

$$V_P = \int_\infty^x k\,\frac{q}{r^2}\, dr,$$

where the symbol $\int_\infty^x$ indicates that the charge must "start" at "infinity" and be moved to the point x. In this illustration, the integral is not an ordinary one since we are concerned with an infinite interval.

From the mathematician's point of view, this new concept must be given a meaning that is consistent with that of the definite integral. Accordingly, we make the following definition.

Definition 15.9a. If f is sectionally continuous on the interval $a \leq x \leq t$, for every t no matter how large, and if

$$\lim_{t\to\infty} \int_a^t f(x)\, dx$$

exists, then

$$\int_a^\infty f(x)\, dx .=. \lim_{t\to\infty} \int_a^t f(x)\, dx.$$

The symbol $\int_a^\infty f(x)\, dx$ is called an **improper integral of the first kind,** and if $\lim_{t\to\infty} \int_a^t f(x)\, dx$ exists, then the improper integral is said to **converge**; otherwise, it is said to **diverge.**

Example 15.9a. If the integral $\int_1^\infty xe^{-x}\, dx$ converges, find its value.

By definition,

$$\int_1^\infty xe^{-x}\, dx = \lim_{t\to\infty} \int_1^t xe^{-x}\, dx$$

$$= \lim_{t\to\infty} [-te^{-t} - e^{-t} + 2e^{-1}].$$

By L'Hôpital's Theorem,

$$\lim_{t\to\infty} te^{-t} = \lim_{t\to\infty} \frac{t}{e^t} = \lim_{t\to\infty} \frac{1}{e^t} = 0,$$

and since $e^{-t} \to 0$ as $t \to \infty$,

$$\lim_{t\to\infty} [-te^{-t} - e^{-t} + 2e^{-1}] = 2e^{-1}.$$

Therefore, the improper integral converges and

$$\int_1^\infty xe^{-x}\, dx = 2e^{-1}.$$

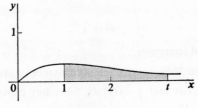

FIGURE 15.9a

A geometric interpretation of $\int_1^\infty xe^{-x}\,dx$ may be helpful. The proper integral $\int_1^t xe^{-x}\,dx$ may be interpreted as the area bounded by the curve $y = xe^{-x}$ and the x-axis between $x = 1$ and $x = t$, as illustrated in Figure 15.9a. The question of convergence essentially depends on whether the curve $y = xe^{-x}$ approaches the x axis "rapidly enough" as $t \to \infty$ to prevent the area from increasing without bound.

In a similar way, improper integrals of the form $\int_{-\infty}^b f(x)\,dx$ or $\int_{-\infty}^\infty f(x)\,dx$ may be defined.

Definition 15.9b. If $f(x)$ is sectionally continuous on the interval $t \leq x \leq b$ for every $t \leq b$, and if

$$\lim_{t \to -\infty} \int_t^b f(x)\,dx$$

exists, then

$$\int_{-\infty}^b f(x)\,dx \,.=.\, \lim_{t \to -\infty} \int_t^b f(x)\,dx.$$

Definition 15.9c. If $f(x)$ is sectionally continuous on $t \leq x \leq T$ for every t and T and if *both*

$$\int_a^\infty f(x)\,dx \quad \text{and} \quad \int_{-\infty}^a f(x)\,dx$$

exist for every a, then

$$\int_{-\infty}^\infty f(x)\,dx \,.=.\, \int_{-\infty}^a f(x)\,dx + \int_a^\infty f(x)\,dx.$$

This last statement may be written as

$$\int_{-\infty}^\infty f(x)\,dx = \lim_{t \to -\infty} \int_t^a f(x)\,dx + \lim_{T \to \infty} \int_a^T f(x)\,dx,$$

but is *not* equivalent to

$$\int_{-\infty}^\infty f(x)\,dx = \lim_{t \to \infty} \left[\int_{-t}^a f(x)\,dx + \int_a^t f(x)\,dx \right].$$

This last limit may exist under circumstances where the preceding one does not. Since $f(x)$ is sectionally continuous on every finite interval, it follows easily that the choice of the point a is unimportant.

Example 15.9b. Find the value of

$$\int_{-\infty}^\infty \frac{x}{x^2 + 1}\,dx$$

provided that the integral converges.

According to Definition 15.9c, we must select a number a and examine the two improper integrals $\int_{-\infty}^a f(x)\,dx$ and $\int_a^\infty f(x)\,dx$. Since any convenient value of a may be used, let us choose $a = 0$. Then

$$\int_{-\infty}^{\infty} \frac{x \, dx}{x^2 + 1} = \int_{-\infty}^{0} \frac{x \, dx}{x^2 + 1} + \int_{0}^{\infty} \frac{x \, dx}{x^2 + 1}$$

and

$$\int_{0}^{\infty} \frac{x}{x^2 + 1} \, dx = \lim_{t \to \infty} \int_{0}^{t} \frac{x}{x^2 + 1} \, dx$$

$$= \lim_{t \to \infty} \frac{1}{2} \ln (t^2 + 1).$$

Since this limit does not exist,

$$\int_{0}^{\infty} \frac{x}{x^2 + 1} \, dx$$

diverges, and consequently

$$\int_{-\infty}^{\infty} \frac{x}{x^2 + 1} \, dx$$

diverges.

It is left as an exercise for the reader to show that

$$\lim_{t \to \infty} \left\{ \int_{-t}^{a} \frac{x}{x^2 + 1} \, dx + \int_{a}^{t} \frac{x}{x^2 + 1} \, dx \right\} = 0.$$

(See Exercises 15.9, Number 16.)

A second type of extension of the definite integral can be made in certain cases to functions having infinite discontinuities on the interval of integration.

Definition 15.9d. Let f have an infinite discontinuity at a point c in the interval $a \leq x \leq b$, and suppose f is sectionally continuous elsewhere in the interval. Then, whenever the limits exist we have

(1) $\int_{a}^{c} f(x) \, dx \, . = . \lim_{\epsilon \to 0^+} \int_{a}^{c-\epsilon} f(x) \, dx$

(2) $\int_{c}^{b} f(x) \, dx \, . = . \lim_{\epsilon \to 0^+} \int_{c+\epsilon}^{b} f(x) \, dx$, and

(3) $\int_{a}^{b} f(x) \, dx \, . = . \int_{a}^{c} f(x) \, dx + \int_{c}^{b} f(x) \, dx$.

If the discontinuity of f occurs at an end point of the interval of integration, then the point of discontinuity is approached from *within* the interval, as indicated by requiring that $\epsilon \to 0^+$. If the discontinuity occurs at an interior point of the interval, then the two integrals on the right side of Equation (3) must converge independently before we may say that $\int_{a}^{b} f(x) \, dx$ converges. Integrals of the kind defined in Definition 15.9d are called **improper integrals of the second kind.**

Example 15.9c. Evaluate

$$\int_{1}^{2} \frac{dx}{\sqrt{x - 1}},$$

if the integral converges.

Since $1/\sqrt{x-1}$ has an infinite discontinuity at $x = 1$, we must consider

$$\lim_{\epsilon \to 0^+} \int_{1+\epsilon}^{2} \frac{dx}{\sqrt{x-1}} = \lim_{\epsilon \to 0^+} [2\sqrt{x-1}]_{1+\epsilon}^{2}$$

$$= 2 - \lim_{\epsilon \to 0^+} 2\sqrt{\epsilon} = 2.$$

Hence the integral converges to the value 2.

If we interpret the results of the preceding example geometrically, then

$$\int_{1+\epsilon}^{2} \frac{1}{\sqrt{x-1}} \, dx$$

represents the area bounded by the curve $y = 1/\sqrt{x-1}$ and the x-axis between $1 + \epsilon$ and 2, as illustrated in Figure 15.9b. The question of convergence

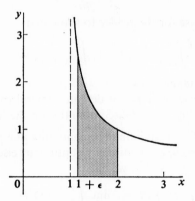

FIGURE 15.9b

then depends on whether or not the curve approaches the asymptote $x = 1$ "sufficiently rapidly" as $\epsilon \to 0^+$ that the area will not increase without bound.

An improper integral may involve infinite discontinuities as well as infinite limits. In this case the integral must be broken up into as many individual improper integrals as are necessary to isolate each of the discontinuities and infinite limits. To illustrate, we may write

$$\int_{0}^{\infty} \frac{1}{x^2} \, dx = \int_{0}^{a} \frac{1}{x^2} \, dx + \int_{a}^{\infty} \frac{1}{x^2} \, dx, \qquad a > 0,$$

and examine each of the resulting integrals for convergence. The original integral converges *only* if each of the component integrals converges. It is left as an exercise for the reader to show that the point a in the preceding illustration is immaterial, so long as a separates the improprieties of the original integral.

It is not uncommon to encounter an improper integral of a function having no elementary inverse derivative. For example, in probability and statistics an integral of the form

$$\int_0^\infty e^{-x^2}\, dx$$

often occurs. This integral cannot be examined for convergence by the procedures discussed up to this point because $\int e^{-x^2}\, dx$ cannot be expressed in terms of elementary functions. Consequently, it is necessary that we develop a means of testing such an integral for convergence or divergence. There are two elementary theorems that will suffice for our needs in this regard. They are stated without proof.

Theorem 15.9a. Suppose that

$$(1)\ \int_a^t f(x)\, dx \text{ exists for all } t > a,$$

$$(2)\ 0 \leq f(x) \leq g(x) \text{ for all } x > a, \text{ and}$$

$$(3)\ \int_a^\infty g(x)\, dx \text{ converges.}$$

Then $\int_a^\infty f(x)\, dx$ also converges.

This theorem is analogous to the theorem on the convergence of a bounded monotonic increasing sequence, and its proof is carried out in a similar fashion.

Theorem 15.9b. If $\int_a^t f(x)\, dx$ and $\int_a^t g(x)\, dx$ both exist for all $t > a$, where $f(x) \geq 0$, $g(x) > 0$ for all $x > a$, and if

$$\lim_{x \to \infty} \frac{f(x)}{g(x)} = A, \qquad A \neq 0,$$

then the integrals $\int_a^\infty f(x)\, dx$ and $\int_a^\infty g(x)\, dx$ converge or diverge together. If $A = 0$, then $\int_a^\infty f(x)\, dx$ converges if $\int_a^\infty g(x)\, dx$ converges.

This theorem is easily made plausible in the following way: Since

$$\lim_{x \to \infty} f(x)/g(x) = A \neq 0,$$

it follows that for all sufficiently large x, $f(x)/g(x) < B$, where the constant $B > A$. Thus $f(x) < Bg(x)$ and so $\int_a^\infty f(x)\, dx$ converges if $\int_a^\infty Bg(x)\, dx$ does. On the other hand, $f(x)/g(x) > C$, where $0 < C < A$, so that $f(x) > Cg(x)$ and thus $\int_a^\infty f(x)\, dx$ diverges if $\int_a^\infty Cg(x)\, dx$ does.

The following examples illustrate the use of these theorems.

Example 15.9d. Determine the behavior with respect to convergence of the integral

$$\int_1^\infty \frac{dx}{\sqrt{x^3 + 1}}.$$

Since $\int (x^3 + 1)^{-1/2}\,dx$ cannot be expressed in terms of elementary functions, we must find a function g that is suitable for use in Theorem 15.9a or in Theorem 15.9b. Our choice for $g(x)$ is somewhat arbitrary, as there may be many functions that meet the requirements of either of the theorems. Accordingly, we try to select as simple a form as possible for $g(x)$. In this case, since

$$\frac{1}{\sqrt{x^3 + 1}} < \frac{1}{x^{3/2}} \quad \text{for all } x > 1,$$

it appears feasible to let $g(x) = x^{-3/2}$. Since $\int_1^\infty x^{-3/2}\,dx$ converges to the value 2, it follows that $\int_1^\infty (x^3 + 1)^{-1/2}\,dx$ converges by Theorem 15.9a. Although the theorem enables us to show that the integral converges in this case, it does not help us to find the value to which it converges. However, we may be certain that this value is not greater than 2.

Example 15.9e. Examine the convergence behavior of the integral $\int_1^\infty e^{-x}x^s\,dx$, where $s \in \mathcal{R}$.

It is easy to show (by the use of L'Hôpital's Theorem, if necessary) that

$$\lim_{x \to \infty} e^{-x}x^k = 0, \qquad k \in \mathcal{R}.$$

Furthermore,

$$\int_1^\infty \frac{dx}{x^2} = \lim_{t \to \infty} \int_1^t \frac{dx}{x^2} = \lim_{t \to \infty} \left(1 - \frac{1}{t}\right) = 1.$$

For any s,

$$\lim_{x \to \infty} \frac{e^{-x}x^s}{x^{-2}} = \lim_{x \to \infty} e^{-x}x^{s+2} = 0,$$

so that Theorem 15.9b applies with $f(x) = e^{-x}x^s$ and $g(x) = x^{-2}$, and we conclude that the given integral converges for all $s \in \mathcal{R}$.

Exercises 15.9

In each of Numbers 1 to 14 test the improper integral for convergence and evaluate the integral if it converges.

1. $\int_1^\infty \frac{dx}{x}$.

2. $\int_0^\infty \frac{dx}{4 + x^2}$.

3. $\int_0^\infty e^{-x}\cos x\,dx$.

4. $\int_0^2 \frac{dx}{\sqrt{4 - x^2}}$.

5. $\int_1^\infty \frac{\ln x}{x}\,dx$.

6. $\int_{-\infty}^\infty xe^{-x^2}\,dx$.

7. $\int_0^1 \frac{\ln x}{\sqrt{x}}\,dx$.

8. $\int_2^\infty \frac{dx}{x(\ln x)^p}$.

9. $\int_0^1 \ln x \, dx.$

12. $\int_{-1}^1 \frac{dx}{x^{2/3}}.$

10. $\int_0^\infty \frac{x \, dx}{1 + x^3}.$

13. $\int_{-a}^a \frac{x \, dx}{\sqrt{a^2 - x^2}}.$

11. $\int_{-\infty}^\infty \frac{dx}{x^2 - a^2}.$

14. $\int_{-\infty}^\infty e^{-|x|} \, dx.$

15. Show that for every value of a,

$$\int_a^\infty \frac{x}{x^2 + 1} \, dx$$

diverges.

16. Verify that

$$\lim_{t \to \infty} \left\{ \int_{-t}^a \frac{x}{x^2 + 1} \, dx + \int_a^t \frac{x}{x^2 + 1} \, dx \right\} = 0,$$

but that

$$\int_{-\infty}^\infty \frac{x}{x^2 + 1} \, dx$$

diverges.

17. If $k \geq 1$, show that

$$\int_0^\infty x^k e^{-x} \, dx = k \int_0^\infty x^{k-1} e^{-x} \, dx.$$

Show further that if $k = n$, a positive integer, then $\int_0^\infty x^n e^{-x} \, dx = n!$.

18. For what values of k is the integral

$$\int_0^\infty \left(\frac{1}{\sqrt{1 + 2x^2}} - \frac{k}{x + 1} \right) dx$$

convergent?

★19. The force of attraction between two masses m_1 and m_2 is $F = k(m_1 m_2 / r^2)$, where r is the distance between their centers. Suppose an infinitely long rod of mass m units per unit length lies along the x-axis, and suppose a unit mass is placed at $(0, a)$. Find the force of attraction exerted between the rod and the unit mass, by considering that the contribution to the total force of attraction between an element of the rod dx units long and the unit mass is given by $dF = km \, dx / r^2$, where $r = \sqrt{a^2 + x^2}$, and finding the x- and y-components of this element.

In each of Numbers 20 to 25, test the given improper integral for convergence, but do not try to evaluate any of the integrals.

20. $\int_0^\infty e^{-x^2} \, dx.$

22. $\int_0^1 \frac{\sin x}{x} \, dx.$

21. $\int_1^\infty x^2 e^{-x^2} \, dx.$

23. $\int_0^\infty e^{-x} x^{s-1} \, dx, \ s \geq 1.$

★24. $\int_0^1 \frac{\cos t}{t^2} \, dt.$ *Hint*: Use the fact that $(\cos t)/t \to \infty$, as $t \to 0^+$.

★25. $\int_1^2 \dfrac{x}{\ln x}\, dx$. *Hint*: Consider the interval from $1 + \epsilon$ to 2 and let $x = e^u$.

15.10 APPROXIMATE INTEGRATION

In many of the practical applications of integration, we often encounter integrals of functions for which the inverse differentiation cannot be performed in terms of elementary functions. In such cases, it is essential to have methods of approximating the value of the definite integral.

Since a definite integral may be interpreted as an area under a curve, any method for finding this area can be used to evaluate the integral. Thus, to obtain an approximate evaluation of $\int_a^b f(x)\, dx$, $f(x) \geq 0$, we need only to approximate the area under the curve $y = f(x)$ and above the x-axis, from $x = a$ to $x = b$.

Let us choose points $x_0, x_1, \ldots, x_n$ so that the interval $a \leq x \leq b$ is divided into n equal parts, and $x_0 = a$, $x_n = b$. Let the corresponding values of the function be $y_0, y_1, \ldots, y_n$, and let $P_0, P_1, \ldots, P_n$ denote the points (x_0, y_0), $(x_1, y_1), \ldots, (x_n, y_n)$ on the curve. A fairly close approximation to the area can

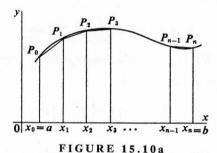

FIGURE 15.10a

be made using trapezoids formed by joining adjacent points $P_0, P_1, \ldots, P_n$ with chords, as shown in Figure 15.10a. The area of the kth trapezoid is

$$\tfrac{1}{2}h(y_{k-1} + y_k),$$

where $h = (b - a)/n$, the width of each subinterval. The sum of the areas of the n trapezoids is

$$T_n = \frac{h}{2}(y_0 + y_1) + \frac{h}{2}(y_1 + y_2) + \cdots + \frac{h}{2}(y_{n-1} + y_n)$$

or

(1) $$T_n = \frac{h}{2}(y_0 + 2y_1 + 2y_2 + \cdots + 2y_{n-1} + y_n).$$

Equation (1) is called the **Trapezoidal Rule** for approximating the integral $\int_a^b f(x)\, dx$.

For an approximation method such as the Trapezoidal Rule to be most useful, it is necessary that a method for estimating the accuracy of the approximation be available. Although it is beyond the scope of our work here to include a derivation, it can be shown that the error, E_n, made by using the Trapezoidal Rule with n trapezoids to approximate $\int_a^b f(x)\,dx$ must satisfy the inequality

$$|E_n| \leq \frac{h^2}{12}(b-a) \max |f''(x)|,$$

where $\max |f''(x)|$ denotes the maximum value of f'' on the interval $a \leq x \leq b$. (For example, see N. Macon, *Numerical Analysis*, Wiley, New York, 1963.)

Another method of approximating the area under a curve $y = f(x)$ is obtained by approximating the curve by a sequence of parabolic arcs, rather than by chords as in the Trapezoidal Rule. In this case, we use a partitioning of the interval $a \leq x \leq b$ as indicated in Figure 15.10a, except that the number of subintervals must be even, say $n = 2m$. A parabolic arc described by an equation of the form

$$y = ax^2 + bx + c$$

is then passed through the points P_0, P_1, P_2, another parabolic arc through the points P_2, P_3, P_4, and so on.

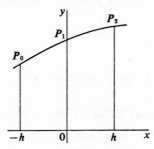

FIGURE 15.10b

Consequently, we need to find the area under a typical parabolic arc through three points. For this purpose, let us choose the points as

$$P_0(-h, y_0), \quad P_1(0, y_1), \quad P_2(h, y_2),$$

as shown in Figure 15.10b. Since the equation of the parabolic arc is of the form

$$y = ax^2 + bx + c,$$

the area under the curve is

$$A = \int_{-h}^{h} (ax^2 + bx + c)\,dx$$

$$= \left[\frac{ax^3}{3} + \frac{bx^2}{2} + cx \right]_{-h}^{h}$$

$$= \frac{2ah^3}{3} + 2ch.$$

Also, since the curve passes through the points $(-h, y_0)$, $(0, y_1)$, (h, y_2), we must have

$$y_0 = ah^2 - bh + c,$$
$$y_1 = c,$$
$$y_2 = ah^2 + bh + c,$$

so that

$$y_0 + y_2 = 2ah^2 + 2c = 2ah^2 + 2y_1.$$

Hence,

$$2ah^2 = y_0 + y_2 - 2y_1$$

and

$$A = \frac{h}{3}(y_0 + y_2 - 2y_1) + 2hy_1,$$

or

$$A = \frac{h}{3}(y_0 + 4y_1 + y_2).$$

This formula for the area under a parabolic arc is known as the **prismoidal formula,** and is independent of the location of the y-axis.

The area under a curve $y = f(x)$ is therefore approximated by adding together the areas under successive parabolic arcs along the curve. This area is

$$S = \frac{h}{3}(y_0 + 4y_1 + y_2) + \frac{h}{3}(y_2 + 4y_3 + y_4) + \cdots + \frac{h}{3}(y_{2m-2} + 4y_{2m-1} + y_{2m})$$

or

(2) $$S = \frac{h}{3}(y_0 + 4y_1 + 2y_2 + 4y_3 + 2y_4 + \cdots + 4y_{2m-1} + y_{2m}).$$

Equation (2) is called **Simpson's Rule** for approximating the integral $\int_a^b f(x)\,dx$. The prismoidal formula is, of course, Simpson's Rule with two subdivisions.

If E_n is the error in Simpson's Rule with n subintervals, then it can be shown that

$$|E_n| \leq \frac{h^4}{180}(b - a)\max |f^{(4)}(x)|, \qquad a \leq x \leq b.$$

(The derivation can be found in N. Macon, *Numerical Analysis*, Wiley, New York, 1963.)

Example 15.10a. Find an approximate value for

$$\int_0^1 \frac{dx}{1 + x^2}$$

(a) by using the Trapezoidal Rule, and (b) by using Simpson's Rule, with eight subintervals in each case.

The work is conveniently arranged in tabular form as follows.

x	$y = 1/(1 + x^2)$		
0.000	1.00000		
0.125		0.98461	
0.250			0.94118
0.375		0.87671	
0.500			0.80000
0.625		0.71910	
0.750			0.64000
0.875		0.56637	
1.000	0.50000		
	1.50000	3.14679	2.38118

For the Trapezoidal Rule, we have $h = \frac{1}{8}$, and

$$T = \frac{1}{16}(1.50000 + 2 \times 3.14679 + 2 \times 2.38118)$$
$$= \frac{1}{16}(12.55594)$$
$$= 0.78475.$$

Since the error is given by $|E_8| \leq \frac{1}{12}h^2 \max |y''(x)|$, we have

$$|E_8| \leq \frac{1}{768} \times 2 \leq 0.0026,$$

so that

$$0.7821 \leq \int_0^1 \frac{dx}{1 + x^2} < 0.7874.$$

For Simpson's Rule, we have $h = \frac{1}{8}$ and

$$S = \frac{1}{24}(1.5000 + 4 \times 3.14679 + 2 \times 2.38118)$$
$$= \frac{1}{24}(18.84952)$$
$$= 0.78540.$$

A calculation of the error, E_8, for Simpson's Rule gives

$$|E_8| < 0.00002.$$

In this example, the integral can be evaluated, and we have

$$\int_0^1 \frac{dx}{1 + x^2} = \text{Tan}^{-1} 1 = \frac{\pi}{4} = 0.78540 \text{ (approx.)}.$$

Thus, it appears that Simpson's Rule gives a much more accurate approximation to the value of the integral than does the Trapezoidal Rule.

Exercises 15.10

In Numbers 1 to 4, use the inverse derivative to evaluate the definite integrals. Then find an approximate value for each integral by using (a) the Trapezoidal Rule, and (b) Simpson's Rule, with four subintervals in each case. Also, use the formulas of this section to estimate the error of each approximation. Compare the results.

1. $\int_0^{0.8} x^3 \, dx.$

2. $\int_1^{1.4} \ln x \, dx.$

3. $\int_0^{\pi/2} \cos x \, dx.$

4. $\int_0^{0.8} e^x \, dx.$

In Numbers 5 to 12, find an approximate value for the given integral by using (a) the Trapezoidal Rule, and (b) Simpson's Rule. Use four subintervals, and round off each answer to four decimal places.

5. $\int_0^{0.8} e^{-x^2} dx.$

6. $\int_0^{0.8} \cos x^2 dx.$

7. $\int_0^{0.4} \sin x^2 dx.$

8. $\int_0^{0.8} \sqrt{1 - x^4} \, dx.$

9. $\int_{0.1}^{0.5} \frac{\cos x}{x} dx.$

10. $\int_{0.2}^{1} \sqrt{\sin x} \, dx.$

11. $\int_1^{1.8} \sqrt{1 + x^3} \, dx.$

12. $\int_0^{\pi/3} \sqrt{1 - \frac{1}{4}\sin^2 x} \, dx.$

13. Use Simpson's Rule to obtain the formula

$$V = \frac{\pi h}{6} (3r_1^2 + 3r_2^2 + h^2)$$

for the volume of a spherical segment of altitude h and base radii r_1 and r_2. Use two subintervals.

14. Use Simpson's Rule to find the formula for the volume of a right circular cone of altitude h and base radius a. Make your own choice as to the number of subintervals to use.

15. Use Simpson's Rule with $n = 4$ to find approximately the area under the probability curve $y = (1/\sqrt{2\pi})e^{-x^2/2}$ from $x = 0$ to $x = 0.4$.

16. Draw a smooth curve through the following points and find an approximation to the area under the curve using Simpson's Rule with $n = 6$:

x	0	2	4	6	8	10	12
y	10	6.8	5.3	4.5	3.6	3.3	3.1

17. If $y = P(x)$, where $P(x)$ is a polynomial of degree three or less, show that Simpson's Rule gives an exact result.

18. The area under the curve $y = \ln x$ from $x = 1$ to $x = 4$ is revolved about the x-axis. Find an approximation to the volume of the resulting solid by using Simpson's Rule with $n = 6$.

15.11 USE OF A TABLE OF INTEGRALS

The formulas in a table of integrals can be derived with standard techniques, and a table of integrals may consist of as many hundreds of formulas as the compiler wishes to include. The table of integrals in the appendix of this book is comparatively short and is essentially a sampling of the formulas that are commonly encountered.

Before using a table of integrals, the student should examine the organization of the table and should study the "items to be observed" at the head of the table.

Example 15.11a. Integrate

$$\int \frac{dx}{x\sqrt{2 + 3x}}.$$

This form contains $\sqrt{a + bu}$ so we look in the integrals listed under this heading and find that Formula (14) will fit with $a = 2$ and $b = 3$. Thus,

$$\int \frac{dx}{x\sqrt{2 + 3x}} = \frac{1}{\sqrt{2}} \ln \left| \frac{\sqrt{2 + 3x} - \sqrt{2}}{\sqrt{2 + 3x} + \sqrt{2}} \right| + C.$$

Example 15.11b. Integrate

$$\int \frac{dy}{y^3(y^2 + 4)}.$$

Formula (21), with $m = 3$ and $a = 2$, may be used as a reduction formula.

$$\int \frac{dy}{y^3(y^2 + 4)} = \frac{-1}{4(2)y^2} - \frac{1}{4} \int \frac{dy}{y(y^2 + 4)}.$$

Now Formula (20) may be used on the last integral to obtain

$$\int \frac{dy}{y^3(y^2 + 4)} = \frac{-1}{8y^2} - \frac{1}{32} \ln \frac{y^2}{y^2 + 4} + C.$$

Example 15.11c. Integrate $\int w^2\sqrt{w^2 - 9}\, dw$.

Formula (27) may be used with $a = 3$. The student should note carefully the choices of sign in the use of this formula.

$$\int w^2\sqrt{w^2 - 9}\, dw = \frac{w}{4}(w^2 - 9)^{3/2} + \frac{9w}{8}\sqrt{w^2 - 9} - \frac{81}{8}\ln |w + \sqrt{w^2 - 9}| + C.$$

Example 15.11d. Integrate $\int \cos^4 3x\, dx$.

Formula (81) may be used with $m = 4$, $u = 3x$, and $du = 3\, dx$. Thus $dx = \frac{1}{3}\, du$, and we may write

$$\int \cos^4 3x\, dx = \frac{1}{3} \int \cos^4 u\, du = \frac{1}{3}\left[\frac{\cos^3 u \sin u}{4} + \frac{3}{4} \int \cos^2 u\, du \right].$$

The last integral fits Formula (79), and the result is

$$\int \cos^4 3x\, dx = \frac{1}{3}\left[\frac{\cos^3 u \sin u}{4} + \frac{3}{4}\left(\frac{u}{2} + \frac{1}{4} \sin 2u \right) \right] + C.$$

Substituting $u = 3x$, the final result is

$$\int \cos^4 3x\, dx = \frac{1}{12} \cos^3 3x \sin 3x + \frac{3x}{8} + \frac{1}{16} \sin 6x + C.$$

Exercises 15.11

In Numbers 1 to 12, derive the indicated formula of the table of integrals.

1. Formula 79.
2. Formula 80.
3. Formula 18.
4. Formula 19.

5. Formula 96.

6. Formula 109.

7. Formula 50.

8. Formula 58.

9. Formula 4.

10. Formula 9.

11. Formula 22.

12. Formula 28.

In Numbers 13 to 32, find the inverse derivative by using the table of integrals.

13. $\int \dfrac{\sqrt{x^2 + 1}}{x^3}\, dx.$

14. $\int \dfrac{(4x^2 - 9)^{3/2}}{x}\, dx.$

15. $\int \dfrac{y^3\, dy}{4y^2 - 1}.$

16. $\int \sqrt{9y^2 - 4}\, dy.$

17. $\int w^3\sqrt{w^2 - 4}\, dw.$

18. $\int \dfrac{dt}{t^3(4t^2 + 9)^{3/2}}.$

19. $\int y^2 \sin 2y\, dy.$

20. $\int w^4 \cos 3w\, dw.$

21. $\int (\ln 2x)^2\, dx.$

22. $\int \dfrac{x^2\, dx}{\sqrt{4x^2 - 1}}.$

23. $\int y^2\sqrt{9 - 4y^2}\, dy.$

24. $\int \dfrac{y^2\, dy}{\sqrt{9 - 4y^2}}.$

25. $\int \dfrac{(4 - y^2)^{3/2}}{y^2}\, dy.$

26. $\int t^2\sqrt{9t^2 - 16}\, dt.$

27. $\int e^{2x} \sin 3x\, dx.$

28. $\int \operatorname{csch} 3y\, dy.$

29. $\int \dfrac{\sqrt{2 + 3x}}{5x}\, dx.$

30. $\int \sin^4 2w\, dw.$

31. $\int \sin 2t \cos 3t\, dt.$

32. $\int \dfrac{2x^4 + 7x^2 - 4x - 2}{(x^2 + 1)^2(x - 2)}\, dx.$

In each of Numbers 33 to 46, evaluate the given definite integral.

33. $\int_0^{\pi/8} \tan^2 2x\, dx.$

34. $\int_0^a t^3(a^2 + t^2)^{3/2}\, dt.$

35. $\int_1^4 \dfrac{3w\, dw}{\sqrt{2 + 3w}}.$

36. $\int_2^3 \dfrac{\sqrt{4x^2 - 9}}{3x}\, dx.$

37. $\int_0^{\pi/4} \sec^5 w\, dw.$

38. $\int_0^{\pi/4} \tan^5 t\, dt.$

39. $\int_0^4 \sqrt{16 - x^2}\, dx.$

40. $\int_0^{\pi/2} e^{-t} \sin 3t\, dt.$

41. $\int_0^1 \operatorname{Tan}^{-1} w\, dw.$

42. $\int_0^1 \dfrac{t^2\, dt}{(9 - 4t^2)^{3/2}}.$

43. $\int_0^{\pi/4} \cos^4 x\, dx.$

44. $\int_0^1 y^2 e^{2y}\, dy.$

45. $\int_0^{1/4} \operatorname{Sin}^{-1} 2w\, dw.$

46. $\int_0^{\pi} u^4 \sin u\, du.$

15.12 MISCELLANEOUS PROBLEMS

The following exercises are intended not only to review a number of applications of integration but also to test the reader's ability to extend the application to a few situations that have not previously been discussed.

Exercises 15.12

1. Find the centroid of the area bounded by the x-axis and the arch of the curve $y = \sin^2 x$ from $x = 0$ to $x = \pi$.
2. Find the centroid of the first quadrant area inside the hypocycloid $x = a \cos^3 t$, $y = a \sin^3 t$.
3. Find the centroid of the area bounded by the x-axis and one arch of the cycloid $x = a(t - \sin t)$, $y = a(1 - \cos t)$.
4. Find the centroid of the area bounded by the curve $y = \sec^2 x$, the x-axis, and the two lines $x = 0$ and $x = \pi/4$.
5. Find the average value with respect to x of $y = \ln x$ from $x = 1$ to $x = 3$.
6. Calculate the average value with respect to x of $y = \operatorname{Tan}^{-1} x$ from $x = 0$ to $x = 1$.
7. What is the average value of $y = a(t - \sin t)$ with respect to $x = a(1 - \cos t)$ from $t = 0$ to $t = \pi$?
8. The area bounded by the axes and the first quadrant portion of the hypocycloid $x^{2/3} + y^{2/3} = a^{2/3}$ is revolved about the y-axis. Find the volume so generated.
9. Find the volume formed by revolving about the y-axis the area that is bounded by the curve $a^{1/2}y = x\sqrt{a - x}$, $a > 0$, and the x-axis.
10. The area above the x-axis and under one arch of the cycloid $x = a(t - \sin t)$, $y = a(1 - \cos t)$ is revolved about the y-axis. Find the volume that is formed.
11. The area bounded by the catenary $y = a \cosh x/a$ and the lines $x = 0$, $y = 0$, $x = a$ is revolved about the x-axis. Locate the centroid of the resulting volume.
12. Through the center of a solid sphere of radius 4 inches a cylindrical hole of radius 2 inches is bored. What volume of material remains?
13. Loudspeaker horns are frequently of the so-called *exponential* type, in which the cross-sectional area increases exponentially with the distance from the throat. Find the volume of air in such a horn if it is 4 feet long and has a throat diameter of 2 inches and a mouth diameter of 2 feet.
14. A horn-shaped solid has for a longitudinal section the region between $y = e^x$ and $y = e^{-x}$ from $x = 0$ to $x = 1$. If every section perpendicular to the x-axis is a square with one diagonal in the xy-plane, find the volume.
15. A vertical water gate is in the shape of a semicircle with its base at the surface of the water. Find the total force on the gate if the radius of the circle is 2 feet.
★16. Locate the point at which a single force would have to be placed to be the equivalent of the total force on the water gate of Number 15.
17. A particle of mass m moves along the x-axis so that its distance (feet) from the origin at time t (seconds) is $x = A \sin \omega t$. This type of motion is called *simple harmonic motion*. The particle makes a complete oscillation in $2\pi/\omega$ seconds. During such an oscillation, what is the average of the kinetic energy, $\frac{1}{2}mv^2$, with respect to the time?

18. A 60 cycle per second alternating electric current is described by the equation $I = I_0 \sin 120\pi t$, where I_0 is in amperes and t is in seconds. Find the average magnitude (absolute value) of the current with respect to the time.

★19. An alternating electric current I (amperes) is described by the equation $I = I_0 \sin \omega t$, where t is the time in seconds and ω is a constant. The effective value I_e of the current is defined to be the direct current (a constant) that will produce the same amount of heat per period in a resistance of R ohms as is produced by the alternating current. If the rate at which heat Q (joules) is produced is given by $D_t Q = RI^2$, find I_e in terms of I_0.

20. Suppose it is conjectured that the cost of an upper atmosphere sounding rocket is $200 + 12\sqrt{x}$ dollars per mile if the rocket is to be propelled to a height of x miles. On this basis, what would be the cost of a rocket that is to be propelled to a height of 100 miles?

★21. Find the force of attraction of a thin semicircle of wire of radius a and of mass m per unit length on a unit mass particle located at the center of the circle.

★22. A thin circle of wire is of radius a and of mass m per unit length. A unit mass particle is located on the axis of the circle at a distance R from the plane of the circle. Show that the force of attraction of the wire on the particle is $2\pi kmaR(a^2 + R^2)^{-3/2}$.

★23. Use the result of Number 22 to find the force of attraction of a thin disk of radius b and of constant mass μ per unit area on a particle of unit mass located on the axis of the disk and at the distance s from the disk.

Summary of Chapter 15

Chapter 15 is primarily devoted to the development of techniques of integration. These techniques include

(1) the recognition of simple inverse derivatives by inspection (Section 15.1);

(2) inverse derivatives of expressions involving trigonometric functions (Section 15.2);

(3) the method of substitution in finding inverse derivatives and in evaluating definite integrals (Section 15.3);

(4) trigonometric and hyperbolic substitutions (Section 15.4);

(5) integration by parts (Section 15.5);

(6) Wallis' formulas and their use (Section 15.6);

(7) integration of rational fractions by means of partial fractions (Sections 15.7, 15.8).

An important extension of the concept of the integral includes integrals having infinite limits and integrals of functions having infinite discontinuities (Section 15.9). Also, the student should understand the need for methods of approximating definite integrals and how to use these methods (Section 15.10). Finally, he must understand how to use a table of integrals (Section 15.11).

APPENDIX A List of Symbols

Greek Alphabet

Alpha	A	α	Iota	I	ι	Rho	P	ρ
Beta	B	β	Kappa	K	κ	Sigma	Σ	σ
Gamma	Γ	γ	Lambda	Λ	λ	Tau	T	τ
Delta	Δ	δ	Mu	M	μ	Upsilon	Υ	υ
Epsilon	E	ϵ	Nu	N	ν	Phi	Φ	φ
Zeta	Z	ζ	XI	Ξ	ξ	Chi	X	χ
Eta	H	η	Omicron	O	o	Psi	Ψ	ψ
Theta	Θ	θ	Pi	Π	π	Omega	Ω	ω

Special Symbols

		PAGE
$=$	equals	3
$\neq$	does not equal	3
$.=.$	is defined to be	3
$[\![\ ]\!]$	greatest integer in	3, 156
$\Rightarrow$	implies	6
$\Leftrightarrow$	if and only if	6
$n!$	factorial n	9
$-p$	negation of a proposition	12
$\{\ldots\}$	set	17, 18
$\{x:\ldots\}$	set of objects x such that	18
$\in$	is an element of	18
$\notin$	is not an element of	18
$\varnothing$	empty set	19
$\subset$	is a subset of	20
$\not\subset$	is not a subset of	20
$\leftrightarrow$	corresponds to	23
$\mathfrak{N}$	the set of natural numbers	23, 33
$\sim$	is equivalent to	24
$\cup$	set union	25
$\cap$	set intersection	25
$\mathfrak{A} - \mathfrak{B}$	set difference	25
$\mathfrak{A}'$	complement of a set	26
$C(\mathfrak{A})$	cardinal number of the set A	33
$<$	less than	34
$>$	greater than	34
$\mathfrak{P}$	the set of primes	35
$\geqq$	greater than or equal to	38, 106
$\mathfrak{N}_0$	the set of natural numbers and zero	42
$\mathfrak{J}$	the set of integers	43
mod	modulo	47
$\mathfrak{F}$	the set of rational numbers	51
$\mathfrak{R}_i$	the set of irrational numbers	57

APPENDIX B   Table of Integrals

In using this table the following items should be observed.

1. The standard formulas listed earlier, and some formulas easily reducible to the standard ones, are not listed.
2. A constant of integration should be supplied for each formula.
3. When the $\pm$ sign is used more than once in a formula, the formula is actually a composite of two formulas, one using the upper signs and another using the lower signs.
4. It is understood that the values of any letters used in the formulas are restricted so that the expressions are always real.
5. This is a brief table of integrals; any standard book of tables will have many times the number of integrals found here.

Forms Containing $(a + bu)$

1. $\displaystyle \int u(a + bu)^m \, du = \frac{(a + bu)^{m+2}}{b^2(m + 2)} - \frac{a(a + bu)^{m+1}}{b^2(m + 1)}, \; m \neq -1, -2.$

2. $\displaystyle \int \frac{u \, du}{(a + bu)^2} = \frac{1}{b^2}\left[\ln |a + bu| + \frac{a}{a + bu}\right].$

3. $\displaystyle \int \frac{u \, du}{(a + bu)^3} = \frac{1}{b^2}\left[-\frac{1}{a + bu} + \frac{a}{2(a + bu)^2}\right].$

4. $\displaystyle \int \frac{u^2 \, du}{(a + bu)^2} = \frac{1}{b^3}\left[a + bu - 2a \ln |a + bu| - \frac{a^2}{a + bu}\right].$

5. $\displaystyle \int \frac{du}{u(a + bu)} = \frac{1}{a} \ln \left|\frac{u}{a + bu}\right|.$

6. $\displaystyle \int \frac{du}{u(a + bu)^2} = \frac{1}{a(a + bu)} - \frac{1}{a^2} \ln \left|\frac{a + bu}{u}\right|.$

7. $\displaystyle \int \frac{du}{u^2(a + bu)} = -\frac{1}{au} + \frac{b}{a^2} \ln \left|\frac{a + bu}{u}\right|.$

8. $\displaystyle \int \frac{du}{u^2(a + bu)^2} = -\frac{a + 2bu}{a^2 u(a + bu)} + \frac{2b}{a^3} \ln \left|\frac{a + bu}{u}\right|.$

Forms Containing $\sqrt{a + bu}$

9. $\displaystyle \int u\sqrt{a + bu} \, du = \frac{2(3bu - 2a)\sqrt{(a + bu)^3}}{15b^2}.$

10. $\displaystyle \int u^2\sqrt{a + bu} \, du = \frac{2(8a^2 - 12abu + 15b^2u^2)\sqrt{(a + bu)^3}}{105b^3}.$

11. $\displaystyle \int u^m\sqrt{a + bu} \, du = \frac{2}{b(2m + 3)}\left[u^m\sqrt{(a + bu)^3} - ma \int u^{m-1}\sqrt{a + bu} \, du\right].$

12. $\int \dfrac{\sqrt{a + bu}}{u} \, du = 2\sqrt{a + bu} + \sqrt{a} \ln \left| \dfrac{\sqrt{a + bu} - \sqrt{a}}{\sqrt{a + bu} + \sqrt{a}} \right|.$

13. $\int \dfrac{\sqrt{a + bu}}{u^m} \, du = -\dfrac{1}{a(m - 1)} \left[\dfrac{\sqrt{(a + bu)^3}}{u^{m-1}} + \dfrac{(2m - 5)b}{2} \int \dfrac{\sqrt{a + bu} \, du}{u^{m-1}} \right],$
$m \neq 1.$

14. $\int \dfrac{du}{u\sqrt{a + bu}} = \dfrac{1}{\sqrt{a}} \ln \left| \dfrac{\sqrt{a + bu} - \sqrt{a}}{\sqrt{a + bu} + \sqrt{a}} \right|.$

15. $\int \dfrac{du}{u^m\sqrt{a + bu}} = -\dfrac{\sqrt{a + bu}}{(m - 1)au^{m-1}} - \dfrac{(2m - 3)b}{(2m - 2)a} \int \dfrac{du}{u^{m-1}\sqrt{a + bu}}.$

16. $\int \dfrac{u \, du}{\sqrt{a + bu}} = \dfrac{2(bu - 2a)}{3b^2} \sqrt{a + bu}.$

17. $\int \dfrac{u^m \, du}{\sqrt{a + bu}} = \dfrac{2u^m\sqrt{a + bu}}{(2m + 1)b} - \dfrac{2ma}{(2m + 1)b} \int \dfrac{u^{m-1} \, du}{\sqrt{a + bu}}.$

Forms Containing $u^2 + a^2$ or $u^2 - a^2$

18. $\int \dfrac{du}{u^2 - a^2} = \dfrac{1}{2a} \ln \left| \dfrac{u - a}{u + a} \right|.$

19. $\int \dfrac{u^m \, du}{u^2 \pm a^2} = \dfrac{u^{m-1}}{m - 1} \mp a^2 \int \dfrac{u^{m-2} \, du}{u^2 \pm a^2}, \; m \neq 1.$

20. $\int \dfrac{du}{u(u^2 \pm a^2)} = \pm\dfrac{1}{2a^2} \ln \left| \dfrac{u^2}{u^2 \pm a^2} \right|.$

21. $\int \dfrac{du}{u^m(u^2 \pm a^2)} = \mp\dfrac{1}{a^2(m - 1)u^{m-1}} \mp \dfrac{1}{a^2} \int \dfrac{du}{u^{m-2}(u^2 \pm a^2)}, \; m \neq 1.$

22. $\int \dfrac{du}{(u^2 \pm a^2)^m} = \pm\dfrac{u}{2a^2(m - 1)(u^2 \pm a^2)^{m-1}} \pm \dfrac{2m - 3}{2a^2(m - 1)} \int \dfrac{du}{(u^2 \pm a^2)^{m-1}},$
$m \neq 1.$

23. $\int \dfrac{du}{u(u^2 \pm a^2)^m} = \pm\dfrac{1}{2a^2(m - 1)(u^2 \pm a^2)^{m-1}} \pm \dfrac{1}{a^2} \int \dfrac{du}{u(u^2 \pm a^2)^{m-1}},$
$m \neq 1.$

24. $\int \dfrac{u^2 \, du}{(u^2 \pm a^2)^m} = -\dfrac{u}{2(m - 1)(u^2 \pm a^2)^{m-1}} + \dfrac{1}{2(m - 1)} \int \dfrac{du}{(u^2 \pm a^2)^{m-1}},$
$m \neq 1.$

Forms Containing $\sqrt{u^2 \pm a^2}$

25. $\int \sqrt{u^2 \pm a^2} \, du = \dfrac{u}{2} \sqrt{u^2 \pm a^2} \pm \dfrac{a^2}{2} \ln |u + \sqrt{u^2 \pm a^2}|.$

26. $\displaystyle\int \frac{du}{\sqrt{u^2 \pm a^2}} = \ln |u + \sqrt{u^2 \pm a^2}|.$

27. $\displaystyle\int u^2\sqrt{u^2 \pm a^2}\, du = \frac{u}{4}(u^2 \pm a^2)^{3/2} \mp \frac{a^2u}{8}\sqrt{u^2 \pm a^2}$
$$- \frac{a^4}{8} \ln |u + \sqrt{u^2 \pm a^2}|.$$

28. $\displaystyle\int u^3\sqrt{u^2 + a^2}\, du = \left(\frac{u^2}{5} - \frac{2a^2}{15}\right)(u^2 + a^2)^{3/2}.$

29. $\displaystyle\int u^3\sqrt{u^2 - a^2}\, du = \frac{1}{5}(u^2 - a^2)^{5/2} + \frac{a^2}{3}(u^2 - a^2)^{3/2}.$

30. $\displaystyle\int \frac{\sqrt{u^2 + a^2}}{u}\, du = \sqrt{u^2 + a^2} - a \ln \left|\frac{a + \sqrt{u^2 + a^2}}{u}\right|.$

31. $\displaystyle\int \frac{\sqrt{u^2 - a^2}}{u}\, du = \sqrt{u^2 - a^2} - a \operatorname{Sec}^{-1}\frac{u}{a}.$

32. $\displaystyle\int \frac{\sqrt{u^2 \pm a^2}}{u^2}\, du = -\frac{\sqrt{u^2 \pm a^2}}{u} + \ln |u + \sqrt{u^2 \pm a^2}|.$

33. $\displaystyle\int \frac{\sqrt{u^2 + a^2}}{u^3}\, du = -\frac{\sqrt{u^2 + a^2}}{2u^2} - \frac{1}{2a} \ln \left|\frac{a + \sqrt{u^2 + a^2}}{u}\right|.$

34. $\displaystyle\int \frac{\sqrt{u^2 - a^2}}{u^3}\, du = -\frac{\sqrt{u^2 - a^2}}{2u^2} + \frac{1}{2a} \operatorname{Sec}^{-1}\frac{u}{a}.$

35. $\displaystyle\int \frac{du}{u\sqrt{u^2 + a^2}} = \frac{1}{a} \ln \left|\frac{u}{a + \sqrt{u^2 + a^2}}\right|.$

36. $\displaystyle\int \frac{du}{u\sqrt{u^2 - a^2}} = \frac{1}{a} \operatorname{Sec}^{-1}\frac{u}{a}.$

37. $\displaystyle\int \frac{u^2\, du}{\sqrt{u^2 \pm a^2}} = \frac{u}{2}\sqrt{u^2 \pm a^2} \mp \frac{a^2}{2} \ln |u + \sqrt{u^2 \pm a^2}|.$

38. $\displaystyle\int \frac{du}{u^2\sqrt{u^2 \pm a^2}} = \mp \frac{\sqrt{u^2 \pm a^2}}{a^2 u}.$

39. $\displaystyle\int \frac{du}{u^3\sqrt{u^2 + a^2}} = -\frac{\sqrt{u^2 + a^2}}{2a^2u^2} + \frac{1}{2a^3} \ln \left|\frac{a + \sqrt{u^2 + a^2}}{u}\right|.$

40. $\displaystyle\int \frac{du}{u^3\sqrt{u^2 - a^2}} = \frac{\sqrt{u^2 - a^2}}{2a^2u^2} + \frac{1}{2a^3} \operatorname{Sec}^{-1}\frac{u}{a}.$

41. $\displaystyle\int (u^2 \pm a^2)^{3/2}\, du = \frac{u}{4}(u^2 \pm a^2)^{3/2} \pm \frac{3a^2u}{8}\sqrt{u^2 \pm a^2}$
$$+ \frac{3a^4}{8} \ln |u + \sqrt{u^2 \pm a^2}|.$$

42. $\displaystyle\int \frac{du}{(u^2 \pm a^2)^{3/2}} = \pm \frac{u}{a^2\sqrt{u^2 \pm a^2}}.$

43. $\displaystyle\int u^2(u^2 \pm a^2)^{3/2}\,du = \frac{u}{6}(u^2 \pm a^2)^{5/2} \mp \frac{a^2 u}{24}(u^2 \pm a^2)^{3/2} - \frac{a^4 u}{16}\sqrt{u^2 \pm a^2}$

$$\mp \frac{a^6}{16}\ln|u + \sqrt{u^2 \pm a^2}|.$$

44. $\displaystyle\int u^3(u^2 \pm a^2)^{3/2}\,du = \frac{1}{7}(u^2 \pm a^2)^{7/2} \mp \frac{a^2}{5}(u^2 \pm a^2)^{5/2}.$

45. $\displaystyle\int \frac{(u^2 - a^2)^{3/2}}{u}\,du = \frac{(u^2 - a^2)^{3/2}}{3} - a^2\sqrt{u^2 - a^2} + a^3 \operatorname{Sec}^{-1}\frac{u}{a}.$

46. $\displaystyle\int \frac{(u^2 + a^2)^{3/2}}{u}\,du = \frac{(u^2 + a^2)^{3/2}}{3} + a^2\sqrt{u^2 + a^2} - a^3 \ln\left|\frac{a + \sqrt{u^2 + a^2}}{u}\right|.$

47. $\displaystyle\int \frac{(u^2 \pm a^2)^{3/2}}{u^2}\,du = -\frac{(u^2 \pm a^2)^{3/2}}{u} + \frac{3u}{2}\sqrt{u^2 \pm a^2}$

$$\pm \frac{3a^2}{2}\ln|u + \sqrt{u^2 \pm a^2}|.$$

48. $\displaystyle\int \frac{u^2\,du}{(u^2 \pm a^2)^{3/2}}\,du = -\frac{u}{\sqrt{u^2 \pm a^2}} + \ln|u + \sqrt{u^2 \pm a^2}|.$

49. $\displaystyle\int \frac{du}{u(u^2 + a^2)^{3/2}} = \frac{1}{a^2\sqrt{u^2 + a^2}} - \frac{1}{a^3}\ln\left|\frac{a + \sqrt{u^2 + a^2}}{u}\right|.$

50. $\displaystyle\int \frac{du}{u(u^2 - a^2)^{3/2}} = -\frac{1}{a^2\sqrt{u^2 - a^2}} - \frac{1}{a^3}\operatorname{Sec}^{-1}\frac{u}{a}.$

51. $\displaystyle\int \frac{du}{u^2(u^2 \pm a^2)^{3/2}} = -\frac{1}{a^4}\left(\frac{\sqrt{u^2 \pm a^2}}{u} + \frac{u}{\sqrt{u^2 \pm a^2}}\right).$

52. $\displaystyle\int \frac{du}{u^3(u^2 + a^2)^{3/2}} = -\frac{1}{2a^2u^2\sqrt{u^2 + a^2}} - \frac{3}{2a^4\sqrt{u^2 + a^2}}$

$$+ \frac{3}{2a^5}\ln\left|\frac{a + \sqrt{u^2 + a^2}}{u}\right|.$$

53. $\displaystyle\int \frac{du}{u^3(u^2 - a^2)^{3/2}} = \frac{1}{2a^2u^2\sqrt{u^2 - a^2}} - \frac{3}{2a^4\sqrt{u^2 - a^2}} - \frac{3}{2a^5}\operatorname{Sec}^{-1}\frac{u}{a}.$

Forms Containing $\sqrt{a^2 - u^2}$

54. $\displaystyle\int \sqrt{a^2 - u^2}\,du = \frac{u}{2}\sqrt{a^2 - u^2} + \frac{a^2}{2}\operatorname{Sin}^{-1}\frac{u}{a}.$

55. $\displaystyle\int u^2\sqrt{a^2 - u^2}\,du = -\frac{u}{4}(a^2 - u^2)^{3/2} + \frac{a^2 u}{8}\sqrt{a^2 - u^2} + \frac{a^4}{8}\operatorname{Sin}^{-1}\frac{u}{a}.$

56. $\int u^3 \sqrt{a^2 - u^2} \, du = \left(-\dfrac{u^2}{5} - \dfrac{2a^2}{15} \right)(a^2 - u^2)^{3/2}.$

57. $\int \dfrac{\sqrt{a^2 - u^2}}{u} \, du = \sqrt{a^2 - u^2} - a \ln \left| \dfrac{a + \sqrt{a^2 - u^2}}{u} \right|.$

58. $\int \dfrac{\sqrt{a^2 - u^2}}{u^2} \, du = -\dfrac{\sqrt{a^2 - u^2}}{u} - \operatorname{Sin}^{-1} \dfrac{u}{a}.$

59. $\int \dfrac{\sqrt{a^2 - u^2}}{u^3} \, du = -\dfrac{\sqrt{a^2 - u^2}}{2u^2} + \dfrac{1}{2a} \ln \left| \dfrac{a + \sqrt{a^2 - u^2}}{u} \right|.$

60. $\int \dfrac{u^2 \, du}{\sqrt{a^2 - u^2}} = -\dfrac{u}{2} \sqrt{a^2 - u^2} + \dfrac{a^2}{2} \operatorname{Sin}^{-1} \dfrac{u}{a}.$

61. $\int \dfrac{u^3 \, du}{\sqrt{a^2 - u^2}} = -\dfrac{2}{3}(a^2 - u^2)^{3/2} - u^2 \sqrt{a^2 - u^2}.$

62. $\int \dfrac{du}{u\sqrt{a^2 - u^2}} = -\dfrac{1}{a} \ln \left| \dfrac{a + \sqrt{a^2 - u^2}}{u} \right|.$

63. $\int \dfrac{du}{u^2 \sqrt{a^2 - u^2}} = -\dfrac{\sqrt{a^2 - u^2}}{a^2 u}.$

64. $\int \dfrac{du}{u^3 \sqrt{a^2 - u^2}} = -\dfrac{\sqrt{a^2 - u^2}}{2a^2 u^2} - \dfrac{1}{2a^3} \ln \left| \dfrac{a + \sqrt{a^2 - u^2}}{u} \right|.$

65. $\int (a^2 - u^2)^{3/2} \, du = \dfrac{u}{4}(a^2 - u^2)^{3/2} + \dfrac{3a^2 u}{8} \sqrt{a^2 - u^2} + \dfrac{3a^4}{8} \operatorname{Sin}^{-1} \dfrac{u}{a}.$

66. $\int \dfrac{du}{(a^2 - u^2)^{3/2}} = \dfrac{u}{a^2 \sqrt{a^2 - u^2}}.$

67. $\int u^2(a^2 - u^2)^{3/2} \, du = -\dfrac{u}{6}(a^2 - u^2)^{5/2} + \dfrac{a^2 u}{24}(a^2 - u^2)^{3/2}$

$$+ \dfrac{a^2 u}{16} \sqrt{a^2 - u^2} + \dfrac{a^6}{16} \operatorname{Sin}^{-1} \dfrac{u}{a}.$$

68. $\int u^3(a^2 - u^2)^{3/2} \, du = \dfrac{1}{7}(a^2 - u^2)^{7/2} - \dfrac{a^2}{5}(a^2 - u^2)^{5/2}.$

69. $\int \dfrac{(a^2 - u^2)^{3/2}}{u} \, du = \dfrac{1}{3}(a^2 - u^2)^{3/2} + a^2 \sqrt{a^2 - u^2} - a^3 \ln \left| \dfrac{a + \sqrt{a^2 - u^2}}{u} \right|.$

70. $\int \dfrac{(a^2 - u^2)^{3/2}}{u^2} \, du = -\dfrac{(a^2 - u^2)^{3/2}}{u} - \dfrac{3u}{2} \sqrt{a^2 - u^2} - \dfrac{3a^2}{2} \operatorname{Sin}^{-1} \dfrac{u}{a}.$

71. $\int \dfrac{u^2 \, du}{(a^2 - u^2)^{3/2}} = \dfrac{u}{\sqrt{a^2 - u^2}} - \operatorname{Sin}^{-1} \dfrac{u}{a}.$

72. $\displaystyle\int \frac{u^3 \, du}{(a^2 - u^2)^{3/2}} = 2\sqrt{a^2 - u^2} + \frac{u^2}{\sqrt{a^2 - u^2}}.$

73. $\displaystyle\int \frac{du}{u(a^2 - u^2)^{3/2}} = \frac{1}{a^2\sqrt{a^2 - u^2}} + \frac{1}{a^3} \ln\left|\frac{a + \sqrt{a^2 - u^2}}{u}\right|.$

74. $\displaystyle\int \frac{du}{u^2(a^2 - u^2)^{3/2}} = \frac{1}{a^4}\left(\frac{u}{\sqrt{a^2 - u^2}} - \frac{\sqrt{a^2 - u^2}}{u}\right).$

75. $\displaystyle\int \frac{du}{u^3(a^2 - u^2)^{3/2}} = -\frac{1}{2a^2u^2\sqrt{a^2 - u^2}} + \frac{3}{2a^4\sqrt{a^2 - u^2}}$
$$- \frac{3}{2a^5} \ln\left|\frac{a + \sqrt{a^2 - u^2}}{u}\right|.$$

Forms Containing Trigonometric Functions

76. $\displaystyle\int \sin^2 u \, du = \frac{u}{2} - \frac{1}{4} \sin 2u.$

77. $\displaystyle\int \sin^3 u \, du = \frac{\cos^3 u}{3} - \cos u.$

78. $\displaystyle\int \sin^m u \, du = -\frac{\sin^{m-1} u \cos u}{m} + \frac{m-1}{m} \int \sin^{m-2} u \, du.$

79. $\displaystyle\int \cos^2 u \, du = \frac{u}{2} + \frac{1}{4} \sin 2u.$

80. $\displaystyle\int \cos^3 u \, du = \sin u - \frac{1}{3} \sin^3 u.$

81. $\displaystyle\int \cos^m u \, du = \frac{\cos^{m-1} u \sin u}{m} + \frac{m-1}{m} \int \cos^{m-2} u \, du.$

82. $\displaystyle\int \frac{du}{a + b \sin u} = \frac{2}{\sqrt{a^2 - b^2}} \operatorname{Tan}^{-1} \frac{a \tan \frac{u}{2} + b}{\sqrt{a^2 - b^2}}.$

83. $\displaystyle\int \frac{du}{a + b \cos u} = \frac{2}{\sqrt{a^2 - b^2}} \operatorname{Tan}^{-1} \frac{\sqrt{a^2 - b^2} \tan \frac{u}{2}}{a + b}.$

84. $\displaystyle\int \sin mu \sin nu \, du = \frac{\sin (m - n)u}{2(m - n)} - \frac{\sin (m + n)u}{2(m + n)}, \; m^2 \neq n^2.$

85. $\displaystyle\int \cos mu \cos nu \, du = \frac{\sin (m - n)u}{2(m - n)} + \frac{\sin (m + n)u}{2(m + n)}, \; m^2 \neq n^2.$

86. $\displaystyle\int \sin mu \cos nu \, du = -\frac{\cos (m - n)u}{2(m - n)} - \frac{\cos (m + n)u}{2(m + n)}, \; m^2 \neq n^2.$

87. $\displaystyle\int \cos^m u \sin^n u \, du = \frac{\cos^{m-1} u \sin^{n+1} u}{m+n} + \frac{m-1}{m+n} \int \cos^{m-2} u \sin^n u \, du.$

88. $\displaystyle\int \tan^2 u \, du = \tan u - u.$

89. $\displaystyle\int \tan^m u \, du = \frac{\tan^{m-1} u}{m-1} - \int \tan^{m-2} u \, du, \ m \neq 1.$

90. $\displaystyle\int \cot^2 u \, du = -\cot u - u.$

91. $\displaystyle\int \cot^m u \, du = -\frac{\cot^{m-1} u}{m-1} - \int \cot^{m-2} u \, du, \ m \neq 1.$

92. $\displaystyle\int \sec^m u \, du = \frac{\tan u \sec^{m-2} u}{m-1} + \frac{m-2}{m-1} \int \sec^{m-2} u \, du, \ m \neq 1.$

93. $\displaystyle\int \csc^m u \, du = -\frac{\cot u \csc^{m-1} u}{m-1} + \frac{m-2}{m-1} \int \csc^{m-2} u \, du, \ m \neq 1.$

Other Forms

94. $\displaystyle\int u \sin u \, du = \sin u - u \cos u.$

95. $\displaystyle\int u^2 \sin u \, du = 2u \sin u - (u^2 - 2) \cos u.$

96. $\displaystyle\int u^3 \sin u \, du = (3u^2 - 6) \sin u - (u^3 - 6u) \cos u.$

97. $\displaystyle\int u^m \sin u \, du = -u^m \cos u + m \int u^{m-1} \cos u \, du.$

98. $\displaystyle\int u \cos u \, du = \cos u + u \sin u.$

99. $\displaystyle\int u^2 \cos u \, du = 2u \cos u + (u^2 - 2) \sin u.$

100. $\displaystyle\int u^3 \cos u \, du = (3u^2 - 6) \cos u + (u^3 - 6u) \sin u.$

101. $\displaystyle\int u^m \cos u \, du = u^m \sin u - m \int u^{m-1} \sin u \, du.$

102. $\displaystyle\int \mathrm{Sin}^{-1} u \, du = u \, \mathrm{Sin}^{-1} u + \sqrt{1 - u^2}.$

103. $\displaystyle\int \mathrm{Sec}^{-1} u \, du = u \, \mathrm{Sec}^{-1} u - \ln |u + \sqrt{u^2 - 1}|.$

104. $\displaystyle\int \mathrm{Tan}^{-1} u \, du = u \, \mathrm{Tan}^{-1} u - \frac{1}{2} \ln (1 + u^2).$

105. $\displaystyle\int u \, e^{au} \, du = \frac{e^{au}}{a^2} (au - 1).$

106. $\int u^m e^{au} \, du = \dfrac{1}{a} u^m e^{au} - \dfrac{m}{a} \int u^{m-1} e^{au} \, du.$

107. $\int e^{au} \sin bu \, du = \dfrac{e^{au}}{a^2 + b^2} (a \sin bu - b \cos bu).$

108. $\int e^{au} \cos bu \, du = \dfrac{e^{au}}{a^2 + b^2} (a \cos bu + b \sin bu).$

109. $\int \ln u \, du = u(\ln u - 1).$

110. $\int (\ln u)^m \, du = u(\ln u)^m - m \int (\ln u)^{m-1} \, du.$

111. $\int u^m \ln u \, du = u^{m+1} \left[\dfrac{\ln u}{m+1} - \dfrac{1}{(m+1)^2} \right], \ m \neq -1.$

112. $\int u^m (\ln u)^n \, du = \dfrac{u^{m+1}(\ln u)^n}{m+1} - \dfrac{n}{m+1} \int u^m (\ln u)^{n-1} \, du, \ m, \ n \neq -1.$

113. $\int \sinh u \, du = \cosh u.$

114. $\int \cosh u \, du = \sinh u.$

115. $\int \tanh u \, du = \ln \cosh u.$

116. $\int \coth u \, du = \ln |\sinh u|.$

117. $\int \operatorname{sech} u \, du = \operatorname{Tan}^{-1} (\sinh u).$

118. $\int \operatorname{csch} u \, du = \ln \left| \tanh \dfrac{u}{2} \right|.$

119. $\int \sinh^2 u \, du = \dfrac{1}{4} \sinh 2u - \dfrac{1}{2} u.$

120. $\int \cosh^2 u \, du = \dfrac{1}{4} \sinh 2u + \dfrac{1}{2} u.$

Wallis' Formulas

121. $\displaystyle\int_0^{\pi/2} \sin^m u \, du = \int_0^{\pi/2} \cos^m u \, du = \dfrac{(m-1)(m-3)\ldots(2) \text{ or } (1)}{m(m-2)\ldots(3) \text{ or } (2)} M,$

   where $M = \pi/2$ if m is even and $M = 1$ if m is odd.

122. $\displaystyle\int_0^{\pi/2} \sin^m u \cos^n u \, du$

   $= \dfrac{[(m-1)(m-3)\ldots(2) \text{ or } (1)][(n-1)(n-3)\ldots(2) \text{ or } (1)]}{(m+n)(m+n-2)\ldots(2) \text{ or } (1)} N,$

   where $N = \pi/2$ if both m and n are even; otherwise, $N = 1.$

APPENDIX C   Numerical Tables

Table 1. Powers, Roots, Reciprocals

1-50

N	N^2	$\sqrt{N}$	$\sqrt{10N}$	N^3	$\sqrt[3]{N}$	$\sqrt[3]{10N}$	$\sqrt[3]{100N}$	$1000/N$
1	1	1.00 000	3.16 228	1	1.00 000	2.15 443	4.64 159	1000.00
2	4	1.41 421	4.47 214	8	1.25 992	2.71 442	5.84 804	500.00 0
3	9	1.73 205	5.47 723	27	1.44 225	3.10 723	6.69 433	333.33 3
4	16	2.00 000	6.32 456	64	1.58 740	3.41 995	7.36 806	250.00 0
5	25	2.23 607	7.07 107	125	1.70 998	3.68 403	7.93 701	200.00 0
6	36	2.44 949	7.74 597	216	1.81 712	3.91 487	8.43 433	166.66 7
7	49	2.64 575	8.36 660	343	1.91 293	4.12 129	8.87 904	142.85 7
8	64	2.82 843	8.94 427	512	2.00 000	4.30 887	9.28 318	125.00 0
9	81	3.00 000	9.48 683	729	2.08 008	4.48 140	9.65 489	111.11 1
10	100	3.16 228	10.00 00	1 000	2.15 443	4.64 159	10.00 00	100.00 0
11	121	3.31 662	10.48 81	1 331	2.22 398	4.79 142	10.32 28	90.90 91
12	144	3.46 410	10.95 45	1 728	2.28 943	4.93 242	10.62 66	83.33 33
13	169	3.60 555	11.40 18	2 197	2.35 133	5.06 580	10.91 39	76.92 31
14	196	3.74 166	11.83 22	2 744	2.41 014	5.19 249	11.18 69	71.42 86
15	225	3.87 298	12.24 74	3 375	2.46 621	5.31 329	11.44 71	66.66 67
16	256	4.00 000	12.64 91	4 096	2.51 984	5.42 884	11.69 61	62.50 00
17	289	4.12 311	13.03 84	4 913	2.57 128	5.53 966	11.93 48	58.82 35
18	324	4.24 264	13.41 64	5 832	2.62 074	5.64 622	12.16 44	55.55 56
19	361	4.35 890	13.78 40	6 859	2.66 840	5.74 890	12.38 56	52.63 16
20	400	4.47 214	14.14 21	8 000	2.71 442	5.84 804	12.59 92	50.00 00
21	441	4.58 258	14.49 14	9 261	2.75 892	5.94 392	12.80 58	47.61 90
22	484	4.69 042	14.83 24	10 648	2.80 204	6.03 681	13.00 59	45.45 45
23	529	4.79 583	15.16 58	12 167	2.84 387	6.12 693	13.20 01	43.47 83
24	576	4.89 898	15.49 19	13 824	2.88 450	6.21 446	13.38 87	41.66 67
25	625	5.00 000	15.81 14	15 625	2.92 402	6.29 961	13.57 21	40.00 00
26	676	5.09 902	16.12 45	17 576	2.96 250	6.38 250	13.75 07	38.46 15
27	729	5.19 615	16.43 17	19 683	3.00 000	6.46 330	13.92 48	37.03 70
28	784	5.29 150	16.73 32	21 952	3.03 659	6.54 213	14.09 46	35.71 43
29	841	5.38 516	17.02 94	24 389	3.07 232	6.61 911	14.26 04	34.48 28
30	900	5.47 723	17.32 05	27 000	3.10 723	6.69 433	14.42 25	33.33 33
31	961	5.56 776	17.60 68	29 791	3.14 138	6.76 790	14.58 10	32.25 81
32	1 024	5.65 685	17.88 85	32 768	3.17 480	6.83 990	14.73 61	31.25 00
33	1 089	5.74 456	18.16 59	35 937	3.20 753	6.91 042	14.88 81	30.30 30
34	1 156	5.83 095	18.43 91	39 304	3.23 961	6.97 953	15.03 69	29.41 18
35	1 225	5.91 608	18.70 83	42 875	3.27 107	7.04 730	15.18 29	28.57 14
36	1 296	6.00 000	18.97 37	46.656	3.30 193	7.11 379	15.32 62	27.77.78
37	1 369	6.08 276	19.23 54	50 653	3.33 222	7.17 905	15.46 68	27.02 70
38	1 444	6.16 441	19.49 36	54 872	3.36 198	7.24 316	15.60 49	26.31 58
39	1 521	6.24 500	19.74 84	59 319	3.39 121	7.30 614	15.74 06	25.64 10
40	1 600	6.32 456	20.00 00	64 000	3.41 995	7.36 806	15.87 40	25.00 00
41	1 681	6.40 312	20.24 85	68 921	3.44 822	7.42 896	16.00 52	24.39 02
42	1 764	6.48 074	20.49 39	74 088	3.47 603	7.48 887	16.13 43	23.80 95
43	1 849	6.55 744	20.73 64	79 507	3.50 340	7.54 784	16.26 13	23.25 58
44	1 936	6.63 325	20.97 62	85 184	3.53 035	7.60 590	16.38 64	22.72 73
45	2 025	6.70 820	21.21 32	91 125	3.55 689	7.66 309	16.50 96	22.22 22
46	2 116	6.78 233	21.44 76	97 336	3.58 305	7.71 944	16.63 10	21.73 91
47	2 209	6.85 565	21.67 95	103 823	3.60 883	7.77 498	16.75 07	21.27 66
48	2 304	6.92 820	21.90 89	110 592	3.63 424	7.82 974	16.86 87	20.83 33
49	2 401	7.00 000	22.13 59	117 649	3.65 931	7.88 374	16.98 50	20.40 82
50	2 500	7.07 107	22.36 07	125 000	3.68 403	7.93 701	17.09 98	20.00 00
N	N^2	$\sqrt{N}$	$\sqrt{10N}$	N^3	$\sqrt[3]{N}$	$\sqrt[3]{10N}$	$\sqrt[3]{100N}$	$1000/N$

Table 1. Powers, Roots, Reciprocals

50-100

N	N^2	$\sqrt{N}$	$\sqrt{10N}$	N^3	$\sqrt[3]{N}$	$\sqrt[3]{10N}$	$\sqrt[3]{100N}$	$1000/N$
50	2 500	7.07 107	22.36 07	125 000	3.68 403	7.93 701	17.09 98	20.00 00
51	2 601	7.14 143	22.58 32	132 651	3.70 843	7.98 957	17.21 30	19.60 78
52	2 704	7.21 110	22.80 35	140 608	3.73 251	8.04 145	17.32 48	19.23 08
53	2 809	7.28 011	23.02 17	148 877	3.75 629	8.09 267	17.43 51	18.86 79
54	2 916	7.34 847	23.23 79	157 464	3.77 976	8.14 325	17.54 41	18.51 85
55	3 025	7.41 620	23.45 21	166 375	3.80 295	8.19 321	17.65 17	18.18 18
56	3 136	7.48 331	23.66 43	175 616	3.82 586	8.24 257	17.75 81	17.85 71
57	3 249	7.54 983	23.87 47	185 193	3.84 850	8.29 134	17.86 32	17.54 39
58	3 364	7.61 577	24.08 32	195 112	3.87 088	8.33 955	17.96 70	17.24 14
59	3 481	7.68 115	24.28 99	205 379	3.89 300	8.38 721	18.06 97	16.94 92
60	3 600	7.74 597	24.49 49	216 000	3.91 487	8.43 433	18.17 12	16.66 67
61	3 721	7.81 025	24.69 82	226 981	3.93 650	8.48 093	18.27 16	16.39 34
62	3 844	7.87 401	24.89 98	238 328	3.95 789	8.52 702	18.37 09	16.12 90
63	3 969	7.93 725	25.09 98	250 047	3.97 906	8.57 262	18.46 91	15.87 30
64	4 096	8.00 000	25.29 82	262 144	4.00 000	8.61 774	18.56 64	15.62 50
65	4 225	8.06 226	25.49 51	274 625	4.02 073	8.66 239	18.66 26	15.38 46
66	4 356	8.12 404	25.69 05	287 496	4.04 124	8.70 659	18.75 78	15.15 15
67	4 489	8.18 535	25.88 44	300 763	4.06 155	8.75 034	18.85 20	14.92 54
68	4 624	8.24 621	26.07 68	314 432	4.08 166	8.79 366	18.94 54	14.70 59
69	4 761	8.30 662	26.26 79	328 509	4.10 157	8.83 656	19.03 78	14.49 28
70	4 900	8.36 660	26.45 75	343 000	4.12 129	8.87 904	19.12 93	14.28 57
71	5 041	8.42 615	26.64 58	357 911	4.14 082	8.92 112	19.22 00	14.08 45
72	5 184	8.48 528	26.83 28	373 248	4.16 017	8.96 281	19.30 98	13.88 89
73	5 329	8.54 400	27.01 85	389 017	4.17 934	9.00 411	19.39 88	13.69 86
74	5 476	8.60 233	27.20 29	405 224	4.19 834	9.04 504	19.48 70	13.51 35
75	5 625	8.66 025	27.38 61	421 875	4.21 716	9.08 560	19.57 43	13.33 33
76	5 776	8.71 780	27.56 81	438 976	4.23 582	9.12 581	19.66 10	13.15 79
77	5 929	8.77 496	27.74 89	456 533	4.25 432	9.16 566	19.74 68	12.98 70
78	6 084	8.83 176	27.92 85	474 552	4.27 266	9.20 516	19.83 19	12.82 05
79	6 241	8.88 819	28.10 69	493 039	4.29 084	9.24 434	19.91 63	12.65 82
80	6 400	8.94 427	28.28 43	512 000	4.30 887	9.28 318	20.00 00	12.50 00
81	6 561	9.00 000	28.46 05	531 441	4.32 675	9.32 170	20.08 30	12.34 57
82	6 724	9.05 539	28.63 56	551 368	4.34 448	9.35 990	20.16 53	12.19 51
83	6 889	9.11 043	28.80 97	571 787	4.36 207	9.39 780	20.24 69	12.04 82
84	7 056	9.16 515	28.98 28	592 704	4.37 952	9.43 539	20.32 79	11.90 48
85	7 225	9.21 954	29.15 48	614 125	4.39 683	9.47 268	20.40 83	11.76 47
86	7 396	9.27 362	29.32 58	636 056	4.41 400	9.50 969	20.48 80	11.62 79
87	7 569	9.32 738	29.49 58	658 503	4.43 105	9.54 640	20.56 71	11.49 43
88	7 744	9.38 083	29.66 48	681 472	4.44 796	9.58 284	20.64 56	11.36 36
89	7 921	9.43 398	29.83 29	704 969	4.46 475	9.61 900	20.72 35	11.23 60
90	8 100	9.48 683	30.00 00	729 000	4.48 140	9.65 489	20.80 08	11.11 11
91	8 281	9.53 939	30.16 62	753 571	4.49 794	9.69 052	20.87 76	10.98 90
92	8 464	9.59 166	30.33 15	778 688	4.51 436	9.72 589	20.95 38	10.86 96
93	8 649	9.64 365	30.49 59	804 357	4.53 065	9.76 100	21.02 94	10.75 27
94	8 836	9.69 536	30.65 94	830 584	4.54 684	9.79 586	21.10 45	10.63 83
95	9 025	9.74 679	30.82 21	857 375	4.56 290	9.83 048	21.17 91	10.52 63
96	9 216	9.79 796	30.98 39	884 736	4.57 886	9.86 485	21.25 32	10.41 67
97	9 409	9.84 886	31.14 48	912 673	4.59 470	9.89 898	21.32 67	10.30 93
98	9 604	9.89 949	31.30 50	941 192	4.61 044	9.93 288	21.39 97	10.20 41
99	9 801	9.94 987	31.46 43	970 299	4.62 607	9.96 655	21.47 23	10.10 10
100	10 000	10.00 000	31.62 28	1 000 000	4.64 159	10.00 000	21.54 43	10.00 00
N	N^2	$\sqrt{N}$	$\sqrt{10N}$	N^3	$\sqrt[3]{N}$	$\sqrt[3]{10N}$	$\sqrt[3]{100N}$	$1000/N$

Table 2. Four-place Common Logarithms of Numbers 100-549

N	0	1	2	3	4	5	6	7	8	9
10	0000	0043	0086	0128	0170	0212	0253	0294	0334	0374
11	0414	0453	0492	0531	0569	0607	0645	0682	0719	0755
12	0792	0828	0864	0899	0934	0969	1004	1038	1072	1106
13	1139	1173	1206	1239	1271	1303	1335	1367	1399	1430
14	1461	1492	1523	1553	1584	1614	1644	1673	1703	1732
15	1761	1790	1818	1847	1875	1903	1931	1959	1987	2014
16	2041	2068	2095	2122	2148	2175	2201	2227	2253	2279
17	2304	2330	2355	2380	2405	2430	2455	2480	2504	2529
18	2553	2577	2601	2625	2648	2672	2695	2718	2742	2765
19	2788	2810	2833	2856	2878	2900	2923	2945	2967	2939
20	3010	3032	3054	3075	3096	3118	3139	3160	3181	3201
21	3222	3243	3263	3284	3304	3324	3345	3365	3385	3404
22	3424	3444	3464	3483	3502	3522	3541	3560	3579	3598
23	3617	3636	3655	3674	3692	3711	3729	3747	3766	3784
24	3802	3820	3838	3856	3874	3892	3909	3927	3945	3962
25	3979	3997	4014	4031	4048	4065	4082	4099	4116	4133
26	4150	4166	4183	4200	4216	4232	4249	4265	4281	4298
27	4314	4330	4346	4362	4378	4393	4409	4425	4440	4456
28	4472	4487	4502	4518	4533	4548	4564	4579	4594	4609
29	4624	4639	4654	4669	4683	4698	4713	4728	4742	4757
30	4771	4786	4800	4814	4829	4843	4857	4871	4886	4900
31	4914	4928	4942	4955	4969	4983	4997	5011	5024	5038
32	5051	5065	5079	5092	5105	5119	5132	5145	5159	5172
33	5185	5198	5211	5224	5237	5250	5263	5276	5289	5302
34	5315	5328	5340	5353	5366	5378	5391	5403	5416	5428
35	5441	5453	5465	5478	5490	5502	5514	5527	5539	5551
36	5563	5575	5587	5599	5611	5623	5635	5647	5658	5670
37	5682	5694	5705	5717	5729	5740	5752	5763	5775	5786
38	5798	5809	5821	5832	5843	5855	5866	5877	5888	5899
39	5911	5922	5933	5944	5955	5966	5977	5988	5999	6010
40	6021	6031	6042	6053	6064	6075	6085	6096	6107	6117
41	6128	6138	6149	6160	6170	6180	6191	6201	6212	6222
42	6232	6243	6253	6263	6274	6284	6294	6304	6314	6325
43	6335	6345	6355	6365	6375	6385	6395	6405	6415	6425
44	6435	6444	6454	6464	6474	6484	6493	6503	6513	6522
45	6532	6542	6551	6561	6571	6580	6590	6599	6609	6618
46	6628	6637	6646	6656	6665	6675	6684	6693	6702	6712
47	6721	6730	6739	6749	6758	6767	6776	6785	6794	6803
48	6812	6821	6830	6839	6848	6857	6866	6875	6884	6893
49	6902	6911	6920	6928	6937	6946	6955	6964	6972	6981
50	6990	6998	7007	7016	7024	7033	7042	7050	7059	7067
51	7076	7084	7093	7101	7110	7118	7126	7135	7143	7152
52	7160	7168	7177	7185	7193	7202	7210	7218	7226	7235
53	7243	7251	7259	7267	7275	7284	7292	7300	7308	7316
54	7324	7332	7340	7348	7356	7364	7372	7380	7388	7396
N	0	1	2	3	4	5	6	7	8	9

Table 2. Four-place Common Logarithms of Numbers
550-999

N	0	1	2	3	4	5	6	7	8	9
55	7404	7412	7419	7427	7435	7443	7451	7459	7466	7474
56	7482	7490	7497	7505	7513	7520	7528	7536	7543	7551
57	7559	7566	7574	7582	7589	7597	7604	7612	7619	7627
58	7634	7642	7649	7657	7664	7672	7679	7686	7694	7701
59	7709	7716	7723	7731	7738	7745	7752	7760	7767	7774
60	7782	7789	7796	7803	7810	7818	7825	7832	7839	7846
61	7853	7860	7868	7875	7882	7889	7896	7903	7910	7917
62	7924	7931	7938	7945	7952	7959	7966	7973	7980	7987
63	7993	8000	8007	8014	8021	8028	8035	8041	8048	8055
64	8062	8069	8075	8082	8089	8096	8102	8109	8116	8122
65	8129	8136	8142	8149	8156	8162	8169	8176	8182	8189
66	8195	8202	8209	8215	8222	8228	8235	8241	8248	8254
67	8261	8267	8274	8280	8287	8293	8299	8306	8312	8319
68	8325	8331	8338	8344	8351	8357	8363	8370	8376	8382
69	8388	8395	8401	8407	8414	8420	8426	8432	8439	8445
70	8451	8457	8463	8470	8476	8482	8488	8494	8500	8506
71	8513	8519	8525	8531	8537	8543	8549	8555	8561	8567
72	8573	8579	8585	8591	8597	8603	8609	8615	8621	8627
73	8633	8639	8645	8651	8657	8663	8669	8675	8681	8686
74	8692	8698	8704	8710	8716	8722	8727	8733	8739	8745
75	8751	8756	8762	8768	8774	8779	8785	8791	8797	8802
76	8808	8814	8820	8825	8831	8837	8842	8848	8854	8859
77	8865	8871	8876	8882	8887	8893	8899	8904	8910	8915
78	8921	8927	8932	8938	8943	8949	8954	8960	8965	8971
79	8976	8982	8987	8993	8998	9004	9009	9015	9020	9025
80	9031	9036	9042	9047	9053	9058	9063	9069	9074	9079
81	9085	9090	9096	9101	9106	9112	9117	9122	9128	9133
82	9138	9143	9149	9154	9159	9165	9170	9175	9180	9186
83	9191	9196	9201	9206	9212	9217	9222	9227	9232	9238
84	9243	9248	9253	9258	9263	9269	9274	9279	9284	9289
85	9294	9299	9304	9309	9315	9320	9325	9330	9335	9340
86	9345	9350	9355	9360	9365	9370	9375	9380	9385	9390
87	9395	9400	9405	9410	9415	9420	9425	9430	9435	9440
88	9445	9450	9455	9460	9465	9469	9474	9479	9484	9489
89	9494	9499	9504	9509	9513	9518	9523	9528	9533	9538
90	9542	9547	9552	9557	9562	9566	9571	9576	9581	9586
91	9590	9595	9600	9605	9609	9614	9619	9624	9628	9633
92	9638	9643	9647	9652	9657	9661	9666	9671	9675	9680
93	9685	9689	9694	9699	9703	9708	9713	9717	9722	9727
94	9731	9736	9741	9745	9750	9754	9759	9763	9768	9773
95	9777	9782	9786	9791	9795	9800	9805	9809	9814	9818
96	9823	9827	9832	9836	9841	9845	9850	9854	9859	9863
97	9868	9872	9877	9881	9886	9890	9894	9899	9903	9908
98	9912	9917	9921	9926	9930	9934	9939	9943	9948	9952
99	9956	9961	9965	9969	9974	9978	9983	9987	9991	9996
N	0	1	2	3	4	5	6	7	8	9

Table 3. Natural Trigonometric Functions for Decimal Fractions of a Degree

0-10, 80-90

Deg.	Sin	Tan	Cot	Cos	Deg.
0.0	.00000	.00000	—	1.00000	90.0
.1	.00175	.00175	572.96	1.00000	.9
.2	.00349	.00349	286.48	0.99999	.8
.3	.00524	.00524	190.98	.99999	.7
.4	.00698	.00698	143.24	.99998	.6
.5	.00873	.00873	114.59	.99996	.5
.6	.01047	.01047	95.489	.99995	.4
.7	.01222	.01222	81.847	.99993	.3
.8	.01396	.01396	71.615	.99990	.2
.9	.01571	.01571	63.657	.99988	.1
1.0	.01745	.01746	57.290	.99985	89.0
.1	.01920	.01920	52.081	.99982	.9
.2	.02094	.02095	47.740	.99978	.8
.3	.02269	.02269	44.066	.99974	.7
.4	.02443	.02444	40.917	.99970	.6
.5	.02618	.02619	38.188	.99966	.5
.6	.02792	.02793	35.801	.99961	.4
.7	.02967	.02968	33.694	.99956	.3
.8	.03141	.03143	31.821	.99951	.2
.9	.03316	.03317	30.145	.99945	.1
2.0	.03490	.03492	28.636	.99939	88.0
.1	.03664	.03667	27.271	.99933	.9
.2	.03839	.03842	26.031	.99926	.8
.3	.04013	.04016	24.898	.99919	.7
.4	.04188	.04191	23.859	.99912	.6
.5	.04362	.04366	22.904	.99905	.5
.6	.04536	.04541	22.022	.99897	.4
.7	.04711	.04716	21.205	.99889	.3
.8	.04885	.04891	20.446	.99881	.2
.9	.05059	.05066	19.740	.99872	.1
3.0	.05234	.05241	19.081	.99863	87.0
.1	.05408	.05416	18.464	.99854	.9
.2	.05582	.05591	17.886	.99844	.8
.3	.05756	.05766	17.343	.99834	.7
.4	.05931	.05941	16.832	.99824	.6
.5	.06105	.06116	16.350	.99813	.5
.6	.06279	.06291	15.895	.99803	.4
.7	.06453	.06467	15.464	.99792	.3
.8	.06627	.06642	15.056	.99780	.2
.9	.06802	.06817	14.669	.99768	.1
4.0	.06976	.06993	14.301	.99756	86.0
.1	.07150	.07168	13.951	.99744	.9
.2	.07324	.07344	13.617	.99731	.8
.3	.07498	.07519	13.300	.99719	.7
.4	.07672	.07695	12.996	.99705	.6
.5	.07846	.07870	12.706	.99692	.5
.6	.08020	.08046	12.429	.99678	.4
.7	.08194	.08221	12.163	.99664	.3
.8	.08368	.08397	11.909	.99649	.2
.9	.08542	.08573	11.664	.99635	.1
5.0	.08716	.08749	11.430	.99619	85.0
Deg.	Cos	Cot	Tan	Sin	Deg.

Deg.	Sin	Tan	Cot	Cos	Deg.
5.0	.08716	.08749	11.430	.99619	85.0
.1	.08889	.08925	11.205	.99604	.9
.2	.09063	.09101	10.988	.99588	.8
.3	.09237	.09277	10.780	.99572	.7
.4	.09411	.09453	10.579	.99556	.6
.5	.09585	.09629	10.385	.99540	.5
.6	.09758	.09805	10.199	.99523	.4
.7	.09932	.09981	10.019	.99506	.3
.8	.10106	.10158	9.8448	.99488	.2
.9	.10279	.10334	9.6768	.99470	.1
6.0	.10453	.10510	9.5144	.99452	84.0
.1	.10626	.10687	9.3572	.99434	.9
.2	.10800	.10863	9.2052	.99415	.8
.3	.10973	.11040	9.0579	.99396	.7
.4	.11147	.11217	8.9152	.99377	.6
.5	.11320	.11394	8.7769	.99357	.5
.6	.11494	.11570	8.6427	.99337	.4
.7	.11667	.11747	8.5126	.99317	.3
.8	.11840	.11924	8.3863	.99297	.2
.9	.12014	.12101	8.2636	.99276	.1
7.0	.12187	.12278	8.1443	.99255	83.0
.1	.12360	.12456	8.0285	.99233	.9
.2	.12533	.12633	7.9158	.99211	.8
.3	.12706	.12810	7.8062	.99189	.7
.4	.12880	.12988	7.6996	.99167	.6
.5	.13053	.13165	7.5958	.99144	.5
.6	.13226	.13343	7.4947	.99122	.4
.7	.13399	.13521	7.3962	.99098	.3
.8	.13572	.13698	7.3002	.99075	.2
.9	.13744	.13876	7.2066	.99051	.1
8.0	.13917	.14054	7.1154	.99027	82.0
.1	.14090	.14232	7.0264	.99002	.9
.2	.14263	.14410	6.9395	.98978	.8
.3	.14436	.14588	6.8548	.98953	.7
.4	.14608	.14767	6.7720	.98927	.6
.5	.14781	.14945	6.6912	.98902	.5
.6	.14954	.15124	6.6122	.98876	.4
.7	.15126	.15302	6.5350	.98849	.3
.8	.15299	.15481	6.4596	.98823	.2
.9	.15471	.15660	6.3859	.98796	.1
9.0	.15643	.15838	6.3138	.98769	81.0
.1	.15816	.16017	6.2432	.98741	.9
.2	.15988	.16196	6.1742	.98714	.8
.3	.16160	.16376	6.1066	.98686	.7
.4	.16333	.16555	6.0405	.98657	.6
.5	.16505	.16734	5.9758	.98629	.5
.6	.16677	.16914	5.9124	.98600	.4
.7	.16849	.17093	5.8502	.98570	.3
.8	.17021	.17273	5.7894	.98541	.2
.9	.17193	.17453	5.7297	.98511	.1
10.0	.17365	.17633	5.6713	.98481	80.0
Deg.	Cos	Cot	Tan	Sin	Deg.

Table 3. Natural Trigonometric Functions for Decimal Fractions of a Degree

10-20, 70-80

Deg.	Sin	Tan	Cot	Cos	Deg.	Deg.	Sin	Tan	Cot	Cos	Deg.
10.0	.17365	.17633	5.6713	.98481	80.0	15.0	.25882	.26795	3.7321	.96593	75.0
.1	.17537	.17813	5.6140	.98450	.9	.1	.26050	.26982	3.7062	.96547	.9
.2	.17708	.17993	5.5578	.98420	.8	.2	.26219	.27169	3.6806	.96502	.8
.3	.17880	.18173	5.5026	.98389	.7	.3	.26387	.27357	3.6554	.96456	.7
.4	.18052	.18353	5.4486	.98357	.6	.4	.26556	.27545	3.6305	.96410	.6
.5	.18224	.18534	5.3955	.98325	.5	.5	.26724	.27732	3.6059	.96363	.5
.6	.18395	.18714	5.3435	.98294	.4	.6	.26892	.27921	3.5816	.96316	.4
.7	.18567	.18895	5.2924	.98261	.3	.7	.27060	.28109	3.5576	.96269	.3
.8	.18738	.19076	5.2422	.98229	.2	.8	.27228	.28297	3.5339	.96222	.2
.9	.18910	.19257	5.1929	.98196	.1	.9	.27396	.28486	3.5105	.96174	.1
11.0	.19081	.19438	5.1446	.98163	79.0	16.0	.27564	.28675	3.4874	.96126	74.0
.1	.19252	.19619	5.0970	.98129	.9	.1	.27731	.28864	3.4646	.96078	.9
.2	.19423	.19801	5.0504	.98096	.8	.2	.27899	.29053	3.4420	.96029	.8
.3	.19595	.19982	5.0045	.98061	.7	.3	.28067	.29242	3.4197	.95981	.7
.4	.19766	.20164	4.9594	.98027	.6	.4	.28234	.29432	3.3977	.95931	.6
.5	.19937	.20345	4.9152	.97992	.5	.5	.28402	.29621	3.3759	.95882	.5
.6	.20108	.20527	4.8716	.97958	.4	.6	.28569	.29811	3.3544	.95832	.4
.7	.20279	.20709	4.8288	.97922	.3	.7	.28736	.30001	3.3332	.95782	.3
.8	.20450	.20891	4.7867	.97887	.2	.8	.28903	.30192	3.3122	.95732	.2
.9	.20620	.21073	4.7453	.97851	.1	.9	.29070	.30382	3.2914	.95681	.1
12.0	.20791	.21256	4.7046	.97815	78.0	17.0	.29237	.30573	3.2709	.95630	73.0
.1	.20962	.21438	4.6646	.97778	.9	.1	.29404	.30764	3.2506	.95579	.9
.2	.21132	.21621	4.6252	.97742	.8	.2	.29571	.30955	3.2305	.95528	.8
.3	.21303	.21804	4.5864	.97705	.7	.3	.29737	.31147	3.2106	.95476	.7
.4	.21474	.21986	4.5483	.97667	.6	.4	.29904	.31338	3.1910	.95424	.6
.5	.21644	.22169	4.5107	.97630	.5	.5	.30071	.31530	3.1716	.95372	.5
.6	.21814	.22353	4.4737	.97592	.4	.6	.30237	.31722	3.1524	.95319	.4
.7	.21985	.22536	4.4373	.97553	.3	.7	.30403	.31914	3.1334	.95266	.3
.8	.22155	.22719	4.4015	.97515	.2	.8	.30570	.32106	3.1146	.95213	.2
.9	.22325	.22903	4.3662	.97476	.1	.9	.30736	.32299	3.0961	.95159	.1
13.0	.22495	.23087	4.3315	.97437	77.0	18.0	.30902	.32492	3.0777	.95106	72.0
.1	.22665	.23271	4.2972	.97398	.9	.1	.31068	.32685	3.0595	.95052	.9
.2	.22835	.23455	4.2635	.97358	.8	.2	.31233	.32878	3.0415	.94997	.8
.3	.23005	.23639	4.2303	.97318	.7	.3	.31399	.33072	3.0237	.94943	.7
.4	.23175	.23823	4.1976	.97278	.6	.4	.31565	.33266	3.0061	.94888	.6
.5	.23345	.24008	4.1653	.97237	.5	.5	.31730	.33460	2.9887	.94832	.5
.6	.23514	.24193	4.1335	.97196	.4	.6	.31896	.33654	2.9714	.94777	.4
.7	.23684	.24377	4.1022	.97155	.3	.7	.32061	.33848	2.9544	.94721	.3
.8	.23853	.24562	4.0713	.97113	.2	.8	.32227	.34043	2.9375	.94665	.2
.9	.24023	.24747	4.0408	.97072	.1	.9	.32392	.34238	2.9208	.94609	.1
14.0	.24192	.24933	4.0108	.97030	76.0	19.0	.32557	.34433	2.9042	.94552	71.0
.1	.24362	.25118	3.9812	.96987	.9	.1	.32722	.34628	2.8878	.94495	.9
.2	.24531	.25304	3.9520	.96945	.8	.2	.32887	.34824	2.8716	.94438	.8
.3	.24700	.25490	3.9232	.96902	.7	.3	.33051	.35020	2.8556	.94380	.7
.4	.24869	.25676	3.8947	.96858	.6	.4	.33216	.35216	2.8397	.94322	.6
.5	.25038	.25862	3.8667	.96815	.5	.5	.33381	.35412	2.8239	.94264	.5
.6	.25207	.26048	3.8391	.96771	.4	.6	.33545	.35608	2.8083	.94206	.4
.7	.25376	.26235	3.8118	.96727	.3	.7	.33710	.35805	2.7929	.94147	.3
.8	.25545	.26421	3.7848	.96682	.2	.8	.33874	.36002	2.7776	.94088	.2
.9	.25713	.26608	3.7583	.96638	.1	.9	.34038	.36199	2.7625	.94029	.1
15.0	.25882	.26795	3.7321	.96593	75.0	20.0	.34202	.36397	2.7475	.93969	70.0
Deg.	Cos	Cot	Tan	Sin	Deg.	Deg.	Cos	Cot	Tan	Sin	Deg.

Table 3. Natural Trigonometric Functions for Decimal Fractions of a Degree

20-30, 60-70

Deg.	Sin	Tan	Cot	Cos	Deg.
20.0	.34202	.36397	2.7475	.93969	70.0
.1	.34366	.36595	2.7326	.93909	.9
.2	.34530	.36793	2.7179	.93849	.8
.3	.34694	.36991	2.7034	.93789	.7
.4	.34857	.37190	2.6889	.93728	.6
.5	.35021	.37388	2.6746	.93667	.5
.6	.35184	.37588	2.6605	.93606	.4
.7	.35347	.37787	2.6464	.93544	.3
.8	.35511	.37986	2.6325	.93483	.2
.9	.35674	.38186	2.6187	.93420	.1
21.0	.35837	.38386	2.6051	.93358	69.0
.1	.36000	.38587	2.5916	.93295	.9
.2	.36162	.38787	2.5782	.93232	.8
.3	.36325	.38988	2.5649	.93169	.7
.4	.36488	.39190	2.5517	.93106	.6
.5	.36650	.39391	2.5386	.93042	.5
.6	.36812	.39593	2.5257	.92978	.4
.7	.36975	.39795	2.5129	.92913	.3
.8	.37137	.39997	2.5002	.92849	.2
.9	.37299	.40200	2.4876	.92784	.1
22.0	.37461	.40403	2.4751	.92718	68.0
.1	.37622	.40606	2.4627	.92653	.9
.2	.37784	.40809	2.4504	.92587	.8
.3	.37946	.41013	2.4383	.92521	.7
.4	.38107	.41217	2.4262	.92455	.6
.5	.38268	.41421	2.4142	.92388	.5
.6	.38430	.41626	2.4023	.92321	.4
.7	.38591	.41831	2.3906	.92254	.3
.8	.38752	.42036	2.3789	.92186	.2
.9	.38912	.42242	2.3673	.92119	.1
23.0	.39073	.42447	2.3559	.92050	67.0
.1	.39234	.42654	2.3445	.91982	.9
.2	.39394	.42860	2.3332	.91914	.8
.3	.39555	.43067	2.3220	.91845	.7
.4	.39715	.43274	2.3109	.91775	.6
.5	.39875	.43481	2.2998	.91706	.5
.6	.40035	.43689	2.2889	.91636	.4
.7	.40195	.43897	2.2781	.91566	.3
.8	.40355	.44105	2.2673	.91496	.2
.9	.40514	.44314	2.2566	.91425	.1
24.0	.40674	.44523	2.2460	.91355	66.0
.1	.40833	.44732	2.2355	.91283	.9
.2	.40992	.44942	2.2251	.91212	.8
.3	.41151	.45152	2.2148	.91140	.7
.4	.41310	.45362	2.2045	.91068	.6
.5	.41469	.45573	2.1943	.90996	.5
.6	.41628	.45784	2.1842	.90924	.4
.7	.41787	.45995	2.1742	.90851	.3
.8	.41945	.46206	2.1642	.90778	.2
.9	.42104	.46418	2.1543	.90704	.1
25.0	.42262	.46631	2.1445	.90631	65.0
Deg.	Cos	Cot	Tan	Sin	Deg.

Deg.	Sin	Tan	Cot	Cos	Deg.
25.0	.42262	.46631	2.1445	.90631	65.0
.1	.42420	.46843	2.1348	.90557	.9
.2	.42578	.47056	2.1251	.90483	.8
.3	.42736	.47270	2.1155	.90408	.7
.4	.42894	.47483	2.1060	.90334	.6
.5	.43051	.47698	2.0965	.90259	.5
.6	.43209	.47912	2.0872	.90183	.4
.7	.43366	.48127	2.0778	.90108	.3
.8	.43523	.48342	2.0686	.90032	.2
.9	.43680	.48557	2.0594	.89956	.1
26.0	.43837	.48773	2.0503	.89879	64.0
.1	.43994	.48989	2.0413	.89803	.9
.2	.44151	.49206	2.0323	.89726	.8
.3	.44307	.49423	2.0233	.89649	.7
.4	.44464	.49640	2.0145	.89571	.6
.5	.44620	.49858	2.0057	.89493	.5
.6	.44776	.50076	1.9970	.89415	.4
.7	.44932	.50295	1.9883	.89337	.3
.8	.45088	.50514	1.9797	.89259	.2
.9	.45243	.50733	1.9711	.89180	.1
27.0	.45399	.50953	1.9626	.89101	63.0
.1	.45554	.51173	1.9542	.89021	.9
.2	.45710	.51393	1.9458	.88942	.8
.3	.45865	.51614	1.9375	.88862	.7
.4	.46020	.51835	1.9292	.88782	.6
.5	.46175	.52057	1.9210	.88701	.5
.6	.46330	.52279	1.9128	.88620	.4
.7	.46484	.52501	1.9047	.88539	.3
.8	.46639	.52724	1.8967	.88458	.2
.9	.46793	.52947	1.8887	.88377	.1
28.0	.46947	.53171	1.8807	.88295	62.0
.1	.47101	.53395	1.8728	.88213	.9
.2	.47255	.53620	1.8650	.88130	.8
.3	.47409	.53844	1.8572	.88048	.7
.4	.47562	.54070	1.8495	.87965	.6
.5	.47716	.54296	1.8418	.87882	.5
.6	.47869	.54522	1.8341	.87798	.4
.7	.48022	.54748	1.8265	.87715	.3
.8	.48175	.54975	1.8190	.87631	.2
.9	.48328	.55203	1.8115	.87546	.1
29.0	.48481	.55431	1.8040	.87462	61.0
.1	.48634	.55659	1.7966	.87377	.9
.2	.48786	.55888	1.7893	.87292	.8
.3	.48938	.56117	1.7820	.87207	.7
.4	.49090	.56347	1.7747	.87121	.6
.5	.49242	.56577	1.7675	.87036	.5
.6	.49394	.56808	1.7603	.86949	.4
.7	.49546	.57039	1.7532	.86863	.3
.8	.49697	.57271	1.7461	.86777	.2
.9	.49849	.57503	1.7391	.86690	.1
30.0	.50000	.57735	1.7321	.86603	60.0
Deg.	Cos	Cot	Tan	Sin	Deg.

Table 3. Natural Trigonometric Functions for Decimal Fractions of a Degree

30-40, 50-60

Deg.	Sin	Tan	Cot	Cos	Deg.
30.0	.50000	.57735	1.7321	.86603	60.0
.1	.50151	.57968	1.7251	.86515	.9
.2	.50302	.58201	1.7182	.86427	.8
.3	.50453	.58435	1.7113	.86340	.7
.4	.50603	.58670	1.7045	.86251	.6
.5	.50754	.58905	1.6977	.86163	.5
.6	.50904	.59140	1.6909	.86074	.4
.7	.51054	.59376	1.6842	.85985	.3
.8	.51204	.59612	1.6775	.85896	.2
.9	.51354	.59849	1.6709	.85806	.1
31.0	.51504	.60086	1.6643	.85717	59.0
.1	.51653	.60324	1.6577	.85627	.9
.2	.51803	.60562	1.6512	.85536	.8
.3	.51952	.60801	1.6447	.85446	.7
.4	.52101	.61040	1.6383	.85355	.6
5	.52250	.61280	1.6319	.85264	.5
.6	.52399	.61520	1.6255	.85173	.4
.7	.52547	.61761	1.6191	.85081	.3
.8	.52696	.62003	1.6128	.84989	.2
.9	.52844	.62245	1.6066	.84897	.1
32.0	.52992	.62487	1.6003	.84805	58.0
.1	.53140	.62730	1.5941	.84712	.9
.2	.53288	.62973	1.5880	.84619	.8
.3	.53435	.63217	1.5818	.84526	.7
.4	.53583	.63462	1.5757	.84433	.6
.5	.53730	.63707	1.5697	.84339	.5
.6	.53877	.63953	1.5637	.84245	.4
.7	.54024	.64199	1.5577	.84151	.3
.8	.54171	.64446	1.5517	.84057	.2
.9	.54317	.64693	1.5458	.83962	.1
33.0	.54464	.64941	1.5399	.83867	57.0
.1	.54610	.65189	1.5340	.83772	.9
.2	.54756	.65438	1.5282	.83676	.8
.3	.54902	.65688	1.5224	.83581	.7
.4	.55048	.65938	1.5166	.83485	.6
.5	.55194	.66189	1.5108	.83389	.5
.6	.55339	.66440	1.5051	.83292	.4
.7	.55484	.66692	1.4994	.83195	.3
.8	.55630	.66944	1.4938	.83098	.2
.9	.56775	.67197	1.4882	.83001	.1
34.0	.55919	.67451	1.4826	.82904	56.0
.1	.56064	.67705	1.4770	.82806	.9
.2	.56208	.67960	1.4715	.82708	.8
.3	.56353	.68215	1.4659	.82610	.7
.4	.56497	.68471	1.4605	.82511	.6
.5	.56641	.68728	1.4550	.82413	.5
.6	.56784	.68985	1.4496	.82314	.4
.7	.56928	.69243	1.4442	.82214	.3
.8	.57071	.69502	1.4388	.82115	.2
.9	.57215	.69761	1.4335	.82015	.1
35.0	.57358	.70021	1.4281	.81915	55.0
Deg.	Cos	Cot	Tan	Sin	Deg.

Deg.	Sin	Tan	Cot	Cos	Deg.
35.0	.57358	.70021	1.4281	.81915	55.0
.1	.57501	.70281	1.4229	.81815	.9
.2	.57643	.70542	1.4176	.81714	.8
.3	.57786	.70804	1.4124	.81614	.7
.4	.57928	.71066	1.4071	.81513	.6
.5	.58070	.71329	1.4019	.81412	.5
.6	.58212	.71593	1.3968	.81310	.4
.7	.58354	.71857	1.3916	.81208	.3
.8	.58496	.72122	1.3865	.81106	.2
.9	.58637	.72388	1.3814	.81004	.1
36.0	.58779	.72654	1.3764	.80902	54.0
.1	.58920	.72921	1.3713	.80799	.9
.2	.59061	.73189	1.3663	.80696	.8
.3	.59201	.73457	1.3613	.80593	.7
.4	.59342	.73726	1.3564	.80489	.6
.5	.59482	.73996	1.3514	.80386	.5
.6	.59622	.74267	1.3465	.80282	.4
.7	.59763	.74538	1.3416	.80178	.3
.8	.59902	.74810	1.3367	.80073	.2
.9	.60042	.75082	1.3319	.79968	.1
37.0	.60182	.75355	1.3270	.79864	53.0
.1	.60321	.75629	1.3222	.79758	.9
.2	.60460	.75904	1.3175	.79653	.8
.3	.60599	.76180	1.3127	.79547	.7
.4	.60738	.76456	1.3079	.79441	.6
.5	.60876	.76733	1.3032	.79335	.5
.6	.61015	.77010	1.2985	.79229	.4
.7	.61153	.77289	1.2938	.79122	.3
.8	.61291	.77568	1.2892	.79016	.2
.9	.61429	.77848	1.2846	.78908	.1
38.0	.61566	.78129	1.2799	.78801	52.0
.1	.61704	.78410	1.2753	.78694	.9
.2	.61841	.78692	1.2708	.78586	.8
.3	.61978	.78975	1.2662	.78478	.7
.4	.62115	.79259	1.2617	.78369	.6
.5	.62251	.79544	1.2572	.78261	.5
.6	.62388	.79829	1.2527	.78152	.4
.7	.62524	.80115	1.2482	.78043	.3
.8	.62660	.80402	1.2437	.77934	.2
.9	.62796	.80690	1.2393	.77824	.1
39.0	.62932	.80978	1.2349	.77715	51.0
.1	.63068	.81268	1.2305	.77605	.9
.2	.63203	.81558	1.2261	.77494	.8
.3	.63338	.81849	1.2218	.77384	.7
.4	.63473	.82141	1.2174	.77273	.6
.5	.63608	.82434	1.2131	.77162	.5
.6	.63742	.82727	1.2088	.77051	.4
.7	.63877	.83022	1.2045	.76940	.3
.8	.64011	.83317	1.2002	.76828	.2
.9	.64145	.83613	1.1960	.76717	.1
40.0	.64279	.83910	1.1918	.76604	50.0
Deg.	Cos	Cot	Tan	Sin	Deg.

Table 3. Natural Trigonometric Functions for Decimal Fractions of a Degree
40-50

Deg.	Sin	Tan	Cot	Cos	Deg.		Deg.	Sin	Tan	Cot	Cos	Deg.
40.0	.64279	.83910	1.1918	.76604	50.0		42.5	.67559	.91633	1.0913	.73728	42.5
.1	.64412	.84208	1.1875	.76492	.9		.6	.67688	.91955	1.0875	.73610	.4
.2	.64546	.84507	1.183	.76380	.8		.7	.67816	.92277	1.0837	.73491	.3
.3	.64679	.84806	1.1792	.76267	.7		.8	.67944	.92601	1.0799	.73373	.2
.4	.64812	.85107	1.1750	.76154	.6		.9	.68072	.92926	1.0761	.73254	.1
.5	.64945	.85408	1.1708	.76041	.5		43.0	.68200	.93252	1.0724	.73135	47.0
.6	.65077	.85710	1.1667	.75927	.4		.1	.68327	.93578	1.0686	.73016	.9
.7	.65210	.86014	1.1626	.75813	.3		.2	.68455	.93906	1.0649	.72897	.8
.8	.65342	.86318	1.1585	.75700	.2		.3	.68582	.94235	1.0612	.72777	.7
.9	.65474	.86623	1.1544	.75585	.1		.4	.68709	.94565	1.0575	.72657	.6
41.0	.65606	.86929	1.1504	.75471	49.0		.5	.68835	.94896	1.0538	.72537	.5
.1	.65738	.87236	1.1463	.75356	.9		.6	.68962	.95229	1.0501	.72417	.4
.2	.65869	.87543	1.1423	.75241	.8		.7	.69088	.95562	1.0464	.72297	.3
.3	.66000	.87852	1.1383	.75126	.7		.8	.69214	.95897	1.0428	.72176	.2
.4	.66131	.88162	1.1343	.75011	.6		.9	.69340	.96232	1.0392	.72055	.1
.5	.66262	.88473	1.1303	.74896	.5		44.0	.69466	.96569	1.0355	.71934	46.0
.6	.66393	.88784	1.1263	.74780	.4		.1	.69591	.96907	1.0319	.71813	.9
.7	.66523	.89097	1.1224	.74664	.3		.2	.69717	.97246	1.0283	.71691	.8
.8	.66653	.89410	1.1184	.74548	.2		.3	.69842	.97586	1.0247	.71569	.7
.9	.66783	.89725	1.1145	.74431	.1		.4	.69966	.97927	1.0212	.71447	.6
42.0	.66913	.90040	1.1106	.74314	48.0		.5	.70091	.98270	1.0176	.71325	.5
.1	.67043	.90357	1.1067	.74198	.9		.6	.70215	.98613	1.0141	.71203	.4
.2	.67172	.90674	1.1028	.74080	.8		.7	.70339	.98958	1.0105	.71080	.3
.3	.67301	.90993	1.0990	.73963	.7		.8	.70463	.99304	1.0070	.70957	.2
.4	.67430	.91313	1.0951	.73846	.6		.9	.70587	.99652	1.0035	.70834	.1
42.5	.67559	.91633	1.0913	.73728	42.5		45.0	.70711	1.00000	1.0000	.70711	45.0
Deg.	Cos	Cot	Tan	Sin	Deg.		Deg.	Cos	Cot	Tan	Sin	Deg.

Table 4a
Radians to Degrees

Radians	Degrees
1	57.295
2	114.592
3	171.887
4	229.183
5	286.479
6	343.775
7	401.070
8	458.366
9	515.662

Table 4b
Degrees to Radians

Degrees	Radians
10	0.17453
20	0.34907
30	0.52360
40	0.69813
50	0.87266
60	1.04720
70	1.22173
80	1.39626
90	1.57080

Table 5. Natural Values of the Trigonometric Functions for Angles in Radians

0-1.00

Rad.	Sin	Tan	Cot	Cos	Rad.	Sin	Tan	Cot	Cos
0.00	.00000	.00000	—	1.00000	0.50	.47943	.54630	1.8305	.87758
.01	.01000	.01000	99.997	0.99995	.51	.48818	.55936	1.7878	.87274
.02	.02000	.02000	49.993	.99980	.52	.49688	.57256	1.7465	.86782
.03	.03000	.03001	33.323	.99955	.53	.50553	.58592	1.7067	.86281
.04	.03999	.04002	24.987	.99920	.54	.51414	.59943	1.6683	.85771
.05	.04998	.05004	19.983	.99875	.55	.52269	.61311	1.6310	.85252
.06	.05996	.06007	16.647	.99820	.56	.53119	.62695	1.5950	.84726
.07	.06994	.07011	14.262	.99755	.57	.53963	.64097	1.5601	.84190
.08	.07991	.08017	12.473	.99680	.58	.54802	.65517	1.5263	.83646
.09	.08988	.09024	11.081	.99595	.59	.55636	.66956	1.4935	.83094
0.10	.09983	.10033	9.9666	.99500	0.60	.56464	.68414	1.4617	.82534
.11	.10978	.11045	9.0542	.99396	.61	.57287	.69892	1.4308	.81965
.12	.11971	.12058	8.2933	.99281	.62	.58104	.71391	1.4007	.81388
.13	.12963	.13074	7.6489	.99156	.63	.58914	.72911	1.3715	.80803
.14	.13954	.14092	7.0961	.99022	.64	.59720	.74454	1.3431	.80210
.15	.14944	.15114	6.6166	.98877	.65	.60519	.76020	1.3154	.79608
.16	.15932	.16138	6.1966	.98723	.66	.61312	.77610	1.2885	.78999
.17	.16918	.17166	5.8256	.98558	.67	.62099	.79225	1.2622	.78382
.18	.17903	.18197	5.4954	.98384	.68	.62879	.80866	1.2366	.77757
.19	.18886	.19232	5.1997	.98200	.69	.63654	.82534	1.2116	.77125
0.20	.19867	.20271	4.9332	.98007	0.70	.64422	.84229	1.1872	.76484
.21	.20846	.21314	4.6917	.97803	.71	.65183	.85953	1.1634	.75836
.22	.21823	.22362	4.4719	.97590	.72	.65938	.87707	1.1402	.75181
.23	.22798	.23414	4.2709	.97367	.73	.66687	.89492	1.1174	.74517
.24	.23770	.24472	4.0864	.97134	.74	.67429	.91309	1.0952	.73847
.25	.24740	.25534	3.9163	.96891	.75	.68164	.93160	1.0734	.73169
.26	.25708	.26602	3.7591	.96639	.76	.68892	.95045	1.0521	.72484
.27	.26673	.27676	3.6133	.96377	.77	.69614	.96967	1.0313	.71791
.28	.27636	.28755	3.4776	.96106	.78	.70328	.98926	1.0109	.71091
.29	.28595	.29841	3.3511	.95824	.79	.71035	1.0092	.99084	.70385
0.30	.29552	.30934	3.2327	.95534	0.80	.71736	1.0296	.97121	.69671
.31	.30506	.32033	3.1218	.95233	.81	.72429	1.0505	.95197	.68950
.32	.31457	.33139	3.0176	.94924	.82	.73115	1.0717	.93309	.68222
.33	.32404	.34252	2.9195	.94604	.83	.73793	1.0934	.91455	.67488
.34	.33349	.35374	2.8270	.94275	.84	.74464	1.1156	.89635	.66746
.35	.34290	.36503	2.7395	.93937	.85	.75128	1.1383	.87848	.65998
.36	.35227	.37640	2.6567	.93590	.86	.75784	1.1616	.86091	.65244
.37	.36162	.38786	2.5782	.93233	.87	.76433	1.1853	.84365	.64483
.38	.37092	.39941	2.5037	.92866	.88	.77074	1.2097	.82668	.63715
.39	.38019	.41105	2.4328	.92491	.89	.77707	1.2346	.80998	.62941
0.40	.38942	.42279	2.3652	.92106	0.90	.78333	1.2602	.79355	.62161
.41	.39861	.43463	2.3008	.91712	.91	.78950	1.2864	.77738	.61375
.42	.40776	.44657	2.2393	.91309	.92	.79560	1.3133	.76146	.60582
.43	.41687	.45862	2.1804	.90897	.93	.80162	1.3409	.74578	.59783
.44	.42594	.47078	2.1241	.90475	.94	.80756	1.3692	.73034	.58979
.45	.43497	.48306	2.0702	.90045	.95	.81342	1.3984	.71511	.58168
.46	.44395	.49545	2.0184	.89605	.96	.81919	1.4284	.70010	.57352
.47	.45289	.50797	1.9686	.89157	.97	.82489	1.4592	.68531	.56530
.48	.46178	.52061	1.9208	.88699	.98	.83050	1.4910	.67071	.55702
.49	.47063	.53339	1.8748	.88233	.99	.83603	1.5237	.65631	.54869
0.50	.47943	.54630	1.8305	.87758	1.00	.84147	1.5574	.64209	.54030
Rad.	Sin	Tan	Cot	Cos	Rad.	Sin	Tan	Cot	Cos

Table 5. Natural Values of the Trigonometric Functions for Angles in Radians
1.00-1.60

Rad.	Sin	Tan	Cot	Cos	Rad.	Sin	Tan	Cot	Cos
1.00	.84147	1.5574	.64209	.54030	1.30	.96356	3.6021	.27762	.26750
1.01	.84683	1.5922	.62806	.53186	1.31	.96618	3.7471	.26687	.25785
1.02	.85211	1.6281	.61420	.52337	1.32	.96872	3.9033	.25619	.24818
1.03	.85730	1.6652	.60051	.51482	1.33	.97115	4.0723	.24556	.23848
1.04	.86240	1.7036	.58699	.50622	1.34	.97348	4.2556	.23498	.22875
1.05	.86742	1.7433	.57362	.49757	1.35	.97572	4.4552	.22446	.21901
1.06	.87236	1.7844	.56040	.48887	1.36	.97786	4.6734	.21398	.20924
1.07	.87720	1.8270	.54734	.48012	1.37	.97991	4.9131	.20354	.19945
1.08	.88196	1.8712	.53441	.47133	1.38	.98185	5.1774	.19315	.18964
1.09	.88663	1.9171	.52162	.46249	1.39	.98370	5.4707	.18279	.17981
1.10	.89121	1.9648	.50897	.45360	1.40	.98545	5.7979	.17248	.16997
1.11	.89570	2.0143	.49644	.44466	1.41	.98710	6.1654	.16220	.16010
1.12	.90010	2.0660	.48404	.43568	1.42	.98865	6.5811	.15195	.15023
1.13	.90441	2.1198	.47175	.42666	1.43	.99010	7.0555	.14173	.14033
1.14	.90863	2.1759	.45959	.41759	1.44	.99146	7.6018	.13155	.13042
1.15	.91276	2.2345	.44753	.40849	1.45	.99271	8.2381	.12139	.12050
1.16	.91680	2.2958	.43558	.39934	1.46	.99387	8.9886	.11125	.11057
1.17	.92075	2.3600	.42373	.39015	1.47	.99492	9.8874	.10114	.10063
1.18	.92461	2.4273	.41199	.38092	1.48	.99588	10.983	.09105	.09067
1.19	.92837	2.4979	.40034	.37166	1.49	.99674	12.350	.08097	.08071
1.20	.93204	2.5722	.38878	.36236	1.50	.99749	14.101	.07091	.07074
1.21	.93562	2.6503	.37731	.35302	1.51	.99815	16.428	.06087	.06076
1.22	.93910	2.7328	.36593	.34365	1.52	.99871	19.670	.05084	.05077
1.23	.94249	2.8198	.35463	.33424	1.53	.99917	24.498	.04082	.04079
1.24	.94578	2.9119	.34341	.32480	1.54	.99953	32.461	.03081	.03079
1.25	.94898	3.0096	.33227	.31532	1.55	.99978	48.078	.02080	.02079
1.26	.95209	3.1133	.32121	.30582	1.56	.99994	92.621	.01080	.01080
1.27	.95510	3.2236	.31021	.29628	1.57	1.00000	1255.8	.00080	.00080
1.28	.95802	3.3413	.29928	.28672	1.58	.99996	−108.65	−.00920	−.00920
1.29	.96084	3.4672	.28842	.27712	1.59	.99982	−52.067	−.01921	−.01920
1.30	.96356	3.6021	.27762	.26750	1.60	.99957	−34.233	−.02921	−.02920
Rad.	Sin	Tan	Cot	Cos	Rad.	Sin	Tan	Cot	Cos

Table 6. Four-place Natural Logarithms

To find ln N when N is beyond the range of this table, write N in the form $P \times 10^m$, where P lies within the range of the table, and m is a positive or negative integer. Then use

$$\ln N = \ln (P \times 10^m) = \ln P + m \ln 10.$$

ln 10 =	2.3026	6 ln 10 =	13.8155
2 ln 10 =	4.6052	7 ln 10 =	16.1181
3 ln 10 =	6.9076	8 ln 10 =	18.4207
4 ln 10 =	9.2103	9 ln 10 =	20.7233
5 ln 10 =	11.5129	10 ln 10 =	23.0259

Table 6. Four-place Natural Logarithms
1.00-5.59

N	.00	.01	.02	.03	.04	.05	.06	.07	.08	.09
1.0	0.0000	0.0100	0.0198	0.0296	0.0392	0.0488	0.0583	0.0677	0.0770	0.0862
1.1	0.0953	0.1044	0.1133	0.1222	0.1310	0.1398	0.1484	0.1570	0.1655	0.1740
1.2	0.1823	0.1906	0.1989	0.2070	0.2151	0.2231	0.2311	0.2390	0.2469	0.2546
1.3	0.2624	0.2700	0.2776	0.2852	0.2927	0.3001	0.3075	0.3148	0.3221	0.3293
1.4	0.3365	0.3436	0.3507	0.3577	0.3646	0.3716	0.3784	0.3853	0.3920	0.3988
1.5	0.4055	0.4121	0.4187	0.4253	0.4318	0.4383	0.4447	0.4511	0.4574	0.4637
1.6	0.4700	0.4762	0.4824	0.4886	0.4947	0.5008	0.5068	0.5128	0.5188	0.5247
1.7	0.5306	0.5365	0.5423	0.5481	0.5539	0.5596	0.5653	0.5710	0.5766	0.5822
1.8	0.5878	0.5933	0.5988	0.6043	0.6098	0.6152	0.6206	0.6259	0.6313	0.6366
1.9	0.6419	0.6471	0.6523	0.6575	0.6627	0.6678	0.6729	0.6780	0.6831	0.6881
2.0	0.6931	0.6981	0.7031	0.7080	0.7129	0.7178	0.7227	0.7275	0.7324	0.7372
2.1	0.7419	0.7467	0.7514	0.7561	0.7608	0.7655	0.7701	0.7747	0.7793	0.7839
2.2	0.7885	0.7930	0.7975	0.8020	0.8065	0.8109	0.8154	0.8198	0.8242	0.8286
2.3	0.8329	0.8372	0.8416	0.8459	0.8502	0.8544	0.8587	0.8629	0.8671	0.8713
2.4	0.8755	0.8796	0.8838	0.8879	0.8920	0.8961	0.9002	0.9042	0.9083	0.9123
2.5	0.9163	0.9203	0.9243	0.9282	0.9322	0.9361	0.9400	0.9439	0.9478	0.9517
2.6	0.9555	0.9594	0.9632	0.9670	0.9708	0.9746	0.9783	0.9821	0.9858	0.9895
2.7	0.9933	0.9969	1.0006	1.0043	1.0080	1.0116	1.0152	1.0188	1.0225	1.0260
2.8	1.0296	1.0332	1.0367	1.0403	1.0438	1.0473	1.0508	1.0543	1.0578	1.0613
2.9	1.0647	1.0682	1.0716	1.0750	1.0784	1.0818	1.0852	1.0886	1.0919	1.0953
3.0	1.0986	1.1019	1.1053	1.1086	1.1119	1.1151	1.1184	1.1217	1.1249	1.1282
3.1	1.1314	1.1346	1.1378	1.1410	1.1442	1.1474	1.1506	1.1537	1.1569	1.1600
3.2	1.1632	1.1663	1.1694	1.1725	1.1756	1.1787	1.1817	1.1848	1.1878	1.1909
3.3	1.1939	1.1969	1.2000	1.2030	1.2060	1.2090	1.2119	1.2149	1.2179	1.2208
3.4	1.2238	1.2267	1.2296	1.2326	1.2355	1.2384	1.2413	1.2442	1.2470	1.2499
3.5	1.2528	1.2556	1.2585	1.2613	1.2641	1.2669	1.2698	1.2726	1.2754	1.2782
3.6	1.2809	1.2837	1.2865	1.2892	1.2920	1.2947	1.2975	1.3002	1.3029	1.3056
3.7	1.3083	1.3110	1.3137	1.3164	1.3191	1.3218	1.3244	1.3271	1.3297	1.3324
3.8	1.3350	1.3376	1.3403	1.3429	1.3455	1.3481	1.3507	1.3533	1.3558	1.3584
3.9	1.3610	1.3635	1.3661	1.3686	1.3712	1.3737	1.3762	1.3788	1.3813	1.3838
4.0	1.3863	1.3888	1.3913	1.3938	1.3962	1.3987	1.4012	1.4036	1.4061	1.4085
4.1	1.4110	1.4134	1.4159	1.4183	1.4207	1.4231	1.4255	1.4279	1.4303	1.4327
4.2	1.4351	1.4375	1.4398	1.4422	1.4446	1.4469	1.4493	1.4516	1.4540	1.4563
4.3	1.4586	1.4609	1.4633	1.4656	1.4679	1.4702	1.4725	1.4748	1.4770	1.4793
4.4	1.4816	1.4839	1.4861	1.4884	1.4907	1.4929	1.4951	1.4974	1.4996	1.5019
4.5	1.5041	1.5063	1.5085	1.5107	1.5129	1.5151	1.5173	1.5195	1.5217	1.5239
4.6	1.5261	1.5282	1.5304	1.5326	1.5347	1.5369	1.5390	1.5412	1.5433	1.5454
4.7	1.5476	1.5497	1.5518	1.5539	1.5560	1.5581	1.5602	1.5623	1.5644	1.5665
4.8	1.5686	1.5707	1.5728	1.5748	1.5769	1.5790	1.5810	1.5831	1.5851	1.5872
4.9	1.5892	1.5913	1.5933	1.5953	1.5974	1.5994	1.6014	1.6034	1.6054	1.6074
5.0	1.6094	1.6114	1.6134	1.6154	1.6174	1.6194	1.6214	1.6233	1.6253	1.6273
5.1	1.6292	1.6312	1.6332	1.6351	1.6371	1.6390	1.6409	1.6429	1.6448	1.6467
5.2	1.6487	1.6506	1.6525	1.6544	1.6563	1.6582	1.6601	1.6620	1.6639	1.6658
5.3	1.6677	1.6696	1.6715	1.6734	1.6752	1.6771	1.6790	1.6808	1.6827	1.6845
5.4	1.6864	1.6882	1.6901	1.6919	1.6938	1.6956	1.6974	1.6993	1.7011	1.7029
5.5	1.7047	1.7066	1.7084	1.7102	1.7120	1.7138	1.7156	1.7174	1.7192	1.7210
N	.00	.01	.02	.03	.04	.05	.06	.07	.08	.09

Table 6. Four-place Natural Logarithms
5.50-10.09

N	.00	.01	.02	.03	.04	.05	.06	.07	.08	.09
5.5	1.7047	1.7066	1.7084	1.7102	1.7120	1.7138	1.7156	1.7174	1.7192	1.7210
5.6	1.7228	1.7246	1.7263	1.7281	1.7299	1.7317	1.7334	1.7352	1.7370	1.7387
5.7	1.7405	1.7422	1.7440	1.7457	1.7475	1.7492	1.7509	1.7527	1.7544	1.7561
5.8	1.7579	1.7596	1.7613	1.7630	1.7647	1.7664	1.7681	1.7699	1.7716	1.7733
5.9	1.7750	1.7766	1.7783	1.7800	1.7817	1.7834	1.7851	1.7867	1.7884	1.7901
6.0	1.7918	1.7934	1.7951	1.7967	1.7984	1.8001	1.8017	1.8034	1.8050	1.8066
6.1	1.8083	1.8099	1.8116	1.8132	1.8148	1.8165	1.8181	1.8197	1.8213	1.8229
6.2	1.8245	1.8262	1.8278	1.8294	1.8310	1.8326	1.8342	1.8358	1.8374	1.8390
6.3	1.8405	1.8421	1.8437	1.8453	1.8469	1.8485	1.8500	1.8516	1.8532	1.8547
6.4	1.8563	1.8579	1.8594	1.8610	1.8625	1.8641	1.8656	1.8672	1.8687	1.8703
6.5	1.8718	1.8733	1.8749	1.8764	1.8779	1.8795	1.8810	1.8825	1.8840	1.8856
6.6	1.8871	1.8886	1.8901	1.8916	1.8931	1.8946	1.8961	1.8976	1.8991	1.9006
6.7	1.9021	1.9036	1.9051	1.9066	1.9081	1.9095	1.9110	1.9125	1.9140	1.9155
6.8	1.9169	1.9184	1.9199	1.9213	1.9228	1.9242	1.9257	1.9272	1.9286	1.9301
6.9	1.9315	1.9330	1.9344	1.9359	1.9373	1.9387	1.9402	1.9416	1.9430	1.9445
7.0	1.9459	1.9473	1.9488	1.9502	1.9516	1.9530	1.9544	1.9559	1.9573	1.9587
7.1	1.9601	1.9615	1.9629	1.9643	1.9657	1.9671	1.9685	1.9699	1.9713	1.9727
7.2	1.9741	1.9755	1.9769	1.9782	1.9796	1.9810	1.9824	1.9838	1.9851	1.9865
7.3	1.9879	1.9892	1.9906	1.9920	1.9933	1.9947	1.9961	1.9974	1.9988	2.0001
7.4	2.0015	2.0028	2.0042	2.0055	2.0069	2.0082	2.0096	2.0109	2.0122	2.0136
7.5	2.0149	2.0162	2.0176	2.0189	2.0202	2.0215	2.0229	2.0242	2.0255	2.0268
7.6	2.0281	2.0295	2.0308	2.0321	2.0334	2.0347	2.0360	2.0373	2.0386	2.0399
7.7	2.0412	2.0425	2.0438	2.0451	2.0464	2.0477	2.0490	2.0503	2.0516	2.0528
7.8	2.0541	2.0554	2.0567	2.0580	2.0592	2.0605	2.0618	2.0631	2.0643	2.0656
7.9	2.0669	2.0681	2.0694	2.0707	2.0719	2.0732	2.0744	2.0757	2.0769	2.0782
8.0	2.0794	2.0807	2.0819	2.0832	2.0844	2.0857	2.0869	2.0882	2.0894	2.0906
8.1	2.0919	2.0931	2.0943	2.0956	2.0968	2.0980	2.0992	2.1005	2.1017	2.1029
8.2	2.1041	2.1054	2.1066	2.1078	2.1090	2.1102	2.1114	2.1126	2.1138	2.1150
8.3	2.1163	2.1175	2.1187	2.1199	2.1211	2.1223	2.1235	2.1247	2.1258	2.1270
8.4	2.1282	2.1294	2.1306	2.1318	2.1330	2.1342	2.1353	2.1365	2.1377	2.1389
8.5	2.1401	2.1412	2.1424	2.1436	2.1448	2.1459	2.1471	2.1483	2.1494	2.1506
8.6	2.1518	2.1529	2.1541	2.1552	2.1564	2.1576	2.1587	2.1599	2.1610	2.1622
8.7	2.1633	2.1645	2.1656	2.1668	2.1679	2.1691	2.1702	2.1713	2.1725	2.1736
8.8	2.1748	2.1759	2.1770	2.1782	2.1793	2.1804	2.1815	2.1827	2.1838	2.1849
8.9	2.1861	2.1872	2.1883	2.1894	2.1905	2.1917	2.1928	2.1939	2.1950	2.1961
9.0	2.1972	2.1983	2.1994	2.2006	2.2017	2.2028	2.2039	2.2050	2.2061	2.2072
9.1	2.2083	2.2094	2.2105	2.2116	2.2127	2.2138	2.2148	2.2159	2.2170	2.2181
9.2	2.2192	2.2203	2.2214	2.2225	2.2235	2.2246	2.2257	2.2268	2.2279	2.2289
9.3	2.2300	2.2311	2.2322	2.2332	2.2343	2.2354	2.2364	2.2375	2.2386	2.2396
9.4	2.2407	2.2418	2.2428	2.2439	2.2450	2.2460	2.2471	2.2481	2.2492	2.2502
9.5	2.2513	2.2523	2.2534	2.2544	2.2555	2.2565	2.2576	2.2586	2.2597	2.2607
9.6	2.2618	2.2628	2.2638	2.2649	2.2659	2.2670	2.2680	2.2690	2.2701	2.2711
9.7	2.2721	2.2732	2.2742	2.2752	2.2762	2.2773	2.2783	2.2793	2.2803	2.2814
9.8	2.2824	2.2834	2.2844	2.2854	2.2865	2.2875	2.2885	2.2895	2.2905	2.2915
9.9	2.2925	2.2935	2.2946	2.2956	2.2966	2.2976	2.2986	2.2996	2.3006	2.3016
10.0	2.3026	2.3036	2.3046	2.3056	2.3066	2.3076	2.3086	2.3096	2.3106	2.3115
N	.00	.01	.02	.03	.04	.05	.06	.07	.08	.09

Table 7. Exponential and Hyperbolic Functions
0.00-0.50

x	e^x	e^{-x}	Sinh x	Cosh x	Tanh x	x
0.00	1.0000	1.00000	.00000	1.0000	.00000	**0.00**
0.01	1.0101	0.99005	.01000	1.0001	.01000	0.01
0.02	1.0202	.98020	.02000	1.0002	.02000	0.02
0.03	1.0305	.97045	.03000	1.0005	.02999	0.03
0.04	1.0408	.96079	.04001	1.0008	.03998	0.04
0.05	1.0513	.95123	.05002	1.0013	.04996	**0.05**
0.06	1.0618	.94176	.06004	1.0018	.05993	0.06
0.07	1.0725	.93239	.07006	1.0025	.06989	0.07
0.08	1.0833	.92312	.08009	1.0032	.07983	0.08
0.09	1.0942	.91393	.09012	1.0041	.08976	0.09
0.10	1.1052	.90484	.10017	1.0050	.09967	**0.10**
0.11	1.1163	.89583	.11022	1.0061	.10956	0.11
0.12	1.1275	.88692	.12029	1.0072	.11943	0.12
0.13	1.1388	.87810	.13037	1.0085	.12927	0.13
0.14	1.1503	.86936	.14046	1.0098	.13909	0.14
0.15	1.1618	.86071	.15056	1.0113	.14889	**0.15**
0.16	1.1735	.85214	.16068	1.0128	.15865	0.16
0.17	1.1853	.84366	.17082	1.0145	.16838	0.17
0.18	1.1972	.83527	.18097	1.0162	.17808	0.18
0.19	1.2092	.82696	.19115	1.0181	.18775	0.19
0.20	1.2214	.81873	.20134	1.0201	.19738	**0.20**
0.21	1.2337	.81058	.21155	1.0221	.20697	0.21
0.22	1.2461	.80252	.22178	1.0243	.21652	0.22
0.23	1.2586	.79453	.23203	1.0266	.22603	0.23
0.24	1.2712	.78663	.24231	1.0289	.23550	0.24
0.25	1.2840	.77880	.25261	1.0314	.24492	**0.25**
0.26	1.2969	.77105	.26294	1.0340	.25430	0.26
0.27	1.3100	.76338	.27329	1.0367	.26362	0.27
0.28	1.3231	.75578	.28367	1.0395	.27291	0.28
0.29	1.3364	.74826	.29408	1.0423	.28213	0.29
0.30	1.3499	.74082	.30452	1.0453	.29131	**0.30**
0.31	1.3634	.73345	.31499	1.0484	.30044	0.31
0.32	1.3771	.72615	.32549	1.0516	.30951	0.32
0.33	1.3910	.71892	.33602	1.0549	.31852	0.33
0.34	1.4049	.71177	.34659	1.0584	.32748	0.34
0.35	1.4191	.70469	.35719	1.0619	.33638	**0.35**
0.36	1.4333	.69768	.36783	1.0655	.34521	0.36
0.37	1.4477	.69073	.37850	1.0692	.35399	0.37
0.38	1.4623	.68386	.38921	1.0731	.36271	0.38
0.39	1.4770	.67706	.39996	1.0770	.37136	0.39
0.40	1.4918	.67032	.41075	1.0811	.37995	**0.40**
0.41	1.5068	.66365	.42158	1.0852	.38847	0.41
0.42	1.5220	.65705	.43246	1.0895	.39693	0.42
0.43	1.5373	.65051	.44337	1.0939	.40532	0.43
0.44	1.5527	.64404	.45434	1.0984	.41364	0.44
0.45	1.5683	.63763	.46534	1.1030	.42190	**0.45**
0.46	1.5841	.63128	.47640	1.1077	.43008	0.46
0.47	1.6000	.62500	.48750	1.1125	.43820	0.47
0.48	1.6161	.61878	.49865	1.1174	.44624	0.48
0.49	1.6323	.61263	.50984	1.1225	.45422	0.49
0.50	1.6487	.60653	.52110	1.1276	.46212	**0.50**
x	e^x	e^{-x}	Sinh x	Cosh x	Tanh x	x

Table 7. Exponential and Hyperbolic Functions
0.50-1.00

x	e^x	e^{-x}	Sinh x	Cosh x	Tanh x	x
0.50	1.6487	.60653	.52110	1.1276	.46212	**0.50**
0.51	1.6653	.60050	.53240	1.1329	.46995	0.51
0.52	1.6820	.59452	.54375	1.1383	.47770	0.52
0.53	1.6989	.58860	.55516	1.1438	.48538	0.53
0.54	1.7160	.58275	.56663	1.1494	.49299	0.54
0.55	1.7333	.57695	.57815	1.1551	.50052	**0.55**
0.56	1.7507	.57121	.58973	1.1609	.50798	0.56
0.57	1.7683	.56553	.60137	1.1669	.51536	0.57
0.58	1.7860	.55990	.61307	1.1730	.52267	0.58
0.59	1.8040	.55433	.62483	1.1792	.52990	0.59
0.60	1.8221	54881	.63665	1.1855	.53705	**0.60**
0.61	1.8404	.54335	.64854	1.1919	.54413	0.61
0.62	1.8589	.53794	.66049	1.1984	.55113	0.62
0.63	1.8776	.53259	.67251	1.2051	.55805	0.63
0.64	1.8965	.52729	.68459	1.2119	.56490	0.64
0.65	1.9155	.52205	.69675	1.2188	.57167	**0.65**
0.66	1.9348	.51685	.70897	1.2258	.57836	0.66
0.67	1.9542	.51171	.72126	1.2330	.58498	0.67
0.68	1.9739	.50662	.73363	1.2402	.59152	0.68
0.69	1.9937	.50158	.74607	1.2476	.59793	0.69
0.70	2.0138	.49659	.75858	1.2552	.60437	**0.70**
0.71	2.0340	.49164	.77117	1.2628	.61068	0.71
0.72	2.0544	.48675	.78384	1.2706	.61691	0.72
0.73	2.0751	.48191	.79659	1.2785	.62307	0.73
0.74	2.0959	.47711	.80941	1.2865	.62915	0.74
0.75	2.1170	.47237	.82232	1.2947	.63515	**0.75**
0.76	2.1383	.46767	.83530	1.3030	.64108	0.76
0.77	2.1598	.46301	.84838	1.3114	.64693	0.77
0.78	2.1815	.45841	.86153	1.3199	.65271	0.78
0.79	2.2034	.45384	.87478	1.3286	.65841	0.79
0.80	2.2255	.44933	.88811	1.3374	.66404	**0.80**
0.81	2.2479	.44486	.90152	1.3464	.66959	0.81
0.82	2.2705	.44043	.91503	1.3555	.67507	0.82
0.83	2.2933	.43605	.92863	1.3647	.68048	0.83
0.84	2.3164	.43171	.94233	1.3740	.68581	0.84
0.85	2.3396	.42741	.95612	1.3835	.69107	**0.85**
0.86	2.3632	.42316	.97000	1.3932	.69626	0.86
0.87	2.3869	.41895	.98398	1.4029	.70137	0.87
0.88	2.4109	.41478	.99806	1.4128	.70642	0.88
0.89	2.4351	.41066	1.0122	1.4229	.71139	0.89
0.90	2.4596	.40657	1.0265	1.4331	.71630	**0.90**
0.91	2.4843	.40252	1.0409	1.4434	.72113	0.91
0.92	2.5093	.39852	1.0554	1.4539	.72590	0.92
0.93	2.5345	.39455	1.0700	1.4645	.73059	0.93
0.94	2.5600	.39063	1.0847	1.4753	.73522	0.94
0.95	2.5857	.38674	1.0995	1.4862	.73978	**0.95**
0.96	2.6117	.38289	1.1144	1.4973	.74428	0.96
0.97	2.6379	.37908	1.1294	1.5085	.74870	0.97
0.98	2.6645	.37531	1.1446	1.5199	.75307	0.98
0.99	2.6912	.37158	1.1598	1.5314	.75736	0.99
1.00	2.7183	.36788	1.1752	1.5431	.76159	**1.00**
x	e^x	e^{-x}	Sinh x	Cosh x	Tanh x	x

Table 7. Exponential and Hyperbolic Functions
1.00-1.50

x	e^x	e^{-x}	Sinh x	Cosh x	Tanh x	x
1.00	2.7183	.36788	1.1752	1.5431	.76159	**1.00**
1.01	2.7456	.36422	1.1907	1.5549	.76576	1.01
1.02	2.7732	.36059	1.2063	1.5669	.76987	1.02
1.03	2.8011	.35701	1.2220	1.5790	.77391	1.03
1.04	2.8292	.35345	1.2379	1.5913	.77789	1.04
1.05	2.8577	.34994	1.2539	1.6038	.78181	**1.05**
1.06	2.8864	.34646	1.2700	1.6164	.78566	1.06
1.07	2.9154	.34301	1.2862	1.6292	.78946	1.07
1.08	2.9447	.33960	1.3025	1.6421	.79320	1.08
1.09	2.9743	.33622	1.3190	1.6552	.79688	1.09
1.10	3.0042	.33287	1.3356	1.6685	.80050	**1.10**
1.11	3.0344	.32956	1.3524	1.6820	.80406	1.11
1.12	3.0649	.32628	1.3693	1.6956	.80757	1.12
1.13	3.0957	.32303	1.3863	1.7093	.81102	1.13
1.14	3.1268	.31982	1.4035	1.7233	.81441	1.14
1.15	3.1582	.31664	1.4208	1.7374	.81775	**1.15**
1.16	3.1899	.31349	1.4382	1.7517	.82104	1.16
1.17	3.2220	.31037	1.4558	1.7662	.82427	1.17
1.18	3.2544	.30728	1.4735	1.7808	.82745	1.18
1.19	3.2871	.30422	1.4914	1.7957	.83058	1.19
1.20	3.3201	.30119	1.5095	1.8107	.83365	**1.20**
1.21	3.3535	.29820	1.5276	1.8258	.83668	1.21
1.22	3.3872	.29523	1.5460	1.8412	.83965	1.22
1.23	3.4212	.29229	1.5645	1.8568	.84258	1.23
1.24	3.4556	.28938	1.5831	1.8725	.84546	1.24
1.25	3.4903	.28650	1.6019	1.8884	.84828	**1.25**
1.26	3.5254	.28365	1.6209	1.9045	.85106	1.26
1.27	3.5609	.28083	1.6400	1.9208	.85380	1.27
1.28	3.5966	.27804	1.6593	1.9373	.85648	1.28
1.29	3.6328	.27527	1.6788	1.9540	.85913	1.29
1.30	3.6693	.27253	1.6984	1.9709	.86172	**1.30**
1.31	3.7062	.26982	1.7182	1.9880	.86428	1.31
1.32	3.7434	.26714	1.7381	2.0053	.86678	1.32
1.33	3.7810	.26448	1.7583	2.0228	.86925	1.33
1.34	3.8190	.26185	1.7786	2.0404	.87167	1.34
1.35	3.8574	.25924	1.7991	2.0583	.87405	**1.35**
1.36	3.8962	.25666	1.8198	2.0764	.87639	1.36
1.37	3.9354	.25411	1.8406	2.0947	.87869	1.37
1.38	3.9749	.25158	1.8617	2.1132	.88095	1.38
1.39	4.0149	.24908	1.8829	2.1320	.88317	1.39
1.40	4.0552	.24660	1.9043	2.1509	.88535	**1.40**
1.41	4.0960	.24414	1.9259	2.1700	.88749	1.41
1.42	4.1371	.24171	1.9477	2.1894	.88960	1.42
1.43	4.1787	.23931	1.9697	2.2090	.89167	1.43
1.44	4.2207	.23693	1.9919	2.2288	.89370	1.44
1.45	4.2631	.23457	2.0143	2.2488	.89569	**1.45**
1.46	4.3060	.23224	2.0369	2.2691	.89765	1.46
1.47	4.3492	.22993	2.0597	2.2896	.89958	1.47
1.48	4.3929	.22764	2.0827	2.3103	.90147	1.48
1.49	4.4371	.22537	2.1059	2.3312	.90332	1.49
1.50	4.4817	.22313	2.1293	2.3524	.90515	**1.50**
x	e^x	e^{-x}	Sinh x	Cosh x	Tanh x	x

Table 7. Exponential and Hyperbolic Functions 1.50-2.00

x	e^x	e^{-x}	Sinh x	Cosh x	Tanh x	x
1.50	4.4817	.22313	2.1293	2.3524	.90515	**1.50**
1.51	4.5267	.22091	2.1529	2.3738	.90694	1.51
1.52	4.5722	.21871	2.1768	2.3955	.90870	1.52
1.53	4.6182	.21654	2.2008	2.4174	.91042	1.53
1.54	4.6646	.21438	2.2251	2.4395	.91212	1.54
1.55	4.7115	.21225	2.2496	2.4619	.91379	**1.55**
1.56	4.7588	.21014	2.2743	2.4845	.91542	1.56
1.57	4.8066	.20805	2.2993	2.5073	.91703	1.57
1.58	4.8550	.20598	2.3245	2.5305	.91860	1.58
1.59	4.9037	.20393	2.3499	2.5538	.92015	1.59
1.60	4.9530	.20190	2.3756	2.5775	.92167	**1.60**
1.61	5.0028	.19989	2.4015	2.6013	.92316	1.61
1.62	5.0531	.19790	2.4276	2.6255	.92462	1.62
1.63	5.1039	.19593	2.4540	2.6499	.92606	1.63
1.64	5.1552	.19398	2.4806	2.6746	.92747	1.64
1.65	5.2070	.19205	2.5075	2.6995	.92886	**1.65**
1.66	5.2593	.19014	2.5346	2.7247	.93022	1.66
1.67	5.3122	.18825	2.5620	2.7502	.93155	1.67
1.68	5.3656	.18637	2.5896	2.7760	.93286	1.68
1.69	5.4195	.18452	2.6175	2.8020	.93415	1.69
1.70	5.4739	.18268	2.6456	2.8283	.93541	**1.70**
1.71	5.5290	.18087	2.6740	2.8549	.93665	1.71
1.72	5.5845	.17907	2.7027	2.8818	.93786	1.72
1.73	5.6407	.17728	2.7317	2.9090	.93906	1.73
1.74	5.6973	.17552	2.7609	2.9364	.94023	1.74
1.75	5.7546	.17377	2.7904	2.9642	.94138	**1.75**
1.76	5.8124	.17204	2.8202	2.9922	.94250	1.76
1.77	5.8709	.17033	2.8503	3.0206	.94361	1.77
1.78	5.9299	.16864	2.8806	3.0492	.94470	1.78
1.79	5.9895	.16696	2.9112	3.0782	.94576	1.79
1.80	6.0496	.16530	2.9422	3.1075	.94681	**1.80**
1.81	6.1104	.16365	2.9734	3.1371	.94783	1.81
1.82	6.1719	.16203	3.0049	3.1669	.94884	1.82
1.83	6.2339	.16041	3.0367	3.1972	.94983	1.83
1.84	6.2965	.15882	3.0689	3.2277	.95080	1.84
1.85	6.3598	.15724	3.1013	3.2585	.95175	**1.85**
1.86	6.4237	.15567	3.1340	3.2897	.95268	1.86
1.87	6.4883	.15412	3.1671	3.3212	.95359	1.87
1.88	6.5535	.15259	3.2005	3.3530	.95449	1.88
1.89	6.6194	.15107	3.2341	3.3852	.95537	1.89
1.90	6.6859	.14957	3.2682	3.4177	.95624	**1.90**
1.91	6.7531	.14808	3.3025	3.4506	.95709	1.91
1.92	6.8210	.14661	3.3372	3.4838	.95792	1.92
1.93	6.8895	.14515	3.3722	3.5173	.95873	1.93
1.94	6.9588	.14370	3.4075	3.5512	.95953	1.94
1.95	7.0287	.14227	3.4432	3.5855	.96032	**1.95**
1.96	7.0993	.14086	3.4792	3.6201	.96109	1.96
1.97	7.1707	.13946	3.5156	3.6551	.96185	1.97
1.98	7.2427	.13807	3.5523	3.6904	.96259	1.98
1.99	7.3155	.13670	3.5894	3.7261	.96331	1.99
2.00	7.3891	.13534	3.6269	3.7622	.96403	**2.00**
x	e^x	e^{-x}	Sinh x	Cosh x	Tanh x	x

Table 7. Exponential and Hyperbolic Functions

2.00-2.50

x	e^x	e^{-x}	Sinh x	Cosh x	Tanh x	x
2.00	7.3891	.13534	3.6269	3.7622	.96403	**2.00**
2.01	7.4633	.13399	3.6647	3.7987	.96473	2.01
2.02	7.5383	.13266	3.7028	3.8355	.96541	2.02
2.03	7.6141	.13134	3.7414	3.8727	.96609	2.03
2.04	7.6906	.13003	3.7803	3.9103	.96675	2.04
2.05	7.7679	.12873	3.8196	3.9483	.96740	**2.05**
2.06	7.8460	.12745	3.8593	3.9867	.96803	2.06
2.07	7.9248	.12619	3.8993	4.0255	.96865	2.07
2.08	8.0045	.12493	3.9398	4.0647	.96926	2.08
2.09	8.0849	.12369	3.9806	4.1043	.96986	2.09
2.10	8.1662	.12246	4.0219	4.1443	.97045	**2.10**
2.11	8.2482	.12124	4.0635	4.1847	.97103	2.11
2.12	8.3311	.12003	4.1056	4.2256	.97159	2.12
2.13	8.4149	.11884	4.1480	4.2669	.97215	2.13
2.14	8.4994	.11765	4.1909	4.3085	.97269	2.14
2.15	8.5849	.11648	4.2342	4.3507	.97323	**2.15**
2.16	8.6711	.11533	4.2779	4.3932	.97375	2.16
2.17	8.7583	.11418	4.3221	4.4362	.97426	2.17
2.18	8.8463	.11304	4.3666	4.4797	.97477	2.18
2.19	8.9352	.11192	4.4116	4.5236	.97526	2.19
2.20	9.0250	.11080	4.4571	4.5679	.97574	**2.20**
2.21	9.1157	.10970	4.5030	4.6127	.97622	2.21
2.22	9.2073	.10861	4.5494	4.6580	.97668	2.22
2.23	9.2999	.10753	4.5962	4.7037	.97714	2.23
2.24	9.3933	.10646	4.6434	4.7499	.97759	2.24
2.25	9.4877	.10540	4.6912	4.7966	.97803	**2.25**
2.26	9.5831	.10435	4.7394	4.8437	.97846	2.26
2.27	9.6794	.10331	4.7880	4.8914	.97888	2.27
2.28	9.7767	.10228	4.8372	4.9395	.97929	2.28
2.29	9.8749	.10127	4.8868	4.9881	.97970	2.29
2.30	9.9742	.10026	4.9370	5.0372	.98010	**2.30**
2.31	10.074	.09926	4.9876	5.0868	.98049	2.31
2.32	10.176	.09827	5.0387	5.1370	.98087	2.32
2.33	10.278	.09730	5.0903	5.1876	.98124	2.33
2.34	10.381	.09633	5.1425	5.2388	.98161	2.34
2.35	10.486	.09537	5.1951	5.2905	.98197	**2.35**
2.36	10.591	.09442	5.2483	5.3427	.98233	2.36
2.37	10.697	.09348	5.3020	5.3954	.98267	2.37
2.38	10.805	.09255	5.3562	5.4487	.98301	2.38
2.39	10.913	.09163	5.4109	5.5026	.98335	2.39
2.40	11.023	.09072	5.4662	5.5569	.98367	**2.40**
2.41	11.134	.08982	5.5221	5.6119	.98400	2.41
2.42	11.246	.08892	5.5785	5.6674	.98431	2.42
2.43	11.359	.08803	5.6354	5.7235	.98462	2.43
2.44	11.473	.08716	5.6929	5.7801	.98492	2.44
2.45	11.588	.08629	5.7510	5.8373	.98522	**2.45**
2.46	11.705	.08543	5.8097	5.8951	.98551	2.46
2.47	11.822	.08458	5.8689	5.9535	.98579	2.47
2.48	11.941	.08374	5.9288	6.0125	.98607	2.48
2.49	12.061	.08291	5.9892	6.0721	.98635	2.49
2.50	12.182	.08208	6.0502	6.1323	.98661	**2.50**
x	e^x	e^{-x}	Sinh x	Cosh x	Tanh x	x

Table 7. Exponential and Hyperbolic Functions
2.50-3.00

x	e^x	e^{-x}	Sinh x	Cosh x	Tanh x	x
2.50	12.182	.08208	6.0502	6.1323	.98661	**2.50**
2.51	12.305	.08127	6.1118	6.1931	.98688	2.51
2.52	12.429	.08046	6.1741	6.2545	.98714	2.52
2.53	12.554	.07966	6.2369	6.3166	.98739	2.53
2.54	12.680	.07887	6.3004	6.3793	.98764	2.54
2.55	12.807	.07808	6.3645	6.4426	.98788	**2.55**
2.56	12.936	.07730	6.4293	6.5066	.98812	2.56
2.57	13.066	.07654	6.4946	6.5712	.98835	2.57
2.58	13.197	.07577	6.5607	6.6365	.98858	2.58
2.59	13.330	.07502	6.6274	6.7024	.98881	2.59
2.60	13.464	.07427	6.6947	6.7690	.98903	**2.60**
2.61	13.599	.07354	6.7628	6.8363	.98924	2.61
2.62	13.736	.07280	6.8315	6.9043	.98946	2.62
2.63	13.874	.07208	6.9008	6.9729	.98966	2.63
2.64	14.013	.07136	6.9709	7.0423	.98987	2.64
2.65	14.154	.07066	7.0417	7.1123	.99007	**2.65**
2.66	14.296	.06995	7.1132	7.1831	.99026	2.66
2.67	14.440	.06925	7.1854	7.2546	.99045	2.67
2.68	14.585	.06856	7.2583	7.3268	.99064	2.68
2.69	14.732	.06788	7.3319	7.3998	.99083	2.69
2.70	14.880	.06721	7.4063	7.4735	.99101	**2.70**
2.71	15.029	.06654	7.4814	7.5479	.99118	2.71
2.72	15.180	.06587	7.5572	7.6231	.99136	2.72
2.73	15.333	.06522	7.6338	7.6991	.99153	2.73
2.74	15.487	.06457	7.7112	7.7758	.99170	2.74
2.75	15.643	.06393	7.7894	7.8533	.99186	**2.75**
2.76	15.800	.06329	7.8683	7.9316	.99202	2.76
2.77	15.959	.06266	7.9480	8.0106	.99218	2.77
2.78	16.119	.06204	8.0285	8.0905	.99233	2.78
2.79	16.281	.06142	8.1098	8.1712	.99248	2.79
2.80	16.445	.06081	8.1919	8.2527	.99263	**2.80**
2.81	16.610	.06020	8.2749	8.3351	.99278	2.81
2.82	16.777	.05961	8.3586	8.4182	.99292	2.82
2.83	16.945	.05901	8.4432	8.5022	.99306	2.83
2.84	17.116	.05843	8.5287	8.5871	.99320	2.84
2.85	17.288	.05784	8.6150	8.6728	.99333	**2.85**
2.86	17.462	.05727	8.7021	8.7594	.99346	2.86
2.87	17.637	.05670	8.7902	8.8469	.99359	2.87
2.88	17.814	.05613	8.8791	8.9352	.99372	2.88
2.89	17.993	.05558	8.9689	9.0244	.99384	2.89
2.90	18.174	.05502	9.0596	9.1146	.99396	**2.90**
2.91	18.357	.05448	9.1512	9.2056	.99408	2.91
2.92	18.541	.05393	9.2437	9.2976	.99420	2.92
2.93	18.728	.05340	9.3371	9.3905	.99431	2.93
2.94	18.916	.05287	9.4315	9.4844	.99443	2.94
2.95	19.106	.05234	9.5268	9.5791	.99454	**2.95**
2.96	19.298	.05182	9.6231	9.6749	.99464	2.96
2.97	19.492	.05130	9.7203	9.7716	.99475	2.97
2.98	19.688	.05079	9.8185	9.8693	.99485	2.98
2.99	19.886	.05029	9.9177	9.9680	.99496	2.99
3.00	20.086	.04979	10.0179	10.0677	.99505	**3.00**
x	e^x	e^{-x}	Sinh x	Cosh x	Tanh x	x

Table 7. Exponential and Hyperbolic Functions
3.00-5.50

x	e^x	e^{-x}	Sinh x	Cosh x	Tanh x	x
3.00	20.086	.04979	10.018	10.068	.99505	**3.00**
3.05	21.115	.04736	10.534	10.581	.99552	3.05
3.10	22.198	.04505	11.076	11.122	.99595	3.10
3.15	23.336	.04285	11.647	11.689	.99633	3.15
3.20	24.533	.04076	12.246	12.287	.99668	3.20
3.25	25.790	.03877	12.876	12.915	.99700	**3.25**
3.30	27.113	.03688	13.538	13.575	.99728	3.30
3.35	28.503	.03508	14.234	14.269	.99754	3.35
3.40	29.964	.03337	14.965	14.999	.99777	3.40
3.45	31.500	.03175	15.734	15.766	.99799	3.45
3.50	33.115	.03020	16.543	16.573	.99818	**3.50**
3.55	34.813	.02872	17.392	17.421	.99835	3.55
3.60	36.598	.02732	18.285	18.313	.99851	3.60
3.65	38.475	.02599	19.224	19.250	.99865	3.65
3.70	40.447	.02472	20.211	20.236	.99878	3.70
3.75	42.521	.02352	21.249	21.272	.99889	**3.75**
3.80	44.701	.02237	22.339	22.362	.99900	3.80
3.85	46.993	.02128	23.486	23.507	.99909	3.85
3.90	49.402	.02024	24.691	24.711	.99918	3.90
3.95	51.935	.01925	25.958	25.977	.99926	3.95
4.00	54.598	.01832	27.290	27.308	.99933	**4.00**
4.05	57.397	.01742	28.690	28.707	.99939	4.05
4.10	60.340	.01657	30.162	30.178	.99945	4.10
4.15	63.434	.01576	31.709	31.725	.99950	4.15
4.20	66.686	.01500	33.336	33.351	.99955	4.20
4.25	70.105	.01426	35.046	35.060	.99959	**4.25**
4.30	73.700	.01357	36.843	36.857	.99963	4.30
4.35	77.478	.01291	38.733	38.746	.99967	4.35
4.40	81.451	.01228	40.719	40.732	.99970	4.40
4.45	85.627	.01168	42.808	42.819	.99973	4.45
4.50	90.017	.01111	45.003	45.014	.99975	**4.50**
4.55	94.632	.01057	47.311	47.321	.99978	4.55
4.60	99.484	.01005	49.737	49.747	.99980	4.60
4.65	104.58	.00956	52.288	52.297	.99982	4.65
4.70	109.95	.00910	54.969	54.978	.99983	4.70
4.75	115.58	.00865	57.788	57.796	.99985	**4.75**
4.80	121.51	.00823	60.751	60.759	.99986	4.80
4.85	127.74	.00783	63.866	63.874	.99988	4.85
4.90	134.29	.00745	67.141	67.149	.99989	4.90
4.95	141.17	.00708	70.584	70.591	.99990	4.95
5.00	148.41	.00674	74.203	74.210	.99991	**5.00**
5.05	156.02	.00641	78.008	78.014	.99992	5.05
5.10	164.02	.00610	82.008	82.014	.99993	5.10
5.15	172.43	.00580	86.213	86.219	.99993	5.15
5.20	181.27	.00552	90.633	90.639	.99994	5.20
5.25	190.57	.00525	95.281	95.286	.99994	**5.25**
5.30	200.34	.00499	100.17	100.17	.99995	5.30
5.35	210.61	.00475	105.30	105.31	.99995	5.35
5.40	221.41	.00452	110.70	110.71	.99996	5.40
5.45	232.76	.00430	116.38	116.38	.99996	5.45
5.50	244.69	.00409	122.34	122.35	.99997	**5.50**
x	e^x	e^{-x}	Sinh x	Cosh x	Tanh x	x

Table 7. Exponential and Hyperbolic Functions
5.50-10.00

x	e^x	e^{-x}	Sinh x	Cosh x	Tanh x	x
5.50	244.69	.00409	122.34	122.35	.99997	**5.50**
5.55	257.24	.00389	128.62	128.62	.99997	5.55
5.60	270.43	.00370	135.21	135.22	.99997	5.60
5.65	284.29	.00352	142.14	142.15	.99998	5.65
5.70	298.87	.00335	149.43	149.44	.99998	5.70
5.75	314.19	.00318	157.09	157.10	.99998	**5.75**
5.80	330.30	.00303	165.15	165.15	.99998	5.80
5.85	347.23	.00288	173.62	173.62	.99998	5.85
5.90	365.04	.00274	182.52	182.52	.99998	5.90
5.95	383.75	.00261	191.88	191.88	.99999	5.95
6.00	403.43	.00248	201.71	201.72	.99999	**6.00**
6.05	424.11	.00236	212.06	212.06	.99999	6.05
6.10	445.86	.00224	222.93	222.93	.99999	6.10
6.15	468.72	.00213	234.36	234.36	.99999	6.15
6.20	492.75	.00203	246.37	246.38	.99999	6.20
6.25	518.01	.00193	259.01	259.01	.99999	**6.25**
6.30	544.57	.00184	272.29	272.29	.99999	6.30
6.35	572.49	.00175	286.25	286.25	.99999	6.35
6.40	601.85	.00166	300.92	300.92	.99999	6.40
6.45	632.70	.00158	316.35	316.35	1.00000	6.45
6.50	665.14	.00150	332.57	332.57	1.00000	**6.50**
6.55	699.24	.00143	349.62	349.62	1.00000	6.55
6.60	735.10	.00136	367.55	367.55	1.00000	6.60
6.65	772.78	.00129	386.39	386.39	1.00000	6.65
6.70	812.41	.00123	406.20	406.20	1.00000	6.70
6.75	854.06	.00117	427.03	427.03	1.00000	**6.75**
6.80	897.85	.00111	448.92	448.92	1.00000	6.80
6.85	943.88	.00106	471.94	471.94	1.00000	6.85
6.90	992.27	.00101	496.14	496.14	1.00000	6.90
6.95	1043.1	.00096	521.57	521.58	1.00000	6.95
7.00	1096.6	.00092	548.32	548.32	1.00000	**7.00**
7.05	1152.9	.00087	576.43	576.43	1.00000	7.05
7.10	1212.0	.00083	605.98	605.98	1.00000	7.10
7.15	1274.1	.00078	637.05	637.05	1.00000	7.15
7.20	1339.4	.00075	669.72	669.72	1.00000	7.20
7.25	1408.1	.00071	704.05	704.05	1.00000	**7.25**
7.30	1480.3	.00068	740.15	740.15	1.00000	7.30
7.35	1556.2	.00064	778.10	778.10	1.00000	7.35
7.40	1636.0	.00061	817.99	817.99	1.00000	7.40
7.45	1719.9	.00058	859.93	859.93	1.00000	7.45
7.50	1808.0	.00055	904.02	904.02	1.00000	**7.50**
7.75	2321.6	.00043	1 160.8	1 160.8	1.00000	7.75
8.00	2981.0	.00034	1 490.5	1 490.5	1.00000	8.00
8.25	3827.6	.00026	1 913.8	1 913.8	1.00000	8.25
8.50	4914.8	.00020	2 457.4	2 457.4	1.00000	8.50
8.75	6310.7	.00016	3 155.3	3 155.3	1.00000	**8.75**
9.00	8103.1	.00012	4 051.5	4 051.5	1.00000	9.00
9.25	10405	.00010	5 202.3	5 202.3	1.00000	9.25
9.50	13360	.00007	6 679.9	6 679.9	1.00000	9.50
9.75	17154	.00006	8 577.1	8 577.1	1.00000	9.75
10.00	22026	.00005	11 013.2	11 013.2	1.00000	**10.00**
x	e^x	e^{-x}	Sinh x	Cosh x	Tanh x	x

ANSWERS, HINTS, AND SOLUTIONS
TO ODD-NUMBERED PROBLEMS

(Some answers have intentionally been omitted.)

Exercises 1.3, Pages 9–10

1. **(a)** 4, 10, undefined, 25, undefined.
   (c) $\bar{\bar{7}} = 1$.
3. $a_n = 2^n$.
5. **(a)** Valid. Multiply members of $x = 3$ by themselves.
   (c) Valid. $x^2 = 4 \Rightarrow x = 2$ or $x = -2$. In either case, $x^2 - 2x + 2 \neq 5$.
   (f) Not valid. The equation is also true for $x = -1$ with y arbitrary.
7. The implication $(y - x)^2 = 4c^2 \Rightarrow y - x = 2c$ is not valid, since the first equation is also true if $y - x = -2c$.

Exercises 1.5, Pages 16–17

1. **(a)** *Converse:* Two triangles have corresponding angles equal $\Rightarrow$ the triangles are congruent. False.
   Contrapositive: Two triangles do not have corresponding angles equal $\Rightarrow$ the triangles are not congruent. True.
   (c) *Converse:* $x^2 = 4 \Rightarrow x = 2$. False.
   Contrapositive: $x^2 \neq 4 \Rightarrow x \neq 2$. True.
3. No. If p stands for *elect A. Crook* and q for *honest government*, then the given proposition is $-p \Rightarrow -q$. This is equivalent to $q \Rightarrow p$ and is not equivalent to $p \Rightarrow q$.
5. **(a)** *Proof:* Suppose $d_1 \neq d_2$. Then, by Axiom 2, the system is not in equilibrium. This is a contradiction of the hypothesis. Consequently, $d_1 = d_2$.
7. **(a)** and **(b)** Suppose there are k distinct lines. Then there must be $\frac{1}{2}k(k - 1)$ pairs of points. However, there are 7 points giving $\frac{1}{2}(7)(6) = 21$ pairs. Thus $\frac{1}{2}k(k - 1) = 21$ and $k = 7$. Furthermore, by Axiom 2, each line must correspond to three pairs of points. If the number of points on each line is m, then $\frac{1}{2}m(m - 1) = 3$, which gives $m = 3$. The lines can easily be enumerated thus: *abc, ade, afg, cdf, bdg, bef, ceg*, and the four axioms checked.
9. True. Number the sides 1, 2, 3, . . . , n in succession. Side n and side 1 intersect in one vertex, side 1 and side 2 in a second vertex, and so on; side $n - 1$ and side n intersect in the nth vertex.
11. $\frac{1}{2}n(n - 1)$.
13. The conjecture is true. See the given reference.

Exercises 1.6, Page 22

1. (a) $\{2, 4, 6, 8, 10\}$;
   (c) $\{0, 1, 2, 3, 4, 5, 6, 7, 8, 9\}$.
3. (a) $\mathfrak{A} \not\subset \mathfrak{B}$; $\mathfrak{B} \not\subset \mathfrak{A}$; no; no.
   (e) $\mathfrak{A} \subset \mathfrak{B}$; $\mathfrak{B} \not\subset \mathfrak{A}$; yes; no.
   (c) $\mathfrak{A} \subset \mathfrak{B}$; $\mathfrak{B} \subset \mathfrak{A}$; no; no.
5. (a) No.
7. Since the empty set is a subset of every set, $\varnothing \subset \varnothing'$ and $\varnothing' \subset \varnothing$. Therefore, $\varnothing = \varnothing'$.

Exercises 1.7, Page 24

1. $\mathfrak{A} \sim \mathfrak{B}$. Let $1 \leftrightarrow 2, 3 \leftrightarrow 4, 7 \leftrightarrow 6, 9 \leftrightarrow 8$.
3. $\mathfrak{A} \sim \mathfrak{B}$. Let $3p \leftrightarrow 5p, p \in \mathfrak{N}$.
5. $\mathfrak{A} \sim \mathfrak{B}$. Let $x = \frac{1}{3}y$.
9. $\mathfrak{A} \sim \mathfrak{B}$. Let $x = \dfrac{b - a}{d - c}y + \dfrac{ad - bc}{d - c}$.

Exercises 1.8, Pages 27–28

1. (a) $\{b, c\}$.
   (g) $\varnothing$.
   (c) $\{c, d\}$.
   (i) $\{c, d\}$.
   (e) $\{c, d, e, f, g, h\}$.
   (k) $\{b, c, h\}$.
3. (a) $\{0, 1, 2, 3, 4\}$, $\{0, 1, 2, 3\}$, $\{0, 1, 2, 4\}$, $\{0, 1, 2\}$, $\{0, 2, 4\}$, $\{1, 2, 3\}$, $\{0, 2\}$, $\{1, 2\}$, $\{2\}$.
5. $\{a, b\}$, $\{b, c\}$, $\{c, a\}$.
7. $\mathfrak{A} = \{a, b, c\}$, $\mathfrak{B} = \{a, c, d\}$.

Exercises 1.9, Page 30

1. (i) Let $x \in (\mathfrak{A} \cup \mathfrak{B})'$. Then $x \notin \mathfrak{A} \cup \mathfrak{B} \Rightarrow x \notin \mathfrak{A}$ and $x \notin \mathfrak{B} \Rightarrow x \in \mathfrak{A}'$ and $x \in \mathfrak{B}' \Rightarrow x \in \mathfrak{A}' \cap \mathfrak{B}'$.
   $\therefore (\mathfrak{A} \cup \mathfrak{B})' \subset \mathfrak{A}' \cap \mathfrak{B}'$.
   Let $y \in \mathfrak{A}' \cap \mathfrak{B}'$. Then $y \in \mathfrak{A}'$ and $y \in \mathfrak{B}' \Rightarrow y \notin \mathfrak{A}$ and $y \notin \mathfrak{B} \Rightarrow y \notin \mathfrak{A} \cup \mathfrak{B} \Rightarrow y \in (\mathfrak{A} \cup \mathfrak{B})'$.
   $\therefore \mathfrak{A}' \cap \mathfrak{B}' \subset (\mathfrak{A} \cup \mathfrak{B})'$.
   Hence, $(\mathfrak{A} \cup \mathfrak{B})' = \mathfrak{A}' \cap \mathfrak{B}'$.
3. $\mathfrak{A} - \mathfrak{B} = \mathfrak{A} \cap \mathfrak{B}'$ (Theorem 1.9g).
   $(\mathfrak{A} - \mathfrak{B})' = (\mathfrak{A} \cap \mathfrak{B}')' = \mathfrak{A}' \cup \mathfrak{B}$ (Theorem 1.9h).
5. $(\mathfrak{A} \cup \mathfrak{B}) - \mathfrak{C} = (\mathfrak{A} - \mathfrak{C}) \cup (\mathfrak{B} - \mathfrak{C})$ is the only correct distributive law for set difference with respect to union or intersection. This can be shown by Venn diagrams.
7. $(\mathfrak{A} - \mathfrak{C}) - (\mathfrak{B} - \mathfrak{C}) = (\mathfrak{A} \cap \mathfrak{C}') \cap (\mathfrak{B} \cap \mathfrak{C}')' = (\mathfrak{A} \cap \mathfrak{C}') \cap (\mathfrak{B}' \cup \mathfrak{C})$
   $= [(\mathfrak{A} \cap \mathfrak{C}') \cap \mathfrak{B}'] \cup [(\mathfrak{A} \cap \mathfrak{C}') \cap \mathfrak{C}]$
   $= (\mathfrak{A} \cap \mathfrak{C}' \cap \mathfrak{B}') \cup (\mathfrak{A} \cap \mathfrak{C}' \cap \mathfrak{C})$
   $= (\mathfrak{A} \cap \mathfrak{B}' \cap \mathfrak{C}') \cup (\mathfrak{A} \cap \varnothing)$
   $= [(\mathfrak{A} \cap \mathfrak{B}') \cap \mathfrak{C}'] \cup \varnothing = (\mathfrak{A} \cap \mathfrak{B}') \cap \mathfrak{C}'$
   $= (\mathfrak{A} - \mathfrak{B}) - \mathfrak{C}$.

9. $(\mathcal{A} - \mathcal{B}) \cup (\mathcal{B} - \mathcal{A}) = (\mathcal{A} \cap \mathcal{B}') \cup (\mathcal{B} \cap \mathcal{A}')$

$$= [\mathcal{A} \cup (\mathcal{B} \cap \mathcal{A}')] \cap [\mathcal{B}' \cup (\mathcal{B} \cap \mathcal{A}')]$$
$$= [(\mathcal{A} \cup \mathcal{B}) \cap (\mathcal{A} \cup \mathcal{A}')] \cap [(\mathcal{B}' \cup \mathcal{B}) \cap (\mathcal{B}' \cup \mathcal{A}')]$$
$$= (\mathcal{A} \cup \mathcal{B}) \cap (\mathcal{B}' \cup \mathcal{A}') = (\mathcal{A} \cup \mathcal{B}) \cap (\mathcal{A} \cap \mathcal{B})'$$
$$= (\mathcal{A} \cup \mathcal{B}) - (\mathcal{A} \cap \mathcal{B}).$$

11. $\mathcal{A} - (\mathcal{B} \cup \mathcal{C}) = \mathcal{A} \cap (\mathcal{B} \cup \mathcal{C})' = \mathcal{A} \cap (\mathcal{B}' \cap \mathcal{C}')$

$$= (\mathcal{A} \cap \mathcal{B}') \cap (\mathcal{A} \cap \mathcal{C}') = (\mathcal{B}' \cap \mathcal{A}) \cap (\mathcal{C}' \cap \mathcal{A})$$
$$= (\mathcal{B}' - \mathcal{A}') \cap (\mathcal{C}' - \mathcal{A}')$$

Exercises 2.1, Pages 35–36

1. Yes. Yes. No.   **3.** Neither.

5. Since m cannot be divisible by any of the first n primes, it either has a prime factor greater than p_n or is itself a prime greater than p_n. Hence p_n cannot be the greatest prime.

Exercises 2.2, Pages 39–41

13. (a) False.   **(b)** True for $r \neq 1$.   **(c)** False.

19. No.

21. $u_1 = 1 < \frac{7}{4}$ and $u_2 = 2 < (\frac{7}{4})^2$. Assume $u_k < (\frac{7}{4})^k$, $k = 3, 4, \ldots, n - 1$. Then
$$u_n = u_{n-1} + u_{n-2} < (\frac{7}{4})^{n-1} + (\frac{7}{4})^{n-2} = (\frac{7}{4})^{n-2}(1 + \frac{7}{4}), \; 1 + \frac{7}{4} = \frac{11}{4} < (\frac{7}{4})^2 = \frac{49}{16}.$$
$$\therefore \; u_n < (\frac{7}{4})^{n-2}(\frac{7}{4})^2 = (\frac{7}{4})^n.$$

This completes the proof by induction.

23. Let $P(n)$ be the proposition that $p(1), p(2), \ldots, p(n)$ are all true. Then apply Theorem 2.2a.

25. (a) $\frac{1}{6}n(n + 1)(n + 2)$.

Exercises 2.3, Page 45

1. $1 + 0 = 1 \Rightarrow x \cdot (1 + 0) = x \cdot 1 \Rightarrow x \cdot 1 + x \cdot 0 = x \cdot 1 \Rightarrow x \cdot 0 = 0.$

3. $(-x)[y + (-y)] = (-x) \cdot 0 = 0 \Rightarrow (-x)(y) + (-x)(-y) = 0$
$$\Rightarrow -xy + (-x)(-y) = 0$$
$$\Rightarrow (-x)(-y) \text{ is the additive inverse of } -xy$$
$$\Rightarrow (-x)(-y) = xy.$$

5. Let $p .=. a - b$. Then, $a = b + p$ and
$$a + (-b) = b + p + (-b) = p + b + (-b) = p \Rightarrow a + (-b) = a - b.$$

7. The Distributive Law.

Exercises 2.4, Pages 49–50

1. Since $\mathfrak{N}$ is not closed under subtraction, subtraction is not a binary operation on $\mathfrak{N}$. Since $\mathcal{I}$ is closed under subtraction, subtraction is a binary operation on $\mathcal{I}$.

3. No. The set $\mathcal{S}$ is not closed under either of the operations. Thus,
$$\{b\} \cup \{c, d\} = \{b, c, d\} \notin \mathcal{S} \quad \text{and} \quad \{a\} \cap \{b\} = \phi \notin \mathcal{S}.$$

5. The set has both the commutative and the associative property under this operation. The symmetry of the table with respect to the diagonal from upper left to lower right corner shows the commutativity. To show the asscciativity, show that $x * (y * z) = (x * y) * z$ for every x, y, z. The set is a group under the operation. The identity element is c, and $a^{-1} = b$, $b^{-1} = a$, $c^{-1} = c$.

7. Yes.

9. No. Neither 2 nor 3 have inverses with respect to multiplication modulo 6.

Exercises 2.5, Pages 54–55

1. $x = ab^{-1} \Rightarrow 1 \cdot x = 1 \cdot (ab^{-1}) = (1 \cdot a)b^{-1} = ab^{-1} = x.$

3. $0 \cdot x = 0 \cdot (ab^{-1}) = (0 \cdot a)b^{-1} = 0 \cdot b^{-1} = 0$ (Number 2).

5. $a^{-1} + (-a^{-1}) = 0 \Rightarrow a \cdot [a^{-1} + (-a^{-1})] = 0 \Rightarrow a \cdot a^{-1} + a \cdot (-a^{-1}) = 0$
$\Rightarrow 1 + a \cdot (-a^{-1}) = 0 \Rightarrow a \cdot (-a^{-1}) = -1$
$\Rightarrow (-1)[a \cdot (-a^{-1})] = 1 \Rightarrow (-a)(-a^{-1}) = 1$
$\Rightarrow (-a)^{-1} = -a^{-1}.$

7. $(ab^{-1})(cd^{-1}) = (ac)(b^{-1}d^{-1}),$
$(b^{-1}d^{-1})(bd) = (b^{-1}b)(d^{-1}d) = 1 \Rightarrow b^{-1}d^{-1} = (bd)^{-1}.$
$\therefore (ab^{-1})(cd^{-1}) = (ac)(bd)^{-1}.$

9. Yes.

11. Yes. This is shown by making tables of the two operations.

13. *Hint:* $(a + b\theta)^{-1} = \dfrac{a - b\theta}{a^2 - 2b^2}.$

Exercises 2.6, Pages 59–60

1. Assume $(a/b)^2 = 3$, a and b have no common factor. Then $a^2 = 3b^2 \Rightarrow a = 3c$ since only multiples of 3 have squares that are multiples of 3, and
$$9c^2 = 3b^2 \Rightarrow 3c^2 = b^2 \Rightarrow b = 3d \Rightarrow a, b$$
have 3 as a common factor. This is a contradiction.

3. No. For example, $\sqrt{2} + (3 - \sqrt{2}) = 3$ and $(1 + \sqrt{2})(1 - \sqrt{2}) = -1.$

5. $\frac{2198}{999}.$ **13.** $0.\overline{64705\ 88235\ 294\ 117}.$

7. $\frac{130}{199}.$ **15.** $0.\overline{9900}.$

9. $\frac{367}{3333}.$ **17.** $0.\overline{6}.$

11. $0.\overline{571428}$

19. No. For instance, $(\sqrt{2} + \sqrt{3})(\sqrt{2} - \sqrt{3}) = -1$, which is not of the form $a\sqrt{2} + b\sqrt{3}$, $a, b \in \mathfrak{F}.$

21. $S \subset \mathfrak{F}$. l.u.b. $= \frac{3}{2} \in \mathfrak{F}.$ **23.** $S \subset \mathfrak{F}$. l.u.b. $= \sqrt{5} \in \mathcal{R}_i.$

Exercises 2.7, Pages 64–65

7. $-1 + 9i$.

9. $11 + 2i$.

11. $x^2 + y^2$.

13. $2 - 2i$.

15. $-\frac{1}{25} + \frac{32}{25}i$.

17. $-\frac{7}{25} + \frac{24}{25}i$.

19. $2i$.

21. $\frac{42}{29} - \frac{40}{29}i$.

Exercises 3.1, Pages 69–70

1. $a^8 b^{13}$.

3. $a^{15} b^{25} c^{14}$.

5. $a^{3n} b^{n+2} c^{7n}$.

7. $a^3 - a^2 b - ab^2 + b^3$.

9. $x^4 - 2x^2 y^2 + y^4$.

11. $a^3 - 3ab - b^3 - 1$.

13. $x^{2n+2} - x^{2n} y^{2n} + 2x^{n+1} y^{n+1} + y^{2n+2}$.

15. $1 + x^2 - x^3 - x^5$.

17. $a^2 + b^2 + c^2 - 2ab + 2ac - 2bc$.

21. 0.

23. 0.

Exercises 3.2, Pages 73–74

1. $(2x - 3)(2x + 3)$.

3. $(2a - 3b^2)(4a^2 + 6ab^2 + 9b^4)$.

5. $(2x^2 - 2xy + y^2)(2x^2 + 2xy + y^2)$.

7. $(x - 5)(x - 2)$.

9. $(2x - y)(2x + y)(4x^2 + y^2)$.

11. $x^3(3x + 2yz^2)(9x^2 - 6xyz^2 + 4y^2 z^4)$.

13. $(2x - 3y)^2$.

15. $(x - \sqrt{3})(x + \sqrt{3})$.

17. $(x - \sqrt{3})^2$.

19. $x(x^2 + 9)$.

21. $(z^2 + z\sqrt{2} + 2)(z^2 - z\sqrt{2} + 2)$.

23. $(x + 2)(x - \sqrt{2})(x + \sqrt{2})$.

25. $(x + 2y)(x^2 - 2xy + 4y^2)$.

27. $(x + iy)(x - iy)$.

29. $(a - 3i)(a - 2i)$.

31. $(a + ib\sqrt{5})(a - ib\sqrt{5})$.

33. $(2x + 3i)(x - 2i)$.

35. $a(a + i\sqrt{3})(a - i\sqrt{3})$.

37. $(b + i\sqrt{2})(b - i\sqrt{2})(b - 1)$.

39. $(3^n + 1)^2$.

41. $(2x + y^k)(x - y^k)$.

43. $9(a - b + 2)(a + b - 2)$.

45. $(1 - y)(x + y + 1)$.

47. $(a - b)(x + y - 1)$.

49. $(a - 1)(a + 1)(b - c)(b + c)$.

51. $(x - a)(x - b)[x^2 + (a - b + 1)x - ab + b]$.

53. $(a + 3b)^2$.

55. $(a + b + 3)(a + b - 2)$.

57. $(y - x)(y - x + 2)$.

59. $(x - 2)(x + 2)(x^2 + 4)(y - 1)(y^2 + y + 1)$.

Exercises 3.3, Pages 80–82

1. $\dfrac{a + 1}{a + 3}$.

3. $\dfrac{yz}{2x - y}$.

5. $\dfrac{x - y}{x + y}$.

7. $\dfrac{x - a + b}{x + a + b}$.

9. $\dfrac{2y^3}{y^2 - 9}$.

11. $\dfrac{2a + b}{a + b}$.

13. $\dfrac{a^2 + ab - b^2}{b(a^2 - b^2)}.$

15. $\dfrac{x^2 + 3x - 5}{(x - 3)(x + 2)(x - 1)}.$

17. $\dfrac{6x^2 - x + y - 3}{x(y - 3)(y + 3)}.$

19. 1.

21. $(x + 1)(x^2 + 1).$

23. $-\dfrac{x}{y}.$

25. $\dfrac{y}{x}.$

27. $\dfrac{(b - 4)(b + 1)}{b(b + 2)}.$

29. $\dfrac{b^2}{a^2 + ab + b^2}.$

31. $\dfrac{x}{x + 1}.$

33. $\dfrac{x(x^2 + y^2)}{(x - y)^2}.$

35. $1 - 2x.$

37. $\dfrac{a(2x - a)}{x}.$

39. $\dfrac{x^2 - 3x + 1}{x^2 - 4x + 1}.$

41. $\dfrac{2x}{y}.$

43. $\dfrac{x - y}{2y}.$

45. $\dfrac{2}{(y + 1)^2}.$

47. $\dfrac{1 - x^3}{2}.$

49. No.

51. $\{x : x \in \mathfrak{F} \text{ and } x > -1\}$

53. (b) No. **(c)** x. **(d)** $\dfrac{x - 1}{x}.$ **(f)** Yes.

Exercises 3.4, Pages 87–89

1. $\dfrac{b^7}{a^7}.$

2. $\dfrac{x^2 y^2}{y - x}.$

3. $\dfrac{x + y}{x^4 y^6}.$

5. $\dfrac{3 - a^2}{a^3}.$

7. $\dfrac{a^2 b^2}{b^2 - a^2}.$

9. 1.

11. $\frac{121}{500}.$

13. 2.

15. $-4.$

17. $0.008.$

19. $(2)(2^{1/6}).$

21. $ab^{1/2}.$

23. $a^{2/15} b^{1/20}.$

25. $\dfrac{b}{a}(a^{23/30}).$

27. $72(108^{1/6}).$

29. $\frac{1}{2}.$

31. $\frac{1}{4}.$

33. 0.

35. $-5\sqrt{3}.$

37. $-3\sqrt[3]{5}.$

39. $7|y|\sqrt{2}.$

41. $6xy\sqrt[3]{xy^2}.$

43. $\sqrt{6} + 3\sqrt{2}.$

45. $\frac{1}{6}\sqrt[3]{18}.$

47. $-6 - 4\sqrt[3]{12} + 3\sqrt[3]{18}.$

49. $xy(\sqrt{x} + \sqrt{y}).$

51. $5\sqrt[4]{5}.$

53. $2\sqrt[6]{2}.$

55. $-\frac{1}{3}(5\sqrt{2} + 4\sqrt{5}).$

57. $5\sqrt{6} - 12.$

59. $2\sqrt{18 + 6\sqrt{3}}.$

61. $2^{13}.$

63. $\frac{1}{7}(1 + i4\sqrt{3}).$

65. 1 if $a > b$, -1 if $a < b$.

69. (i) Let $u = a^{p/q}$, $v = a^{r/s}$. Then

$$u^q = a^p \quad \text{and} \quad v^s = a^r,$$
$$u^{qs} = a^{ps} \quad \text{and} \quad v^{qs} = a^{qr}.$$

Thus,

$$u^{qs}v^{qs} = a^{ps}a^{qr} = a^{ps+qr}$$
$$\Rightarrow (uv)^{qs} = a^{ps+qr}$$
$$\Rightarrow uv = a^{(ps+qr)/qs}$$
$$\Rightarrow a^{p/q}a^{r/s} = a^{(ps+qr)/qs}.$$

The proofs of (ii) and (iii) are similar to this.

71. *Hint:* $\theta^6 - 1 = 0 \Rightarrow \theta^2 + \theta + 1 = 0$ or $\theta^2 - \theta + 1 = 0$.

Exercises 3.5, Page 91

1. $x^2 + 3x + 1$.

3. $2x^2 - x + 3$.

5. $x^2 - x - 4 - \dfrac{31}{x - 4}$.

7. $4x^3 + 12x^2 + 2x - 11 - \dfrac{3}{x - 3}$.

9. $y^2 + (2 - i)y - 2i - \dfrac{1}{y + i}$.

11. $3x^2 - 4x - 6 - \dfrac{1}{2x - 3}$.

13. $3y^2 - 2a^2 + \dfrac{a^3}{y - 2a}$.

15. $2u^3 + (3 + 2\sqrt{3})u^2 + (1 + 3\sqrt{3})u + \sqrt{3} - \dfrac{4}{u - \sqrt{3}}$.

17. $2x^2 - 3x + 1 - \dfrac{2}{3x - 4}$.

Exercises 3.6, Pages 96–97

1. (a) $r(x) = 0$, $s(x) = 2x^2 - x + 3$.

   (b) $r(x) = x + 1$, $s(x) = \frac{3}{2}x + 1$.

3. $-1; -9$.

5. $152; 37$.

7. $0; 320$.

9. $-326; 4$.

11. 2 is a zero.

13. 2 is not a zero.

15. $A = 2, B = 1, C = -2$.

17. $A = 2, B = -24, C = -60, D = 83$.

19. $-1, -2$.

21. $-2, 1$.

23. $-2i, 2, -1$.

25. $2 - i, -2, 1$.

27. $-2, -2$.

29. $2 - \sqrt{3}, -2, -1$.

Exercises 3.7, Pages 103–104

1. $\{3, 4\}$.

3. $\{-2, -1, 0\}$.

5. $\{-1, 2, 3\}$.

7. $\{-\frac{5}{2}\}$.

9. $\Re - \{0, \frac{1}{2}\}$.

11. $\varnothing$.

13. $\{5\}$.

15. $\{14\}$.

17. $\{-2, 2\}$.

19. $\{x : 4 \leq x < 5\}$.

21. $\varnothing$.

23. $\{\frac{1}{4}, \frac{11}{2}\}$.

25. $\{-2, 2\}$.

27. $\{\frac{5}{2}\}$.

29. $\varnothing$.

31. $\{-\frac{27}{8}\}$.

33. $\{-\frac{1}{243}\}$.

35. Since $a = b, \dfrac{a}{c} = \dfrac{a}{c} \Rightarrow \dfrac{a}{c} = \dfrac{b}{c}$.

Since $c \neq 0, \dfrac{a}{c} = \dfrac{b}{c} \Rightarrow \dfrac{a}{c} - \dfrac{b}{c} = 0 \Rightarrow \dfrac{1}{c}(a - b) = 0 \Rightarrow a - b = 0 \Rightarrow a = b$.

37. $12\sqrt{3}$ inches, 24 inches.

39. $A = V^{2/3}$.

41. $\frac{1}{2}$ ounce short on silver, long on copper.

43. 55 mph.

Exercises 3.8, Page 108

5. *Hint:* Add corresponding members of the inequalities

$$(a - b)^2 \geqq 0, \quad (b - c)^2 \geqq 0, \quad (c - a)^2 \geqq 0.$$

7. $\sqrt{15} - \sqrt{5} > 3 - \sqrt{2}$.

9. $\sqrt{19} - \sqrt{14} < \sqrt{29} - \sqrt{22}$.

11. $a > b > 0 \Rightarrow a^2 > b^2$ (Theorem 3.8e). Assume $a^k > b^k$. Then, by Theorem 3.8e,

$$a \cdot a^k > b \cdot b^k \Rightarrow a^{k+1} > b^{k+1}.$$

This completes the proof by mathematical induction.

13. $a < b \Rightarrow b = a + p, p > 0 \Rightarrow -a = -b + p \Rightarrow -a > -b$.

15. False. Try it for $a = 1, b = 2, c = 3, d = 4$.

17. Let $a^{1/p} = x, b^{1/p} = y$. Then $a = x^p, b = y^p$,

$$a > b \Rightarrow x^p > y^p.$$

Suppose $x \leqq y$. Then $x^p \leqq y^p \Rightarrow a \leqq b$, which is a contradiction. Hence, $x > y$, as was to be shown.

19. $1 < a \Rightarrow a < a^2 \Rightarrow a^2 < a^3 \Rightarrow \cdots \Rightarrow a^{p-1} < a^p \Rightarrow a < a^p$.

$1 < a < a^p \Rightarrow 1 < a^{1/p} < a$.

21. $y = ax^2 + bx + c = a\left(x + \dfrac{b}{2a}\right)^2 + c - \dfrac{b^2}{4a}$. $y > 0$ for all $x \in \mathfrak{R} \Leftrightarrow a > 0$ and

$c - \dfrac{b^2}{4a} > 0$, or $a > 0$ and $b^2 - 4ac < 0$.

Exercises 3.9, Page 112

1. $\{x : x > \frac{5}{3}\}$.

3. $\{x : x < -\frac{9}{2}\}$.

5. $\mathfrak{R} - \mathcal{G}$.

7. $\varnothing$.

9. $\varnothing$.

11. $\{x : x \geqq 11\}$.

13. $\{y : y > 0\}$.

15. $\mathfrak{R}$.

17. Division by $x + 1$ without change of sense is valid only if $x + 1 > 0$.

19. $x_0 \in \mathcal{S}[f(x) > g(x)] \Rightarrow f(x_0) > g(x_0)$. Then

$$p(x_0) > 0 \Rightarrow f(x_0)p(x_0) > g(x_0)p(x_0)$$
$$\Rightarrow x_0 \in \mathcal{S}[f(x)p(x) > g(x)p(x)].$$

If $p(x_0) > 0$, then the order of steps may be reversed to complete the proof.

23. $25 < t < 400$.

Exercises 4.1, Pages 118–119

1. (a) $4, -4$. (c) $3, +3$. (f) $\sqrt{3} + \sqrt{6}, -\sqrt{6} - \sqrt{3}$.
5. (a) $\{x: x < -2\} \cup \{x: x > 5\}$.
   (c) $\{x: x \leq 2\} \cup \{x: x \geq 4\}$.
7. The largest number d (if there is one) such that $d \leq \sqrt{(x_1 - x_2)^2}$ for all $x_1 \in \mathcal{I}_1$ and $x_2 \in \mathcal{I}_2$ may be defined as the distance between the intervals. In this problem, the distance is 2 units.

Exercises 4.2, Pages 123–124

1. (a) The points are on a straight line.
   (b) The points are not on a straight line.
3. The quadrilateral is a parallelogram.
5. The triangle is a right triangle because the sides satisfy the Pythagorean Theorem.
7. $(4, 5), (4, -1), (-2, 7)$. 11. (a) $(\frac{1}{5}, -\frac{2}{5})$. (d) $(-7, \frac{19}{2})$.
9. $(-1, -2)$. 13. $(4, 7), (8, 1), (2, -3)$.

Exercises 4.3, Pages 128–129

1. The figure is a trapezoid and includes two right angles.
7. *DE*: $[-5, 12]$, *DF*: $[33, 56]$.
9. *Altitudes:* $[5, 1], [2, -2], [7, -1]$.
   Medians: $[1, 3], [0, 1], [1, -1]$.
11. $-\frac{20}{3}$. 13. $(-3, 0)$ and $(6, 3)$.

Exercises 4.4, Pages 131–132

1. (a) $\sqrt{30}$. (c) $\sqrt{83}$.
3. Since $(PR)^2 = (PQ)^2 + (QR)^2$, the triangle is a right triangle.
5. $(-\frac{11}{5}, -\frac{1}{5}, \frac{23}{5})$.
9. $\left(\dfrac{x_1 + x_2}{2}, \dfrac{y_1 + y_2}{2}, \dfrac{z_1 + z_2}{2}\right)$.
11. (a) $(-2, 5, 3)$. (c) $(2, 5, -3)$. (e) $(-2, -5, 3)$.
13. Two: $[0, 1, 1]$ and $[0, 1, -1]$.

Exercises 4.5, Pages 137–138

1. (a) $(6, 1)$. (d) $\sqrt{74}$. (e) $(16, -1)$. 3. 0.
5. (b) $-2i + 4j$. (d) $\sqrt{221}$. (f) $\sqrt{13} + \sqrt{17}$. (h) $3\sqrt{13} - 2\sqrt{17}$.
11. $\dfrac{5}{\sqrt{41}}i + \dfrac{4}{\sqrt{41}}j$.

13. $|\mathbf{a} + \mathbf{c}| \leq |\mathbf{a}| + |\mathbf{c}|$. Let $\mathbf{c} = \mathbf{b} - \mathbf{a}$. Then
$$|\mathbf{b}| \leq |\mathbf{a}| + |\mathbf{b} - \mathbf{a}| \Rightarrow |\mathbf{b}| - |\mathbf{a}| \leq |\mathbf{b} - \mathbf{a}|.$$
Similarly, $|\mathbf{a}| - |\mathbf{b}| \leq |\mathbf{a} - \mathbf{b}|$. Therefore, $|\mathbf{a} - \mathbf{b}| \geq ||\mathbf{a}| - |\mathbf{b}||$.

15. $\sqrt{505}$.

17. No. Another base set is $(1, 1)$, $(1, -1)$. In fact, any two nonparallel vectors may be used.

19. No. For general rotations, $\mathbf{a} + \mathbf{b} \neq \mathbf{b} + \mathbf{a}$.

Exercises 4.6, Pages 141–142

1. $\sqrt{113}$ in the direction $[8, 7]$.

3. $\sqrt{70 + 48\sqrt{2}}$ in the direction $[3\sqrt{2} + 4, -1]$.

5. 96.9 pounds, approximately in the direction $[19, -12]$.

7. $\sqrt{641}$ knots in the direction $[4, 25]$.

9. $5\sqrt{169 + 60\sqrt{2}}$ pounds in the direction $[5 + 12\sqrt{2}, 5]$.

11. $[\sqrt{17}, 1]$.   **13.** $1500\sqrt{2}$ pounds, $300\sqrt{5}$ pounds.

Exercises 5.1, Page 146

1. *Domain:* $\{1, 2, 3, 4\}$, *range:* $\{1, 2, 3\}$.

3. *Domain:* $\{1, 2, 3, 4, 5, 6, 7, 8, 9, 10\}$, *range:* $\{1, 4, 9, 16, 25, 36, 49, 64, 81, 100\}$.

5. *Domain:* $\{0, 1, 4, 9, 16, 25, 36, 49, 64, 81, 100\}$,
    range: $\{0, \pm 1, \pm 2, \pm 3, \pm 4, \pm 5, \pm 6, \pm 7, \pm 8, \pm 9, \pm 10\}$.

7. *Domain:* $\mathfrak{R}$, *range:* $\mathfrak{R}$.

9. *Domain:* $\{x: 0 \leq x \leq 2\}$, *range:* $\{y: 0 \leq y \leq 5\}$.

11. *Domain:* $\{x: 0 \leq x \leq 2\}$, *range:* $\{y: 0 \leq y \leq 4\}$.

13. *Domain:* $\{x: x = 1/n, n \in \mathfrak{N}\}$, *range:* $\mathfrak{N}$.

15. *Domain:* $\{x: -2 \leq x \leq 2\}$, *range:* $\{y: -2 \leq y \leq 2\}$.

17. *Domain:* $\mathfrak{R}$, *range:* $\mathfrak{R}$.

19. *Domain:* $\{x: 0 < x \leq 3\}$, *range:* $\{y: y > \frac{1}{2}\}$.

21. *Domain:* $\{-\frac{4}{5}, \frac{4}{5}\}$, *range:* $\{\frac{3}{5}\}$.

Exercises 5.2, Pages 148–149

1. (a) $\{(2, 3), (4, 3), (2, 5), (6, 3)\}$. (b) $2^3 = 8$.

3. *Domain:* $\mathfrak{R}$, *range:* $\mathfrak{R}$.

5. *Domain:* $\{x: -2 \leq x \leq 2\}$, *range:* $\{y: -2 \leq y \leq 0\}$.

7. *Domain:* $\mathfrak{R} - \{0\}$, *range:* $\mathfrak{R} - \{0\}$.

9. *Domain:* $\mathfrak{R} - \{2\}$, *range:* $\mathfrak{R} - \{4\}$.

11. Not a function. There are two values of y for each $x > 0$.

13. *Domain:* $\mathfrak{R}$, *range:* $\{y: y \leq 1\}$.

15. Not a function. There are two values of y for each value of $x \in \{x: -3 < x < 2\}$.

17. -1; undefined; $\dfrac{h}{1-4h}$; $\dfrac{x}{1-4x}$.

19. $2x + 2h + 3$; $\dfrac{2}{x} + 3$.   **21.** -3; -3; $\frac{27}{20}$.

Exercises 5.3, Page 154

1. *Domain:* $\{-3, -2, -1, 0, 1, 2, 3\}$, *range:* $\{0, 1, 2, 3\}$. Not a function. Symmetry with respect to the y-axis.

3. *Domain:* $\mathcal{R}$, *range:* $\mathcal{R}$. A function. Symmetry with respect to the origin.

5. *Domain:* $\{-4\}$, *range:* $\mathcal{R}$. Not a function. Symmetry with respect to the x-axis.

7. *Domain:* $\{x: x \leq 0\}$, *range:* $\mathcal{R}$. Not a function. Symmetry with respect to the x-axis.

9. *Domain:* $\mathcal{R}$, *range:* $\{y: y \leq 4\}$. A function. Symmetry with respect to the y-axis.

11. *Domain:* $\mathcal{R}$, *range:* $\{y: y \geq 0\}$. A function. Symmetry with respect to the y-axis.

13. *Domain:* $\mathcal{R}$, *range:* $\{y: y \geq 0\}$. A function. No symmetry.

15. *Domain:* $\{x: -4 \leq x \leq 4\}$, *range:* $\{y: -4 \leq y \leq 4\}$. Not a function. Symmetry with respect to both axes and the origin.

17. Satisfied by no real (x, y).

19. *Domain:* $\mathcal{R}$, *range:* $\{y: |y| \geq \sqrt{2}\}$. Not a function. Symmetry with respect to both axes and the origin.

21. *Domain:* $\mathcal{R}$, *range:* $\mathcal{R}$. Not a function. Symmetry with respect to the line $y = -x$.

23. *Domain:* $\{0\}$, *range:* $\{1\}$. A function.

25. *Domain:* $\mathcal{R}$, *range:* $\mathcal{R}$. Not a function. Symmetry with respect to the line $y = x$.

Exercises 5.4, Pages 159–160

1. *Domain:* $\mathcal{R}$, *range:* $\mathcal{I}$. No symmetry with respect to the axes or the origin.

3. *Domain:* $\{x: |x| \geq 2\}$, *range:* $\{y: y \geq 0\}$. Symmetry with respect to the y-axis.

5. *Domain:* $\mathcal{R}$, *range:* $\{y: y \geq 0\}$. No symmetry with respect to the axes or the origin.

7. *Domain:* $\mathcal{R}$, *range:* $\{y: 0 \leq y < 1\}$. No symmetry. Periodic with period 1.

9. *Domain:* $\mathcal{R}$, *range:* $\{-1, 0\}$. No symmetry with respect to the axes or the origin.

11. *Domain:* $\mathcal{R}$, *range:*
$$\{y: 0 \leq y < 1\} \cup \{y: -2 \leq y < -1\} \cup \{y: -4 \leq y < -3\} \cup \cdots$$
$$\cup \{y: -2n \leq y < -2n + 1\} \cup \cdots, \qquad n = 1, 2, 3, \ldots.$$
No symmetry.

13. *Domain:* $\mathcal{R}$, *range:* $\{-1, 0, 1\}$. Symmetry with respect to the origin.

15. *Domain:* $\mathcal{R}$, *range:* $\{y: 0 \leq y < 1\}$. Symmetry with respect to the y-axis.

17. *Domain:* $\mathcal{R}$, *range:* $\{y: 0 \leq y \leq 1\}$. No symmetry with respect to the axes or the origin.

19. *Domain:* $\mathcal{R}$, *range:* $\{0, 1\}$. No symmetry with respect to the axes or the origin.

21. $L = 1000[U(x) + 2U(x - c) - 3U(x - 2c)]$.

Exercises 5.5, Pages 165–166

1. (b) All points in $\{x: 0 < x < 1\}$. **(d)** None.

3. (b) For each $k > 0$, there is an $h > 0$ such that
$$x \in \mathfrak{N}^*(2, h) \Rightarrow y \in \mathfrak{N}(4, k).$$
(e) For each $M_1 > 0$, there is an $h_1 > 0$ such that
$$x \in \mathfrak{N}^*(1^-, h_1) \Rightarrow y < -M_1,$$
and for each $M_2 > 0$, there is an $h_2 > 0$ such that
$$x \in \mathfrak{N}^*(1^+, h_2) \Rightarrow y > M_2.$$

5. $A = \frac{5}{4}, B = -2.$ **7.** $A = 12, B = 5.$ **9.** $A = 2, B = -2.$

Exercises 5.6, Pages 170–171

1. *Intercepts:* None.
    Asymptotes: x-axis, y-axis.
    Symmetry: Origin (and the lines $y = x, y = -x$.)

3. *Intercepts:* $x = 0 \Rightarrow y = -3.$
    Asymptotes: $x = 1, y = 0.$
    Symmetry: None with respect to the axes or the origin.

5. *Intercepts:* $x = 0 \Leftrightarrow y = 0.$
    Asymptotes: $y = 0.$
    Symmetry: Origin.

7. *Intercepts:* $x = 0 \Leftrightarrow y = 0.$
    Asymptotes: $x = 1, x = 3, y = -1.$
    Symmetry: None.

9. *Intercepts:* $x = 0 \Rightarrow y = \frac{1}{2}.$
    Asymptotes: $x = -2, x = 2, y = 0.$
    Symmetry: y-axis.

11. *Intercepts:* $x = 0 \Leftrightarrow y = 0.$
    Asymptotes: $x = -1, x = 1, y = 0.$
    Symmetry: Origin.

13. *Intercepts:* $x = 0 \Leftrightarrow y = 0.$
    Asymptotes: $x = 3, y = 0.$
    Symmetry: None.

15. *Intercepts:* $x = 0 \Rightarrow y = -1; y = 0 \Rightarrow x = \pm 3$
    Asymptotes: $y = 1.$
    Symmetry: y-axis.

17. *Intercepts:* $x = 0 \Rightarrow y = -\frac{4}{9}; y = 0 \Rightarrow x = \pm 2.$
    Asymptotes: $y = -1, x = 3, x = -3.$
    Symmetry: y-axis.

19. *Intercepts:* $x = 0 \Rightarrow y = \frac{1}{2}.$
    Asymptotes: $x = -2, y = 0.$
    Symmetry: None.
    Note that y is undefined at $x = 2.$

21. *Intercepts:* $x = 0 \Leftrightarrow y = 0$.
  Asymptotes: $y = 1, x = -1$.
  Symmetry: None.
23. *Intercepts:* $x = 0 \Rightarrow y = \pm\frac{2}{3}$.
  Asymptotes: $y = 0$.
  Symmetry: x-axis, y-axis, origin.
25. *Intercepts:* None.
  Asymptotes: $x = 0$, $y = \frac{1}{3}x$.
  Symmetry: Origin.
  Note that for x very large $1/(2x)$ is negligible and $y = \frac{1}{3}x$, approximately. This
  leads to the oblique asymptote.
27. $h = (2/r)\sqrt{4 - 2r^2}, 0 < r \leq \sqrt{2}$.
  Intercepts: $h = 0 \Rightarrow r = \sqrt{2}$.
  Asymptotes: $r = 0$ (upper portion).
  Symmetry: None.

Exercises 5.7, Pages 174–176

1. (a) $f^{-1} = \{(10, 1), (20, 2), (30, 3)\}$.
  (c) The inverse relation is $\{(1, 2), (3, 4), (5, 6), (1, 8), (2, 10)\}$. Since there are two
  distinct pairs, $(1, 2)$ and $(1, 8)$, with the same first number, the inverse relation
  is not a function.
  (f) $G^{-1} = \{(x, \sqrt{-x}), x \leq 0\}$.
  (h) $F^{-1} = \{(u, v): v = 1 - \frac{1}{2}u\}$.
3. $f = \{(x, y): y = f(x)\} \Rightarrow f^{-1} = \{(y, x): y = f(x)\}$
$$\Rightarrow (f^{-1})^{-1} = \{(x, y): y = f(x)\} = f.$$
5. (a) Let $f(y) = y - (1/y), y \neq 0$, and $g(x) = \sqrt{x}, x > 0$. Then $h(x) = f[g(x)]$,
  $x > 0$.
  (b) Let $f(y) = \sqrt{y}, y \geq 0$, and $g(x) = x/(x - 1), x \leq 0$ or $x > 1$. Then
$$h(x) = f[g(x)], \qquad x \leq 0 \text{ or } x > 1.$$
7. (a) $y = \dfrac{x - 1}{x + 1} \Rightarrow x = \dfrac{y + 1}{1 - y}, x \neq -1, y \neq 1$.
$$\therefore f(x) = \frac{x - 1}{x + 1} \Rightarrow f^{-1}(y) = \frac{y + 1}{1 - y}.$$
$$f[f^{-1}(x)] = \frac{\dfrac{x + 1}{1 - x} - 1}{\dfrac{x + 1}{1 - x} + 1} = \frac{x + 1 - 1 + x}{x + 1 + 1 - x} = x, x \neq \pm 1.$$
  (b) Let $\mathcal{D}_f$ be the domain and $\mathcal{R}_f$ the range of f. Then $f[f^{-1}(x)] = x$ for $x \in \mathcal{R}_f$,
  and $f^{-1}[f(y)] = y$ for $y \in \mathcal{D}_f$. Hence, $f[f^{-1}(x)] = f^{-1}[f(x)]$ for $x \in \mathcal{D}_f \cap \mathcal{R}_f$.
9. (a) $[f(x)]^n = f(nx)$. Let $u = f(x) \Rightarrow x = f^{-1}(u)$. Then
$$u^n = f[nf^{-1}(u)] \Rightarrow f^{-1}(u^n) = nf^{-1}(u).$$

11. $f[g(x)] = \sqrt{x^2 - 4}$, $|x| \geq 2$.

For f, the domain is $\{x: x \geq 1\}$ and the range is $\{y: y \geq 0\}$. For g, the domain is $\{x: x \in \mathcal{R}\}$ and the range is $\{y: y \geq -3\}$. For $f(g)$, the domain is $|x| \geq 2$ and the range is $\{y: y \geq 0\}$.

13. $f(xy) = f(x) + f(y)$.

$y = 1 \Rightarrow f(x) = f(x) + f(1) \Rightarrow f(1) = 0$.

$x = 2, y = 2 \Rightarrow f(4) = f(2) + f(2) = 1 + 1 = 2$.

$x = 4, y = 2 \Rightarrow f(8) = f(4) + f(2) = 2 + 1 = 3$

$\Rightarrow f^{-1}(3) = 8$.

Exercises 6.1, Pages 182–183

1. (a) $2x + 3y = 5$. (c) $x - y = 1$. (e) $3y = 4x - 12$.

3. $(\frac{7}{8}, 0)$.

5. $(y_2 - y_1)x - (x_2 - x_1)y = x_1 y_2 - x_2 y_1$.

7. $(\frac{35}{13}, \frac{33}{13})$.   **11.** $x - x_0 = k(y - y_0)$.

9. $2y = 3x + 2$.   **13.** $x = 4t + 2$, $y = -t + 3$.

15. No. If the line did pass through $(14, 2)$, there would be a value of t such that $14 = 5 - 3t$ and $2 = -3 + 2t$. But the first of these gives $t = -3$ and the second $t = \frac{5}{2}$.

17. $(3, -3)$.   **19.** $(-2, -4)$.

21. Direction numbers of $ax + by = c_1$ are $[b, -a]$, and of $bx - ay = c_2$ are $[a, b]$. Since $(a)(b) + (b)(-a) = 0$, the lines are perpendicular.

Exercises 6.2, Pages 185–186

1. (a) $m = \frac{2}{3}, b = \frac{7}{3}$. (c) $m = -30, b = 60$. (f) $m = -\frac{3}{2}, b = 12$.

3. (a) $m = -\frac{7}{5}, a = \frac{11}{7}, b = \frac{11}{5}$. (c) $m = 1, a = -1, b = 1$.

5. No. The equation of the line is $y = -4x + 2$, which is not satisfied by $(100, -392)$.

7. $\frac{4}{5}\sqrt{5}$. *Hint:* Draw a figure and use the similar right triangles.

9. $(-\frac{25}{11}, \frac{7}{11})$.   **13.** Yes.

11. $(1, \frac{4}{3})$.   **15.** Yes. $3x + 2y = 22$.

17. $F = 40x$, where x is the number of inches and F the number of pounds.

Exercises 6.3, Page 189

1. $\{-\frac{7}{2}, \frac{7}{2}\}$.   **5.** $\{x: x < \frac{5}{2}\}$.   **9.** $\emptyset$.

3. $\{x: 1 < x < 3\}$.   **7.** $\emptyset$.   **11.** $\{x: 0 < x < 2\}$.

Exercises 6.4, Pages 193–194

1. $\{-1 + i, -1 - i\}$.

3. $\left\{\dfrac{3 + \sqrt{41}}{8}, \dfrac{3 - \sqrt{41}}{8}\right\}$.

5. $\{-p + \sqrt{p^2 - q}, -p - \sqrt{p^2 - q}\}$.

7. $\{-\sqrt{3}\}$; $-\sqrt{3}$ is a double root.

9. $\left\{\dfrac{-1 + \sqrt{321}}{400}, \dfrac{-1 - \sqrt{321}}{400}\right\}$.

11. $-\dfrac{b}{a}$.

15. $x = -\frac{1}{2}, -4$.

17. $\{-1 + i, -1 - i, -1 + \sqrt{2}, -1 - \sqrt{2}\}$.

19. $x = -2, 1$.

21. $x = 16$.

23. *Hint:* Solve for $\dot{x}$.

25. $\pm 8\sqrt{2}$.

27. $3y = x^2 + 6x + 15$.

29. $\frac{1}{2}(1 + i\sqrt{3})$ or $\frac{1}{2}(1 - i\sqrt{3})$.

31. 15 (inches)^2.

Exercises 6.5, Page 196

1. $\{x: x < -1\} \cup \{x: x > 3\}$.

3. $\{w: -\frac{1}{2} \leqq w \leqq 2\}$.

5. $\{x: x < 2\} \cup \{x: x > \frac{5}{2}\}$.

7. $\{x: -3 < x < -2\}$.

9. $\varnothing$.

11. $\{x: -\frac{3}{2} \leqq x < 3\}$.

13. $\left\{x: x \leqq \dfrac{1 - \sqrt{13}}{2}\right\} \cup \left\{x: \dfrac{1 - \sqrt{5}}{2} \leqq x \leqq \dfrac{1 + \sqrt{5}}{2}\right\} \cup \left\{x: x \geqq \dfrac{1 + \sqrt{13}}{2}\right\}$.

15. $\{x: -2 < x < 0\} \cup \{x: x > 1\}$.

17. $3 < x < 3.5$.

19. $\{x: x < -1\} \cup \{x: x > 3\}$.

21. $0 < R_1 \leqq 2$ or $8 \leqq R_1 < 10$.

Exercises 6.6, Page 201

1. Parabola; vertex at origin; axis, $x = 0$; opens downward.

3. Circle; center at origin; radius $\frac{3}{2}$.

5. Two straight lines: $y = \pm\frac{1}{2}x$.

7. Parabola; vertex at $(1, 2)$; axis, $x = 1$; opens upward.

9. Parabola; vertex at $(-3, 2)$; axis, $y = 2$; opens to the left.

11. Ellipse; intercepts $(0, 3)$, $(0, -3)$, $(2, 0)$, $(-2, 0)$.

13. Hyperbola in second and fourth quadrants; asymptotes, $x = 0$, $y = 0$.

15. No graph since equation is satisfied by no real values of (x, y).

17. $x^2 + y^2 = 17$.

19. Two: $y = 4x^2 + 8x$, $16x = y^2 + 8y$.

21. $h = 18\frac{3}{4}$ feet.

23. The line is tangent to the parabola. Tangents to curves are discussed in Chapter 9.

Exercises 6.7, Pages 205–206

1. $y + 1 = m(x - 3)$.

3. $3x + 2y = c$.

5. $y = mx + m$.

7. All have the same y-intercept, 3.

9. All pass through the point $(6, -6)$.

11. Since the equation is linear, it is that of a straight line. Also
$$aL_1(x_1, y_1) + bL_2(x_1, y_1) = a \cdot 0 + b \cdot 0 = 0.$$
Hence, every line passes through (x_1, y_1).

13. They all have a common axis of length 4 units along the x-axis.

15. (a) The vertices are all at the origin. All have the y-axis for axis.

(c) The vertices are all on the x-axis. The parabolas all open up and have exactly the same shape.

(e) The line $y = -1$ is the common axis for the entire family.

Exercises 7.1, Pages 209–210

1. (a) $\frac{3}{4}\pi$. (b) $\frac{19}{12}\pi$.   **3.** 600π radians/minute.

5. (a) $425°, -295°$. (c) $245°, -475°$.

7. (a) $\frac{16}{3}\pi$ (inches)^2. (c) $\frac{104}{9}\pi$ (inches)^2. (e) $\frac{16}{3}\pi$ (inches)^2.

9. The 95¢ piece is a better buy.   **11.** Yes.

Exercises 7.2, Page 217

1. $\cos \frac{1}{4}\pi = 1/\sqrt{2}$, $\sin \frac{1}{4}\pi = 1/\sqrt{2}$, $\tan \frac{1}{4}\pi = 1$.

3. $\cos \frac{4}{3}\pi = -\frac{1}{2}$, $\sin \frac{4}{3}\pi = -\sqrt{3}/2$, $\tan \frac{4}{3}\pi = \sqrt{3}$.

5. $\cos \frac{13}{4}\pi = -1/\sqrt{2}$, $\sin \frac{13}{4}\pi = -1/\sqrt{2}$, $\tan \frac{13}{4}\pi = 1$.

7. $\cos \frac{7}{4}\pi = 1/\sqrt{2}$, $\sin \frac{7}{4}\pi = -1/\sqrt{2}$, $\tan \frac{7}{4}\pi = -1$.

9. $\cos 4\pi = 1$, $\sin 4\pi = 0$, $\tan 4\pi = 0$.

11. $\cos(-\frac{3}{2}\pi) = 0$, $\sin(-\frac{3}{2}\pi) = 1$, $\tan(-\frac{3}{2}\pi)$ is undefined.

13. $\cos \frac{5}{12}\pi = \sin \frac{1}{12}\pi$, $\sin \frac{5}{12}\pi = \cos \frac{1}{12}\pi$, $\tan \frac{5}{12}\pi = \cot \frac{1}{12}\pi$.

15. $\cos(-\frac{1}{7}\pi) = \cos \frac{1}{7}\pi$, $\sin(-\frac{1}{7}\pi) = -\sin \frac{1}{7}\pi$, $\tan(-\frac{1}{7}\pi) = -\tan \frac{1}{7}\pi$.

17. $\cos \frac{10}{7}\pi = -\sin \frac{1}{14}\pi$, $\sin \frac{10}{7}\pi = -\cos \frac{1}{14}\pi$, $\tan \frac{10}{7}\pi = \cot \frac{1}{14}\pi$.

33. Area triangle $OAD <$ Area sector $OAC <$ Area triangle OPC
$$\Rightarrow \tfrac{1}{2}r^2 \cos\theta \sin\theta < \tfrac{1}{2}r^2\theta \quad < \tfrac{1}{2}r^2 \tan\theta, \, 0 < \theta < \tfrac{1}{2}\pi.$$
$$\Rightarrow \qquad \cos\theta < \theta/\sin\theta < \sec\theta, \, 0 < \theta < \tfrac{1}{2}\pi.$$

Exercises 7.3, Pages 222–223

1. $A = 55°$, $a = 5.71$, $c = 6.97$.

3. $C = 90°$, $a = 5.30$, $b = 2.82$.

5. $C = 110°$, $a = 3.16$, $b = 1.59$.

7. $A = 27°55'$, $C = 130°5'$, $c = 8.17$.
$A' = 152°5'$, $C' = 5°55'$, $c' = 1.10$.

9. $A = 12°49.1'$, $B = 152°10.9'$, $b = 12.626$.

11. $A = 46°34'$, $B = 57°54.6'$, $C = 75°31.6'$.

13. $A = 53°8'$, $B = 89°52'$, $c = 3.009$.

15. $x + \sqrt{3}y + 3 = 0$.   **17.** $30°, 150°$.

19. 51.55 pounds inclined at an angle of $88°4'$ to the x-axis.

21. 14.83 pounds inclined at an angle of $155°44'$ to the x-axis.

23. 272.4 mph.

25. The angle from the 50-pound force to the 75-pound force is $96°54'$; from the 75-pound force to the 85-pound force, $144°16'$; from the 85-pound force to the 50-pound force, $118°50'$.

Exercises 7.4, Page 226

Note that $n = 0, \pm1, \pm2, \pm3, \ldots$ throughout this set of answers.

15. $\frac{1}{6}(2n + 1)\pi$.

17. $\frac{1}{8}(4n + 1)\pi$.

19. $\frac{1}{6}(6n + 1)\pi$.

21. $\frac{1}{3}(3n \pm 1)\pi$.

23. No real roots.

25. No real roots.

27. $n\pi, \frac{1}{4}(4n + 1)\pi$.

29. $n\pi + (-1)^{n+1}\frac{1}{3}\pi, \frac{1}{2}(4n + 3)\pi$.

Exercises 7.5, Pages 230–232

1. $\frac{1}{4}(\sqrt{2} + \sqrt{6})$.

3. $-2 - \sqrt{3}$.

5. $\frac{1}{4}(\sqrt{2} - \sqrt{6})$.

7. $\dfrac{\cot A \cot B - 1}{\cot A + \cot B}$.

9. $\cos A \cos B \cos C - \sin A \sin B \cos C - \sin A \cos B \sin C - \cos A \sin B \sin C$.

25. (a) $\frac{33}{65}$. (c) $\frac{33}{56}$.

27. $\frac{1}{4}(2n + 1)\pi$.

29. $n\pi, \frac{1}{4}(4n + 3)\pi$.

31. $13°17' + n \cdot 360°, -119°33' + n \cdot 360°$.

Exercises 7.6, Pages 235–236

1. $\sin 3A = 3 \sin A - 4 \sin^3 A$.

3. (a) $\frac{1}{2}\sqrt{2 + \sqrt{2}}$.

5. $\tan B$.

21. Yes.

23. $\frac{1}{8}[4n - 1 - (-1)^n]\pi$.

25. $2n\pi, \frac{1}{2}(2n + 1)\pi$.

27. No roots.

29. $\frac{1}{2}(4n + 3)\pi$.

31. $2n\pi \pm \frac{1}{6}\pi$.

33. $x = b\sqrt{\dfrac{h + b}{h - b}}$ for $h > b$. There is no solution for $h \leq b$.

Exercises 7.7, Page 241

1. $z_1 = x_1 + iy_1, z_2 = x_2 + iy_2 \Rightarrow \bar{z}_1 = x_1 - iy_1, \bar{z}_2 = x_2 - iy_2$.

$$\overline{z_1 + z_2} = \overline{x_1 + iy_1 + x_2 + iy_2} = \overline{x_1 + x_2 + i(y_1 + y_2)}$$
$$= x_1 + x_2 - i(y_1 + y_2) = (x_1 - iy_1) + (x_2 - iy_2)$$
$$= \bar{z}_1 + \bar{z}_2.$$

3. This is essentially equivalent to the geometric theorem that the sum of the lengths of two sides of a triangle is greater than the length of the third side.

5. Let $z_1 = z_2 z_3 w$. By Number 4, $|z_1| = |z_2||z_3||w|$. Hence, $|w| = \left|\dfrac{z_1}{z_2 z_3}\right| = \dfrac{|z_1|}{|z_2||z_3|}$.

7. $3 + i3\sqrt{3}$.

9. $\dfrac{1}{128} + i\dfrac{\sqrt{3}}{128}$.

11. $-\dfrac{1}{2} - i\dfrac{\sqrt{3}}{2}$.

13. $\dfrac{1}{32} - i\dfrac{\sqrt{3}}{32}$.

15. $-\dfrac{1}{2} + i\dfrac{\sqrt{3}}{2}$.

Exercises 8.1, Pages 247–248

1. (a) $h \leq \frac{1}{50}$ will suffice. (b) $h \leq \frac{1}{500}$ will suffice. (c) $h \leq$ the smaller of $\frac{1}{5}\epsilon$ and 1 will suffice.

3. (a) $h \leq 0.6$ will suffice. (b) $h \leq 0.06$ will suffice. (c) $h \leq$ the smaller of 6ϵ and 1 will suffice.

5. Suppose such an h exists. Then
$$x \in \mathfrak{N}^*(0^-, h) \Rightarrow f(x) \in \mathfrak{N}(1, \tfrac{1}{10}),$$
or
$$-h < x < 0 \Rightarrow |x^3 - 1| < \tfrac{1}{10}.$$
Let $x = -a$, where $-h < -a < 0$. Then
$$|-a^3 - 1| < \tfrac{1}{10} \quad \text{or} \quad a^3 + 1 < \tfrac{1}{10},$$
which is impossible for $a > 0$.

7. (a) $h \leq 0.01$, $h \leq 10^{-6}$, $h \leq \epsilon^2$.

9. (a) No. If there were such an h for each ϵ, then
$$x \in \mathfrak{N}^*(0^-, h) \Rightarrow y \in \mathfrak{N}(\tfrac{1}{2}, \epsilon),$$
or
$$-h < x < 0 \Rightarrow \tfrac{1}{2} - \epsilon < y < \tfrac{1}{2} + \epsilon.$$
But $y = |x| = -x$, so $\tfrac{1}{2} - \epsilon < -x < \tfrac{1}{2} + \epsilon$. Suppose $\epsilon = \tfrac{1}{10}$, then
$$0.4 < -x < 0.6, \quad \text{or} \quad -0.6 < x < -0.4.$$
This means that values such that $-0.4 < x < 0$ are excluded, which contradicts $x \in \mathfrak{N}^*(0^-, h)$. The graph shows that $y \to 0$ (not $\tfrac{1}{2}$) as $x \to 0^-$.

(b) Yes. Take $h \leq$ the smaller of ϵ and 1.

Exercises 8.2, Pages 252–253

1. $|x^2 - x + 1 - 3| = |x^2 - x - 2| = |x - 2||x + 1|$.
$$|x - 2| < h \Rightarrow 2 - h < x < 2 + h.$$
If $h < 1$, then $1 < x < 3 \Rightarrow 2 < x + 1 < 4$. Thus, $|x - 2||x + 1| < 4|x - 2|$, and
$$4|x - 2| < \epsilon \Rightarrow |x - 2| < \tfrac{1}{4}\epsilon.$$
Therefore, for $h = \min(\tfrac{1}{4}\epsilon, 1)$,
$$x \in N^*(2, h) \Rightarrow (x^2 - x + 1) \in N(3, \epsilon),$$
so that $\lim_{x \to 2} (x^2 - x + 1) = 3$.

3. $|x^3 - 2x^2 + x - 2| = |x - 2|(x^2 + 1)$.
$$|x - 2| < h \Rightarrow 2 - h < x < 2 + h.$$
If $h < 1$, then $1 < x < 3 \Rightarrow 2 < x^2 + 1 < 10$. Thus, $|x - 2||x^2 + 1| < 10|x - 2|$, and
$$10|x - 2| < \epsilon \Rightarrow |x - 2| < \tfrac{1}{10}\epsilon.$$

Therefore, for $h = \min\left(\frac{1}{10}\epsilon, 1\right)$,
$$x \in \mathfrak{N}^*(2, h) \Rightarrow (x^3 - 2x^2 + x) \in \mathfrak{N}(2, \epsilon),$$
so that $\lim_{x \to 2}(x^3 - 2x^2 + x) = 2$.

5. Take $h = \epsilon$.

7. *Hint:* For $x \neq 3$, $\dfrac{x^2 - 9}{x - 3} = x + 3$.

9. $\dfrac{x - 2}{x^2 + 2x - 8} = \dfrac{1}{x + 4}$ for $x \neq 2$.

$$\left|\frac{1}{x + 4} - \frac{1}{6}\right| = \frac{|x - 2|}{6|x + 4|}.$$

$$|x - 2| < h \Rightarrow 2 - h < x < 2 + h.$$

If $h < 1$, then $1 < x < 3 \Rightarrow 5 < x + 4 < 7$. Thus, $\dfrac{|x - 2|}{6|x + 4|} < \dfrac{|x - 2|}{30}$, and

$$\frac{|x - 2|}{30} < \epsilon \Rightarrow |x - 2| < 30\epsilon.$$

Therefore, for $h = \min(30\epsilon, 1)$,

$$x \in \mathfrak{N}^*(2, h) \Rightarrow \frac{x - 2}{x^2 + 2x - 8} \in \mathfrak{N}(\tfrac{1}{6}, \epsilon),$$

so that $\lim_{x \to 2} \dfrac{x - 2}{x^2 + 2x - 8} = \tfrac{1}{6}$.

11. $\lim_{x \to 0^-} \dfrac{x}{|x|} = -1$, $\lim_{x \to 0^+} \dfrac{x}{|x|} = 1$. Since these are not equal, $\lim_{x \to 0} \dfrac{x}{|x|}$ does not exist.

13. $\lim_{x \to 0} \dfrac{|x|}{x^2} = \lim_{x \to 0} \dfrac{1}{|x|}$, which does not exist since $\dfrac{1}{|x|} \to \infty$ as $x \to 0$.

15. $\left|\sin \dfrac{1}{x}\right| \leq 1 \Rightarrow \left|x \sin \dfrac{1}{x}\right| \leq |x|$. Since $|x| \to 0$ as $x \to 0$, $\lim_{x \to 0} x \sin \dfrac{1}{x} = 0$.

17. No. For $0 < x - 2 < h$, we have $\sqrt{x - 2} < \sqrt{h}$ and $\dfrac{1}{\sqrt{x - 2}} > \dfrac{1}{\sqrt{h}} \to \infty$ as $h \to 0$.

Exercises 8.3, Pages 259–260

1. -6.   **3.** -4.

5. The absolute value of the fraction $\to \infty$ as $x \to \infty$.

7. $\tfrac{3}{2}$.

9. The limit from the left is -3. What is it from the right?

11. 0.   **13.** 0.

15. *Hint:* Multiply by $\dfrac{\sqrt{x^2 + 1} + x}{\sqrt{x^2 + 1} + x}$.

17. -1.

19. $\lim_{x \to a} f(x) = A \Rightarrow$ corresponding to each ϵ_1, there is an $h > 0$ such that
$$|f(x) - A| < \epsilon_1 \text{ for } |x - a| < h.$$
Also, $|cf(x) - cA| = |c||f(x) - A| < |c|\epsilon_1$ for $|x - a| < h$, and $c \neq 0$. Therefore, the choice $\epsilon_1 = \epsilon/|c|$ yields $|cf(x) - cA| < \epsilon$ for $|x - a| < h$.

     For $c = 0$, the theorem is trivial.

21. For each $\epsilon > 0$, there is an M such that
$$x > M \Rightarrow f(x) \in \mathfrak{N}(A, \epsilon).$$

23. $\lim_{x \to a} f_1(x) = A \Rightarrow$ corresponding to each $\epsilon > 0$, there is an h_1 such that
(1) $\qquad A - \epsilon < f_1(x) < A + \epsilon$ for $|x - a| < h_1$.
$\lim_{x \to a} f_2(x) = A \Rightarrow$ corresponding to each $\epsilon > 0$, there is an h_2 such that
(2) $\qquad A - \epsilon < f_2(x) < A + \epsilon$ for $|x - a| < h_2$.
Both (1) and (2) are true for $h = \min(h_1, h_2)$. Therefore,
$$A - \epsilon < f_1(x) < g(x) < f_2(x) < A + \epsilon,$$
or
$$|g(x) - A| < \epsilon \quad \text{for } |x - a| < h.$$
Hence, $\lim_{x \to a} g(x) = A$.

Exercises 8.4, Pages 265–266

1. Continuous everywhere except at $x = \pm 1$. The discontinuities are infinite ones.
3. Continuous everywhere.
5. Continuous except for a finite discontinuity at $x = 2$.
7. An infinite discontinuity at $x = -3$. A removable discontinuity at $x = 2$. The latter can be removed by defining $f(2) = \frac{1}{5}$. The function is otherwise continuous everywhere.
9. Continuous for $x < 1$. A removable discontinuity at $x = 1$. Can be made (one-sided) continuous there by defining $f(1) = 0$.
11. Infinite discontinuity at $t = -a$. Removable discontinuity at $t = a$. Can be made continuous at $t = a$ by defining $f(a) = 0$. Otherwise function is continuous everywhere.
13. Continuous for $t > 0$ except for a removable discontinuity at $t = 2$. The latter can be removed by defining $g(2) = 0$.
15. Continuous everywhere on $-2 \leqq x < 2$, except at $x = 0$, where there is a finite discontinuity.
17. Let $1/t = n + x$, $0 \leqq x < 1$, $n \in \mathfrak{N}$. Then $\left[\!\left[\dfrac{1}{t}\right]\!\right] = n$, $t = \dfrac{1}{n + x}$, and
$$g(t) = \left[\!\left[\dfrac{n}{n + x}\right]\!\right] = \begin{cases} 0 & \text{for } 0 < x < 1, \\ 1 & \text{for } x = 0. \end{cases}$$
Thus, there is a removable discontinuity at each integral value of x. These discontinuities can be removed by defining $g(n) = 0$ in place of $g(n) = 1$.
19. Since $\lim_{x \to a} P(x) = P(a)$ and $\lim_{x \to a} Q(x) = Q(a) \neq 0$,
$$\lim_{x \to a} \frac{P(x)}{Q(x)} = \frac{P(a)}{Q(a)}.$$
21. For $a = 0$, take $h = \epsilon^3$, since $|x| < \epsilon^3 \Rightarrow |x^{1/3}| < \epsilon$. For $a \neq 0$, proceed as follows:
$$|x^{1/3} - a^{1/3}| = \frac{|x - a|}{|x^{2/3} + a^{1/3}x^{1/3} + a^{2/3}|}.$$
If $|x - a| < h$, then $a - h < x < a + h$. For $a > 0$, let $h \leq \frac{7}{8}a$ so that $\frac{1}{8}a < x < \frac{15}{8}a$. Thus $x^{2/3} + a^{1/3}x^{1/3} + a^{2/3} > (\frac{1}{8}a)^{2/3} + a^{1/3}(\frac{1}{8}a)^{1/3} + (\frac{1}{8}a)^{2/3} = a^{2/3}$, and so $|x^{1/3} - a^{1/3}| < a^{-2/3}|x - a| < a^{-2/3}h$.

Consequently, if $h = \min(\tfrac{7}{8}a, \epsilon a^{2/3})$, then
$$x \in \mathfrak{N}(a, h) \Rightarrow y \in \mathfrak{N}(a^{1/3}, \epsilon).$$
Thus $y = x^{1/3}$ defines a continuous function for $a \geq 0$. By symmetry, the function is also continuous for $a < 0$.

23. f is continuous only if $g(b) = \lim_{x \to b^+} h(x)$.

Exercises 8.5, Pages 273–274

1. Continuous for all x.   3. Continuous for all x.

5. Continuous except at $x = 0$, where the function has a removable discontinuity.

7. Yes. Since f is continuous on the closed interval, Theorem 8.5c does apply.

9. $M = 97$.   11. $M = 1$.   13. $M = 4$.

15. (a) l.u.b. $= 1$, not attained.

 g.l.b. $= 0$, $f(1) = 0 = f(2) = f(3) = f(0)$.

 (b) l.u.b. $= 1$, $f\left(\dfrac{1}{n}\right) = 1$, $n = 1, 2, 3, \ldots$.

 g.l.b. $= 0$, $f(x) = 0$ for all $x > 1$.

17. No. A function may be discontinuous on an interval but still be bounded. Consider any function with only finite discontinuities.

19. Since for each c in the interval $\lim_{x \to c} f(x) = f(c)$ and $\lim_{x \to c} g(x) = g(c)$, then
$$\lim_{x \to c} [f(x)g(x)] = [\lim_{x \to c} f(x)][\lim_{x \to c} g(x)] = f(c)g(c).$$
Therefore, the product function is continuous at each point where both factors are continuous.

21. Simply replace $>$ with $<$ in the statement of Theorem 8.5c.
 Proof: f is continuous at $c \Rightarrow$ for each $\epsilon > 0$, there is a $\mathfrak{N}(c, h)$ such that
$$x \in \mathfrak{N}(c, h) \Rightarrow f(c) - \epsilon < f(x) < f(c) + \epsilon.$$
Choose $\epsilon = -\tfrac{1}{2}f(c)$. Then $\tfrac{3}{2}f(c) < f(x) < \tfrac{1}{2}f(c)$ for $x \in \mathfrak{N}(c, h)$. Since $f(c) < 0$, this proves the theorem.

23. No, because f is not continuous on the interval.

25. (a) False. For example, let $f(x) \doteq 1/x$, $0 < x \leq 1$, $f(0) \doteq 0$. Then f is defined on the closed interval $0 \leq x \leq 1$, but is not bounded there.

 (b) False. For example, let $f(x) \doteq x$, $0 \leq x < 1$, $f(x) \doteq x - 1$, $1 \leq x \leq \tfrac{3}{2}$. Then the l.u.b. is 1, but $f(x) = 1$ for no x in the domain.

27. Take $f(x) = x^2$, $-1 \leq x \leq 1$.

29. f is not strictly increasing (decreasing) on its entire domain. The theorem does apply for $x \leq \tfrac{1}{2}$ or for $x \geq \tfrac{1}{2}$.

Exercises 9.1, Page 280

1. *Tangent:* $4x - y = 7$, *normal:* $x + 4y = -11$.

3. *Tangent:* $5x + y = 4$, *normal:* $x - 5y = 6$.

5. *Tangent:* $x - 4y = -8$, *normal:* $4x + y = 36$.

7. *Tangent:* $x + y = 0$, *normal:* $x - y = -2$.

9. *Tangent:* $x + 4y = 12$, *normal:* $4x - y = 14$.

11. $4x - y = 4$.   13. $(1, 2)$ and $(-1, -4)$.

Exercises 9.2, Page 283

1. 9 feet/second.   **5.** -9 feet/second.   **9.** $v = v_0 - gt_1$.

3. -24 feet/second.   **7.** $\frac{1}{4}$ foot/second.   **11.** $18\frac{3}{4}$ feet.

13. Motion in positive direction for $0 < t < 2$ and for $t > 4$. Motion in negative direction for $2 < t < 4$.

15. $t = 0$, $v_1 = -4$ feet/second, $v_2 = 3$ feet/second.

$\quad\;\; t = \frac{7}{2}$, $v_1 = 3$ feet/second, $v_2 = -4$ feet/second.

Exercises 9.3, Page 286

1. 10 (inches)^2/inch.   **5.** 3π (inches)^3/inch.

3. 64π (inches)^3/inch.   **7.** -0.4096π (inches)^3/minute.

9. $t = 0$, $a = -6$ feet/(second)^2; $t = 2$, $a = 6$ feet/(second)^2.

11. $(-\frac{1}{2}, -\frac{3}{4})$, $(-\frac{3}{2}, -\frac{3}{4})$.   **13.** πr^2 (linear units)^3/linear unit.

Exercises 9.4, Pages 290–291

1. $10x - 21x^2$.   **11.** $-1/(2\sqrt{3}x^{3/2})$.

3. $4x + 3$.

5. $3y^2 + 4y$.   **13.** $-\dfrac{1}{t^2} + \dfrac{6}{t^3} - \dfrac{1}{t^4}$.

7. $3(t - 1)^2$.   **15.** $-\frac{3}{2}u^{-5/2}$.

9. $-1/x^3$.   **17. (a)** 2. **(b)** 2.

19. (a) $\frac{1}{8}$. **(b)** $-\frac{3}{32}$.

21. $t = 0$, $s = 0$ feet, $v = 16$ feet/second, $a = -32$ feet/(second)^2.

$\quad\;\; t = \frac{1}{2}$, $s = 4$ feet, $v = 0$ feet/second, $a = -32$ feet/(second)^2.

23. $t = 1$, $s = 2$ feet, $v = 1$ foot/second, $a = -\frac{1}{2}$ foot/(second)^2.

$\quad\;\; t = 4$, $s = 4$ feet, $v = \frac{1}{2}$ foot/second, $a = -\frac{1}{16}$ foot/(second)^2.

25. $\pm 6\sqrt{3}$.   **29.** $\frac{1}{4}\sqrt{S/\pi}$.

27. $y = -4$ and $y = 4x$.   **31.** 1.00425 calories/degree.

Exercises 9.5, Pages 293–294

1. $\frac{1}{2}x^4 - x^3 - x^2 + 7x + C$.   **7.** $9x + 4x^3 + \frac{4}{5}x^5 + C$.

9. $\frac{1}{3}x^3 + \frac{3}{2}x^2 + 4x - (1/x) + C$.

3. $-\dfrac{1}{4x^2} - \dfrac{3}{x} + 4x + C$.   **11.** $\frac{3}{2}t^{2/3} - \frac{24}{11}t^{11/3} + C$.

5. $\frac{2}{3}\sqrt{2}s^{3/2} + \sqrt{2}s^{1/2} + C$.

13. $\dfrac{(2s^3 - 1)^4}{24} + C$.

15. $\frac{2}{3}x^{3/2} - \frac{12}{7}x^{7/2} + \frac{24}{11}x^{11/2} - \frac{16}{15}x^{15/2} + C$.

17. $y = 2x^3 + 2x^2 + 3x + 4$.   **23.** $s = \frac{1}{6}t^4 + \frac{1}{2}t^3 + 2t^2 + 10t$.

19. $y = \frac{1}{4}x^4 - 2x^2 + x + 9$.   **25.** 164 feet, $-16\sqrt{41}$ feet/second.

21. $3y = 2x\sqrt{2x} + 4$.   **27.** $12y = x^3 + 16$.

Exercises 10.1, Pages 297–298

1. $\mathcal{D}_f = \mathcal{R}$; $\mathcal{D}_{f'} = \mathcal{R}$.

3. $\mathcal{D}_f = \{x: x \geq 0\}$; $\mathcal{D}_{f'} = \{x: x > 0\}$.

5. $\mathcal{D}_f = \mathcal{R} - \{0\}$; $\mathcal{D}_{f'} = \mathcal{R} - \{0\}$.

7. $f'_+(1) \neq f'_-(1)$; f is continuous at 1.

9. $f'_+(0) \neq f'_-(0)$; f is continuous at 0.

11. $f'_+(-3) \neq f'_-(-3)$; f is continuous at -3.

13. $f'_+(0) \neq f'_-(0)$; f is continuous at 0.

15. (a) f_1 is differentiable on $0 < x < 1$ except at $x = \frac{1}{2}$.

    (b) f_n is continuous on $0 \leq x \leq 1$ and is differentiable on this interval except at $x = k \cdot 2^{-n}$, where $k = 1, 2, 3, \ldots, 2^n - 1$.

    (c) The limit function F is given by $F(x) = 0$, $0 \leq x \leq 1$. It is continuous and differentiable on its entire domain.

Exercises 10.2, Page 302

1. $2x$.

3. $4x^3 + 18x^2 + 22x + 6$.

5. $-2(x - 1)^{-2}$.

7. $\dfrac{1}{(x + 1)^2}$.

9. $\dfrac{2 + \sqrt{x}}{2(1 + \sqrt{x})^2}$.

11. $t = 2$.

13. $t = 1$.

15. $25y + 2x = 7$.

17. $y = -x$.

19. *Hint:* Apply the Product Rule for Differentiation n times, first writing the product as $(f_1)(f_2 f_3 \cdots f_n)$ and then proceeding in the obvious fashion.

21. $D_x(uv^{-1}) = (D_x u) v^{-1} + u D_x(v^{-1}) = v^{-1} D_x u - uv^{-2} D_x v$
$$= v^{-2}(v D_x u - u D_x v).$$

Exercises 10.3, Pages 306–307

1. $\dfrac{1}{2\sqrt{x + 2}}$.

3. $\dfrac{1}{2(2 - t)^{3/2}}$.

5. $\dfrac{2}{(2s - 1)^{1/2}(2s + 1)^{3/2}}$.

7. $\dfrac{-6u^2}{(u^3 + 8)^{1/2}(4 + u^3)^{3/2}}$.

9. $\dfrac{1}{t^2}$, $t \neq 0, 1$.

11. $\dfrac{2x(x^2 - 9)}{\sqrt{(x^2 - 9)^2}}$.

13. $\dfrac{2x^2 - 1}{\sqrt{x^2 - 1}}$.

15. $\dfrac{z^3 + 2z}{(1 + z^2)^{3/2}}$.

17. $1 - \dfrac{a^{1/2}}{x^{1/2}}$.

19. $(0, 1)$.

21. $y = \sqrt{|x|} = \begin{cases} \sqrt{x}, & x \geq 0, \\ \sqrt{-x}, & x < 0. \end{cases}$

$y' = \dfrac{1}{2\sqrt{x}}$, $x > 0$ and $y' = -\dfrac{1}{2\sqrt{-x}}$ for $x < 0$.

Thus, $|y'| \to \infty$ as $x \to 0$ and there is a vertical tangent at $(0, 0)$.

23. Let $y = u^n$, where $u = f(x)$ and apply the chain rule to get
$$D_x y = (D_u y)(D_x u) = nu^{n-1} D_x u.$$

25. Suppose $f'(x_0) = 0$. Then, if $y = [f(x)]^n$, $y' = n[f(x)]^{n-1}f'(x)$. Therefore, $y' = 0$ for $x = x_0$, and the curve $y = [f(x)]^n$ has a horizontal tangent at $x = x_0$.

The converse is not necessarily true since, for $n \geq 2$, it is possible that $y' = 0$ and $f'(x) \neq 0$ at a point where $f(x) = 0$. An example is furnished by $y = (x^2 - 1)^2$.

27. $v = 0$ for $t = 0$ only. There are no times when $v = 1$ foot/second.

29. By Theorem 10.3a, if f and g are differentiable on $a < x < b$ and if $f(x)$ is a value such that $a < f(x) < b$, then $g(f)$ is differentiable there. If $f(x)$ is not a value in this interval, then nothing can be guaranteed. Hence, in general, the answer is no. For example, let the interval be $0 < x < 2$ and take $g(x) .=. 1/x, f(x) .=. (x - 1)^2$. Is $g(f)$ differentiable at $x = 1$?

Exercises 10.4, Pages 308–309

1. $\dfrac{4}{(x - 1)^3}$.

3. $-\dfrac{x + 4}{4(x + 1)^{5/2}}$.

5. $10(1 + 3t)^{-8/3}$.

7. $y' = \frac{1}{2}x^{-1/2}$, $y^{(n)} = (1/2^n)(-1)^{n-1}(1)(3) \cdots (2n - 3)x^{-(2n-1)/2}$, $n = 2, 3, 4, \ldots$.

9. $t = 1$, $s = 0$ feet, $v = 3$ feet/second.

11. $t = 2$, $s = -68$ feet, $v = -52$ feet/second.

13. $t = 2$, $s = 2$ feet, $v = -\frac{1}{2}$ foot/second.

15. At $(0, 0)$, $y' = 1$; at $(2, -222)$ and at $(-2, 222)$, $y' = -239$.

17. 72.

19. $f'(x) = \begin{cases} 2x, & x \geq 0, \\ -2x, & x < 0. \end{cases}$

$f''(x) = \begin{cases} 2, & x > 0, \\ -2, & x < 0. \end{cases}$

21. (b), (c), (e) are true; (a) and (d) are false.

Exercises 10.5, Pages 313–314

1. The equation defines no real function.

3. The equation defines no real function.

5. $-\dfrac{4x}{y}$.

7. $\dfrac{5 - x}{y + 2}$.

9. $\dfrac{x^2}{t^2 - 1}$.

11. $\frac{1}{10}$.

13. Undefined.

15. $-\frac{1}{4}$.

17. $-\dfrac{1}{y^3}$.

19. 0.

21. $\frac{1}{3}a^{2/3}x^{-4/3}y^{-1/3}$.

23. 0.

25. $\frac{1}{4}$ and $-\frac{1}{4}$.

Exercises 10.6, Pages 318–319

7. $(-7, -2)$, $(-7, 2)$.

9. $(0, \sqrt{2})$.

11. $(0, 2\sqrt{2})$.

13. $y = 3x$.

15. $4x - 3y = 1$.

17. $\dfrac{9u}{4}$, $u \neq 0$; $\dfrac{9}{16u}$.

19. $\dfrac{2b}{a} t^{1/2} + \dfrac{4c}{a} t^{3/2}$; $\dfrac{2b}{a^2} + \dfrac{12c}{a^2} t$.

21. Hypotheses are satisfied on any interval in $\mathcal{R} - \{0\}$.

23. Hypotheses are satisfied on any interval in $\mathcal{R} - \{-1, 1\}$.

Exercises 10.7, Pages 324–325

1. $\Delta y = 3.25$, $dy = 3$.

3. $\Delta y = 0.00998$, $dy = 0.01$.

5. $-\dfrac{x}{y}$.

7. $-\dfrac{x^2 + y}{x + y^2}$.

9. $\dfrac{4t}{1 + t^2}$.

11. 0.3988.

13. 3.0067.

15. 0.0101.

17. $V = V_0(1 + \alpha t)^3$, $dV = 3\alpha V_0(1 + \alpha t)^2 \, dt$.

19. $8\frac{1}{3}\%$.

21. $8\frac{1}{3}\%$.

23. 2.099 centimeters.

25. $d(u + v) = du + dv$.

Exercises 11.1, Pages 330–331

1. Increasing for $x > 0$; decreasing for $x < 0$.

3. Decreasing on $\mathcal{R} - \{1\}$.

5. Increasing on $\mathcal{R}$.

7. Increasing for $x < -1$ and for $x > \frac{1}{3}$; decreasing for $-1 < x < \frac{1}{3}$.

9. Increasing for $x > -2$; decreasing for $x < -2$.

11. $f(0) = 0$ is the least value of f, and f' does not exist at $x = 0$.

13. At $x = \pm a$, $y = 0$. This is the least value of y, and y' does not exist at $x = 0$.

15. The greatest value is $\frac{1}{5}$; the least is 0.

Exercises 11.2, Pages 337–338

1. Concave up for $-1 < x < 0$, $x > 1$.
Concave down for $x < -1$, $0 < x < 1$.
Inflection points: $(-1, 7)$, $(0, 0)$, $(1, -7)$.

3. Concave up for $0 < x < 2$.
Concave down for $x < 0$, $x > 2$.
Inflection points: $(0, 0)$, $(2, 16)$.

5. Concave up for $x < 0$.
Concave down for $x > 0$.
No inflection points.

7. Concave up for $-a\sqrt{3} < x < 0$, $x > a\sqrt{3}$.

Concave down for $x < -a\sqrt{3}$, $0 < x < a\sqrt{3}$.

Inflection points: $(-a\sqrt{3}, -\frac{1}{4}a\sqrt{3})$, $(0, 0)$, $(a\sqrt{3}, \frac{1}{4}a\sqrt{3})$.

9. *Hint:* The inflection point occurs for $x = -\frac{1}{3}(b/a)$.

11. $22y = -x^4 + 2x^3 + 12x^2 + 13x + 22$.

13. Falling curve with a horizontal inflectional tangent at $[a, f(a)]$. Concave up to the left and down to the right of $x = a$.

15. Rising curve, concave down.

17. Falling curve with inflection point $[a, f(a)]$. Concave up to the right and down to the left of $x = a$.

19. Impossible. The conditions are inconsistent since f' is discontinuous for $x = a$, so that f'' cannot exist there.

Exercises 11.3, Page 345

1. $f(-3) = -2$, min; $f(-1) = 2$, max; $f(3) = -14$, min.

3. $F(0) = 1$, max. **5.** No extremes. **7.** $f(0) = 0$, min.

9. $(-2, 4 + \sqrt[3]{4})$, max point; $(0, 4)$, min point; $(3, 4 + \sqrt[3]{9})$, max point.

11. $(1, 0)$, min point. **17.** $(-1, 2)$, min point.

13. No max or min points. **19.** $(4, \frac{3}{4})$, min point.

15. $(1, 1)$, min point; $(\frac{13}{9}, \frac{31}{27})$, max point. **21.** $c = 0$, $b > 0$, $3a + 2b = 0$.

23. $\left[\dfrac{m}{m + n}, \dfrac{m^m n^n}{(m + n)^{m+n}}\right]$ is always a max point.

For m even, $(0, 0)$ is a min point.

For n odd, $(1, 0)$ is a min point.

No other extremes occur.

25. x_c is the only critical point $\Rightarrow$ no extreme on the interval $a < x < x_c$ or $x_c < x < b$. Hence, f has only end point extremes for $a \leq x \leq x_c$ and $x_c \leq x \leq b$. Since $f(x_c) > f(a)$ and $f(x_c) > f(b)$, then $f(x_c)$ is the greatest value of f on the interval $a \leq x \leq b$.

27. (a) A rising curve with a vertical inflectional tangent or else a sharp corner at $x = a$, concave up to the left and down to the right of $x = a$.

Exercises 11.4, Page 349

1. 1. **3.** $1 + \sqrt{3}$. **5.** $\frac{1}{6}(\sqrt{39} - 3)$. **7.** $1/\sqrt{2}$.

11. No, since f' does not exist at $x = 0$, which is in the given interval.

Exercises 11.5, Pages 356–357

1. *Intercepts:* $x = 0 \Leftrightarrow y = 0$; $y = 0 \Rightarrow x = \pm 2\sqrt{2}$.

Symmetry: y-axis.

y increasing for $-2 < x < 0$, $x > 2$, decreasing for $x < -2$, $0 < x < 2$.

Max point $(0, 0)$. Min points $(\pm 2, -16)$.

Concave up, $x < -\frac{2}{3}\sqrt{3}, x > \frac{2}{3}\sqrt{3}$.

Concave down, $-\frac{2}{3}\sqrt{3} < x < \frac{2}{3}\sqrt{3}$.

Inflection points $(\pm\frac{2}{3}\sqrt{3}, -\frac{80}{9})$.

3. *Intercepts:* $y = 0 \Rightarrow x = \pm 3$.

 Symmetry: y-axis.

 Extent: $|x| \geq 3, y \geq 0$.

 y increasing for $x > 3$, decreasing for $x < -3$.

 Min points $(\pm 3, 0)$. Vertical tangents at these points.

 Concave up, $x > 3$; concave down, $x < -3$.

5. *Intercepts:* $x = 0 \Leftrightarrow y = 0$.

 Symmetry: y-axis.

 y decreasing for $x < 0$, increasing for $x > 0$.

 Min point $(0, 0)$. Derivative does not exist there.

 Concave up, $x < 0$ and $x > 0$.

7. *Intercepts:* $x = 0 \Rightarrow y = -1; y = 0 \Rightarrow x = 1$.

 Asymptotes: $x = -1, y = 1$.

 y increasing on $x < -1$ and $x > -1$.

 Concave up, $x < -1$; concave down, $x > -1$.

9. *Intercepts:* $y = 0 \Rightarrow x = \pm 2$. Note that $(0, 0)$ is an isolated point.

 Symmetry: Origin.

 Extent: $x = 0, |x| \geq 2$.

 y increasing for $x < -2$, decreasing for $x > 2$.

 Max point $(-2, 0)$; min point $(2, 0)$. Vertical tangents at these points.

 Concave up, $-\sqrt{6} < x < -2, x > \sqrt{6}$; concave down, $x < -\sqrt{6}, 2 < x < \sqrt{6}$.

 Inflection points $(-\sqrt{6}, -2\sqrt{3}), (\sqrt{6}, 2\sqrt{3})$.

11. *Intercepts:* $x = 0 \Leftrightarrow y = 0$.

 Symmetry: y-axis.

 Asymptotes: x-axis.

 y increasing for $x < -1, 0 < x < 1$, decreasing for $-1 < x < 0, x > 1$.

 Max points $(\pm 1, \frac{1}{2})$; min point $(0, 0)$. Note that the derivative has a finite discontinuity at $x = 0$.

 Concave up, $x < -\sqrt{3}, x > \sqrt{3}$; concave down, $-\sqrt{3} < x < 0, 0 < x < \sqrt{3}$.

 Inflection points $(\pm\sqrt{3}, \frac{1}{4}\sqrt{3})$.

13. *Intercepts:* $y = 0 \Rightarrow x = -5, 3; x = 0 \Rightarrow y = 20.80$.

 y increasing for $x < -\frac{1}{5}, x > 3$, decreasing for $-\frac{1}{5} < x < 3$.

 Min point $(3, 0)$; max point $(-\frac{1}{5}, 20.85)$. Vertical tangent at $(3, 0)$.

 Concave up, $x > 4.6$; concave down, $x < 3, 3 < x < 4.6$.

 Inflection point $(4.6, 26.81)$.

15. *Intercepts:* $y = 0 \Rightarrow x = 0, 5$.

 Asymptotes: $y = -1, x = -2$.

 y decreasing for $x < -2, x > \frac{10}{9}$, increasing for $-2 < x < \frac{10}{9}$.

 Max point $(\frac{10}{9}, \frac{25}{56})$.

Concave up, $x > \frac{8}{3}$; concave down, $x < -2$, $-2 < x < \frac{8}{3}$. Inflection point $(\frac{8}{3}, \frac{2}{7})$.

17. *Intercepts:* $x = 0 \Rightarrow y = 2a$.
Symmetry: y-axis.
Asymptotes: $y = 0$.
y increasing for $x < 0$; decreasing for $x > 0$.
Max point $(0, 2a)$.
Concave up, $|x| > \frac{2}{3}\sqrt{3}a$; concave down, $|x| < \frac{2}{3}\sqrt{3}a$.
Inflection points $(\pm\frac{2}{3}\sqrt{3}a, \frac{3}{2}a)$.

19. *Intercepts:* $y = 0 \Rightarrow x = -a, 0$.
Asymptotes: $x = a$.
Symmetry: x-axis.
Extent: $-a \leqq x < a$.
For $y_1 = x\sqrt{\dfrac{a+x}{a-x}}$,
y_1 increasing for $\frac{1}{2}a(1 - \sqrt{5}) < x < a$, decreasing for $-a < x < \frac{1}{2}a(1 - \sqrt{5})$.
Min point $(-0.62a, -0.49a)$.
Concave up, $-a < x < a$. Vertical tangent at $(-a, 0)$.
For $y_2 = -x\sqrt{\dfrac{a+x}{a-x}}$, use the symmetry.

21. Parabola, vertex at $(-2, 1)$, axis $x = -2$. Opens upward.

23. The curve is symmetric to the x-axis, so consider only $t \geqq 0$.
Intercepts: $y = 0 \Rightarrow x = 0, -6$.
y increasing for $x > -4$, decreasing for $-6 < x < -4$.
Min point $(-4, -8)$.
Concave up, $x > -6$. Vertical tangent at $(-6, 0)$.
Use symmetry for $t \leqq 0$.

25. (a) $f(x) + g(x) = 0$ or $g(x) = -f(x)$.
(b) If $y_1 = f(x)$ has a max point at x_1 then there is a $\mathfrak{N}(x_1, h)$ such that
$x \in \mathfrak{N}(x_1, h) \Rightarrow f(x_1) > f(x) \Rightarrow -f(x') < -f(x) \Rightarrow g(x_1) < g(x) \Rightarrow g$
has a min value at x_1.
(c) *Hint:* Consider the difference $f(x) - t(x)$, where t is the linear function defined in the proof of Theorem 11.2b.

Exercises 11.6, Pages 362–364

1. 6, 6.

3. $x = \frac{1}{2}A\sqrt{2} = y$.

7. 3 inches.

9. Height $= \frac{1}{2}$ length of base.

11. $\frac{1}{3}h$.

13. Rectangle twice as wide as high.

15. Height $=$ radius at base.

17. $R = r$.

19. Depth $= \sqrt{2}$ times the width.

21. $1\frac{1}{2}\%$.

23. $AB = 37\frac{1}{2}$ feet.

Exercises 11.7, Pages 366–367

1. $\dfrac{4\pi}{r}$ (inches)²/second.

3. 6.4 mph; no.

5. 1.8 feet/second.

7. $\frac{5}{18}$ foot/minute; $\frac{1}{6}$ foot/minute.

9. $\frac{84}{73}\sqrt{73}$ inches/minute.

11. 12.5 mph.

13. $32\sqrt{5}$ mph. No, since $D_t^2 s$ is not zero.

Exercises 12.1, Pages 372–373

1. (a) $\displaystyle\sum_{k=1}^{n} 2^k$.

(b) $\displaystyle\sum_{k=0}^{n}\left[7+\frac{k(k+1)}{2}\right]$.

3. (a) $a_1 + a_2 + a_3 + a_4$.

(c) $\dfrac{1}{n-1}+\dfrac{1}{n-2}+\dfrac{1}{n-3}+\dfrac{1}{n-4}+\dfrac{1}{n-5}$.

(e) $0+1+0+1$.

9. 2^n; 0.

11. (a) $64a^6 - 576a^5b^2 + 2160a^4b^4 - 4320a^3b^6 + 4860a^2b^8 - 2916ab^{10} + 729b^{12}$.

(b) $\dfrac{a^7}{128} - \dfrac{7a^4}{32} + \dfrac{21a}{8} - \dfrac{35}{2a^2} + \dfrac{70}{a^5} - \dfrac{168}{a^8} + \dfrac{224}{a^{11}} - \dfrac{128}{a^{14}}$.

13. (a) $14{,}784a^7$.

(c) $\dfrac{12{,}155x^9y^{16}}{128}$.

15. $\dfrac{1001}{248{,}832}$.

19. $(n+1)! - 1$.

Exercises 12.2, Pages 378–379

1. $\frac{1}{4}, \frac{2}{5}, \frac{3}{6}, \frac{4}{7}, \frac{5}{8}, \ldots$ Cluster point 1; limit 1.

3. $-\frac{1}{2}, \frac{1}{4}, -\frac{1}{8}, \frac{1}{16}, -\frac{1}{32}, \ldots$ Cluster point 0; limit 0.

5. $-\frac{3}{2}, \frac{3}{4}, -\frac{9}{8}, \frac{15}{16}, -\frac{33}{32}, \ldots$ Cluster points $-1, 1$; limit does not exist.

7. $a, a^2, a^3, a^4, a^5, \ldots$

If $|a| < 1$, then 0 is a cluster point and the limit is 0.

If $|a| > 1$, there are no cluster points and the limit does not exist.

If $a = 1$, then 1 is a cluster point and the limit is 1.

If $a = -1$, then 1 and -1 are cluster points and the limit does not exist.

9. $-\frac{3}{5}, -\frac{15}{17}, -\frac{63}{65}, -\frac{255}{257}, -\frac{1023}{1025}, \ldots$ Cluster point -1; limit -1.

11. $-8, -\frac{13}{2}, -\frac{56}{9}, -\frac{49}{8}, -\frac{152}{25}, \ldots$ Cluster point -6; limit -6.

13. Nine terms $\notin \mathfrak{N}(0, 0.001)$.

15. $s_n = \dfrac{2n+1}{2n+3} < 1$, so that the sequence is bounded above.

$\dfrac{2n+3}{2n+5} > \dfrac{2n+1}{2n+3}$ since $4n^2 + 12n + 9 > 4n^2 + 12n + 5$.

Therefore, the sequence is increasing. By Theorem 12.2b, the sequence converges.

17. $s_n = 1 - \dfrac{1}{2^n} < 1$ so that the sequence is bounded above.

$1 - \dfrac{1}{2^n} < 1 - \dfrac{1}{2^{n+1}} \Rightarrow$ the sequence is increasing. By Theorem 12.2b, the sequence converges.

Exercises 12.3, Pages 383–384

1. 10 (linear units)^2.　　　　　　　　　　　**3.** $15\frac{1}{3}$ (linear units)^2.

5. $A_n = \sum_{k=0}^{n-1} \frac{1}{n}\left(\frac{k}{n}\right)^2 = \frac{1}{n^3}\sum_{k=1}^{n-1} k^2 = \frac{(n-1)(n)(2n-1)}{6n^3}$.

$\lim_{n\to\infty} A_n = \lim_{n\to\infty}\left[\left(1 - \frac{1}{n}\right)\left(\frac{1}{3} - \frac{1}{6n}\right)\right] = \frac{1}{3}$.

7. $A = \lim_{n\to\infty}\sum_{k=1}^{n} \frac{r}{n}\sqrt{r^2 - \frac{k^2 r^2}{n^2}} = \frac{\pi r^2}{4} \Rightarrow \lim_{n\to\infty}\sum_{k=1}^{n}\frac{1}{n}\sqrt{1 - \frac{k^2}{n^2}} = \frac{\pi}{4}$.

Exercises 12.4, Page 389

1. $V_n = nhr^2 \sin\frac{\pi}{n} = \pi r^2 h \frac{\sin \pi/n}{\pi/n}$.

$\lim_{n\to\infty} \pi r^2 h \frac{\sin \pi/n}{\pi/n} = \pi r^2 h$.

3. $V_n = \frac{\pi r^2 h}{n^3}\sum_{k=1}^{n} k^2 = \frac{\pi r^2 h}{6n^3}(n)(n+1)(2n+1)$.

$\lim_{n\to\infty} V_n = \frac{1}{3}\pi r^2 h$.

5. $\frac{1}{2}wb^3\sqrt{2}$ pounds.　　　　　　　　　**7.** $\frac{1}{6}wbh(3H+b)$ pounds.

9. Example 12.4b: $F_n = \sum_{k=1}^{n} \frac{\rho b a}{n}\left(H + b - \frac{kb}{n}\right)$.

Let $\Delta x_k = \frac{b}{n}$, $f(x) = \rho a(H + b - x)$, $x_k = \frac{kb}{n}$. Then, $F_n = \sum_{k=1}^{n} f(x_k)\,\Delta x_k$.

Exercises 12.5, Pages 393–394

1. *c*.　　　　　　　　　**5.** 8.　　　　　　　　　**9.** $\int_1^2 dx/x$.

3. 2*m*.　　　　　　　　**7.** $\frac{1}{2}$.

Exercises 12.7, Page 400

1. This follows the same line of argument as the first part of the theorem. Replace the words "greatest lower bound" by "least upper bound," and proceed as in the first half of the proof.

3. Repeat the proof of the first part of the theorem but with upper sums rather than lower sums.

5. A succession of refinements starting with s_p always produces a *nondecreasing* sequence with limit equal to $\lim_{n\to\infty} s_n$. Hence

$$s_p \leq \lim_{n\to\infty} s_n.$$

Exercises 12.8, Page 404

1. $\int_b^a f(x)\,dx = \lim\limits_{\delta\to 0} \sum\limits_{k=1}^{n} f(x_k^*)\,\Delta\bar{x}_k = \lim\limits_{\delta\to 0} \sum\limits_{k=1}^{n} -f(x_k^*)\,\Delta x_{n-k}$

$$= -\lim\limits_{\delta\to 0} \sum\limits_{\alpha=1}^{n} f(x_\alpha^*)\,\Delta x_\alpha = -\int_a^b f(x)\,dx.$$

3. $\int_2^7 x^2\,dx = \dfrac{335}{3},\ \int_2^5 x^2\,dx = \dfrac{117}{3},\ \int_5^7 x^2\,dx = \dfrac{218}{3}.$

$$\dfrac{117}{3} + \dfrac{218}{3} = \dfrac{335}{3}.$$

5. $\int_2^7 x^2\,dx = \dfrac{335}{3},\ \int_2^9 x^2\,dx = \dfrac{721}{3},\ \int_9^7 x^2\,dx = -\dfrac{386}{3}.$

$$\dfrac{721}{3} + \left(-\dfrac{386}{3}\right) = \dfrac{335}{3}.$$

7. $\int_a^b [f(x) + g(x)]\,dx = \lim\limits_{\delta\to 0} \sum\limits_{k=1}^{n} [f(x_k^*) + g(x_k^*)]\,\Delta x_k$

$$= \lim\limits_{\delta\to 0} \left[\sum\limits_{k=1}^{n} f(x_k^*)\,\Delta x_k + \sum\limits_{k=1}^{n} g(x_k^*)\,\Delta x_k \right]$$

$$= \lim\limits_{\delta\to 0} \sum\limits_{k=1}^{n} f(x_k^*)\,\Delta x_k + \lim\limits_{\delta\to 0} \sum\limits_{k=1}^{n} g(x_k^*)\,\Delta x_k$$

$$= \int_a^b f(x)\,dx + \int_a^b g(x)\,dx,$$

since both f and g are integrable.

9. For the same partitions for both integrals,

$$\int_a^b f(x)\,dx = \lim\limits_{\delta\to 0} \sum\limits_{k=1}^{n} f(x_k^*)\,\Delta x_k \le \lim\limits_{\delta\to 0} \sum\limits_{k=1}^{n} g(x_k^*)\,\Delta x_k = \int_a^b g(x)\,dx.$$

Exercises 12.9, Pages 410–411

1. $-\frac{4}{3}$. **5.** $\frac{251}{15}$. **9.** $\frac{16}{105}a^3$. **13.** 10.

3. $\frac{1}{3}(9 - 4\sqrt{2})$. **7.** 2. **11.** $\frac{1}{8}$. **15.** $\frac{2}{3}\sqrt{2}$.

17. $\frac{1}{3}(2t + 1)^{3/2} - 9$ for $t \ge 0$ and $-\frac{1}{3}(1 - 2t)^{3/2} - \frac{25}{3}$ for $t < 0$.

19. $2(x^{1/2} + 2x^{1/4} - 3)$.

21. $\frac{3}{2}t^2$ for $t \ge 0$, $-\frac{3}{2}t^2$ for $t < 0$.

23. $\sqrt{1 + x^4}$.

25. $\dfrac{s - a}{s + a}$.

27. $\dfrac{2}{1 - x^2}$.

Exercises 12.10, Pages 414–415

1. 36 (l.u.)². **5.** $\frac{17}{20}$ (l.u.)². **9.** $\frac{8}{3}$ (l.u.)². **13.** 16 (l.u.)².

3. $\frac{8}{3}$ (l.u.)². **7.** 1 (l.u.)². **11.** 8 (l.u.)². **15.** $\frac{81}{2}$ (l.u.)².

17. $A = \int_0^1 [(1 + \sqrt{x}) - (1 - \sqrt{x})]\,dx + \int_1^4 [(1 + \sqrt{x}) - (x - 1)]\,dx = \frac{8}{3}$ (l.u.)².

Exercises 12.11, Pages 418–419

1. $V = \frac{1}{12}a^3\sqrt{2}$.
3. $\frac{16}{3}$ (l.u.)^3.
5. $V = \frac{4}{3}\pi b^3$.
7. $V = \frac{4}{3}\pi ab^2$.

9. (a) $\frac{2}{5}\pi a^3$ (l.u.)^3. (c) $\frac{2}{3}\pi a^3$ (l.u.)^3.
11. $V = \frac{1}{12}na^2h \cot(\pi/n)$.
13. $\frac{128}{15}\pi$ (l.u.)^3.
15. (a) $\frac{32}{105}\pi$ (l.u.)^3.

Exercises 12.12, Pages 427–429

1. $\frac{2}{3}a$.
3. $\frac{4}{3}\sqrt{2}$.
5. $\frac{1}{2}r^2$.
7. $(\frac{55}{16}, \frac{17}{8})$.

9. $(0, \frac{4}{3}(a/\pi))$.
11. $(\frac{1}{2}, \frac{2}{5})$.
13. $(\frac{3}{7}, \frac{12}{25})$.
15. $(\frac{1}{2}, \frac{8}{5})$.

17. $(1, \frac{6}{5})$.
19. $(\frac{8}{5}, -\frac{88}{35})$.
23. $\frac{408}{5}\pi$ (l.u.)^3.
25. π (inches)^3.

Exercises 12.13, Pages 432–434

1. $9\frac{3}{8}$ foot-pounds.
3. $22\frac{2}{9}\%$.
5. $27648\pi w$ foot-pounds.
7. $640,000\pi w/3$ foot-pounds.
9. $12,480w$ foot-pounds.
11. $2w \int_{-4}^{4} (4-y)\sqrt{16-y^2}\, dy$.
13. $\frac{5}{8}bh^2w$ pounds.

15. $256w/5$ pounds.
17. $\frac{1}{10}(k/a)(5\sqrt{2} - 2\sqrt{5})$.
19. 384×10^7 foot-pounds.
21. 736 foot-pounds.
23. $8\frac{1}{2}$ inches.
25. $\dfrac{km^2}{(x_3 - x_1)(x_3 - x_2)}$.

Exercises 12.14, Pages 438–439

1. 0.   3. $\frac{64}{3}$.   5. $\frac{2}{3}n$.   7. $\frac{1}{2}n(n+1)$.
9. $T - 2k$ for $2k \leqq T \leqq 2k + 1 \leqq n$,
$2k + 2 - T$ for $2k + 1 \leqq T \leqq 2k + 2 \leqq n$,
$k = 0, 1, 2, \ldots$.

Exercises 13.1, Page 447

1. $\dfrac{\log_{10} 3}{\log_{10} 2} = 1.59$.   3. $\dfrac{\log_{10} 2}{\log_{10} 3 - \log_{10} 2} = 1.71$.   5. $\frac{1}{9}$.   7. $\frac{1}{5}$.

9. $x = \log_a M, y = \log_a N \Rightarrow a^x = M, a^y = N$
$\Rightarrow \dfrac{M}{N} = a^{x-y} \Rightarrow \log_a \dfrac{M}{N} = x - y = \log_a M - \log_a N$.

11. $x = \log_a N \Rightarrow a^x = N$. Then, by substitution, $a^{\log_a N} = N$.

13. $-\log_5 y$.
15. $\frac{1}{4}(y \log_2 3 - 1)$.
21. 0.69897.
23. -0.69897.

25. 2.17609.
27. 0.82660.
29. 0.59272.

Exercises 13.2, Pages 454–455

1. $\dfrac{1 - 3 \ln x}{x^4}$.

3. $\dfrac{18 \ln x}{x}$.

5. $\dfrac{x(2 \ln x - 1)}{3(\ln x)^2}$.

7. $-\dfrac{y}{x}$.

9. $\dfrac{4 - x^2}{x(4 + x^2)}$.

11. $-\dfrac{\ln t}{2 + \ln t}$.

13. $\dfrac{1}{\sqrt{x^2 + 1}}$.

15. $\dfrac{4x}{x^4 - 1}$.

17. $x + 2x \ln 3x$; $3 + 2 \ln 3x$.

19. $2s^2$; $4s^2$.

21. *Intercepts:* $y = 0 \Rightarrow x = 1$.
   Extent: $x > 0$.
   y decreasing for $0 < x < e^{-1}$, increasing for $x > e^{-1}$.
   Min point $(e^{-1}, -e^{-1})$.
   Concave up for $x > 0$.

23. *Intercepts:* $y = 0 \Rightarrow x = 9$.
   Extent: $x > 0$.
   Asymptotes: Lower portion of y-axis.
   y increasing for $x > 0$.
   Concave down for $x > 0$.

25. *Intercepts:* $y = 0 \Rightarrow x = 1$.
   Extent: $x > 0$.
   Asymptotes: $x = 0$, $y = 0$.
   y increasing for $0 < x < e$, decreasing for $x > e$.
   Max point $(e, 3e^{-1})$.
   Concave up for $x > e^{3/2}$, down for $0 < x < e^{3/2}$.
   Inflection point $(e^{3/2}, \frac{9}{2}e^{-3/2})$.

27. $\ln y = kt \Rightarrow y = e^{kt} \Rightarrow D_t y = ke^{kt} = ky$.

29. Let $f(x) = \ln x$. Then $f'(x) = 1/x$, so that the Mean Value Theorem gives
$$\ln (x + h) = \ln x + \frac{h}{x + \theta h}, \qquad 0 < \theta < 1.$$
   For $x = 1$ and $h = 0.01$, this becomes
$$\ln 1.01 = \ln 1 + \frac{0.01}{1 + 0.01\theta}$$
   or
$$\ln 1.01 = \frac{1}{100 + \theta}.$$
   Thus, $0 < \theta < 1 \Rightarrow 1/101 < \ln 1.01 < 1/100$.

31. $D_x R = \dfrac{k}{(x - a)^2}\left(1 - \dfrac{a}{x} - \ln \dfrac{x}{a}\right)$, and $\dfrac{k}{(x - a)^2} > 0$.

   Let $y = 1 - \dfrac{a}{x} - \ln \dfrac{x}{a}$. Then $y' = \dfrac{a}{x^2} - \dfrac{1}{x} = \dfrac{a - x}{x^2}$. By inspection, $y = 0$ for
   $x = a$ and $y' < 0$ for $x > a$. Thus y is decreasing for $x > a$ and therefore $y < 0$
   for $x > a$. Hence, $D_x R < 0$ for $x > a$, and R is decreasing.

Exercises 13.3, Pages 457–458

1. $3x^2 \exp(x^3)$.

3. $3^{2y}(1 + 2y \ln 3)$.

5. $\dfrac{5^{\sqrt{4+u^2}}u \ln 5}{\sqrt{4 + u^2}}$.

7. $\dfrac{y(x - 1 - xye^{xy})}{x(1 + xye^{xy})}$.

9. $e^u(u + 1)$.

11. $x^x(\ln x + 1)$.

13. 0.

15. $\dfrac{e^w}{w}(1 + w \ln w)$.

17. $-\dfrac{6e^{3x}}{e^{6x} - 1}$.

19. $\dfrac{e^x - e^{-x}}{e^x + e^{-x}} \log_{10} e$.

21. $y'' = 2x(2x^4 - 7x^2 + 3) \exp(-x^2)$.

23. $y'' = (4x^2 - 4x + 3) \exp(x^2 - x)$.

25. *Intercepts:* $y = 0 \Rightarrow x = 1$.
Symmetry: y-axis.
Asymptotes: $y = 0$.
y increasing for $x < 0$, decreasing for $x > 0$.
Max point $(0, 1)$.
Concave up for $|x| > 1/\sqrt{2}$, down for $|x| < 1/\sqrt{2}$.
Inflection points $(\pm 1/\sqrt{2}, e^{-1/2})$.

27. *Intercepts:* $y = 0 \Leftrightarrow x = 0$.
Symmetry: Origin.
y increasing for all x.
Concave down for $x < 0$, up for $x > 0$.
Inflection point $(0, 0)$.

29. *Intercepts:* $x = 0 \Leftrightarrow y = 0$.
Asymptotes: $y = -1$.
y increasing for all x.
Concave up for all x.

31. *Intercepts:* $x = 0 \Rightarrow y = 1$.
Symmetry: y-axis.
y increasing for $x > 0$, decreasing for $x < 0$.
Min point $(0, 1)$.
Concave up for $x < 0$ and for $x > 0$.

33. 2.7998.

35. 61.34.

37. Let $f(x) = e^x$. Then $f'(x) = e^x$, and
$$e^{x+h} = e^x + he^{x+\theta h}, \qquad 0 < \theta < 1.$$
For $x = 1$ and $h = 0.02$,
$$e^{1.02} = e + 0.02e^{1+0.02\theta}.$$
$$0 < \theta < 1 \Rightarrow e^{1.02} > e + 0.02e = 1.02e$$
and
$$e^{1.02} < e + 0.02e^{1.02}, \text{ or } 0.98e^{1.02} < e.$$
Hence,
$$1.02e < e^{1.02} < \frac{e}{0.98}.$$

That is,

$$2.7726 < e^{1.02} < 2.7737.$$

39. $x + y = \frac{1}{2}(1 + \ln 2)$.

Exercises 13.4, Pages 461–462

1. $\frac{1}{3} \ln |1 + x^3| + C$.

3. $-\sqrt{1 - x^2} + C$.

5. $-\frac{1}{2} \exp(-x^2) + C$.

7. $\ln(e^x + e^{-x}) + C$.

9. $\frac{1}{2}t^2 + \ln |t^2 - 1| + C$.

11. $-e^{1/x} + C$.

13. $3^{3x-1} \log_3 e + C$.

15. $-\ln(1 + e^{-t}) + C$.

17. $\frac{1}{3}e^{2+3x} + C$.

19. $-\dfrac{1}{2(1 + y^2)} + C$.

21. $\frac{3}{2} \ln \frac{5}{17}$.

23. $2(\sqrt{2} - 1)$.

25. $1 - \ln 2$.

27. $\frac{1}{2}(e - e^9)$.

29. $\frac{1}{2} \ln \frac{3}{2}$.

31. $\frac{1}{2} \ln 5$ (l.u.)^2.

33. $\ln 3$ (l.u.)^2.

35. 46.4 minutes (approx.).

37. 1700 years (approx.).

39. $(1/\ln 2, 1/\ln 2)$.

Exercises 13.5, Pages 463–464

1. $\dfrac{2y}{x} \ln x$.

3. $\dfrac{y}{x} e^{-x}(1 - x \ln x)$.

5. $x \left[\dfrac{5}{y} - \dfrac{2y}{3(1 - y^2)} - \dfrac{3}{2(1 + 3y)} \right]$.

7. $u \left[\ln \ln 2v + \dfrac{1}{\ln 2v} \right]$.

9. $\dfrac{1}{4} y \left[\dfrac{2x}{x^2 + 4} - \dfrac{x}{1 + x^2} - \dfrac{3x^2}{x^3 + 2} \right]$.

11. $(w/u^2)(1 - \ln u)$.

13. $u^v(D_x v) \ln u + v u^{v-1} D_x u$.

Exercises 14.1, Pages 467–468

1. The limit does not exist.   **3.** 1.   **5.** 0.

9. Continuous except for infinite discontinuities at $v = n\pi$, $n = 0, \pm 1, \pm 2, \ldots$.

11. Continuous except for infinite discontinuities at $x = n\pi$, $n = 0, \pm 1, \pm 2, \ldots$.

13. Continuous except for infinite discontinuities at $s = (2n - 1)\pi/2$, $n = 0, \pm 1, \pm 2, \ldots$.

Exercises 14.2, Page 470

3. $D_x \cos x = \lim\limits_{h \to 0} \dfrac{\cos(x + h) - \cos x}{h}$

$= \lim\limits_{h \to 0} \dfrac{\cos x \cos h - \sin x \sin h - \cos x}{h}$

$= \lim\limits_{h \to 0} \left(-\sin x \dfrac{\sin h}{h} - \cos x \dfrac{1 - \cos h}{h} \right)$

$= \lim\limits_{h \to 0} \left(-\sin x \dfrac{\sin h}{h} - \cos x \dfrac{\sin h/2}{h/2} \sin \dfrac{h}{2} \right)$

$= -\sin x$.

5. $-5 \sin 5x$.

7. $2t \cos t^2$.

9. $2 \csc 2\theta$.

11. $-e^w \csc e^w \cot e^w$.

13. $e^{\sin x} \cos x$.

15. $12 \sin^3 3x \cos 3x$.

17. $8 \tan 4x \sec^2 4x$.

19. $-9 \sec^2 3w$.

21. $8 \cos (2 - 4z)$.

23. $-\frac{1}{2}[(n + m)^2 \sin (n + m)t + (n - m)^2 \sin (n - m)t]$.

25. $\dfrac{t \cos t^2}{\sqrt{\sin t^2}}$.

31. $-\dfrac{\sin t}{2 \cos 2t}$.

27. $-\dfrac{\sec y}{1 + x \sec y \tan y}$.

29. $\dfrac{\cos x \cos^2 y - \sin^2 x \sin y}{\cos^3 y}$.

33. $\cot \frac{1}{2}u$.

35. $-\cot t$.

37. $-\cos x$.

39. $D_x \cos x = -\sin x = \cos (x + \frac{1}{2}\pi)$.

Assume $D_x^k \cos x = \cos (x + \frac{1}{2}k\pi)$. Then

$$D_x^{k+1} \cos x = D_x \cos (x + \tfrac{1}{2}k\pi) = -\sin (x + \tfrac{1}{2}k\pi)$$
$$= \cos (x + \tfrac{1}{2}k\pi + \tfrac{1}{2}\pi) = \cos [x + \tfrac{1}{2}(k + 1)\pi].$$

This completes the proof by Mathematical Induction.

Exercises 14.3, Pages 475–476

1. Concave up, $\pi < x < 3\pi$; concave down, $0 < x < \pi$ and $3\pi < x < 4\pi$.
Max points $(0, 2)$, $(4\pi, 2)$; min point $(2\pi, -2)$.
Inflection points $(\pi, 0)$, $(3\pi, 0)$.

3. Concave up, $0 < x < \frac{1}{2}\pi$; concave down, $\frac{1}{2}\pi < x < \pi$.
Min points $(\frac{1}{4}\pi, -4)$, $(\pi, 0)$; max points $(0, 0)$, $(\frac{3}{4}\pi, 4)$.
Inflection point $(\frac{1}{2}\pi, 0)$.

5. Concave up, $\pi < x < \frac{3}{2}\pi$; concave down, $0 < x < \pi$ and $\frac{3}{2}\pi < x < 2\pi$.
Max point $(\frac{1}{2}\pi, 1)$.
Inflection point $(\frac{3}{2}\pi, 0)$.

7. Concave up, $-\pi < x < -\frac{1}{2}\pi$ and $\frac{1}{2}\pi < x < \pi$; concave down, $-\frac{1}{2}\pi < x < 0$ and $0 < x < \frac{1}{2}\pi$.
Max points $(\pm\pi, 0)$, $(\pm\frac{1}{4}\pi, 5)$; min points $(\pm\frac{3}{4}\pi, -5)$.
Inflection points $(\pm\frac{1}{2}\pi, 0)$.

9. Concave up, $\frac{1}{4}(4n - 1)\pi < x < \frac{1}{4}(4n + 1)\pi$, $n \in \mathcal{I}$;
concave down, $\frac{1}{4}(4n + 1)\pi < x < \frac{1}{4}(4n + 3)\pi$, $n \in \mathcal{I}$.
Max points $(\frac{1}{2}(2n - 1)\pi, 3)$; min points $(n\pi, 1)$, $n \in \mathcal{I}$.
Inflection points $(\frac{1}{4}(2n - 1)\pi, 2)$, $n \in \mathcal{I}$.

11. No max or min points.
Inflection points $(n\pi, 2n\pi)$, $n \in \mathcal{I}$.

13. Max points $(\frac{1}{4}\pi, \sqrt{2})$, $(2\pi, 1)$; min points $(0, 1)$, $(\frac{5}{4}\pi, -\sqrt{2})$.
Inflection points $(\frac{3}{4}\pi, 0)$, $(\frac{7}{4}\pi, 0)$.

15. Max points $(n\pi + \frac{1}{3}\pi, n\pi + \frac{1}{3}\pi - 2 + \frac{1}{2}\sqrt{3})$, $n \in \mathcal{I}$;
min points $(n\pi - \frac{1}{3}\pi, n\pi - \frac{1}{3}\pi - 2 - \frac{1}{2}\sqrt{3})$, $n \in \mathcal{I}$.
Inflection points $(\frac{1}{2}n\pi, \frac{1}{2}n\pi - 2)$, $n \in \mathcal{I}$.

17. Max points $(2n\pi - \pi, \frac{3}{2})$, $(2n\pi, -\frac{1}{2})$, $n \in \mathcal{I}$; min points $(2n\pi \pm \frac{1}{3}\pi, -\frac{3}{2})$, $n \in \mathcal{I}$.

19. *Hint:* Use the formula for sin A − sin B.

Max points $(2n\pi, -1)$, $(2n\pi \pm \frac{2}{5}\pi, 4.05)$, $n \in \mathcal{I}$;

min points $(2n\pi + \pi, -5)$, $(2n\pi \pm \frac{1}{5}\pi, -1.55)$, $n \in \mathcal{I}$.

21. The curve $y = \sin x$ goes through one cycle in 2π units and the curve $y = \sin \sqrt{2}x$ goes through $\sqrt{2}$ cycles in 2π units. Since $\sqrt{2}$ is irrational, the two component curves have no common period. Hence, the given curve is not periodic.

23. $3r$.

25. Largest volume, $r = h = 2$ inches; smallest volume, $h = 3$ inches, $r = 1\frac{1}{2}$ inches.

27. $\text{Tan}^{-1}(\frac{1}{6}\sqrt{3})$.

29. $\frac{1}{12}\pi a\sqrt{3}$ l.u./second; $\frac{1}{12}\pi a$ l.u./second; $-\frac{1}{12}\pi a$ l.u./second.

31. Approx. 0.53 millimeters/minute.

Exercises 14.4, Pages 479–480

1. $\frac{3}{2}\sin \frac{2}{3}x + C$.

3. $\frac{1}{2}\ln |\sin 2x| + C$.

5. $\frac{1}{3}\sec 3r + C$.

7. $\frac{1}{3}\cos(2 - 3t) + C$.

9. $-\frac{1}{2}\cot 2w + C$.

11. $\frac{1}{3}\ln |\sec 3x + \tan 3x| + C$.

13. $e^{\sin y} + C$.

15. $-\frac{1}{4}\csc 4y + C$.

17. $-\frac{1}{2}\cos(1 + x^2) + C$.

19. $-\frac{1}{3}\ln(1 + \cos 3\theta) + C$.

21. $\dfrac{\pi^3 + 24}{24}$.

23. $\dfrac{1}{2\pi}$.

25. $2\sqrt{2} - 2$.

27. 4.

29. $-\frac{1}{2}$.

31. $\displaystyle\int \csc x \, dx = \int \frac{\csc^2 x - \csc x \cot x}{\csc x - \cot x} \, dx$

$$= \ln |\csc x - \cot x| + C = \ln \left|\frac{1 - \cos x}{\sin x}\right| + C$$

$$= \ln |\tan \tfrac{1}{2}x| + C.$$

33. 4 (l.u.)^2.

35. $\dfrac{2a}{b}$ (l.u.)^2.

37. π (l.u.)^3.

39. $\dfrac{\pi}{3}(1 - \ln 2)$ (l.u.)^3.

41. $\dfrac{A}{k}(1 - \cos k\xi)$.

Exercises 14.5, Page 485

1. $n\pi + (-1)^{n-1}\frac{1}{3}\pi$, $n \in \mathcal{I}$.

3. $2n\pi \pm \frac{1}{4}\pi$, $n \in \mathcal{I}$.

5. $-\frac{1}{4}\pi$.

7. $\frac{5}{6}\pi$.

9. 0.

11. $\frac{3}{4}\pi$.

13. $\{(x, y): x = \cot y\}$.

15. $\{(x, y): x = \csc y\}$.

17. Yes. Let $y = \text{Sin}^{-1}(-x)$; then

$$(-\tfrac{1}{2}\pi \leq y \leq \tfrac{1}{2}\pi \text{ and } \sin y = -x) \Rightarrow \sin(-y) = x \Rightarrow y = -\text{Sin}^{-1} x.$$

19. $x = \frac{1}{2}\tan 2y$.

21. $x = -1 + \cos \frac{1}{2}(y + 1)$.

23. *Hint:* The graph is that of $x = \frac{1}{3}\sin 2y$.

25. *Hint:* The graph is that of $x = 1 + \tan \frac{1}{3}y$ for $-\frac{3}{2}\pi < y < \frac{3}{2}\pi$.

27. $\dfrac{x}{\sqrt{1 - x^2}}$.

29. $\dfrac{1}{\sqrt{x^2 - 3}}$.

31. $\dfrac{840}{841}$.

33. $\frac{3}{4}$.

35. $\frac{2}{5}(1 + \sqrt{10})$; $\frac{1}{9}(4\sqrt{2} - \sqrt{5})$; $\frac{2}{3}(\sqrt{2} + \sqrt{5})$.

37. $\frac{1}{10}(3\sqrt{3} - 4)$; $\frac{1}{10}(4\sqrt{3} + 3)$; $\frac{1}{39}(48 - 25\sqrt{3})$.

39. $\frac{253}{325}$; $\frac{204}{325}$; $\frac{253}{204}$.

41. $\frac{1}{4}$.

43. -2.

45. 1.

47. $\dfrac{h + k}{1 - hk}$.

Exercises 14.6, Pages 488–490

3. Let $y = \text{Cos}^{-1} u$, where $0 < y < \pi$. Then $u = \cos y$ and

$$D_x u = -\sin y\, D_x y \Rightarrow D_x y = \frac{-D_x u}{\sin y} = -\frac{D_x u}{\sqrt{1 - u^2}},$$

since $\sin y > 0$.

5. $\dfrac{2}{4 + s^2}$.

7. $\dfrac{1}{\sqrt{2u - 4u^2}}$.

9. $2e^{2x} \text{Tan}^{-1} e^{2x} + \dfrac{2e^{4x}}{1 + e^{4x}}$.

11. $3 \text{Sin}^{-1} 2x + \dfrac{6x}{\sqrt{1 - 4x^2}}$.

13. $\dfrac{2}{(4 + s^2) \text{Tan}^{-1} (s/2)}$.

15. $\dfrac{(1 + 4v^2) \text{Tan}^{-1} 2v - 2v}{(1 + 4v^2)(\text{Tan}^{-1} 2v)^2}$.

17. $2 \text{Tan}^{-1} (s/2) + C$.

19. $-\frac{1}{4}\sqrt{1 - 4x^2} + C$.

21. $\frac{1}{2} \text{Tan}^{-1} 2e^v + C$.

23. $t - \ln (1 + t) + C$.

25. $\text{Tan}^{-1} (\sin u) + C$.

27. $\frac{1}{6}\pi$.

29. $\text{Tan}^{-1} e - \frac{1}{4}\pi$.

31. $\frac{1}{8}\pi$ (l.u.)^2.

33. *Intercepts:* $y = 0 \Rightarrow x = 0$, $x = 2$.

Extent: $0 \leq x \leq 2$, $0 \leq y \leq \frac{1}{2}\pi$.

y increasing for $0 < x < 1$; decreasing for $1 < x < 2$.

Max point $(1, \frac{1}{2}\pi)$; min points $(0, 0)$, $(2, 0)$.

Concave down, $0 < x < 1$, $1 < x < 2$.

35. $\text{Tan}^{-1}\left(\dfrac{1 + x}{1 - x}\right) = \text{Tan}^{-1} x + \dfrac{\pi}{4}$.

37. $x = \pm\dfrac{1}{\sqrt{2}} \exp\left(\dfrac{\pi}{4} - 1\right) = y$.

39. $\frac{1}{6}\pi$ (l.u.)^2.

41. $30\sqrt{5}$ feet.

43. $\text{Tan}^{-1} (x + h) = \text{Tan}^{-1} x + \dfrac{h}{1 + (x + \theta h)^2}$, $0 < \theta < 1$

$\Rightarrow \text{Tan}^{-1} 1.02 = \text{Tan}^{-1} 1 + \dfrac{0.02}{1 + (1 + 0.02h)^2}$

$\Rightarrow \dfrac{\pi}{4} + \dfrac{0.02}{1 + (1.02)^2} < \text{Tan}^{-1} 1.02 < \dfrac{\pi}{4} + \dfrac{0.02}{1 + 1^2}$

$\Rightarrow 0.7952 < \text{Tan}^{-1} 1.02 < 0.7954$.

45. 0.0308 radian/second. **49.** $\frac{4}{101}$ radian/minute.

47. $-\frac{24}{73}$ radian/minute.

Exercises 14.7, Pages 496–497

27. $\frac{1}{6}\sinh^2 3x + C.$

29. $\frac{1}{2}\ln\cosh 2x + C.$

31. $\ln\cosh x - \frac{1}{2}\tanh^2 x + C.$

33. $\frac{3}{2}\mathrm{Cosh}^{-1}\frac{2}{3}x + C.$

35. $\frac{1}{2}\mathrm{Tanh}^{-1}\frac{1}{2}x + C.$

37. $-\dfrac{1}{12}\mathrm{Tanh}^{-1}\dfrac{4}{3x} + C.$

39. $-\frac{1}{18}\ln|4 - 9x^2| + C.$

41. $\frac{1}{4}\pi a^3(2 + \sinh 2)$ (l.u.)^3.

43. The curve is the hyperbola $\frac{1}{9}x^2 - \frac{1}{16}y^2 = 1.$

Exercises 14.8, Pages 504–505

1. (a) The graph is the ray $y = x$, $x \geqq 0$.

   (c) The graph is the circle $x^2 + y^2 = y$.

3. (a) $-2\sin 2s + i2\cos 2s$.

   (c) $(-1 + i)\sin 2u$.

5. (a) $4e^{i7\pi/6}$.

11. (a) $i\sinh 1$.

   (c) $-\frac{1}{2}\sqrt{2}\cosh 1 + i\frac{1}{2}\sqrt{2}\sinh 1$.

   (e) $\frac{1}{2}\sqrt{2} + i\frac{1}{2}\sqrt{2}$.

(c) $10\exp(i\,\mathrm{Cos}^{-1}\frac{3}{5})$.

(g) $\ln 2 + i\frac{1}{2}\pi$.

(i) $\ln 3 + i\pi$.

Exercises 14.9, Page 508

1. $2,\ -1 + i\sqrt{3},\ -1 - i\sqrt{3}$.

3. $i,\ -\frac{1}{2}\sqrt{3} - \frac{1}{2}i,\ \frac{1}{2}\sqrt{3} - \frac{1}{2}i$.

5. $\sqrt{2} + i\sqrt{2},\ -\sqrt{2} + i\sqrt{2},\ -\sqrt{2} - i\sqrt{2},\ \sqrt{2} - i\sqrt{2}$.

7. $\sqrt{3} + i,\ -\sqrt{3} + i,\ -2i$.

9. $-\frac{1}{2}\sqrt{6} + \frac{1}{2}\sqrt{2}i,\ \frac{1}{2}\sqrt{6} - \frac{1}{2}\sqrt{2}i$.

11. $\sqrt[3]{5}\exp(i\frac{1}{3}\alpha),\ \sqrt[3]{5}\exp(i\frac{1}{3}\alpha + i\frac{2}{3}\pi),\ \sqrt[3]{5}\exp(i\frac{1}{3}\alpha + i\frac{4}{3}\pi)$, where $\alpha = \mathrm{Cos}^{-1}(-\frac{3}{5})$.

13. $2\sqrt[4]{2}\exp(i\frac{5}{8}\pi),\ 2\sqrt[4]{2}\exp(i\frac{13}{8}\pi)$.

15. $\exp(i\frac{1}{4}n\pi)$, $n = 0, 1, 2, 3, 4, 5, 6, 7.$

17. $\frac{1}{2} + \frac{1}{2}\sqrt{3}i,\ -\frac{1}{2} + \frac{1}{2}\sqrt{3}i,\ -\frac{1}{2} - \frac{1}{2}\sqrt{3}i,\ \frac{1}{2} - \frac{1}{2}\sqrt{3}i$.

19. $2\exp(i\frac{1}{5}2n\pi)$, $n = 1, 2, 3, 4.$ **21.** -64.

25. *Hint:* $\omega^4 + \omega^3 + \omega^2 + \omega + 1 = 0$.

Exercises 14.10, Page 512

1. k.

3. The fraction $\to \infty$ as $x \to 0$.

5. 0.

7. The fraction $\to \infty$ as $t \to \infty$.

9. 0.

11. $-\frac{1}{2}$.

13. 0.

15. $\ln(a/b)$.

17. 1.

19. $\frac{1}{16}$.

21. $\frac{1}{4}$.

Exercises 14.11, Page 514

1. The expression $\to \infty$ as $x \to \infty$.

3. 1.   **9.** $-\frac{1}{3}$.   **15.** 1.

5. 0.   **11.** $-\frac{1}{2}$.   **17.** 1.

7. 0.   **13.** e^{-1}.   **19.** e^{2a}.

Exercises 14.12, Pages 520–521

1. 0.703.   **5.** 0.443.   **9.** 0.682.   **13.** 2.053.

3. 2.104.   **7.** 1.306.   **11.** 2.551.   **15.** 335°2.4′.

Exercises 15.1, Pages 524–525

1. $x^4 + \frac{8}{3}x^3 + 7x + C$.

3. $\frac{1}{3}\sin^3 t + C$.

5. $\frac{1}{3}(w^2 + 1)^{3/2} + C$.

7. $x - \ln|x + 1| + C$.

9. $\frac{1}{3}e^{3u} + C$.

11. $\sec v + C$.

13. $2\ln|\sec\sqrt{x}| + C$.

15. $\sqrt{w^2 + 4} + C$.

17. $\frac{1}{2}\ln|t^2 - 9| + C$.

19. $(2x^{2-1}/\ln 2) + C$.

21. $\sqrt{u^2 - 4} + C$.

23. $\frac{1}{10}\operatorname{Tan}^{-1}(\frac{2}{5}x) + C$.

25. $\operatorname{Sin}^{-1}(\frac{1}{2}y) + C$.

27. $-\frac{1}{3}\ln|\csc u^3 + \cot u^3| + C$.

29. $w^2 + \frac{4}{3}\sqrt{2}w^{3/2} + w + C$.

31. $\frac{1}{8}\sin^4 2x + C$.

33. $(2^w/\ln 2) + C$.

35. $9 - 6\sqrt{2}$.

37. 1.

39. $\frac{3}{2}(e^4 - 1)$.

41. 0.

43. $\frac{1}{4}\pi$.

Exercises 15.2, Pages 527–529

1. $\frac{1}{9}\cos^3 3x - \frac{1}{3}\cos 3x + C$.

3. $\tan\theta + C$.

5. $\frac{1}{4}\sec^2 2r + C$.

7. $\frac{1}{21}\sec^7 3y - \frac{2}{15}\sec^5 3y + \frac{1}{9}\sec^3 3y + C$.

9. $\frac{1}{4}\sec^2 2s + \frac{1}{2}\ln|\cos 2s| + C$.

11. $\frac{1}{3}\sin^3 y - \frac{1}{5}\sin^5 y + C$.

13. $\frac{1}{10}\sin^5 2w - \frac{1}{3}\sin^3 2w + \frac{1}{2}\sin 2w + C$.

15. $-\frac{1}{2}\csc^2 x + C$.   **19.** $\frac{2}{3}\sin^3 x + C$.

17. $\frac{1}{8}x - \frac{1}{64}\sin 8x + C$.   **21.** $\frac{1}{3}\ln(1 + \sin 3y) + C$.

23. $-\frac{1}{8}\csc^4 2r + \frac{1}{4}\csc^2 2r + \frac{1}{2}\ln|\sin 2r| + C$.

25. $\sqrt{2}\sin x + C$ for $2n\pi - \frac{1}{2}\pi \leq x \leq 2n\pi + \frac{1}{2}\pi$,

$-\sqrt{2}\sin x + C$ for $(2n + 1)\pi - \frac{1}{2}\pi < x < (2n + 1)\pi + \frac{1}{2}\pi$.

27. $\frac{1}{2}\ln|\csc 2\theta - \cot 2\theta| + \frac{1}{2}\ln|\sin 2\theta| + C$.

29. $2\cot\frac{1}{2}w - 2\csc\frac{1}{2}w + w + C$.

31. $-\frac{1}{10}\cot^5 2u + \frac{1}{6}\cot^3 2u - \frac{1}{2}\cot 2u - u + C$.

33. $\frac{1}{2}(1 - \ln 2)$.

35. $\frac{3}{16}\pi$.

37. $\sqrt{3} - 1$.

39. $\frac{2}{3}$.

41. $\frac{28}{15}$.

43. $\frac{1}{5} \ln \left| \dfrac{2(5 + 4 \sin t - 3 \cos t)}{4 \cos t + 3 \sin t} \right|$.

45. $\dfrac{\sin x}{3(3 \cos x - 4 \sin x)}$.

47. $-\frac{2}{5}$.

49. $\frac{1}{48}(3\sqrt{3} + 8)$.

53. $\frac{1}{4}(4 - \pi)$ (l.u.)^2.

55. $\frac{1}{8}(\pi - 2)$ (l.u.)^2.

57. $\pi(1 - \frac{1}{4}\pi)$ (l.u.)^3.

59. $30RI_0^2$ joules.

Exercises 15.3, Pages 534–535

1. $\frac{2}{3}(x - 8)\sqrt{x + 4} + C$.

3. $-\frac{1}{5}(s^2 + 6)(9 - s^2)^{3/2} + C$.

5. $\mathrm{Sin}^{-1}\left[\frac{1}{3}(x - 1)\right] + C$.

7. $\sqrt{u^2 - 4u + 8} + 2 \sinh^{-1}\left[\frac{1}{2}(u - 2)\right] + C$.

9. $\frac{1}{2} \ln (w^2 - 4w + 13) + C$.

11. $\frac{1}{3}\sqrt{x^2 - 9} - \mathrm{Tan}^{-1}\left(\frac{1}{3}\sqrt{x^2 - 9}\right) + C$.

13. $\dfrac{1}{\sqrt{2}} \mathrm{Tan}^{-1}\left(\dfrac{t + 1}{\sqrt{2}}\right) + C$.

15. $(y^2 + 8)(y^2 + 4)^{-1/2} + C$.

17. $\frac{5}{9}x^{9/5} + \frac{15}{4}x^{4/5} + C$.

19. $\frac{2}{15}(3s^2 - 4s + 8)\sqrt{s + 1} + C$.

21. $\frac{3}{4}(y - 3)\sqrt[3]{y + 1} + C$.

23. 14.1.

25. $\frac{1}{12}\pi$.

27. $\frac{5832}{35}$.

29. $\frac{1}{3}(9\sqrt{3} - 10\sqrt{2})$.

31. $\frac{5}{3}$.

33. $\frac{1}{2}(2\sqrt{2} - \sqrt{5})$.

35. 4 (l.u.)^2.

37. $(15 - \ln 16)$ (l.u.)^2.

39. $\frac{1}{5}\pi(717 - 20 \ln 4)$ (l.u.)^2.

Exercises 15.4, Pages 539–540

3. $\frac{9}{2} \mathrm{Sin}^{-1}\left(\frac{1}{3}x\right) - \frac{1}{2}x\sqrt{9 - x^2} + C$.

5. $\frac{1}{2} \mathrm{Sin}^{-1} t + \frac{1}{2}t\sqrt{1 - t^2} + C$.

7. $-\dfrac{\sqrt{4 - s^2}}{4s} + C$.

9. $\frac{1}{3}(y^2 - 8)\sqrt{y^2 + 4} + C$.

11. $\dfrac{x}{4\sqrt{4 + x^2}} + C$.

13. $\dfrac{1}{2} \ln \left| \dfrac{\sqrt{x^2 + 4} - 2}{x} \right| + C$.

15. $-\frac{1}{3}(18 + x^2)(9 - x^2)^{1/2} + C$.

17. $2 \mathrm{Sin}^{-1}\left(\frac{1}{2}\sqrt{y}\right) + C$.

19. $\frac{1}{6}(2\pi - 3\sqrt{3})$.

21. $\frac{1}{30}(2\sqrt{15} - 5\sqrt{3})$.

23. $\frac{1}{2} \mathrm{Sec}^{-1} 3 - \frac{1}{6}\pi$.

25. $\dfrac{2\pi + 3\sqrt{3}}{192}$.

27. 6π (l.u.)^2.

29. $\frac{1}{5}\pi$ (l.u.)^2.

31. $\left[\ln (2 + \sqrt{3}) - \frac{1}{2}\sqrt{3}\right]$ (l.u.)^2.

33. $\frac{1}{8}\pi$ (l.u.)^2.

35. $\frac{3}{8}\pi a^2$ (l.u.)^2.

Exercises 15.5, Pages 542–543

1. $\frac{1}{3}w \sin 3w + \frac{1}{9} \cos 3w + C$.

3. $(2 - x^2) \cos x + 2x \sin x + C$.

5. $w \mathrm{Tan}^{-1} w - \frac{1}{2} \ln (1 + w^2) + C$.

7. $\frac{3}{8}(2x^2 - 1) \cos 2x + \frac{1}{4}(2x^3 - 3x) \sin 2x + C.$

9. $\frac{1}{4}y^2(2 \ln y - 1) + C.$

11. $\frac{1}{4}(2y^2 - 1) \mathrm{Sin}^{-1} y + \frac{1}{4}y\sqrt{1 - y^2} + C.$

13. $-x \cot x + \ln \sin x + C.$

15. $\frac{1}{13}e^{2x}(3 \sin 3x + 2 \cos 3x) + C.$

17. $\frac{1}{4}(x^4 - 1) \mathrm{Tan}^{-1} x - \frac{1}{12}(x^3 - 3x) + C.$

19. $\theta \tan \theta + \ln \cos \theta + C.$

21. $\frac{2}{25}y^{5/2}(5 \ln 3y - 2) + C.$

23. $\frac{1}{2} \sec t \tan t + \frac{1}{2} \ln |\sec t + \tan t| + C.$

25. 1.

27. $\frac{1}{4}\pi - \frac{1}{2} \ln 2.$

29. $\frac{1}{5}(2 + e^{\pi/4}).$

31. $\frac{506}{15}.$

33. $(1 - 2e^{-1})$ (l.u.)$^2.$

35. $(\frac{1}{12}\sqrt{3}\pi - \frac{1}{4})$ (l.u.)$^2.$

37. $\left(\dfrac{25 \ln 5 - 12}{10 \ln 5 - 8}, \dfrac{5 \ln^2 5 - 10 \ln 5 + 8}{10 \ln 5 - 8} \right).$

39. 1.

Exercises 15.6, Pages 547–548

1. $\frac{2}{3}.$

3. $\frac{3}{16}\pi.$

5. $\frac{2}{15}.$

7. $\frac{2}{35}.$

9. $\frac{1}{2}\pi.$

11. $\frac{2}{3}.$

13. $\frac{8}{3}.$

15. $\frac{1}{8}\pi.$

17. $\frac{4}{15}.$

19. $\frac{5}{128}\pi.$

21. $\frac{8}{35}.$

23. $\frac{5}{16}\pi.$

25. $\frac{1}{2}\pi.$

27. $4\pi.$

29. $\frac{1}{2}\pi.$

31. $\frac{3}{32}\pi a^2.$

33. $\frac{4}{9}$ (l.u.)$^2.$

35. $\frac{3}{16}\pi^2$ (l.u.)$^3.$

37. $\frac{1}{16}\pi$ (l.u.)$^2.$

39. $\dfrac{4(2m)(2m - 2)\cdots(2)(2n - 1)(2n - 3)\cdots(1)}{(2m + 2n + 1)(2m + 2n - 1)\cdots(1)}$ (l.u.)$^2.$

Exercises 15.7, Pages 554–555

1. $\dfrac{1}{4} \ln \left| \dfrac{x - 2}{x + 2} \right| + C.$

3. $2 \ln |w - 2| + 3 \ln |w + 2| + C.$

5. $\ln \dfrac{|x^3(x - 1)|}{(x + 1)^2} + C.$

7. $\ln w^2 - \dfrac{3}{w + 2} + C.$

9. $t + \ln \dfrac{(t - 2)^4}{|t - 1|} + C.$

11. $\ln |x| - \dfrac{3}{x + 1} + C.$

13. $3 \ln |w| - \frac{2}{3} \ln |3w - 1| + \frac{1}{3} \ln |3w + 1| + C.$

15. $2 \ln |t| + 3 \ln |t + 1| + \dfrac{1}{t + 1} + C.$

17. $4 \ln |w - 1| + \frac{1}{3} \ln |w + 1| + \frac{5}{3} \ln |w - 2| + C.$

19. $\ln \frac{9}{8}.$

21. $\frac{3}{28} + \ln 16.$

23. $\ln \frac{20}{9}.$

25. $\frac{1}{2} + \ln \frac{36}{25}.$

27. $\ln \frac{9}{2}$ (l.u.)$^2.$

29. $(\frac{29}{112} + \frac{1}{6} \ln \frac{7}{4})$ (l.u.)$^2.$

31. $\dfrac{6 \ln 3 - 2 \ln 2 + 2}{\ln 9 - \ln 2}.$

33. $2\pi(6 \ln 3 - 2 \ln 2 + 2)$ (l.u.)$^3.$

Exercises 15.8, Pages 559–560

1. $\ln |y + 1|(y^2 + 1) + C.$

3. $9 \ln |t + 3| - \frac{5}{2} \ln (t^2 + 4t + 8) - 2 \mathrm{Tan}^{-1} [\frac{1}{2}(t + 2)] + C.$

5. $2 \ln |w| + \frac{3}{2} \operatorname{Tan}^{-1} (\frac{1}{2}w) + C.$

7. $\ln |x - 2| + \ln (x^2 + 2x + 10) + \frac{7}{3} \operatorname{Tan}^{-1} [\frac{1}{3}(x + 1)] + C.$

9. $\dfrac{1}{3\sqrt{2}} \operatorname{Tan}^{-1} \left(\dfrac{s}{\sqrt{2}}\right) + \dfrac{1}{3} \ln \left|\dfrac{s - 1}{s + 1}\right| + C.$

11. $-\ln |x| + 3 \operatorname{Tan}^{-1} (x - 1) + C.$

13. $\ln |w - 1| + \ln (w^2 + 3w + 8) + C.$

15. $\ln |w + 1| + 2w + \frac{3}{2} \operatorname{Tan}^{-1} (\frac{1}{2}w) + C.$

17. $3 \ln |x| + 2 \ln (x^2 + 4x + 5) - 9 \operatorname{Tan}^{-1} (x + 2) + C.$

19. $3 \ln |x + 1| + \dfrac{5}{2(x^2 + 1)} + C.$

21. $\frac{1}{4} \operatorname{Tan}^{-1} (\frac{1}{2}x^2) + C.$

23. $\frac{5}{2} \ln 2 - \frac{1}{12}\pi.$

25. $\ln \frac{9}{2} - \frac{1}{3}\pi.$

27. $2 \ln \frac{9}{5} + \frac{1}{2} \ln 2 - \frac{3}{4}\pi.$

29. $2 \ln 2 + \frac{3}{2} \ln 3 + \pi - 4 \operatorname{Tan}^{-1} 3.$

31. $1 + \frac{1}{36}(12 - \pi)\sqrt{3}.$

33. $\frac{1}{96}(12 - 4\sqrt{3} - \pi)$ (l.u.)$^2.$

35. $(\frac{1}{3}\pi\sqrt{3} + \ln \frac{2}{3}\sqrt{3})$ (l.u.)$^2.$

Exercises 15.9, Pages 566–568

1. Divergent.

3. $\frac{1}{2}.$

5. Divergent.

7. $-4.$

9. $-1.$

11. Divergent.

13. $0.$

17. *Hint:* Write $\displaystyle\int_0^\infty x^k e^{-x}\, dx = \lim_{t\to\infty} \int_0^t x^k e^{-x}\, dx$, and use integration by parts.

19. $2km/a$ force units.

21. Converges.

23. Converges.

25. Diverges.

Exercises 15.10, Pages 571–572

1. (a) $T = 0.1088,\ |E| \leq 0.0128.$ (b) $S = 0.1024,\ E = 0.$

3. (a) $T = 0.9871,\ |E| \leq 0.0202.$ (b) $S = 1.0001,\ |E| \leq 0.00021.$

5. (a) $T = 0.6549.$ (b) $S = 0.6577.$

7. (a) $T = 0.0220.$ (b) $S = 0.0213.$

9. (a) $T = 1.6240.$ (b) $S = 1.5629.$

11. (a) $T = 1.5716.$ (b) $S = 1.5690.$

13. *Hint:* If r_m is the radius of the midsection, then Simpson's Rule gives
$$V = \frac{1}{6}\pi h(r_1^2 + 4r_m^2 + r_2^2).$$
Show that $4r_m^2 = 2r_1^2 + 2r_2^2 + h^2.$

15. $0.1544.$

17. *Hint:* See the error formula.

Exercises 15.11, Pages 573–574

9. *Hint:* Use partial fractions.

11. *Hint:* Use a trigonometric substitution and integration by parts.

13. $-\dfrac{\sqrt{x^2 + 1}}{2x^2} - \dfrac{1}{2} \ln \left|\dfrac{1 + \sqrt{x^2 + 1}}{x}\right| + C.$

15. $\frac{1}{8}y^2 + \frac{1}{32}\ln|4y^2 - 1| + C.$

17. $\frac{1}{5}(w^2 - 4)^{5/2} + \frac{4}{3}(w^2 - 4)^{3/2} + C.$

19. $\frac{1}{2}y\sin 2y - \frac{1}{4}(2y^2 - 1)\cos 2y + C.$

21. $x\ln^2 2x - 2x\ln 2x + 2x + C.$

23. $-\frac{1}{16}y(9 - 4y^2)^{3/2} + \frac{9}{32}y(9 - 4y^2)^{1/2} + \frac{81}{64}\operatorname{Sin}^{-1}\left(\frac{2}{3}y\right) + C.$

25. $-\dfrac{(4 - y^2)^{3/2}}{y} - \dfrac{3}{2}y(4 - y^2)^{1/2} - 6\operatorname{Sin}^{-1}\left(\dfrac{1}{2}y\right) + C.$

27. $\frac{1}{13}e^{2x}(2\sin 3x - 3\cos 3x) + C.$

29. $\dfrac{2}{5}\sqrt{2 + 3x} + \dfrac{1}{5}\sqrt{2}\ln\left|\dfrac{\sqrt{2 + 3x} - \sqrt{2}}{\sqrt{2 + 3x} + \sqrt{2}}\right| + C.$

31. $\frac{1}{2}\cos t - \frac{1}{10}\cos 5t + C.$

33. $\frac{1}{8}(4 - \pi).$

35. $\frac{2}{9}(8\sqrt{14} + \sqrt{5}).$

37. $\frac{7}{8}\sqrt{2} + \frac{3}{8}\ln(1 + \sqrt{2}).$

39. $4\pi.$

41. $\frac{1}{4}\pi - \frac{1}{2}\ln 2.$

43. $\frac{1}{32}(8 + 3\pi).$

45. $\frac{1}{24}(\pi - 12 + 6\sqrt{3}).$

Exercises 15.12, Pages 575–576

1. $(\frac{1}{2}\pi, \frac{3}{8}).$

3. $(\pi, \frac{5}{6}a).$

5. $\frac{3}{2}\ln 3 - 1.$

7. $\frac{1}{4}\pi a.$

9. $\frac{32}{105}\pi a^3$ (l.u.)³.

11. $\bar{x} = \dfrac{(3 + 2\sinh 2 - \cosh 2)a}{4 + 2\sinh 2}.$

13. $\dfrac{143\pi}{72\ln 2}$ (feet)³.

15. $\frac{16}{3}w$ pounds.

17. $\frac{1}{4}mA^2\omega^2.$

19. $I_e = \frac{1}{2}\sqrt{2}I_0.$

21. $\dfrac{2km}{a}$ force units.

23. $2\pi k\mu\left(1 - \dfrac{s}{\sqrt{s^2 + b^2}}\right)$ force units.

INDEX